ION BOMBARDMENT OF SOLIDS

ION BOMBARDMENT OF SOLIDS

by

G. Carter, B. Sc., Ph. D.

Department of Electrical Engineering and Electronics, University of Liverpool

and

J. S. Colligon, B. Eng. Ph. D.

Royal Aircraft Establishment, Farnborough

AMERICAN ELSEVIER PUBLISHING COMPANY, INC.

52 Vanderbilt Avenue

New York, New York 10017

AMERICAN ELSEVIER PUBLISHING, INC.
52 Vanderbilt Avenue
New York, New York 10017

Library of Congress Catalog Card Number: 67–31195

PRODUCED BY UNEOPRINT
set on electric keyboards
photo-reproduced and printed offset
at The Gresham Press
UNWIN BROTHERS LIMITED
Old Woking Surrey England

Preface

Although the effects of the ion bombardment of solids have been known for over one hundred years, for most of that time, the effects were inadequately understood and regarded as positively undesirable. Ion bombardment studies have, however, as in almost all other branches of scientific endeavour, multiplied extensively since the mid 1950's. Indeed a book on the present topic, written at that time would have been probably only one-tenth the size of this volume.

Probably the two major stimuli for the increased activity were the positive uses of the phenomena as applied to ion pumping and surface reactions, and the realization that a study of the interaction between ions and surfaces could give basic information on the nature of interatomic forces at separation distances between atoms not normally accessible to observation by other techniques. In addition to these earlier applications, ion bombardment techniques are in current use for the implantation of dopant ions into semiconductors, for the preparation of thin sputtered films for micro-electronic circuitry, for the simulation of space environmental conditions and much is being learnt about the basic nature of atomic collisions and the structure of solid materials.

It is becoming clear that bombardment studies are being carried out at two levels. One designed to understand the basic phenomena involved, the other to exploit practically, the knowledge of these phenomena. It is the aim of this text to bring together these aspects and to attempt to correlate the various branches of the subject which are under current investigation. This latter intention is all the more important when it is realised that world-wide attention is being given to the problem and the relevant literature is contained in many publications in several languages. In addition, international symposia in various aspects of the topic and related studies are held regularly and we have attempted to include the relevant data from these symposia in this book.

In order to acquaint the investigator, concerned primarily with practical applications, with the underlying theoretical concepts, we have deliberately included detailed theoretical sections which start at quite elementary levels, but which proceed to embrace more sophisticated recent developments. At the same time the current experimental position is reviewed in some detail so that the theoretician may have access to the wealth of available data.

In view of the basic nature of the theoretical discussion, particularly in Chapter 2 which deals with the physics of atomic collisions, it is believed that this book would be relevant to many undergraduate Physics and Materials Science courses and should serve as an introduction for new research workers in the field. Indeed one of the motivating influences for the authors in writing this book has been the desire to provide postgraduate students at the University of Liverpool and elsewhere, with an integrated view of ion bombardment induced phenomena and elucidate the logical theoretical and experimental development of the subject. On the other hand, the inclusion of all available data at the time of writing should provide the experienced research worker with a source of contemporary knowledge.

It is, in fact, this duality of purpose, which the authors felt to be desirable and necessary, that has resulted in the production of a text of the present extended length. It is hoped, however, that the discerning reader will be able to extract the type of information required, and theoretical and experimental sections of each chapter are clearly differentiated.

In Chapters 1 and 2 the reader is reminded of crystal terminology and basic atomic collision processes where the simple equations required for Chapters 5 and 6 dealing with ion penetration and radiation damage, respectively, are derived. Chapters 3, 4 and 7 treat emission processes from the solid, since, as the ion transmits its energy to the target, electrons, ions and neutral particles are emitted. Whilst the majority of work on these three processes has been of an experimental nature, theoretical treatments are being developed and good predictions of experimental trends are possible. One major factor which arises in all the phenomena discussed is the critical effect which crystal structure and orientation exerts on all experimental measurements, a factor which has only recently been thoroughly appreciated.

This influence is stressed also in Chapters 5 and 6, in the former case the emphasis is on the path of the projectile ion whilst in the latter case it is the effect of ion bombardment upon the lattice atoms which are discussed. In Chapter 8, the retention of ions by a solid is investigated, whilst Chapter 9 presents a more detailed consideration of the practical application of ion bombardment phenomena.

As the work recorded here has been drawn from many different sources no fully consistent use of symbols has been attempted. The reader will find the appropriate symbols defined near the set of equations concerned. We have, however, made one exception to this rule and reversed the Russian symbols M_1, M_2 for target and ion masses respectively to the conventional system ion mass M_1, target mass M_2.

As many investigators in ion bombardment studies generally require numerical data, comprehensive sets of tables and figures are presented where possible.

It is difficult to single out individuals from the many to whom our thanks are due in the preparation of this book. The completion of the book has been greatly assisted by the patience of our wives who have given untiring help in editing and typing preliminary drafts of the manuscript. We are grateful also to many research colleagues throughout the world for discussions, for allowing us to use their figures and data and for providing pre-prints of current work. In particular we would like to thank Dr. M. Kaminsky who loaned us the proofs of his book on Atomic and Ionic Impact Phenomena.

J.S.C. G.C.

ACKNOWLEDGMENTS:

The following Figures are published by courtesy of:-

Academic Press Inc:-6. 13; 6. 16; 6. 17; 6. 23;

Akademie—Verlag, Berlin:-8. 43; 8. 44; 8. 45; 8. 46;

The American Institute of Physics:- 2. 5; 2. 7; 2. 8; 2. 9; 2. 10; 2. 12; 3. 3; 3. 4; 3. 5; 3. 6; 3. 7; 3. 9; 3. 10; 3. 11; 3. 12; 3. 13; 3. 13; 3. 14; 3. 15; 3. 21; 3. 22; 3. 26; 3. 27; 3. 28; 3. 29; 3. 31; 3. 32; 3. 33; 3. 34; 3. 35; 3. 36; 3. 37; 3. 39; 3. 40; 3. 41; 3. 42; 3. 43; 3. 44; 4. 5; 4. 6; 4. 7; 4. 8; 4. 8; 4. 9; 4. 17; 4. 18; 4. 19; 4. 21; 5. 7; 5. 8; 5. 9; 5. 10; 5. 11; 5. 12; 5. 13; 5. 14; 5. 15; 5. 16; 5. 17; 5. 18; 5. 22; 5. 23; 5. 24; 5. 25; 5. 26; 5. 27; 5. 28; 5. 29; 5. 30; 5. 31; 5. 32; 5. 35; 5. 36; 5. 37; 5. 38; 5. 39; 5. 40; 5. 41; 5. 45; 5. 46; 5. 47; 5. 48; 5. 49; 5. 50; 5. 51; 5. 52; 5. 53; 5. 57; 5. 60; 5. 85; 5. 87; 5. 96; 6. 14; 6. 18; 6. 19; 6. 20; 6. 21; 6. 22; 6. 25; 6. 31; 6. 32; 6. 33; 6. 35; 6. 42; 6. 43; 6. 44; 6. 45; 6. 46; 6. 47; 6. 51; 6. 52; 6. 53; 6. 54; 6. 59; 7. 1; 7. 4; 7. 5; 7. 10; 7. 12; 7. 14; 7. 15; 7. 17; 7. 18; 7. 19; 7. 24; 7. 27; 7. 28; 7. 31; 7. 33; 8. 4; 8. 22; 8. 23; 9. 5; 9. 13;

The American Vacuum Society:- 7. 6; 7. 16; 8. 12; 8. 15; 8. 27; 8. 29;

The Australian Journal of Physics:- 6. 61; 6. 62;

C.N.R.S. Bellevue, France:- 4. 4; 6. 60; 6. 63; 6. 64; 6. 66; 7. 29;

Columbia Technical Translations:- 3. 18; 4. 15; 4. 16; 7. 13; 9. 14; 9. 15;

The Danish Atomic Energy Commission:- 2. 11;

The Faraday Society/Taylor & Francis:- 6. 40; 6. 41; 6. 48;

Institute of Petroleum:- 7. 30;

The Institute of Physics & The Physical Society:- 8. 1; 8. 2; 8. 7; 8. 11; 8. 13; 8. 14; 8. 24; 8. 25; 8. 26; 8. 30; 8. 32; 8. 36;

The International Atomic Energy Agency:- 2. 6; 5. 1; 5. 42; 5. 43; 6. 2; 6. 3; 6. 4; 6. 49; 6. 50;

Interscience Publishers:- 6. 12;

The Italian Physical Society:- 8. 28;

McGraw-Hill Book Co: - 9. 4;

National Aeronautics & Space Administration:- 7. 9;

National Research Council of Canada:- 5. 61; 5. 62; 5. 63; 5. 64; 5. 69; 5. 70; 5. 71; 5. 72; 5. 74; 5. 76; 5. 79; 5. 80; 5. 81; 5. 82; 5. 83; 5. 84; 5. 86; 5. 88; 5. 89; 5. 90; 5. 94; 5. 95; 8. 9; 8. 16; 8. 33; 8. 34; 8. 35; 8. 37;

North Holland Publishing Co:- 4. 20; 4. 22; 5. 67; 5. 68; 6. 29; 6. 30; 6. 34; 6. 39; 7. 21; 7. 34; 7. 35; 8. 10; 8. 17; 8. 18; 8. 19; 8. 20; 8. 21; 8. 38; 8. 39; 8. 40; 8. 41; 8. 42; 8. 47; 8. 48;

Office of Aerospace Research. U.S. Air Force:- 5. 33; 5. 34; 5. 56; 5. 58;

Pergamon Press:- 6. 36; 6. 57; 8. 8;

The Physical Society of Japan:- 3. 16; 5. 44;

Princeton University Press:- 6. 5; 6. 6;

The Royal Danish Academy of Sciences & Letters:- 2. 16; 2. 18; 5. 2; 5. 3; 5. 4; 5. 5; 5. 6; 5. 59;

The Royal Society (London):- 6. 25; 6. 38; 8. 49; 8. 50;

The Royal Swedish Academy of Sciences:- 5. 66; 5. 73; 5. 75; 5. 77; 5. 78; 5. 93;

Springer-Verlag, Berlin:- 2. 14; 2. 15; 4. 2; 4. 10; 4. 11; 4. 12; 4. 14; 6. 15; 6. 24; 6. 26; 7. 7;

Taylor & Francis:- 5. 19; 5. 20; 5. 21; 5. 65; 6. 27; 6. 28; 6. 55; 6. 56; 7. 23; 9. 10;

The Times Science Review:- 6. 58;

United States Atomic Energy Commission:- 3. 19; 3. 20; 3. 23; 3. 24; 3. 25; 3. 30; 3. 38; 4. 13; 4. 23; 4. 24; 4. 25;

Zeitschrift für Naturforschung:- 5. 91; 5. 92;

Contents

CHAPTER 1

Introduction

It is more then a century since the first qualitative observations of the effects of ion bombardment of surfaces were reported. In 1851 Plucker observed that in X-ray tubes a continuous removal of gas occurred and the X-rays became 'harder' since increasingly high voltages were required to operate the tubes. This phenomena was ascribed to ionization of the residual gases after which the energetic ions struck, penetrated, and were trapped in exposed regions of the tubes. A little later, in 1852, Grove noted that surfaces struck by these energetic ions were slowly eroded due to removal of the target material by the impinging ions. Following these early observations, the subject lay more or less dormant for 100 years except for a few exploratory experiments by Langmuir, Dushman and their collaborators at the General Electric Laboratory on the gas removal phenomenon, and preliminary investigation of the target erosion or 'sputtering' process by Güntherschulze. During this period the phenomena were regarded with some disapprobation since they were generally an undesirable adjunct of other experiments and the major concern was for their elimination. In addition, other phenomena associated with the ion bombardment of solids were also noted and subjected to a superficial analysis. These processes included the ejection of electrons from ion bombarded surfaces (secondary electron emission) the reflection and neutralization of the incident ions, and the ejection of charged target particles as well as the neutral atoms which form the bulk of the sputtering process. The results of these early investigations have been collected by Massey and Burhop, Dushman and Güntherschulze and reference to these publications reveals the unsatisfactory understanding of the subject existing even as recently as 1940.

Even during the 1939-45 period in which so much scientific research accelerated astronomically, very little further knowledge of this subject was acquired. However, several of the well known developments of this period did have a bearing on later activity in this field and led to renewed endeavour in the post 1950 era. One such development was radar with the requirements of high power transmitting valves, in which the gas disappearance phenomenon was particularly obnoxious. A second development was the increasing size of machines for producing and accelerating nuclear particles, which required and posed new problems in the maintenance and measurement of very low pressures. These requirements led in turn to investigation of the operation of pressure measuring devices which relied upon gas ionization phenomena and inevitably suffered from the gas trapping processes. Indeed, as a result of these investigations the possible use of the ion trapping process as a pumping effect was realised and the phenomenon was exploited in pumps based upon the trapping phenomenon. The importance of sputtering as a means of producing clean, fresh metal films which were highly chemically reactive to many gas molecules, and could therefore act as pumps, was also realised and exploited. It was also recognised that the sputtering phenomenon could be used to produce clean target surfaces by removal of contaminants and that targets so produced could be used for investigation of other surface phenomena.

In this initial period of expanding experimental activity most emphasis was placed upon utilising the phenomena for practical purposes, and with the exception of an enlightened, premature theoretical treatment of ion penetration processes by Bohr, very little was achieved in obtaining a clearer understanding of the phenomena either through careful experimental investigation or theoretical interpretation. Inevitably, however, investigators came to realize that in order to be able to predict device behaviour it was necessary to possess fundamental knowledge of the important phenomena, and it is since 1955 that the majority of basic research has been conducted on ion bombardment induced phenomena and it is with this research that this book is largely concerned. A further development of the decades from 1940 onwards was the increasing investigation, and use, of nuclear reactors in which many materials were subjected to intense irradiation from highly energetic light particles. The results of these investigations have been well documented and it is not our intention to dwell on this type of irradiation in this text. Nevertheless, subsequent investigations of target reactions induced by lower energy but larger mass particles, appreciated that many of the target reactions would be similar whether induced by either type of irradiation, differing only in magnitude. The most important of the target reactions from our present point of view was the production of lattice damage in the target materials due to the collision of the energetic particles with lattice atoms and electrons and the displacement of these from their normal equilibrium positions. Indeed current investigations and theories of many ion-target interactions draw heavily on concepts initially developed in radiation damage work.

In this text we will be almost wholly concerned with the effects resulting from the collision of quite low energy ions with solid targets, although reference will be made, where appropriate, to higher energy investigations with primary particles from accelerators and nuclear reactors. Low energy, in the present context therefore refers to particle energies in the region of about 0-100 KeV. Apart from the fact that such low energy particles will be unable to cause nuclear transmutations in the irradiated targets there will generally be a different dominant type of interaction between the ions and the target. As we suggested earlier, energetic particles will collide and interact with both target atoms as a whole and the individual electrons of these atoms. In the next chapter we will consider in some detail the nature of the interaction between two colliding atoms and will show that at high particle energies the dominant collision effect is the interaction of the incident particle with the atomic electrons. At energies below about A KeV, however, where A is the lower atomic weight of the colliding particles, it transpires that the colliding particles can be treated as perfectly elastic entities and that energy transfer processes can be adequately described by classical mechanical considerations. In this energy region, therefore, we will be mainly interested in interactions between the incident ion and the individual lattice atoms rather than with processes which involve only the atomic electrons.

Since all ion bombardment induced phenomena are essentially due to the successive interactions of the incident ions with target atoms, it is clear that a basic understanding of the collision mechanics of two particles is desirable. In Chapter 2 we consider this fundamental collision process in detail and examine the methods used to determine the collision dynamics exactly and the simplified methods of solution through the use of appropriate approximations. We will see that the collision dynamics are conditioned wholly by the forces of interaction (and therefore the interaction potential energies) between the colliding particles and consideration will be given to the analytical form of these forces in determining the effects of ion bombardment due to a succession of atomic collisions and will be stressed again and again.

Although we will see in Chapter 2 that the majority of low energy collisions are adequately described using essentially wholly elastic particles in which there is no overall loss of energy, we will also see that some inelasticity is always present due to quantized processes involving electronic excitation phenomena. One such excitation process is the ion induced electron ejection, or secondary electron emission, from bombarded surfaces, and the experimental observations and theoretical interpretation of measurements on this process are surveyed in Chapter 3. This topic has been the subject of sporadic investigation since 1889 but much of the credit for the introduction of elegant experimental techniques and understanding of the electron emission process must go to Hagstrum and his collaborators, particularly in the ion energy region from 10 ev to 1000 ev. More recently investigators have tended to concentrate upon higher ion energies (>1 keV) where, as we shall see, the emission process tends to be conditioned by somewhat different factors from those at the lower energies. Parameters of particular importance appear to be the ion penetration into the lattice and the structure of the lattice itself.

However, when ions are incident upon a solid target one may anticipate that not all are able to penetrate into the lattice, but that some will be reflected back from the surface and Chapter 4 summarizes measurements of this reflection process. Current investigations of this phenomenon are indicating the importance of lattice structure in determining reflection effects, since this structure will determine the nature of the spatial force distribution experienced by an incident ion. In addition to ion reflection one may also anticipate that electron excitation processes may cause ion neutralization at the surface and influence atomic reflection and these matters are also investigated in Chapter 4. Finally the possibility of emission of charged target particles, other than electrons, is also considered in this Chapter.

As the incident ion energy is increased it is expected that a larger fraction of the ions will be able to penetrate the surface force fields and enter the bulk of the lattice. Any particular ion will then experience a sequence of collisions, each described by the dynamics investigated in Chapter 2, losing a certain fraction of its energy at each atomic encounter until it has degraded to such an energy that it can no longer migrate. Because of the wide variety of possible incidence positions on a surface the trajectories of different ions through the target lattice can be completely different, before coming to rest, and in Chapter 5, we examine the nature and statistics of the ion paths in the lattice. The earliest theoretical work on this topic was conducted by Bohr and this investigation has been continued by the Danish school, notably by Lindhard. In addition the Oak Ridge group in the United States have made significant contributions to the theory of ion penetration problems and introduced the method of solving the particle trajectory equations with very fast computational techniques. As a result of this latter method of study the Oak Ridge investigators were able to predict the probable importance of lattice structure in determining ion penetration and this has led to considerable experimental activity which in turn has confirmed the theoretical predictions. Outstanding in the experimental field on this topic has been Davies and his collaborators at Chalk River in Canada, who has introduced some very sophisticated methods of determining ion penetration in an ever expanding range of target materials. These workers have conducted most of the important investigations on this subject and were first to confirm the importance of lattice structure. In Chapter 5 we first examine the theoretical evaluations of ion penetration, since to a large extent these preceded the experimental observations which are currently being reported at an ever increasing rate. The computational methods of approximating the theory are then examined and finally the available experimental data is surveyed.

A similar approach is employed in Chapter 6 where the effects of ion bombardment upon the individual target atoms within the lattice are appraised. Since, in slowing down in the lattice, the incident ion must impart considerable energy to the lattice atoms it is reasonable to suppose that considerable destruction of the original lattice order will result from ejection of the target atoms from their normal equilibrium positions, and these bulk disordering effects are summarised under the title of Radiation Damage. Several excellent texts have been published on radiation damage due to high energy particle bombardment but these have paid little attention to the energy range of interest in this book. Relatively recent theoretical work has shown that at low particle energies the lattice structure has a determining influence upon the nature and extent of radiation damage, and apart from a recent text by Leibfried (1. 1) the theories of lattice effects have not been collected together nor their importance summarized. In Chapter 6 we give a brief survey of possible defects in irradiated lattices and recapitulate the important results of 'conventional' radiation damage theory which pertain properly to a random spatial distribution of target atoms but which have some applicability to our current interest. The theories of the influence of lattice structure are then summarized, in particular the phenomena of 'focusing' where energy is transmitted efficiently along rows of atoms in a billiard ball type of collision sequence, and 'channelling', where energetic atoms can move long distances near the central axes of adjacent rows of atoms which are relatively devoid of interatomic force, and examine the importance of these processes in radiation damage theory. Many of the significant advances in the theories of lattice influence have been made by Leibfried and his collaborators in Germany and at Oak ridge. We then continue with a description of the collective interaction of an ion with several lattice particles which can induce somewhat different types of lattice damage, and can also result in re-ordering of the damaged regions, and conclude the theoretical survey with an analysis of a further type of lattice reordering due to thermal activation and migration of displaced atoms. The computational methods of studying lattice damage, due particularly to Vineyard and Erginsoy and their co-workers, and Beeler and Besco, are then examined and finally the experimental studies of radiation damage are reviewed.

In this latter section the contributions of Trillat and his group at Bellevue on microscopic observations of damage are notable whilst the high resolution studies of damage on the atomic scale using electron microscopic techniques by the Harwell group and ion emission microscopy by Brandon et al and Müller are outstanding for their elegance.

Since atomic displacement occurs in the bulk of the target during irradiation, it is logical to suppose that such displacements should also occur at the free surface, resulting in ejection of surface atoms in the process known as sputtering. This phenomenon is the subject of discussion in Chapter 7. The order of presentation is reversed in this Chapter since this phenomenon has been subjected to the highest degree of experimental study of any discussed in this book. Only recently have relatively reliable theoretical and computational evaluations of the sputtering phenomenon been produced although many, rather abortive, attempts have been made in the past.

Initial experimental studies of sputtering were concerned mainly with evaluating the efficiency of the process as a function of the ion and target material i.e. in determining the number of sputtered atoms per incident ion. Wehner and his co-workers noted however, in studies of the directions of emission of sputtered atoms, that there was a high degree of correlation with the known structure of the target lattice. In fact it was quickly realised that this symmetry resulted from the preferential conduction of energy along atomic rows in the target, i.e. in the focusing events mentioned in connection with Chapter 6. Since this initial observation, numerous studies of the focusing process have been undertaken with valuable contributions from Wehner himself, Robinson at Oak Ridge, Thomson's group at Harwell, Kistemaker and his co-workers at Amsterdam, Yurasova and Molchanov in the Soviet Union and Perovic et al at Belgrade. Significant theoretical advances have been made by Robinson and by Thomson and Nelson and various groups have initiated computer studies. The present situation in studies of the sputtering phenomenon is very encouraging and substantial agreement has been reached between experiment and theory as Chapter 7 will reveal and both types of study are advancing rapidly.

As a result of the sputtering process it is expected that not only the target will be eroded but that ions trapped in the lattice will be simultaneously released. The simple calculations and experimental results discussed in Chapter 5 refer largely to targets where the sputtering, radiation damage and gas release processes are supposed to be minimal. In Chapter 8 we explore the influence of these processes on gas trapping phenomena in greater detail and discuss the mechanisms involved in solution of the trapped gas in the target and the various gas release effects including ion bombardment induced emission and thermally activated processes.

Finally, whereas most of the work discussed in Chapters 1 to 8 is heavily biassed in favour of the results of basic theoretical and experimental investigations without paying detailed attention to the experimental techniques or to practical applications of these results, this situation is rectified in Chapter 9. Here the discussion centres firstly upon the methods of production and manipulation of energetic ion beams and then upon the practical devices and techniques which rely upon the phenomena associated with ion bombardment such as ion pumping, ion doping, ionic etching and surface cleaning.

Most of these introductory remarks may appear to be as much a catalogue of investigators in the field as of the work they have performed. This was our deliberate intention since it is indicative of the wide prominence being given to ion bombardment studies at the present time and of the global interest in these studies. In addition to the ever increasing literature on ion bombardment phenomena, symposia are regularly held which bring together the interested workers and at which the participants represent laboratories from several scientific disciplines and from many nations.

As we have noted above, investigators in many scientific disciplines are using ion bombardment techniques as a research tool and as a practical technique. Since most of the remainder of this work will be concerned with the effects of ion bombardment on real lattice structures, and since some readers may be unfamiliar with the structures of crystalline materials, it is useful to recapitulate briefly the major structures and the methods of atomic designation of crystals with which we shall be concerned. Figure 1.1 which is duplicated in most elementary Physics, Chemistry or Metallurgy texts, indicates the arrangement of atoms in the structures of the face centred, body centred and hexagonal close packed crystal lattices. The unit cells depicted here are replicated throughout space to form a macroscopic perfect crystal, and the arrangement of the atoms in each cell then typifies the crystal structure. Any deviation from the unit cell structures of Figure 1.1 leads to defects in the crystal, and indeed thermodynamic considerations soon show that any real crystal at a finite temperature differs in some degree from the replicated unit cell structure.

When considering the atomic arrangements of crystals it is convenient to be able to specify directions and planes in the crystal in order to identify the atomic configuration of interest.

The general method of crystal indexing is due to Miller and is briefly as follows. Consider the atom O in the f.c.c. structure of Figure 1.1 a as the origin of co-ordinates, with the co-ordinates axes Ox, Oy, Oz atoms along the axes are then equally spaced at intervals of $\underline{a}$ units, and may be assigned numerical values according to the number of units which each is displaced from the origin. Clearly any atom can then be specified by these co-ordinate numbers, and atoms A, B and C, for example in Figure 1.1 have position defined by $(1, 0, 0)$, $(1, 0, 1)$, $(\frac{1}{2}, \frac{1}{2}, 0)$ respectively.

Since the lattices are merely reproductions of the unit cells it is more convenient to define planes and rows of atoms rather than individual atoms. Considering a plane ABPQ parallel to the Oyz plane, which cuts the x axis at 1 unit, and the Oy and Oz axes at effectively infinite units, then the indices $(1, \infty, \infty)$ specify this plane. Clearly planes specified by (n, ∞, ∞) are parallel to this plane, where n is integral

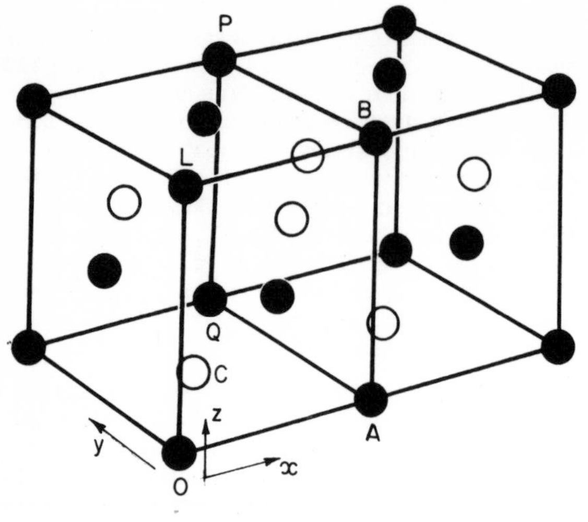

Fig. 1.1a The arrangement of atoms in a face centred cubic crystal

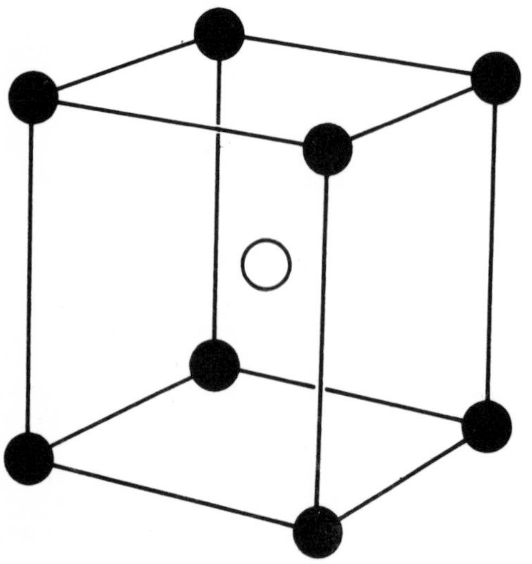

Fig. 1.1b The arrangement of atoms in a body centred cubic crystal

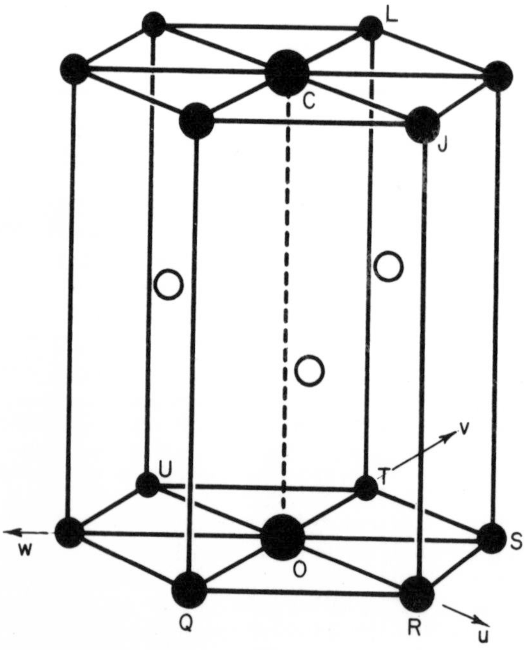

Fig. 1.1c The arrangement of hexagonal close packed crystals

or fractional. The Miller system of plane indexing then considers the reciprocals of these indices, normalised to render the values the smallest possible integers. Thus the ABPQ plane is the plane (1,0,0) and all parallel planes are specified by (1/n, 0, 0) or when normalised to make n integral, (1, 0, 0). Thus a set of planes is generally specified by the notation (h, k, l) where 1/h, 1/k, 1/1 are intersections of the plane on the Ox, Oy and Oz axes measured in a units. Clearly the Oxy plane is the (0, 0, 1) plane, and the plane OLPQ the $(1, \bar{1}, 0)$ plane where the $\bar{1}$ indicates a negative intersection on the y axis. (This latter plane is of course perpendicular to the (1, 0, 1) plane.) In symmetrical crystals, such as the f.c.c. and b.c.c. considered here, planes such as (1, 0, 0) (0, 1, 0) (0, 0, 1) are in fact identical in the disposition of atoms within them, since a 90° reorientation of the axes will change one plane to either of the others. It is convenient to refer to this set of symmetrical planes by the notation {1, 0, 0}.

The directions of crystal rows may also be readily obtained, by taking the ⟨h k l⟩ row as that perpendicular to the (h k l) plane. The h, k, l, in this designation are thus proportional to the direction cosines of the row ⟨h k l⟩. In hexagonal close packed (h c p) structure it is often convenient to specify a fourth index, since these lattices do not possess cubic symmetry. Reference to Figure 1.1 c shows that there are three axes Ou, Ov, Ow which are mutually inclined at 120° in the plane defined by PQRSTU and which are perpendicular to the axis Oc. PQRSTU is defined as a basal plane of the crystal and Oc the symmetry axis, and it is evident that the crystal structure has sixfold symmetry about this axis since 6 × 60° orientations about this axis leads to identical atomic configurations. In order to specify the orientation of a given plane within this symmetric arrangement it is necessary to specify intercepts on all these axes Ou, Ov, Ow (only 3 not 6 are required). It is readily shown that a plane which intersects the Ou and Ov axes at a/h units and a/k units respectively, will also intersect the Ow axis at $-\frac{a}{h + k}$ units (e.g. plane RJLT meets the Ou and Ov axes at a units and the Ow axis at −a/2 units). Thus the Miller indices describing orientation with respect to the C axis, gives the final specification (h, k, −(h + k), l). F.c.c. and b.c.c. structures are those commonly associated with many metals whilst many semiconductors, including silicon and germanium, crystallize in the h.c.p. structure.

Finally we should mention one aspect of ion bombardment which we will not consider in this book, namely the phenomenon of surface adsorption. Generally speaking this term is applied to the reactions between atoms or molecules with energies typical of the thermal ambient and solid (or liquid) surfaces, where the atoms become attached to the surface via physical or chemical binding forces. There is no reason to suppose that very low energy incident ions should not suffer a similar interaction, but since, to our knowledge, no specific measurements with ions have been made and since the subject of surface adsorption has been admirably and fully discussed in other texts (notably in a recent work by Kaminsky (1.2)) we will not consider it further. We may note, however, that surface adsorption of atoms upon a target can influence the nature of the interaction of a faster ion with that surface and where this influence is of some importance we shall take due cognizance of the effect.

REFERENCES

1 Leibfried, G. (1965) Einführung in die Theorie der. Bestrahlungseffekte in Festkorpen. Teubner Verlag. Stuttgart (1965)

2 Kaminsky, M. (1965) Atomic and Ionic Impact Phenomena on Metal Surfaces. Springer-Verlag. Berlin (1965)

Other books and conference symposia which are of relevance are:

Dienes, G. J. and Vineyard, G. H. (1957) Radiation Effects in Solids. Interscience Publishers. New York (1957)

Billington, D. S. and Crawford, J. H. (1965) Radiation Damage in Solids. Princeton Univ. Press. Princeton (1961)

Arifov, U. A. (1965) Interaction of atomic Particles with the surface of metals. Tashkent Uzbekhistan (1961) English Translation in AEC-tr 6089

Chadderton, L. T. (1965) Radiation Damage in Crystals. Methuen & Co. Ltd. London (1965)

Proceedings of the International School of Physics 'Enrico-Fermi' (1960) No. 18. Radiation damage in Solids. Ed. by D.K. Holmes. Academic Press Inc. New York (1962)

Radiation Effects in Inorganic Solids (1961) Disc. Faraday. Soc. **31** (1961)

Radiation Damage in Solids, Venice Symposium (1962) International Atomic Energy Agency–Vienna (1962)

Le Bombardement Ionique (1962) Ed. by J. J. Trillat. C.N.R.S. Bellevue. Paris (1962)

Conference on Crystal Lattice Defects. Kyoto. Japan 1963. Conf. J. Phys. Soc. Japan. **18** (1963)

The Interaction of Radiation with Solids. Proceedings of the International Summer School on Solid State Physics (1963) (Mol. Belgium). Edited by Strumane, Nihoul, Gevers and Amelinckx. North Holland Publishing Co. Amsterdam (1964)

CHAPTER 2

Collisions between atoms

2.1 INTRODUCTION

When an energetic ion strikes a solid surface there is a very high probability of electron capture by one of the mechanisms which will be described in detail in Chapter 3. One therefore becomes concerned with the interaction between a fast moving atom and a solid lattice in many problems of ion bombardment. Early explanations of the effects occurring during ion bombardment envisaged a macroscopic interaction between an incident ion and the solid as a whole. For example the removal of surface material during ion bombardment (sputtering) was interpreted by Von Hippel[1,2] as the result of evaporation of the surface due to heating induced by the ions. Modern descriptions of the interaction however, appreciate that the solid lattice is composed of individually sited atoms and that the effects of ion bombardment are the result of the forces between the incident ion and each individual particle. In some cases this microscopic approach leads to results which can also be predicted on a macroscopic scale, but there are many instances in which a macroscopic view fails to explain certain phenomena observed under ion bombardment.

Since an understanding of the interaction between the ion and lattice atom is clearly basic to an appreciation of the observed phenomena, it is proposed in this chapter to investigate in some detail the mechanics of the collision of particles between which there are relative movements and forces of interaction. This study is desirable also for the converse reason: that experimental observation of the theoretical predictions of the collision mechanics will lead to a better understanding of interatomic forces. Indeed, as we shall see in this chapter, the mechanics of any collision between atoms depend very sensitively upon the assumed force of interaction between the atoms. Comparison of experimental data, as considered in later chapters, with the theoretical derivations presented here will therefore allow a better definition of the nature of interatomic forces.

It is plain that the forces between neutral atoms arise from the repulsion and attractions between the nuclei and electron clouds of the atoms and will therefore operate over all distances of separation between the atoms. This implies that an energetic atom, striking a solid surface, will interact simultaneously with all atoms of the lattice and the collision mechanics can only be deduced by integration over the whole lattice. Thus, in order to study the collision mechanics one could, in principle, construct the wave functions for the incident and lattice atoms and solve to determine the collision parameters. Indeed for high incident particle energies, it would be necessary to apply relativistic correlations. Such methods are extremely difficult, and it is fortunate that in most cases in which we are interested, the problem can be greatly simplified when it is recognised that the interaction forces between two atoms decrease very rapidly above a distance of approach of the order of the atomic diameter. This circumstance allows one to consider an encounter between the incident atom and a lattice atom individually and to virtually ignore the contributions due to more remote lattice atoms.

A fuller justification of the validity of this two-body collision approach will be given later and for the present we consider the interaction mechanics of an isolated event only. It is fortunate also that, in the energy range of interest here, quantum mechanical considerations can be very adequately approximated by classical collision mechanics. The conditions necessary to allow this approximation will also be considered in this chapter, after using the approximations to investigate the problem which is clearly one of a collision of two particles moving under the action of an (unknown) central force.

It is readily apparent that in any collision, in which two atoms are concerned, one may expect at least some quantum effects to occur. For example one may expect excitation and ionization of the incident or lattice atom, and indeed such effects do occur in the type of collisions known as 'inelastic collisions'. This type of collision predominates at higher incident particle energies and is of not so great interest in this book as the other collision interaction 'the elastic collision'. In this latter collision the energy is transferred only in kinetic energy changes of the incident and target atoms, whereas, in inelastic collisions, changes in potential energy of the individual atoms (rather than the system as a whole) occur also. Obviously there is an intermediate energy region, over which both processes are of comparable magnitude.

In keeping with what was said in Chapter 1 about the scope of the book, in that we are mainly interested in relatively low energy processes, (the region of almost entirely elastic collisions) the majority of this chapter will be devoted to discussion of collisions of this type.

However, since recent experimental investigations have been concerned with the intermediate energy range (competition between elastic and inelastic collisions), and for the sake of completeness, a short discussion on inelastic losses will also be given. Further the limits of the regions of both type of collision will be briefly discussed. For a fuller discussion on the inelastic collision region the reader is referred to texts on reactions between particles from reactors,[3] accelerators, and from fission fragments[4] with solids, since it is in this region of the energy spectrum that inelastic collisions dominate.

2.2 COLLISION KINETICS

If it is assumed initially that collisions between the incident (primary) and the lattice atoms can be treated classically by isolated two body events, then it is obvious that the problem under investigation is that of the complete determination of the trajectory of the primary when acted upon by the interatomic force between the primary and the atom with which it is in collision (i.e. the struck or target atom). If the collision partners (primary and struck atom) are considered merely as centres of force, then the trajectory of the primary may be depicted as in figure 2.1. Here, in the absence of any force of interaction $F(r)$ between the partners (where r is the distance between the

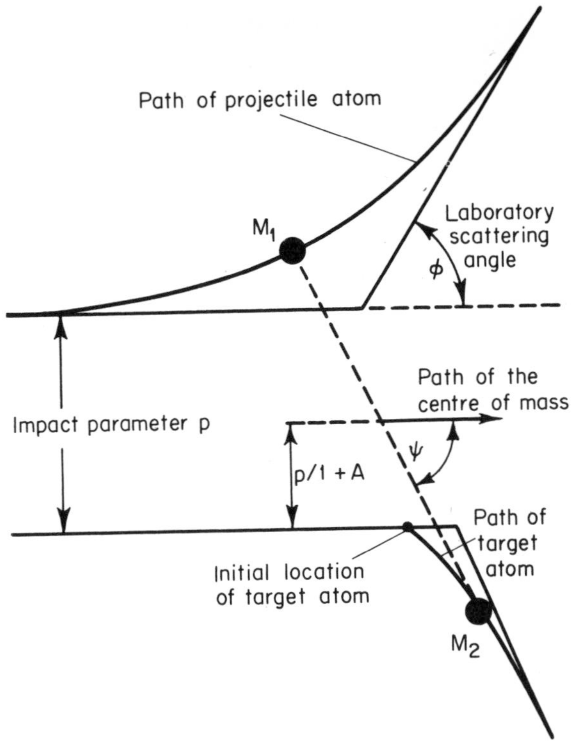

Fig. 2. 1 The scattering of a projectile atom by a target atom

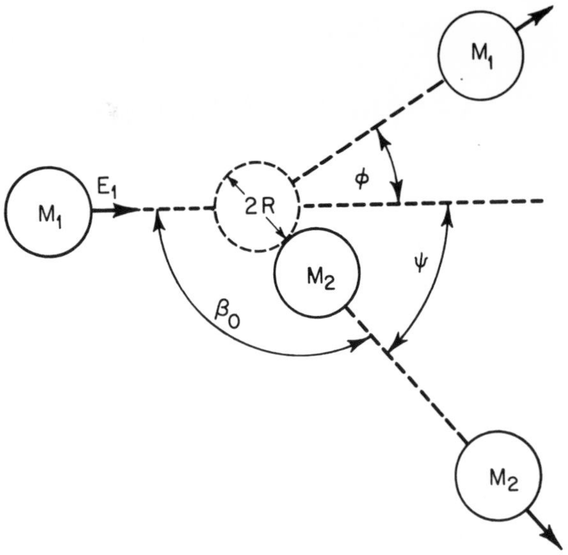

Fig. 2. 2a The collision of two hard spheres in the laboratory system

partners) the primary would pass within a (minimum) distance p, known as the impact parameter, from the struck atom and continue undeflected.

However because of the force F(r) the primary is deflected through an angle ϕ measured in the laboratory system (i.e. as seen by a stationary external observer) and the struck atom moves away at some angle ψ to the original direction of motion of the primary. Energy is patently transferred from the primary to the struck atom and the amount of energy transferred or remaining with each collision partner can be calculated. The general treatment of this energy transfer and deflection angle for an unknown force law F(r) will be returned to shortly since it is the basic interaction which determines the particle trajectories. However considerable simplification results if one assumes that the atoms are not merely centres of force with a given interaction force F(r), but that they can be represented by hard, perfectly elastic spheres of radius R. Again we will justify the assumption of the hard sphere approximation and determine the value of R typical of a certain interaction force and primary energy later, but for the present use the assumption to evaluate approximately the properties of the collision.

2. 3. 1. Collisions between elastic spheres

Assuming hard spheres of radius R for the collision partners then, for an impact parameter p (defined above as the distance of closest approach of the sphere centres in the absence of a collisions), a typical collision would appear as in Figure 2. 2a. Clearly the maximum value of p is 2R, and in a head on collision, the minimum value of p = 0. If the angle which the velocity vector v_0, of the primary makes with the line of centres of the partners at collision, is β_0 and since the kinetic energy of the incident primary is very much greater than the translational energy of the lattice atom so that the latter may be effectively considered at rest, then the lattice atom moves off after impact along the line of centres of the collision partners (since no energy can be transferred perpendicular to the line of centres). Thus the angle between the trajectory of the struck atom and the original direction of motion ψ is given by $180-\beta_0$. The primary moves from the collision position in a direction with respect to the original velocity vector which depends upon the masses of the primary and struck particles M_1 and M_2 respectively and the primary energy E_0. In order to evaluate the angle through which the primary is deflected we introduce, at this stage, the use of the centre of mass system. In Figure 2. 2a motion of the primary and struck atom is depicted as seen through the eyes of a stationary observer, however since the primary is moving towards the (effectively) stationary lattice atom, then if one views the primary and struck atom from an instantaneous position of the centre of mass of the collision partners, one sees both approaching this centre from opposite directions along a direction joining the centres. After collision both partners will move away in certain directions but their centre of mass will continue to move in the original direction with unchanged velocity. An observer moving with the centre of mass simply sees the collision partners receding in opposite directions from the instantaneous centre of mass position. This system of observation is denoted by the centre of mass system and is of particular value in that it allows considerable facilitation of the arithmetic associated with the collision processes, as follows.

In Figure 2. 2b we follow the motion in the centre of mass system, where the primary is deflected through an angle θ with respect to its original direction of motion. The direction of motion of the centre of mass is plainly parallel to that of the primary (for a stationary target atom) for an impact parameter p, the centre of mass passes within a distance $\dfrac{M_1 \cdot p}{M_1+M_2}$ from the original centre of the target atom. This direction of motion is unchanged after collision and it is further evident from momentum considerations that the centre of mass moves with an effective velocity

$$\nu_c = M_1\nu_0/M_1 + M_2 \qquad 2.1$$

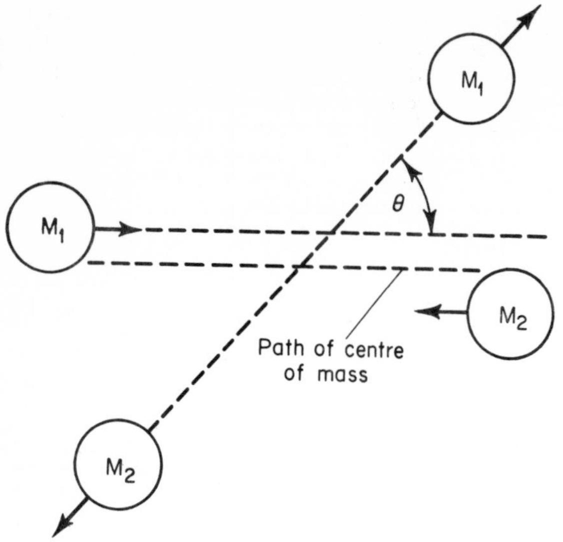

Fig. 2. 2b The collision of two hard spheres in the centre of mass system

Thus, with respect to the centre of mass, before collision, the primary has a velocity

$$\nu_0 - M_1\nu_0/M_1 + M_2 = M_2\nu_0/M_1 + M_2 \qquad 2.2$$

and the struck atom

$$-M_1\nu_0/M_1 + M_2 \qquad 2.3$$

Multiplication by the appropriate masses shows that the total momentum in the C.M. (centre of mass) system before collision, is zero, and must therefore be zero after collision also. Thus if the velocities of the primary and target atoms after collision are V_1 and V_2 in the C.M. system and the primary deflection angle is θ then the absolute values of the atom velocities in the L (laboratory) system are given by vectorially adding the velocity of the mass centre to the velocities V_1 and V_2 in the C.M. system. Because of the zero momentum condition in the C.M. system, it is required that

$$M_1V_1 = -M_2V_2 \qquad 2.4$$

and from the conservation of energy condition it is also required that

$$\tfrac{1}{2}M_1V_1^2 + \tfrac{1}{2}M_2V_2^2 = \tfrac{1}{2}M_1\left\{\frac{M_2\nu_0}{M_1 + M_2}\right\}^2 + \tfrac{1}{2}M_2\left\{\frac{M_1\nu_0}{M_1 + M_2}\right\}^2 \qquad 2.5$$

Solution of equations 2.4 and 2.5 results in values for V_1 and V_2

as $$V_1 = \frac{M_2\nu_0}{M_1 + M_2}$$

$$V_2 = -\frac{M_1\nu_0}{M_1 + M_2} \qquad 2.6$$

It is now a simple matter to deduce the velocities V_a and V_b of the primary and struck atoms in the L system by vector addition as in Figure 2. 2c. One consequently obtains

$$V_a^2 = \nu_0^2 \frac{[1 + A^2 + 2A\cos\theta]}{(1 + A)^2} \qquad 2.7a$$

$$V_b^2 = \left[\frac{2\nu_0 \sin\theta/_2}{1 + A}\right]^2 \qquad 2.7b$$

where $A = M_2/M_1$

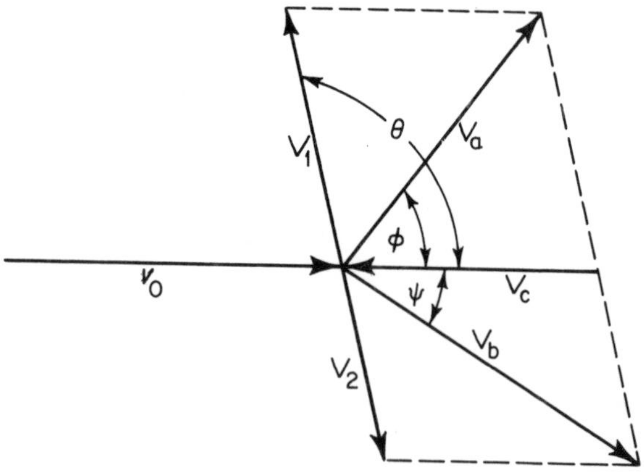

Fig. 2. 2c Velocity vector diagram in the centre of mass system

It is also evident that the relation between the scattering angle ϕ in the L and θ in the C.M. systems is

$$\tan\phi = \frac{V_1\sin\theta}{V_c + V_1\cos\theta} = \frac{A\sin\theta}{1 + A\cos\theta} \qquad 2.8a$$

and $\psi = \frac{\pi}{2} - \frac{\theta}{2}$ for the struck atom in the L system.

2.8b

The energy lost by the primary in the collision, T, is equal to that gained by the struck atom, and use of Equation 2. 7b leads to the results

$$T = \frac{2M_2\nu_0^2 \sin^2\theta/2}{(1 + A)^2} \qquad 2.9a$$

or, in terms of the primary energy E_0,

$$T = (1 - \alpha)\, E_0 \sin^2\theta/2 \qquad 2.9b$$

where

$$\alpha = \left[\frac{A - 1}{A + 1}\right]^2$$

In a head-on collision between partners $\beta_0 = 0$ and hence $\psi = 180°$ i.e. the struck atom moves parallel to the original direction of motion, $\theta = -180°$ and the motion of the primary is reversed. The maximum energy transfer in such a collision is thus

$$T = (1 - \alpha)\, E_0 = \frac{4M_1M_2}{(M_1 + M_2)^2} \cdot E_0 \qquad 2.10a$$

and therefore

$$T = T_m \sin^2 \theta/2 \quad 2.10b$$

The minimum energy transfer, for a collision at grazing incidence is zero.

The energy E_2 retained by the primary in a collision of deflection angle θ is thus

$$E_2 = E_0(1 - (1 - \alpha)\sin^2 \theta/2) \quad 2.11a$$

or, in terms of the angle of incidence

$$E_2 = E_0(1 - (1 - \alpha)\cos^2\beta_0 \quad 2.11b$$

and the energy of the struck atom

$$E_s = E_0(1 - \alpha) \cos^2\beta_0 \quad 2.11c$$

It is evident, therefore, that as the collision angle β_0, varies between 0° and $\pi/2$, the deflection angle in the C.M. system varies between π and 0° and the energy transfer falls from a maximum of E_0 $(1-\alpha)$ to zero. The deflection angle in the system is also of some importance, and vector resolution in Figure 2.2c leads to the relation:

$$\cos \phi = \tfrac{1}{2} \left\{(1 + A) \left(\frac{E_2}{E_0}\right)^{1/2} + (1 - A) \left(\frac{E_0}{E_2}\right)^{1/2} \right\} \quad 2.12$$

In the important case of equal primary and target atom masses, the useful relationships become

$$T = E_0 \sin^2 \theta/2 = E_0\cos^2 \beta_0 \quad 2.13a$$

$$\tan \phi = \tan \theta/2, \text{ or } \phi = \theta/2 \quad 2.13b$$

and

$$\cos \phi = (E_2/E_0)^{1/2} \quad 2.13c$$

2.3.2 Collision Probabilities

In addition to the total energy transfer for given collision scattering angles it is necessary to investigate the probability for the energy transfer to occur during collision. Reference to Figure 2.2 shows that

$$\sin \beta_0 = \cos \theta/2 = p/2R \quad 2.14a$$

and differentiation then shows that

$$-\sin \theta d\theta = pdp. \quad 2.14b$$

It is then readily deduced that

$$p^2 = 4R^2[1 - T/T_m] \quad 2.14c$$

and hence that

$$2\pi p \cdot \frac{dp}{dT} = \pi \cdot \frac{4R^2}{T_m} \quad 2.14d$$

The importance of these results is evident when it is realised that all angles of incidence β_0 are equally probable and hence, all values of the scattering angle θ are equally probable. This may be interpreted that scattering is isotropic in the C.M. system. Moreover, since the probability of collision with impact parameters between p and p + δp is simply the ratio of the areas between radii p and p + δp, projected onto the total projected cross sectional area $\pi \cdot 4R^2$ of the hard spheres this probability is seen, immediately, to be $\frac{2\pi pdp}{4\pi R^2}$. Thus the probability for an energy transfer between T and T + dT is simply

$$\frac{dT}{T_m} \quad 2.15$$

Since the primary and target atom centres must approach within a distance 2R to ensure collision, the area $\pi . 4R^2$ is defined as the total cross section for collision, σ, and by analogy $d(\pi p^2) = 2\pi pdp$ is the differential cross section $d\sigma(p)$ for impact parameters between p and p + p, scattering angles θ and $\theta + \delta\theta$ and energy transfers T and T + δT. Thus, since scattering angles are azimuthally symmetrically distributed over a solid angle $2\pi \sin \theta\delta\theta$, the probability of scattering into unit solid angle between θ and $\theta + \delta\theta$ is defined as $\frac{d\sigma(\theta)}{d(2\pi \cos \theta)}$, which from 2.14b, is constant and unity, independent of θ, i.e. isotropic scattering. It may also be noted that, although scattering is isotropic in the C.M. system, this is not true of the L system. Reference to Equation 2.8a shows that for the the primary mass $\ll$ target atom mass ($A \gg 1$) the scattering is still approximately isotropic even in the L system. (Thus neutron scattering from heavy solid atoms may equally well be supposed to be isotropic in the L system). However, for primary masses much greater than target atom masses ($A \ll 1$), there is a preponderance of small angle scattering in the L system. This must be anticipated heuristically in that the primary always retains most of its energy in a collision, in the forward direction. It may also be appreciated that in this case the possibility of complete reversal of direction of the primary is zero i.e. $\frac{d\sigma}{d\phi} = O$, for $\phi = 180°$. Another parameter of interest is the average energy transfer during a collision definable from $\int Td\sigma(T)/\int d\sigma(T)$, this clearly has limits O and T_m and is readily deduced as $T_m/2$, an expected result.

Finally we may evaluate the probability of a primary obtaining energies in the range E_2 to $E_2 + \delta E_2$, which is clearly equivalent to the probability of an energy transfer dT, after collision, for the incident energy E_0. If this probability is $g(E_0, E_2)\delta E_2$ we observe that since E_2 is a function only of the scattering angle (2.11a) the probability of finding primary energies between E_2 and $E_2 + \delta E_2$ is simply that of scattering between θ and $\theta + \delta\theta$. Thus $g(E_0, E_2)\delta E_2 =$ $f(\theta) \frac{d\theta}{dE_2} \cdot \delta E_2$ where $f(\theta)$ is the probability of finding angles between θ and $\theta + \delta\theta$ and is simply $\frac{\sin \theta}{2}$, $\left(\text{i.e.} \frac{2\pi \sin \theta}{4\pi}\right)$ Use of Equation 2.11a then allows deduction of $g(E_0, E_2)$ as

$$g(E_0, E_2)\delta E_2 = -\frac{\delta E_2}{E_0(1-\alpha)} \qquad 2.16a$$

Which, in the equal mass case is simply

$$g(E_0, E_2)dE_2 = -\frac{dE_2}{E_0} \qquad 2.16b$$

The independence of the primary energy after collision is notable. We observe also that $g(E_0, E_2)\delta E_2 = -\frac{\delta E_2}{E_0}$, i.e. the probability of energy transfer into δE_2 is just the ratio of the differential cross section for this event, to the total cross section.

2.4 COLLISIONS INFLUENCED BY THE INTERATOMIC FORCES

In the previous section it was noted that the collision between the primary and target atoms could, in many circumstances, be approximated by a collision between two perfectly hard spheres of definable radius R. In general terms however, the collision partners interact, not only at the instant of collision, but over all times via the mutual forces of interaction F(r). The interaction force can be thought of as composed of two terms; one attractive, which is of importance only at large interatomic distances and represents the cohesive forces which bind the crystal, the other which is repulsive dominates over the close interaction distances with which we are concerned here. The repulsive force increases rapidly with decreasing internuclear distance and this may be represented diagramatically as in Figure 2.3 where the potential

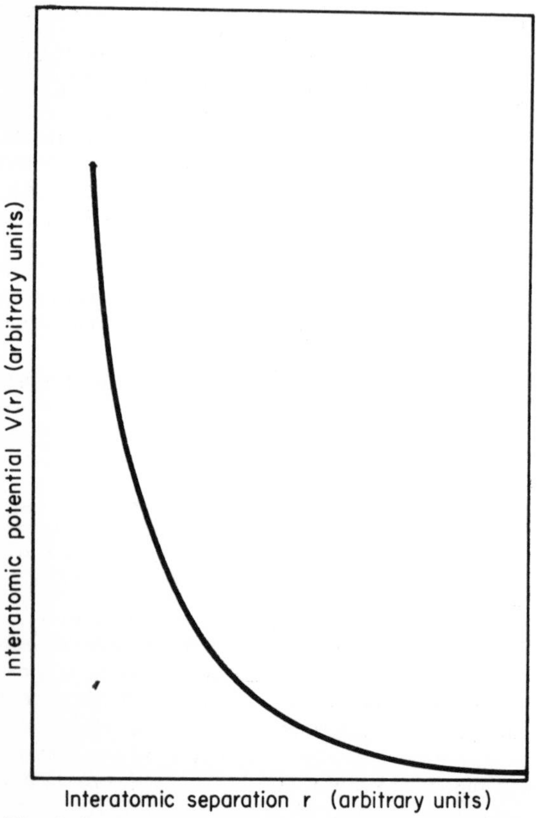

Fig. 2.3 Qualitative representation of the interatomic potential as a function of the interatomic separation

of the collision partners V(r),

where $F(r) = \frac{\partial}{\partial r}\{V/(r)\}$ increases rapidly at low separations between the force centres.

When the primary is projected at the target atom, under the influence of the interatomic potential, it is deflected from its initial trajectory through a C.M. angle θ and the formal deduction of this scattering angle θ is a straight-forward exercise in particle dynamics under a central force. We may quote the results (Goldstein)[5,6] for the angular momentum conservation

$$Mr^2\dot{\theta} = \text{constant} = (2ME_R)^{1/2}p \qquad 2.17a$$

for the total energy conservation

$$E_R = \frac{M}{2}\{\dot{r}^2 + r^2\dot{\theta}^2\} + V(r) \qquad 2.17b$$

which, upon insertion of $u \equiv \frac{1}{r}$ may be solved to yield the differential equation for the primary trajectory

$$\dot{u}^2 + u^2 = \frac{1}{p^2}\left\{1 - \frac{V(r)}{E_R}\right\} \qquad 2.17c$$

which, as shown by Lehman and Shapiro,[7] can be expressed in the integral equation

$$u = \frac{1}{p}\sin\theta - \int_0^\theta \sin(\phi - \phi')f(u(\phi'))d\phi' \qquad 2.17d$$

the prime on u denotes differentiation with respect to ϕ and p is the impact parameter as defined earlier.

$f(u(\phi'))$ is defined as $f(u) = \frac{1}{2}p^{-2}(E_R)^{-1}\left(\frac{\partial V}{\partial u}\right)$

and E_R is the primary energy measured with respect to the centre of mass, i.e.

$$E_R = E_0 - \frac{M_1}{M_1 + M_2} \cdot E_0 = \frac{A_1}{1 + A} \cdot E_0 \qquad 2.18$$

for a real primary energy E_0.

Solution of 2.17a shows that the scattering angle is given by

$$\theta = \pi - 2p\int_0^{u_0} \frac{du}{\left(1 - \frac{V(u)}{E_R} - p^2u^2\right)^{1/2}} \qquad 2.19a$$

where u_0 is the value of u for which the denominator in this expression vanishes.

The energy of the primary after collision E_2, can be related to the energy before collision via equation 2.11a or

$$\frac{E_2}{E_0} = 1 - \frac{4A}{(1 + A)^2}\sin^2\theta/2 \qquad 2.20$$

as for the hard sphere case, and the probability of finding the energy of the primary between E_2 and $E_2 + dE_2$ is

$$g(E_0, E_2) = -C \frac{pdp}{d\theta} \left| \frac{d\theta}{dE_2} \right| \qquad 2.21a$$

where the constant C is determined from the normalisation condition that

$$\int_0^{\alpha E_0} g(E_0, E_2)dE_2 = 1 \qquad 2.21b$$

Thus the minimum energy transfer, for zero angle scattering and large impact parameter, is zero, and the maximum energy transfer is αE_0 for direct collisions, as in the hard sphere case.

The scattering angle θ upon which the differential and total energy transfers depend, may be evaluated in closed form from Equation 2.19 only for a few distinct forms of the interaction potential V(r). For example

(a) The Coulomb potential $V(r) = Z_1Z_2\, e^2/r$ (e is the electronic charge and Z_1 and Z_2 are the atomic numbers of the incident and struck atoms.

(b) The inverse r^2, potential $V(r) = C/r^2$ 2.22

(c) The hard sphere potential, $V(r) = 0$ for $r > R$
$V(r) = \infty$ for $r < R$

Case (a), which has been exhaustively treated, e.g. by Bohr,[8] Rutherford[9] etc. is the form of potential often used for the scattering of α particles in passing through materials and one deduces the well known results given below where b is the impact parameter for head on collisions and θ, the scattering angle, is the angle between the asymptotes of one branch of the hyperbola performed by the primary in the C.M. system. In this system, the struck atom moves on the other branch of the hyperbola at an angle $\Omega = \pi/2 - \theta/2$. The trajectories in the laboratory system appear as in Figure 2.1 however. One also deduces, for the energy transfer

$$T = E_0 \sin^2 \theta/2 \qquad 2.23a$$

for the impact parameter

$$p/b = \cot \theta/2 \qquad 2.23b$$

and the differential cross section for scattering between θ and $\theta + \delta\theta$ is

$$d\sigma = \pi b^2/4 \cdot \operatorname{cosec}^3 \theta/2 \cos \theta/2\, d\theta \qquad 2.23c$$

which indicates that $d\sigma$ is proportional to $\frac{1}{T^2}$, i.e.

$$d\sigma = \frac{\pi b^2}{4} E_0 \frac{dT}{T^2} \qquad 2.23d$$

The other widely used case (c), the hard sphere approximation, when evaluated leads to the results given in Equations 2.10 to 2.16. A brief comparison of cases (a) and (c) shows that in the former case, there is a preference for small angle scattering as opposed to the isotropic scattering in the latter case.

For the inverse r^2 potential, (case b) Lindhard, Scharff and Schiøtt[10] have suggested

$$d\sigma\ \alpha\ \frac{1}{E_R^{1/2}} \frac{dT}{T^{3/2}}$$

2.5 COMPARISON OF THE REAL COLLISION WITH A HARD SPHERE COLLISION

We can at this point indicate how a hard sphere radius may be assigned to the collision partners. If we consider the primary approaching the target atom with a relative energy E_R as shown in Figure 2.1, then one would expect that the deflection angle θ would be determined largely by the force (and potential) at the distance of closest approach r_0 in the figure. This will be particularly true if the potential changes rapidly with interatomic distance as in Figure 2.3 since the closest approach distance will be the position of a very pronounced maximum interaction. Plainly the distance of closest approach is where the primary radial velocity is zero. It can be seen that use of equation 2.17a gives this distance r_0 in the expression

$$V(r_0) = E_R \{1 - p^2/r_0^2\} \qquad 2.24$$

If as suggested by Figure 2.3 the variation of V(r) with r is rapid, $\frac{\partial(V(r))}{\partial r}$ approaches infinity, and one may expect that the force centres may be replaced by hard spheres $\left(\text{for which } \frac{\partial(V(r))}{\partial r} = \infty\right)$ having a radius $R = r_0/2$ determined from equation 2.24, i.e. the two hard spheres approach to within a distance r_0. Clearly R depends upon the primary energy and the form of the potential chosen. The faster the variation of V(r) with distance, the harder is the potential and the smaller R for a given primary energy E_R. Similarly, a soft potential is associated with a less rapid variation of V(r). Silsbee[11] has shown that this hard sphere approximation is very reasonable, particularly in the range of small impact parameters, i.e. high energy transfers. Under these conditions Equation 2.24 is adequately represented by $V(r_0) = E_R$, and the hard sphere radius R is determined by the distance of closest approach where the interatomic potential energy equals the kinetic energy of the system for a head on collision. This approximation is used frequently in scattering calculations and is expressed generally as

$$V(2R) = E_R \qquad 2.25a$$

and in the equal mass case

$$V(2R) = E_0/2 = T_{max}/2 \qquad 2.25b$$

These equations show that the kinetic energy of motion of the colliding atoms with respect to the centre of mass is completely transformed to potential energy where these atoms just come to rest, i.e. the kinetic energy of the centre of mass is unchanged since no external constraints act upon the system if the forces due to other atoms are ignored as in the two body approximation.

A fuller consideration of the hard sphere approximation will follow shortly since it is often necessary to consider other parameters associated with the interatomic potential in order to specify R with higher precision. The hard sphere treatment leads to isotropic scattering, as noted in Equation 2.14b, but clearly a real potential will lead to conditions far from isotropic scattering and the hard sphere approximation may be quite poor.

In order to evaluate the form of the scattering law, which is of utmost importance in most problems associated with ion bombardment, it is necessary to evaluate equation 2.19 for a realistic interatomic potential.

The question is naturally posed; what is a realistic form for the interatomic potential?

2.6.1 The Interatomic Potential

The potential due to a point charge $Z_1 \cdot e$ at a distance r is given by the well known Coulomb law, $V(r) = \frac{Z_1 e}{r}$. However, in classical terms a neutral atom consists of a central, positively charged nucleus surrounded by an orbiting cloud of electrons. At a point distance r from the nucleus, the full potential due to the nucleus can be expected to be reduced by the screening effect of these orbital electrons. The exact analytical form of this screening effect has been evaluated by several authors and is obtained by integration over the contribution due to each individual electron. In general form however the potential may be expressed as

$$V(r) = f(r/a) \cdot \frac{1}{r} \cdot Z_1/e \qquad 2.26$$

where $f(r/a)$ is the screening function and a is a screening length, which for example as Bohr[8] has suggested for an isolated atom, may be expressed by $a = a_0 Z_1^{-1/3}$, where a_0 is the first Bohr orbit for the electron in the hydrogen atom and $Z_1 e$ is the nuclear charge.

Thus the exact specification of the potential depends critically upon the form chosen for the screening function.

Bohr[8] has also shown that a further expression for the screening function is

$$f(r/a) = \exp(-r/a) \qquad 2.27a$$

but other forms of $f(r/a)$ have also been proposed. These include

$$f(r/a_1) = r/a_1 \exp\{-C_1 r/a_1\} \qquad 2.27b$$

the Born-Mayer[12] function

$$f(r/a_2) = \psi(r/a_2) - C_2 a_2/r \qquad 2.27c$$

the Thomas-Fermi function

where $\psi(r/a_2)$ is the Thomas-Fermi function and is the solution of

$$\psi''(r/a_2) = \{\psi(r/a_2)\}^{3/2} \cdot \left(\frac{r}{a_2}\right)^{-1/2} \cdot \psi\left(\frac{r}{a_2}\right)$$

has been tabulated by Gombas.[13] This has been modified to

$$f(r/a_3) = \psi(r/a_3) - C_3 a_3/r \qquad 2.27d$$

where $\psi(r/a_3)$ is the solution of

$$\psi''(r/a_3) = r/a_3 \left\{ \frac{[\psi(r/a_3)]^{1/2}}{(r/a_3)} + \left(\frac{C_3 a_3}{2e}\right)^{1/2} \right\}^3$$

Similarly Holmes[14] and Oen et al[15] have proposed slight modification of the Bohr function by replacing the Bohr screening distance a as defined above by a new distance a*, equal to k.a. with k as an adjustable constant. If the potential due to one atom is as defined by any of these functions then the interatomic potential between two interacting atoms will be composed of contributions from the potential of each atom. Brinkman[16,17] has shown, using the Bohr screening function, that the energy of interaction of two atoms is obtainable from $2V(r)_A \cdot (\rho(r)_B)$ where V_A is the potential due to atom A and ρ_B is the effective charge distribution of atom B. When evaluated the mutual interatomic potential turns out to be

$$V(r) = \frac{Z_1 Z_2 e^2}{r} \left\{ \frac{a_1^2 \exp(-r/a_B) - a_2^2 \exp(-r/a_A)^2}{r a_A{}^2 - a_B{}^2} \right\} \qquad 2.28a$$

where a_A, a_B refer to atoms A and B.

For identical atoms A and B, one has

$$V(r) = \frac{Z^2 e^2}{r} \exp\left(\frac{-r}{a}\right)\{1 - r/2a\} \qquad 2.28b$$

This form which is clearly similar to the Bohr potential itself is in fact often approximated by the Bohr potential, and it is this unmodified form which is often employed in scattering calculations. Firsov[18,19,20] and Abrahamson[21-26] have also obtained the interatomic potential from the Thomas-Fermi Dirac statistical picture of the atom where Firsov has replaced a, by

$$a_F = \left(\frac{9\pi}{128}\right)^{1/2} a_0 \{Z_1^{1/2} + Z_2^{1/2}\}^{-2/3}$$

We should note that interatomic potentials of the Brinkman, Firsov or Thomas-Fermi type are repulsive at small distances of separation ($r \lesssim a$) and are weakly attractive for large separations ($r \gg 2a$) representing the mutual binding of atoms in the solid state. Thus for small approach distances, one may reasonably approximate these interatomic potentials by one of the Bohr type, although it is probable that for large distances this latter is slightly too strong a potential. On the other hand for a potential of the Born-Mayer type which has also been employed in collision problems, one recognises that this is probably too weak at small separations but better for larger separation distances.

A comparison of the various interatomic potentials is shown on Figure 2.4 with appropriate assumptions about the magnitudes of the constants involved indicated in the legend to that Figure. It is not felt meaningful to make any further comparison of the acceptability of these potentials at this stage, since to do this we should know how they were derived and what accuracy may be anticipated. The manner of derivation of the potentials for various solids will be outlined in subsequent chapters. However, in view of the frequent use of the Bohr potential in ion bombardment studies it is interesting to investigate this a little further.

From the expression $V(r) = Z_1Z_2e^2\left(\frac{1}{r}\right)\exp\left(\frac{-r}{a}\right)$

which is the form of the Bohr potential for two interacting atoms of atomic number Z_1 and Z_2, and a is given by $a = a_0(Z_1^{2/3} + Z_2^{2/3})^{-1/2}$ it is evident that at small values of the interatomic separation r the potential closely approximates to the inverse r (i.e. the Coulomb) potential. Thus for small values of the impact parameter and quite energetic collisions, the electron cloud has only a very minor screening effect. This corresponds to Rutherford scattering which as mentioned earlier, is far from isotropic. At values of r large compared with a the potential falls off more rapidly than the Coulomb potential or any power law potential and is indicative of the excessive screening effect of the electron cloud at large impact parameters. With this potential there results a preference for small angle scattering (i.e. for large impact parameters).

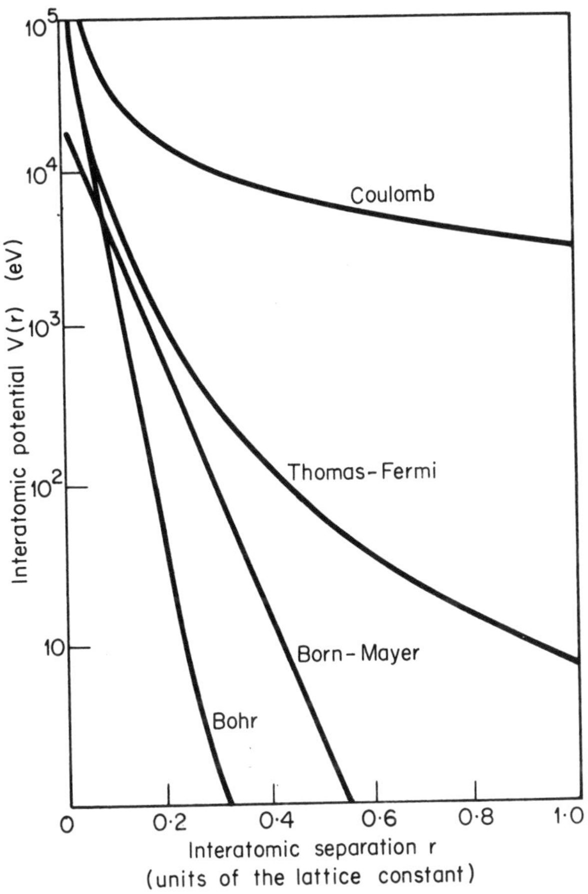

Fig. 2.4 Interatomic potentials for copper. The constants in the Coulomb, Bohr and Thomas-Fermi potentials are given in references 2.8; 2.8; and 2.13 respectively. The constants in the Born-Mayer potential have been given by Gibson et al (Ref. 2.74) from consideration of elasticity data.

It is quite clear from this very brief consideration of the Bohr potential that the hard sphere scattering will not represent the actual scattering problem with any degree of accuracy at all. To investigate the magnitude of the discrepancy we must return to our original problem of the exact solution of equation 2.19.

2.6.2 The form of the scattering law for a realistic potential

If we assume initially that the interatomic potential can be represented by the Bohr equation, then equation 2.19a becomes

$$\theta = \pi - 2p\int_0^{u_0} \frac{du}{\left\{1 - \frac{Z_1Z_2e^2}{E_R}\cdot u\exp\left(-\frac{1}{au}\right) - p^2u^2\right\}^{1/2}} \qquad 2.29$$

As noted earlier the equation is soluble in closed analytic form for a very few forms of V(r) only and, unfortunately, the Bohr potential does not belong to this class. However the equation can be evaluated numerically and this has been undertaken by Everhart, Stone and Carbone[27]. The details of the calculation are unnecessary to our present discussion except to note that accuracy can only be maintained if the equation is rewritten in the form

$$\theta = \pi - 2p/a\left\{\int_0^Z y_0^{-1/2}\,dz - \int_0^Z (y_0^{-1/2} - y^{1/2})\,dz\right\} \qquad 2.30$$

where

$$\left.\begin{aligned} y &= 1 - (p/a)^2Z^2 - (b/a)\,Z\,.\,\exp(-1/Z); \\ y_0 &= 1 - (p/a)^2Z^2 - (b/a)\,Z\,.\,\exp(-1/Z_0) \end{aligned}\right\}$$

with Z_0 the root of the equation for y, since in the former equation one becomes concerned with the difference between two closely equal quantities.

These authors have evaluated the integral in equation 2.30 for various values of the incident particle energy E_R and obtained the scattering angle as a function of the impact parameter for each energy. The differential cross section for scattering is then derived from the equation $d\sigma = p\delta p/\sin\theta\delta\theta$ and this parameter is plotted as a function of the scattering angle, as in Figure 2.5. The variable parameter in this figure is

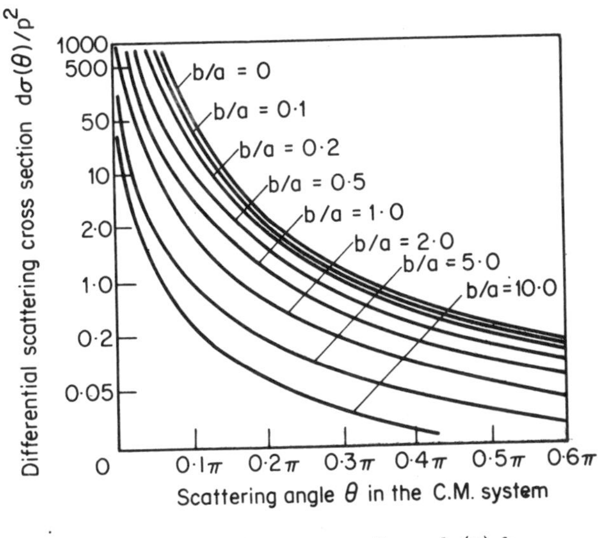

Fig. 2.5 Differential cross sections $d\sigma(\theta)$ for scattering from a Bohr potential plotted as a function of the C.M. scattering angle θ b is the collision diameter and a the screening radius. For $b/a = 0$, or $a = \infty$, the curve corresponds to that for Rutherford scattering (Ref. 2.27)

the distance of closest approach b in a head on collision which is defined with reference to an unscreened Coulomb potential as before, for a given primary energy E_R as $b = Z_1Z_2e^2/E_R$. Thus in figure 2.5, b/a is representative of the energy of the collision and the curve for b/a = 0 corresponds to quite high energies where the distance of closest approach is small, the potential is unscreened and the scattering reduces to the Rutherford type with the differential cross section as given earlier

$$d\sigma(\theta) = \frac{\pi b^2}{4} \ \mathrm{cosec}^3\ \theta/2 \ .\ \cos\theta/2 \ d\sigma$$

It is clear for smaller impact energies that the form of the scattering departs markedly from the Rutherford type.

Since the scattering angle is intimately connected to the energy transfer in a collision through equation 2.10 then it is instructive to replot the figure as a function of the energy transfer T. This has been accomplished in figure 2 6 (taken from an article by Holmes[14]), again for the equal primary and struck atom mass case, and for comparison the scattering due to an exact Coulomb potential, due to an inverse r^2 potential and for the hard sphere case have been included. The former two cases can be evaluated analytically, but the Bohr case uses the numerical technique of Everhart et al. In order to make comparison with the hard sphere case meaningful, the hard sphere radius must be chosen appropriately. This is accomplished by use of the relation given previously $V(2R) = E_R$. For the Bohr potential $(E_B/2.) \exp(-2R/a_B)/(2R/a_B) = A(1 + A)^{-1}\ .\ (E)^{-1}$ where E_B is the Bohr energy, defined as $E_B = 2Z_1Z_2e^2/a_B$ and the factor 2 appears for convenience in the important equal mass case where $E_R = E/2$. Thus a hard sphere radius is chosen for a given primary energy and in the case of figure 2.6 the incident energy has been adopted such that $2R = 5.25\ a_B$., thus allowing appropriate choice of a curve from the Everhart[27] data. We should note that this is in the range where excessive screening can be expected to occur.

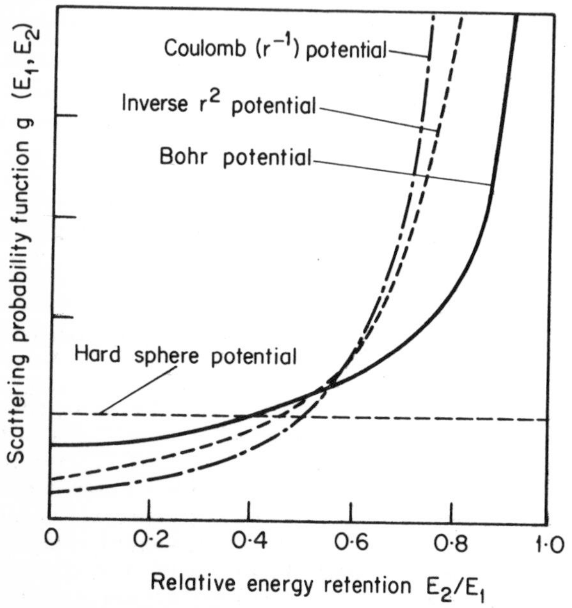

Fig. 2.6 The scattering probability function $g(E_1, E_2)$ as a function of the relative energy retention E_2/E_1 for the equal mass case for four interatomic potentials (Ref. 2.14)

It is immediately apparent that there is some similarity between the inverse power potentials (r^{-1} and r^{-2}) results but there is considerable deviation from the Bohr potential scattering at both low and high values of the transferred energy. The hard sphere scattering is clearly a very much poorer approximation to the real scattering since, at all energy transfers, the probability is constant and there is not even a suggestion of the increased probability for large and small energy transfers which is notable in the Bohr and the inverse power potential cases. This, however, should not cause us to reject the hard sphere approximation completely since the hard sphere model possesses some desirable features and allows considerable simplification to many problems. One such desirable feature of the hard sphere approximation is that the total collision cross section in this case is finite, equal to $\pi(2R)^2$ whereas all potentials which extend to infinity lead naturally to infinite cross sections. Of course one method of ensuring finite cross section is to cut off the real potential to zero at some specific interatomic separation, but the exact point at which this should be performed is one of the most critical assumptions in any calculation, and it appears that the hard sphere model, correctly applied could lead to results of similar validity but at the expense of less arduous mathematics. A further advantage of the hard sphere model is that the average energy transfer in a collision, for the equal mass case is given by

$$\overline{T} = \int_0^{E_0} (E_0 - E_2) g(E_0, E_2) dE_2 = \frac{\int_0^{E_0} T\, d\sigma(T)}{\int_0^{E_0} d\sigma(T)} \qquad 2.31$$

which is finite for the Bohr and hard sphere cases but is divergent for the Coulomb potential. Finally a large improvement in the agreement between the scattering in the Bohr and hard sphere cases could be obtained by allowing an infinite spike in the latter cross section just where the energy transfer is 50% of the maximum. Further consideration will be given to this important approximation shortly.

In the same way as Everhart et al,[27] computed differential cross sections for the Bohr potential it must be anticipated that similar calculations can be performed for the alternative potentials proposed in equations 2.26 and 2.27 For example Lindhard et al.[10,28] have deduced differential cross sections for a Thomas-Fermi potential. However, it is clear that such computations are laborious and moreover do not give analytical expressions which can be used for calculations. It thus seems desirable to see if any approximations can be introduced in order to facilitate evaluation of equation 2.19a.

We should also note that Robinson[29] has prepared tables, similar to those of Everhart et al, for the scattering angle as a function of impact parameter, for various relative collision energies, with the interatomic potential assumed as the Bohr type, the Born-Mayer type or the Thomas-Fermi type. Values of transferred energy are also deduced together with the distance travelled by the centre of mass during the interaction. The results agree well, in the common region, with those of Everhart et al, and the extension to other potentials render these tables valuable as a reference source.

2.7.1 Approximations to the exact scattering law

Baroody[30,31] has considered solutions to the scattering equation 2.19a for the class of potentials described by

$$V(r) = Br^{-n} \exp(-\frac{r}{a}), \qquad 2.32$$

which is equivalent to the Bohr potential for n = 1, the exponential (or Born-Mayer) potential for n = 0 and the hard sphere potential for a = ∞. A convenient method of approach is to define a parameter

$$\gamma = \frac{\partial \log V(r)}{\partial \log r}\bigg|_{r=c} = n + \frac{c}{a} \qquad 2.33$$

where c is the distance of closest approach in a head on collision and is therefore related to the energy of the incident particle. Equation 2.19a can be rewritten

$$\theta = \pi - \frac{2p}{c} \cdot I \qquad 2.34$$

where

$$I = \int_{x_0}^{\infty} \{1 - (p/cx)^2 - v(x)\}^{-1/2} . dx . x^{-2} \quad 2.35$$

$v(x) = V(r)/V(c)$ and the distance of closest approach for an impact parameter p is $r_0 = cx_0$. Thus

$$v(x_0) = x^{-n} \exp\{-(\gamma - n)(x - 1)\} \qquad 2.36a$$

and x_0 satisfies

$$x_0^2[1 - v(x_0)] = (p/c)^2 \qquad 2.36b$$

If one substitutes $y = 1 - (p/c)^2$, then

$$x_0 = 1 + \frac{\log_e y}{\gamma^2}\left[-\gamma + \frac{2}{y}(1 - y) + \frac{n}{2\gamma} \log_e y\right] \qquad 2.36c$$

A further parameter $R(\theta)$ is defined such that

$$p = R(\theta) \cos \theta/2 \qquad 2.37a$$

and I may be rewritten

$$I = c/p \sin^{-1} (p/cx_0) + J \qquad 2.37b$$

where

$$J = \int_{x_0}^{\infty} (\{1 - (p/cx)^2 - v(x)\}^{-1/2} - \{1 - (p/cx)^2\}^{-1/2})x^{-2}dx \qquad 2.37c$$

For large γ most of the contribution to J arises for x values close to x_0 (the distance of closest approach) and letting $x = x_0(1 + \epsilon)$ one may expand the integral for J in powers of ϵ.

$$\text{i.e. } x_0[v(x_0)]^{1/2} . J = \int_0^{\infty} \left\{\left(1 - \frac{v(x)}{v(x_0)}\right)^{-1/2} - 1\right\} d\epsilon \qquad 2.38a$$

When this integral is evaluated in powers of γ up to γ^{-2} using equation 2.36 one obtains

$$x_0[v(x_0)]^{1/2} . J = \frac{D_0}{\gamma} + \frac{1}{\gamma^2}\left[\left(1 - \frac{n}{\gamma}\right)(D_0 \log_e y - D_1) - \frac{(D_1 + D_0)}{y} + 2D_0\right] \qquad 2.38b$$

where

$$D_0 = \log_e 4, D_1 = \pi^2/6 - 2(\log_e 2)^2$$

From equation 2.37a

$$\frac{p}{R(\theta)} = \cos \theta/2 = \sin \frac{pI}{c} = (p/cx_0) \cos \frac{pJ}{c} + \{1 - (p/cx_0)^2\}^{-1/2} \times . \sin \left(\frac{pJ}{c}\right) \qquad 2.39a$$

which can be expanded in terms of γ to give

$$\frac{x_0 c}{R(\theta)} = 1 + x_0[v(x_0)]^{1/2} . J - 0.5\left(\frac{pJ}{c}\right)^2 \qquad 2.39b$$

Combining equations 2.38b and 2.39b one finally obtains

$$\frac{R(\theta)}{c} = 1 - \frac{\log_e w}{\gamma} + \frac{1}{\gamma^2}\left[\pi^2/6\left(1 - \frac{n}{\gamma} + \frac{4}{w}\right) + \frac{n}{2\gamma} (\log_e w)^2\right] \qquad 2.40$$

where $w = 4 \sin^2\theta/2$. The differential scattering probability $\frac{d\sigma(\theta)}{d\Omega}$ is then related to $R(\theta)$ via

$$\frac{d\sigma(\theta)}{d\Omega} = \frac{d(\pi p^2)}{d(2\pi \cos \theta)} = \frac{d}{dw}\left\{\left(\frac{w}{4} - 1\right) R^2(\theta)\right\} \qquad 2.41a$$

and from equation 2.40 one obtains

$$\frac{d\sigma(\theta)}{d\Omega} = \frac{c^2}{4}\{1 + A_1/\gamma + A_2/\gamma^2\} \qquad 2.41b$$

where

$$A_1 = 2\{4/w - 1 - \log_e w\}$$
$$A_2 = \pi^{2/3}\{1 - n/\gamma + 16/w^2\} + (1 + n/\gamma) \log_e w (\log_e w + 2 - 8/w)$$

Baroody has compared the results of equation 2.41b with exact calculations for inverse sixth and twelfth power potentials (which may be obtained since solutions of equation 2.19a are known elliptic integrals) and shown that agreement is very good. For small scattering angles it is found necessary to use only the first two terms of equation 2.41b to obtain good agreement, but for large angles the use of all three terms is mandatory.

2.7.2 Asymptotic Trajectory Approximation

A second approximation was proposed by Lehman and Shapiro,[7] in which solution of the scattering equation was effected by assuming that the actual path of the primary could be approximated by two intersecting straight line elements. These linear paths were considered to be the asymptotes to the actual trajectory at infinite separation in the C.M. system. This approximation amounts to setting u(=1/r) in the trajectory equation equal to $p^{-1} . \sin \theta^1$, where θ^1 is the instantaneous scattering angle appropriate to the value of r. With this approximation the equation for the scattering angle can be transformed to an energy equation

$$V(R). + p.(R^2 - p^2)^{-1/2} \times H(R). = E_R. \quad 2.42$$

where

$$H(R). = -\int_R^{\infty} dr.\frac{p}{(r^2 - b^2)^{1/2}}\frac{d}{dr}V(r)$$

and $R = p.\sec(\theta/2)$ = distance of closest approach in the collision with impact parameter p.

It was then shown that, for physically interesting forms of the potential V(R), the function H(R). has the approximate form $V(R).[\sec(\theta/2) - \tan(\theta/2)]$ which, when substituted into the energy equation, leads to $\sin\theta/2 = V(R)./2E_R$. Since $p = R\cos\theta/2$, these relations allow derivation of R for any arbitrary potential and subsequently the scattering angle in terms of the impact parameter. Lehman and Shapiro[7] have evaluated the impact parameter, p, R, and the differential cross section for the potential defined in equation 2.28a for several values of the characteristic parameters a_1 and a_2 of this equation. In view of the fact that this potential is used very infrequently in scattering studies we shall not reproduce the results here. It is notable, however, that comparison of the approximate results for a potential of the type $V(R) = (\exp(R)-1)^{-1}$ with machine computed data give satisfactory agreement as can be seen from table 2.1. The differential cross sections are particularly satisfactory for large energy transfers, where, it can be shown that the approximation simulates the hard sphere behaviour.

TABLE 2.1 (Ref. 2.7).

Comparison of approximate and exact differential scattering cross sections for the potential $V(R) = (\exp(R) - 1)^{-1}$ as a function of incident atom energy E_0 and fractional energy transferred to struck atom, T/T_m.

T/T_m	$(T_m/4\pi)\sigma_1$	$E_0 = 10$	$E_0 = 10^{-1}$	$E_0 = 10^{-3}$	$E_0 = 10^{-5}$
1	Exact	5.3×10^{-4}	7.1×10^{-1}	8.3	26.3
	Approx	6.0×10^{-4}	8.0×10^{-1}	9.7	29.3
10^{-1}	Exact	5.9×10^{-2}	11.2	43.7	85.1
	Approx	5.1×10^{-2}	8.0	30.2	62.8
10^{-2}	Exact	5.0	1.5×10^2	3.3×10^2	5.3×10^2
	Approx	3.4	1.0×10^2	2.3×10^2	3.7×10^2
10^{-3}	Exact	2.5×10^2	1.8×10^3	2.9×10^3	4.5×10^3
	Approx	1.5×10^2	1.3×10^3	2.4×10^3	3.6×10^3
10^{-4}	Exact	6.0×10^3	2.1×10^4	3.2×10^4	5.0×10^4
	Approx	3.7×10^3	1.6×10^4	2.7×10^4	3.8×10^4

We should also note that Lehman and Shapiro,[7] in evaluating the exact scattering cross-sections numerically, have employed a somewhat different approach to that of Everhart et al[27] which removes some of the difficulties inherent in the latter treatment.

2.7.3 Matching Potential Approximation

2.7.3.1 Inverse Power Potentials

An alternative approach to the problem of the solution of the scattering equation is to approximate the real atomic potential by one which can be used to give exact solutions of the equations. This method of 'matching potentials' has been discussed by numerous authors including Bohr,[8] Lindhard et al[10,28], Holmes[14] and Leibfreid and Oen[32,33], and several forms of matching potential have been proposed. One useful class of potential is the inverse power form

$$V(r). = Z_1Z_2e^2a_s^{s-1}/sr^s \qquad 2.43$$

where $a_s = c.a_0.Z^{-1/3}$ and $s \geqslant 1$, which has been discussed by Bohr[8], Nielsen[34], Lindhard et al[28] and Baroody[30,31]. The basis of the method is to compare the power potential with a realistic potential at some convenient interatomic separation, for example, the distance of closest approach in the absence of a collision or, in the extreme, in a head on collision. From this matching a value of s may be deduced which can be used in the scattering equation to allow deduction of the differential cross section. We may take, as an example the matching of a potential of the form $V(r) = c/r^s$., to the Bohr potential.

Thus at the distance of closest approach in a collision under either potential one obtains,

$$\frac{E_B}{2}.\exp(-r_0/a_B)/r_0/a_B = E_R = c/r_0^s \qquad 2.44$$

from which s may be deduced in terms of r_0. However we may anticipate that a value of s obtained in this way may not be too exact since only the potential V(r) and the matching potential $V_m(r)$ are equal at the distance of closest approach. An improvement can be expected if we require the rate of change of these potentials to match at this spacing also. With this condition applied we observe that

$$\frac{E_B}{2}\frac{\exp(-r_0/a_B)}{r_0/a_B}[1/a_B + 1/r_0] = \frac{sc}{r_0^{s+1}} \qquad 2.45$$

which, with the earlier equation leads to the identification

$$s = 1 + r_0/a_B \qquad 2.46$$

This value of s can now be used with the inverse power potential and this can then in principle at least, be substituted into the scattering equation to obtain the cross section. In all except the simplest cases of $s = 1$ or $s = 2$, this equation is still difficult to evaluate, although Leibfried et al[33] have shown that for arbitrary s the differential cross section for maximum energy transfer T_m is

$$d\sigma(T_m) = \frac{\pi r_0^2}{T_m}\left\{\frac{s\Gamma(\frac{1}{2} + \frac{1}{s})}{\Gamma\frac{1}{2}.\Gamma\frac{1}{s}}\right\}^2 .dT \qquad 2.47a$$

which for large s has the asymptotic expansion

$$d\sigma(T_m) \to \frac{\pi r_0^2}{T_m}\{1 - \tfrac{4}{s}\log_e 2\}dT \simeq \frac{\pi r_0^2}{T_m}\left(1 - \frac{2.8}{s}\right)dT \qquad 2.47b$$

This can be compared with the result that can be obtained from the Lehman and Shapiro treatment, which is

$$d\sigma(T_m) \to \frac{\pi r_0^2}{T_m}\left(1 - \frac{1.4}{s}\right)dT \qquad 2.47c$$

Lindhard et al[10,28] have also shown that the differential cross section for any energy transfer T can be given approximately by

$$d\sigma(T) = K_s.\frac{\pi r_0^2}{T_m^{1/s}}.\frac{dT}{T^{1+1/s}} \qquad 2.48$$

where K_s is a function of the maximum energy transfer and s. Probably the most physically interesting values of s are those where s = 1 and 2, which correspond to (a) Coulomb scattering, which according to Equation 2.46 occurs for $r_0 \ll a$, i.e. close encounters and minor screening, and (b) Inverse distance squared scattering, which corresponds to $r_0 \cong a$ where the electron clouds begin to overlap. It should be noted that Lindhard et al have evaluated the above Equation for s = 1 and 2 and compared the results with those obtained with a Thomas-Fermi screened potential. These authors show that the Thomas-Fermi function represents the r^{-1} (Rutherford) scattering quite adequately for large energy transfers, and approximates the inverse r^2 potential relatively well for small energy transfers (large impact parameters).

2.7.3.2 Hard Sphere Approximation

A further approximation[14] which is often introduced, and is very convenient for calculation purposes, is the hard sphere approximation, in which the distance of closest approach r_0 as obtained from the matching criteria such as Equations 2.25 and 2.44 is considered to be simply twice the radius of the hard spheres. The intermediate use of the matching potential assists in defining this hard sphere radius, since from equation 2.46 for the Bohr Potential. $s = 1 + r_0/a_B$ and $E_R = \dfrac{c}{r_0^{(1+r_0/a_B)}}$ giving r_0 for each energy E_R.

Thus both the total collision cross section $\pi r_0^2 = 4\pi R_0^2$ and the differential collision cross section

$$\frac{\pi r_0^2}{T_m}dT = \frac{4\pi R_0^2}{T_m}dT$$

can be evaluated in terms of E_R.

Clearly this evaluation must be performed numerically for each incident energy but the result is considerably simpler than if the hard sphere radius had been calculated directly from the Bohr potential. The technique can also be applied to encounters which are not head on since for an impact parameter p the distance of closest approach is given as in equation 2.24 by $p^2 = r_0^2(1 - V(r_0)/E_R)$ and this relation can be used to evaluate r_0 for each value of p. Essentially this procedure allows the hard sphere radius to vary as the impact parameter varies, and so the scattering is no longer isotropic as for the sphere of constant radius. Beeler and Besco[35] have compared the C.M. scattering angle as a function of the impact parameter for the exact case (Everhart et al calculation), with the constant radius hard sphere model and the variable radius hard sphere model. Their results for a collision of relative energy of 1 KeV between two Beryllium atoms are presented in table 2.2. It is

TABLE 2.2

Comparison of centre of mass scattering angle (cos θ) given by Everhart et al. (Ref. 2.27) Holmes (hard sphere Ref. 2.14) and the variable radius hard sphere model (Ref. 2.35) for a 2 keV (laboratory system energy) beryllium-beryllium collision. p is the common impact parameter in Å.

Everhart et al.	Beeler -Besco	Holmes	Impact Parameter. p.
−1.0000	−1.0000	−1.0000	0
−0.7193	−0.8886	−0.8782	0.0330
0.0174	−0.5276*	−0.3438	0.0767
0.3090	−0.3014*	0.1764	0.1027
0.5878	−0.0284*	1.0000	0.1388
0.8090	0.2928*	1.0000	0.1955
0.8910	0.4860*	1.0000	0.2361
0.9511	0.6744*	1.0000	0.3046
0.9686	0.7298*	1.0000	0.3471
0.9823	0.8240	1.0000	0.4014
0.9921	0.8856	1.0000	0.4769
0.9956	0.9130	1.0000	0.5312
0.9980	0.9404	1.0000	0.6115
0.9995	0.9960	1.0000	0.7555

* Possibly unrealistic scattering range.

clear that in numerical terms the variable radius model is probably a poorer approximation to the exact case than the constant radius model, but it should be noted also that in the results of the constant radius model many correspond to complete misses between the spheres (i.e. for $p > 2R_0$). The variable radius model however always ensures a collision even at large impact parameters, which is clearly closer to the true state of affairs. Lee and Robinson[36] have drawn similar conclusions in a comparison of the constant and variable hard sphere radius models with exact computer calculations for the Bohr potential. Again there will be the drawback with this model of an effectively infinite collision cross section, which will be a severe restriction for many calculational purposes. Despite the obvious limitations of the hard sphere model, for example the unrealistic scattering law, it is often used successfully to predict the general aspects of a collision problem, as we shall see in subsequent chapters, since a great simplification in the analytical computations often results.

2.7.3.3 *The Potential $V(r) = A(a'/r - 1)$ and other Truncated Potentials*

The inverse power matching potentials, can, as we have seen lead to an adequate approximation to the scattering law, although the computations associated with these often become laborious. An an alternative Leibfried and Oen[37] have suggested the matching potential

$$V_m(r) = A\left(\frac{a'}{r} - 1\right) \quad \text{for } r < a'$$
$$= 0 \quad \text{for } r > a' \qquad 2.49$$

with A and a' as determinable constants, and which is clearly cut off arbitrarily to zero at $r = a'$.

The constants A and a' are determined by comparison of the real and matching potentials at the distance of closest approach. Thus if $V(r_0)$ is the real potential and $V_m(r_0)$ the matching potential at $r = r_0$, one matching condition is $V(r_0) = V_m(r_0)$ while a second condition may be derived by requiring, as earlier, that the first potential derivatives should match at $r = r_0$.

Thus $V'(r_0) = V'_m(r_0)$ and using $V_m(r_0) = A(a'/r_0 - 1)$ these criteria lead to $A = -r_0V'(r_0)$ and

$$Aa' = -r_0^2V'(r_0) \qquad 2.50$$

The procedure is reasonable only for positive A and a', which requires that $-r_0V'(r_0)/V(r_0) \geqslant 1$. This effectively means that $V(r)$ must decrease at least as fast as r^{-1}. In view of the fact that at close approach distances, the real Bohr potential decreases according to r^{-1} and at larger approach distances according to r^{-n} (where $n > 1$) the procedure appears acceptable.

Having obtained A and a' by matching at the distance of closest approach (where $V(r_0) = E_R$) the values can be substituted back into 2.49 and this potential then substituted into Equation 2.19a to obtain the scattering law. The real value of this matching potential lies in the fact that it allows direct evaluation of the integral in Equation 2.19a which in turn leads to the relations for the matching impact parameter p_m and differential cross sections $d\sigma_m(T)$

$$p_m^2(T) = \left(\frac{Aa'}{2E_R}\right)^2 \frac{1 - T/T_m}{\left(1 + \frac{A}{E_R}\right)\frac{T}{T_m} + \left(\frac{A}{2E_R}\right)^2} \qquad 2.51a$$

$$d\sigma_m(T) = \frac{\pi}{T_m}\left\{\frac{Aa'}{2E_R} \cdot \frac{1 + A/2E_R}{\left(1 + \frac{A}{E_R}\right)\frac{T}{T_m} + \left(\frac{A}{2E_R}\right)^2}\right\} dT \qquad 2.51b$$

Since the matching potential vanishes at $r_0 = a'$, the total cross section is finite and equal to $\pi(a')^2$. Further the differential cross section behaves like hard sphere scattering if

$$\frac{A}{2E_R} \gg 1; \text{i.e. } d\sigma_m(T) \simeq \frac{\pi(a')^2dT}{T_m}$$

(i.e. at low impact energies) whereas at high impact energies, and

$$\frac{A}{2E_R} \ll 1$$

the behaviour approximates the anticipated Coulomb scattering law, i.e.

$$d\sigma_m(T) \propto \frac{1}{T^2}\, dT$$

The real test of the success of this matching potential is whether it duplicates the behaviour of realistic or assumed scattering potentials. Thus Leibfried and Oen[37] have compared the results obtained from this matching potential with those obtained from an inverse r^2 potential, the general inverse power potential r^{-n} and the Bohr Potential. In Figure 2.7 a comparison

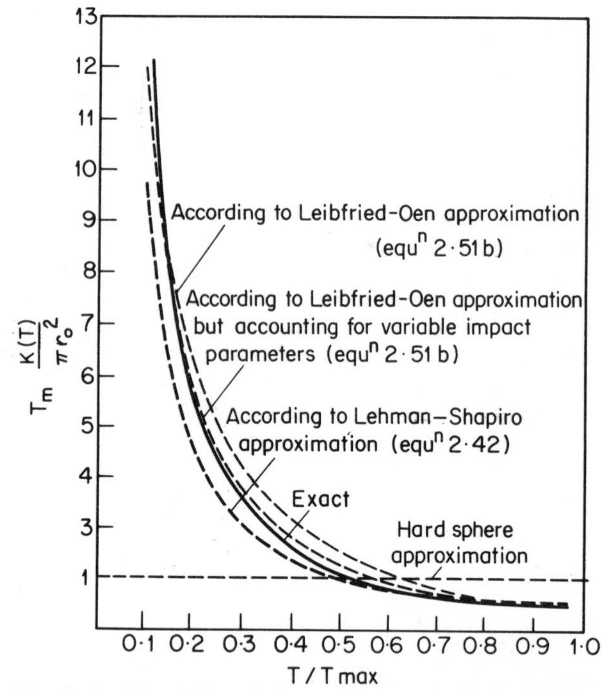

Fig. 2.7 The differential cross section as a function of the relative energy transfer for the inverse r^2 potential according to various approximations. [Ref. 2.37]

of the differential cross section (relative to the sphere cross section) is made for the inverse r^2 case, (in which exact evaluation of $p(T)$ and $d\sigma(T)$ are possible) where the above Equation 2.51b has been used to deduce

$$d\sigma_m(T) = \frac{\pi r_0^2}{T_m}\left\{\frac{3}{4\frac{T}{T_m} + \frac{1}{2}}\right\}^2$$

and where a refinement of this equation has been made in that matching has been performed for all impact parameters, using Equation 2.24 to obtain r_0 for each value of p, thence obtaining A and a' and using these values in 2.51b rather than for a head on collision only. The agreement with the exact solution, for both approximations is clearly good, except perhaps for very low energy transfers, but is always considerably better than the Lehman-Shapiro and the hard-sphere approximations.

Comparison of the cross section for $T = T_{max}$ and for a parameter known as the STOPPING POWER, defined from $\int_0^{T_m} T \,.\, d\sigma(T)$ is also valuable and the agreement of the exact and approximating potentials is evident from Table 2.3 (N.B. The stopping power is of importance in particle penetration problems and will be defined and investigated in further detail in Chapter 5).

TABLE 2.3

Comparison of the relative stopping power $\int_0^{T_m} T d\sigma(T)/\pi r_0^2$ deduced exactly (Ref. 2.33) and by the Leibfried-Oen (Ref. 2.37) and Lehman-Shapiro (Ref. 2.7) approximations for the inverse r^2 potential.

	Exact	Ref. 2.7	Ref. 2.33 (matched for head on case only)	Ref. 2.33 (matched for all impact parameters)
Relative Stopping Cross Sections	0.795	0.667	0.736	0.875

The agreement of the differential cross section maximum energy transfer $d\sigma(T_{max})$ when compared with that from the general inverse power (r^{-s}) potential is also found to be better than the Lehman and Shapiro approximation. As shown before, $d\sigma(T_{max})$ for an inverse power potential, is for large s, equal to $\left(1 - \frac{2.8}{s}\right)\frac{\pi r_0^2 dT}{T_m}$, whereas the matching potential leads to $(1 - 2/s)\frac{\pi r_0^2}{T_m} dT$ and the Lehman-Shapiro[7] treatment to $(1 - 1.4/s)\frac{\pi r_0^2}{T_m} dT$. Finally, comparison with the realistic Bohr potential, shows the utility of the matching potential.

The differential cross section in this case turns out to be

$$d\sigma(T_{max}) = \frac{\pi r_0^2}{4T_m}\left\{\frac{(1 + r_0/a)(1 + r_0/2a)}{(1 + r_0/a)\frac{T}{T_m} + (r_0/2a)^2}\right\}^2 \qquad 2.52a$$

and the total cross section

$$\sigma_m = \pi(a')^2 = \pi(r_0 + a)^2 \qquad 2.52b$$

with r_0 determined for the relative energy E_R.

Again Equation 2.52a shows the transition from almost Coulomb (Rutherford) scattering at high energies ($r_0 \ll a$) to hard sphere scattering at low energies ($r_0 \gg a$). In Figures 2.8a and 2.8b the differential cross sections deduced from Equation 2.52a and exactly by an Everhart et al[27] type of calculation for the Bohr potential are compared for two different values of r_0 (corresponding to different values of E_R). The agreement is again remarkably good except possibly at high impact parameters (low energy transfers). This is to be expected on inspection of Figures 2.9a and 2.9b where the real and matching potentials themselves are compared for both values of r_0. It is apparent that at large separations only do the two diverge, indeed the matching potential is cut off to zero at $r_0 = a'$, above which one can hardly anticipate accurate reproduction of the scattering.

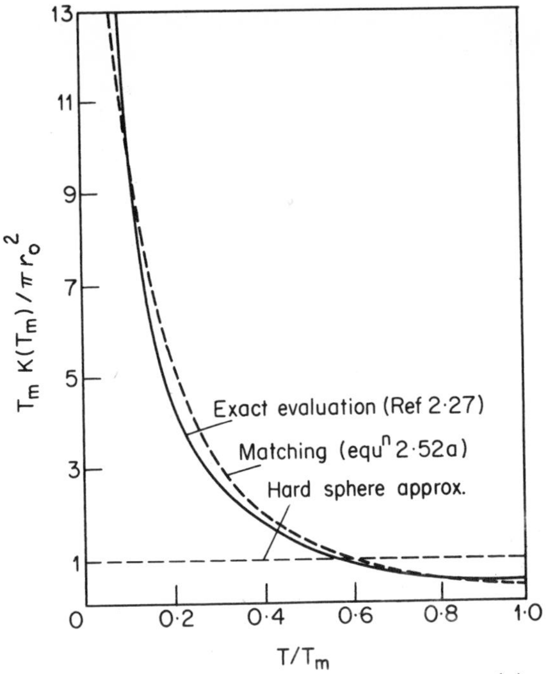

Fig. 2.8a Matching for a Bohr potential $V(r) = C_{a/r} \cdot \exp(-r/a)$ according to the Leibfried-Oen method [Ref. 2.37]. The differential cross section as a function of the relative energy transfer for $r_0/a = 1.05$

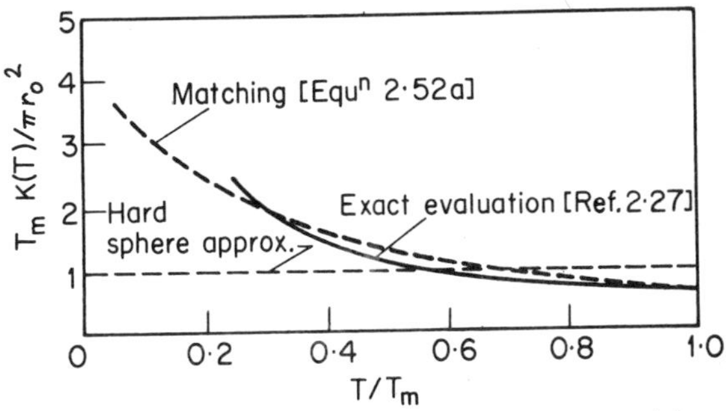

Fig. 2.8b Matching for a Bohr potential $V(r) = C.a/r \exp(-r/a)$ according to the Leibfried-Oen method (Ref. 2.37]. The differential cross section as a function of the relative energy transfer for $r_0/a = 3.4$

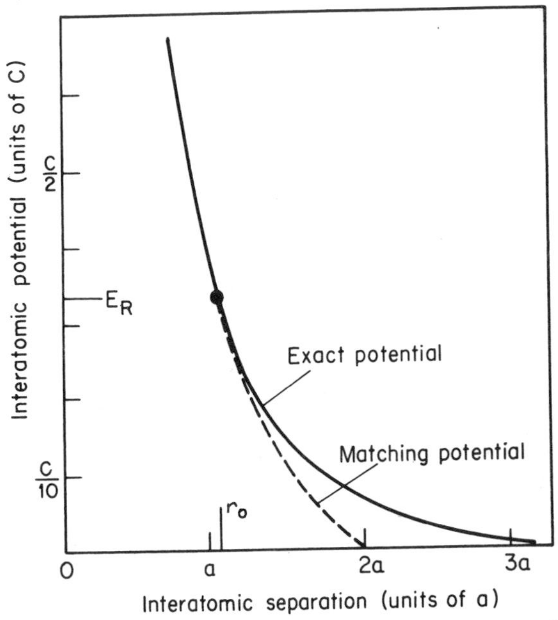

Fig. 2.9a Matching of the interatomic potential $V(r) = C.a/r \exp(-r/a)$ according to the Leibfried-Oen method [Ref. 2.37] for $r_0/a = 1.05$

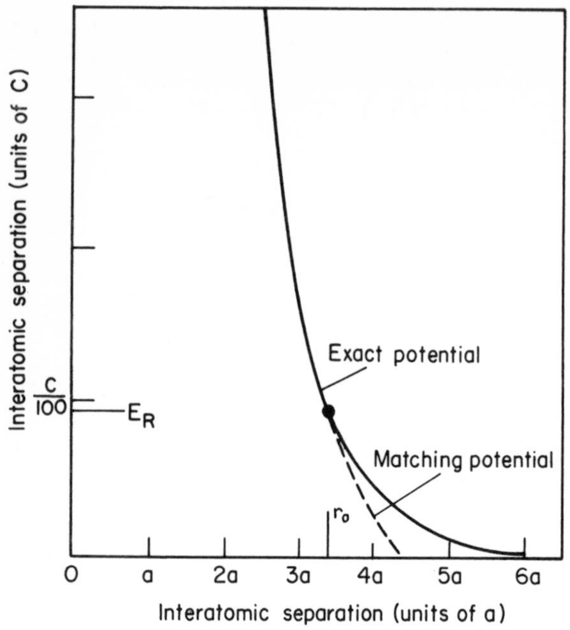

Fig. 2. 9b Matching of the interatomic potential $V(r) = C.a/r \exp(-r/a)$ according to the Leibfried-Oen method [Ref. 2. 37] for $r_0/a = 3.4$

Comparison of the function $\int_0^{T_m} T d\sigma(T)$ for the Bohr and matching potential is also valuable and instructive, as seen in Figure 2. 10, where again, only at low energy transfers is there appreciable divergence. There is clearly a divergence between the exact and the hard sphere values however, the latter always giving too small results.

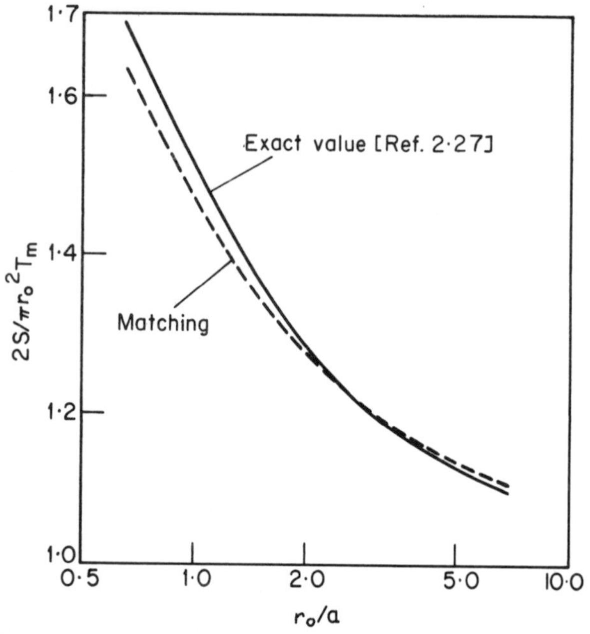

Fig. 2. 10 Matching of the interatomic potential $V(r) = C.a/r \exp(-r/a)$ according to the Leibfried-Oen method [Ref. 2. 37]. The stopping power $2s/\pi r_0^2 T_m$ plotted as a function of the approach distance.

The inability of any matching potential, and particularly the hard sphere approximation, to duplicate the behaviour of a screened potential such as the Bohr potential, at low energy transfers, must be largely anticipated. This is apparent in that the Bohr screening function $\exp\left(-\frac{r}{a}\right)$ must fall more rapidly with increasing r than any inverse power screening function (r^{1-s} in the inverse s power potential). In the case of cut off potentials such as that of Leibfried and Oen, [37] and the hard sphere approximation, the divergence must be expected to be particularly severe (as comparison of exact and hard sphere cross sections in the appropriate figures indicate).

The potential $V_m(r) = A\left(\frac{a'}{r} - 1\right)$, is of course, only one of a family of truncated potentials which can be matched to the real potential. In general

$$V_{mn}(r) = \frac{\alpha_n}{n}\left[\left(\frac{\beta_n}{r}\right)^n - 1\right]; 0 < r < \beta_n \qquad 2.53a$$

$$= 0 \qquad ; \beta_n < r < \infty$$

can be matched to the real potential V(r) at the distance of closest approach r_0, both for magnitude and slope.

This matching results in values for the constants α_n and β_n given by

$$\alpha_n = -[nV(r_0) + r_0 V'(r_0)] \qquad 2.53b$$

$$\beta_n = r_0[-r_0 V'(r_0)/\alpha_n]^{1/n} \qquad 2.53c$$

which may be inserted in equation 2. 53a to give

$$V_{mn}(r) = V(r_0) + [r_0 V'(r_0)/n][1 - (r_0/r)^n] \qquad 2.54$$

The value of the matching potential V_{m1}, where n = 1, has been seen to lie in the fact that it allows straightforward evaluation of the integral

$$\theta = \pi - 2p\int_{r_0}^{\infty} \frac{dr}{r^2(1 - p^2/r^2 - V(r)/E_R)^{1/2}} \qquad 2.19b$$

The same is true of the generalised potential, only for values of n = 1, n = ±2 & $-\infty$ the last value corresponding to the hard sphere case, and it is these values which are of most use practically.

In the earlier analysis for the n = 1 case, the r value was taken as that corresponding to the distance of closest approach in a head on collision, i.e. $V(r_0) = V_{m1}(r) = E_R$. However, as Lehmann and Robinson[38] point out in a complete analysis of the generalised potential, the distance of closest approach r at impact parameter p, is given by $V(r) = E_R(1 - p^2/r^2)$, i.e. r is a function of p_2, E_R and the real interatomic potential. Thus, upon insertion of the matching potential $V_m(r)$ into the relation for θ, one obtains a C.M. deflection angle θ_{APP} as a function of the impact parameter p and energy E_R. Further since $\frac{T}{T_m} = \sin^2 \theta/2$, the energy transfer may be deduced as a function of the impact parameter. Defining $\sigma = p/\beta_n$, $\gamma = \frac{\alpha_n}{|n| . E_R}$, one deduces, through integration of equation 2.19a

$$n = 1; \quad \frac{T}{T_m} = 1 - \sigma^2/\rho^2 \text{ where } \rho^2 = 1 + 4\sigma^2(1 + \gamma)/\gamma^2 \qquad 2.55a$$

$$n = 2; \quad \frac{T}{T_m} = \sin^2\left\{\cos^{-1}\sigma - \left[\frac{\sigma}{(\gamma + \sigma^2)^{1/2}}\right] \times\right.$$

$$\times \quad \mathrm{Cos}^{-1}\left(\frac{\gamma + \sigma^2}{1 + \gamma}\right)^{1/2}\Bigg\} \qquad 2.55b$$

$n = -\infty$, hard sphere;

$$\frac{T}{T_m} = 1 - p^2/r^2 \qquad 2.55c$$

In these equations α_n and β_n and thus σ are functions of p and E_R, since r itself is a function of p. In the previous analysis, where matching was effected only at the distance of closest approach in a head-on collision, α_n and β_n were independent of p. Consequently two approximations for T/T_m as functions of p may be formulated, one in which matching is effected only for head on collision, and a second where matching is effected for all values of p. The first approximation has the advantage that the total cross section is finite ($= \pi r_0^2$), which is valuable in many calculations, whereas the second is infinite, since β_n increases with p, but more accurate.

For a given real interatomic potential V(r), certain considerations regarding the plausibility of matching potentials may be applied to determine probable values of n. i.e. $V_{mn}(r)$ must be positive for all r and

$$\lim_{r \to \infty}\left\{ r\, \frac{\partial V_{mn}(r)}{\partial r} \right\} \to 0$$

The success of using the matching potentials may be judged by comparison of T/T_m as a function of impact parameter, obtained from equations 2.55 and by exact numerical calculation for a specific real potential. Lehmann and Robinson[38] have effected this comparison for the Bohr potential $V(r) = C(a/r)\exp(-r/a)$ in copper and their results for a relative energy $E_R = 0.04$ C are reproduced in Figure 2.11. In this Figure, V^0_{m1} and V^0_{m2} refer to T/T_m evaluated for n = 1 and 2, and with the values of α_n and β_n determined only for the head on collision, whereas $V_{m1}{}^p$ and $V_{m2}{}^p$ refer to T/T_m deduced with values of α_n and β_n as functions of p. V^0_{mH} and $V_{mH}{}^p$ are corresponding curves deduced for the hard sphere approximation. It is clear, that both $V_{m1}{}^p$ and $V_{m2}{}^p$ are in excellent agreement with the exact calculation, but that V^0_{m1} and V^0_{m2} are also satisfactory over a limited range of impact parameters. Both approximations are a considerable improvement on the hard sphere model, but even this is rather good at low impact parameter. Also included in the Figure is the T/T_m relation deduced by the momentum approximation, which will be discussed shortly, and this is seen to be a very good approximation at large impact parameters.

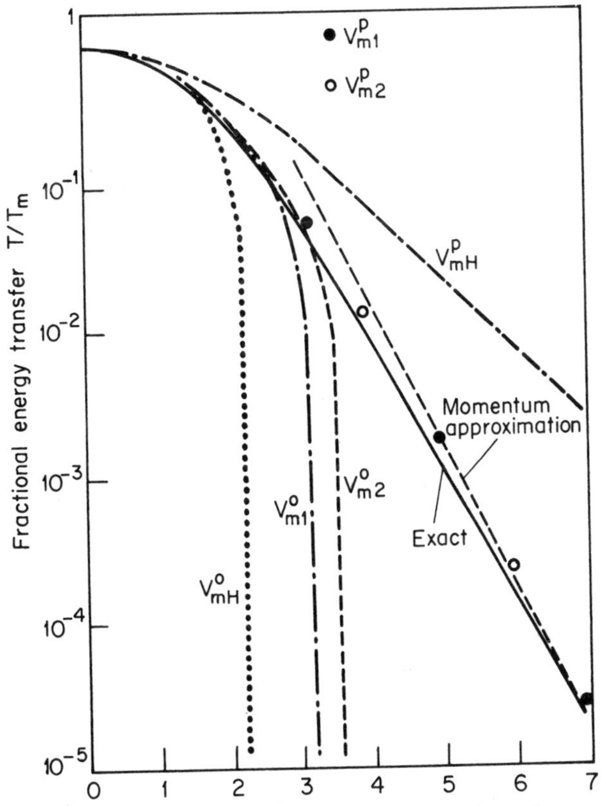

Fig. 2.11 Comparison of exact and approximate values of the factional transferred energy for the Bohr potential & $E_R = 0.05$ C. [Ref. 2.38]

The matching potential approximation was also found to be very good for a Born-Mayer and a Thomas-Fermi potential, and one way of displaying this is to evaluate the exact θ and the θ_{APP} deduced with a matching potential as functions of the impact parameter.

If the difference between V(r) and the matching potential $V_{mn}(r)$ is written as $\Delta V_n(r)$, then equation 2.19a may be rewritten

$$\theta = \pi - 2p\int_{r_0}^{\infty} \frac{dr}{r^2\left(1 - p^2/r^2 - \dfrac{(V_{mn}(r) + \Delta_n V(r))}{E_R}\right)^{1/2}} \qquad 2.19b$$

This may be expanded in powers of $\Delta V_n(r)$ to give

$$\theta = \pi - \sum_{k=0}^{\infty} \theta_k;$$

where

$$\theta_k = 2p\gamma_k \int_{r_0}^{\infty} \left\{ r^2\left(1 - p^2/r^2 - \frac{V_{mn}(r)}{E_R}\right)^{-1/2} \right\} \left\{ \frac{\Delta_n V(r)}{E_R\left(1 - p^2/r^2 - \dfrac{V_{mn}(r)}{E_R}\right)^{1/2}} \right\}^k . \, dr$$

and

$$\gamma_k = \lfloor 2k / 2^{2k} (\lfloor k)^2 \qquad 2.56$$

If only the k = 0 term is retained, the result is identical to that obtained by replacing V(r) by $V_{mn}(r)$ in equation 2.19b i.e. $\theta \to \theta_{APP}$. Higher order terms adjust the derived θ_{APP} to closer agreement with θ. Thus table 2.4 illustrates exact values of θ, $\theta = \pi - \theta_0(2)$ and $\theta = \pi - \theta_0(2) - \theta_1(2)$ i.e. the 1st and 2nd order approximation to θ, for a matching potential with n = 2 matched to a Born-Mayer potential $V(r) = C_{BM}\exp(-r/a_{BM})$ at a relative energy $E_R = 0.05\, C_{BM}$. Clearly the second order approximation is very close to the exact θ, but even the first order, which is the simple matching procedure is quite satisfactory.

As pointed out earlier it is difficult to obtain specific expressions for the differential cross section for scattering with the matching potential, when matching is performed at all impact parameters, and the results obtained through matching only in a head on collision must be considered satisfactory. However,

TABLE 2.4 (Ref. 2.38)

First- and second-order r^{-2} approximations to scattering from the Born-Mayer potential at $E_r = 0.05\ C_{BM}$.

Impact parameter p/a_{BM}	c.m. scattering angle, radians Approximate $\pi - \theta_0(2)$	$\pi - \theta_0(2) - \theta_1(2)$	Exact θ
2	1.5255	1.5087	1.5048
3	0.9619	0.9387	0.9355
4	0.5579	0.5363	0.5337
5	0.2923	0.2758	0.2752
6	0.1382	0.1286	0.1284
7	0.0602	0.0559	0.0554
8	0.0249	0.0228	0.0227

it is clear that if only the dependence of T upon impact parameter p is required, or, as has been shown by Lehmann and Robinson, [38] the positional change of the mass centre during a collision, the above treatment, including impact parameter matching is excellent. The general matching potential, with n = 1 or 2 is therefore seen to be most useful.

Sigmund and Vajda[39] have also used a variant of the matching technique to obtain tractable analytic approximations to the Thomas-Fermi and Born-Mayer potentials. Whereas the Leibfried-Oen[37] and Lehmann-Robinson[38] treatments suggested cutting off the matching potential at a distance $r_c (= a')$ determined from matching at the distance of closest approach considerations and therefore a function of the primary atom energy, Sigmund and Vajda[39] suggested that the cut off radius should be a constant. The reason for doing this is that, using realistic Thomas-Fermi and Born-Mayer potentials, the cut off radius in copper falls considerably below half the interatomic spacing for primary energies above 6 keV i.e. the lattice appears to become very transparent and small angle scattering is underestimated. To remedy this Sigmund and Vajda employed a matching potential of the form

$$V_m(r) = V(r);\ r \leq R'$$

$$V_m(r) = B(a'/r - 1);\ R' \leq r \leq a'$$

$$V_m(r) = 0;\ r > a' \qquad 2.57$$

where the cut off radius a′ was maintained constant (half the lattice spacing) and B and R′ were then obtained by matching potential and slope at the distance R′ determined by the conditions $V_m(R') = V(R')$, $V_m'(R') = V'(R')$.

Since a′ is constant this latter condition leads to primary energy independent values for R′ and B also, and equation 2.57 shows that the potential employed is the correct one up to R′ and then a potential matched at R′, eroded to zero at a′.

Using this treatment the scattering integral is readily evaluated in a similar manner to that given by Leibfried and Oen[37] and Sigmund and Vajda[39] have shown that for very small angle deflections this matching procedure is considerably better than that employed by Leibfried and Oen, [37] for the Thomas-Fermi potential, as revealed in Fig. 2.12 where the differential

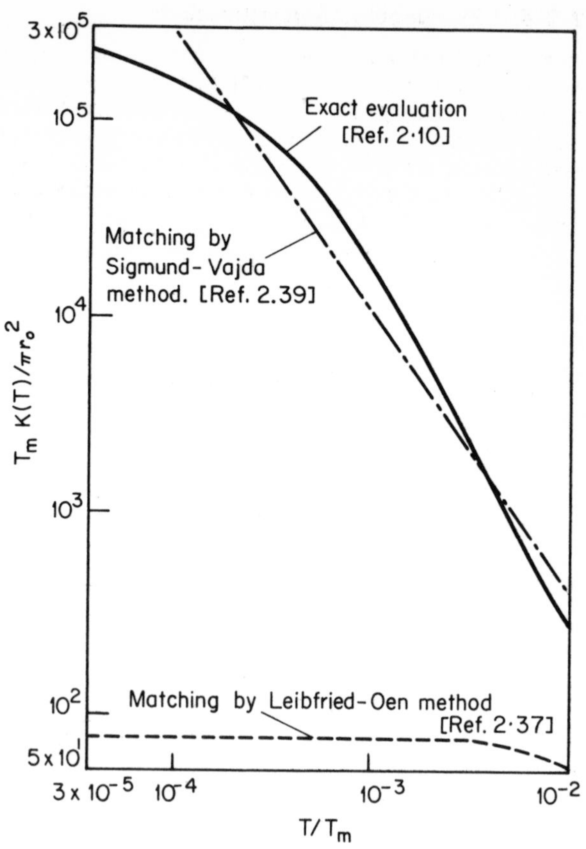

Fig. 2.12 Matching of the Thomas-Fermi Potential according to two methods. The differential cross section plotted as a function of the fractional energy transfer.

cross section, for low energy transfers using the Leibfried-Oen[37] method, the above method, and the exact Lindhard[10] evaluation for 60 KeV Cu primaries are compared. The Sigmund-Vajda[39] method is clearly superior in this region, but for larger energy transfer, the Figure suggests that all treatments have similar validity. These predictions were also confirmed by comparison of the matching techniques with an exact evaluation for the r^{-2} potential. We should expect these results on purely intuitive grounds since the Leibfried-Oen[37] treatment, which is matched and cut off at distances close to the head on collision distances should be adequately representative for large and intermediate energy transfers. The Sigmund-Vajda[39] treatment, which matches at larger impact parameters is therefore best suited to lower energy transfers (10^{-6}-$10^{-3}T_m$) whilst at smaller energy transfers still, any cut off potential will underestimate the forward scattering and the best approach is to use the real potential, and its scattering laws, itself. A similar improvement[40] for lower primary energies was obtained using this matching procedure with the Born-Mayer potential.

Vajda[40a] has also shown that even better agreement with exact data can be obtained for the Born-Mayer potential using a quadratic form for the matching potential (as suggested by Lehmann and Robinson) with two adjustable constants determined by matching the potentials, slope and curvature.

However, if one requires more precise information about distant collisions, in a tractable analytic form, one may resort to a final approximation, which finds frequent application in collision problems. This is the Impulse or Momentum Approximation.

2.7.4 The Impulse Approximation

In a distant collision the path of the primary atom is almost undisturbed by the collision with the target atom and it is possible, to a first approximation, to describe the trajectory of the primary by a straight line passing within a perpendicular distance from the centre of mass equal to the distance of closest approach r_0 as shown in Figure 2.13. However, a collision does occur and the primary will lose energy to the struck atom. If we consider the x direction to lie along a direction joining the centre of mass and the point where the asymptotes to the real trajectory intersect, then the momentum lost by the primary of initial energy E_R and velocity v_0 i.e. the impulse, in reaching the distance of closest approach, is given by

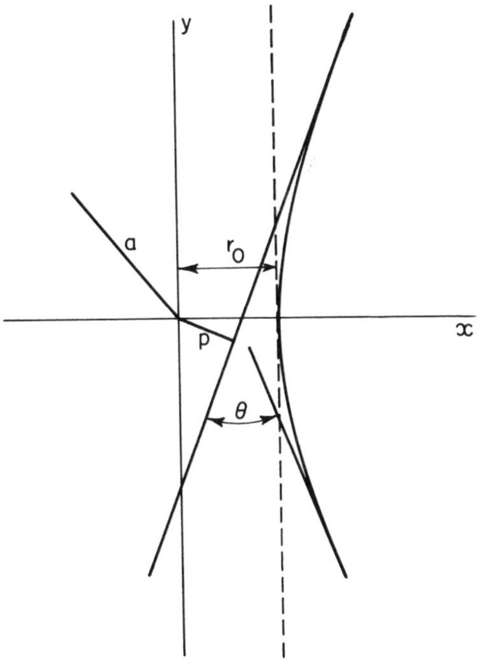

Fig. 2.13 Orbit of a particle scattered through an angle θ, to illustrate the impulse approximation

$$M_1 v_x = \int_0^{\infty} \left\{-\frac{\partial V(r)}{\partial r}\right\} \frac{x}{r} \cdot dt \qquad 2.58$$

along the x direction, which is perpendicular to the assumed straight line path. This integral becomes a function of time alone if it is assumed, for an undisturbed trajectory, that $x = r_0$ and that $r = (r_0^2 + v_0^2 t^2)^{1/2}$. The ratio of the transferred x momentum to the momentum along the assumed path thus gives half the scattering angle i.e.

$$\tan\theta/2 \approx \theta/2 = \frac{M_1 v_x}{M_1 v_0} \qquad 2.59$$

As an example, if an inverse r potential (Coulomb) is employed and it is assumed that approximately $r_0 = p$. Then the transferred momentum is twice that in Equation 2.58 i.e. the transferred momentum

$$M = \int_{-\infty}^{+\infty} \frac{Z_1 Z_2 e^2}{r^2} \cdot \frac{x}{r}\, dt$$

which as shown by Bohr[8] is simply

$$M = \frac{2 Z_1 Z_2 e^2}{p v_0} \qquad 2.60$$

The scattering angle is thus given by

$$\tan\theta/2 = \frac{Z_1 Z_2 e^2}{M_1 p v_0^2} = \frac{b}{2p} \qquad 2.61a$$

and the energy transfer to the struck atom, is,

$$T = \frac{M^2}{2M_2} = \frac{2(Z_1 Z_2 e^2)^2}{M_2 v_0^2} \cdot \frac{1}{p^2} =$$

$$\frac{(Z_1 Z_2)^2 e^4}{p^2} \cdot \frac{M_1}{M_2} \cdot \frac{1}{E_R} \qquad 2.61b$$

From this latter Equation it is clear that the differential cross section $d(\pi p^2) = d\sigma(T)$ is given by

$$d\sigma(T) = \pi \left(\frac{Z_1 Z_2 e^2}{E_R}\right)^2 \frac{M_1}{M_2} \cdot \frac{dT}{T^2}$$

which is the Rutherford scattering law as noted earlier. Thus, in a distant collision, the impulse approximation appears to simulate the exact scattering adequately.

For the Bohr screened potential Everhart et al[27] have evaluated the integral contained in Equation 2.30 using numerical integration and some transformation of the equation and have compared the results with exact evaluation of 2.19a. They found extremely good agreement (to within 1%) with the accurately computed scattering even at scattering angles as large as 0.1π. It should be noted that although the distance of closest approach and the impact parameter are approximately equal, Everhart et al[27] have maintained higher accuracy by using the Equation

$$p^2 = r_0^2 \left\{1 - \frac{V(r_0)}{E_R}\right\}$$

to evaluate p. It is convenient for the Bohr potential, to use numerical integration techniques since for this case Equation 2.19a reduces to the non-elementary integral

$$\theta = \frac{b}{a} \int_1^{\infty} \frac{\left(\frac{a}{r_0} + u\right) \exp(-u r_0/a)}{u^2 (u^2 - 1)^{1/2}} du \qquad 2.62$$

where an infinity has to be handled carefully because of the zero in the denominator.

One may note at this time that the Lehman/Shapiro[7] approximation is a first order approximation to the trajectory i.e. tangent to the path for small angle scattering, whereas the impulse approximation is a zero order approximation. One may thus anticipate that the Lehman/Shapiro[7] approach should give good agreement with the exact scattering law at small angles since as Everhart et al[27] have shown, even the impulse approximation is adequate in this region. This expectation is confirmed by inspection of Figure 2.7 which show the results of Lehman and Shapiro,[7] compared with the exact results obtained by Everhart[27] and those derived from the Leibfried and Oen[37] matching potential. It is clear that the asymptotic approximation becomes quite good at small scattering angles, just where matching potentials begin to lose accuracy. Thus, whereas matching potentials appear to be most useful for small impact parameters, the Lehman-Shapiro[7] and Impulse approximation are clearly best suited to large impact parameter problems.

Although Everhart et al[27] have employed numerical techniques to evaluate θ it would be desirable to be able to express the results analytically, for computational purposes. Lehmann and Leibfreid[32] have shown, by an elegant mathematical technique, that such analytical expressions can be deduced, by circumventing the infinity involved in the integration of Equation 2.19a. Essentially the technique is to replace the real trajectory C in the complex r plane which contains the singularity at $r = r_0$ (where the denominator in Equation 2.19a is zero) by an alternative path C'' which leads to the correct results but avoids the r_m position. The integral can then be evaluated by expansion in powers of V(r) and by replacing $\frac{V(r)}{E_R} = v(r)$ one obtains:

$$\theta = \pi - \int_{C''} \frac{pdr}{r^2\{1 - v(r) - p^2/r^2\}^{1/2}} \qquad 2.63a$$

by expansion

$$\theta = \pi - \int_{C''} \left\{ \frac{1}{(1 - p^2/r^2)^{1/2}} + \sum_{n=1}^{\infty} \frac{\gamma_n (v/r))^n}{(1 - p^2/r^2)^{n+1/2}} \right\} \frac{pdr}{r^2} \qquad 2.63b$$

where

$$\gamma_n = \frac{\underline{|2n-1}}{2^{2n-1} \cdot \underline{|n-1} \cdot \underline{|n}}$$

Since the first term in the integral cancels π, one obtains finally,

$$\theta = -\sum_{n=1}^{\infty} \gamma_n \int_{C''} \frac{pdr}{r^2} \cdot \frac{(v(r))^n}{(1 - p^2/r^2)^{n+1/2}} = \sum_{1}^{\infty} \theta_n \qquad 2.64$$

This expression can now be transferred back to the C trajectory, using the results

$$\theta_n = -\frac{2}{\underline{|n}} \int_p^{\infty} \frac{rpdr}{(2p^2)^n (r^2 - p^2)^{1/2}} \{D(r) \,.\, r^3\}^n \frac{(v(r))^n}{r^2} \qquad 2.65a$$

or alternatively

$$\theta_n = -\frac{2}{2^n \underline{|n}} \int_p^{\infty} \frac{pdr}{(r^2 - p^2)^{1/2}} \{D(r) \,.\, r^{-1}\}^n (v(r))^n \,.\, r^{2n-1} \qquad 2.65b$$

where D(r) is the differential operator d/dr.
The first term θ_1 in the summation 2.64 is clearly equal to

$$-\tfrac{1}{2} \int_p^{\infty} \frac{pdr}{r^2} \cdot \frac{v(r)}{(1 - p^2/r^2)^{3/2}}$$

This integral can be evaluated by parts, assuming that v(r) vanishes at infinity with the result that

$$\theta_1 = -\tfrac{1}{2} \int_p^{\infty} \frac{pdr}{(r^2 - p^2)^{1/2}} \cdot \frac{d(v(r))}{dr} \qquad 2.66$$

which, it is easy to show, is an alternative form of the impulse approximation expressed by Equation 2.58. We may also note here that the Lehman-Shapiro[7] function H(R) is in fact the impulse approximation for small θ (i.e. $R \approx p$), whilst their energy equation 2.42 leads to the hard sphere approximation for large energy transfers. The impulse approximation is therefore the evaluation of the first term in a power expansion of the potential. Consequently it is advisable to investigate the contributions to θ due to higher orders in the power expansion (i.e. $\theta_2, \theta_3 \ldots$ etc.). Lehmann and Leibried[32] have done this for (a) Inverse power potentials $V(r) = B_s(a_s/r)^s$; $s > 0$ and (b) A Bohr type screened potential $V(r) = \frac{Ba}{r} \exp(-r/a)$ and (c) a purely exponential, Born-Mayer potential $V(r) = B.\exp(-r/a_s)$. It is necessary only to quote the results for θ_1 and θ_2 which are

$$\theta_1 = \frac{B_s}{E_R} (a_s/p)^2 \frac{|\overline{s+1}}{2} \,.\, |\overline{\tfrac{1}{2}} / |\overline{\tfrac{s}{2}} \quad \text{for potential (a)} \qquad 2.67a$$

$$\theta_1 = \frac{B}{E_R} K_1(\alpha) \quad \text{for potential (b)} \qquad 2.67b$$

where $K_1(\alpha)$ is the modified Hankel[41] function

$$\theta_1 = \frac{B}{E_R} \alpha K_0(\alpha) \quad \text{for potential (c)} \qquad 2.67c$$

and

$$K_0(\alpha) = \int_1^{\infty} \frac{e^{-\alpha z}}{(z^2 - 1)^{1/2}} \,.\, dz$$

$$\theta_2 = -\frac{B^2}{{E_R}^2} K_1(2\alpha) \quad \text{for potential (b)} \qquad 2.67d$$

and

$$\theta_2 = -\frac{B^2}{{E_R}^2} \left\{ \alpha^2 K_1(2\alpha) - \frac{3d}{2} K_0(2\alpha) \right\} \quad \text{for potential (c)} \qquad 2.67e$$

Third and higher order terms can, of course, be evaluated with greater difficulty.

Clearly the utility of any approximation depends upon its ability to successfully reproduce the exact results. In order to test the impulse approximation Lehmann and Leibfried[32] have evaluated the scattering angle θ_1 from Equations 2.67 for the potentials (b) and (c) and compared these graphically with the exact results from a numerical computation. This comparison is shown in Figures 2.14a and 2.14b where θ_1 refers to impulse approximation values and θ to exact values. In this computation a value of $\frac{B}{E_R} = 20$ has been assumed and it is clear that accuracy is maintained down to impact parameters of $p \sim 4a$ (a is the screening radius). One must expect improved accuracy if the second term θ_2 is added to θ_1 and that this is true is seen immediately in Figure 2.14a and 2.14b in which $\theta_1 + \theta_2$ is also plotted. The

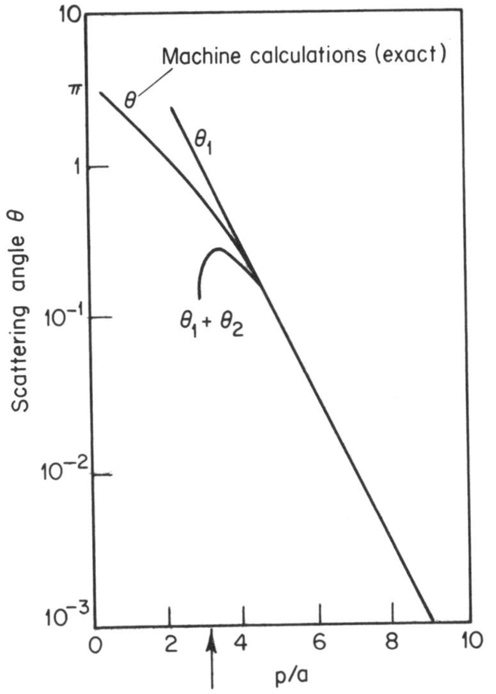

Fig. 2.14a Scattering angle as a function of the input parameter using the momentum approximation for the potential $V(r) = \frac{Ba}{E_R \cdot r} \exp(^-r/_a)$ according to the Lehmann-Leibfried method [Ref. 2.32]. The arrow indicates the value of p, where the series for $\Sigma\theta_n$ becomes divergent

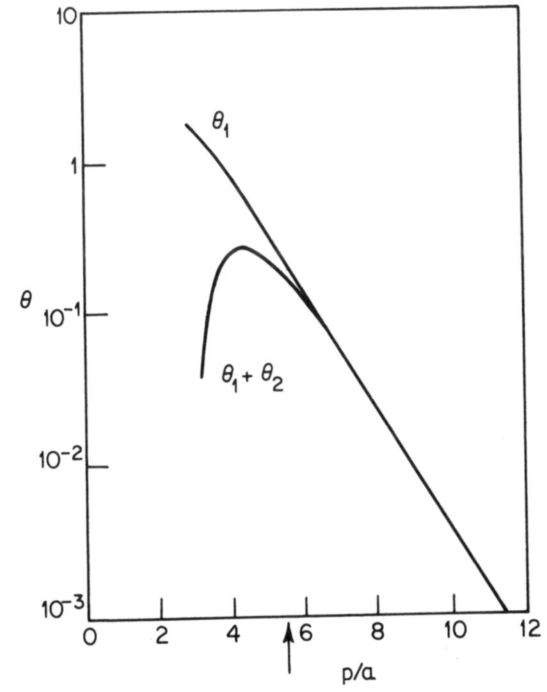

Fig. 2.14b Scattering angle as a function of the impact parameter using the momentum approximation for the potential $V(r) = B \exp(^-r/a)$ according to the Lehmann-Leibfried method [Ref. 2.32]. The arrow indicates the value of p where the series for $\Sigma\theta_n$ becomes divergent

error between $\theta_1 + \theta_2$ and θ is reduced from 25% (θ_1 and θ) to 5% at $p \sim 4a$. Another method of illustrating the accuracy of the impulse approximation is to require that θ_2 shall be no more than, say, 10% of θ_1 and this requires, for the Bohr screened potential that

$$\theta_2/\theta_1 = B/E_R \cdot \frac{K_1(2p/a)}{K_1(p/a)} = 0.1$$

which for $p/a \gg 1$ (large impact parameters) reduces to

$$E_R/B \simeq \frac{10}{\sqrt{2}} \exp(-p/a).$$

This condition is plotted on a semi-logarithmic scale as in Figure 2.15 and indicated by θ_1 which shows that at any point above the line the impulse approximation is accurate to better than 10%.

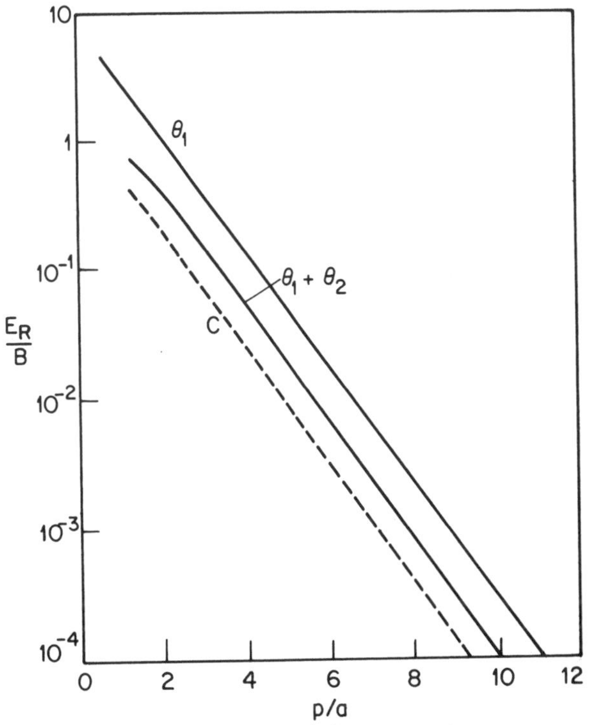

Fig. 2.15 The accuracy of the momentum approximation for the potential $V(r) = \frac{B.a}{E_R \cdot r} \exp(^-r/a)$ according to the Lehmann-Leibfried method. See text for an explanation of the curves (Ref. 2.32)

One can further enquire as to the accuracy of approximating θ by $\theta_1 + \theta_2$ by requiring that $\frac{\theta_3}{\theta_1 + \theta_2} \leqslant 0.1$ (the 10% criterion) and one then obtains a line ($\theta_1 + \theta_2$) in Figure 2.15 which shows that between the θ_1 and ($\theta_1 + \theta_2$) lines the error obtained by assuming that p is approximated by $\theta_1 + \theta_2$ is less than 10%. Similar procedures can be adopted by higher order approximations. At small values of p/a, the expansion $\sum_1^\infty \theta_n$ is no longer an adequate approximation and the impulse method becomes invalid. Lehmann and Leibfried[32] investigate the limit of applicability further in their original publication, but a general result is that this approximation starts to lose accuracy around p values comparable to a, depending in detail upon the values of E_R. These authors have also investigated the use of the impulse approximation for potentials which are cut off at some arbitrary distance r_c (such as hard sphere potential and the potential expressed in equation 2.49) and show that the approximation is only valid in certain cases e.g. where not only $v(r_c) = 0$ at $r = r_c$ but $r_c \left|\frac{\partial v(r)}{\partial r}\right|_c$ tends to zero also. The reason for this, briefly, is that the cut off, introduces an essentially hard sphere condition, at $r = r_c$ and the scattering is thus isotropic around r_c. If however the potential approaches zero smoothly at $r = r_c$ the scattering is due to the real potential.

2.8 DEDUCTION OF THE INTERATOMIC POTENTIAL FROM SCATTERING MEASUREMENTS

Up to this point we have been concerned with the deduction of the scattering law from assumed specific interatomic potentials. However the converse problem of the deduction of the potential from knowledge of the scattering law is equally important, since experimental data may be used to determine the form of the latter. Keller, Kay and Shmoys[42] have investigated this problem with the following results.

From Equation 2.19a

$$\theta_p = \pi - 2\int_{r_0}^{\infty} \frac{dr}{r^2\left(1/p^2 - 1/r^2 - \frac{V(r)}{E_R \cdot p^2}\right)^{1/2}}$$

for an impact parameter p.

Also if the differential cross section for scattering into unit solid angles between θ and $\theta + \delta\theta$, is $d\sigma(\theta)$, the differential cross section for scattering into all angles between θ and $\theta + \delta\theta$ is $d\sigma(\theta)(2\pi \sin\theta\delta\theta)$ which is, in fact, just the differential cross section for collision with impact parameters between p and $p + \delta p$, i.e. $2\pi p\delta p$.

Thus $d\sigma(\theta) = pdp/\sin\theta d\theta$

or integrating from θ to π and 0 to p.

$$\int_\theta^\pi d\sigma(\theta) \sin\theta d\theta = p^2/2$$

$d\sigma(\theta)$ can be measured experimentally by observing the probability of scattering into unit solid angle, as a function of θ, and so evaluation of the integral leads to observation of a functional dependence of p upon θ.

Introducing the variables $x = \frac{1}{p^2}$ and $u = 1/r$ we obtain

$$\theta_x = \pi - \int_0^{u_0} \frac{du}{\left\{x\left(1 - \frac{V(u)}{E_R}\right) - u^2\right\}^{1/2}}$$

and upon defining

$$v(u) = 1 - \frac{V(u)}{E_R} \quad \text{and} \quad w = u^2/v(u)$$

then

$$\frac{\pi}{2} - \frac{\theta_x}{2} = \int_0^x \frac{g(w)dw}{(x-w)^2} \qquad 2.64$$

where

$$g(w) = v^{-1/2} \cdot \frac{du}{dw}$$

and it is assumed that $V(r) \to 0$ as $r \to \infty$

Equation 2.64 is an Abel[41] type integral and may be solved explicitly to give g(w) in terms of θ_x.

i.e.

$$g(w) = \frac{d}{dw}\left\{\frac{1}{2\pi}\int_0^w \frac{\pi - \theta_x}{(-x+w)^{1/2}} \cdot dx\right\} \qquad 2.70$$

Now the relation between v and g(w) is

$$v^{-1/2}\frac{du}{dw} = \frac{1}{2w^{1/2}} + \frac{w^{1/2}}{2v}\frac{dv}{dw} = g(w) \qquad 2.71$$

This Equation may be solved readily for v, as

$$v = \exp\int_0^w \left\{\frac{2g(w)}{w^{1/2}} - \frac{1}{w}\right\}dw \qquad 2.72$$

Since g(w) is given from 2.70 then 2.72 yields v in terms of w.

Thus, to determine V(r) one deduces from experimental data, θ as a function of $x\left(=\frac{1}{p^2}\right)$, (generally by integrating the observed differential scattering cross section as above) and the result is then used to compute g(w) as a function of w.

Finally the result is used to obtain v from 2.72 and hence V(u) and V(r). The calculation is facilitated by integrating 2.70 by parts to give

$$g(w) = \frac{d}{dw}\left\{w^{1/2} - \frac{1}{\pi}\int_0^w (w-x)^{1/2}\theta^1(x)dx\right\}$$

$$\therefore g(w) = \frac{1}{2w^{1/2}} + \frac{1}{2\pi}\int_0^w \frac{\theta^1(x)dx}{(w-x)^{1/2}} \qquad 2.73$$

where

$$\theta^1(x) = \frac{d\theta(x)}{dx}$$

Changing the variable to $\theta(x)$, one obtains

$$g(w) = \frac{1}{2w^{1/2}} + \frac{1}{2\pi}\int_0^{\theta(w^1)} \frac{d\theta}{[w - x(\theta)]^{1/2}} \qquad 2.74$$

and finally

$$v = \exp\frac{1}{\pi}\int_0^w \frac{1}{(w^1)^{1/2}}\int_0^{\theta(w^1)} \frac{d\theta dw^1}{[w^1 - x(\theta)]^{1/2}} \qquad 2.60$$

from identification of Equations 2.72 and 2.74. Thus as $x(\theta)$ is computed as a function of θ (from $x = \frac{1}{p^2}$ and the observed experimental relation between θ and p), then v(u), V(u), and V(r) follow from 2.64. It is readily shown that the form of the scattering laws for the Coulomb and inverse square potentials, for example, lead back to these potential forms; the method should therefore be useful for all forms of the scattering law. Lane and Everhart[43] have in fact used a closely analogous method to determing the interatomic potential between inert gas atoms from scattering data obtained by Fuls et al,[44] Jones et al[45] and

Kaminker Afrosimov Fedorenko[46–49] for inert gas ions of energy between 25 and 100 KeV incident into inert gas targets. Although not directly concerned with the ion bombardment of solids it is interesting to note that the form of the interatomic potential observed was close to that suggested earlier by Firsov.[18–20] The Coulomb potential however was not a considerably poorer approximation, as might be expected in the high energy range where the approach distances are of order $\underline{a}$.

Conclusions

It is apparent that of the several approximations we have discussed, each has its own merits and disadvantages over certain ranges of applicability. Clearly the ideal solution would be exact evaluation of a representative potential by numerical techniques, but it is evident that matching to the real potential by the potentials employed by Leibfried and Oen,[37] Lehmann and Robinson[38] and Sigmund and Vajda[39,40] for large energy transfers, and higher order impulse approximations for low energy transfers, are very adequate approximations. One may possibly anticipate that a marriage of the two at the region where each loses accuracy may be forthcoming and can prove valuable. The hard sphere model, although possessing many inadequacies is of considerable utility in many calculations and must also be considered as at least a reasonable approximation. Finally the Lehman-Shapiro[7] model is a compromise solution leading to the 1st order impulse approximations at one extreme and hard sphere at the other. One must not accept any of these approximations, nor even the exact solution, without reservation however, since all have been evaluated assuming strictly classical mechanical laws. Many authors, notable amongst whom are Bohr,[8] who largely initiated scattering problem studies, have shown that only in certain limited cases is the true quantum mechanical scattering process soluble by classical methods. In the following section we shall investigate these validity criteria and show that, fortunately, in the energy range with which one is largely concerned in ion bombardment problems, classical considerations are sufficient.

2.9 VALIDITY CRITERIA FOR THE USE OF CLASSICAL MECHANICS

The collisions between atoms can properly be expressed in terms of the superposition of the wave functions of primary and target atoms and the scattering law can be determined by solutions of the wave equations. Clearly much simplification results from the ability to approximate the quantum mechanical treatment by classical methods as we have done in this chapter. In order to have confidence in the approximation we must discuss the limits of its validity.

Scattering problems have been considered from the quantum mechanical point of view by numerous authors and the reader, interested in a more exhaustive discussion than will be attempted here, is referred to texts such as those by Mott and Massey[50] and by Massey and Burhop.[51] On the other hand Bohr[8] has considered the classical approximation for scattering in some detail and shown in what circumstances the more exact treatment can be adequately approximated by the classical mechanical methods. In the present section we shall attempt a brief resume of Bohr's[8] findings.

In quantum mechanical terms a particle of velocity v has an effective wavelength

$$\lambda = h/M_1 v, \qquad 2.75$$

where h is Planck's constant and the collision is thus one of the interaction of two superimposed wave systems. Naively one can adopt the analogy of diffraction in physical optics and expect that diffraction or wave effects will only become observable when the physical dimensions of the interacting systems becomes comparable to the wavelength of the effective waves. If the physical dimensions of the colliding systems are large in comparison with the effective wavelength one can expect that classical collision mechanics will apply with high accuracy. To impose the most restrictive criteria for the validity of the use of classical mechanics it is necessary to require that the smallest physical dimension of the systems shall be larger than the effective wavelength.

If we initially consider the case of two particles influenced by a mutual Coulomb repulsion then the smallest physical distance associated with such a collision will be the distance of closest approach in a head on encounter b. Thus one may express the limit for the validity of classical considerations as $b \gg \lambda$ or writing $\frac{b}{\lambda} = \psi$ it is required that $\psi \gg 1$. Since $b = Z_1 Z_2 e^2/E_R$ for a Coulomb potential, and

$$\lambda = h/\frac{M_1 M_2 v}{M_1 + M_2} = h/\{2E_R\}^{1/2} \cdot \left\{\frac{1 + A}{A}\right\}^{-1/2}$$

the sufficient condition for the applicability of classical pictures is

$$\frac{Z_1 Z_2 e^2}{h}\left\{\frac{2}{E_R} \cdot \frac{A}{1 + A}\right\}^{1/2} \gg 1 \qquad 2.76$$

This is the limiting case for a head on collision, but in a collision with impact parameter p the criterion can be established with equal facility through use of the relation

$$\frac{V(r_0)}{E_R} = 1 - p^2/r_0^2,$$

$$\text{or} \quad b_1^2 - \frac{Z_1 Z_2 e^2 b_1}{E_R} - p^2 = 0,$$

where b_1 and r_0 are identical for the Coulomb repulsion for the distance of closest approach for the given impact parameter p. The validity criterion then becomes $\frac{b_1}{\lambda} \gg 1$.

Generally speaking, however, we are concerned not with scattering from a Coulomb potential (except in the case of close encounters) but with scattering from a screened Coulomb potential, probably of the Bohr type, and in such cases the above validity criterion is inadequate. In remote collisions which occur in the screened part of the field, i.e. $b > a$ (the characteristic screening length) the smallest physical dimension associated with the collision is clearly not b, but a. It will therefore be convenient to introduce a parameter ξ equal to b/a, to investigate the validity criteria in the region of scattering for a screened potential.

If the condition $\psi \gg 1$ is not fulfilled i.e. if the relative energy E_R or if $\frac{h}{Z_1 Z_2 e^2}\left\{\frac{1+A}{A}\right\}^{1/2}$ is large, one is confronted with a typical quantum-mechanical problem for which a complete treatment depends upon solution of the appropriate wave equations. However, one may arrive at a good approximation to the solution by use of the first step of the Born approximation (c.f. Mott[52]) in which it assumed that the plane wave representing the incident particle passes practically unaltered through the field of force of the scattering atom. Consequently the diffracting effect of the scattering potential may be represented by the superposition of all wavelets originating from all space elements about the centre of force (Normal Diffraction practice). One then obtains, for a relative deflection θ the reduced amplitude A_s of the scattered wave at a large distance ρ from the scattering centre, given by

$$A_s(\theta) = \frac{A_i}{\rho}\frac{Z_1 Z_2 e^2}{4E_R}\frac{1}{\sin^2\theta/2 + (\bar{\lambda}/2a)^2} \qquad 2.77a$$

for scattering from a Bohr type potential, where A_i and $\bar{\lambda}$ are the amplitude and wavelength of the incident wave divided by 2π. Of more interest is the scattering law to which this leads, and this is clearly

$$d\sigma(\theta) = R(\theta)\left\{1 + \left(\frac{\bar{\lambda}}{2a\sin\theta/2}\right)^2\right\}^{-2} \qquad 2.77b$$

where $R(\theta)$ is the Rutherford scattering law distribution. One may also deduce the total scattering cross section by a integration over all scattering angles and obtain

$$\sigma = \pi a^2\, \psi^2/1 + (\bar{\lambda}/2a)^2 \qquad 2.77c$$

where ψ is as defined earlier. If $\psi \ll 1$ (very large primary energies for example) the total cross section is small compared with the quantity πa^2 which represents the number of particles entering the unscreened part of the field. Thus the number of particles deflected in the screened field will be small and the necessary small perturbation required by the Born approximation is valid. Thus it appears that for $\psi \ll 1$ and screened fields, one may, with some restrictions use the methods of simplified wave diffraction rather than classical collision mechanics, but it is unnecessary to employ a full quantum mechanical analysis.

We observe from Equation 2.77b that for $\bar{\lambda} \ll a$ the scattering law approaches the Rutherford form, i.e. although the distance of closest approach b is very small the screening radius a is large and so almost all collisions are in the unscreened part of the field. However, for $\bar{\lambda} \gg$ a the scattering approaches a uniform distribution, as may be anticipated since collisions occur in the screened part of the field. The lower angular limit of the Rutherford distribution is thus given by an angle $\theta''/2 \approx \frac{\lambda}{2a}$, according to 2.77b which may be written as $\theta'' = \xi/\psi$ since $\xi = b/a$ and $\psi = b/\lambda$. On the other hand, in a simple Coulomb field, where $\psi \gg 1$, the deflection angle θ is given by tan $\theta/2 = b/2p$. Thus scattering would be expected to occur in the unscreened Coulomb field for impact parameters p less than a, and an angle $\theta' \simeq b/a = \xi$ gives the upper limit for Rutherford scattering in this case.

We may thus summarise, that for $\psi \gg 1$, the upper limit for Rutherford scattering is $\theta' = \xi$, and Classical Mechanics can always be used below this angle. Whilst for $\psi \ll 1$, the limit for Rutherford scattering is $\theta'' = \xi/\psi$. For $\psi \to 1$, the two estimates give the same value for θ, provided $\xi \ll 1$, and the scattering is largely in the unscreened part of the field, although, strictly speaking, in neither case is the application of Classical Mechanics or simple wave diffraction justifiable, and an intermediate region will exist where quantum mechanical considerations must be applied.

In the case where the major part of the scattering occurs in the screened part of the fields (for small relative energies of approach) one may anticipate that classical mechanics will be applicable for angles θ less than $\bar{\lambda}/a$, just as for unscreened fields, angles less than $\bar{\lambda}/b$ will be discernible. Thus, for screened fields the criterion for classical scattering will be $\bar{\lambda} \ll$ a or $\psi \gg \xi$. If $\xi > 1$ the scattering certainly occurs in the screened part of the field (i.e. $b > a$) and the validity criterion is more restrictive than $\psi \gg 1$ for the unscreened case where $\psi < 1$.

If $\bar{\lambda} > a$, classical mechanics are inapplicable but it is clear from Equation 2.77b that the scattering cross section is smaller than πa^2 if $\psi < \bar{\lambda}/2a$ i.e. if $\psi \ll \sqrt{\xi}$ and simplified wave diffraction methods are valid.

One may represent these criteria diagrammatically in Figure 2.16 where each point represents values of ψ and ξ and the co-ordinates are chosen as log ψ and log ξ for convenience. The line T corresponds to $\psi = \xi$ and the line U to $\psi = \sqrt{\xi}$.

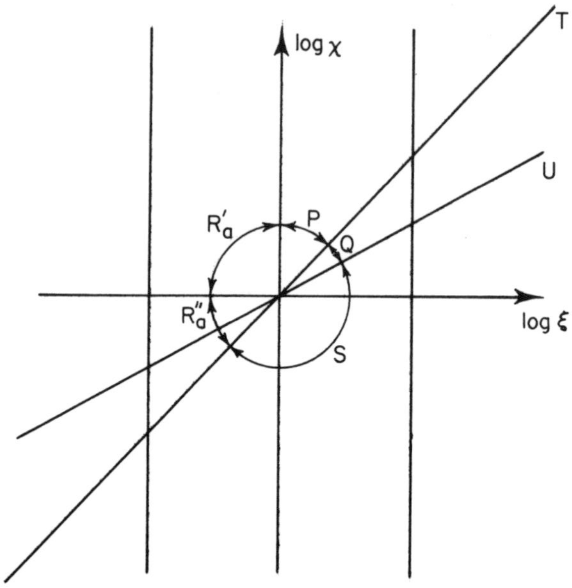

Fig. 2.16 Diagrammatic representation of the criteria for using various methods of solution of the scattering problem (Ref. 2.8) See text for an explanation of the symbols

In the third and fourth segments, where $\psi \ll 1$, high relative energies, the regions S can be treated by simplified wave diffraction methods as can the area below the line U in the first segment since $\psi < \sqrt{\xi}$. The region S corresponds to uniform scattering. The region R in the third segment corresponds to $\psi \ll 1$ and $\psi > \xi$ (i.e. $a > \bar{\lambda}$) thus the scattering will be of the Rutherford type and can also be treated by simplified wave diffraction. In the second segment $\psi \gg 1$ and $\xi < 1$, (i.e. $b < a$) thus all collisions are of the Rutherford type in an unscreened field and treatable by classical methods as denoted by R^1. In the first segment where ψ and ξ are both greater than unity and thus collisions occur exclusively in the screened field, classical considerations are valid only in the region where $\psi \gg \xi$ i.e. above the line T.

In the intermediate region between the lines T and U, neither classical mechanics nor simplified wave diffraction is adequately representative of the collision and real quantum effects must be expected.

Such criteria are of course only valuable when reviewed with the values of collision parameters appropriate to a typical encounter between the energetic ion and a solid lattice atom. We may note, from definition of ψ and ξ that the line $\xi = \psi$ in the first segment of Figure 2.16 corresponds to

$$a = a_0\{Z_1^{2/3} + Z_2^{2/3}\}^{-1/2} = \lambda = \frac{h}{\sqrt{(2E_0M_1)}}\,\frac{1 + A}{A} \qquad 2.78a$$

This may be rewritten as

$$E_0 = \left(\frac{h}{a_0}\right)^2 \left(\frac{1 + A}{A}\right)^2 \cdot \frac{1}{2M_1}\{Z_1^{2/3} + Z_2^{2/3}\} \qquad 2.78b$$

and, for energies higher than this, classical considerations may be applied. a_0, the Bohr radius, is equal to 0.528 Angstrom units, and upon substitution of this value and of h, the condition for classical scattering becomes

$$E_0 > 3.85 \times 10^{-38} \left\{\frac{Z_1^{2/3} + Z_2^{2/3}}{2M_1}\right\} \left(\frac{1 + A}{A}\right)^2.$$

In problems with which we will be concerned in the ion bombardment of solids, the extreme values of M_1 will be 4 m_n (for Helium) and 200 m_n (Mercury) and the lattice atom masses will also lie in this range (m_n = nucleon mass).

Thus extreme ratios A, will be approximately 50 (for mercury incident on a solid helium lattice) and $^1/_{50}$ (helium incident on mercury).

For the $^1/_{50}$ ratio, and $M_1 = 200\ m_n$ one deduces $E_0 \gtrsim$ 20 eV whilst for the 50 ratio, $E_0 \geqslant 0.4$ eV. Thus, provided $E_0 \gtrsim 25$ eV, classical considerations will apply for all cases in which we will be interested.

Of course, this analysis only holds in the region where, not only $\psi \gg \xi$ but $\psi \gg 1$ (i.e. b must be greater than λ), which it is easy to show requires that

$$E_0 \ll 2M_1 \left\{\frac{Z_1Z_2e^2}{h}\right\}^2 \qquad 2.79$$

Again, for the extreme cases of helium and mercury bombardment, the values of E must, respectively, be below 2 MeV and 500 MeV; this will be largely obeyed in the problems with which we are concerned in this book. These latter values have been derived assuming head on collisions. Clearly, however, if the impact is remote from the scattering centre, the generalised condition for classical collision validity is $\frac{r_0}{\lambda} = \frac{b_1}{\lambda} \gg 1$. Since r_0 is energy dependent one may expect different criteria to apply for large impact parameters.

Lehmann and Leibfreid[32] have examined validity criteria for the impulse approximation, and it is valuable to reproduce their arguments since this approximation is of great importance in many penetration phenomena.

In the impulse approximation, the scattering angles are necessarily small and so, for large impact parameters the scattering angle θ is approximately given by $\theta \approx b/p$. In this case the condition $\psi \gg 1$ (i.e. $\frac{b}{\lambda} \gg 1$) then reduces to $\frac{p\theta}{\lambda} \gg 1$ as a necessary condition for classical scattering.

Most calculations involving the impulse approximation (as we shall see in later chapters on particle penetration, radiation damage and sputtering) have considered the case of a Copper atom colliding with a Copper lattice atom. For this Cu-Cu case the Bohr potential may be written $V(r) = B\frac{a}{r}\exp(-r/a)$ where according to Leibfreid[53] and others, values of B = 10^5 eV and a = 0.12 Å are realistic. As we have seen, the Lehmann-Leibfreid[32] impulse first order approximation gives, for the Bohr potential, $\theta = \frac{B}{E_R}K_1(p/a)$. Thus the necessary condition for the applicability of classical methods becomes

$$p\,.\,\frac{B}{E_R}\,\frac{K_1(p/a)}{\lambda} \gg 1 \qquad 2.80$$

After insertion of the value for

$$\lambda = \frac{h}{\sqrt{2M_1E_R}} \cdot \frac{1 + A}{A} = \frac{\sqrt{2}.h}{\sqrt{M_1E_R}}$$

use of the approximation $K_1(p/a) \simeq (\pi a/2p)^{1/2}\exp(-p/a)$ for $p \gg a$ and insertion of numerical values for a, h and B, one obtains the validity condition, $E_R \ll 3.46 \times 10^{10}\ p/a\ \exp(-2p/a)$ eV if one assumes arbitrarily that $p\theta/\lambda = 10$ (i.e. $\gg 1$).

When a copper atom collides with its own lattice, characteristic values of the impact parameter p will be of the order of half the nearest neighbour distance: D = 2.56 Å for Cu. If this value for p is inserted, one obtains $E_R < 300$ eV or $E_0 < 600$ eV. Lehmann and Leibfreid[32] have also deduced the energy limit assuming a Born-Mayer type potential for copper and it turns out that in this case $E_0 < 100$ KeV.

Clearly these energies are much more restrictive than those derived earlier where large angle scattering in the screened fields was implicitly assumed. (i.e. the earlier condition was $b/\lambda \gg 1$ not $p/\lambda \gg 1$) and one must therefore exercise caution in applying the impulse approximation to specific problems, particularly if particle energies are greater than about 1 KeV.

If one investigates the other criterion for classical considerations, viz. $\psi \ll \xi$, it is easily shown, for the Cu-Cu case, that $E_0 \gtrsim 10^{-3}$ eV a condition which is always satisfied in the present region of interest.

It may thus be concluded that, for many calculations, particularly for almost head on collisions, the classical methods adopted in the first part of this chapter are adequate at all energies of current interest. However, one must be circumspect in applying the impulse approximation for high particle energies since it may be that the range of classical validity is exceeded.

Even the head-on collision case must be viewed carefully at high energies however, since the assumption of elastic collisions, which has been used up to this point, begins to lose validity. Ionisation and excitation of atomic electrons assume importance at energies, low in comparison to the 'less than several MeV' condition for classical scattering and, in fact one cannot describe the collisions by the earlier relationship even at energies considerably below these limits. Although we have already pointed out that relatively low energies of bombardment ($\lesssim$ 100 KeV) are of greatest interest in this book where elastic collisions dominate, even at these comparatively low energies inelastic collisions, in certain cases, assume importance. It is to this type of collision that we briefly turn our attention in the next section.

2.10 INELASTIC COLLISIONS

This type of collision is, as we have stated, characterised by the loss of energy from the primary to the struck atom, not only in nuclear motion but in excitation and ionization of the electrons of this latter. As an extremely rough approximation to obtain the energy range in which we will be concerned with energy losses to the atomic electrons, we recall Equation 2.10a for the maximum energy transfer from a particle of mass M_1 to one of mass M_2 with an incident energy E_0, i.e. $T_m = \frac{4M_1M_2}{(M_1 + M_2)^2} \cdot E_0$. If the struck particle is an electron, then

$$T_m = E_0 \frac{4m}{M_1} \qquad 2.81$$

where m is the nuclear mass relative to the electron mass. Clearly this energy transfer is much less efficient than when the masses involved are equal ($T_m = E_0$), and so the transfer of energy to electrons, sufficient to excite them to higher levels in the struck atom, only becomes adequate when $T_m \simeq E$

E /(Excitation) $= 4E_0 \frac{m}{M_1}$. To obtain a crude order of magnitude for E_0, we may assume $E_{excitation}$ is in the region of several electron volts, and we thus obtain E_0 is of order $\frac{M_1}{m}$ eV or writing A_1, for the atomic mass number of the incident atom, E_0 should be of the order of

$$A_1 \text{ KeV} \qquad 2.82$$

For Helium atoms this requires 4 KeV, whilst for mercury, some 200 KeV are required. Obviously these energies are in the range of interest of this book although in many cases the effect will be marginal. One can look at the ion energy required for excitation or ionization in a rather different way by noting that the kinetic energy of an electron in the state of highest binding energy is approximately equal to the ionization energy for the removal of that electron. Thus the criterion for ionisation may be written $T_m \approx E_{ionization} = \frac{1}{2} m v_e^2 = 4 \frac{m}{M_1} E_0$ and, replacing E_0 by $\frac{1}{2} M_1 v_0^2$ the minimum ion velocity required for ionization is given by $v \gtrsim 2v_e$ or, stated differently, if the ion velocity falls below the order of the electron orbital velocity, ionization effects are unimportant (here v_e = electron orbital velocity).

In a many-electron target atom, excitation and ionization energies for the various states will be lower than those for the innermost electrons and the above criterion will be optimistic. If the various bound states are considered then Seitz,[54] from considerations of the velocity matching, suggested that the lower limits for ionization are (1) For insulators

$$E_0 = \frac{M_1}{m} \cdot Eg/8 \qquad 2.83a$$

where Eg is the optical width of the forbidden gap (2) For metals

$$E_0 = \frac{M_1}{m} \cdot \frac{E_f}{16} \qquad 2.83b$$

where E_f is the Fermi Energy. Dienes and Vineyard[55] have assumed as a rough approximation for all materials

$$E_0 = \frac{1}{2} \frac{M_1}{m} \text{ eV} \qquad 2.83c$$

which is closely similar to our simple estimate given above.

None of these estimates have yet been shown to be correct, and indeed all assume a sharp cut off of ionization or excitation below E_0, which can hardly be expected to be realistic. Indeed recent experimental measurements have suggested that inelastic losses may occur at substantially lower energies than predicted by the simple velocity matching criterion. Nevertheless these considerations do give an order of magnitude for the limiting ion velocity or energy below which excitational losses are relatively unimportant and are therefore useful as a guide to the types of collision mechanism with which we will be concerned later.

These estimates indicate that, at least, a superficial appraisal of inelastic collisions is a necessary part of this chapter. The region where inelastic and elastic collisions assume comparable importance has, in fact, been treated only briefly in the literature, and the time is opportune for further theoretical and experimental investigation of this energy region. Lindhard, Scharff and Schiøtt[10] and Firsov[56] have in fact made some estimates of ionization losses just inside the region where $v_0 \sim v_e$ and we will return to the former treatment shortly. Recent experimental work[57-64] has been conducted in this interesting region and this may turn out to be of some considerable importance in providing a foundation for realistic theoretical calculations. On the other hand Bohr[8] has considered in some detail the excitation and ionization processes which occur at energies considerably in excess of the lower limits evaluated above. Nevertheless the concepts introduced have considerable bearing on this lower energy range. Bohr[8] and others have shown that, for $v_1 \sim v_e$ the collisions between the ion and the electrons can be considered as free and uninfluenced by the electron binding forces. For such cases, the maximum energy transfer to an electron is exactly as written earlier, $T_m = 4E_0 \cdot \frac{m}{M_1}$ which is a small fraction of the incident particle energy. If this is the case the incident particle suffers only a small deflection, and it is therefore permissible to treat the collision by the impulse approximation which, as we have seen, holds with high accuracy for small scattering angles.

Just as in the example of the impulse approximation in a Coulomb field given earlier, the energy transfer to an electron is given by

$$T = \frac{Z_1^2 e^4}{E_0 p^2} \frac{M_1}{m} \qquad 2.84$$

for an impact parameter p and an interaction potential $V(r) = \frac{Z_1 e^2}{r}$ (c.f. Equation 2.22). Further, the differential cross section for this energy transfer is

$$d\sigma(T) = \frac{\pi Z_1^2 e^4}{E_0} \cdot \frac{M_1}{m} \cdot \frac{dT}{T^2}$$

which, as shown previously, is the Rutherford scattering law.

One can also deduce the quantity $\int T d\sigma(T) = \Sigma$, defined earlier as proportional to the stopping power, in which the limits of integration extend from the energy required to ionize an atom, I_i, to the maximum energy transfer $4E_0 \frac{m}{M_1}$

One thus deduces

$$\Sigma = \frac{2\pi Z_1 e^4}{m v_1^2} \log_e \frac{2 m v_1^2}{I} \qquad 2.85a$$

with v_1 = incident atom velocity.

The lower limit I plainly applies to one electron orbit only and all collisions with energy-transfers less than this are assumed not to result in any energy loss (excitation is ignored). If account is taken of such collisions and I_e is defined as an average over all electrons in an atom i.e.

$$\sum_i n_i \log_e c/I = nZ \log_e c/I_e$$

Then an accurate value for

$$\Sigma \text{ is } \frac{4\pi Z_1 e^4}{m v_1^2} \log_e \frac{2 m v_1^2}{I_e} \qquad 2.85b$$

i.e. just twice the approximate result.

Σ may be plotted as a function of E_0 as in Figure 2.17

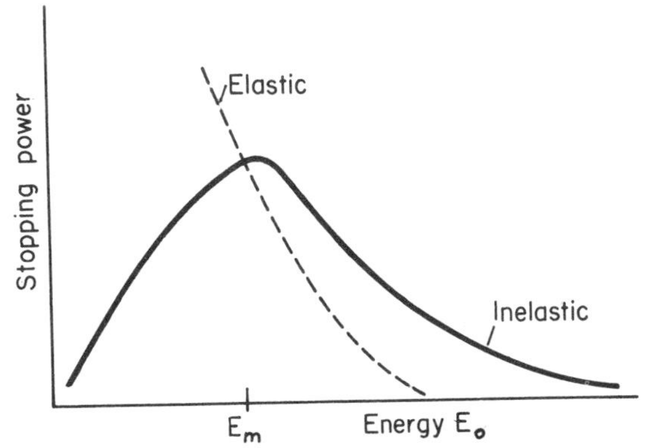

Fig. 2.17 Qualitative representation of the elastic and inelastic stopping powers as a function of the ion energy E_0.

and is clearly a decreasing function of E_0 above an energy E_m which, differentiation of shows, gives a maximum value of Σ for which $v_1 \approx v_e$.

Below this energy, the region of doubtful validity prevails but qualitatively at least, Σ falls rapidly. It is just in this region that elastic collisions begin to dominate, since these, in this energy range at least, generally increase with decrease of energy (shown qualitatively in Figure 2.17). Thus, in the completely inelastic collision range, accurate values for collision parameters can be deduced, whereas, just at the region where present analysis is inadequate and $v_1 \approx v_e$, both inelastic and elastic losses assume equal importance. In order to investigate the relative importance of elastic and inelastic collisions at velocities $v_1 \gg v_e$ one may consider the stopping powers for inelastic collisions given by Equation 2.85b and for elastic collisions. In the former case one must multiply by a term n_e (the number of ionisable electrons per atom) since each can receive energy from the incident atom—to a first approximation we may write $n_e = Z$. In the latter case one may use the hard sphere approximation to obtain

$$\Sigma_{HS} = \int_0^{T_m} \frac{\pi r_0^2}{T_m} \cdot T dT \text{ where } r_0 = \frac{2Z^2 e^2}{E_1}$$

for like colliding atoms and a Coulomb interaction potential. One finally deduces, therefore

$$\frac{\Sigma \text{ inelastic}}{\Sigma \text{ elastic}} \approx \frac{M_1}{Zm} \log_e \frac{4E_0}{I} \cdot \frac{m}{M_1} \qquad 2.86$$

For an energy in the inelastic range, say $v_1 = \sqrt{5}\, v_e$, we may choose as an example $M_1 = 100$ atomic mass units, with $Z_1 \approx 50$ and $E_0 = 500$ KeV (i.e. $E_0 = 5 \times$ limiting energy), and to simplify matters let $I_e \approx$ 10 eV. We then obtain

$$\frac{\Sigma \text{ inelastic}}{\Sigma \text{ elastic}} \approx 3500,$$

indicating the dominance of inelastic collisions.

For lower energies this ratio falls more rapidly than indicated by the simple equation above since the struck electrons have time to readjust to the varying field of the moving atom ($v_1 \sim v_e$) and remain bound. In this lower energy region as previously mentioned, there has been little theoretical work performed. Apart from the difficulties which arise in such analysis no doubt one reason for the lack of effort has been the lack of experimentation in this range with which to compare theoretical results. However quite recent experimental work[57-64] is beginning to remedy this situation and concurrently Lindhard et al[10] have made some initial theoretical estimates of the effects at lower energies. Lindhard et al[10] have shown that it is most useful to consider the stopping cross section ($\Sigma_i = \int T d\sigma(T)$ and have found that Σ inelastic is approximately proportional to v_e at low primary velocities where $v_1 < Z_1^{2/3} v_e$ (v_e is the electron velocity in the hydrogen atom). One simple way of showing the proportionality of Σ_i upon v_1 is to consider the energy loss of slowly moving atoms in an electron gas (Lindhard[65], Lindhard and Scharff[66], Lindhard and Winther[67]) where a lower limit to the energy transfer is set by polarisation effects during the collisions. Lindhard and Scharff,[66] and Lindhard[65] have shown that in these cases, the term $\log_e \frac{2 m v_1^2}{I}$ may be replaced by one of the form $C v_1^3$ and the stopping power becomes directly velocity dependent. Using a Thomas-Fermi model of the atom, it is then deduced that

$$\Sigma_i = \xi_e \cdot 8\pi e^2 a_0 \frac{Z_1 Z_2}{(Z_1^{2/3} + Z_2^{2/3})} \cdot \frac{v_1}{v_e}$$

$$\text{for } v_1 < v_e Z_1^{2/3} \qquad 2.87$$

and ξ_e is of the order $Z_1^{1/6}$.

This relation is believed to hold down to low values of v_1 (and hence incident energy), but at higher energies ($v_1 > v_e$) there is a transition to the behaviour of the type expressed in Equation 2.85b. In the transition range there is unfortunately as yet, no satisfactory theoretical treatment available but this may be anticipated in the not too distant future. In addition it should be pointed out that equation 2.87 is essentially a smoothed function over all electron orbits. Evidence has recently been obtained in both ion-gas atom [57,61,62,63] and ion-surface studies[58,59,64] that electron excitation losses occur in a stepwise manner and electrons are ejected with rather discrete energies due to overlapping of successive electron levels and theoretical explanations of the effect have been advanced by Amusia[68] and Fano and Lichten.[69] For our present considerations we shall consider only the simple theory however.

At low energies it is clear that Equations 2.85 and 87 lead to low values of inelastic energy loss compared with elastic losses and so one may justifiably neglect the former in many of the problems with which we will be confronted in subsequent analysis. At these energies, one method of assessing the contribution of inelastic processes would be to allow Σ inelastic $= K.E_0^{1/2}$ where K is an adjustable constant which can be determined by comparison with experiment. In the chapter on ion penetration we will investigate the utility of this method further.

An alternative method of determining the inelastic energy loss, discussed by Firsov[56,70] should also be mentioned. If one constructs a hypothetical surface S between two colliding atoms, defining the regions of action of the potentials of the atoms then, on the average, electrons crossing from one side of the surface interact with the field of the other atom and quickly assume the momentum of this atom. Thus if the number density of electrons in the first atom is n and v their velocity, the energy loss of these electrons is

$$\xi = m \iint_S \frac{nv}{4} \, ds\dot{R}dR \qquad 2.88$$

where R is the radius vector between the two nuclei.

The Thomas-Fermi model of the atom then allows one to write v in terms of n, and n in terms of the spatial potential ϕ, such that 2.88 becomes

$$\xi = \frac{m^2e^2}{4\pi^2h^3} \iint_S \phi^2 \, ds \, . \, \dot{R}dR \qquad 2.89$$

For distant collisions, one can use the momentum approximation to define $\dot{R}dR = v_0 dx$ where v_0 is the relative velocity of the colliding atoms and if the distance from one nuclei to any point in the plane is r then the potential

$$\phi = \frac{Z_1 + Z_2}{r} \psi \left[1.13\,(Z_1 + Z_2)^{1/3} \frac{r}{a_0}\right]$$

in the Thomas-Fermi-Firsov model. Further, if the distance from this point in the plane to the line of atomic centres (radius vector R) is ρ, then $ds = 2\pi\rho d\rho$, $r^2 = (R/2)^2 + \rho^2$ and $R^2 = r_0^2 + x^2$ where r_0 is the distance of closest approach.

With these substitutions, equation 2.89 is readily integrable to

$$\xi = \frac{0.35\,(Z_1 + Z_2)^{5/3} \, . \, \frac{hv_0}{a_0}}{\{1 + 0.16\,(Z_1 + Z_2)^{1/3} r_0/a_0\}^5} \ \text{eV} \qquad 2.90$$

For close collisions, with impact parameter p, equation 2.89 must be solved with the trajectory equations 2.17 to give.

$$\xi(p) = \frac{hv_0}{\pi a_0^2} (Z_1 + Z_2)^2 \int_{r_0}^{\infty} \frac{\left[1 - \frac{V(R)}{E_R}\right] dR}{\left\{1 - \frac{V(R)}{E_R} - p^2/R^2\right\}^{1/2}} \times$$

$$\int_{R/2}^{\infty} \frac{\psi^2(\rho) d\rho}{\rho} \qquad 2.91$$

If p_1 is the impact parameter for ejection of a single electron, then the cross section for single ionization is

$$\sigma_1 = 2\pi \int_0^{p_1} \frac{\xi(p)\, 2\pi p dp}{J}$$

where J is the average ionization potential for outer shell electrons. On performing the integration it is found, that to a good approximation

$$\sigma = \frac{1.39\, a_0 h}{J} \left\{\frac{Z_1 + Z_2}{Z_1^{1/2} + Z_2^{1/2}}\right\}^2 . \ 5.25\, v_0$$

$$\tan^{-1}\{6 \times 10^8 (v_0 - v_{min})\} \qquad 2.92$$

where v_{min} is a threshold velocity for ionization.

At high atom velocities this relation becomes linear in v_0, as found by Lindhard,[10] but at lower velocities ($< 3 \times 10^7$ cm/sec) becomes quadratic in v_0.

Before concluding this section we may note that all that has been said in relation to ionization and excitation of target atom electrons will apply by and large to the incident atomic electrons. Thus an atom, or ion, colliding with a solid lattice may lose electrons, or emit radiation, during its passage through the solid. Simultaneously there can be a capture of electrons by this particle and, at high energies, there will be a continual competition between electron excitation, loss and capture. This topic has been the subject of much research at high energies and Bohr has given careful consideration to the processes involved. At the energies of major interest here, however, we will largely ignore this type of interaction, except for one notable exception: that of electron ejection at low particle energies which forms the bulk of the next chapter. At these low energies ($\approx$10 eV) the interactions with the lattice atoms are not amenable to the type of collision mechanics outlined in this chapter since these atoms are constrained to remain bound to their lattice positions. The interactions between the incident and lattice atoms must therefore be treated from the quantum mechanical point of view.

We should also note that because of the differing electron structure of a neutral and of an ionised atom, subtle difference may occur in low energy interactions of the different particles with a solid surface. Such differences have in fact been observed in ion reflection experiments as we shall see in Chapter 4.

2.11 CONDITION FOR ISOLATED COLLISION MODEL

In view of these constraining forces on the motion of the lattice atoms, and because of the proximity of the surrounding atoms to the partners in a collision, one must enquire as to the applicability of the results of this chapter, where isolated two body events have been assumed, to a real collision between an energetic ion and a lattice. We have seen that the interatomic potential may be expressed generally by a form which exhibits a large repulsive term for small approach distances and a weakly attractive term for large separations. The former dominate the restoring forces for small atomic displacements whilst the latter characterise the cohesive forces of the crystal. (This may not be altogether true for covalent crystals since some displacements will produce only large angular bond distortion with little change in interatomic separation).

However for metals, we may enquire as to the displacement, δ, of a given atom for which the restoring forces are provided by only one other (nearest) atom.

Clearly the magnitude of the forces will depend upon the direction of the displacement, but for a force $\frac{\partial V(r)}{\partial r}$ derivable from the potential $V(r)$, the condition for this dependence upon one atom restoring force is given in order of magnitude by $\delta\left|\frac{\partial^2 V(r)}{\partial r^2}\right| \gtrsim \frac{\partial V(r)}{\partial r}$ i.e. the variation of the restoring force over small distances is large compared to the equilibrium force.

If we consider that the interatomic potential can be expressed as the difference of two inverse power terms, $\left(\frac{1}{r^n} - \frac{1}{r^m}\right)$ which is a fair approximation to the actual potential, then the condition becomes $\delta > \frac{d}{n}$ where d is the equilibrium separation. The energy E_c required to produce this displacement may be expressed in terms of the binding energy per bond E_L and is $E_c \approx E_L \frac{m}{n}$. For $E_L \approx 1$ eV and $\frac{m}{n} \approx 10$, one obtains a rough estimate for E_c of 0.1 eV. Above this energy one may thus expect the forces between only the two nearest atoms to be important in determining the collision mechanics, i.e. the collision partners may be considered as isolated from the rest of the lattice. Somewhat higher values of E_c must be anticipated for covalent crystals and alkali metals where the core repulsion is not important in determining the equilibrium separation. E_c values are not expected to exceed the binding energy however and are thus well below the energies of interest.

Thus isolated two body events are acceptable, at least at energies greater than say 10 eV generally, and we may accept this assumption for a large part of the remainder of this work. At lower energies, however, the quantum mechanical effects will assume importance and it is necessary to treat the lattice as a whole.

2.12 COLLECTIVE INTERACTIONS

In the low energy range below some tens of eV Arifov[71] and Gurvich[72] have examined the scattering of ions by solid surfaces in some detail. For the high energy region the scattering problem is treatable by two body collisions to a high degree of accuracy so that the Lagrange function for the system of moving and struck particles is according to equation 2.17

$$L = m_R \frac{\dot{\underline{r}}^2}{2} - V(\underline{r}) \qquad 2.17c$$

or in polar coordinates

$$L = \frac{m_R}{2}(\underline{r}^2 + \underline{r}^2\dot{\phi}^2) - V(\underline{r}) \qquad 2.17d$$

where

$$m_R = \frac{M_1 M_2}{M_2 + M_2}$$

is the reduced mass, $\underline{r} = |\underline{r}_1 - \underline{r}_2|$ is the vector distance between the atoms and $V(\underline{r})$ the instantaneous interatomic potential.

The C.M system scattering angle is then deduced, as before, to be

$$\theta = -\int_{\underline{r}_0}^{\infty} \frac{2p\,d\underline{r}}{\underline{r}^2\left\{1 - p^2/\underline{r}^2 - \frac{V(\underline{r})}{E_R}\right\}^{1/2}} + \pi$$

$$\text{or } \theta = \pi - 2\theta_x \qquad 2.19a$$

When the energy of the incident ion is low however, there will be considerable interaction between this ion and other target atoms apart from the one considered to be struck, and in this case the Lagrangian is

$$L = \sum_{i=1}^{n} \frac{m_i \dot{\underline{r}}_i^2}{2} - \frac{1}{2}\sum_{\substack{i=1,k=1\\ i\neq k}}^{n} V|\underline{r}_i - \underline{r}_k| \qquad 2.93a$$

One can simplify the problem by assuming that it is only the struck atom which is influenced by the forces of other atoms of the solid, these constraining it to prevent motion. Because of this constraint however the primary atom will experience a different type of collision than with a free atom, and this will lead to changes in the trajectory of the primary. Thus the lattice acts upon the primary through the intercession of the struck atom.

Consequently one may write

$$L = \frac{m_R \dot{r}^2}{2} - V(\underline{r}, \alpha_{12}) - V(\underline{r}, \alpha_{2i}) \qquad 2.93b$$

and thus the scattering angle

$$\theta_x^1 = \int_{\underline{r}_0}^{\infty} \frac{p\,d\underline{r}}{\underline{r}^2\left\{1 - \frac{p^2}{\underline{r}^2} - \left[\frac{V(\underline{r}, \alpha_{12} + V(\underline{r}, \alpha_{2i})}{E_R}\right]\right\}^{1/2}} \qquad 2.93c$$

This integral may be expressed in an analogous manner to equation 2.19a if one defines

(1) an effective mass

$$m_e = m_R\left(1 + \frac{V(\underline{r}, \alpha_{2i})}{E_R}\right) \qquad 2.94a$$

(2) an effective kinetic energy

$$E_e = E_R\left(1 + \frac{V(\underline{r}, \alpha_{2i})}{E_R}\right) \qquad 2.94b$$

or

(3) an effective impact parameter

$$p_e = p\left\{1 + \frac{V(\underline{r}, \alpha_{2i})}{E_R}\right\}^{-1/2} \qquad 2.94c$$

i.e.

$$\theta_x^1 = \int_{\underline{r}_0}^{\infty} \frac{p_e d\underline{r}}{\underline{r}^2\left\{1 - p_e^2/\underline{r}^2 - \frac{V(\underline{r}, \alpha_{12})}{E_R}\right\}^{1/2}} \qquad 2.94d$$

Thus the problem is essentially a two body problem with revised values for the mass and kinetic energy of the collision partners.

It is immediately seen that for high energies, $p_e \to p$, $m_e \to m$ and $E_e \to E_R$ and the normal two body collision treatment is permissible. For low E_R however the effective mass of the target atom M_{2_e} is

$$M_{2_e} = \frac{M_2 + (M_1 + M_2)\,.\,V(\underline{r}, \alpha_{2i})/E_R}{1 - (M_1 + M_2)\,.\,V(\underline{r}, \alpha_{2i})/M_1E_R} \qquad 2.95$$

Generally speaking $V(\underline{r}, \alpha_{2i})$ will be less than E_R, even for low E_R values but on the other hand $M_1 + M_2 > M_1$, and so as E_R decreases M_{2_e} increases i.e. the constraining influence of the surrounding atoms increases the effective mass of the struck atom.

$V(\underline{r}, \alpha_{2i})$ will be of the order of the energy required to displace the struck atom i.e. E_d and so a reasonable choice for $V(\underline{r}, \alpha_{2i})$ will be

$$V(\underline{r}, \alpha_{2i}) = 0, \text{ for } \underline{r} > a$$

$$V(\underline{r}, \alpha_{2i}) = -E_d, \text{ for } \underline{r} \lesssim a$$

where a is the distance of primary atom approach at which the interaction potential due to all lattice atoms must be considered.

With this assumption, one obtains

$$\theta_x^1 = \cos^{-1} p/a + \int_{\underline{r}_0}^{a} \frac{p d\underline{r}}{\underline{r}^2\left\{1 - p^2/\underline{r}^2 - \frac{(V(\underline{r}) + E_d)}{E_R}\right\}^{1/2}} \qquad 2.96$$

which is identified with equation 2.19a by setting

$$m_e = m_R\left(1 + \frac{E_d}{E_R}\right)$$

$$p_e = p\left(1 + \frac{E_d}{E_R}\right)^{-1/2}$$

$$E_e = E_R\left(1 + \frac{E_d}{E_R}\right)$$

and

$$M_{2_e} = \frac{M_2 + (M_1 + M_2)E_d/E_R}{1 - (M_1 + M_2)E_d/M_1E_R}$$

which again illustrates the increase of M_{2_e} with decreasing Energy E_R. In fact M_{2_e} tends to infinity wnere

$$E_R \to \frac{M_1 + M_2E_0}{M_1}.$$

The above treatment is that due to Gurvich,[72] but the Arifov[71] calculations lead to essentially similar conclusions regarding the increase of M_{2_e} with decreasing energy, differing only slightly in the exact dependence upon the energy ratio, E_d/E_R. We conclude therefore, that at low energies, the target commences to act as a macromolecule rather than a collection of isolated atoms.

It should be noted, however, that this evaluation still effectively treats the atoms merely as force centres and neglects any quantum effects which may occur because of electron transitions between the primary and target atoms i.e. the collisions are assumed to be elastic. However, we shall see in the next chapter that, at these low primary energies, considerable inelastic energy changes occur and to some extent this renders the above treatment only partly correct.

2.12.1 Nearest Neighbour Collective Interactions

Although the above calculation is applicable to essentially any point of impact on a surface there are certain phenomena where it is required to know the mechanics of the collision process for rather specific impact points. These phenomena include channelling (to be discussed in Chapter 5) and assisted focusing as occurs in sputtering (discussed in further detail in Chapters 6 and 7) and these are essentially processes in which an ion is acted upon simultaneously by several nearest neighbour atoms. Since, as we have already seen, interatomic forces reduce rapidly with atomic separation it is generally only necessary to consider these nearest neighbour interactions rather than the full lattice interaction as above. In a randomly distributed array of target atoms the problem is further simplified to binary collisions, but in a real lattice, ion starting positions may be simultaneously equally, or almost equally, spaced from several nearest neighbours and one must consider the collective interaction with all of these. As an example for discussion of the methods which have been used to study this collective interaction we consider the situation, depicted in Figure 2.18, where an ion of mass

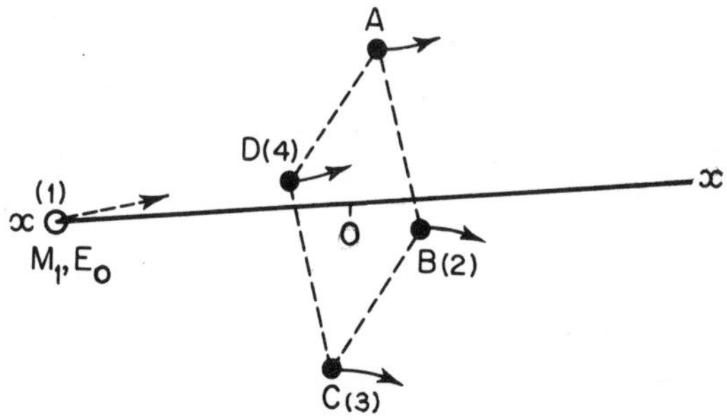

Fig. 2.18 Collision between an ion (energy E) and a "ring"of four equally spaced atoms of mass M_1, equal to the ion mass

M_1, energy E_0, is incident on a plane containing the four interacting 'ring' atoms, also considered to be of mass M_1. The distance of each atom to the ring axis xOx is d, and we consider the motion of the atom ① started at an angle θ to xOx and in the plane A①C. Because of symmetry the subsequent motion of atom ① will always be confined to this plane although all ring atoms will suffer an energy transfer.

If the ion energy is large, the distance d large (which is true for most cases under consideration) and the angle θ small, it is legitimate to treat the interactions by the impulse approximation discussed earlier. For an impact parameter p_1 between the ion ① and atom A and a Born-Mayer interatomic potential if it is considered that the ring atoms remain fixed during the interaction due to the influence of the surrounding lattice atoms, then equation 2.67c shows that the angular deflection of atom ϕ_1 in the laboratory system is given by

$$\phi_1 = \frac{A}{E_0} p_1/a . K_0 (p_1/a)$$

and the velocity loss of atom ① perpendicular to xOx is given by $v_0\phi_1$

$$\text{i.e. } v_\perp = \frac{v_0}{E_0} A p_1/a . K_0(p_1/a)$$

If θ is small then $p_1 = d - dy$ and the impact parameter with atom ③ is $p_3 = d + dy$. Thus the velocity loss perpendicular to xOx and the total deflection angle is

$$\phi_1 - \phi_3 = \frac{v_{\perp_1} - v_{\perp_3}}{v_0} = \beta$$

$$= \frac{A}{E_0} p_1/a . K_0(p_1/a) - \frac{A}{E_0} p_3/a . K_0(p_3/a)$$

or by expansion

$$\beta = \frac{A}{E_0} 2 . \frac{dy}{a} \left\{ \frac{d}{a} K_1(d/a) - K_0 (d/a) \right\}$$

The energy loss, including that to atoms ② and ④ can also be calculated from the momentum approximation to be

$$\Delta E_0 = 4 . \tfrac{1}{2} M_1 v_\perp^2 = 4\frac{A^2}{E_0}\left(\frac{d}{a}\right)^2 \{K_0(d/a)\}^2 \text{ for}$$

small θ.

This type of approach has been employed by Nelson and Thompson in calculation of the focussing action of ring atoms in collision sequences important in sputtering phenomena (viz. Chapters 6 and 7) and Lehmann and Leibfried in channelling processes (Chapter 5) but has been criticised by Weijsenfeld[73] on the grounds that, because interaction of ring atoms with the surrounding lattice is weak, the ring atoms can move during the passage of atom ① and weaken the overall interaction. It would appear to be preferable to consider therefore not the impact parameter p in the momentum approximation, but the distance of closest approach r_0 during a collision, since as the ring atoms relax, r_0 will give a truer representation of the maximum interaction force. Thus, for an impact parameter p, the distance of closest approach is derived from

$$\left\{1 - \frac{V(r_0)}{E_R}\right\} = p^2/r^2$$

and as Weijsenfeld has shown by expansion of equation 2.19a, in powers of V(r) to first order, one obtains

$$\phi_1 = \frac{A}{E_0}\frac{r_0}{a} K_0 (r_0/a),$$

whilst the equation for the energy loss is unchanged. Thus

$$\beta = \frac{A}{E_0} 2 dr_0 \left\{\frac{r_0}{a} K_1\left(\frac{r_0}{a}\right) - K_0\left(\frac{r_0}{a}\right)\right\}$$

with dr_0 determined from differentiation of equation 2.24. Weijsenfeld has shown that this evaluation leads to smaller scattering angles at low energies than predicted by the simple momentum approximation and that the results are in better agreement with machine calculations made by Gibson et al.[74]

Andersen and Sigmund[75] have also applied this treatment to studying the energy loss to the ring atoms during the collision as a function of the particle energy for axially directed ions. In addition these authors considered a further approximation, the distant collision approximation, in which the real, elliptically symmetric potential of the ring atoms (in the C.M system) was replaced by a matching spherically symmetric potential which agreed in magnitude and curvature at the position where the ion crosses the plane of the ring. It was found that for large energies (~100 eV but dependent upon the ion and ring atom masses) the momentum approximation, the distant collision approximation (D.C.A) and the Weijsenfeld[73] method (the constant velocity approximation, C.V.A.) were all adequate. At low particle energies however both the momentum approximation (M.A) and the C.V.A. leads to excessive values of ΔE_0 (because of the E_0^{-1} dependence) but the D.C.A. approximates to an energy loss relation $\Delta E_0 = E_0$, which is more sensible. Indeed for the incident ion to penetrate the ring, an energy E_p is required to overcome the ring potential energy, which is just 4A exp (–d/a) and below this energy one may expect to lose an appreciable fraction of E_0.

REFERENCES

1. Von Hippel, A. (1926) Ann. Physik **80,** 672
2. Von Hippel, A. (1926) Ann. Physik **81,** 1043
3. Glasstone, S. and Edlund, M. C. (1953) The Elements of Nuclear Reactor Theory. Macmillan. London (1953)
4. Billington, D. S. and Crawford, J. H. (1961) Radiation Damage in Solids. Princeton. Univ. Press. Princeton (1961)
5. Goldstein, H. (1950) Classical Mechanics. Addison-Wesley. Cambridge Mass. U.S.A. Chapter 3
6. Leibfried, G. (1965) Einfuhrung in die Theorie der Bestrahlungseffekte in Festkorpern (Stuttgart: (1965) Teubner Verlag)
7. Lehman, W. and Shapiro, K. A. (1960) Phys. Rev. **120,** 32
8. Bohr, N. (1948) Mat. Fys. Medd. Dan. Vid. Selsk. **18.** No. 8
9. Rutherford, E. (1911) Phil. Mag. (6), **21,** 669
10. Lindhard, J., Scharff, M. and Schiøtt, H. E. (1962) Mat. Fys. Med. Dan. Vid. Selsk. **33,** No. 14, 3
11. Silsbee, R. H. (1957) J. Appl. Phys. **28,** 1246
12. Born, M. and Mayer, J. E. (1932) Zeits. f. Physik **75,** 1
13. Gombas, P. (1956) Handbuch der Physik **36.** Springer-Verlag. Berlin. 109
14. Holmes, D. K. (1962) Radiation Damage in Solids. Vol. 1. International Atomic Energy Agency. Vienna (1962) p. 1
15. Oen, O. S., Holmes, D. K. and Robinson, M. T. (1963) J. Appl. Phys. **34,** 302
16. Brinkman, J. A. (1954) J. Appl. Phys. **25,** 961
17. Lee, C., Longmire, C. L. and Rosenbluth, M. N. (Unpublished.)
18. Firsov, O. B. (1957) Zh. Eksper i Teor. Fiz. **32,** 1464. English Translation in Sov. Phys. J.E.T.P. (1957) **5,** 1192
19. Firsov, O. B. (1957) Zh. Eksper i Teor. Fiz. **33,** 696. English Translation in Sov. Phys. J.E.T.P. (1958) **6,** 534
20. Firsov, O. B. (1958) Zh. Eksper i Teor. Fiz. **34,** 447. English Translation in Sov. Phys. J.E.T.P. (1958) **7,** 308
21. Abrahamson, A. A., Hatcher, R. D. and Vineyard, G. H. (1961) Phys. Rev. **121,** 159
22. Abrahamson, A. A. (1963) Phys. Rev. **130,** 693
23. Abrahamson, A. A. (1964) Phys. Rev. **133A,** 990
24. Slater, J. C. and Khutter, H. M. (1935) Phys. Rev. **47,** 559
25. Feynman, R. P., Metropolis, N. and Teller, E. (1949) Phys. Rev. **75,** 1561
26. Abrahamson, A. A. (1961) Phys. Rev. **123,** 538
27. Everhart, E., Stone, G. and Carbone, R. J. (1955) Phys. Rev. **99,** 1287
28. Lindhard, J. and Scharff, M. (1961) Phys. Rev. **124,** 128
29. Robinson, M. T. (1963) Oak Ridge National Laboratory Report. ORNL-3493
30. Baroody, E. M. (1961) Phys. Fluids. **4,** 1182
31. Baroody, E. M. (1962) Aeronautical Research Laboratory Report. ARL 62-321
32. Lehmann, C. and Leibfried, G. (1963) Zeits. f. Physik **172,** 465
33. Holmes, D. K., Leibfried, G. and Oen, O. S. (1959) Oak Ridge National Lab. Report. No. ORNL-2829. p. 1
34. Nielsen, K. O. (1956) Electromagnetically Enriched Isotopes and Mass Spectrometry. Butterworths. London (1956) p. 68
35. Beeler, J. R. Jr. and Besco, D. G. (1963) J. Appl. Phys. **34,** 2873. References contained therein
36. Lee, E. J. and Robinson, M. T. (1962) Oak Ridge National Laboratory Report. ORNL-3364 (1962) p. 11
37. Leibfried, G. and Oen, O. S. (1962) J. Appl. Phys. **33,** 2257
38. Lehmann, C. and Robinson, M. T. (1964) Phys. Rev. **134A,** 37
39. Sigmund, P. and Vajda, P. (1964) Danish Atomic Energy Commission. Riso Report No. 83
40. Sigmund, P. and Vajda, P. (1964) Danish Atomic Energy Commission. Riso Report No. 84

40a. Vajda, P. (1965) Danish Atomic Energy Commission. Riso Report No. 115, and Phys. Letters (1965) **19,** 204

41. See for example Jahnke, E., Emde, F. and Lösch, F. (1960) Tafeln höherer Funktionen. Stuttgart
42. Keller, J. B., Kay, I. and Shmoys, J. (1956) Phys. Rev. **102,** 557
43. Lane, G. H. and Everhart, E. (1960) Phys. Rev. **120,** 2064
44. Fuls, E. N., Jones, P. R., Ziemba, F. P. and Everhart, E. (1957) Phys. Rev. **107,** 704
45. Jones, P. R., Ziemba, F. P., Moser, H. A. and Everhart, E. (1959) Phys. Rev. **113,** 182
46. Kaminker, D. M. and Fedorenko, N. V. (1955) Zh. Tekh. Fiz. **25,** 2239
47. Afrosimov, V. V. and Fedorenko, N. V. (1957) Zh. Tekh. Fiz. **27,** 2557. English Translation in Soviet Physics—Tech. Physics (1957) **2,** 2378
48. Afrosimov, V. V. and Fedorenko, N. V. (1957) Zh. Tekh. Fiz. **27,** 2573. English Trans. in Soviet Physics. Tech. Physics (1957) **2,** 2389
49. Fedorenko, N. V. (1959) Fiz. Uspekhi. **68,** 481. English Translation in Soviet Phys. Usp. **2,** 526 (1959)
50. Mott, W. F. and Massey, H. S. W. (1952) The Theory of Atomic Collisions. Oxford University Press. Oxford (1952)
51. Massey, H. S. and Burhop, E. H. S. (1952) Electronic and Ionic Impact Phenomena. Oxford. Clarendon Press (1952)
52. Mott, N. F. (1930) An Outline of Wave mechanics. Cambridge University Press. Cambridge
53. Leibfried, G. (1962) Radiation Damage in Solids. Proc. International School of Physics. Enrico-Fermi. Academic Press. Inc., New York (1962) p. 227
54. Seitz, F. and Koehler, J. S. (1956) Progress in Solid State Physics. **2.** New York (1956) p. 305
55. Dienes, G. J. and Vineyard, G. H. (1957) Radiation Effects in Solids. Interscience Publishers.; New York (1957)
56. Firsov, O. B. (1959) Zhur. Eksper. i. Teor. Fiz. **36,** 1517. English Translation in Soviet Physics—J.E.T.P. (1959) **9,** 1076
57. Morgan, G. H. and Everhart, E. (1962) Phys. Rev. **128,** 667 (and references contained therein)

58a. Datz, C. and Snoek, S. (1964) Phys. Rev. **134,** A347

58b. Dahl, P. and Magyer J. (1965) Phys. Rev. **140,** A1420

59. Piercy, G. R., McCargo, M., Brown, F. and Davies, J. A. (1964) Can. J. Phys. **42,** 1116
60. Russek, A. (1963) Phys. Rev. **132,** 246
61. Afrosimov, V. V., Gordeev, Yu. S., Panov, M. N. and Fedorenko, N. V. (1964) Zhur. Tekh. Fiz. **34,** 1613, 1624 and 1637. English Translation in Soviet Physics—Tech. Phys. (1965) **9,** 1248, 1256 and 1265
62. Everhart, E. and Kessel, Q.C. (1965) Phys. Rev. Letters **14,** 484
63. Kessel, Q.C., Russek, A. and Everhart. (1965) Phys. Rev. Letters **14,** 484
64. Rol, P., Snoek, C., VanderWeg, W. F. and Geballe, R. (1965) Proc. 7th. International Conference on Phenomena in Ionized Gases. Belgrade (1965)

65. Lindhard, J. (1954) Dan. Vid. Selsk. Mat. Fys. Medd. **27**, 15

66. Lindhard, J. and Scharff, M. (1953) Dan. Vid. Selsk. Mat. Fys. Medd. **27**, 15

67. Lindhard, J. and Winther, A. (1964) Dan. Vid. Selsk. Mat. Fys. Medd. **34**, 3.

68. Amusia, M. Ya. (1965) Phys. Letters **14**, 36

69. Fano, V. and Lichten, W. (1965) Phys. Rev. Letters **14**, 627

70. See also Parilis, E. S. and Kishinevskii, L. M. (1960) Fiz. Tver. Tela. **3**, 1219. English Translation in Soviet Physics—Solid State (1960) **3**, 885

71. Arifov, U. A. (1961) Interaction of atomic particles with the surface of a metal. Tashkent. University. Uzbekhistan. English Translation in AEC-tr 6089

72. Gurvich, L. G. (1962) Izv. Akad. Nauk. S.S.R. **26**, 1418. English Translation in Bull. Acad. Sci. U.S.S.R. (1962) **26**, 1443

73. Weijsenfeld, C. H. (1965) To be Published

74. Gibson, J. B., Goland, A. N., Milgram, M. and Vineyard, G. H. (1960) Phys. Rev. **120**, 1229

75. Andersen, H. H. and Sigmund, P. (1965) To be Published

CHAPTER 3

Secondary Electron Emission

3.1 INTRODUCTION

When, under suitable conditions, a beam of ions strikes a metal surface electrons are liberated. This process is known as secondary electron emission and a coefficient γ is defined as the number of electrons liberated per incident ion.

The phenomenon of electron emission during ion bombardment was first observed by Villard in 1889[1] who explained the occurrence of cathode rays in a discharge tube as being due to the 'knocking-out' of electrons at the cathode by positive ions. Similar effects occurring during the bombardment by α particles were reported by Rutherford[2] Thomson[3] and Logeman[4].

The importance of studying electron emission will be apparent to the reader who has carried out experiments in which accurate measurements of low intensity charged particle currents are required. Since an electron leaving the collector surface is equivalent to an ion arriving as far as a current detector is concerned then it is imperative that the value of the coefficient γ applicable to the bombardment conditions be known, unless some reliable electron suppressor device can be operated. The problem is thus shared by all devices where ion currents need to be recorded such as collectors of ion gauges and mass spectrometers.

Of course the secondary emission effect is not always unwanted and can in fact be used to amplify the ion current signal, or, to detect the arrival of neutral particles at the collector surface.[5,6,7] Present day research shows that certain Copper-Beryllium compounds are remarkably efficient in producing secondary electrons having yields in the region of ten electrons per incident ion at 20 keV and use of compounds such as this arė favoured in the construction of secondary electron multiplier detectors.

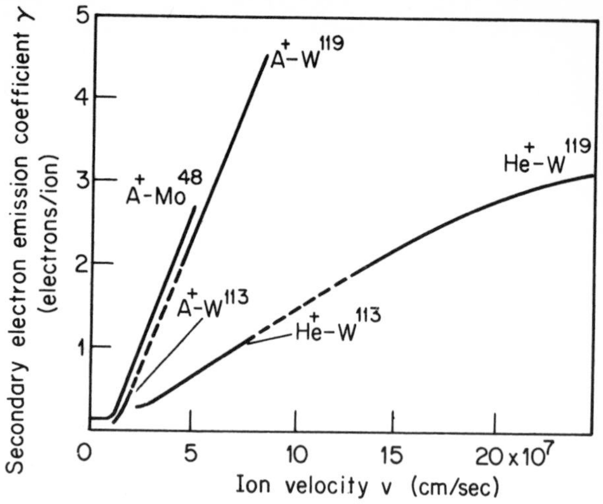

Fig. 3.2 Secondary electron emission coefficient as a function of ion velocity

The secondary electron emission coefficient is also important as a parameter in the equations governing the Townsend discharge phenomenon. The 'γ' actually used in the Townsend equations is not the same coefficient as discussed here but the two are interrelated.

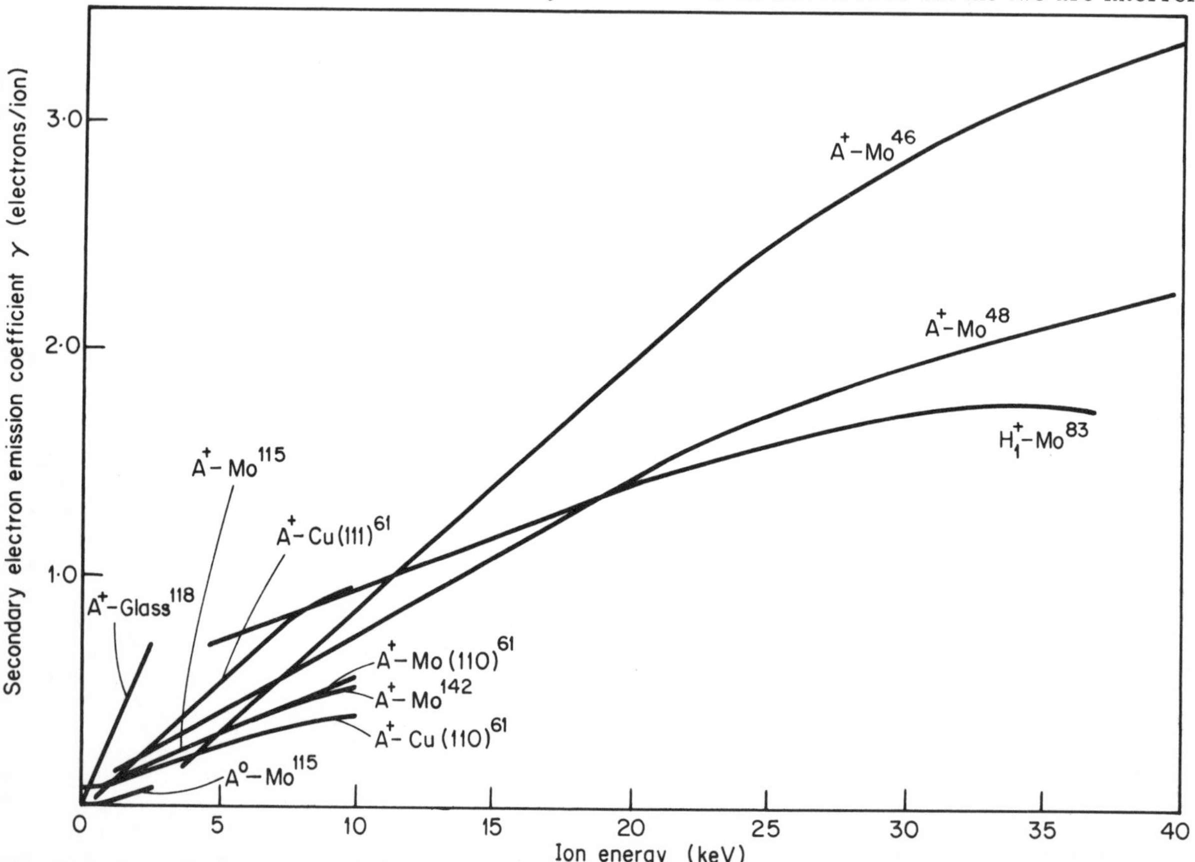

Fig. 3.1 Secondary electron emission coefficient as a function of ion energy

TABLE 3.1.a

Secondary Electron Emission Coefficients for Bombardment at 10 eV

Ion / Target	He^+	He^{++}	Ne	A	Kr	Xe
Si (111)	0.188[75]		0.128[75]			
Si (100)	0.172[75]		0.115[75]	0.024[75]	0.007[75]	0.0005[75]
Ni (111)	0.171[98]		0.123[98]	0.034[98]		
Ge (111)	0.196[75]		0.138[75]	0.032[75]	0.008[75]	0.0006[75]
Mo	0.300[74]	0.71[76]	0.254[74]	0.122[74]	0.069[74]	0.022[74]
Ta	0.13* [77]	0.52* [77]				
W	0.289[138]		0.213[138]	0.096[138]	0.050[138]	0.013[138]

* Evidence of surface contamination

TABLE 3.1.b

Secondary Electron Emission Coefficients for Bombardment at 100 eV

Ion / Target	H_2	He^+	He^{++}	N	Ne	N_2	O_2	A	Kr	Xe
Si (111)		0.180[75]			0.145[75]					
Si (100)		0.168[75]			0.131[75]			0.027[75]	0.009[75]	0.0007[75]
Ni (111)		0.170[98]			0.138[98]			0.036[98]		
Ge (111)		0.191[75]			0.144[75]			0.037[75]	0.010[75]	0.0003[75]
Mo		0.274[74]	0.72[76]	0.031[85]	0.281[74]	0.032[85]	0.026[85]	0.115[74]	0.061[74]	0.019[74]
Ta		0.14* [77]	0.55* [77]							
W		0.263[138]			0.246[138]			0.095[138]	0.051[138]	0.012[138]
W	0.029[91]	0.27[91]				0.0245[91]	0.015[91]			

* Evidence of surface contamination

In the following rather brief treatise we first discuss early investigations and then proceed to a discussion of more recent work including current theories of the two types of emission process found to exist. For the reader purely interested in magnitudes of the coefficient a table of yields is presented and typical curves showing the variations of yield with energy and also with ion velocity are included (Tables 3.1 and Figs. 3.1 and 3.2).

3.2 EARLY RESEARCH

In spite of the fact that the electron emission from metals under the influence of ion bombardment has been under investigation since the turn of the century significant results have been obtained only in the past decade. Earlier work was carried out on dirty surfaces (i.e. surfaces covered with background gases) and results were not therefore reliable. Jackson [8,9] found, by baking his targets, that the secondary emission was very dependent on the surface conditions when the bombarding ions were Na^+, Rb^+, Cs^+ or K^+ and concluded correctly that this was due to removal of adsorbed layers of gas in the baking cycle. Yields were generally much higher on the unbaked contaminated target whilst they were sometimes not large enough for detection after baking. Jackson also observed a dependence of the yield on the orientation of the target with respect to the incident beam, an effect which has been confirmed in recent work.[10,11]

The dependence of γ on target cleanliness was demonstrated conclusively by Linford[12] who made measurements on Ni, Cu, Sb, Ag, Cd, Na, K, and Li targets whilst bombarding with a 0.75-2.5 MeV mercury ion beam. Paetow and Walcher[13] bombarded tungsten targets with cesium ions and found that the secondary electron coefficient was low initially, when the surface was clean, but increased to a constant value as the bombardment continued and the surface became contaminated. This effect was also observed by Koch[14] who found yields increased to a constant value of 0.05 electrons/ion for cesium coverages of 10 per-cent. Oliphant[15] showed that γ was less for a hot target than for a cold one which again suggested that the adsorbed layer, present to a greater extent on the cold target, caused an increase in the electron emission. He further found that a relation of the form

TABLE 3.1.c

Secondary Electron Emission Coefficients for Bombardment at 1 keV

	H_1	H_2	H_3	D_2	He	Li	Ni	O	Ne	Na	N_2	O_2	K	A	Kr	Rb	Xe	Cs	Hg
Al (poly-x)														0.09[142]					
Al (111)														0.1[61]	0.047[61]		0.015[61]		
Al (100)														0.09[61]	0.045[61]		0.015[61]		
Al (110)														0.08[61]	0.04[61]		0.010[61]		
Si (111)					0.191[75]				0.181[75]										
Si (100)					0.178[75]				0.169[75]					0.039[75]	0.019[75]		0.0018[75]		
Ni (poly-x)		0.27[140]		0.32[140]	0.17[48] 0.82[140]									0.07[142] 0.135[140]					
Ni (111)									0.17[61]					0.07[61]	0.03[61]		0.01[61]		
Ni (100)									0.14[61]					0.06[61]	0.04[61]		0.01[61]		
Ni (110)									0.16[61]					0.05[61]	0.025[61]		0.01[61]		
Cu (poly-x)									0.13[142]					0.08[142]	0.06[142]		0.03[142]		
Cu (111)									0.18[61]					0.11[61]	0.06[61]		0.04[61]		
Cu (100)									0.16[61]					0.09[61]	0.07[61]		0.035[61]		
Cu (110)									0.15[61]					0.08[61]	0.04[61]		0.025[61]		
Ge (poly-x)		0.46* [117]				0.11[117]							0.11[117]					0.00[117]	
Ge (111)					0.193[75]				0.160[75]					0.047[75]	0.019[75]		0.002[75]		
Zr														0.14[142]					
Mo (poly-x)	0.232[85]	0.230[85] 0.17[143]	0.134[85]	0.08[143]	0.25[48] 0.263[138] 0.28[114]	0.064[82] 0.16[42]	0.088[85]	0.176[85]	0.23[142] 0.21[48] 0.306[74] 0.27[87]	0.02[87] 0.017[82]	0.082[85]	0.059[85]	0.005[87] 0.010[82]	0.09[142] 0.092[115] 0.095[114] 0.132[48] 0.118[74] 0.105[104] 0.128[87]	0.072[87] 0.073[74] 0.04[142]	0.005[87]	0.02[142] 0.025[74]		0.80[95]
Mo (111)									0.22[61]					0.08[61]	0.03[61]		0.01[61]		
Mo (100)									0.225[61]					0.08[61]	0.052[61]		0.01[61]		
Mo (110)									0.23[61]					0.09[61]	0.042[61]		0.01[61]		
Ag (111)									0.20[61]					0.07[61]	0.04[61]		0.015[61]		
Ag (100)									0.19[61]					0.07[61]	0.045[61]		0.015[61]		
Ag (110)									0.18[61]					0.07[61]	0.038[61]		0.015[61]		
Ta					0.23[77] 0.28[139]				0.30[87]					0.135[87] 0.10[139] 0.10[142]					
W					0.20[48] 0.252[138] 0.26[113]				0.250[138] 0.20[113] 0.24[87]					0.099[138] 0.095[113] 0.105[87]	0.06[187] 0.061[138]		0.016[138]	0.0022[141]	
Pt						0.26[42]			0.46[42] 0.47[140]										
No. 46 Glass	0.69[110]	0.85[110]	0.86[110]		0.82[118] 0.83[110]									0.23[110] 0.28[118]					
KCl (mono-x)						0.83[112]							0.95[112]						
NaCl (mono-x)						4.0[112]													

* extrapolated value

TABLE 3.1.d

Secondary Electron Emission Coefficients for Bombardment at 10 keV

	H_1	H_2	D_1	D_2	He	Li	N	Ne	Na	K	A	Kr	Rb	Mo	Xe	Cs	Ba
Al poly x											0.61[142]						
Al (111)											0.63[61]	0.325[61]			0.30[61]		
Al (100)											0.43[61]	0.219[61]			0.163[61]		
Al (110)											0.42[61]	0.185[61]			0.13[61]		
Ni poly x					0.65[48]						0.63[142]						3.1[137]
Ni (111)								0.91[61]			0.875[61]	0.88[61]			0.55[61]		
Ni (100)								0.60[61]			0.48[61]	0.44[61]			0.26[61]		
Ni (110)								0.56[61]			0.38[61]	0.31[61]			0.20[61]		
Cu poly x								0.73[142]			0.74[142]	0.68[142]			0.46[142]		
Cu (111)								0.83[61]			0.95[61]	1.08[61]			0.74[61]		
Cu (100)								0.52[61]			0.49[61]	0.52[61]			0.34[61]		
Cu (110)								0.43[61]			0.38[61]	0.39[61]			0.27[61]		
Ge		1.0[117]				1.5*[117]				1.77[117]						0.69[117]	
Zr	0.7[83] 0.95[83]										0.075[83] 0.60[142]						
Mo poly x	1.0†[143] 1.0[46]	1.5†[143]	0.68†[143]	0.95†[143]	0.95[83] 1.2†[143] 1.07[46] 1.01[48]		1.1[83] 1.38[46]	1.18[48] 1.25[83] 0.88[142] 0.86[87]	0.51[87]	0.40[87]	1.05[83] 0.55[142] 0.57[87] 0.83[48]	0.225[87] 0.24[142]	0.16[87]	0.03[83]	0.24[142]		
Mo (111)								0.77[61]			0.52[61]	0.24[61]			0.262[61]		
Mo (100)								0.81[61]			0.55[61]	0.26[61]			0.286[61]		
Mo (110)								0.91[61]			0.59[61]	0.305[61]			0.334[61]		
Ag (111)								1.38[61]			0.61[61]	0.282[61]			0.30[61]		
Ag (100)								0.81[61]			0.44[61]	0.175[61]			0.163[61]		
Ag (110)								0.68[61]			0.38[61]	0.145[61]			0.13[61]		
Ta		0.97[109]						0.83[87]			0.58[87] 0.49[142]	0.225[87]					
W					0.95*[113] 0.97[48]			0.81[87] 0.88*[113]			0.56[87] 0.58*[113]	0.22[87]				0.029[116]	
Pt										2.5[137]							
No. 46 Glass		2.90[110]			2.15[110]												

* Extrapolated value † Kinetic component only

$$\gamma = f(a - b \cos \theta) \qquad 3.1$$

described his results, where θ was the angle between the incident ion beam and the normal to the target surface.

Veith[16] found that not only was the secondary emission coefficient dependent on the state of the target surface, but also the energy distribution of the ejected electrons was changed; low energy electrons being produced in greater numbers from dirty surfaces. (this is again confirmed by more recent experiments.[92]) He further demonstrated that the ejected electrons fell into two distinct groups; one a group of small velocity of about 1-3 eV irrespective of primary ion energy and the second a relatively narrow group of greater energy which was dependent on the nature of the target material and the energy of the incident ions. For potassium ions of 560 eV incident on platinum the energy of this second group was about 21 eV whilst, on an aluminium surface, the corresponding energy was as high as 50 eV.

Penning[17,18] and Oliphant[15] applied better vacuum techniques to their studies than earlier researchers, though Hagstrum is of the opinion that these pressures were still too high. Penning obtained values of γ from 0.08 to 0.14 at 100 eV and from 0.3 to 0.6 at 1000 eV energy for neon ions on an iron target.

Healea and Houtermans[19] investigated the dependence of yield on ion mass and found that it increased as the ion mass decreased. These workers studied bombardment of hot nickel targets which were baked prior to experiment for times as long as two months! Results were then reproducible and showed a linear increase in γ for energies between 600 and 1400 eV for He^+, Ne^+ and A^+ ions in agreement with the trend seen in an earlier study of H_2^+ ions[20]. It was noted that the H_2^+ and He^+ curves had a tendency to level off at energies above 1000 eV. No electron emission was observed for energies below about 100 eV however which contradicts present day results.

The above inverse dependence of γ on ion mass was not observed by Hill et al[21] though they admit that their results were possibly for surfaces covered with an oxide film as seen by Schneider[22]. Variations of electron emission with target mass were small and bore little relation to the value of this mass.

Variation of yield with target mass was studied by Pavlov et al[23] for Na^+ and K^+ bombardment of tungsten, molybdenum and platinum targets at 10-70 eV energy. Secondary emission coefficients were found to increase slightly with target temperature, and coverage of adsorbed gases and were such that

$$\gamma_W > \gamma_{Mo} > \gamma_{Pt}$$

By control studies of thorium contamination on tungsten Pavlov et al were able to show that the change in yield satisfied the empirical equation

$$\gamma = B \exp(-C\phi) \qquad 3.2$$

where ϕ is the work function of the contaminated tungsten target and B and C constants determined by curve-fitting.

We thus have the situation in all the pre-1940 work on electron emission that the experimenters were very conscious of the need to keep surfaces clean, but were not always successful in their ideals. It is certainly very strange that many workers concerned with sputtering yields in this period (discussed in Chapter 7) payed an almost equal 'disregard' to the state of the surface when obtaining their results! This in itself leads one to the conclusion that electron emission must be much more critically surface dependent than sputtering, a hypothesis which is certainly confirmed by more recent research discussed in the following sections.

3.3 DEVELOPMENT OF A THEORETICAL MODEL OF SECONDARY EMISSION

An ion travelling toward a target surface has both potential energy, due to its elevation to the ionized state, and kinetic energy, due to its velocity relative to the target material. Various theories have been proposed to demonstrate how electron emission can occur as a result of the re-arrangement of either potential or kinetic energies in the ion-metal system and from experimental results it appears that to a first approximation, for ion energies below about 1 keV, the yields are independent of kinetic energy and depend only on the potential energy of the ion; i.e. a so-called 'Potential Ejection' process predominates whereas, for ion energies above 1 keV, kinetic energy considerations start to be important. It should be mentioned at this point that potential ejection is not energetically possible for all ion-target combinations whilst kinetic emission is always feasible at energies above a minimum threshold value.

The possible transitions which can occur due to liberation of the potential energy of an excited particle fall into the categories (a) resonance processes, (b) auger processes and (c) radiative events. Shekhter[24] has calculated the probability of (c) to be of the order 5×10^{-7} so we shall ignore this in our following treatment. The remaining processes are

(1) Resonance Neutralization of an ion,

(2) Resonance Ionization of an atom,

(3) Auger Neutralization of an ion and

(4) Auger De-excitation of an excited atom.

These processes are illustrated in Figs. 3.3-3.5 and will now be discussed in detail.

3.3.1 Resonance Neutralization

This process was first suggested by Oliphant and Moon[25] who proposed the tunnelling of an electron from the metal surface through the potential barrier to populate an excited atomic level of the incident ion. Let us look at the potential energy of an idealised ion-metal system as the ion is neutralized to obtain a clear picture of the changes occurring. (see Fig. 3.6) Initially we have N electrons in the metal and an ion situated at infinity, state A of Fig. 3.6. At the next stage (M) we have an electron and an ion at infinity and N − 1 electrons remaining in the metal. The energy gained by the system therefore has values anywhere between ϕ, if the electron was taken from the top of the Fermi level, and W_a, if an electron from the bottom of the band of metallic states was removed. In general the electron will be removed from some state between the above extremes, that is anywhere in the band of N states between y_M and x_M.

In stage 3 the ion and electron combine at infinity to form an excited atom of excited potential state V_e. This lowers the energy of the system by V_i-V_e where V_i is the ionization potential of the ion. Thus we have a band of possible final states (B), $x_B \rightarrow y_B$, resulting

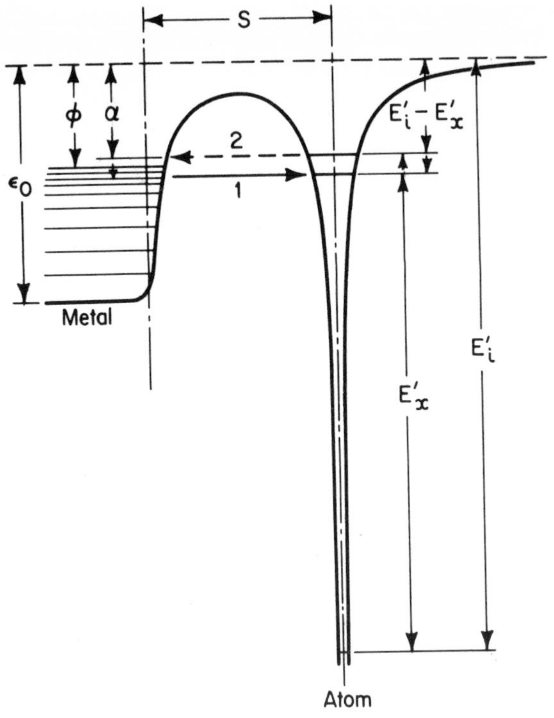

Fig. 3.3 Schematic diagram illustrating resonance neutralization of an ion (transition 1) or resonance ionization of an excited atom (transition 2) at a metal surface. Transition 1 can only occur at energy levels which are filled inside the metal, transition 2 at levels which are empty. ϵ_0 = energy of vacuum level above bottom of conduction band in the metal, ϕ = work function, α = energy below vacuum level of transition electron, s = distance of ion from surface of metal and E_i' and E_x' are the effective ionization and excitation energies near the metal surface, respectively (viz. Ref. 3.26).

from a single initial state. In practice the model is not as simple as this since all the potential states are influenced by the attractive coulombic force due to the image potential and the repulsive interatomic forces. The energy levels of initial and final states thus change with ion-target distance in the manner indicated in Fig. 3.7.

According to the Franck-Condon principle, an electronic transition can only occur with appreciable pro-

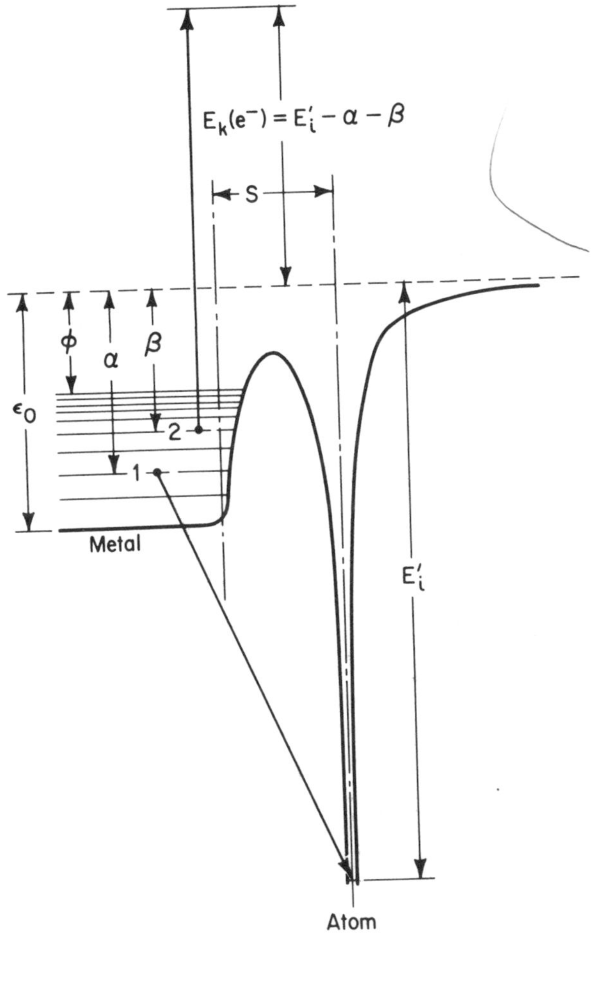

Fig. 3.4 Schematic diagram illustrating Auger neutralization of an ion at a metal surface. Symbols as in Fig. 3.3 with β = energy below vacuum of second participating electron which is ejected with energy $E_K(e^-)$ (viz. Ref. 3.26)

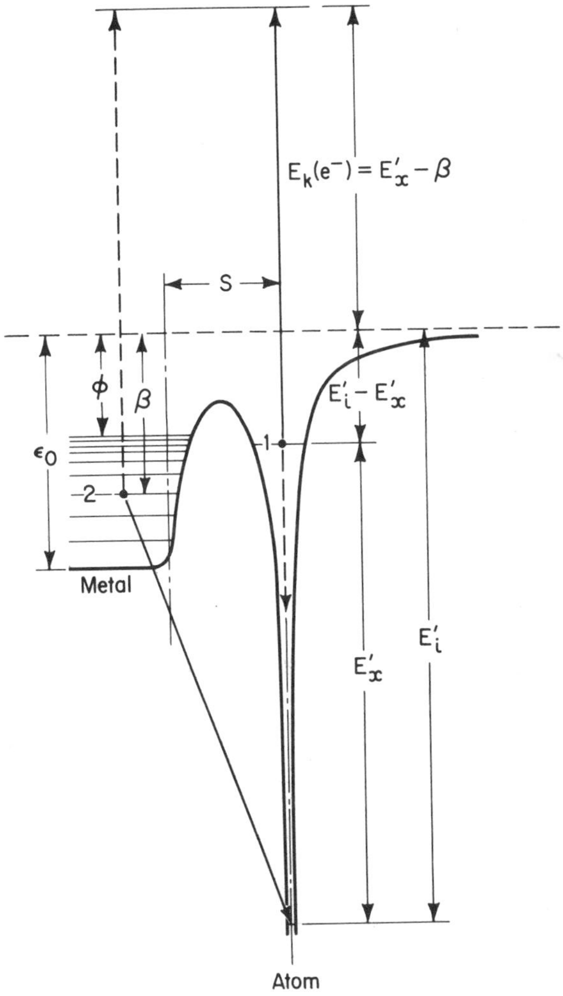

Fig. 3.5 Schematic diagram illustrating Auger de-excitation of an excited atom at a metal surface. Symbols are as in Figs. 3.3 and 3.4 (viz. Ref. 3.26)

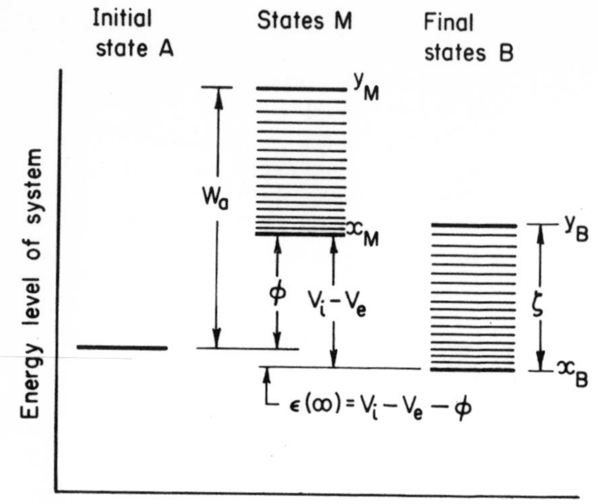

Fig. 3.6 Energy levels of system for neutralization of an ion at infinite separation. Initial state A: N-1 electrons in metal plus an ion and an electron at infinity. Final states B: N-1 electrons in metal plus an excited atom at infinity. For comparison with preceding figures $W_a \equiv \epsilon_0$ and V_i, V_e = ionization potential and excitation potential of the ion respectively (Ref. 3.143)

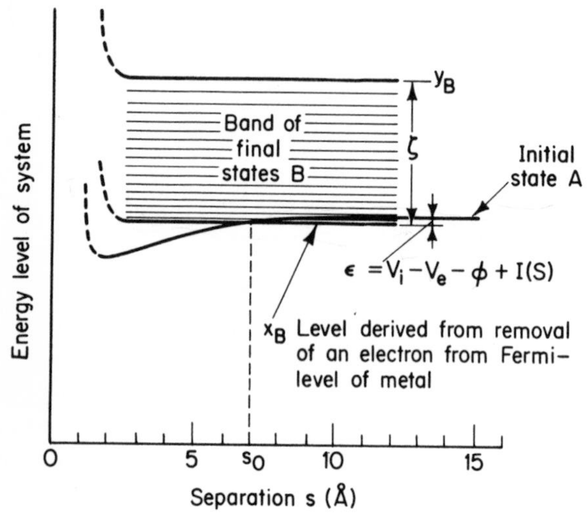

Fig. 3.7 Energy levels of system as a function of separation for neutralization of a He^+ ion to the $He(^3S_1)$ metastable state at a molybdenum surface (Ref. 3.143)

bability when the position and velocity of the approaching particle is unaltered by the transition. Since the initial velocity is unaltered the kinetic energy is therefore conserved and, as the total energy must also be conserved within the system, then the potential energy of the system must remain unchanged. We require therefore a cross-over point of the potential energy curves of the initial and final states. This is in fact seen in Fig. 3.7 (which represents a helium ion approaching a molybdenum surface). The curves cross for separations s greater than approximately 7Å and do not re-cross at very low values of s. The simple band picture is altered slightly due to the potential energy contributions of the image potential $I_{(s)} = (-e^2/4s)$. Taking this extra term into account we know that neutralization will be possible (as discussed above) if a curve representing an initial state crosses a curve for a possible final state.

The overlap of the curves for possible final states with the initial state is, from Fig. 3.7, $(V_i - V_e) - \phi$ and, including the image potential contribution I(s), this becomes:

$$(V_i - V_e) - \phi + I(s)$$

Consequently, since the curves must cross, this overlap must be greater than zero, so we have the condition for neutralization to be possible as

$$(V_i - V_e) - \phi + I(s) > 0$$

that is

$$(V_i - V_e) + I(s) \quad > \phi$$

For a cross-over at the other end of the scale we require

$$(V_i - V_e) - \phi + I(s) < W_a - \phi$$

that is

$$(V_i - V_e) + I(s) < W_a$$

Thus the condition for resonance neutralization being possible may be written

$$\phi < (V_i - V_e) + I(s) < W_a \qquad 3.3$$

3.3.2 Resonance Ionization

We have so far seen how an ion can become neutralized (i.e. reduced to a lower excited state). It is also possible and worth mentioning at this point that an excited atom or metastable atom can equally well become ionized as it approaches a metal surface. We look at the system as a whole once again (Fig. 3.8)

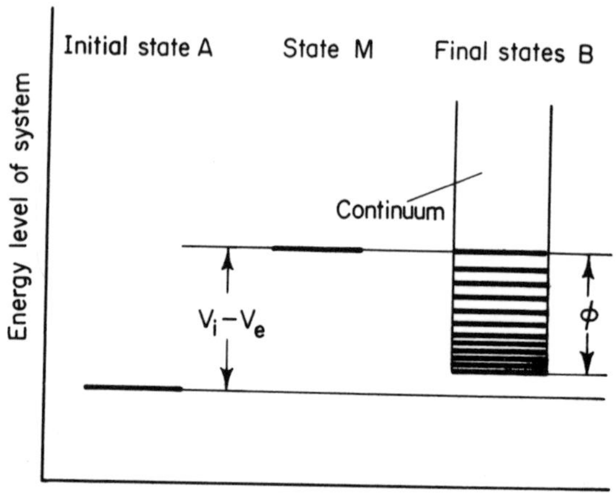

Fig. 3.8 Energy levels of system for ionization of an excited atom. Initial state A: Excited atom at infinity. State M: ion and electron at infinity. Final States B: the electron has occupied any of the non-filled levels above the Fermi level which extend above the vacuum level so that the electron may in fact be ejected

and find initially an excited atom at infinity which is ionized into an ion and an electron at infinity (state M). In stage 3 the electron has occupied any of the non-filled available states above the Fermi level. Here there exists a continuum of available states since the electron could be liberated as a secondary electron.

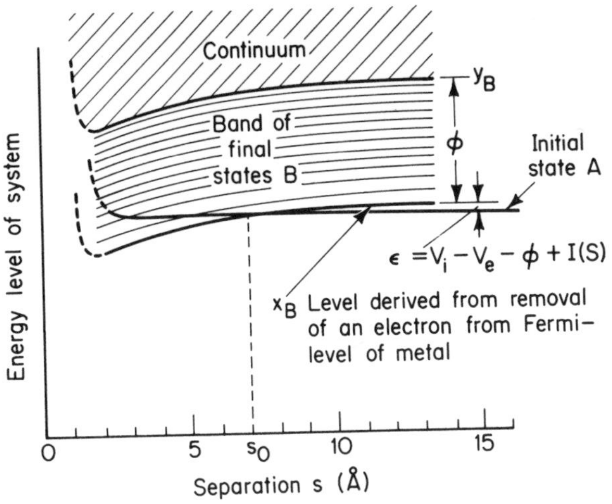

Fig. 3.9 Potential energy diagram for a He($^3S_1$) metastable atom as it undergoes resonance ionization at a molybdenum surface. (Ref. 3.143)

The curves for initial and final states are now as shown in Fig. 3.9; the initial states being independent of the atom-target separation as the metastable atom is uncharged and the final states being modified by the image potential at low values of ion-atom separation s. Again by the Franck-Condon principle a transition is possible where curves for initial and final states cross, this condition being fulfilled for values of s less than some critical value s_0. The transition is energetically possible provided the initial state lies below a possible final state by a finite amount, that is if:

$$V_i - V_e + I(s) - \phi > 0 \qquad 3.4$$

If the atom is initially highly excited then the curve representing the initial state in Fig. 3.9 is raised and may cross the continuum of final states at small values of s. Thus the excited atom may be ionized at close approach with the possibility of production of a free secondary electron.

The two processes discussed in detail above are possible events which certainly must be considered as an ion, or an excited atom, approaches a surface, but are not the main processes governing electron emission. Where energetically possible it is apparent that an ion approaching a surface has considerable probability of being neutralized in the region from $s = \infty$ to $s = s_0$. At distances closer than s_0 the neutral excited atom has a high probability of further ionization.

3.3.3 Auger neutralization of an ion

The so-called 'Auger' processes involve transitions of two electrons simultaneously and occur at distances of approach of the order 3Å or less, according to theoretical estimates by Shekhter[24] and Hagstrum[26]. In general terms we can write the process:

$$X^+ + ne_m^- \rightarrow X + e^- + (n-2)\, e_m^- \qquad 3.5$$

That is, an ion (X^+) combining with a system of n electrons in the metal (e_m^-) transforms to an atom (X) a free electron (e^-) and leaves the metal with (n − 2) electrons. The process is indicated schematically in Fig. 3.4 and the potential curves associated with the initial and possible final states of the system are presented in Fig. 3.10 for the case of a helium ion approaching a tungsten surface.

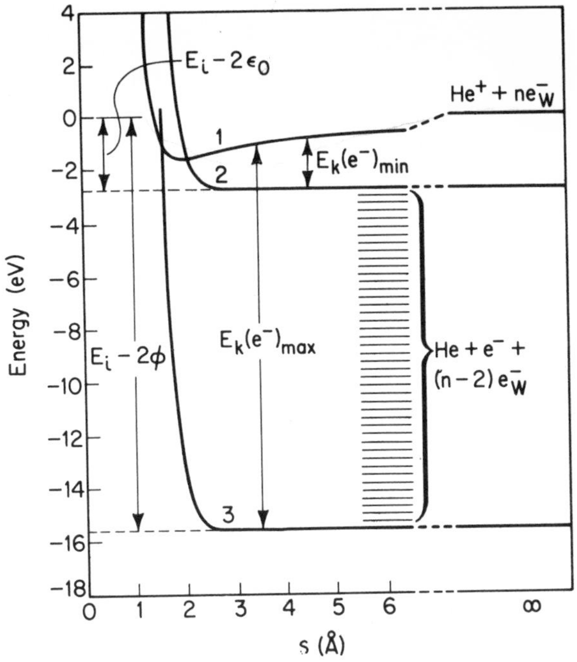

Fig. 3.10 Potential energy diagram for a helium ion as it undergoes Auger neutralization at a tungsten surface. (Ref. 3.26)

The energy of the system $He^+ + ne_W^-$ with the ion at rest at infinity is taken as zero. As the ion approaches the surface the potential curve of the system is depressed due to the image potential (curve 1 Fig. 3.10). After the transition the energy of the system has changed due to the supply of one electron to neutralize the ion and another electron which is liberated. Thus there is a band of n^2 possible final states between curves 2 and 3. This band extends from $-(E_i - 2\epsilon_0)$* (both electrons from the bottom of the conduction band) to $-(E_i - 2\phi)$ (both electrons from the top of the conduction band) below the above defined 'zero' energy level. In Fig. 3.10 the total energy would be a horizontal line ($E = E_T$) corresponding to the energy of the helium ion at infinity. At any value of s the total energy of the helium ion is the vertical distance from $E = E_T$ to the curve 1 and any energy level between curves 2 and 3 is the energy of the neutralized atom plus the energy of the free electron. According to the Franck-Condon principle, the total energy of the helium ion before transition equals the energy of the helium atom just after a transition. It does not however equal the energy of the helium atom plus the free electron which is represented by the band of curves in Fig. 3.10 so we do not now look for an intersection of initial and final states as in the 'resonance' treatments. We do know however that the energy of the helium atom will, according to the Franck-Condon rule, be exactly equal to the energy of the helium ion just before transition so that, if we draw a vertical line at the transition distance in Fig. 3.10, the energy interval between the intersection of this line with curve 1 and the intersection with the curve for the appropriate final state will equal the kinetic energy gained by the liberated electron. Thus we can assign minimum ($E_K(e^-)_{min}$) and maximum ($E_K(e^-)_{max}$) possible energies to the secondary electron so formed, as indicated in the figure.

---

* The terms E_i, V_i (ionization potential of the ion); E_e, V_e (excitation potential) and W_a, ϵ_0 (energy of vacuum level above bottom of the valence band) are used interchangeably throughout the discussion.

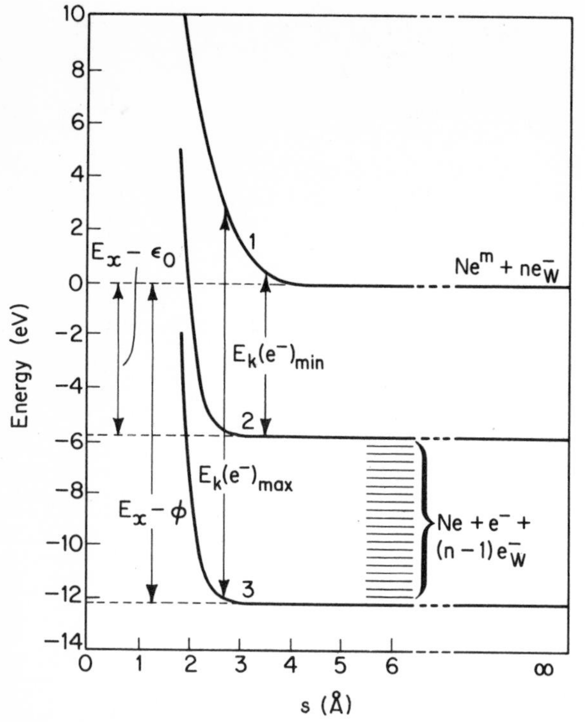

Fig. 3.11 Potential energy diagram for a metastable helium atom as it undergoes Auger de-excitation at a tungsten surface. (Ref. 3.26)

3.3.4 Auger de-excitation of an excited atom

This process may be written in general terms

$$X^m + ne_m^- \rightarrow X + e^- + (n-1)\,e_m^- \qquad 3.6$$

where the terms are as in equation 3.5, X^m being the excited metastable state. The relevant potential curves for a typical case of $Ne^m \rightarrow W$ are presented in Fig. 3.11 and it is clear that the main difference from Fig. 3.10 lies in the fact that the initial state curve is not modified by the image potential. The kinetic energy of the ejected electron is again the vertical distance from curve 1 to a curve in the band between curves 2 and 3 at the distance at which the transition occurs.

Massey[27, 28], Shekhter[24] and Cobas and Lamb[29] have considered a metastable de-excitation mechanism for secondary electron emission based on a resonance neutralization process for helium ions striking molybdenum, followed by an Auger de-excitation as described above. The helium ion is first assumed to neutralize to the He^3S_1 metastable state. At closer approach this metastable is assumed to de-excite by capturing a further metal electron (which falls to the ground state) and ejecting a 2s atomic electron. Cobas and Lamb calculated that the metastable de-excitation process could occur with appreciable probability at approach distances of less than one angstrom. However the value of s_0 for this ion-atom combination is 7Å so that the metastables will re-ionize in the majority of cases before de-excitation becomes probable. Consequently this process is of minor importance in this case. Hagstrum[26] has shown that this type of process, although still the minor contributor to the secondary yield, occurs more appreciably for neon ions striking tungsten.

Hagstrum[26] has developed theoretical expressions for secondary electron yields and the energy distribution of the emitted electrons, but the mathematics is protracted and will not be included in this brief treatise. In his treatment Hagstrum has first calculated a transition rate $R_t(s)$ for electrons within the conduction band reaching an energy in the interval $\varepsilon_K \rightarrow \varepsilon_K + d\varepsilon_K$ when the ion is at distance s from the metal surface. From this transition rate, and taking into account the velocity of the approaching ion, v_0, a probability function for the formation of electrons with energies in the above limits can be derived, $P_t(s, v_0)$. Finally, having described the distribution of possible electron energies produced within the metal,

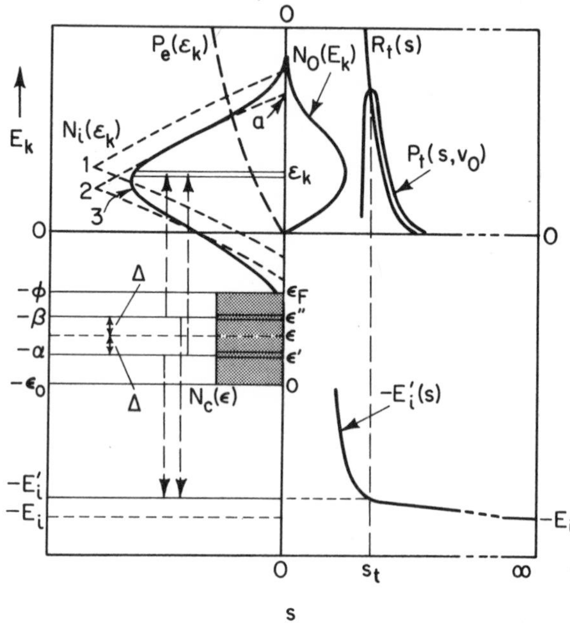

Fig. 3.12 Illustration of transition rate ($R_t(s)$), probability of electron formation ($P_t(s, V_0)$) and probability of electron escape ($P_e(\varepsilon_K)$) functions considered by Hagstrum in his theoretical model for Auger emission. (Ref. 3.26)

TABLE 3.2.

Comparison of theoretical (T) and experimental (E) potential emission coefficients

Target	Ion Energy	He	Ne	A	Kr	Xe
W(E)[138]	40 eV	0.279	0.220	0.095	0.050	0.013
W(T)[26]	40 eV	0.282	0.232	0.097	0.048	0.017
Ni(111) (E)[98]	5 eV	0.172	0.122	0.034	—	—
Ni(polyx) (T)[34]	5 eV	0.159	0.128	0.051	—	0.006

an escape probability function has to be taken into account $P_e(\varepsilon_K)$ to obtain the energy distribution curve of the escaping electrons. The functions discussed above are illustrated in Fig. 3.12 which is taken from Hagstrum's paper.

The theory predicts yields and energy distributions with reasonable accuracy and Hagstrum has been able to show that, for noble gas ions on tungsten, the Auger neutralization process accounts for all electron ejection by very slow ions (less than 10 eV) whilst, at higher energies, only in the case of Ne^+ — W does a two-stage ejection process play any role (resonance neutralization followed by Auger de-excitation). Even then only ten percent of the encounters result in Auger de-excitation processes. A table of theoretical and experimental yields is presented in Table 3.2 and Fig. 3.13 shows theoretically predicted electron energy distributions (both for noble gas ions on tungsten at 40 eV).

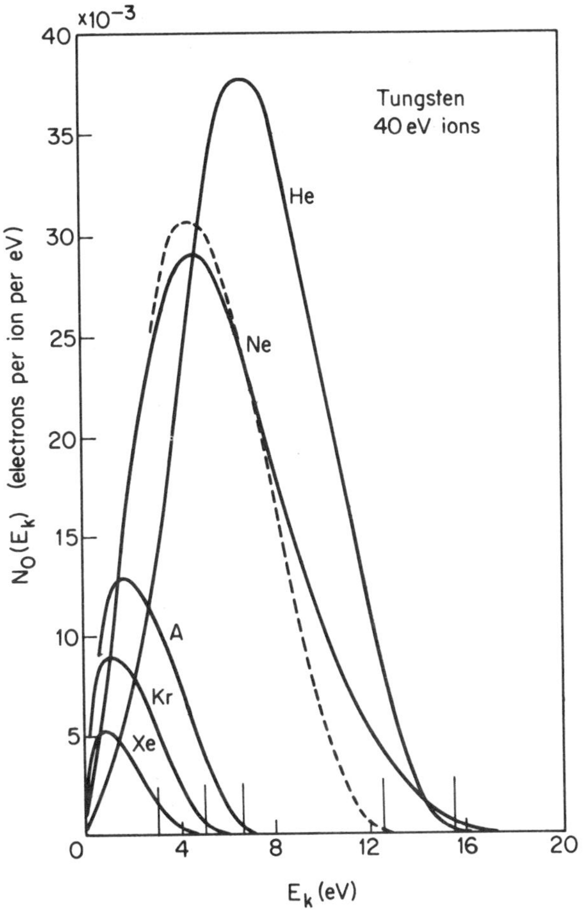

Fig. 3.13 Theoretical electron energy distributions for noble gas ion bombardment of tungsten. (Ref. 3.26)

A similar treatment to Hagstrum's is presented by Propst[30] who shows that only about 50% of Auger interactions give rise to free electrons. The other 50% create energetic electrons within the solid which can pass on their energy to other electrons and these latter then escape. Propst showed that, if the transition probability were

$$R_t(s) = B(d) \exp\{-a(d).(E_f - E)\} \qquad 3.7$$

where B and a are functions of distance at which the transition occurred and E_f is the fermi energy, then the energy distribution of electrons created within the metal was given by

$$N_i(E) = B\int_{-\eta}^{\eta} \exp[-a(E_f - \eta - x)]\,dx$$

$$R \leqslant E \leqslant R + E_f$$

$$= B\int_{-(E_f-\eta)}^{E_f-\eta} \exp[-a(E_f - \eta - x)]\,dx$$

$$R + E_f \leqslant E \leqslant R + 2E_f \qquad 3.8$$

where $R = E_i' - E_f - \phi$ = minimum energy of excited electrons, E_i' = effective ionization energy and $\eta = \frac{1}{2}(E - R)$.

By integrating and normalizing to one electron per incident ion

$$N_i(E) = \frac{\exp\{-a(E_i'(d) - \phi - E)\} - \exp(-aE_f)}{E_f[1 - \exp(-aE_f)]}$$

$$R < E < R + E_f$$

$$= \frac{1 - \exp\{-a[E_i'(d) + E_f - \phi - E]\}}{E_f[1 - \exp(-aE_f)]}$$

$$R + E_f < E < R + 2E_f \qquad 3.9$$

Curves showing the $N_i(E)$ distribution as a function of energy E are plotted in Propst's paper for various values of 'a'.

The probability of escape of these $N_i(E)$ electrons was then considered assuming an isotropic distribution and was found to be

$$F(E) = \tfrac{1}{2}[1 - (E_b/E)^{1/2}] \qquad 3.10$$

where $E_b = E_f + \phi$. The number of electrons actually escaping per incident ion with energy E′ was thus given by

$$N_p(E') = F[E' + E_f + \phi] \,.\, N_i(E' + E_f + \phi) \qquad 3.11a$$

where $E'(= E - E_b)$ is the energy with which an electron of initial energy E escapes.

The theoretical curve obtained from this treatment is shown together with Hagstrum's experimental curve in Fig. 3.14 and is seen to fill the top energy portion only. To explain the presence of lower energy electrons in the distribution the electrons which do not escape must be considered, that is the fraction

$$N_i'(E) = (1 - F(E)) \,.\, N_i(E) \qquad 3.11b$$

Using available data for electron-electron emission[31] Propst showed that the energy distribution of electrons emitted due to bombardment with electrons of energy distribution $N_i'(E)$ when added to the direct Auger distribution brings the theoretical energy distribution into line with the experimental data (see Fig. 3.15). For He^+ ions on tungsten the proportion of electrons liberated directly by the Auger process was found to be 12.4% of the incident ion current whilst the indirect emission amounted to 12.0%. This gave a total yield of 0.24 which was in good agreement with experimental values of Hagstrum[32].

Other theoretical calculations on similar lines to Hagstrum have been carried out by Takeishi[33, 34].

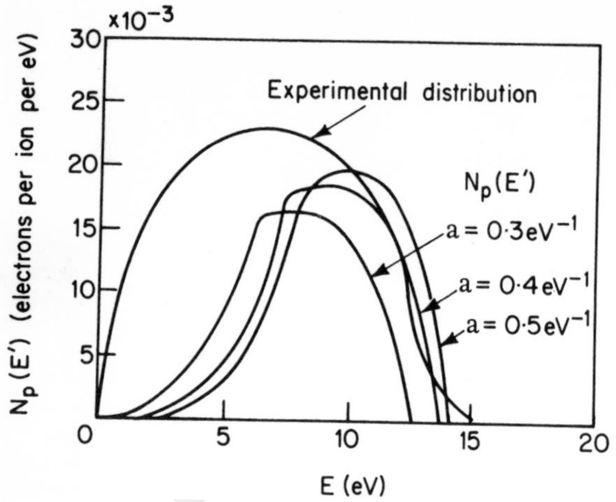

Fig. 3.14 Experimental and theoretical distributions of ejected electrons for 100 eV He^+ ions on tungsten. Experimental data is taken from Hagstrum et al[32 92]. Parameter 'a' is a constant appearing in an approximate expression for the integral of the transition probability and varies with ion-target separation 'd' (For $\lambda a = 0.3, 0.4$ and $0.5\ eV^{-1}$, d = 2.05, 2.35 and 2.66 Å, respectively) (Ref. 3.30)

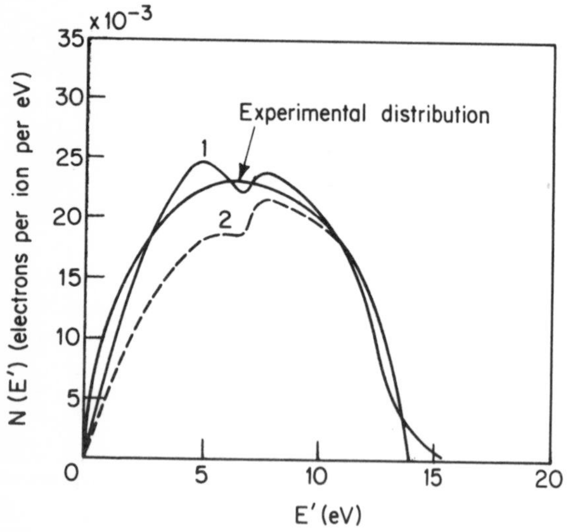

Fig. 3.15 Modified theoretical distributions of ejected electrons for 100 eV He^+ ions on tungsten taking into account electron collisions within the metal. Curve 1 was deduced using electron-electron emission profiles derived from data of Harrower[31], curve 2 using data of Gorodetskii[31a]. Experimental curve was obtained by Hagstrum et al [32 92]. (Ref. 3.30)

In the later article Takeishi derives the electron energy distributions obtained when inert gas ions bombard nickel targets. He first obtained an expression for the electrons with energy ε_K, $N_i(\varepsilon_K)$, resulting from transitions of pairs of electrons with energies $\varepsilon_1 = \epsilon_0 - \alpha$ and $\varepsilon_2 = \epsilon_0 - \beta$ (see Fig. 3.4):

$$N_i(\varepsilon_K) = C_1 \rho(\varepsilon_K) \int\int_0^{\epsilon_F} n_c(\epsilon_1) \cdot n_c(\epsilon_2) \times \delta(\varepsilon_K - \varepsilon_1 - \varepsilon_2 + \epsilon_0 - E_i) d\varepsilon_1 \cdot d\varepsilon_2 \qquad 3.12$$

Here $\epsilon_0 = \epsilon_F + \phi$, E_i = ionization energy of the inert gas atom (in this treatment not corrected for energy level shifts near the metal), C_1 is a normalization factor, $\rho(\varepsilon_K)$ the density of final states and $n_c(\varepsilon)$ the initial conduction band state density. The Dirac δ-function assures that the transitions integrated are energetically possible. Takeishi next made the assumptions $n_c(\varepsilon) \propto \varepsilon^{1/2}$ and $\rho(\varepsilon_K) = c\, \varepsilon_K^{1/2}$ and thereby obtained

1. for $E_i - \epsilon_0 < \varepsilon_K < E_i - \epsilon_0 + \epsilon_F$

$$N_i(\varepsilon_K) = \tfrac{1}{2} \cdot C_2 \cdot \pi \cdot \varepsilon_K^{1/2}(\varepsilon_K + \epsilon_0 - E_i)^2 \qquad 3.13$$

and

2. for $E_i - \epsilon_0 + \epsilon_F < \varepsilon_K < E_i - \epsilon_0 + 2\epsilon_F$

$$N_i(\varepsilon_K) = C_2 \varepsilon_K^{1/2} \Big[4\{\varepsilon_K - \tfrac{1}{2}(\varepsilon_K + \epsilon_0 - E_i)\, \epsilon_F (\varepsilon_K + \epsilon_0 - E_i) - \epsilon_F^2\}^{1/2} + (\varepsilon_K + \epsilon_0 - E_i)^2 \sin^{-1}\left\{ \frac{\epsilon_F - \tfrac{1}{2}(\varepsilon_K + \epsilon_0 - E_i)}{\tfrac{1}{2}(\varepsilon_K + \epsilon_0 - E_i)} \right\} \Big] \qquad 3.14$$

C_2 is a normalization factor = 1.197×10^{-3} for He^+, Ne^+ and A^+ ions
and = 1.265×10^{-3} for Xe^+ ions.

From the above expressions for $N_i(\varepsilon_K)$, the number of electrons escaping can be derived by multiplying by an escape probability function $P_e(\varepsilon_K)$ which can be written

$$P_e(\varepsilon_K) = \tfrac{1}{2}[1 - (\epsilon_0/\varepsilon_K)^{1/2}] \quad \varepsilon_K > \epsilon_0 \qquad 3.15$$

if the angular distribution of excited electron velocities is isotropic. Thus the electron energy distribution is given by

$$N_0(\varepsilon_K) = N_i(\varepsilon_K) \times P_e(\varepsilon_K) \qquad 3.16$$

Electron energy distributions obtained by this calculation are shown in Fig. 3.16 and, by integrating, total yields predicted by Takeishi are as shown in Table 3.2.

3.3.5 Kinetic ejection

We now consider briefly the kinetic ejection theories which, at the present time, are not as complete as those for the potential mechanism. There are three possible mechanisms of kinetic ejection of electrons;

(1) acceleration of nearly free electrons inside the metal[35,36]

(2) thermal emission by local heating[37-41], or

(3) release of bound electrons from atoms either at the surface or inside the metal[42,43].

According to (1) the release of electrons would be dependent on the maximum energy transferable to them in collisions and, because of their relatively low mass, the energy transferred would be extremely small. This process is certainly not important therefore at low ion energies and it is also of note that secondary emission occurs during bombardment of dielectrics where there are no conduction electrons available. One concludes that this is not the main mechanism responsible for kinetic emission.

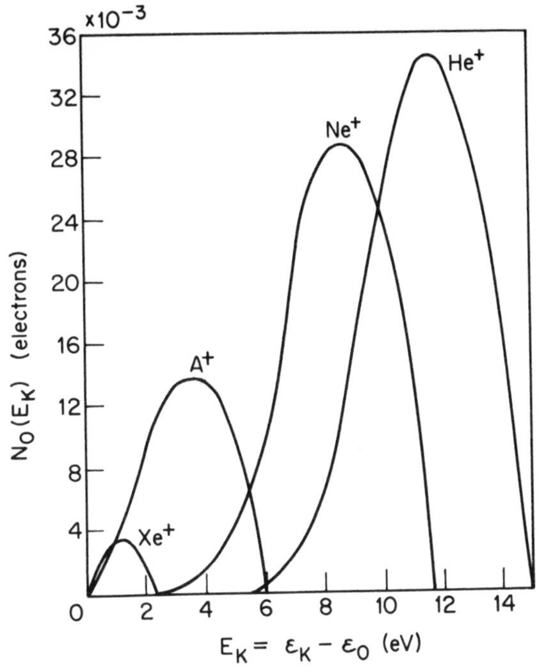

Fig. 3.16 Theoretical energy distributions of secondary electrons ejected from nickel during bombardment by He^+, Ne^+, A^+ and Xe^+ ions. (Ref. 3.34)

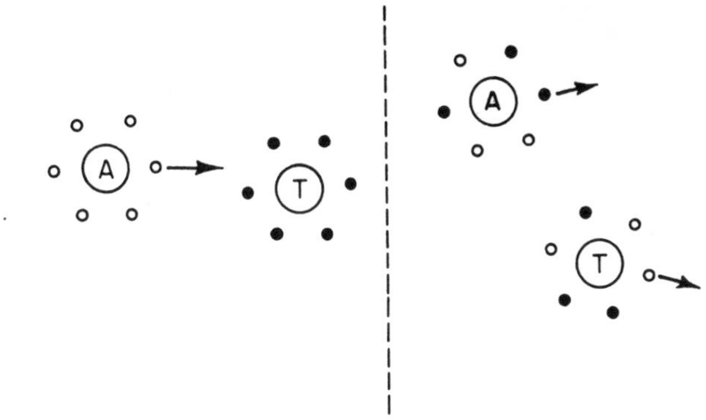

Fig. 3.17 Illustration of Kinetic energy exchange by electrons during a collison between a fast ion and target atom.

Theories based on thermal emission by local heating, (2), do not account for the dependence of kinetic emission on the work function (observed by Paetow and Walcher[13]) nor the dependence on ion mass of the kinetic ejection by isotopic ions (Ploch[41]) and the model has been proved invalid by Morgulis[38-40] and Izmailov[41]. Thus, the last process (3), release of bound electrons from atoms of the metal, seems most probable, at least for ion energies in the range 0-1 keV.

According to Ploch[42], the release of bound (i.e. valence band) electrons is purely dependent on ion velocity. Since lighter ions have a higher velocity corresponding to a given energy one would expect the kinetic process to show itself first with lighter ions as ion energies are increased. This does in fact appear to be the case; Hagstrum[32] has found that yields for helium increase with ion energy above 400 eV to an extent not explicable by the pure potential ejection processes.

For the release of bound electrons from metals we require the transfer of energy greater than the energy interval from the vacuum level to the bottom of the conduction band plus the energy of the forbidden gap. Even if all this incoming ion energy could be utilized in this process, kinetic emission would not be expected at ion energies below 15-20 eV. However, it is possible that the transfer of energy sufficient to raise a valence electron into the conduction band may subsequently enable electron emission to occur since, when the excited electron falls back to recombine with a positive hole, an Auger effect can occur exciting another conduction band electron and it is possible that sufficient energy will be transferred to this second electron for it to escape.

According to Parilis and Kishinevskii[44] the process of energy transfer to electrons is along the lines described by Firsov[45] where the electron exchange between the colliding atoms is accompanied by the transport of an average pulse of forward motion by the electrons originally in the moving atom, as illustrated schematically in Fig. 3.17. An additional energy exchange occurs between the electrons due to forces on them as the atoms slide past each other, this force being similar to a frictional force. The work done by this force determines the energy transferred to electrons from the forward motion of the incoming atom.

Having established the methods by which electron energy exchange can be provided Parilis and Kishinevskii used the Thomas-Fermi model of the electron-atom cloud to calculate, by a statistical process, the electron density and the exchange frequency and also the repulsive potential between atoms. Their equation for the transferred energy takes the form:

$$\epsilon = \frac{m^2 \, . \, e^2}{4\pi^2 h^3} \int \left(\int_S \phi^2 \, . \, dS \right) \dot{\underline{R}} \, . \, dR \qquad 3.17$$

where $\underline{R}$ is the radius vector connecting colliding atoms, $\overline{S}$ is the surface separating the domain of action for the potential of the two atoms and ϕ is the potential on this surface expressed in terms of a Thomas-Fermi function:

$$\phi = [(Z_1 + Z_2)e/r]X(1.13(Z_1 + Z_2)^{1/3} \, r/a),$$

$$a = h^2/me^2 \qquad 3.18$$

For near head-on collisions leading to scattering at small angles

$$\dot{\epsilon} = \frac{0.35\,(Z_1 + Z_2)^{5/3}\, hu_0/a_0}{[1 + (0.16(Z_1 + Z_2)^{1/3}\, R_0/a_0)]^5} \qquad 3.19$$

u_0 is the relative velocity of the atoms and R_0 the distance of closest approach. In general,

$$\epsilon(p) = \frac{h(u_0)}{\pi a^2} (Z_1 + Z_2)^2$$

$$\int_{R_0}^{\infty} \frac{[1 - (V(R)/E)]dR}{R_0[1 - (V(R)/E) - (p^2/R^2)]^{1/2}} \, .$$

$$\int_{R/2}^{\infty} \frac{X^2(\rho)d\rho}{\rho} \qquad 3.20$$

where E is the energy of relative motion of the atoms, p is the collision parameter (defined in Chapter 2) and V(R) the repulsive potential at small separations.

The mechanism of energy transfer discussed above is only effective for bound electrons. One can look at the process as equivalent to the 'ionization' of the atomic residue (the atomic residue being the atom with all its conduction electrons removed) where excitation of electrons from filled valence bands to the conduction band occurs. An electron in the valence band at an energy level δ cannot occupy any filled level in the conduction band, by the Pauli exclusion principle, so it must receive energy greater than $\epsilon = \delta - \phi$ where ϕ is the work function. The probability cross-section for this collision is thus $\sigma_1 = \pi p_1^2$ where p_1 is the impact parameter at which $\epsilon(p_1) = \delta - \phi$.

Parilis and Kishinevskii next calculated, by an approximate method, the probability cross-section of ejecting an electron into the conduction band;

$$\sigma = 2\pi \int_0^{p_1} (\epsilon(p)/J)\ p\ .\ dp \qquad 3.21$$

J is the average ionization potential for the outer shells of an atom. Assuming p small and ion energies greater than several thousand electron volts, and also restricting the calculation to the condition $\frac{1}{4} < Z_1/Z_2 < 4$

$$\sigma(u_0) = \frac{1.39\ a_0 h}{J} \cdot \left(\frac{Z_1 + Z_2}{(Z_1)^{1/2} + (Z_2)^{1/2}}\right)^2 \cdot S(u_0) \qquad 3.22$$

The equation for the surface separating the domain of action is shown to be

$$S(u_0) = \frac{1.28\ u_0}{a_0^2} (Z_1^{1/2} + Z_2^{1/2})^2$$

$$\int_0^{p_1} p\ .\ dp \int_{R_0}^{\infty} \frac{1 - (V(R)/E)\ .\ dR}{[1 - (V(R)/E) - (p^2/R^2)]^{1/2}}$$

$$\int_{R/2}^{\infty} \frac{X^2\ .\ 1.13(Z_1 + Z_2)^{1/3} (\rho/a_0)}{\rho}\ .\ d\rho \qquad 3.23$$

which includes an integral which must be solved numerically. However an approximate form, found by calculating the above for argon and krypton bombardment of tungsten and molybdenum, is given by:

$$S(u_0) = 5.25\ u_0\ .\ \tan^{-1} [0.6 \times 10^{-7} (u_0 - u_{min})] \qquad 3.24$$

where u_{min} is the threshold velocity. Its value depends on the ion-target combination and varies between 0.6 and 0.7 × 10^7 cm./sec. Detailed calculation of $\sigma(u_0)$ shows that, for $u_0 < 3 \times 10^7$ cm/sec, $\sigma(u_0)$ is very nearly a quadratic function of u_0 whilst, for high velocities, $\sigma(u_0)$ is approximately linear.

The model has so far obtained a probability for excitation of electrons from the valence band. This probability also includes the formation of positive holes (left behind in the valence band) so that $\sigma(u_0)$ is, in fact the probability of formation of an electron-hole pair. This is very important since, in a metal target, the remaining hole has a high probability of recombination with a conduction electron and the energy produced by this recombining electron can be passed on to another conduction electron, the whole process being described as an Auger recombination (equivalent to Auger neutralization in the potential ejection theory). The second electron will be emitted provided the hole depth δ exceeds 2ϕ, and the probability of electron escape $w(\delta)$ is larger the deeper the potential level of the positive hole. Parilis et al have presented an empirical formula for this probability as follows;

$$w(\delta) = 0.016\ (\delta - 2\phi) \qquad 3.25$$

Finally, it is necessary to take into account two depth effects; one the change in the velocity of the incoming ion as it penetrates the target and the other the loss of electrons produced at a finite depth as they make their way to the surface. Parilis et al computed the average loss in velocity as

$$\overline{du} = (-M_1 M_2)/(M_1 + M_2)^2\ .\ u\ .\ N\ .\ \sigma_d\ .\ dx \qquad 3.26$$

where σ_d is the diffusion scattering cross-section. For a Firsov[45] potential this is given by:

$$\sigma_d = \frac{1.24\ \pi a_0 e^2 Z_1 Z_2 (M_1 + M_2)}{u^2 (Z_1^{1/2} + Z_2^{1/2})^{2/3} M_1 M_2} \qquad 3.27$$

which, combined with equation 3.26 yields a simple law for the decrease in velocity with depth,

$$u_0^2 - u^2 = k\ .\ x\ . \qquad 3.28$$

The electron loss due to diffusion to the surface from the depth of formation is assumed to decrease with $\exp(-x/\lambda)$ hence,

$$\gamma = \int_0^{x_n} \sigma(u)\ .\ w(\delta)\ .\ N\ .\ \exp(-x/\lambda)\ .\ dx \qquad 3.29$$

where N is the number of metal atoms per cubic centimetre and x_n is the maximum depth at which ions can still produce electrons (here their velocity is u_{min}). Substituting for x from 3.28 ($-2u\,du = k.dx$)

$$\gamma = (2Nw(\delta)/k) \int_{u_{min}}^{u_0} u\sigma(u) \exp\{(u^2 - u_0^2)/k\lambda\}\ du$$

$$= N\ .\ w(\delta)\ .\ \lambda\ [\sigma(u_0) - \Delta\sigma(u_0)] \qquad 3.30$$

where

$$\Delta\sigma(u_0) = \exp(-u_0^2/k\lambda) \int_{u_{min}}^{u_0} \exp(u^2/k\lambda) \frac{d}{du} (\sigma(u))\ .\ du \qquad 3.31$$

and is the factor which takes into account the decrease in the ionization cross-section of the ion as it penetrates the metal. Parilis et al propose that $\Delta\,\sigma(u_0)$ can be adequately approximated by:

$$\Delta\,\sigma(u_0) = \exp(-u_0^2/k\lambda) \Big\{ \tfrac{1}{2}\pi (k\lambda)^{1/2} \left[\Phi\left(\frac{u_0}{(k\lambda)^{1/2}}\right) - \Phi\left(\frac{u_{min}}{(k\lambda)^{1/2}}\right)\right] - \tfrac{1}{2} u_{min} \times (\tfrac{1}{2}\pi - 0.6 \times 10^{-7}\ u_{min}) \times \left[E_i\left(\frac{u_0^2}{k\lambda}\right) - E_i\left(\frac{u_{min}^2}{k\lambda}\right)\right]\Big\} \qquad 3.32$$

where

$$\Phi(x) = \int_0^x e^{t^2} dt$$

and

$$E_i(x) = \int_{-\infty}^{x} (e^t/t)\, dt$$

The effect of $\Delta\,\sigma(u_0)$ is most important at low velocities since here the ionization occurs throughout at depths from which the electrons can escape. At high ion velocities the probability of secondary electron production becomes nearly constant over the whole range of depths from which the liberated electrons can escape, $\Delta\,\sigma(u_0)$ is then insignificant.

Writing $\sigma^*(u_0)$ as the effective ionization cross-section, where ionization means ionization of the ionic residue of the atoms and the term cross-section means the probability of formation of an electron-hole pair (i.e. conventional terminology for conduction electrons applied to valence electrons) we have:

$$\sigma^*(u_0) = \sigma(u_0) - \Delta\,\sigma(u_0) \qquad 3.33$$

and the secondary electron emission coefficient for kinetic processes γ is given by:

$$\gamma = N \,.\, \sigma^*(u_0) \,.\, \lambda \,.\, w(\delta) \qquad 3.34$$

We re-list the basic factors of this equation:

N = atomic density,

$\sigma^*(u_0) = f\{[(Z_1 + Z_2)/(Z_1^{1/2} + Z_2^{1/2})]^2,\ u_0[u_0 - u_{min}],\ \Delta\,\sigma(u_0)\}$

λ = constant

$w(\delta) = f(\delta - 2\phi)$

Thus we see that for high velocity ions γ is predominantly governed by $F_1 = [(Z_1 + Z_2)/(Z_1^{1/2} + Z_2^{1/2})]^2$. However, although this dependence has been shown to be true for heavy ions[46] it is not true for bombardment by lighter ions where the electrons available in the initial collision are fewer. Kishinevskii and Parilis show, in a later article[47], that the governing function for light ions is of the form:

$$F_2(Z_1, Z_2) = (Z_1^{1/2} + Z_2^{1/2}) \,.\, (Z_1^{1/6} + Z_2^{1/6})^3 \qquad 3.35$$

Curves relating the two cases (F_1, F_2), together with a curve drawn from experimental results of Tel'kovskii[46] and Arifov et al[48], are presented in Fig. 3.18.

The main trends predicted by the theory of Parilis and Kishinevskii can be listed as follows

1. Low velocity region: $u_0 \simeq u_{min}$, $\Delta\,\sigma(u_0)$ term is important (equation 3.32), γ increases slowly with u_0 . $\sigma^*(u_0) \simeq u_0^2 - (\tfrac{3}{2}\, u_{min})^2$. Hence, initially $\gamma \propto u_0^2$ i.e. γ is a linear function of energy.

2. High velocity region:

$$\sigma^*(u_0) \simeq u_0 \tan^{-1}\{0.6 \,.\, 10^{-7}\, (u_0 - u_{min})\}$$

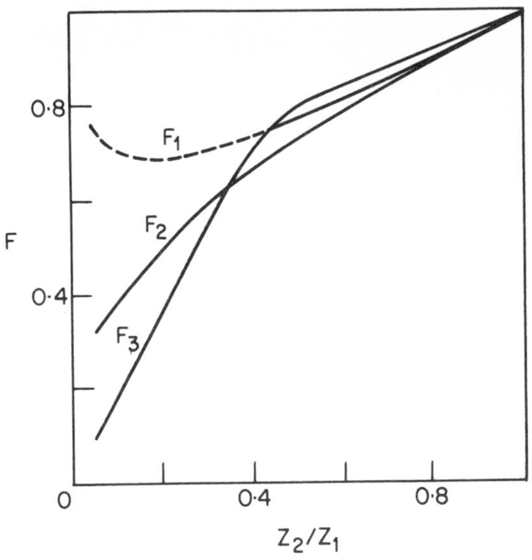

Fig. 3.18 Variation with ion/atom number ratio of the functions F_1, F_2 (defined in the text) which are the principal factors governing the secondary electron emission coefficient. F_3 is the functional dependence required to fit the theory to experimental data of Tel'kovskii[46] and Arifov et al[48]. (Ref. 3.47)

This expression asymptotically approaches the straight line

$$\sigma(u_0) = C(u_0 - u_{min})$$

therefore γ increases linearly with velocity. Extrapolating the linear portion back to $\sigma(u_0) = 0$ a value of the intercept $u_1 = 1.05 \times 10^7$ cm/sec is obtained; this is independent of the ion-target combination.

3. Very high velocities:
Here penetration depths of the ions are greater so that electrons are formed further from the surface. The number escaping to the surface and therefore the yield is expected to pass through a maximum. This is confirmed experimentally.[21,49-51]

4. No yield dependence on ion charge is predicted.

5. A dependence of yield on the ion-target combination of the form $[(Z_1 + Z_2)/(Z_1^{1/2} + Z_2^{1/2})]^2$ for heavy ions and $(Z_1^{1/2} + Z_2^{1/2}) \,.\, (Z_1^{1/6} + Z_2^{1/6})^3$ for light ions. If the term $\Delta\,\sigma(u_0)$ is important however (i.e. at low velocities) then the yield is independent of ion-atom combination to a first approximation.

6. The dependence of the yield on the angle of incidence 'θ' is expected to be of the form

$$\gamma_i \simeq \gamma_0 \sec\theta$$

since the probability of electron escape is a function of the shortest distance to the surface d and the probability of formation of electrons is a function of the actual distance traversed, d sec θ.

7. The effect of isotopic mass on the yield (observed by Brunnée[82]) is anticipated to be connected with the different retardation rates for the isotope pairs.

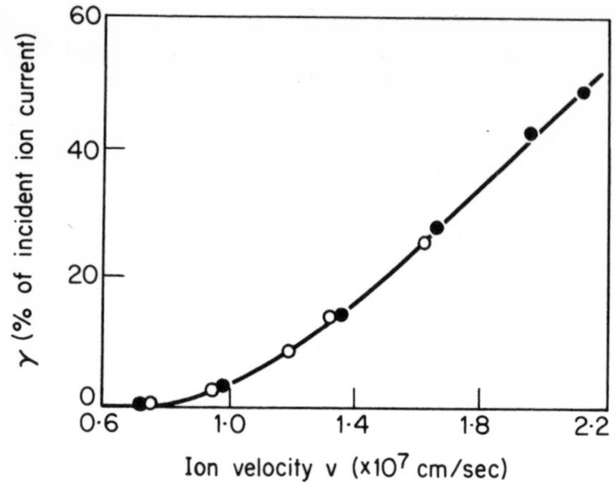

Fig. 3.19 Comparison of theoretical curve (continuous line) obtained from the theory of Parilis and Kishinevskii[44 47] with experimental values of Arifov et al[52] (●) and Petrov[53] (○) for the kinetic emission coefficient as a function of ion velocity during bombardment of tungsten by A^+ ions. (Ref. 3.81)

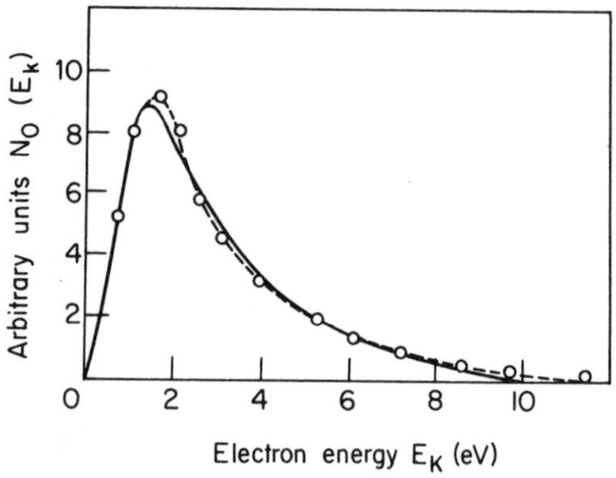

Fig. 3.20 Comparison of theoretical and experimental electron energy distributions for kinetic emission from tungsten by 1 keV Li^+ ions. Continuous curve is derived from theory of Parilis and Kishinevskii[44 47] and experimental points are from the work of Waters[54]. (Ref. 3.81)

The success of the theory of Parilis and Kishinevski is illustrated in Figs. 3.19 and 3.20. Fig. 3.19 shows the kinetic component of the secondary emission coefficient against the ion velocity; the solid line being the theoretical curve and the points values obtained experimentally by Arifov et al[52] and Petrov[53] whilst Fig. 3.20 shows the predicted energy distribution of the ejected electrons compared with those obtained experimentally by Waters[54].

Izmailov[55-7] has presented an alternative theory for kinetic emission which depends on the release of free conduction electrons by transient fields produced during the collisions of the incoming particle with target atoms. At a time $t = -\tau$ the ion and atom are about to collide and the peripheral parts of the electronic shells are retarded. At time $t = 0$ the positive frameworks of the atoms are retarded and proceed to fly apart and, at a later time $t = +\tau$ the peripheral parts of the electronic shells separate and move with the velocities of the positive frameworks. During the collision therefore transient fields exist due to the relative motion of the positive and negative frameworks of the colliding partners and these fields make probable a transition of an electron in the conduction band to an excited state. The mathematics of the theory is complicated and will not be reproduced here, but the following relations are predicted:

1. For $E_e \ll E_0 \ll M_1 E_e/m$ (where E_e is the energy expended by the ion in emitting an electron and m is the electron mass), the secondary yield γ is approximately proportional to E_0/M_1. This is confirmed by the experimental results of Eremeev et al.[145, 146]
2. For $E_0 \geqslant M_1 E_e/m$, γ = constant, independent of ion energy.
3. By assuming a rectangular potential barrier at the metal-vacuum boundary the energies of emitted electrons can be predicted:

$$E_{e_m}' = E_f(1 + (\phi/E_f))(0.132 + 0.119(\phi/E_f)) + \ldots \qquad 3.36$$

where E_f is the Fermi energy. Thus, the higher the work function, the greater the energy possessed by the emitted electrons.

Sternglass[58], on the other hand, presents a theory for electron emission from metals by high energy ions and predicts that the energies of the emitted electrons are independent of the work function. Here the model is based on the formation of secondaries within the metal by excitation and ionization as the primary ions are retarded. The secondaries formed are then considered to diffuse through the 'gas' of ordered atoms so that their escape probability from a depth x is given by:

$$P(x) = \tau(A)\exp(-x/L_s) \simeq 0.5\exp(-x/L_s) \qquad 3.37$$

where τ is a surface emission coefficient, $L_s = (\alpha' N\sigma_g)^{-1}$, $\alpha' = \alpha(3/\bar{n}_c)^{1/2}$ and

$$\alpha = \sigma_{sc}/\sigma_g = \frac{\text{scattering cross-section of secondary electron}}{\text{geometric area of outermost filled shells}}$$

By considering fast ions only, the electrons which can escape are produced in a region where the retardation is negligible, so that a constant average energy loss may be assumed:

$$\left\langle \frac{dE}{dx} \right\rangle_{AV} = 2\pi N e^4 Z_i^2 \left[4 Z_1^{1/3}/I_0^{1/2}\, E_{eq}^{1/2}\right] \qquad 3.38$$

N is the atomic density, e the electron charge, Z_i the ion charge, Z the ion atomic number, I_0 the Rydberg energy

$$E_{eq} = \tfrac{1}{2} m_0 v_i^2,$$

where m_0 is the electron mass, and v_i the ion velocity. The number of electrons formed at depth x proceeding initially toward the surface is then:

$$n_{se}(v_i, x) = \tfrac{1}{2}\,\frac{1}{E_0}\left\langle \frac{dE_i}{dx} \right\rangle_{AV} (1 + F(v_i, x)) \qquad 3.39$$

where $\overline{E}_0$ is the mean energy loss per secondary electron formed and $F(v_i, x)$ the fraction of energy available for formation of electrons in higher order processes at depth x.

The yield is thus the integral of the above number over all depths from which electrons can escape to the surface (i.e. up to x_{max}) multiplied by the probability of escape by diffusion:

$$\gamma = \int_0^{x_{max}} n_{se}(v_i, x) \cdot P(x) \cdot dx \qquad 3.40$$

and the expression reduces to $\gamma = 38V_{eq}^{-1/2}$ for proton bombardment. This final equation agrees with the data of Hill et al[21] and also Aarset et al[49] in the 0.1-3 MeV energy region. The yield is here decreasing as E increases but is still a linear function of the ion velocity.

A similar treatment to that presented by Sternglass has been given by Ghosh and Khare,[59] the principal difference being that where Sternglass described the rate of production of secondary electrons by a stopping-power expression Ghosh and Khare used an ionization cross-section for ejection of electrons from the target atoms. Their expression for the yield was

$$\gamma = \tfrac{1}{2}(N/\alpha) \sum_{nl} \sigma_{nl} \qquad 3.41$$

where N is the number of target atoms per unit volume, σ_{nl} the ionization cross-section of these atoms for the nl shell and α an absorption coefficient for electrons. An expression derived by Bethe[60] for σ_{nl} was used to obtain the final expression

$$\gamma = \tfrac{1}{2}(N/\alpha m E_0)\pi Z_1{}^2 e^4 M \sum_{nl} (c_{nl}/|E_{nl}|)\ln(4mE_0/MC_{nl}) \qquad 3.42$$

where e = electron charge, Z_i = ion atomic number, m = electron mass, C_{nl} = certain mean of $E_k - E_{nl}$ and is assumed to be equal to $(E_{nl}/10)$, E_0 = ion energy and

$$c_{nl} = (Z_{eff}{}^2/n^2a_0^2)\int |x_{nl,k}|^2 \, dk$$

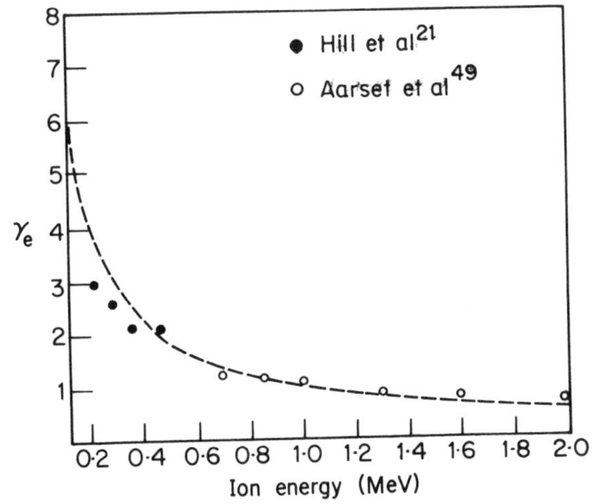

Fig. 3.21 Comparison of theoretical values of the kinetic emission coefficient obtained by Ghosh and Khare[59] with experimental values of Hill et al[21] and Aarset et al[49] for hydrogen ion bombardment of aluminium. (Ref. 3.59)

and ranges from a value 0.28 for the 1s shell to 0.04 for the 4f shell of a hydrogen atom. Fig. 3.21 shows the theoretical curve against experimental values obtained by Hill et al[21] and Aarset et al[49] for hydrogen ion bombardment of aluminium targets and the comparison is seen to be very satisfactory. The parameter α was adjusted to give the best fit to the experimental curves and was seen to be 8×10^5 indicating that emitted secondaries can be produced in a section of surface material extending to a depth of approximately 120Å.

All the theories discussed above do not take into account the crystal structure which, experiments now indicate,[61-7] greatly influences the yield values. Harrison et al[68] have developed a theory based on the lines of Parilis and Kishinevskii[44,47] which takes the crystal orientation into account by adjusting the limits on the inelastic energy transfer integral. The expression for the yield on an (hkl) surface due to an ion of energy E_0 is given by

$$\gamma^{hkl}(E_0) = K\int_0^{s_{max}(hkl)} n_e(s, E_{TFF})\, P^{hkl}(s)\, ds \qquad 3.43$$

where s is the impact parameter, E_{TFF} the inelastic energy transferred, $P^{hkl}(s)$ the probability that the impact parameter s will occur in the (hkl) surface and K a constant which is assumed independent of E_0 and crystal orientation. The factor K represents the probability of escape of electrons produced within the target, a factor between 1 and 2 which takes account of additional high energy electrons being created by the Auger process, and the probability that a high energy electron escapes before it is scattered into the conduction band.

The model proposed by Harrison et al considers that the ion is first neutralised, then undergoes a binary collision with a target atom in which some energy transfer is inelastic and causes multiple ionization of the incoming particle. The ion so formed can then become neutralized as in the potential emission case, the energy liberated by electrons in neutralizing the ion being absorbed by a second group of electrons, some of which can escape.

The difficult part of the calculation involves assigning the amount of energy available for the above inelastic collision events. Harrison et al derive an expression similar to equation 3.20, the different limits of integration taking account of the orientation dependence

$$E_{TFF}(s, E_0) = K_{TFF}\int_{r_{min}}^{r_{max}(s)} \frac{[1-(V(r)/E_0)]dr}{[1-(V(r)/E_0)-(s^2/r^2)]^{1/2}} \cdot \int_{r/2}^{r_{EM}} \frac{\phi^2(\rho)}{\rho} \cdot d\rho \qquad 3.44$$

In practice r_{EM} is taken as being approximately equal to the smallest value of r_{max} its actual value not affecting the second integral greatly as $\phi^2(\rho)/\rho \to 0$ for $r > r_0$, the equilibrium lattice spacing. The limit r_{max} is completely determined by the lattice orientation, i.e. the fact that one collision must be terminated because another is beginning. It is a function of the impact parameter so that a calculation of impact parameter probability densities is necessary. In equation 3.44 Harrison et al use the Sommerfeld approximation for the Thomas Fermi function $\phi(\rho)$ which describes the mutual interaction of the electrons

$$\phi(\rho) = [1 + (a_F \cdot \rho)^{0.8034}]^{-3.734} \qquad 3.45$$

where

$$a_F = a_{TF}((Z_1 + Z_2)/144)^{1/3}/0.8853$$

and a_{TF} is an adjustable parameter.

All distances above are measured in units of $a_0 = h^2/4\pi^2 me^2 = 0.529\text{Å}$ (the Bohr radius). A further modification made by Harrison et al was to express V(r), the repulsion potential describing the atom-atom collisions, in the Born-Mayer form $V(r) = \exp(A + Br)$ where constants A and B were determined by matching this potential to a Thomas-Fermi function over a prescribed set of interatomic distances.

The distribution of impact probability densities involves an essentially geometric calculation and the main problem is to decide how many atomic layers contribute to the ejection process. Harrison et al have found that the distribution of smallest impact parameters when all target atoms are considered provides the best fit to experimental curves.

The problem of calculating the inelastic energy transfer has thus been tackled and the remaining calculation has to determine the number of electrons emitted as this energy, E_{TFF}, is dissipated. Harrison et al have used a probability function of a form derived by Russek[69]:

$$p_n^{(M)} \simeq \binom{M}{n} \sum_{i=0}^{k} (-1)^i \times \binom{M-n}{i} \left[1 - \frac{nE_n^{ION} + iE_{n+1}^{ION}}{E_{TFF}}\right]^{M-1} \qquad 3.46$$

where

$$k \geq (E_{TFF}/E_{n+1}^{ION}) - (nE_n^{ION}/E_{n+1}^{ION}) \leq k + 1$$

In the above $p_n^{(M)}$ is the probability that n electrons will be liberated from a shell containing M electrons, the terms in parenthesis are matrices, and E_n^{ION} is the energy required to remove the nth of the M electrons.

The above expressions were combined to give a solution for equation 3.43 adjusting the model where necessary to give the best solution for the A^+-Cu results. However having developed the theory to fit this ion-target combination Harrison et al have found that yields for other combinations are also well predicted. Figs. 3.22(a), (b) and (c) show the experimental points and predicted curves for A^+-Cu and A^+-Ni and A^+-Mo. The parameters are the matching constants for the Thomas Fermi and Born-Mayer repulsion potentials, and the constants A and B in the Born-Mayer potential are determined completely from these.

For the bcc target studied (Mo) the theory does not agree as well with experimental values as for the fcc targets though it does predict crossing of the (111)

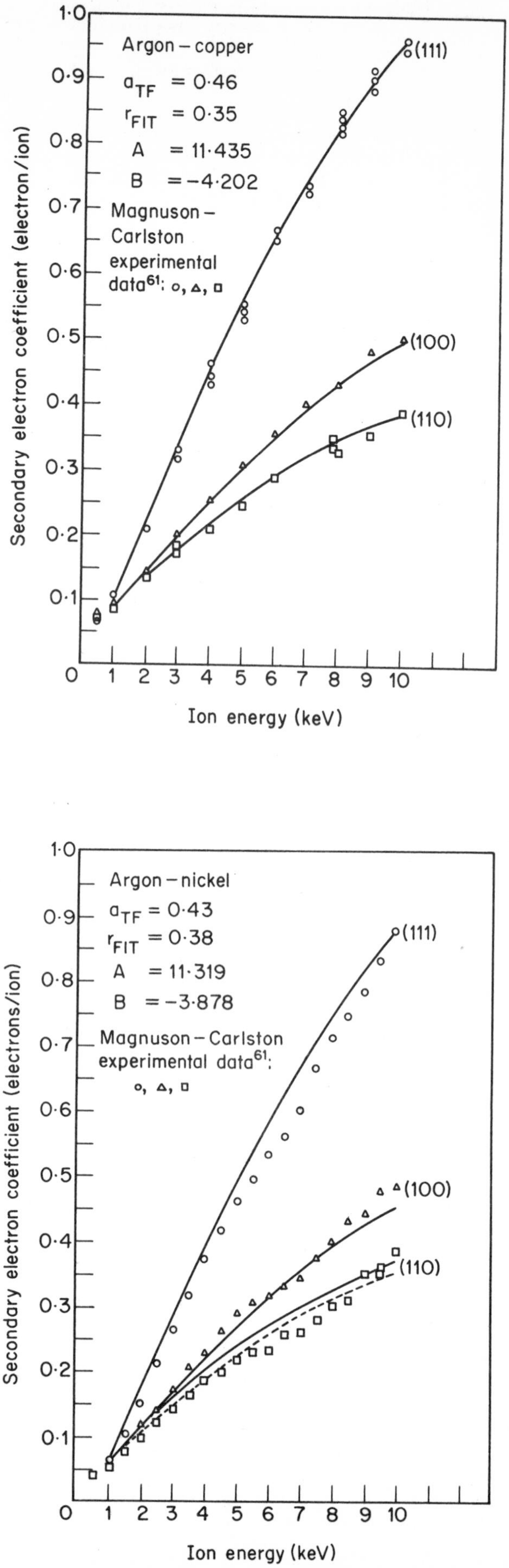

Fig. 3.22 Theoretical kinetic emission coefficients for A^+ ion bombardment of single crystal targets as a function of the incident ion energy (a) copper (b) nickel and (c) molybdenum. (Ref. 3.68)

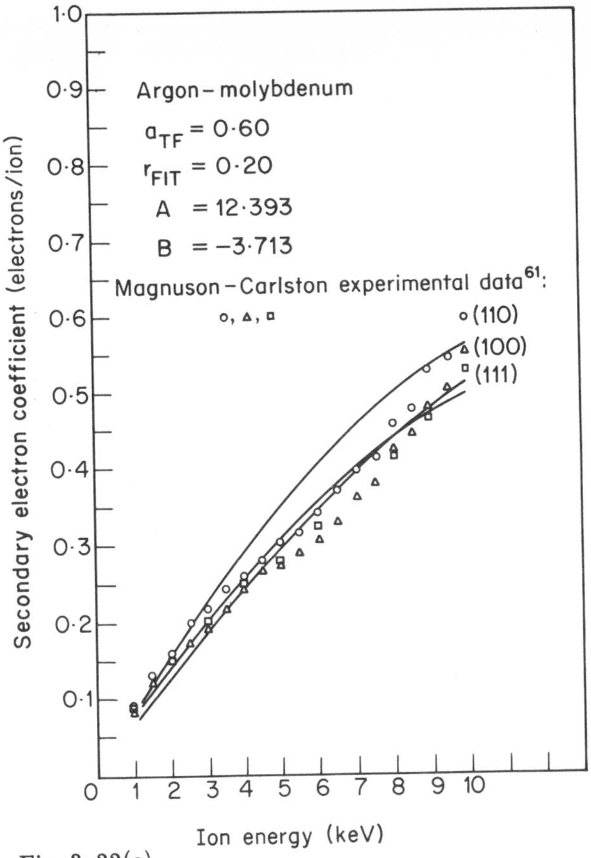

Fig. 3. 22(c)

and (100) curves as observed experimentally (Fig. 3. 22(c)). Harrison et al have suggested that some uncertainty in the predicted curves is due to the unknown form of the potential ejection contribution to the yield at higher ion energies. In the present calculations the potential yield has been assumed constant over the whole range of energies studied.

One satisfactory point about the present theory is that the calculations show that electrons liberated must originate from the incident ion rather than the target atom whilst Everhardt et al[70,71,72] have presented experimental evidence that both of the excited atoms participating in the binary collision first separate completely and then emit electrons.

It is interesting to observe in conclusion that, from the curve fitting processes, Harrison et al have been able to determine the inter-atomic potentials and have shown them to be predominantly harder than the potentials applicable in radiation damage studies and uniformly softer than those derived from diatomic molecular theoretical studies.

It is clear that further work on the development of a theory of secondary emission is required to describe more accurately effects observed in single crystal studies. Meanwhile the theories of Parilis and Kishinevskii, [44,47] at lower incident ion energies, and of Sternglass, [58] at high energies, are seen to be well substantiated by the experimental results which are discussed in the following section. The theory of Izmailov, [55-7] although in agreement with certain experimental results, does not explain secondary emission from insulators.

3.3.6 Resumé of theoretical processes for an ion approaching a surface

If conditions are favourable an ion approaching a surface can, as we have seen (3. 3. 1), undergo resonance neutralization. The excited atom then continues its journey toward the surface and may either, de-excite in an Auger process and emit a secondary electron, or, become re-ionized. In the latter case, as the ion comes nearer to the surface conditions become favourable for Auger neutralization and again emission of a secondary electron. It should be noted that by this time the initial identity of the particle has been forgotten and had it been an excited metastable atom it would also have a large probability of becoming ionized as it approaches the surface so that no sharp distinction between the bombardment of ions and metastables should be observable. The energy distributions obtained by Green[73] for incident metastable atoms do in fact look similar to those characteristic of Auger neutralization (the process which the ions undergo) rather than of Auger de-excitation.

For ions of energy less than 100 eV, Hagstrum[26] finds that Auger processes occur with a high probability on the inward journey of the ion before kinetic processes can occur and, in fact, the potential mechanism of ejection is dominant for most ions (where available potential energies are adequate) so that yields are to a first approximation independent of ion energy. At higher energies kinetic ejection processes become of increasing importance and yields begin to increase initially linearly with the ion energy and, later, linearly with velocity, eventually approaching a maximum and then decreasing again.

3.4 RECENT WORK ON POTENTIAL EJECTION

A considerable amount of research has been done on secondary electron yields over the past decade; in particular a most thorough and noteworthy investigation of the potential ejection process by Hagstrum, [32,74-79,80,138]. His papers include treatments on bombardment by noble gas ions of tungsten[32], molybdenum[74], and monocrystalline germanium (111) and silicon (111) and (100)[75]. Hagstrum has also studied helium ion bombardment in more detail; observing effects of single and double charged ion bombardment and also bombardment by the molecular ion He_2^+ on molybdenum. [76] and tantalum[77]. Further experimental contributions of Hagstrum include the investigation of the production of metastable states of the bombarding ions and their effects on the yields. [78,79]

The apparatus used in the above work comprised a Nier source (described in Chapter 9), an electrostatic extractor-focusing system which allowed differential pumping, a 90° magnetic mass analyzer and a final electrostatic focusing array of cylinders and slits encased in a third stage of differential pumping. The complete system was bakeable and ultimate pressures as low as 3×10^{-10} Torr were recorded, though this was the x-ray limit on an unmodified ion gauge and pressures may therefore have been even lower. A complete description of the apparatus is presented by Hagstrum in a separate publication[80]. Some experiments have been carried out without the magnetic analyzer, the argument being that, provided electron energies in the ion source were maintained below the second ionization potential and gases introduced to the system were spectroscopically pure, then the potential results would not be affected. Later investigations with metastable ions however[78 79] showed this assumption to be in error so that the early results have had to be adjusted.

Arifov[81] has also carried out many useful experiments on secondary electron and ion emission, principally investigating kinetic emission but, at the same time, presenting a few results on potential ejection which are in excellent agreement with those obtained by Hagstrum. The ultimate pressure in the apparatus used by Arifov et al was two orders of magnitude higher than that obtained by Hagstrum but, by an ingenious experimental technique, Arifov has been able to overcome the problem of contamination and, in fact, demonstrate how emission characteristics change as the surface becomes covered with an adsorbed layer of background gases.

The basic technique used by Arifov was to display a signal proportional to the charged particle secondary current on the y-plates of an oscilloscope and to apply the saw-tooth repetitive stopping potential voltage between his target and collector to the x-plates of the oscilloscope. By synchronizing the oscilloscope output a steady trace of the stopping potential curve could be obtained within seconds of switching off the out-gassing current from the ribbon target. However it was not easy to determine from the scope trace where the zero-current line should be placed so Arifov modulated the incident ion beam, thus marking the zero line in the half cycles when the beam was switched off and indicating the magnitude of the secondary emission current in the other half cycles.

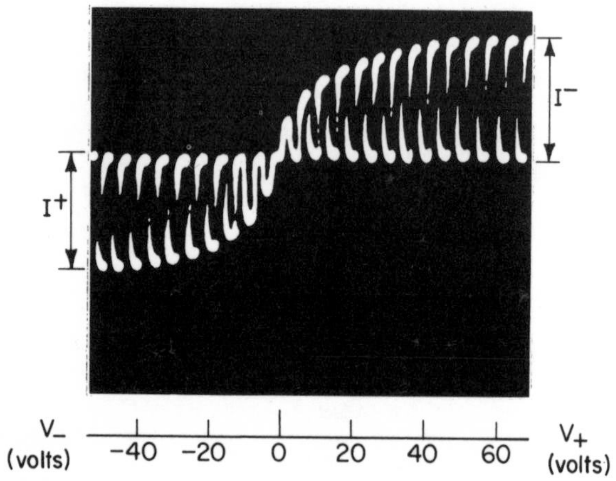

Fig. 3.23 Typical oscilloscope trace of the stopping potential characteristic obtained by Arifov et al. Case shown is for 400 eV Rb^+ bombardment of a Rb film on a 300°K tantalum surface. (Ref. 3.81)

A typical trace obtained by Arifov using this technique is presented in Fig. 3. 23. Arifov succeeded in separating the electron current from the negative ion current by applying a magnetic field normal to the target which caused ejected electrons to travel along a tight helix around the target-normal direction. They could thus be made to pass through a small aperture in the usual collector on to a second-collector. The negative ions were not constrained by this magnetic field and proceeded to the first collector as usual. An alternative technique, also used by Brunnée[82], was to assemble a split-hemisphere collector, the forward portion being held at −50 eV with respect to the target and the rear section at +40 eV. Thus all the electrons were collected by the rear hemisphere. The success of the double modulation technique for obtaining secondary electron emission coefficients characteristic of clean surfaces is clear from Fig. 3. 24 which compares the results for noble gas ion bombardment of tungsten obtained by Hagstrum (broken curves) and Arifov (continuous curves). Further the change in yield from the clean surface

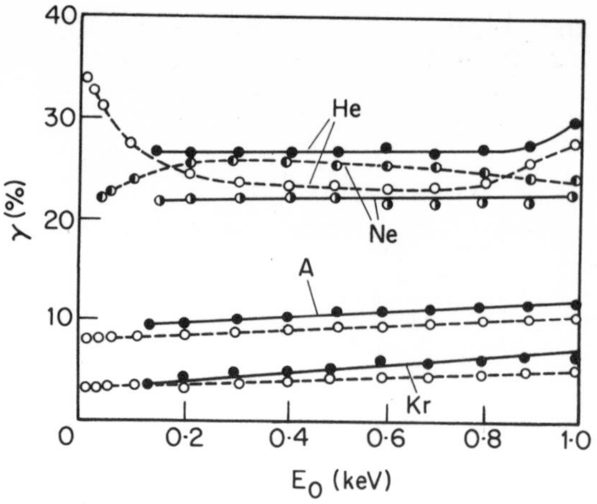

Fig. 3. 24 Comparison of potential emission coefficients obtained for noble gas bombardment of tungsten by Hagstrum[32] (broken curves) and Arifov[81] (continuous curves). (From U. A. Arifov[81] by courtesy of U.S. Atomic Energy Commission)

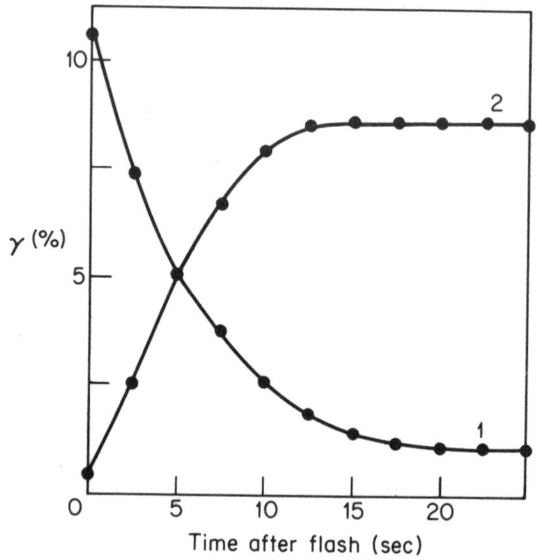

Fig. 3. 25 Dependence of potential emission coefficient on adsorption time for 200 eV A^+ bombardment of molybdenum. Curve 1 mercury pumped system, curve 2 oil pumped system. (Ref. 3 81)

value could be easily investigated by observing the change in oscilloscope trace and is shown for 200 eV argon ions on molybdenum (Fig. 3. 25). A most interesting result emanates from this study since it is clear that the yields represented by curve 1 are entirely different to those represented by curve 2, the former demonstrating the change in yield after flashing a target in a mercury-pumped system and the latter the change in yield in an oil-pumped system. From the curves it is clear that even an outgassed target does not give the clean-surface yield in an oil pumped apparatus. Arifov et al demonstrate this point further by deliberately introducing oil into the mercury pumped system. The change in yield with time from degassing immediately takes the form of curve 2 and the process cannot be reversed. This important result explains conclusively why the results obtained by Tel'kovskii[83 84] for inert gases on molybdenum using an oil-pumped system did not confirm the existence of potential emission found for similar ion-atom bombardment in a mercury pumped system by Hagstrum[74]. Many other discrepancies in the literature on the subject of surface interactions may likewise be explained by this surprising effect.

We shall now discuss the general pattern of results obtained by Hagstrum with reference to theoretical predictions and will compare his results with those of other workers where the latter are available.

3.4.1 Dependence of yield on ion species

All the available data indicates that, for a given target, the ion giving the largest yield is (for noble gases) helium, followed by neon, argon, krypton and xenon, respectively, in decreasing order of magnitude. This state of affairs is anticipated by Hagstrum's theory since the probability of electron production is related to the maximum energy available after neutralization of the ion. This, as we have seen, is equal to $E_i - \phi$. Referring again to the potential curves for helium ions bombarding tungsten (Fig. 3.10) it is clear that the curves for initial and final states of the system are well separated, so that the energies carried by the emitted electrons on transition between states is always large. If the $E_i - \phi$ term is reduced, as it is for other noble gases, for the hydrogen molecular ion (which undergoes pure potential ejection at bombarding energies of about 50 eV) and for nitrogen, the band of possible final states for these gases moves up in the figure towards the curves for the initial states. Hence, average electron energies gained in the transitions are reduced and, since the probability of escape for lower energy electrons is smaller, secondary electron yields will be less. For a given target therefore the yields should increase in relation to the ionization potential E_i, that is, in the order xenon, krypton, argon, neon, and helium and this state of affairs is confirmed experimentally.

Mahadevan et al[85] have shown that this simple potential rule is violated when the bombardment is by molecular ions of hydrogen and nitrogen. Although these ions have approximately the same ionization potential as argon their secondary electron yield is much lower and Mahadevan et al conclude that some of the available potential energy is absorbed in excitation of atomic vibrational levels of the molecular species.

3.4.2 Dependence of yield on ion energy

To a first approximation the yields obtained by Hagstrum for the noble gases are independent of the energy of the bombarding ions, as would be expected for a pure potential ejection mechanism. A more critical study of the results however shows many deviations from this rule, but all these can be satisfactorily explained by considering the theoretical processes in more detail.

For helium bombardment of tungsten and molybdenum[32 74] Hagstrum's results show an initial decrease in γ, a minimum at about 400 eV energy and then a further rise in the yield to 1 keV (the maximum energy used in the experiments). In the 0 — 400 eV region Hagstrum suggests that the transition occurs nearer to the metal surface as the ion velocity increases so that the effective ionization energy of the ion is lowered. This results in the whole $N_i(\mathcal{E}_k) - \mathcal{E}_k$ electron energy distribution being displaced toward lower energies so that relatively fewer electrons will have sufficient energy to escape. A further effect is that the $N_i(\mathcal{E}_k)$ distribution broadens so that again some electrons move to lower energies and cannot escape and γ is further reduced. At energies above 400 eV for helium ions it is thought that kinetic ejection is possible, thus the ions undergo the usual Auger neutralization, but still have sufficient kinetic energy to release further electrons.

The slight rise in yield with ion energy for A^+, Kr^+ and Xe^+ ions is attributed again to the broadening of the electron energy distributions; in these instances the broadening is advantageous and more electrons are liberated. Neon is an exception since, at low energies (10 eV) the ejection process is predominantly single stage, as for the other noble gases, but at higher bombarding energies a larger proportion of the two-stage 'resonance neutralization-Auger de-excitation' process occurs. The electrons liberated by this latter mechanism have larger energies and therefore escape more easily and the yields are seen to increase quite sharply with ion energy at the onset of this process (Fig. 3.24).

3.4.3 Yield dependence on ion charge

According to the potential ejection theory it is anticipated that the yields will be proportional to the ionization potential of the ion less the work function of the target and, where the ion is doubly charged, the appropriate ionization potential to consider is the value for second ionization and the effective work function is twice ϕ since two electrons are now involved (three, counting the ejected one). In his work on helium bombardment of tantalum and molybdenum Hagstrum[76 77] has shown that the yields for He^{++}, He^+ and the yield for molecular $He_2{}^*$ are, in fact, in the approximate ratios

$$E_{i_2} - 2\phi : E_{i_1} - \phi : E_i{}^{\nu} - \phi$$

where E_{i_2} is the second and E_{i_1} the first ionization potential of helium and $E_i{}^{\nu}$ is the energy liberated on neutralization of the stable He_2^+ to the repulsive He_2 state. For molybdenum the above experimental ratios are, respectively, 2.9: 1: 0.52 whilst the predicted ratios are 3.5: 1: 0.62.

Hasted[86] has shown that yields from metals including molybdenum and tungsten during bombardment by He (2^3S) and Ne (3P) metastable atoms at thermal velocities were consistently lower than those observed for ionic bombardment of the same metals by He^+ and Ne^+. This again confirms the potential ejection mechanism since these metastable atoms have less available excitation energy to promote ejection of electrons than their ionic counterparts.

It is of particular interest to observe that the liberated electron energy distributions for Auger ejection by singly charged ions always lie within the distributions produced by double charged ions. Further reference to the energy limits of these distributions indicates that the neutralization of doubly charged ions must occur by a step-by-step process; first, resonance neutralization to an excited metastable state of the singly charged ion, second, an Auger de-excitation of the singly charged ion to the first ionization ground state and, finally, the usual Auger neutralization of the singly charged ion.

3.4.4 Effect of target material on yield

As mentioned in the discussion of the effect of ion species on the yield, one of the critical factors is the maximum available energy, $E_i - \phi$, which is clearly dependent on the target material through the work function ϕ. Other factors influenced by the target are the width of the filled portion of the conduction band ϵ_F and the variation of the state density function. Clearly if ϕ decreases γ is expected to increase. If ϵ_F decreases then Auger transitions will produce on average more energetic electrons as is clear from a study of the possible N_i ($\mathcal{E}_k$) distribution functions in Fig. 3. 26. The width of the N_i ($\mathcal{E}_k$) distribution is

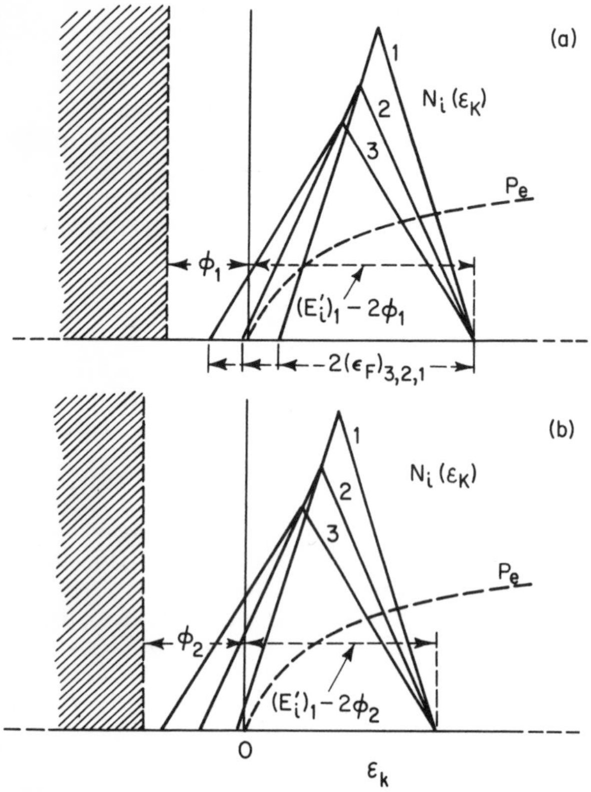

Fig. 3. 26 Illustrating the change in internal electron state density distribution N_i ($\mathcal{E}_k$) for targets with different work functions ((a) and (b)), each showing three different widths of the filled band ϵ_F. (Ref. 3. 74)

given by 2 ϵ_F and the maximum possible electron energy is fixed at $E_i' - 2\phi$, thus, as ϵ_F increases, the N_i ($\mathcal{E}_k$) curve becomes broader thereby increasing the fraction of electrons with energies less than the minimum value required for escape. Consequently the secondary electron emission coefficient will decrease on changing to a target with a smaller conduction band width. The state density function influences yields in a similar manner since, if more electrons are available in higher energy levels in the metal, then there is a larger probability that they will receive the energy released in the Auger transitions so that the average energy of electrons awaiting escape is increased. Consequently the probability of escape is high. It was found experimentally by Hagstrum that yields for molybdenum were larger than those for tungsten and this can be accounted for by the first of the above three effects: the change in ϕ.

Further confirmation of the importance of ϕ on the yield is indicated by the results of Arifov and Rakhimov[87] who have obtained results on well degassed targets for ion energies between 0. 1 and 1 keV and have found a linear relation between the secondary emission coefficient and the work function; the yield decreasing as ϕ increased.

Using their double modulation technique Arifov et al[88] were able to study the change in secondary electron yield as a tantalum surface was covered with an evaporated film of sodium, during bombardment by 400 eV A^+ ions. Two groups of ejected negative species were identified, one being shown to be negative ions and the other due to potential emission of electrons. Yields were seen to vary from 0. 06 for clean tantalum to a maximum of 0. 22 after deposition of about 100 monolayers of sodium and then γ decreased again to the clean sodium value of 0. 165. The work function of sodium is less than that of tantalum so that the above result again confirms that the secondary electron emission coefficient decreases as the work function increases.

3. 4. 5 Importance of the state of the target surface

Most experiments confirm the fact that secondary electron yields are critically dependent on the cleanliness of the target surface[81 89-92]. Hagstrum[89] and Propst and Lüscher[91] found that yields generally decreased in the presence of sorbed gases and, further, that it was the electrons at the high energy end of the emitted spectrum that were eliminated. Figs. 3. 27 and 3. 28 obtained by Hagstrum[92] show conclusively the change in the electron emission yield and the energy spectrum of secondary electrons as a tungsten surface is cleaned from its original contaminated condition and Fig. 3. 25, discussed earlier, shows that the possible change in yield with contamination time can have distinctly different forms depending whether the system has oil or mercury pumps.

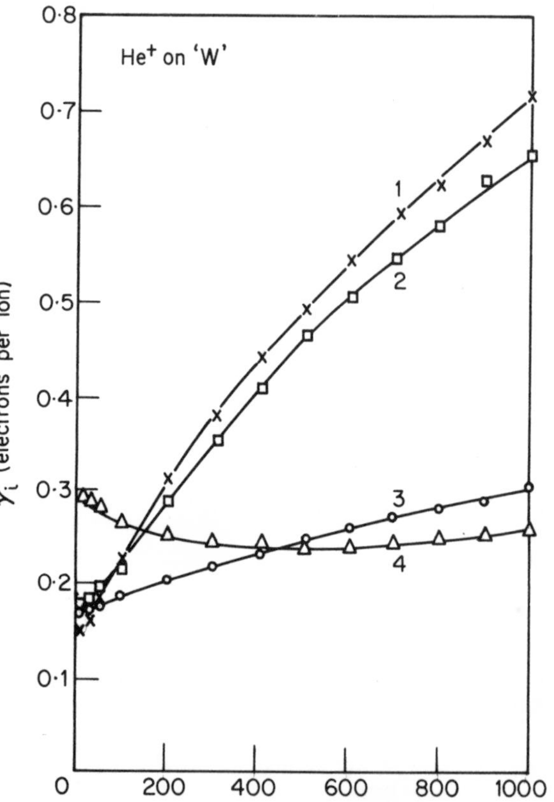

Fig. 3. 27 Variation of secondary electron emission coefficient with surface contamination for He^+ ions on tungsten. Curve 1: untreated target, curve 2: after heating to 800°K, curve 3: after heating to 1330°K and curve 4: after further outgassing at 1500°K and flashing to 2200°K. (Ref. 3. 92)

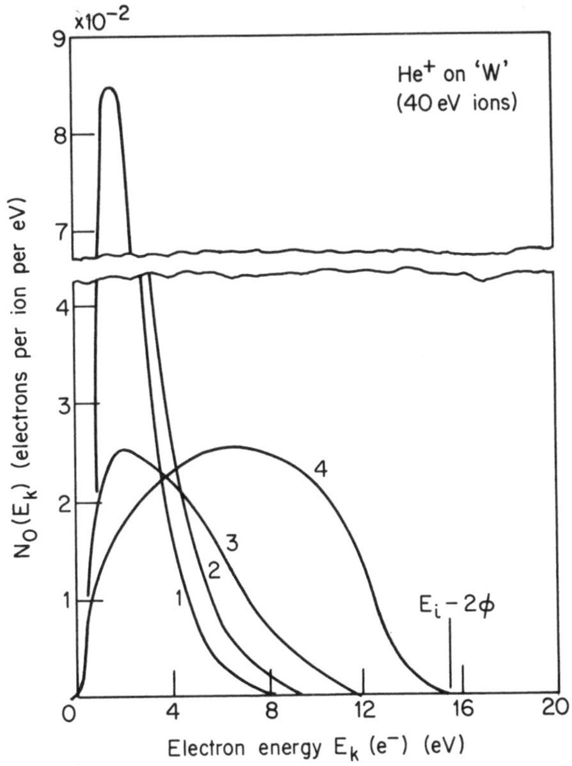

Fig. 3. 28 Kinetic energy distribution of ejected electrons during 40 eV He^+ ion bombardment of tungsten. Curves 1-4 demonstrate the change in characteristic as the surface is progressively cleaned according to the sequence listed in Fig. 3. 27 (Ref. 3. 92)

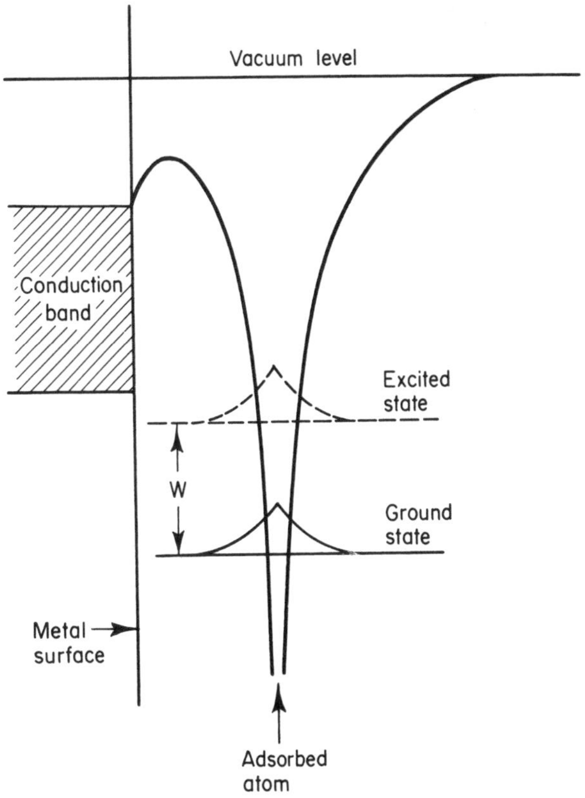

Fig. 3. 29 Potential model for an adsorbed atom on a surface which introduces an extra electronic state at an energy W above the ground state of the target atom. (Ref. 3. 91)

Hall and Weston[93] have carried out an interesting experiment which involves the use of two ionization gauges; one with a molybdenum collector which is used as a reference and the other as a test gauge. The collector current is equal to

$$i_c = i_e . S (1 + \gamma) p \qquad 3.46$$

where i_e = filament emission current, S = gauge sensitivity and p = pressure. The experiment comprises adjusting the emission currents for the two gauges so that the collector currents are equal and noting the values i_{e_1}, i_{e_2}. The surface of the test gauge collector then either receives an evaporated layer of another metal, or is oxidized, the currents i_{e_1}, i_{e_2} are re-established and, from the new value of the collector current in the test gauge, the change in γ can be determined. Using this technique Hall and Weston have observed the change in yield for neon ions as molybdenum becomes covered with oxygen and have found that γ values are reduced. However oxygen is a rather special case in that it has a great affinity for electrons and will trap many excited ones which would otherwise have escaped. This particular technique of Hall and Weston appears to be ideal for studying surface effects on the yield values and it is hoped that more results are forthcoming.

Propst and Lüscher[91] considered that the adsorbed gas atoms introduced localized electronic states at the surface of the metal from which the primary Auger electrons can be scattered as indicated in Fig. 3. 29, where the new electronic state is at an energy W above the ground state of the target atom.

On leaving the metal an Auger electron may be scattered from an electron in the ground state imparting sufficient energy (W) to the latter to excite it to the higher state. Such electrons will be emitted with energies equal to a value W below those expected from a clean surface.

By an elegant curve fitting technique Propst and Lüscher were able to evaluate the approximate values of the energy W for hydrogen and nitrogen coverage of tungsten. If E_M is the maximum energy of the electrons emitted from the covered surface and assuming that some electrons will be liberated with the energies anticipated for a clean surface, then electrons with energies between E_M-W and E_M cannot have encountered a sorbed gas atom. If one assumes that the fraction of electrons comprising this group is independent of their energy over the range E_M-W < E < E_M then the curve for this end of the distribution will be an exact scaled-down version of the same portion of the curve for a clean target. It is found, by this scaling down method, that the high energy portions of the curves do in fact coincide; from E_M down to E_M − 4. 5 eV for hydrogen adsorption and from E_M to E_M − 5. 5 eV for nitrogen adsorption. Thus the excited states for hydrogen and nitrogen-covered tungsten lie 4. 5 eV and 5. 5 eV, respectively, above the ground state of the tungsten atom.

A mechanism similar to the one described above was suggested by Parker[94] to explain his results for electron emission from tantalum and platinum targets which had been subjected to controlled contamination by hydrogen, nitrogen or oxygen gases. It was clear from these results that the change in work function of the surface did not entirely account for the change in ion-electron emission coefficient which occurred during bombardment by 30-100 eV He^+ and A^+ ions. At the lower energies the yields were reduced by the smallest amounts after hydrogen contamination, slightly more after nitrogen contamination and by a considerable amount after oxygen contamination. At 100 eV the order was similar on platinum, although absolute magnitudes were higher, whilst on tantalum the yields on a hydrogen covered surface were higher than for the uncontaminated surface and were very near the atomically clean values after nitrogen and oxygen contamination. One concludes from these results that the surface is actually being cleaned by bombardment at these higher energies. At the lower energies the change in yield is due both to a change in the work function and the introduction of new electronic levels in the sorbed gases which affect the electron emission process.

It is possible to take the above argument a step further and predict the new electron energy distribution for a covered surface by assuming that the electrons that scatter from the surface states escape from the metal with a probability of escape reduced appropriately for their reduced energy. If the probability of escape at energy E is P(E) then, electrons which scatter will have a probability of escape P(E-W). If the fraction that scatter is F(E) then the number of electrons escaping at (E-W) is given by

$$N_{COVERED}(E-W) = \frac{P(E-W)}{P(E)} F(E). N_{CLEAN}(E) + [1 - F(E-W)] N_{CLEAN}(E-W) \qquad 3.47$$

Using the escape probability derived by Hagstrum[26] which is derived on the assumption of an isotropic angular distribution of excited electrons and a value of F(E) of 0.64 for hydrogen, from the scaling factor required for curve fitting described above, Propst and Lüscher have deduced the gas covered electron energy distribution and have found very good agreement considering the approximations involved.

A final note on the state of the surface deserves mention at this point. No systematic studies have yet been carried out, but it is apparent that whilst electron emission is very dependent on surface cleanliness, it is not affected by surface morphology. In experiments on the bombardment of germanium (111) monocrystals by noble gas ions Hagstrum[75 94a] has shown that the electron energy distribution after sputtering the surface is little different to that obtained after sputtering followed by annealing. This insensitivity of the Auger processes to some surface disarray must indicate that the valence band electronic work functions at the surface accommodate themselves to such lattice distortion without much relative change throughout the band.

3.4.6 Variation of potential emission coefficient with target temperature

Although many results have been presented in the literature on the variation of potential emission with temperature, nearly all are questionable since the main effect of raising target temperatures was to improve the cleanliness of the surface and this in itself changes the secondary electron yield.

Arifov[94b], using his double-modulation technique described earlier, is one of the few experimenters contributing reliable information on the temperature

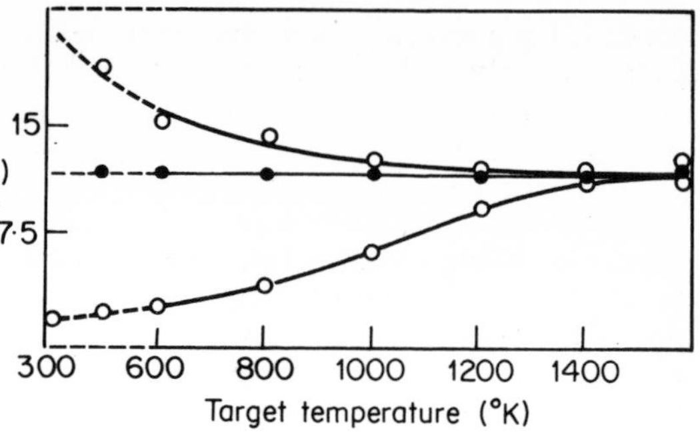

Fig. 3.30 Effect of target temperature on secondary electron emission coefficient for A^+ ions on Mo. Upper curve shows variation of γ for surface contaminated with electropositive species; lower curve for electronegative species. Middle curve is true variation for an atomically clean target. (Refs. 3.81 and 3.94b)

dependence of yields. Fig. 3.30 illustrates the situation very clearly. The upper curve shows the fall in yield which would occur as the temperature was increased if the vacuum system contained a predominantly electropositive residual gas whilst the lower curve the corresponding curve for an adsorbed film of an electronegative gas. The central curve is the true variation of yield with temperature in the region 300 to 1600°K and is clearly a constant. This situation has also been observed by Dorozhkin and Petrov[95] who found that yields for 0.5 to 8 keV A^+ ions bombarding tungsten and molybdenum targets were independent of temperature over the range 300-2100°K. The energy region included the kinetic ejection region so that kinetic yields must also be independent of temperature. Yields for 0.5-2.8 keV Hg^+ bombardment of the same metals where emission is purely potential were, however, critically dependent on temperature as indicated in Fig. 3.31. Thus the available data is not conclusive and indicates that, for inert gases the potential yield for clean surfaces is not dependent on temperature whilst for mercury ion bombardment yields increase with temperature. Dorozhkin and Petrov have suggested that the temperature dependence observed for mercury bombardment of tungsten and molybdenum may

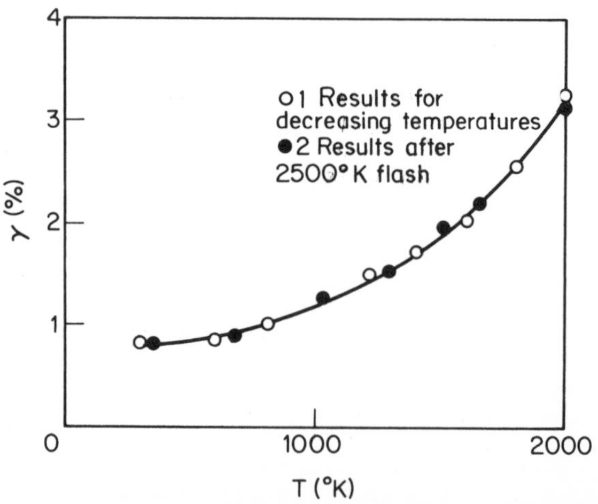

Fig. 3.31 Effect of target temperature on secondary electron emission coefficient for Hg^+ ion bombardment of molybdenum and tungsten. (Ref. 3.95)

occur (a) because in these two cases the ionization energy is only just in excess of 2ϕ so that only the electrons near the Fermi level may contribute and therefore a slight change in temperature could possibly greatly influence the number of participating electrons and (b) because a two-stage process of resonance neutralization followed by auger de-excitation may be possible. If the incoming particle provides excited electron energy levels slightly above the Fermi-level this two stage process will only become possible after a small increase in temperature, thus the emission would be very temperature dependent in the unique cases where the bombarding ion has appropriate excited levels. Eremeev and Petrov[96] have shown that once the two-stage ejection is possible it is more likely to occur than the direct Auger process and is more efficient in production of secondary electrons.

In conclusion therefore it appears that the potential ejection process is not basically temperature dependent, but certain unique conditions, governed by the available energy levels in the particular ion, may make the process extremely temperature sensitive.

3.4.7 Single Crystal studies

Using atomically clean Ge (111) and (100) surfaces Takeishi and Hagstrum[97] have shown that both total yields and ejected electron energy distributions produced by bombardment with He^+, Ne^+ and A^+ ions at energies between 4 and 100 eV were very similar. The secondary electron yield curves for the Ge (100) surface were slightly lower at a given energy than for the (111) surfaces for He^+ and Ne^+ bombardments, but otherwise exhibited similar trends whilst the A^+ curves were coincident for the two germanium faces studied. Since the ejected electron energy distributions were similar for the two faces investigated Takeishi and Hagstrum inferred that the parameters controlling these distributions must likewise be equally effective at the two crystal surfaces, that is, (i) the state density variation through the filled bands of the solid and (ii) the variation with band energy of the magnitude of the electron wave function must both be very similar on each crystal face, for the germanium sample studied.

This condition does not hold for copper monocrystalline surfaces which, as Magnuson and Carlston[62] have found, have very different yields on the (111) (100) and (110) faces. They proposed that the change in yield may have been due to the different work function which is known to vary from face to face thereby influencing the factor $E_i - \phi$. However the trend in the yields was in the wrong direction e.g. $\gamma_{111} < \gamma_{100}$ whilst $\phi_{111} < \phi_{100}$ and hence $E_i - \phi_{111} > E_i - \phi_{100}$. Thus it may be that the electron parameters (i) and (ii) proposed by Hagstrum[97] are not similar on the different copper crystal faces studied and thereby cause the changed emission characteristics.

3.4.8 Electron energy distributions

Using an improved version of their experimental apparatus Hagstrum et al[97-99] have been able to obtain ejected electron distributions for He^+, Ne^+ and A^+ ions of energy between 4 and 100 eV and have shown that the general trend was for the high energy tails of the distributions to extend to even higher energies and the peaks in the distributions to become less pronounced as the bombarding ion energy was increased (Fig. 3.32). Three possible competing processes were proposed to account for this broadening: (1) the onset of kinetic ejection, (2) tertiary electron-electron emission by the faster Auger electrons and (3) Auger de-excitation in which the excited states of the incoming atom are partially populated by electrons from the solid. Of the above three possibilities the first two were discounted on the grounds that the electrons produced would be of relatively low energy only. Factors governing energy broadening in the Auger process comprise (1) initial state lifetime (2) final state lifetime (3) shift in the atomic energy levels near the surface (4) the variation of impact parameter near the surface and (5) non-adiabatic excitation of electrons in the solid as a result of the ions' motion. Of these (2) is independent of the incident ion velocity so will not contribute to the change in spectrum with increasing ion energy, and factors (3) and (4) will cause production of more electrons with lower energy rather than increase the high energy tail. It is concluded therefore that factors (1) and (5) are the main parameters causing the distribution to change, each contributing approximatley an equal amount to the observed energy broadening. The initial state lifetime conributes a fraction b_i to the broadening function (which is discussed below) which is governed mainly by the Heisenberg uncertainty principle and is approximated by

$$b_i = hav \qquad 3.48$$

where h = Planck's const., v = ion velocity and a is a term governing the total transition probability per unit time at distance 5 from the surface: $R_t(s) = A\exp(-as)$. Hagstrum[26, 100] has estimated a value for a of approximately 3 $Å^{-1}$ from consideration of wave function tails so that the contribution b_i amounts to

$$b_i \simeq 0.3 \text{ eV for He at 4 eV}$$

and

$$b_i \simeq 4 \text{ eV for He at 1000 eV}$$

assuming that the surface barrier does not collapse. In practice the surface barrier will collapse so that the high energy value of b_i will be much lower than the 4 eV predicted.

The non-adiabatic contribution to the broadening arises due to the electric perturbation caused by an ion as it passes electrons in orbit around surface atoms. The perturbation can cause excitation of these electrons to elevated states from which they may participate in Auger transitions, the excess energy being transferred in this process to the ejected electron. Consideration of the perturbing potential at an electron site a distance d from a moving ion leads to the approximate expression.

$$b_n \simeq hv/d \qquad 3.49$$

If d is taken as 0.5 Å then

$$b_n \simeq 0.2 \text{ eV for 4 eV } He^+$$
$$\simeq 3 \text{ eV for 1000 eV } He^+$$

The states available for non-adiabatic excitation are very dependent upon the ion-target species so that the marked change of broadening for various ion-target combinations may well be accounted for by the non-adiabatic process. (see Figs. 3.33 and 3.34)

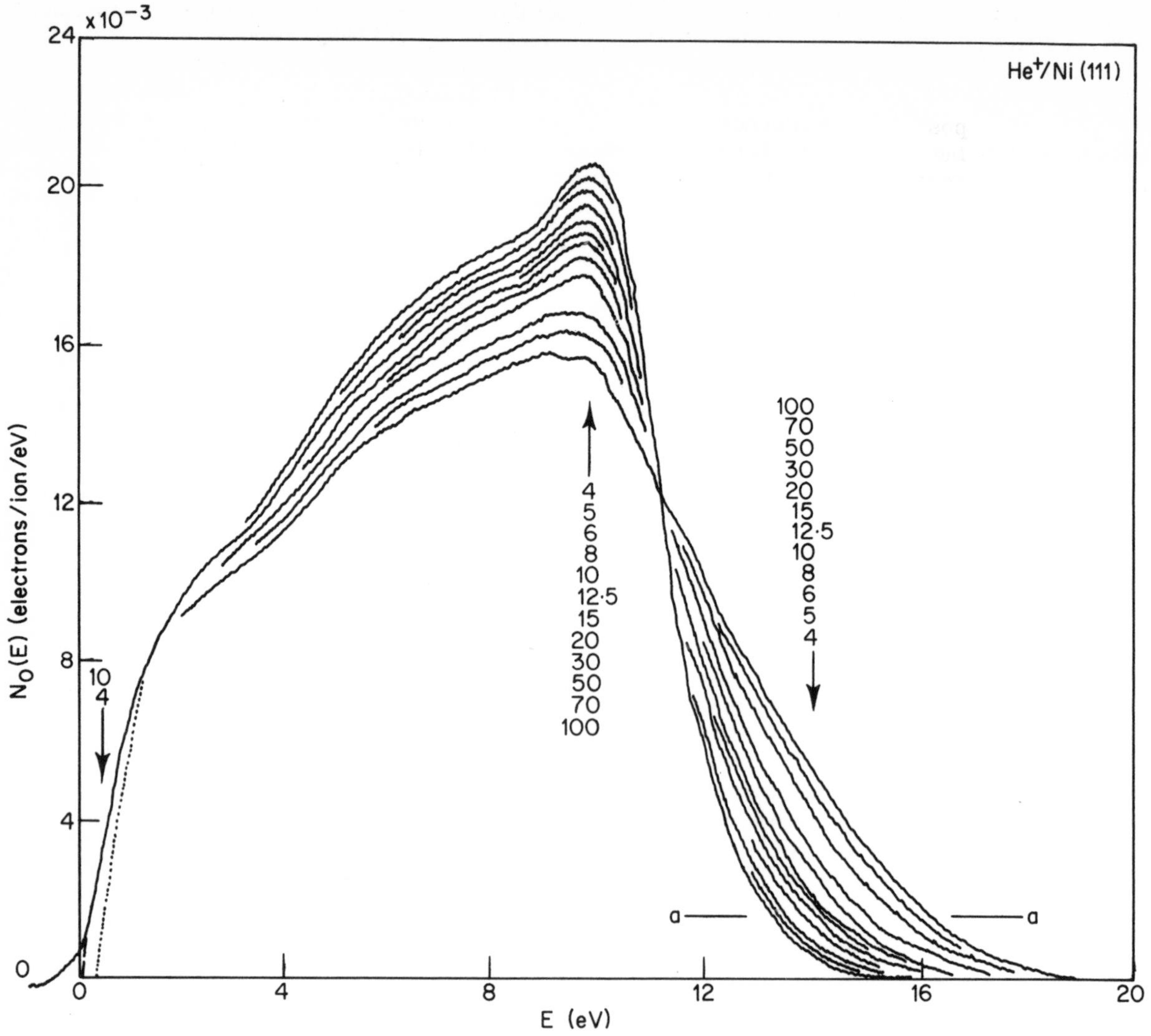

Fig. 3. 32 Change in electron energy distribution with bombarding ion energy for He^+ ions incident on atomically clean Ni (111). Incident ion energies are listed in sequence at three points on the curves. (Ref. 3. 99)

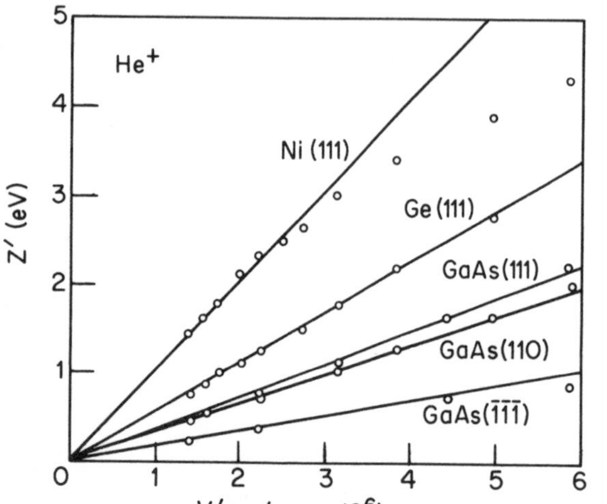

Fig. 3. 33 Variation of parameter Z′ (defined in text) with ion velocity for He^+ ions incident on various monocrystalline surfaces. (Ref. 3. 99)

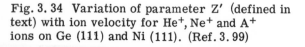

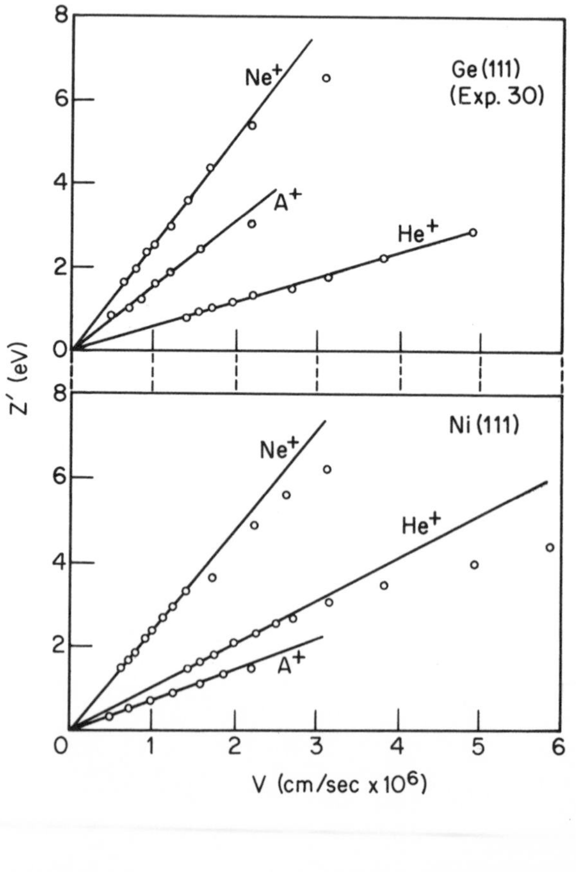

Fig. 3. 34 Variation of parameter Z′ (defined in text) with ion velocity for He^+, Ne^+ and A^+ ions on Ge (111) and Ni (111). (Ref. 3. 99)

The above arguments indicate the manner in which the electron energy distribution can be broadened on a physical basis. Hagstrum et al have also expressed the broadening mathematically by assuming that it is introduced by the convolution of the internal electron energy distribution $N_{io}(E)$ by a broadening function. The distribution at energy K_2 is related to that at a lower bombarding energy K_1 by

$$N_{iK_2} = \int_{-\infty}^{\infty} B(x, L_{K_1K_2}) N_{iK_1}(E - x)dx \qquad 3.50$$

where $B(x, L_{K_1K_2})$ is the broadening function and $L_{K_1K_2}$ is a parameter expressing its width. The externally observed electron energy distribution can be obtained by multiplying $N_{iK}(E)$ by a suitable probability function for electron escape over the surface barrier $P_e(E)$. This probability function varies only relatively slowly for $E > 5$ eV so that the observed distribution can be approximated to the internal distribution in most cases.

If $N_{iK_1}(E) = 1 \quad E < E_1$

$= 0 \quad E > E_1$ i.e. a sudden cutoff in the energy distribution and the broadening function is expressed by the Lorentzian

$$B(x, L_{K_1K_2}) = (L_{K_1K_2}/\pi)/(L_{K_1K_2}^2 + x^2) \qquad 3.51$$

then equation 3.50 yields the extension $Z = E - E_1$ at the level f due to broadening as

$$Z = E - E_1 = L_{K_1K_2} \cdot \tan(\tfrac{1}{2}\pi - f\pi) \qquad 3.52$$

(see Fig. 3.35).

Since $2L_{K_1K_2}$ is the total width at half maximum of the broadening function (=b) then it is clear that, in the simplified expression derived above, the extension Z is proportional to broadening.

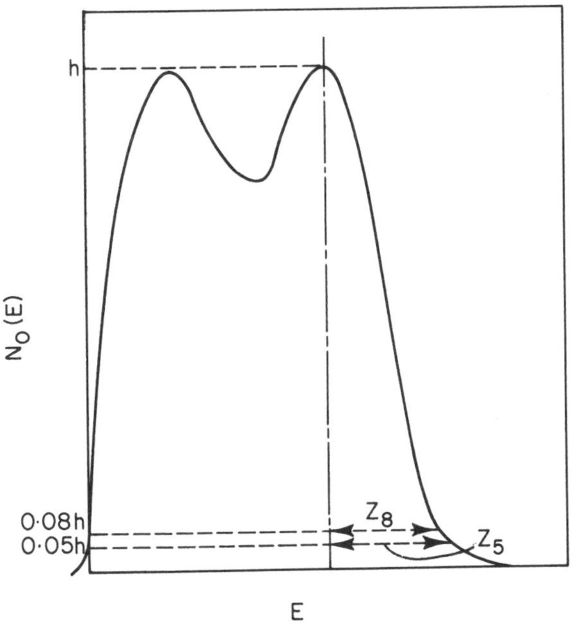

Fig. 3.35 Diagram illustrating the definitions of the relative extensions Z_5 and Z_8 used to provide a measure of the relative broadening in the electron kinetic energy distributions. (Ref. 3.99)

Hagstrum et al have analysed their experimental curves and have been able to derive from them the relationship between broadening and ion velocity. To do this they have first measured off the distances Z_8 and Z_5 (Fig. 3.35) where

Z_8 = distance from second peak to curve at height 0.08h

Z_5 = distance from second peak to curve at height 0.05h and

Z' = distance from specially chosen zero to curve at a height 1.5×10^{-3} electrons/ions/eV (a-a in Fig 3.32). The zero is chosen arbitrarily and then adjusted so that the linear plot of Z' against V passes through (O, O).

These Z values were then plotted as a function of ion velocity. Next a machine calculation was carried out on the experimental 4 eV distribution, convoluting this curve by a series of Lorentzian functions of increasing parameter L_{4K}. The Z_8, Z_5 and Z' values were then measured on these theoretically broadened curves and plotted as a function of L_{4K}. From these curves ($Z - V$ experimental, $Z - L_{4K}$ theoretical) the Z parameters were eliminated and the parameter L_{4K} plotted as a function of V (Fig. 3.36). Adjustment of the zero for the ordinates as indicated in

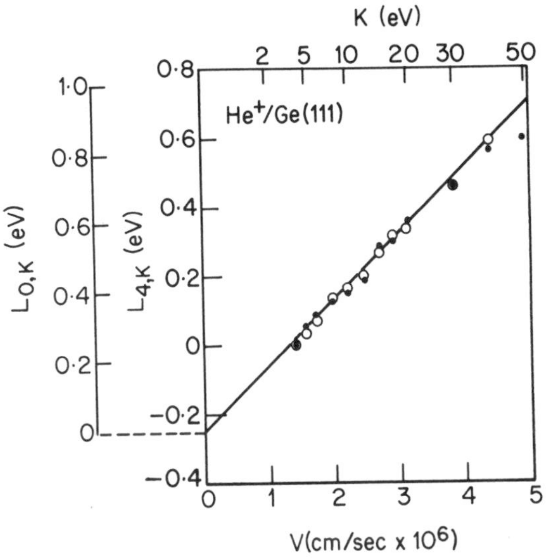

Fig. 3.36 Plot of the Lorentzian parameter L_{4K} versus ion velocity for He^+ on Ge (111): ● Data for f = 0.05 ○ Data for f = 0.08. Extrapolation to v = 0 defines the L_{OK} scale as discussed in text. (Ref. 3.99)

Fig. 3.36 was then carried out, the linear extrapolation to V = O defining the zero of L_{OK}. Thus Hagstrum et al were able to determine the velocity dependence of broadening from their results and demonstrate that the broadening $b = 2L_{OK}$ is linearly dependent on the impinging ion velocity. The two values Z_5 and Z_8 were used in the calculation above to check that the Lorentzian function was applicable and the Z' value was used to enable comparison between different ion-target combinations. (See Figs. 3.33 and 3.34).

3.5 RECENT WORK ON KINETIC EJECTION

We now proceed to study the various aspects of kinetic ejection in a parallel survey to the preceding one for potential ejection.

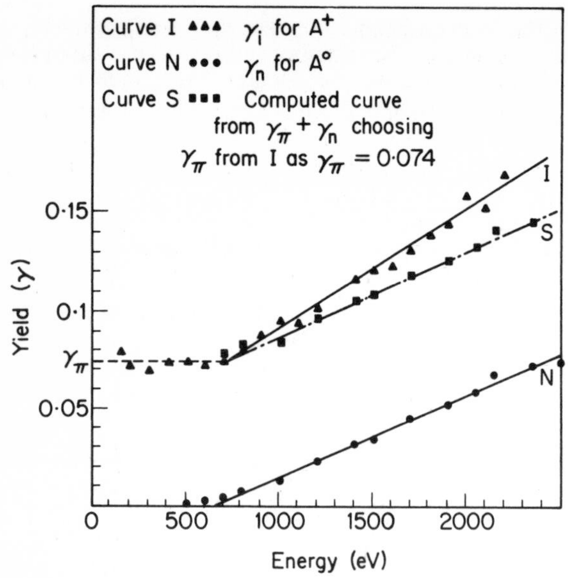

Fig. 3. 37 Secondary electron emission as a function of ion energy for argon and neutral atom bombardment of molybdenum. (Ref. 3. 101).

A convenient introduction to the kinetic ejection field is provided by a paper by Medved et al[101] who have studied potential and kinetic ejection by argon ions and the corresponding kinetic ejection by argon neutral bombardment. The curves obtained by Medved are presented in Fig. 3. 37 and, to a first approximation, it is clear that they are identical for the ion and neutral bombardments except for a vertical displacement equal to the magnitude of the potential emission for the argon ions. ($\gamma_{\text{POTENTIAL}}$). A closer investigation shows however that the slope of the yield against energy curve for the ions is slightly larger than for the neutrals so that the potential energy component must be energy dependent (or, the ion with its different shell structure undergoes collisions which are more efficient in producing electrons by kinetic ejection than the neutral atom). At higher bombarding ion energies (20-60 keV) Chambers[102] and others[59 103] (see a later discussion) have found that emission during neutral atom bombardment is greater than for bombardment by the corresponding ion. Chambers shows that a calculation, based on the assumption that it is the extra electron travelling with the neutral species that contributes to this extra emission, gives reasonable results for the difference in secondary emission. However at low energies the extra electron will not contribute to the ejection process. The energy dependence could of course be explained by the potential theory as due to the penetration of the incoming ion nearer to the target at higher energies before the Auger transition occurs, so that the effective ionization energy is altered. It is interesting to find that Arifov et al[104] who also studied secondary emission for the argon ion and neutral atom on molybdenum did not detect a divergence of the curves at higher energies, in other words the potential emission was found to be a constant independent of ion energy. It is not clear which of these results is correct, they may have been taken for polycrystals with a slightly different preferred orientation in which case the different energy transfer processes for the ion and neutral may have been more marked on the surface studied by Medved et al than on that studied by Arifov. With regard to the different energy transfer to a surface bombarded by a neutral and ionic particle Medved et al[105] have shown that the neutral atom does in fact transfer less energy and this in itself would explain the different slopes of the A^+ and A^0 yield curves. (Peterson[106] has shown that the apparent difference in energy transfer could be caused by the scattering of ions and neutrals out of the beam, but Mahadevan et al[107] have presented further evidence refuting this possibility). However, in spite of the slight contradiction in results, the data of both Medved[101] and Arifov[104] demonstrate the distinct difference in potential and kinetic emission characteristics. Similar curves have been obtained by Petrov[108] for K^+ and A^+ bombardment of tungsten and again show that the only difference in yields is due to a constant additional potential component in the argon characteristic.

Mahadevan et al[85] have obtained interesting data for atomic oxygen, nitrogen, and argon ions striking a molybdenum target which has been degassed, or has a layer of adsorbed gas. The curves show the transition from potential to kinetic emission, the gas-covered curve lying parallel to and below the clean molybdenum curve throughout the energy regime studied. It thus appears that it is the potential contribution to the secondary electron emission which is so critically affected by the adsorbed layer whilst the kinetic emission characteristic remains relatively stable.

3.5.1 Dependence of yield on the ion-target combination

The theory of Parilis and Kishinevskii[44 47] predicts that at energies near threshold for kinetic emission, the yield will be relatively independent of ion-atom combination. Experimental data of Tel'kovskii[83] indicates that this is true to a first approximation for various ions bombarding molybdenum, zirconium, nickel and tantalum targets. At higher ion energies a thorough investigation has been carried out by Fogel et al[109] for 10-40 keV H^+, He^+, Ne^+, A^+, Kr^+ and O^+ bombardment of molybdenum and H^+, Ne^+ and A^+, bombardment of tantalum, tungsten, copper and iron. The general observation was that the electron emission coefficient increased with increase in ion mass for a given velocity.

Arifov and Rakhimov[87] have made a thorough study of the secondary emission coefficient in the 1 to 10 keV range using noble gas ions and their nearest alkali ion counterpart, i.e. Ne-Na, A-K, Kr-Rb. After subtracting the potential emission from the noble gas curves the yield-energy curves for the above pairs of ions were seen to nearly coincide (see Fig. 3. 38). It was clear that the kinetic ejection from metals was governed largely by the nature of the impinging ion since results for tungsten, tantalum and molybdenum were all very similar, whilst yields for different ions changed by a factor of three or more.

It is clear from the table of yields (Table 3.1) that secondary emission from glass surfaces is more efficient than from metals and, again, yields from alkali-halide crystals are even larger. Batanov[110] records yields for argon ions on a glass surface described as 'number 46 glass' at energies of 2 keV which are some twenty times the yields for the same ion on tantalum targets. Furthermore, the slope $d\gamma/dE$ for the argon-glass combination is also greatly in excess of that for tantalum (approximately seven times). Batanov[111 112] observes even larger yields

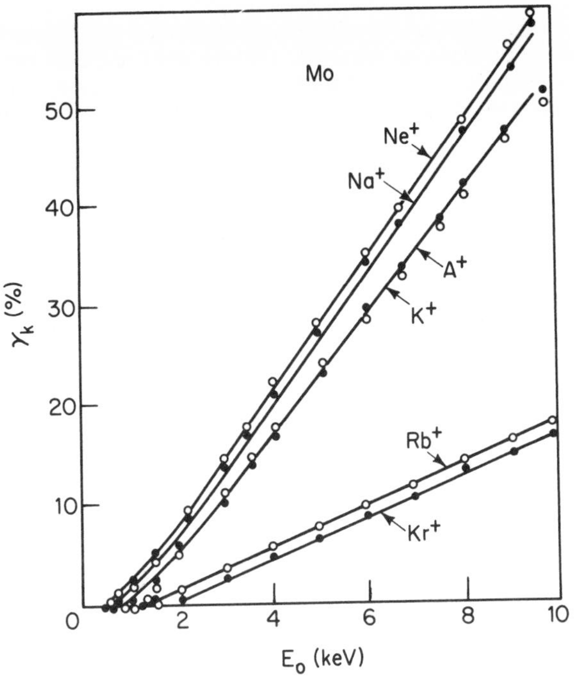

Fig. 3. 38 Comparative yield-energy data for Ne^+ -Na^+, A^+ -K^+ and Kr^+ -Rb^+ for 1-10 keV ion bombardment of molybdenum. (Ref. 3. 87)

for Li^+ and K^+ bombarding NaCl and KCl targets and concludes that the yields are large because the excitation probability for electrons in these targets is much greater than for metals and, further, the energy losses of the electrons produced are much less.

3.5.2. Yield dependence on ion energy

The theory of Parilis[44] predicts that no kinetic emission can occur up to a certain threshold energy: the yield then proceeds to increase in a linear form with energy and then, at higher energies, the yield increases at a lesser rate and becomes a linear function of the ion velocity. The predicted threshold energy is that energy corresponding to an ion velocity of $0.6 - 0.7 \times 10^7$ cm/sec regardless of the ion-target combination, provided $1/4 < (Z_1/Z_2) < 4$. An alternative reference velocity could be the intercept on the velocity axis obtained by extrapolating the linear γ vs v portion of the curve to zero. This latter value is predicted theoretically to be 1.05×10^7 cm./sec., again independent of the participating atoms.

The majority of available results confirm the above predicted trends and therefore indicate that the basic assumptions of this theory are correct. Curves obtained by Petrov and Dorozhkin[113] for He^+, Ne^+, A^+, N_1^+, and N_2^+ ion bombardment of a clean tungsten target embrace the two regions discussed above (i.e. γ vs E linear and γ vs v linear). Threshold energies are not apparent from these curves however as the presence of the potential component of electron emission disguises the true kinetic cut-off.

Results obtained by Parilis and Kishinevski[44] themselves for A^+, Kr^+, K^+ and Mo^+ bombardment of tungsten and molybdenum targets indicate threshold velocities of $0.6 - 0.7 \times 10^7$ cm/sec. Mahedevan et al[114] find a similar value for the threshold for A^+ ions on molybdenum and, in a later paper[115], these workers find the predicted linear dependence of yield on ion energy. Bosch and Kuskevics[116] have also found a linear dependence of yield on energy in the 0-20 keV region for Cs^+ ion bombardment of clean and cesiated tungsten and their data is in fair agreement with Brunnée[82]. Threshold energies obtained on clean tungsten correspond to velocities of 0.6×10^7 cm/sec, again in excellent correspondence with Parilis et al's predicted value.

This linear dependence of yield with ion energy does not only apply to metal targets as demonstrated by Abroyan[117] who bombarded n-type germanium of resistivity 37 ohm-cm. with K^+, Li^+ and Cs^+ ions. Threshold energies were, respectively, 500, 500 and 1000 eV, corresponding to velocities of 1.2×10^7, 0.5×10^7 and 0.4×10^7 cm/sec. the potassium and cesium results are a good confirmation of the theory, but the lithium result is not. This is expected since for lithium-germanium the ratio Z_1/Z_2 is $1/10$ which is outside the limits $1/4 < (Z_1/Z_2) < 4$ over which the theory applies. On glass surfaces Batanov and Petrov [118] have again found a linear dependence of yield on energy for He^+ and A^+ bombardment. The apparent threshold for A^+ is at 0.3 keV, corresponding to a velocity of about 0.4×10^7 cm/sec whilst the He^+ threshold is difficult to determine due to the presence of potential ejection. Further confirmation comes from work by Batanov[111 112] who bombarded alkali-halide compounds with potassium ions and found threshold energies all in the region of 200 eV (i.e. 3.14×10^6 cm/sec). Yields were again found to increase linearly with energy in the range studied (0-2 keV).

Other examples of the general rule of a linear relationship between yield and energy can be found in the literature[53 85 87]. At higher energies however $d\gamma/dE$ decreases as is indicated in most of the results of Ploch[42] whose studies extended over this critical range of energy and included results for 1-8 keV Li^+ and Ne^+ ions on molybdenum, beryllium, copper and platinum targets. Of these the platinum surface only was thoroughly degassed so that results for other targets applied to surfaces contaminated with residual gases. At these higher energies the yield is found to become proportional to the ion velocity, again as predicted by the Parilis theory. Tel'kovskii[83] has shown that yields for Mo^+, A^+, Ne^+, N^+, He^+, and H_1^+ on molybdenum increase linearly with the ion velocity over the higher energy range. The linearity is seen to hold for argon ions in the range $1/8 - 1/2 \times 10^8$ cm/sec, that is, approximately 4-50 keV whilst the linear γ-E region, according to Mahadevan et al[115], occurs for argon on molybdenum in the range 0.7-2.5 keV, which would be insignificant on Tel'kovskii's curves.

A similar linear relationship between yield and velocity is obtained by Large[119] for H^+, He^+, O^+, Ne^+, N^+ and A^+ bombarment of tungsten and the He^+ and A^+ curves are included in Fig. 3.2 for comparison. In all cases the linear rule is found to be obeyed for ion velocities up to about 10^8 cm/sec. Secondary electron emission coefficients are also seen to be linearly related to velocity for non-metallic targets, as can be seen from the results of Batanov[110 118] for hydrogen, helium and argon bombardment of a glass surface.

At extremely high energies however the electron yield is seen to reach a maximum value as observed for proton bombardment of tungsten by Ewing[120]. The maximum was seen to occur at an energy of about 125 keV as anticipated by the theory of Sternglass[58]. In this theory the main postulate was that the electrons escaped from a thin layer near the surface so that proton energies in the region concerned were approximately constant and neither the zone depth nor the fraction of electrons emitted from the zone would be a strong function of the proton energy. The only changing parameter would be therefore the cross-section for free electron production in tungsten by protons and the γ-E curve will illustrate this change. This conclusion is backed by the work of Whaling[121] who showed that the differential energy loss cross-sections for protons in metals exhibit maxima at approximately 125 keV proton energy.

3.5.3 Yield dependence on ion charge and composition

The general impression conveyed by the experimental results is that the ion charge is important only in that it affects the impinging ion velocity. Daly and Powell[122] have presented results for single and double-charged He^+, A^+, Kr^+, and Xe^+ ions on aluminium targets at energies of 40 keV showing that the double-charged species gave yields in excess of their single charge counterparts by only about 16 percent, even though they arrived at the surface with twice the energy. It is apparent that these ions penetrated further into the target so that their extra energy was dissipated mainly in atom layers too deep to allow diffusion of the electrons produced to the surface. An experiment allowing a better comparison of the performance of single and multiply charged ions would be to compare the yields for these ions when they arrive at the surface with identical velocities. This has been done by Tel'kovskii[83] for argon ions of one, two, or three charges on molybdenum and zirconium and the yield curves as a function of velocity were shown to be identical.

Regarding the composition of the bombarding particles, most workers conclude that the constituents of a molecular ion dissociate on impact and then each atomic component reacts as if it had the same energy as its parent molecule. Large[119] shows that, for a given velocity, the yields for the molecular species O_2^+, N_2^+ and H_2^+ are, approximately, twice those for their corresponding atomic ions. Also Tel'kovskii[83] finds for H_3^+, H_2^+ and H_1^+ bombardment of molybdenum and zirconium that the yields are directly in proportion to the number of atoms in the bombarding particle. Mahadevan et al[85] disagree with these results finding, in a lower energy regime (1-2 keV) that yields for atomic nitrogen exceeded those for the molecular ion and similarly for oxygen and hydrogen. In a controlled experiment, where the molybdenum target was deliberately contaminated with background gases, Mahadevan et al were able to reverse the order of yields for the hydrogen ions, making the molecular species produce slightly higher electron yields than the atomic ions and have therefore suggested that previous results were representative of contaminated surfaces only.
Arifov et al[123] have studied secondary yields for hydrogen, deuterium and helium ions on molybdenum which has been flashed to 2000°K and then held at about 1300-1400°K for the experiment. This heating cycle was shown to ensure that the molybdenum surface remained clean for the duration of the experiment in the rather poor vacuum (2×10^{-7} torr) existing in their apparatus. When yields were plotted as a function of the velocity the curves of H_2^+, D_2^+ and HD^+ ions were seen to coincide and have a magnitude approximately twice that for H_1^+, or D_1^+, these latter curves also being coincident. No isotopic dependence was apparent however, except at velocities near threshold where H_2^+ yields remained slightly above those for D_2^+ ions. Arifov et al concluded that the difference was due to the different slowing down of the two isotopes in the target; an effect which is only of importance at low velocities. It is notable that the curve obtained for helium bombardment was not the same as for the equal mass hydrogen molecules and one concludes that the extra electron in the helium atom must be responsible for this (i.e. collision cross-sections are changed).

Further confirmation of the independence of the isotope on the yield on a γ vs v plot is provided by Ploch[42] who studied secondary emission for the isotopes of lithium and neon on platinum, beryllium and copper targets. Ploch has plotted out the curves against energy and then taken points for one isotope s and adjusted its energy E to $E' = EM_H/M_s$. Having re-plotted the yield for isotope s at this new energy he found that the new curve was superimposed upon the curve for isotope H, in other words the yield against velocity curves would coincide. This state of affairs was also observed by Daly and Powell for Li^6 and Li^7 yield values at 40 keV on gas-covered aluminium surfaces, but was not found to be the case by Krebs[124] for bombardment of nickel targets by krypton and xenon isotopic ions at 12-25 keV. Background pressures in all these studies were rather high (order 10^{-7}) so that changes in surface conditions may have influenced the results.

It was noted above that the results of Arifov[123] showed that yields of mass 4 hydrogen molecular species were less than those for helium although the latter is of equal mass. The main difference in the two cases is the extra electron which is travelling toward the surface with the helium ion. On a similar argument it is anticipated that yields due to neutral particles (which also have an extra electron compared to the ion) will be greater than those for the corresponding ions. Chambers[102] has recently demonstrated this effect for proton bombardment of copper-beryllium surfaces in the energy range 9-60 keV at angles of incidence of 60°. The neutral to ionic ratios were shown to be: $1.11 + 0.001E_0$ for H, $1.18 + 0.003E_0$ for H_2 and $1.32 + 0.003E_0$ for H_3. Chambers assumes that the extra electron travelling with the ion is capable of reacting independently and producing the extra fraction in the yield factor. Carrying out this calculation for 6 keV H^+, the electron energy equivalent to this speed is 3.3 eV. As it reaches the target it gains energy equal to the work function, but at higher energies this can be neglected. The maximum energy transfer that the H_1 atom can give to an electron in a head-on collision is given by $(4 M_e M_H/(M_e + M_H)^2)$. E_0 and this is found to be 13.2 eV for a 6 keV H^+ ion. Thus the H^+ ion can impart 13.2 eV to an electron and the accompanying electron in the H neutral bombardment can transfer all its energy, 3.3 eV, so that the fractional increase in the yield due to neutral bombardment might be expected to be $3.3/13.2 = 0.25$. Thus this simple treatment predicts that the ratio γ^0/γ^+ will be 1.25. In fact it turns out to be 1.14 which is fair agreement and Chambers concluded that the electron contribution must be reduced as a result of its close binding to the H ion, thus restricting its energy transfer capabilities.

Further confirmation of the above theory was obtained by Bethge and Lexa[103] who compared yields for 20-60 keV lithium ion and neutral atom bombardment of Be, Al, Ag, Ta, Pt, Au and W and Ag-Mg, Cu-Be alloys. The ratio of the yields for neutral γ^0 and ionic γ^+ bombardment was found to be:

$$\gamma^0/\gamma^+ = 1.1 \pm 10\%$$

for all the targets studied, except for Be and Al which had slightly larger ratios. By making a theoretical calculation along the lines of Ghosh and Khare[59] which was similar, but more detailed than that of Chambers[102], the predicted ratio was shown to be:

$$y^0/y^+ = 1.03 \text{ (20 keV)}$$
$$= 1.09 \text{ (60 keV)}$$

which is again in good agreement with experimental measurements.

Thus we can conclude that the increase in emission for neutral atom bombardment of a surface is mainly due to the presence of the extra electron which contributes a fraction of its energy to the process of secondary electron emission.

3.5.4 State of the target surface

Arifov et al[48] have carried out a controlled experiment involving the bombardment of clean and background gas contaminated molybdenum by 0-50 keV argon ions and have demonstrated that yields for a clean surface exceed those for the contaminated surface for energies up to 18 keV, above which the curves coincide. They concluded that the cleaning efficiency of the ions increased with energy up to 18 keV so that, in fact at higher energies the measured yields were for clean targets in both cases. However Large[125] has found the opposite state of affairs for 0-100 keV hydrogen ions on titanium where the yields on contaminated surfaces were shown to be higher than those on clean surfaces. Large proposed that since the ion has to expend energy in penetrating the adsorbed layer it has more chance of losing energy to atoms near the surface of the metal. The electrons are thus formed nearer to the surface and their diffusion through the adsorbed layer is easier than through the corresponding thickness of metal so that their escape is easier.

The results of Fogel et al[109] confirm the findings of Large in that yields for a molybdenum target immediately after baking were about 50% lower than yields for the same target with a monolayer of residual gas on its surface. Both Brunnée[82] and Waters[54] observed the same trends in yields so one must conclude that the results of Arifov et al are the exception rather than the rule in this instance.

3.5.5 Dependence of yield on angle of incidence

It is generally found that the secondary electron emission coefficient for polycrystalline targets varies with the angle of incidence of the ion beam θ according to the equation;

$$\gamma_\theta = \gamma_0 \sec\theta \qquad 3.53$$

where, γ_0 and γ_θ are the yields at 0 and θ to the normal. This is confirmed experimentally by Allen[126] and Tel'kovskii[84] and yields obtained by Bosch[127] for normal and 40° incidence for cesium on molybdenum were in the ratio predicted by the sec θ dependence. The equation is anticipated in the theoretical treatments as, at any given angle θ the path length for electron-producing collisions will be unaltered whilst the distance through which the liberated electrons have to diffuse to the surface before escaping is less than for normal incidence in the proportion cos θ to 1.

3.5.6 Yields on single crystals

At the time of writing there is very little experimental evidence available for kinetic emission from different faces of single crystal targets. According to the theory of Parilis and Kishinevskii the yield is anticipated to be proportional to the velocity of the incident ion as it penetrates the target. It is clear that, in an ordered array, the ion will retain its velocity if it enters the crystal along open channel directions (for a discussion of channelling see Chapter 5) and the collision will occur at a greater depth than in a non-ordered amorphous target. The electrons will not escape as easily from this greater depth so that one anticipates a yield against crystal direction pattern similar to that for sputtering (Chapter 7) where yields are lowest for bombardment directions which coincide with open channel directions.

Fagot et al[63,64,64a,b] and Zscheile[128] have carried out experiments in which the secondary electron emission coefficient was found to vary markedly with the crystal orientation, thus confirming the above conclusion. The results of Fagot et al were observed on monocrystalline copper, iron and germanium targets during bombardment by 50-100 keV A^+ ions and the minima in the values of γ were shown to occur in directions most transparent to the ion beam. In the experiments of Zscheile[128] 17.5-35 keV protons and noble gas ions were fired at copper monocrystalline targets and it was shown that the influence of the lattice orientation was greater for bombardment by heavier ion species, a fact confirmed by Mashkova et al[67] for bombardment of the (100) face of copper at the same energies by H_1^+, H_2^+, H_3^+, N_1^+ and N_2^+ ions. Here the nitrogen ions were seen to produce the anticipated peaks and minima in the emission characteristic (the minima corresponding to bombardment in open channel directions Fig. 3.39) whilst the hydrogen ions produced an almost smooth function of yield against incident angle.

Magnuson and Carlston[62] have carried out an experiment in which the low-index planes of copper were bombarded with argon ions. Yields for (111), (110) and (100) surfaces were found to be widely different, but the ratios of the yields were seen to follow the ratios of the closed (hard-sphere) area to the total area for the directions considered. For example; if an ion approaching a (jkl) surface sees 90% of its path clear and 10% closed, then only 10% of the beam will undergo collisions capable of producing electrons near enough to the surface to escape. Similarly, if the ion now approaches a (j'k'l') surface where 50% of its path is closed then we expect a higher yield from bombardment in this direction in the ratio 50 to 10, i.e. five times. Fig. 3.40 shows that the ratio of yields on the different crystal faces can be fairly accurately predicted in this way.

Kaminsky et al[129] have found that the yields are still approximately in the ratio of the closed to open areas

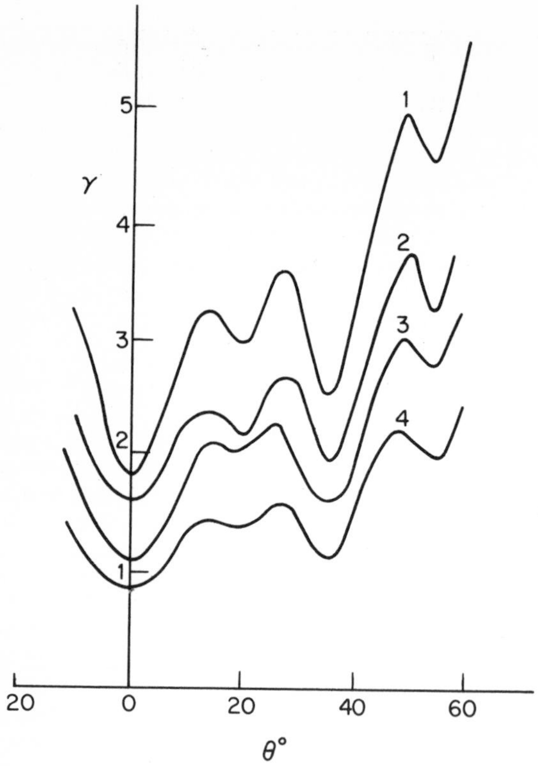

Fig. 3. 39 Secondary electron emission coefficient as a function of angle of incidence for bombardment of a (100) face of copper. Curve 1, N_2^+ ions at 35 keV; 2, N_2^+ at 17. 5 keV; 3, N_1^+ at 35 keV; 4, N_1^+ at 35 keV; 4, N_1^+ at 17. 5 keV. (Ref. 3. 67)

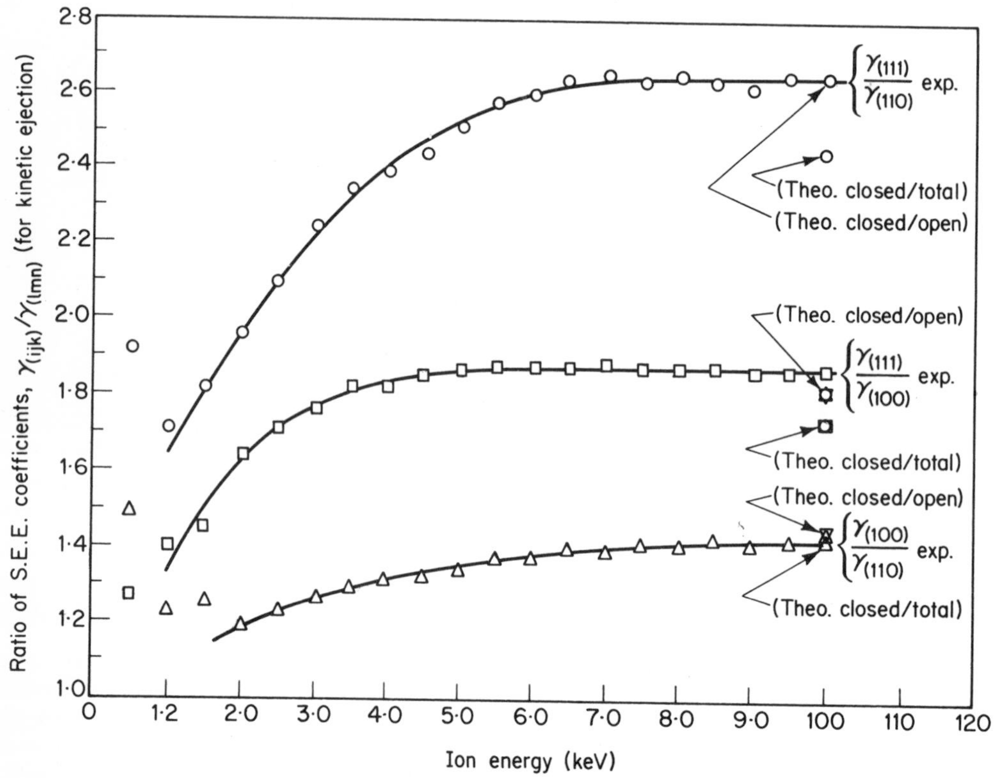

Fig. 3. 40 Theoretical estimates of the ratio of secondary electron emission coefficients for 10 keV A^+ ions on different crystal faces of copper based on a transparency model. Points ○ $\gamma_{111}/\gamma_{110}$; □ $\gamma_{111}/\gamma_{100}$ and Δ $\gamma_{100}/\gamma_{110}$, are experimental values and theoretical values at 10 keV are indicated by arrows. (Ref. 3. 62)

as described above at energies as high as 0. 2 MeV; for example for D^+ ions on copper targets $\gamma_{111} = 1.25\,\gamma_{100}$ whilst the ratio of the total collision areas on the (111) and the (100) faces was 1. 75. Kaminsky et al explain that this larger difference is due to channelling of the incident ions to regions away from the surface, especially in the (111) bombardment, so that emission of electrons is not as efficient for bombardments in this direction as would be expected from calculation of the total closed area. The channelling process will be discussed fully in Chapter 5, but it will suffice for the moment to explain that at high energies the ion is actually constrained to move within certain planes of atoms in the crystal. Thus a calculation based on random collisions with atoms having a total cross-section determined from geometric considerations becomes invalid since the crystal structure 'guides' the impinging ion and the ion-atom interactions are no longer random.

In later work the single crystal studies of Magnuson et al[62] were extended to include bombardment of Al, Ag, Cu, Mo, and Ni (110), (100) and (111) surfaces by 1-10 keV Ne^+, A^+, Kr^+ and Xe^+ ions[61] and again the ratios of yields between two given planes were found to be generally similar, although there were one or two wide deviations. Figs. 3.41 show variations of yield with energy for A^+ bombardment of (111), (100) and (110) surfaces of nickel, aluminium, silver and molybdenum and Fig. 3.42 shows the variation of the 10 keV yield with bombarding ion mass for the (111) surfaces of aluminium, copper, silver and nickel targets. It is particularly interesting to note that the curves all cross at a value M = 29 in the above figure which indicates the rather surprising result that the yield is independent of target material for bombardment by ions of mass 29.

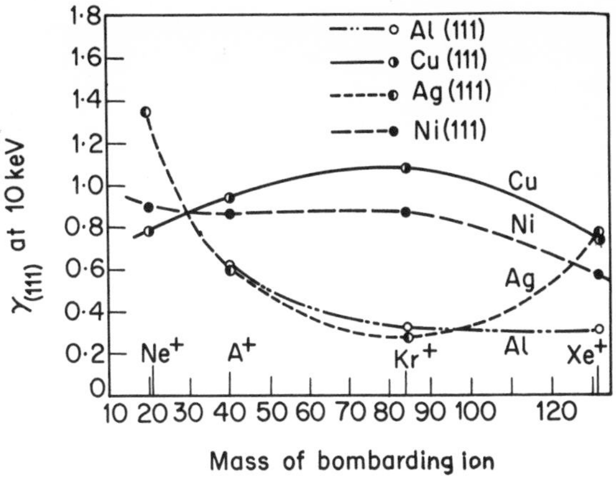

Fig. 3.42 Variation of 10 keV electron emission coefficient with bombarding ion mass for the (111) surfaces of aluminium(○), copper (◑), silver (◐) and nickel (●). (Ref. 3.61)

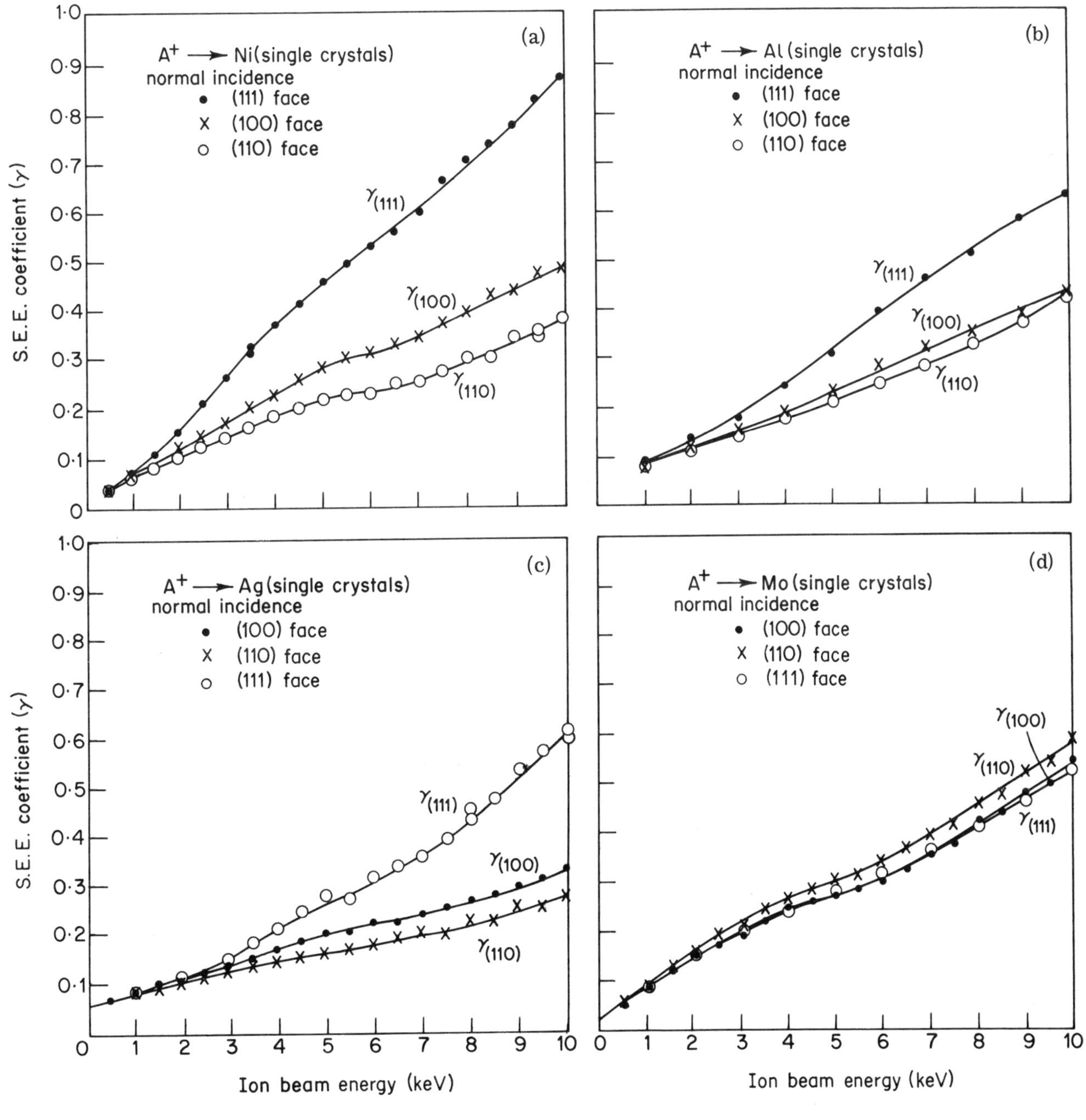

Fig. 3.41 Variation of γ with ion energy for A^+ bombardment of (111), (100) and (110) surfaces of (a) nickel, (b) aluminium, (c) silver and (d) molybdenum. (Ref. 3.61)

A combined study of the anisotropy of sputtering yields and electron emission coefficients for single crystals has been carried out by Mashkova et al[10, 65-7] for 20-30 keV argon ions on (110) and (100) faces of copper and also, for comparison, the yields from polycrystalline targets. It was found that, when the primary ion direction corresponded to principal crystallographic axes of the target, there was a sharp reduction in the number of emitted electrons. Further work by Mashkova et al[11] confirmed this pattern for secondary emission from nickel and zinc targets. In order to explain the variation of yield Mashkova et al postulated that the yield due to collision with atoms in the 'i' th plane below the surface is a function of three parameters; β_i, a coefficient of proportionality which depends on the angle of incidence θ, $\overline{E}_i$, the mean energy transmitted by the ion to atoms in the 'i' th plane, and σ_i the effective collision cross-section of the ion with the atom lying in this plane. Thus, integrating over all planes, the yield is given by

$$\gamma = \Sigma\beta_i(\theta) \cdot \sigma_i \cdot \overline{E}_i \qquad 3.54$$

The average energy transferred to an atom in the case where part of it is hidden by an atom above is calculated by the formula:

$$\overline{E}_i\sigma_i = E_{max}\left[\frac{\pi\delta^2}{2} - \frac{R\delta}{2}\left(1 + \frac{\delta^2}{2R^2}\right)\left[1 - \frac{\delta^2}{4R^2}\right]^{1/2} + R^2 - \delta^2 \sin^{-1}\left(\frac{\delta}{2R}\right)\right] \qquad 3.55$$

where δ is the projection of the distance between the centres of the atoms on a plane perpendicular to the direction of incidence of particles, R is the radius of the colliding sphere (equal to the sum of the hard sphere radii of the ion and target atom) and E_{max} is the maximum energy transferrable to the hit atom in a head-on collision $(4M_1M_2/(M_1 + M_2)^2)\ E_0$. If the angle of incidence is varied in such a way that atoms in planes 2, 4, 6, etc. do not overlap their corresponding neighbouring atoms in planes 1, 3, 5, etc., then the appropriate coefficients for planes 1, 2, 3 and 4, ... 2j-1 and 2j, ... will be equal (i.e. $\beta_1 = \beta_2 = \beta_{12}$; $\beta_3 = \beta_4 = \beta_{34}$; .... etc.) Also, the surface atoms are fully exposed, so that

$$\overline{E}_{12} \cdot \sigma_{12} = \beta_{12}\frac{\pi R^2}{A_0 \cos^2\theta} \cdot \frac{E_{max}}{2} \qquad 3.56$$

where A_0 is the area of the face of the elementary unit cell of the crystal per surface atom. The projected area is thus $A_0 \cdot \cos\theta$ and the additional $1/\cos\theta$ term appears (making a $1/\cos^2\theta$ term) since yields vary with sec θ as for polycrystalline targets (discussed in the preceding section). We also have

$$\overline{E}_{34} \cdot \sigma_{34} = \beta_{34}\frac{\overline{E}_{34}}{A_0 \cos^2\theta} \cdot S_{34} \qquad 3.57$$

Where S_{34} is the exposed area of the colliding spheres in planes 3 and 4. Thus the total yield may be written:

$$\gamma = \frac{1}{A_0 \cos^2\theta}\left[\beta_{12}\pi R^2\frac{E_{max}}{2} + \beta_{34}S_{34}\overline{E}_{34} + \beta_{56}S_{56}\overline{E}_{56} + \ldots\right] \qquad 3.58$$

The unknown parameters of this equation were determined by fitting the curve to experimental results. The radii of collision spheres were fitted from γ values at 48° and $\beta_{i,\,i+1}$ from values at 0, 13 and 19°. It was found that

$$\beta_{12} = \beta_{34} = \frac{5}{3}\beta_{56} = 0.23\ (\text{keV})^{-1} \qquad 3.59$$

$\beta_{i,\,i+1}$ with $i \geq 7$ were set equal to zero. The curves calculated from equation 3.58 are shown together with experimental results in Fig. 3.43 and indicate a reasonable agreement. In a later paper however

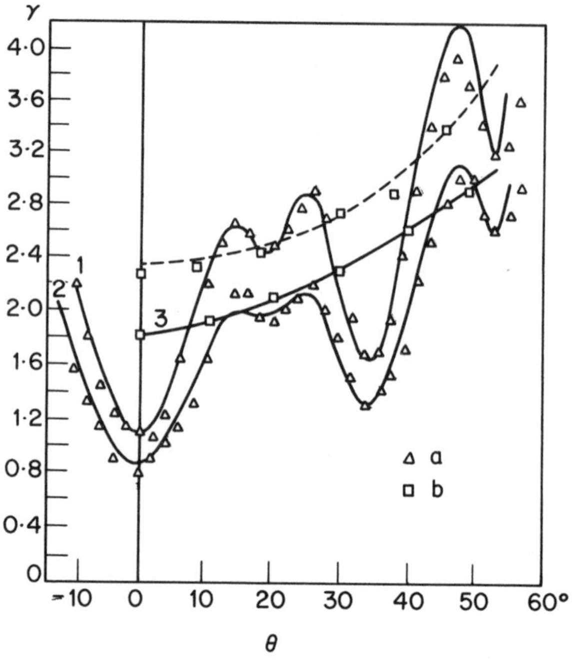

Fig. 3.43 Comparison of experimental and theoretical secondary emission coefficients of a (100) single crystal copper target as the angle of incidence is varied. Curve 1 calculated yield for 30 keV A^+ ions; Δ, experimental values 30 keV A^+; curve 2 theoretical yield for 20 keV A^+ ions; Δ, experimental values 20 keV A^+; curve 3, experimental yield for polycrystalline copper; broken curve, data of Tel'kovskii[46]. (Ref. 3.10)

Mashkova et al[66] showed that the theoretical curves did not agree as well for small angles of incidence for 30 keV A^+ ions on a copper (110) face. They concluded that, at these small angles, atom layers lower then the seventh are exposed and contribute to the emission process. They further suggest that the energy transfer from these deep-seated layers to the surface is by generation of plasma waves which can propagate to the surface and there have an energy in excess of the work function ϕ so that an electron is liberated.

3.5.7 Electron Energy Distributions

A thorough investigation of the energy distribution of the ejected electrons due to kinetic emission on the lines of Hagstrum et al[97-99] for potential emission has not yet been presented in the literature. Fig. 3.44 illustrates the change in form of the distribution for He^+ ions on molybdenum as their energy is increased[74] and the kinetic emission mechanism begins to

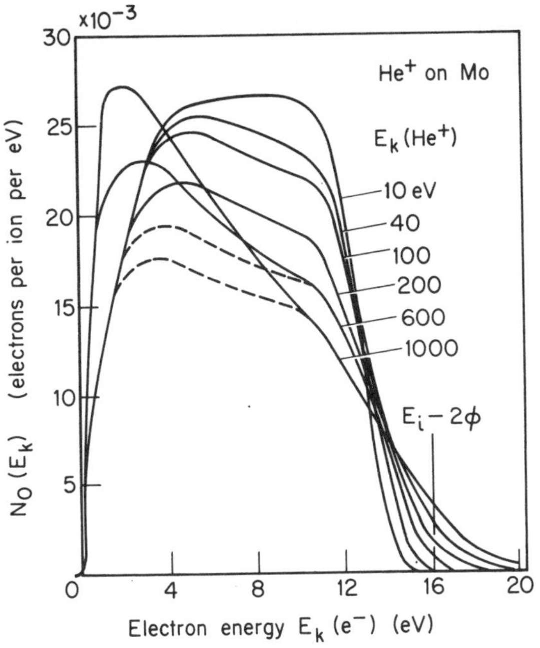

Fig. 3.44 Change in ejected electron energy distribution with onset of kinetic emission for He^+ ions on Molybdenum. (Ref. 3.74)

predominate. It is seen that the peak in the distribution $N_0(E_k)$ vs E_k moves from about 8 eV to 2 eV, indicating that a greater proportion of low energy electrons are liberated by the kinetic emission process. This form of the kinetic emission curve is also observed by Sugiura[130] for helium ions of 540, 840 and 1240 eV on an electropolished copper-beryllium surface.

It should be noted that whilst the most probable electron energy is reduced for kinetic emission processes, the maximum energy can be increased to a value in excess of 100 eV[68]. Snoek et al[131] have shown that when gold targets were bombarded by argon ions at 90 keV a continuum of ejection energies existed with two principal peaks one at a most probable energy of 40 eV and the other belonging to a smaller group at an energy of 190 eV. No explanation was given for this second high energy peak. However Kaminsky et al[129] have shown that secondary peaks on their ejected electron energy distributions could well be a reflection of the internal electron density distributions of the target. Two subsidiary peaks appear on the main distribution curve for bombardment of copper (111) surfaces by H^+, D^+ or He^+ and were seen to occur 3 eV apart. As it is known that copper has a narrow (5.5 eV wide) 3d band with a high density of states and exceptionally large concentrations near its extremites; about 3 eV apart, Kaminsky et al proposed that the subsidiary peaks were due to ejection of electrons from these denser 3d regions, especially as the form of the curve is unaltered when bombardment is by different ion species and must therefore be a characteristic of the copper target.

3.6 CONCLUSIONS

We mention here points of general interest which have not fitted into the categories discussed earlier in this chapter.

An interesting investigation has been carried out by Moroz et al[132] to determine the depth of emergence of the secondary electrons in the bombarded material. Yields were determined for Na^+ ions at various energies striking a NaCl surface of various thicknesses and it was seen that the yield reached a saturation value as the thickness t was increased. Presumably, as the NaCl thickness increased more electrons were produced and, to a first approximation, they all escaped with the same probability. As the thickness t increased further however the electrons formed deeper in the target were recaptured as they diffused towards the surface so that the yield reached a maximum. It was found that the thickness of NaCl at which electron-electron emission reached a maximum was the same. Gomoyunova[133] quotes a value 6×10^{-6} cm. for sodium ions of energy greater than 1 keV in NaCl targets. Sternglass and Wachtel[134] give a mean electron escape depth of 0.3×10^{-6} cm. which is consistent with the above value of Gomoyunova as this latter presumably represents the maximum escape depth. Zarutskii[135] has also found that yields from thin films of 150-400 Å bombarded by potassium ions were unaffected by the change in film thickness; in other words the principal electron producing layer was less than 150×10^{-8} cm. thick which is again consistent with the above estimates.

Another important and interesting experiment has been undertaken by Abroyan and Movnin[136]. They have shown that electron-electron emission yields from an oxide cathode can be increased by as much as 5000 times due to bombardment with hydrogen, helium, argon or potassium ions. The authors explain this effect as due to donor-type displacement defects which are formed by the retardation of the fast ions in the oxide cathode material.

The preceding brief survey has dealt only with the major trends in research on secondary electron emission. Much more experimental detail could have been included, but it was considered that this would only obscure the main details of the phenomenon and would make the treatise over long. Single crystal studies are at the moment providing the most interesting information since, from these results, the form of the interatomic potentials can be deduced. It is hoped that further work in this field will throw much additional light on the phenomenon of atom-atom collision processes and, from potential ejection studies, the electron state density functions of various materials.

REFERENCES

1. Villard, M. P. (1889) Journal de Phys. **8**, 5
2. Rutherford, E. (1905) Phil. Mag. **10**, 193
3. Thomson, J. J. (1905) Proc. Camb. Phil. Soc. **13**, 49
4. Logeman, W. H. (1907) Proc. Roy. Soc. A **78**, 212
5. Devienne, F. M. (1961) Comptes Rendus. Acad. Sci. (Paris) **253**, 1750
6. Utterback, N. G. and Miller, G. H. (1961) Rev. Sci. Instr. **32**, 1101
7. Berry, H. W. (1958) J. Appl. Phys. **29**, 1219
8. Jackson, W. J. (1926) Phys. Rev. **28**, 524
9. Jackson, W. J. (1930) Phys. Rev. **30**, 473
10. Mashkova, E. S., Molchanov, V. A. and Odintsov, D. D. (1963) Dokl. Akad. Nauk. SSSR 151, 1074. English translation in Soviet Physics—Doklady (1964), 806
11. Mashkova, E. S. and Molchanov, V. A. (1964) Fiz. Tver. Tela **6**, 3486. English translation in Soviet Physics-Solid State (1965), **6**, 2792
12. Linford, L. H. (1935) Phys. Rev. **47**, 279
13. Paetow, H. and Walcher, W. (1938) Zeits. f. Physik **110**, 69
14. Koch, J. (1936) Zeits f. Physik **100**, 685
15. Oliphant, M. L. E. (1930) Proc. Roy. Soc. A **127**, 373
16. Veith, H. (1937) Ann. Physik **29**, 189
17. Penning, F. M. (1928) Koninkl. Akad. Amst. Proc. **31**, 14
18. Penning, F. M. (1930) Koninkl. Akad. Amst. Proc. **33**, 841
19. Healea, M. and Houtermans, C. (1940) Phys. Rev. **58**, 608
20. Healea, M. and Chaffee, E. L. (1936) Phys. Rev. **49**, 925
21. Hill, A. G., Buechner, W. W., Clark, J. S. and Fisk, J. B. (1939) Phys. Rev. **55**, 463
22. Schneider, E. G. (1938) Phys. Rev. **54**, 185
23. Pavlov, V. I. and Starodubtsev, S. V. (1937) Zh. Eksper. i teor. fiz. **7**, 409
24. Shekhter, S. S. (1937) Zh. Eksper i teor. fiz. (USSR), **7**, 750
25. Oliphant, M. L. E. and Moon, P. B. (1930) Proc Roy, Soc. A127, 388
26. Hagstrum, H. D. (1954) Phys. Rev. **96**, 336
27. Massey, H. S. W. (1930) Proc. Camb. Phil. Soc. **26**, 386
28. Massey, H. S. W. (1931) Proc. Camb. Phil. Soc. **27**, 469
29. Cobas, A. and Lamb, W. E. Jr. (1944) Phys. Rev. **65**, 327
30. Propst, F. M. (1963) Phys. Rev. **129**, 7
31. Harrower, G. A. (1956) Phys. Rev. **104**, 52

31a. Gorodetskii, D. A. (1958) Zh. Eksper. i teor. fiz. (USSR). English translation in Soviet Physics—JETP (1958), **7**, 4

32. Hagstrum, H. D. (1954) Phys. Rev. **96**, 325
33. Takeishi, Y. (1956) J. Phys. Soc. (Japan) **11**, 676
34. Takeishi, Y. (1958) J. Phys. Soc. (Japan) (Notes) **13**, 766
35. Becker, A. (1924) Ann. Physik **75**, 217
36. Schneider, G (1931) Ann. Physik **111**, 357
37. Kapitza, P. L. (1923) Phil. Mag. **45**, 989
38. Morgulis, N. D. (1934) Zh. eksper. i teor. fiz. (USSR) **4**, **449**
39. Morgulis, N. D. (1939) Zh. eksper. i teor. fiz. (USSR) **9**, 1484
40. Morgulis, N. D. (1941) Zh. eksper. i teor. fiz. (USSR) **11**, 300
41. Izmailov, S. V. (1939) Zh. eksper. i teor. fiz. (USSR) **9**, 1473
42. Ploch, W. (1951) Zeits. f. Physik **130**, 174
43. Gurtovoy, M. E. (1940) Zh. eksper. i teor. fiz. **10**, 483
44. Parilis, E. S. and Kishinevskii, L. M. (1960) Fiz. tver. tela **3**, 1219. English translation in Soviet Physics-Solid State (1960) **3**, 885
45. Firsov, O. D. (1959) Zh. eksper. i teor. fiz. **36**, 1517. English translation in Soviet Physics—J. E. T. P. (1959) **9**, 1076
46. Tel'kovskii, V. G. (1956) Izv. Akad. Nauk SSSR Ser. fiz. **20**, 1179. English translation in Bulletin Acad. Sci. USSR Physics Series (1956) **20**, 1070
47. Kishinevskii, L. M. and Parilis, E. S. (1962) Izv. Akad. Nauk (SSSR) Ser fiz. **26**, 1409. English translation in Bulletin Acad.Sci. (USSR) Physics Series (1963) 26, 1432
48. Arifov, U. A., Rakhimov, R. R. and Khozinskii, O. V. (1962) Izv. Akad. Nauk (SSSR) Ser. fiz. **26**, 1398. English translation in Bulletin Acad. Sci. (USSR) Physics Series (1963) **26**, 1422
49. Aarset, B., Cloud, R. W. and Trump, J. G. (1954) J. Appl. Phys. **25**, 1365
50. Bourne, and Cloud, R. W. (1955) J. Appl. Phys. **28**, 596
51. Akishin, A. I. and Vasil'ev, S. S., (1959) Fiz. tver. tela **1**, 833. English translation in Soviet Physics-Solid State (1959) **1**, 755
52. Arifov, U. A. and Rakhimov, R. R. (1958) Izv. Akad. Nauk (UzSSR) ser fiz-mat nauk **6**, 49
53. Petrov, N. N. (1959) Fiz. tver. tela **2**, 949. English translation in Soviet Physics-Solid State (1960) **2**, 865
54. Waters, P. M. (1958) Phys. Rev. 111, 1053
55. Izmailov, S. V. (1959) Fiz. tver. tela **1**, 1546. English translation in Soviet Physics-Solid State (1960) **1**, 1415
56. Izmailov, S. V. (1959) Fiz. tver. tela **1**, 1557. English translation in Soviet Physics-Solid State (1960) **1**, 1425
57. Izmailov, S. V. (1962) Fiz. tver. tela **3**, 2804. English translation in Soviet Physics-Solid State (1962) **3**, 2046
58. Sternglass, E. J. (1957) Phys. Rev. 108, 1
59. Ghosh, S. N. and Khare, S. P. (1962) Phys. Rev. 125, 1254.
60. Bethe, H. A. (1930) Ann. Physik **5**, 325
61. Carlston, C. E., Magnuson, G. D., Mahadevan, P., and Harrison, D. E. Jr. (1965) Phys. Rev. 139A, 729
62. Magnuson, G. D. and Carlston, C. E. (1963) Phys. Rev. **129**, 2409
63. Fagot, B. and Fert, C. (1964) Comptes Rendus Acad. Sc. (Paris) **258**, 1180
64. Fagot, B. and Fert, C. (1964) Comptes Rendus Acad. Sc. (Paris) **258**, 6670

64a. Fagot, B., Colombie, N. and Fert, C. (1965) Comptes Rendus Acad. Sc. (Paris) **261**, 2855

64b. Fagot, B., Colombie, N., Thiry, R. and Fert, C. (1966) Comptes Rendus Acad. Sc. (Paris) **262**, 173

65. Molchanov, V. A., Tel'kovskii, V. G. and Chicherov, V. M. (1961) Dokl. Akad. Nauk SSSR **137**, 58. English translation in Soviet Physics-Doklady (1961) **6**, 222
66. Mashkova, E. S., Molchanov, V. A. and Odintsov, D. D. (1963) Fiz. tver. tela **5**, 3426. English translation in Soviet Physics-Solid State (1964) **5**, 2516
67. Mashkova, E. S. and Molchanov, V. A. (1965) Zh. tekh. fiz. **35**, 575. English translation in Soviet Physics-Tech. Phys. (1965) **10**, 449
68. Harrison, D. E. Jr., Carlston, G. E. and Magnuson, G. D. (1965) Phys. Rev. 139A, 737

69. Russek, A. (1963) Phys. Rev. **132**, 246

70. Everhart, E. (1965) Bull. Am. Phys. Soc. **10**, 96

71. Everhart, E. and Kessel, Q. C. (1965) Phys. Rev. Letters **14**, 247

72. Kessel, Q., Russek, A. and Everhart, E. (1965) Phys. Rev. Letters **14**, 484

73. Greene, D. (1950) Proc. Phys. Soc. B **63**, 876

74. Hagstrum, H. D. (1956) Phys. Rev. **104**, 672

75. Hagstrum, H. D. (1960) Phys. Rev. **119**, 940

76. Hagstrum, H. D. (1953) Phys. Rev. **89**, 244

77. Hagstrum, H. D. (1953) Phys. Rev. **91**, 543

78. Hagstrum, H. D. (1956) Phys. Rev. **104**, 309

79. Hagstrum, H. D. (1960) J. Appl. Phys. **31**, 897

80. Hagstrum, H. D. (1953) Rev. Sci. Instr. **24**, 1122

81. Arifov, U. A. (1961) 'Vzaimodeistvie Atomnykh Chastits s Poverkhnost'yu Metalla', Izdatel'stvo Akademii Nauk Uzbekskoi SSR. Tashkent. English translation: 'Interaction of Atomic Particles with the Surface of a Metal', U. S. Joint Publications Research Service, U. S. Atomic Energy Commission, Washington D. C. AEC-tr-6089 (1963)

82. Brunnée, C. (1957) Zeits f. Physik. **147**, 161.

83. Tel'kovskii, V. G. (1956) Dokl. Akad. Nauk SSSR **108**, 444. English translation in Soviet Physics-Doklady (1957) **1**, 334

84. Tel'kovskii, V. G. (1959) Dissertation, Moscow

85. Mahadevan, P., Magnuson, G. D., Layton, J. K. and Carlston, C. E. (1965) Phys. Rev. **140A**, 1407

86. Hasted, J. B. (1959) J. Appl. Phys. **30**, 22

87. Arifov, U. A. and Rakhimov, R. R. (1960) Izv. Akad. Nauk. SSSR ser. fiz. **24**, 657. English translation in Bull. Acad. Sci. (USSR) Physics Series (1961) **24**, 666

88. Arifov, U. A. and Tashkanova, D. A. (1960) Izv. Akad. Nauk SSSR ser fiz. **24**, 664. English translation in Bull. Acad. Sci. USSR Physics Series (1961) **24**, 673

89. Hagstrum, H. D. (1956) Phys. Rev. **104**, 1516

90. Devienne, F. M., Roustan, J. C. and Souquet, J. (1964) Comptes Rendus Acad. Sc. (Paris) **258**, 140

91. Propst, F. M. and Lüscher, E. (1963) Phys. Rev. **132**, 1037

92. Hagstrum, H. D. and D'Amico, C. (1960) J. Appl. Phys. **31**, 715

93. Hall, R. F. and Weston, G. F. (1963) J. Sci. Instr. **40**, 573

94. Parker, J. H. Jr. (1954) Phys. Rev. **93**, 1148

94a. Hagstrum, H. D. (1961) J. Appl. Phys. **32**, 1015

94b. Arifov, U. A. and Rakhimov, R. R. (1958) Izv. Akad. Nauk. Uz SSR **12**, 15

95. Dorozhkin, A. A. and Petrov, N. N. (1965) Fiz. tver. tela **7**, 118. English translation in Soviet Physics-Solid State (1965) **7**, 88

96. Eremeev, M. A. and Petrov, N. N. (1956) Problemy Sovremennoi Fiziki **9**, 133

97. Takeishi, Y. and Hagstrum, H. D. (1965) Surface Sci. **3**, 175

98. Takeishi, Y. and Hagstrum, H. D. (1965) Phys. Rev. **137A**, 641

99. Hagstrum, H. D., Takeishi, Y. and Pretzer, D. D. (1965) Phys. Rev. **139A**, 526

100. Hagstrum, H. D. (1961) Phys. Rev. **122**, 83

101. Medved, D. B., Mahadevan, P. and Layton, J. K. (1963) Phys. Rev. **129**, 2086

102. Chambers, E. S. (1964) Phys. Rev. **133A**, 1202

103. Bethge, K. and Lexa, P. (1966) Brit. J. Appl. Phys. **17**, 181

104. Arifov, U. A., Rakhimov, R. R. and Dzhurakulov, Kh. (1962) Dokl. Akad. Nauk (SSSR) **143**, 309. English translation in Soviet Physics-Doklady (1962) **7**, 209

105. Mahadevan, P., Layton, J. K., Comeaux, A. R. and Medved, D. B. (1963) J. Appl. Phys. **34**, 2810

106. Petersen, J. R. (1965) J. Appl. Phys. (Comm) **36**, 652

107. Mahadevan, P. and Marriott, R. (1965) J. Appl. Phys. (Comm.) **36**, 863

108. Petrov, N. N. (1962) Izv. Akad. Nauk (SSSR) ser. fiz. **26**, 1327. English translation in Bull. Acad. Sci. (USSR) Physics Series (1963) **26**, 1350

109. Fogel, Ya. M., Slabospitskii, R. P. and Rastrepin, A. B. (1960) Zh. tekhn. fiz. **30**, 63. English translation in Soviet Physics-Tech. Phys. (1960) **5**, 58

110. Batanov, G. M. (1960) Fiz. tver. tela **2**, 2048. English translation in Soviet Physics-Solid State (1961) **2**, 1839

111. Batanov, G. M. (1962) Fiz. tver. tela **4**, 1778. English translation in Soviet Physics-Solid State (1963) **4**, 1306

112. Batanov, G. M. (1961) Fiz. tver. tela **3**, 558. English translation in Soviet Physics-Solid State (1961) **3**, 409

113. Petrov, N. N. and Dorozhkin, A. A. (1961) Fiz. tver. tela **3**, 53. English translation in Soviet Physics-Solid State (1961) **3**, 38

114. Mahadevan, P., Layton, J. K. and Medved, D. B. (1963) Phys. Rev. **129**, 79

115. Medved, D. B., Mahadevan, P. and Layton, J. K. (1963) Phys. Rev. **129**, 2086

116. Bosch, S. H. and Kuskevics, G. (1964) Phys. Rev. **134A**, 1357

117. Abroyan, I. A. (1961) Fiz. tver. tela **3**, 588. English translation in Soviet Physics-Solid State (1961) **3**, 431

118. Batanov, G. M. and Petrov, N. N. (1959) Fiz. tver. tela **1**, 1856. English translation in Soviet Physics-Solid State (1960) **1**, 1701

119. Large, L. N. (1963) Proc. Phys. Soc. **81**, 1101

120. Ewing, R. I. (1965) Phys. Rev. **139A**, 1840

121. Whaling, W. (1958) Handbuch. der. Physik **34**, 193

122. Daly, N. R. and Powell, R. E. (1964) Proc. Phys. Soc. **84**, 595

123. Arifov, U. A., Rakhimov, R. R., Abdullaeva, M. and Gaipov, S. (1962) Izv. Akad. Nauk SSSR ser. fiz. **26**, 1403. English translation in Bull. Acad. Sci. USSR Physics Series (1963) **26**, 1427

124. Krebs, K. H. von (1965) Ann. Physik **15**, 111

125. Large, L. N. (1963) Proc. Phys. Soc **81**, 175

126. Allen, J. S. (1939) Phys. Rev. **55**, 336

127. Bosch, S. H. (1965) Phys. Rev. **137A**, 255

128. Zscheile, H. (1965) Phys. Status Solidi **11**, 159

129. Kaminsky, M. and Goodwin, G. (1965) 25th Annual Conf. on Physical Electronics M. I. T. p 213

130. Sugiura, T. (1961) Bull. Chem. Soc. (Japan) **34**, 1475

131. Snoek, C., Weg, W. F. van der, Geballe, R. and Rol, P. K. (1965) F. O. M. Laboratories Report. Amsterdam

132. Moroz, L. P. and Ayukhanov, A. Kh. (1962) Izv. Akad. Nauk (SSSR) ser. fiz. **26**, 1322. English translation in Bull. Acad. Sci. (USSR) Physics Series (1963) **26**, 1345

133. Gomoyunova, M. V. (1959) Fiz. tver. tela. **1**, 315. English translation in Soviet Physics-Solid State (1959) **1**, 329

134. Sternglass, E. J. and Wachtel, M. M. (1955) Phys. Rev. **99**, 646

135. Zarutskii, E. M. (1964) Fiz. tver. tela. **6**, 3734. English translation in Soviet Physics-Solid State (1965) **6**, 2995

136. Abroyan, I. A. and Movnin, S. M. (1961) Fiz. tver. tela **3**, 567. English translation in Soviet Physics-Solid State (1961) **3**, 416

137. Dunaev, Yu. A. and Flaks, I. P. (1953) Dokl. Akad. Nauk **91**, 43

138. Hagstrum, H. D. (1956) Phys. Rev. **104**, 317

139. Petrov, N. N. (1960) Izv. Akad. Nauk (SSSR) ser. fiz. 24, 673. English translation in Bull. Acad. Sci. (USSR) Physics Series (1960) **24**, 682

140. Healea, M. (1939) Phys. Rev. **55**, 984

141. Waters, P. M. (1958) Phys. Rev. **109**, 1466

142. Magnuson, G. D. and Carlston, C. E. (1963) Phys. Rev. **129**, 2403

143. Varnerin, L. J. (1953) Phys. Rev. **91**, 859

144. Petrov, N. N. (1960) Fiz. tver. tela **2**, 1182. English translation in Soviet Physics-Solid State (1960) **2**, 857

145. Eremeev, M. A. (1951) Dokl. Akad. Nauk (SSSR) **79**, 775

146. Eremeev, M. A. and Shestukhina, V. V. (1952) Zh. tekhn. fiz. (SSSR) **22**, 1262

CHAPTER 4

Ionic Emission

4.1 INTRODUCTION

In the preceding chapter we saw that bombardment of a surface by positive ions caused ejection of electrons; the so-called secondary emission process. It is clear that these electrons are not the only charged species liberated by the bombardment and that, under suitable conditions, (1) ions of the incident beam may be reflected without neutralization, (this process is generally called Ion Reflection or Scattering) (2) ionized species of the target atoms may be liberated, and (3) species characteristic of gaseous impurity atoms adsorbed on the surface of the targets can be ejected as ions.

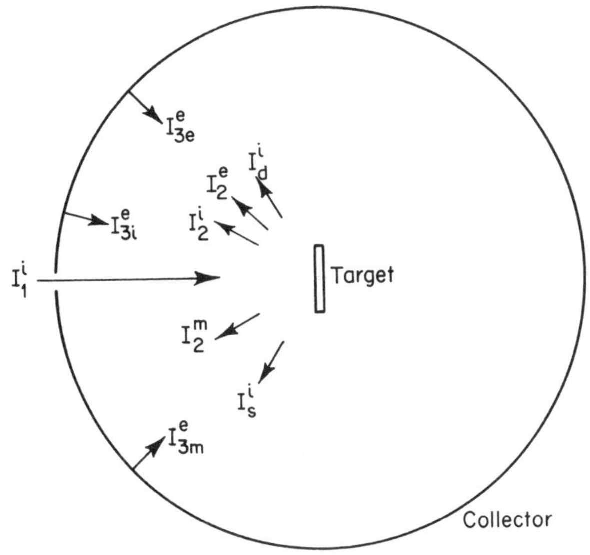

Fig. 4.1 Illustrating possible secondary and tertiary emission currents in a conventional target and collector assembly (Symbols are defined in the text).

Fig. 4.1 is a schematic diagram representing the target and collector system and indicating the secondary and tertiary emissions which must be considered. Referring to the figure, we see that the incident ion beam (I_1^i) can give rise to ionic secondary species which may be either positively or negatively charged and arise from pure ion reflection (I_2^i), ejection of sorbed species as ions (I_d^i), or, sputtering of target species as ions (I_s^i). In addition to these are metastable secondaries (I_2^m) and secondary electrons (I_2^e). All these secondary beams are able to produce tertiary electron currents on neutralization at the collector surface $I_{3e}^e, I_{3i}^e, I_{3m}^e$ and, of course, further tertiary emission of ionic species is possible but is generally very small and can be neglected. Hagstrum[1] has shown that, by appropriate choice of experimental conditions, certain of the currents enumerated above can be suppressed so that the total currents comprise

$$I_T = I_1^i - I_2^i - I_{3m}^e \qquad 4.1$$

and

$$I_C = I_2^i + I_{3i}^e + I_{3m}^e \qquad 4.2$$

(where the collector is negative with respect to the target).

Many authors have taken the ratio of collector current to target current and presented the answer as a reflection coefficient

$$R = \frac{I_C}{I_T} \qquad 4.3$$

However, the preceding equations illustrate that this is not a true reflection coefficient so we will hereafter adopt the terminology of Kaminsky[2] and refer to 'R' as the 'secondary emission coefficient'. The term 'reflection coefficient' is clearly defined by

$$\rho = \frac{I_2^i}{I_1^i} \qquad 4.4$$

and can be related to R by

$$R = \rho + \gamma_2 \cdot \rho + y_m \cdot \rho_m \qquad 4.5$$

where

$\gamma_2 = I_{3_i}^{\ e}/I_2^i$ is the secondary electron coefficient for reflected ions striking the collector, $\gamma_m = I_{3m}^e/I_2^m$ the same coefficient for secondary metastables striking the collector and $\rho_m = I_2^m/I_2^i$ the conversion coefficient for the transfer of secondary ions to metastable atoms.

Coefficients of secondary ion emission are generally small (of the order 10^{-2} ion/ion) though Arifov et al[3] found values for alkali ion bombardment of heated targets approaching 0.3 and, at energies below 50 eV, scattering coefficients approached 100%. However corrections to recorded ion currents due to ionic emission can usually be ignored. It is apparent that the principal reason for studying this phenomenon in detail was, initially, that it was an event accompanying the more useful aspects of ion bombardment such as electron emission and sputtering and that it represented a fundamental research problem. However recent research has shown that analysis of the secondary ions produced during bombardment can yield information of the species present at the target surface; in other words a qualitative chemical analysis is possible. Further, there is now little doubt that the majority of negative ions which are liberated during positive ion bombardment originate from gases adsorbed on the target surface so that an analysis of these can yield information not only on the surface cleanliness of the target, but also on the nature of the gases which are causing the contamination. Of course, electron emission coefficients are the most sensitive surface coverage monitors, but these can only indicate whether the surface is clean or not clean so that secondary ion studies are more descriptive in this context.

Another associated phenomenon is the emission of photons by excited atoms during ion bombardment. This process is perhaps to be expected as it represents the group of secondaries which have either not quite reached, or, reach only temporarily, their ionized state during the exchanges leading to emission. The excited atoms or ions liberate their characteristic emission line as they decay again to the ground state so that identification is relatively simple.

4.2 EARLY RESEARCH

Very little data concerning ionic emission was presented in the literature before 1950. Early work by Klein[4] on secondary electron and ion emission from nickel bombarded by 0-500 eV Na^+ and K^+ ions showed that negative ions were ejected and that there were two distinct groups, one having energies up to 2 eV and the other with energies close to the primary ion energy. Arnold and Beckett[5] described 'A New Process of Negative Ion Formation' in 1938. In this work they mass-analyzed the species ejected during bombardment of tungsten by A^+, N^+ and Hg^+ ions.

The liberated ions were found to include C^-, O^-, $C_3H_2^-$, CO_2^- and various other combinations of C, O and H which were clearly representative of background gases in the experimental chamber and were presumably adsorbed on the tungsten surface. Similar results were presented by Sloane and Press[6] who also attributed the presence of negative ions to the presence of an adsorbed gas film. In addition to C and H combinations in the emitted ion spectrum (which included some positive ions CO^+ and C_3H^+) less intense peaks of Ni^- and Cr^- were observed. Overall yields were in the region 10^{-4}-10^{-3} ions/ion and ejection energies were seen to be fairly high. For example, the energies of CO^- species ejected from Ni by Hg^+ bombardment at 2.57 keV ranged up to 30 eV. In later work Sloane et al[7] observed peaks in the secondary spectrum corresponding to Li_6^- and Li_7^- due to bombardment of nickel by Li^+ ions. The peaks were found to be in the ratio 1 to 10 respectively which was as expected for the relative abundancies of the lithium isotopes. This work showed results basically different to those of Sloane and Press[6] as it was the incident particle rather than an adsorbed molecular species that was reflected as the negative ion. This process, where the incident ion species was reflected as a negative ion, was also observed by Arnot and Milligan[8].

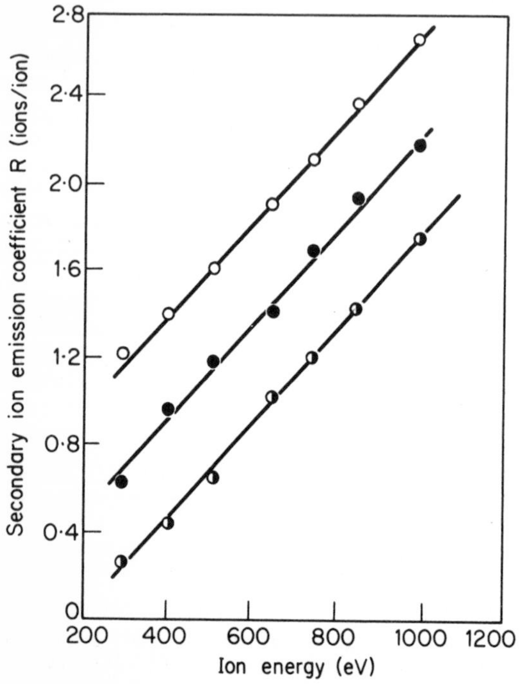

Fig. 4.2 Secondary ion emission coefficient as a function of incident ion energy for Cs^+ ion bombardment of a clean (●), oxygen covered (○) and cesium contaminated (◑) tungsten surface. (Ref. 4.12)

Chaudri and Khan[9], whilst determining secondary electron emission from nickel and molybdenum targets bombarded by neutral species of Hg and K, observed emission of secondary electrons from neighbouring electrodes and concluded these were liberated by scattered primary atoms impinging on these surfaces. It was found that the scattering coefficient for mercury increased as the molybdenum target became contaminated whilst the coefficient for potassium decreased. Presumably this discrepancy was connected with the new collision parameters as atoms of mass different to molybdenum proceeded to cover its surface. This surface dependence was observed by Oliphant[10], who found that the secondary ion emission coefficient for K^+ bombardment of molybdenum or nickel surfaces increased from 0.01 to 0.03 ion/ion when the residual gas was allowed to contaminate the target surfaces, Koch,[11] who observed the change in ion emission as a tungsten target became contaminated with the Cs^+ ion species bombarding it and found that the secondary ion coefficient decreased to 0.12 at a coverage of 0.1 monolayer and Paetow and Walcher[12], who carefully controlled the contamination of a tungsten target and observed the change in the curve of ion reflection coefficient R as a function of energy. The curves were found to be essentially linear for cesium ion bombardment in the range of energies studied (200-1200 eV) as indicated in Fig. 4.2. The curve for an oxygen-covered tungsten surface was seen to lie parallel to and above the R versus E_0 curve for clean tungsten whilst the curve after bombardment of a clean target (i.e. for a cesiated surface) was seen to lie parallel to and below the clean tungsten curve. Paetow and Walcher concluded that the change in work function of the surface was the main factor governing ion reflection from a contaminated target.

A linear dependence of ion reflection coefficient on incident ion energy was observed by Healea and Houtermans[13] who studied 400-1400 eV He^+, Ne^+ and A^+ bombardment of a heated nickel target. These results further showed that the secondary emission coefficient R decreased as the ion mass increased

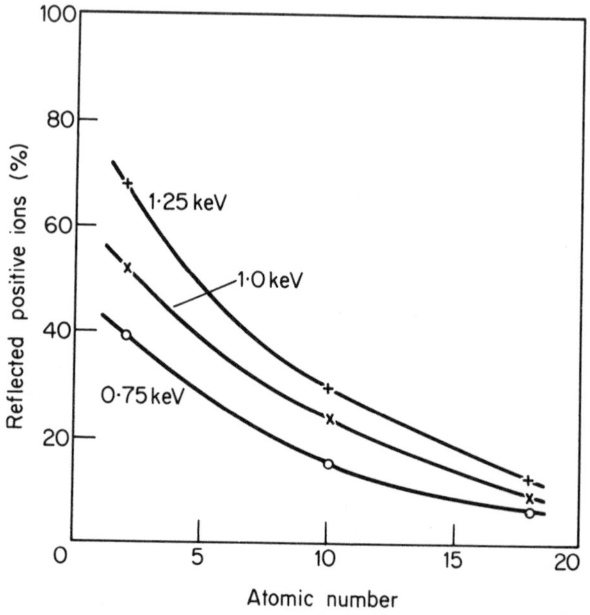

Fig. 4.3 Variation of secondary emission coefficient with incident ion mass for noble gas ions on nickel (Ref. 4.13)

(Fig. 4. 3.). Actual magnitudes for R obtained in this work were however exceptionally large and contamination is suspected even though the nickel target had been outgassed for two months prior to the experiment.

The early research has thus indicated many useful trends, especially the importance of target cleanliness for observations of reflection phenomena. It is not clear however from most of these early papers what fraction of the ionic emission can be ascribed to pure reflection of the incident beam and the contribution of other currents represented in Fig. 4. 1. We shall attempt to distinguish these components in the following review of recent research and shall first consider the rather sparse data on emission of excited particles and photons.

4. 3 EXCITED ATOM EMISSION

The phenomenon of the emission of excited atoms during the bombardment of metal targets with energetic alkali metal ions was first recorded by Mayer[14] who showed that the emission would only occur when the target was covered by an alkali-metal film. Sporn[15] studied the decay of radiation intensity with distance from the target surface and, by assuming that the particles all had the same initial velocity, was able to determine the average ejection energies of the particles. In fact the ejected particles have a wide spectrum of energies as will be seen in Chapter 7 so that the values obtained by Sporn were subject to large error.

Stuart and Wehner[16] have devised a sensitive detector for observing ejected particles which is based on the emission of characteristic radiation from the excited atoms as they pass through an observation region. However it is doubtful whether any of these atoms were actually liberated from the target in an excited state as the discharge conditions near the target would make excitation of all the ejected particles most probable. Consequently it is not possible to obtain useful information on excited atom emission from this work. Fluit et al[17] bombarded copper and aluminium surfaces with 10-15 keV Ne^+, A^+ and Cu^+ ions and attempted to detect secondary metastable particles by recording the secondary electron emission from a copper collector plate. This current was assumed to result from de-excitation of the metastable atoms which caused Auger emission of electrons from the copper plate. In later work with an improved detector however Kistemaker and Snoek[18] discovered that the ejected particles had much higher energies than the ten electronvolts or so which had been anticipated; in fact energies as high as several kiloelectronvolts for the ejected species were apparent. These particles may have been reflected atoms of the incident beam, or even sputtered species. In any event their energy was sufficient to cause appreciable kinetic emission from the copper detector so that the existence of ejected metastables could not be verified. Kistemaker and Snoek were however able to produce evidence for the existence of excited components in the secondary beam by detecting photon emission of wavelength characteristic of the decay of these excited particles to a lower electronic state. The studies were carried out in an isotope separator so that there was no question of the ejected particles becoming excited after emission as was the case in Wehner's discharge apparatus. Monocrystalline aluminium and copper, and polycrystalline copper targets were bombarded by 10-15 keV Ne^+ and A^+ ions, and the emitted light was detected by a grating monochromator and photo-multiplier capable of studying emissions of wavelength 2000-6000 Å.

The optical axis of the spectrograph and the direction of the ion beam were fixed relative to each other at 90°. Consequently for bombardment near normal the photon emission was viewed along a line parallel to the target surface. Kistemaker et al were able to observe photon emission at these near-grazing angles and concluded therefore that the emission was occurring a small distance above the surface. The emitted spectra indicated that de-excitation of both excited copper atoms and excited ions was occurring, with the former providing the dominant emission (Cu 1 spectra) whilst only de-excitation of excited ions of the bombarding species could be detected. The light intensity of the Cu 1 lines were seen to be closely related to the sputtering yield since the intensity for bombardment by A^+ was approximately twice that obtained during Ne^+ bombardment, that is, in a similar ratio to the sputtering yields (see Chapter 7). Furthermore, when the surface of a (100) copper target was rotated about a ⟨100⟩ axis in the crystal surface the intensity of emission varied in a similar manner to that obtained during sputtering with a pronounced minimum at 45°, as shown in Fig. 4. 4.

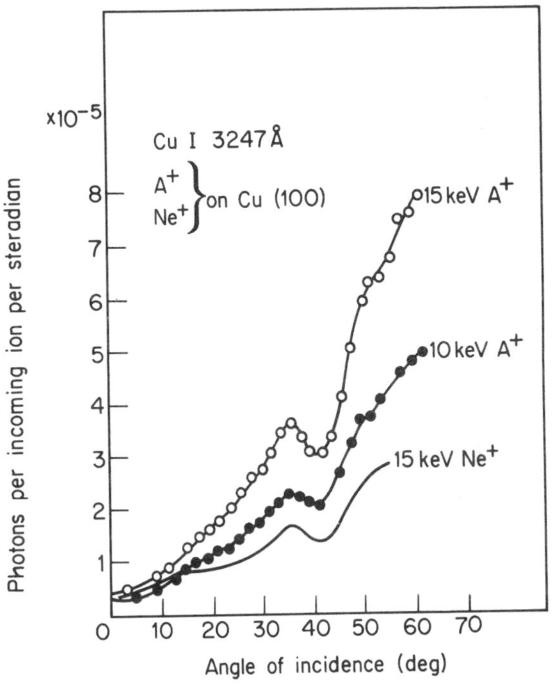

Fig. 4. 4 Excited atom emission intensity (Cu 1 line) as a function of the angle of incidence of Ne^+ and A^+ ions on a (100) surface of copper. (Ref. 4. 18)

For polycrystalline targets the intensity of emission of the Cu 1 spectra was seen to vary with the angle of incidence in the manner

$$I_\theta = I_0 \frac{4 - 3\cos\theta}{\cos\theta} \qquad 4.6$$

whereas the corresponding variation of sputtering yield with θ (the angle between the incident beam and the normal to the target) was seen to be

$$I_\theta = I_0 \frac{2 - \cos\theta}{\cos\theta} \qquad 4.7$$

This is a surprising result and may in fact be due to an experimental shortcoming since for larger angles of incidence the detector was approaching a near normal position so that it may have received photons reflected from the target surface, this would make the apparent dependence on θ stronger for photon emission.

Further experiments by Snoek et al[19] for 60 keV A^+ bombardment of copper confirmed that the photon emission occurred slightly above the target, its intensity dropping to 1/e at a distance 0. 25-0. 35 mm. from the surface. As the mean lifetime of excited copper atoms is 0.5×10^{-8} sec. Snoek et al concluded that the mean velocity of the ejected species in a direction perpendicular to the target was 6×10^6 cm/sec. This velocity is consistent with the value anticipated if the mechanism of ejection comprised simple two-atom collisions, the incident ion striking the target atom as if it were isolated from its neighbours.

Snoek et al further showed that the photon emission for a Cu_2O target was higher than for the clean Cu surface, but a full study of this has not yet been published.

Veksler[20] studied the emission of excited cesium atoms which were produced by the bombardment of a molybdenum ribbon by 0. 56-2. 5 keV Cs^+ ions. The emission was recorded photographically, each exposure covering a bombardment of 5×10^{-6} A for 40 minutes. The camera was positioned to view the surface of the target and the region above it from one end of the ribbon, i.e. the objective axis and the long target axis were coincident. The ions approached the target in a plane at right-angles to the ribbon (broadside) and struck the surface at 60° to the normal. The negatives obtained showed darkened elliptical shapes which corresponded to the regions in which secondary excited atoms were returning to their ground state. Veksler was able to calculate from the variations in intensity across these elliptical shapes in eight chosen directions the distribution of excited atoms as a function of ejected angle ϕ (ϕ is the angle with respect to the target surface) and also the r.m.s. values of velocity of the excited atoms as a function of ϕ. (see Figs. 4. 5. and 4. 6.) Veksler contradicts the assertion of Mayer [14] that a layer of adsorbed cesium atoms is necessary before excitation is possible since, in his experiments the emission was observed immediately after flashing the target to 2100°K, that

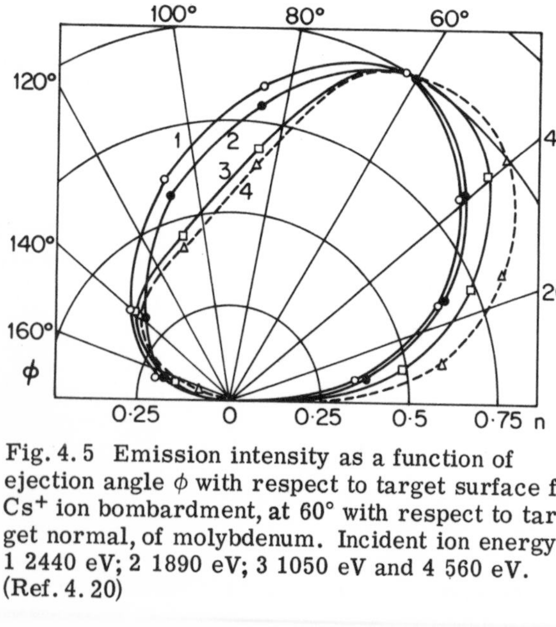

Fig. 4. 5 Emission intensity as a function of ejection angle ϕ with respect to target surface for Cs^+ ion bombardment, at 60° with respect to target normal, of molybdenum. Incident ion energy 1 2440 eV; 2 1890 eV; 3 1050 eV and 4 560 eV. (Ref. 4. 20)

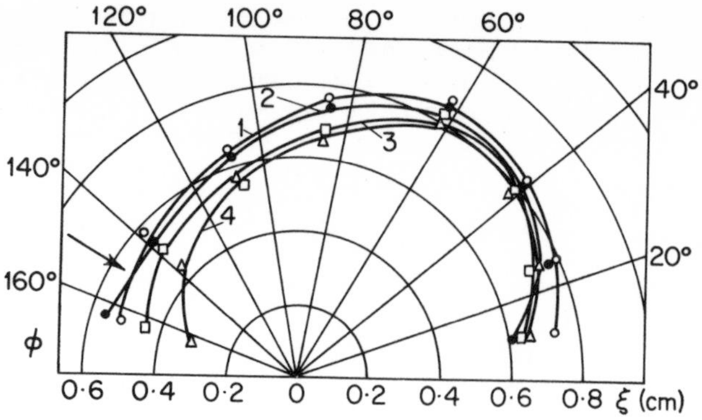

Fig. 4. 6 Ejected atom r.m.s. velocities (proportional to parameter ξ) as a function of ejection angle ϕ with respect to the target surface for Cs^+ ion bombardment of molybdenum at 60° with respect to the target normal. Incident energy 1) 2440 eV; 2) 1890 eV; 3) 1050 eV and 4) 560 eV. (Ref. 4. 20)

is, before an appreciable quantity of cesium could have been adsorbed. However he does show that the ejected atoms were not reflected, but accommodated on the surface and re-liberated by a sputtering process. For example Fig. 4. 6. shows that the velocity distribution of ejected particles is only slightly dependent upon the primary ion energy which, Veksler suggests, indicates that the secondaries in question were sputtered from the surface rather than scattered since, for scattering, energies have been found to increase almost proportionally with the incident ion energy [21 22]. Certain other features of the distributions in Figs. 4. 5. and 4. 6. were shown by Veksler to be similar to those anticipated for sputtering rather than direct reflection of the cesium beam.

Photon emission produced when low energy ions strike a metal surface has been observed by Böhmer and Lüscher[23] for 25-100 eV Ne^+ and He^+ bombardment of well-degassed tungsten surfaces. It is not clear whether these results represent emission from ejected species or from decay of the incident ion as it approaches the surface. Photon energies were found to cover a wide range with 10% having values between 4 and 6. 5 eV and the remaining 90% energies in excess of 6. 5 eV. The logarithm of intensity was seen to be a linear function of ion energy and the yield for Ne^+ under given conditions less than half the corresponding yield during He^+ bombardment. Results obtained by Böhmer and Lüscher indicated photon yields several orders of magnitude higher than those predicted by Sternberg[24] for a 10 eV He^+ ion approaching a metal surface. Sternberg's value indicated that one He^+ ion in 10^4 should photo-emit, and this prediction is again several orders of magnitude higher than that of Shekhter[25] who predicted one emission per 10^7-10^8 He^+ ions. The discrepancy in results and theory would suggest that Böhmer and Lüscher were in fact observing emission from excited reflected species as well as the chance emission which occurs as the ions approach the surface. The theoretical calculations only apply to the latter component and will therefore be expected to be smaller.

4.4 CHARGED PARTICLE EMISSION; QUALITATIVE STUDIES

We discuss here experiments designed to distinguish qualitatively the many types of ion which are liberated during ion bombardment rather than to determine absolute magnitudes of emission. In Chapter 9 dealing with applications of ion bombardment we see that such studies yield much useful data on the state and composition of the target surface, but up to the present time only qualitative results can be relied upon. For example Castaing and Soldzian[26] have bombarded a copper-aluminium alloy having 5% aluminium with 20 keV H^+ and A^+ ions and found that the ionic emission of copper is seven times the magnitude of emission from a pure copper target whilst the emission of aluminium ions is only one half the emission from a pure aluminium target. Bradley[27] has found a similar situation during bombardment of platinum where the Pt^+ peak was found to have comparable magnitude to the Ca^+ peak, the latter representing an impurity present in a quantity less than 1 part in 100, 000. Until new techniques are discovered therefore we can disregard any magnitude of the various secondary species and concentrate solely on qualitative data, i.e. whether a given mass peak exists or not.

The difficulties encountered when using sputtering of secondary ions as a quantitative measuring device were further demonstrated by Honig[28] who bombarded a twinned Ge-Si crystal (11% Si by density) with noble gas ions of various energies from 100-400 eV. Some of the typical ejected species are shown in Table 4. 1.

TABLE 4. 1

Ionic species ejected from a twinned Ge-Si (89-11) crystal by rare gas ions A^+, Kr^+ and Xe^+ at energies 100-400 eV. (Ref. 4. 28)

Na^+	Al^+	Si^+	Ge^+	K^+	$GeSi^+$	Ge_2^+
—	—	SiH^+	GeH^+	—	—	—
—	—	$SiOH^+$	$GeOH^+$	—	—	—
—	—	—	—	—	$GeSiO^+$	Ge_2O^+

The ratio of the peaks Si_1^+/Ge_1^+ was investigated and found to have a value of approximately 6% for bombarding energies of 100 eV. However this ratio increased almost linearly with energy to a value near 20% at 400 eV. For bombardment of silver by 300-400 eV Xe^+ ions Honig was able to detect masses corresponding to Ag_1^+, Ag_2^+, Ag_3^+, Ag_2O^-, Ag_2^- and AgO_2^- representing species characteristic of the target and Xe^+ and Xe^{++} peaks characteristic of the bombarding ion. He points out that the bombarding current intensity in these experiments was insufficient for maintaining a clean surface, a fact which was apparent from the full spectrum of secondary species which contained many hydrocarbons, especially in the negative ion spectrum.

In later work Honig[29] again bombarded germanium targets but this time after the surfaces had undergone an ethylation treatment before the 400 eV A^+ bombardment. The secondary positive ion species characteristic of the clean germanium surface (Ge^+, $GeOH^+$, Ge_2^+, Ge_2O^+) were found to be present in the spectra for the ethylated germanium samples together with many $C_2H_x^+$ species indicative of the ethyl radicals on the treated surface. In the negative ion spectrum the only observed species characteristic of the surface was GeO_2^-. Other species, all of which were due to impurities, were F^-, Cl^-, O^- and plain carbon groups of C_1^- to C_6^-. It was noted that the carbon group had alternating intensities, the even numbered groups (C_2^-, C_4^-, C_6^-) having the higher yields. This is explained by Pitzer and Clementi[30] as being due to the fact that even-numbered neutral species can accommodate the extra electron in a half-filled bonding π-orbital while odd-numbered carbon groups cannot.

This pattern of C_x^- emission was observed for other targets by Honig and appears to be a characteristic feature of carbon-containing surfaces. Other principal species detected by Honig during bombardment of graphite, coal, silver and diamond are presented in Table 4. 2.

A further interesting experiment using the silicon carbide target showed the variation of intensity of certain characteristic secondary negative ion species with incident ion energy[31]. It was found that the peaks characteristic of sorbed gases or surface impurities (O^-, F^-, C_2H^-) decreased as the ion energy increased whilst species representative of the bulk increased with ion energy. This is to be expected since the ion penetration increases with energy so that bulk atoms

TABLE 4. 2

Ionic species ejected from graphite, coal, silicon-carbide and diamond during positive ion bombardment at 400-600 eV energy. (Ref. 4. 29)

Positive Ions

Target										
Graphite	Na^+	K^+	C—H^+ combinations							
Coal	Na^+	K^+	C—H^+ combinations							
SiC	C^+	Si^+	SiH^+	SiO^+	$SiOH^+$	SiC_2H^+				
	Si_2^+	$Si_2^+OH^+$	Si_xC_γ	$(x = 1, 2, 3, 4; y = 1, 2, 3)$						
Diamond	Na^+	K^+	27	(Al^+)	C^+	O^+	24	(Mg^+ or C_2^+)	C_3^+	C_4^+

Negative Ions

Target									
Graphite	Cl^-	F^-	Br^-	O^-	OH^-	O_2^-	C_{1-10}^-	C—H^-	combinations
Coal	Cl^-	F^-	Br^-	O^-	OH^-	O_2^-	C_{1-10}^-	C—H^-	combinations
SiC	C_{1-9}^-	SiC_{0-7}^-	$Si_2C_{0-3}^-$		O^-	F^-	C_2H^-		
Diamond	C_{1-12}^-								

are involved more and more at higher bombarding energies.

A similar thorough investigation of ejected positive ion species from metal targets has been carried out by Bradley et al[32-35]. Background pressures in these investigations were of the order 10^{-7} Torr and targets were flashed prior to bombardment by an ion beam of several micro-amperes per square centimetre intensity so that results should be representative of clean surfaces. For bombardment of molybdenum, tantalum and platinum targets with rare gas ions of about 500 eV energy the secondary spectrum comprised species characteristic of the particular metal (Mo^+ or Pt^+), alkali metal ions and some compound species (e.g. MoC_2^+, TaN^+, PtO_3^+). There was however no observable molecular species of the target material (Mo_2^+ etc.). Although the vacuum was reasonably satisfactory there was evidence of some oxide formation, detected as MoO_2^+ and $Mo_2O_3^+$. These oxide peaks disappeared on flashing the target to 1800°C, a temperature sufficient to remove oxygen contamination and, at the same time, the Mo^+ peak increased in magnitude. Similarly with a platinum target a peak identified as $PtO(CO)^+$ could be observed which increased with the duration of ion bombardment. Thus it was clear that the bombardment under these conditions produced additional contamination rather than a cleaning action, a point which should be considered in all experiments which rely on bombardment cleaning.

In the same paper Bradley et al[32] were able to observe a secondary Xe^+ ion peak during the Xe^+ ion bombardment which comprised secondaries with very low energies (average < 1 ev) and whose yield could be expressed by an equation of the same form as a Langmuir adsorption equation.[36] Bradley et al concluded that this peak was due to sputtering of adsorbed Xe atoms which were then ionized and emitted as Xe^+. The xenon adsorption was shown to occur only during ion bombardment and is not the usual adsorption described by Langmuir, but rather the process described in Chapter 8. They point out that true Xe^+ reflection may also occur, but this second group would possess much larger energies and would probably escape detection in their apparatus.

A typical record of ionic emission from a copper surface obtained by Ruedl and Bradley[35] is presented in Table 4.3. and shows species characteristic of the incident beam (argon, xenon or nitrogen) both singly and doubly charged, CO^+ impurity, alkali impurities and copper and copper oxide ions. These latter were apparently only formed by decomposition of the oxides on the copper surface so that, unlike the earlier results for molybdenum and platinum, there was no ionic ejection identifiable with the target material. Results for tantalum targets were similar to those for copper in that the parent ion was present only when the surface was contaminated, thus indicating that it originated from a surface impurity rather than the bulk.

TABLE 4.3

Positive ions emitted from copper due to bombardment by Z^+ ions where Z is A^+ Xe^+ or N_2^+. (Ref. 4.35)

Incident species	Z^+	Z^{++}				
Bulk impurities	Na^+	K^+				
Surface species	CO^+	Cu^+	Cu_2^+	CuO^+	Cu_2O^+	CuO_2^+

Further studies of Ta targets have been made by McHugh and Sheffield[37] who observed ejection of Ta^+, Ta_2^+, Ta_3^+ and many oxide combinations during bombardment by mercury ions of energies 0.3-14 keV. Surfaces were frequently cleaned by flashing so that they should not have been contaminated. However the tantalum oxides were obviously present during the bombardment as could be seen from the secondary spectra so that it is not clear whether the Ta^+ peaks originated from decomposition of oxides or not. Hagstrum[38] has demonstrated that tantalum is unusual in that it appears to adsorb its surface impurities on baking and release them to the surface again when cooling so that the presence of oxides in McHugh et al's experiments is most probable. The detection of molecular and triatomic species of the target material by McHugh et al is also unusual and may again indicate that these components originate directly from decomposition of oxides.

An interesting result from the above work was that for bombardment of the tantalum target by a wide range of ions (Ne^+, A^+, Kr^+, Xe^+, N_2^+, CO^+, CO_2^+, Hg^+) at energies from 0.2 to 9 keV there was no evidence of a secondary ion peak corresponding to the incident species, this was true even for bombardment by doubly charged particles. From their results McHugh et al have evaluated a secondary emission coefficient of the order 10^{-3} ions/ion, but the foregoing clearly indicates that this is not a reflection coefficient. Hagstrum[1] has reported reflection coefficients of the same order and has assumed them to be due to ions of the incident beam, but this assumption does not appear to be justified in the light of these results.

Further work on identification of secondary species has been carried out by Fogel et al[39] who bombarded outgassed molybdenum targets with noble gas ions at energies from 5 to 40 keV and obtained the spectrum indicated in Table 4.4.

Veksler and Shuppe[40] found a similar secondary spectrum, but excluding the ions underlined in Table 4.4. for 0-600 eV Hg^+ bombardment of molybdenum and, again, the negative ion spectrum was very similar to that obtained by Mitropan and Gumeniuk[41, 42] for 200-1000 keV hydrogen and deuterium ion bombardment of outgassed, aluminium, stainless steel and copper targets. (Table 4.5.) After outgassing, their results were seen to be dependent on time throughout the first 20 minutes which indicated contamination during this interval and it is clear that these results for negative ion spectra are still very dependent on the surface conditions even at energies near 1 MeV as the spectra are not greatly affected by changing the ion-target combination. Mitropan et al further demonstrated this fact by outgassing their targets more vigorously and noting that the secondary negative emission was decreased. The surface dependence may however be directly related to the change in work function ϕ as the target is cleaned. For example it was demonstrated by Krohn[43] that the yield of negative ions from a copper surface increased after

TABLE 4.4

Charged species ejected from molybdenum during bombardment by 5-40 keV noble gas ions. (Ref. 4.39). Veksler and Shuppe[40] obtained the same secondary ion spectrum for 0-600 eV Hg^+ bombardment excluding the species underlined.

Negative ions	H	C	CH	OH	C_2	C_2H	O_2	MoO_2	MoO_3	Mo_2O_3
Positive ions	H	Mo								

TABLE 4.5

Negative species ejected from aluminium, stainless steel and copper targets during bombardment by 200-1000 keV hydrogen and deuterium positive ions. (Refs. 4.41 and 4.42)

Negative ions	H	C	O	OH	C_2	CH_2	C_2H_2

bombardment by a cesium neutral beam, the main effect presumably being due to the cesium layer lowering the work function.

By using their double-modulation technique and simultaneously bombarding a tantalum surface with sodium ions and depositing sodium films from an evaporation source Arifov et al[44 45] were able to monitor the stopping potential characteristic and thereby determine the change in energy distribution of ejected ions throughout the sequence: clean tantalum to tantalum plus sodium contamination to sodium. The scattered sodium ions initially had a wide energy spectrum, but the form of this spectrum changed as the sodium contamination proceeded, a larger contribution to the ejected ion current being due to sputtering of the sodium film as ions. There was no negative ion emission from the clean tantalum surface, but negative ejection immediately occurred in the presence of a trace of sodium impurity and the intensity of the negative ion current increased with sodium film thickness. Mass analysis of these negative ions indicated that the majority of them resulted from the contamination of the surface by background gases during the experiment and species such as H^-, C^-, Ca^-, N^-, OH^- and Cl^- could be eliminated by increasing the sodium deposition rate. O^- and O_2^- ions were however still ejected at the higher deposition rate and Arifov et al concluded that these were produced by decomposition of chemical compounds on the surface, again confirming the work of Hagstrum[38] on tantalum who concluded that the tantalum surface is never completely free of oxygen.

Abroyan and Lavrov[46] have studied ejection from alkali halides during potassium ion bombardment and concluded that the negative ions, when present, were derived from target components whilst positive ions were representative of both the incident ion beam and target atoms. A record of the principal species ejected during potassium ion bombardment is presented in Table 4.6 and it is interesting to note that, in spite of the wide difference in actual composition of the secondary current, the total reflected positive ion yields vary with bombarding ion energy in an almost identical manner. Fig. 4.7. shows the variation K_+ with ion energy for K^+ ions bombarding KBr and the yield is seen to tend to a maximum value at 6 keV. This maximum value lies between 0.26 and 0.32 for all the crystals studied.

TABLE 4.6

Ionic emission from alkali-halides due to K^+ ion bombardment. (Ref. 4.46). Fluorine peaks were obscured by secondary electron emission in this experiment.

Target	Positive Ions	Negative Ions
NaF	Na, K	NaF (F)
NaCl	Na, K	Cl
CsCl	—	K, Cl
LiF	Li	LiF (F)
KBr	K	Br

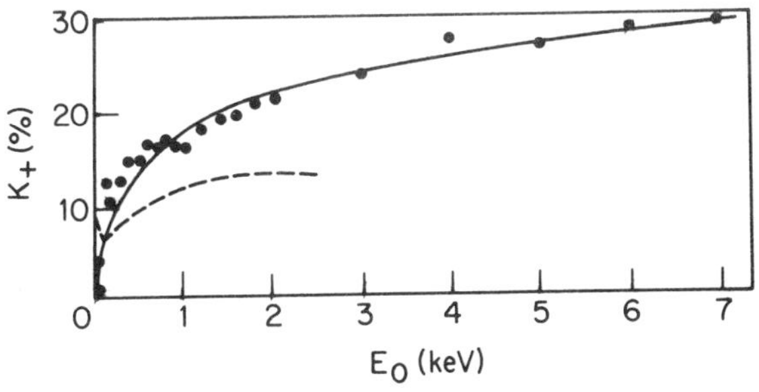

Fig. 4.7 Variation of K_+ with energy for potassium ion bombardment of potassium bromide. Broken curve shows data obtained by Hagstrum[118]. (Ref. 4.46)

TABLE 4.7

Positive ions emitted during 2-6 keV A^+ bombardment of various glasses. (Ref. 4.47)

Soda Lime			Na	Mg	Al	Si	K	A	Ca	SiOH
Phosphate			Na	Mg	Al	P	K^{39}		Ca	K^{41}
Borosilicate	B^{10}	B^{11}	Na		Al	Si^{29}		SiH	Si^{30}	

Analysis of secondary species ejected from various types of glass surface during bombardment by 2.6 keV A^+ ions has been carried out by Kerr[47] and the principal positive ion peaks are presented in Table 4.7. The negative ion peaks were found to be affected by the cleaning treatment (hydrofluoric acid), for example for soda lime glass the un-treated surfaces had relatively low F^- peaks compared with the OH^- peak whilst targets treated with HF had much higher F^- peaks.

4.5 IONIC EMISSION COEFFICIENTS

The preceding discussion will have made the reader aware of the complexities of secondary emission studies and, with such a wide variation of ejected species, simple measurements of yields on an incident-ejected current ratio basis seem to be fairly useless, and certainly not reproducible. However determination of current ratios have been carried out in the literature and whilst the expected inconsistencies do exist certain general trends are apparent. The principal ratios of secondary to incident ion currents have already been defined. True reflection coefficient:

$$\rho = \frac{\text{current of incident particles ejected as ions}}{\text{ion current striking target}} \qquad 4.8$$

and secondary emission coefficient

$$R = \frac{\text{collector current}}{\text{target current}} \qquad 4.9$$

For suitably applied potentials between the target and collector the coefficient R exceeds ρ only by the contribution of current due to the secondary emission of electrons from the collector surface and also the non-incident species ejected from the target as ions such as adsorbed gas or ions of the target material. The actual magnitude will therefore be very similar, but care must be taken in interpreting variations of R with experimental parameters as the apparent changes could be entirely due to the fraction of the current due to electron emission being disturbed. Russian workers introduce the factors K_- and K_+ to distinguish reflection and emission of positive ions from negative ion emission where

$$K_+ = \frac{\text{Number of Positive ions ejected from target}}{\text{Number of incident positive ions}} \qquad 4.10a$$

$$\text{and } K_- = \frac{\text{Number of Negative ions ejected from target}}{\text{Number of incident positive ions}} \qquad 4.10b$$

The parameters ρ and K_+ differ only by the extra ions which are ejected from the target due to the liberation of adsorbed gases or target species in a positively charged state by sputtering or evaporation. Thus K_+ values are slightly higher than true reflection coefficients.

Other coefficients describing this phenomenon appear in the literature and are generally slight variations of those described above with some of the spurious secondary electron currents biased out.

4.6. REFLECTION COEFFICIENTS (ρ, K_+)

4.6.1 Energy dependence

Hagstrum[1] has studied reflection of noble gas ions. He^+, Ne^+ and A^+ at a clean tungsten surface in the energy range 0-1 keV and shown that values of the reflection coefficient vary between 10^{-4} and 10^{-2} and are almost independent of incident ion energy (Fig. 4.8). Similar studies on molybdenum targets for helium ion bombardment showed that yields were again between 8×10^{-4} and 10^{-3} ions/ion and generally slightly lower than those for a tungsten surface.

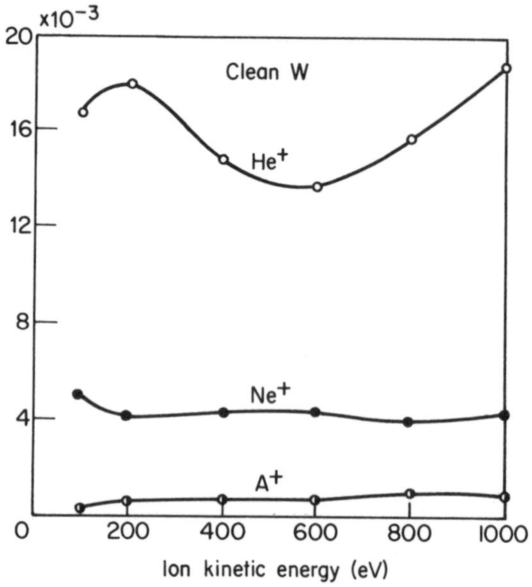

Fig. 4.8 Variation of ion reflection coefficient $\rho(=R_{ii})$ with energy for He^+, Ne^+ and A^+ ions on tungsten. (Ref. 4.1)

Bradley[27] confirmed that yields were relatively independent of energy for 0.1-0.9 keV Xe^+ bombardment of platinum though there was evidence here that results depended upon the background pressure of xenon. Eremeev et al[48 49] have also shown that the secondary coefficient K_+ was independent of energy over the range 2-14 keV for potassium and lithium ion bombardment of tantalum, tungsten and tin targets. The targets were heated to 2500°C and K_+ was found to remain constant throughout, except for a sharp jump at 800-1000°K, presumably due to a re-emission of atoms of the incident beam in the ionic form.

Fogel et al[39 50] have found that K_+ increases with ion velocity at higher energies for noble gas bombardment of molybdenum. However, it is a little disconcerting to read in their report that the results varied during the first twenty minutes of bombardment before settling to a constant value!

An interesting technique has been developed by Batanov[51] for determining secondary emission parameters. His detector region comprised a target surrounded by a concentric grid and this in turn was surrounded by the collector assembly. The grid was maintained at -7.5 volts with respect to the collector to eliminate tertiary electron currents and the ion current was pulsed. By selecting a sufficiently short pulse-time and observing the collector current trace, peaks corresponding to individual ion masses could be identified so that not only could the secondary ion emission coefficients be obtained, but also the actual composition of the secondary current could be interpreted. This technique was applied to the study of ionic emission from monocrystalline alkali halides by K^+ ions in the energy range 0-4 keV and it was seen that the coefficient K_+ first decreased and then increased for many of the targets studied. (Fig. 4. 9.).

contamination which is known to increase reflection coefficients[21], or, it could have been caused by some secondary reaction occurring as ions struck the collector surface.

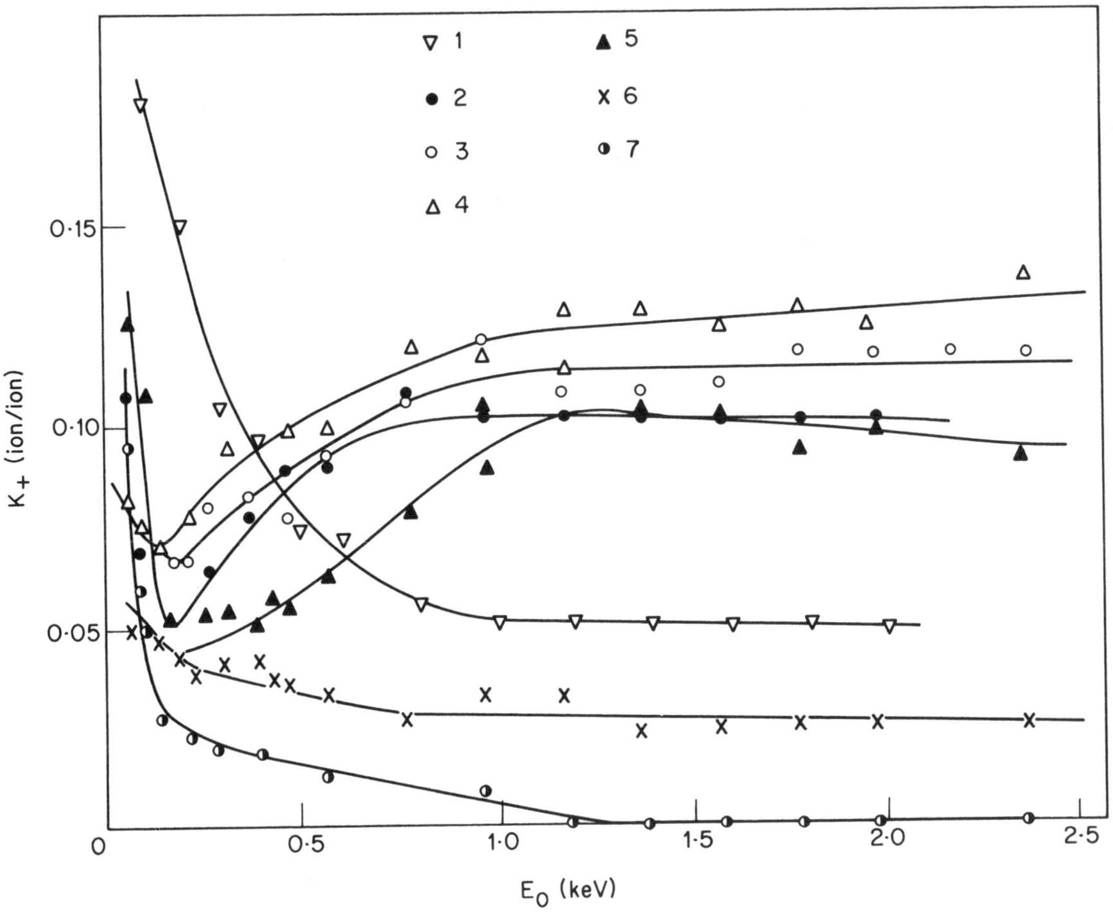

Fig. 4. 9 Variation of ion reflection coefficient K_+ with energy for K^+ ions on alkali-halides, nickel and glass

▽ Ni ▲ NaF after prolonged bombardment

● KCl x NaF before bombardment

○ NaCl ◑ No. 46 Glass

△ KBr

(Ref. 4. 51)

This was explained as being due to the straightforward reflection of incident K^+ ions at lower energies which decreased as the ion energy, E_0, increased. At higher energies cathodic sputtering would predominate the sputtered particles being liberated in the ionic form since $E_i < \phi$ for alkali atoms[30]. The ionic yield, therefore, proceeded to increase with energy again in the manner of a sputtering yield curve (See Chapter 7). These results were further confirmation of work carried out by Batanov[52] on Li^+ bombardment of monocrystalline NaCl where, again, the K_+-E_0 curve showed a minimum at 300 eV.

Again using the pulse technique Abroyan and Lavrov[46] have shown that the secondary positive ion coefficient increased monotonically with energy for K^+ ions bombarding monocrystalline LiF, NaF, NaC, KBr, CsCl and Si in the manner shown in Fig. 4. 7. These workers did not observe a minimum in the K_+-E_0 curve at low energies in normal experiments, but found that this minimum was produced when their ion beam was intentionally defocused to partially miss the target. No explanation of this effect was attempted, but it may have resulted from greater surface

All the higher energy work described above for alkali ions indicates that reflection coefficients approach constant values of order 5-10%. This fact was also observed by Petrov and Dorozhkin[53] for noble gas bombardment of tungsten though their measurements were of the coefficient R. At 5 keV yields were 6, 4. 5 and 2% for He^+, Ne^+ and A^+ ion bombardment, respectively. Evidence for an increase in yield as the ion energy decreased for Ca^+ ions was again observed, though the minimum occurred at a higher energy than previously obtained by Batanov[51 52] (about 1-2 keV).

Results presented by Brunnée[22] show a markedly different trend, the reflection coefficient K_+ decreasing rapidly in the region 0-2 keV and then levelling off to a constant value between 1 and 15% (See Fig. 4. 10). The experiments of Brunnée were conducted, however, in a much better vacuum system than that of the Russian workers and the molybdenum surface was shown to be clean enough to produce a secondary electron emission curve almost identical to that obtained by Hagstrum[119], Fig. 4. 11 demonstrates how sensitive the reflection coefficient is to the sur-

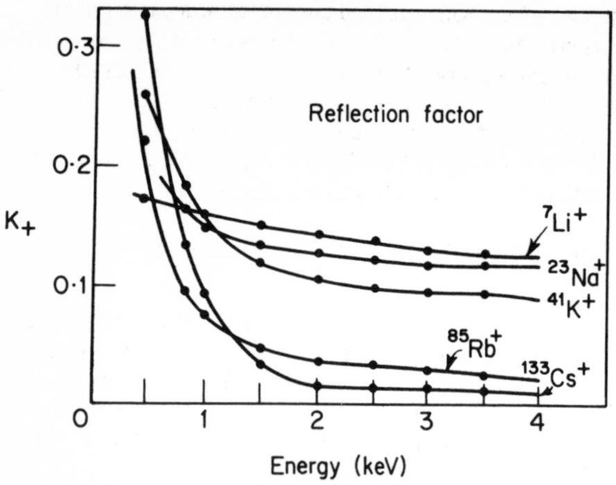

Fig. 4. 10 Variation of Ion reflection coefficient K_+ with energy for Li^+, Na^+, K^+, Rb^+ and Cs^+ ions on clean molybdenum surfaces. (Ref. 4. 22)

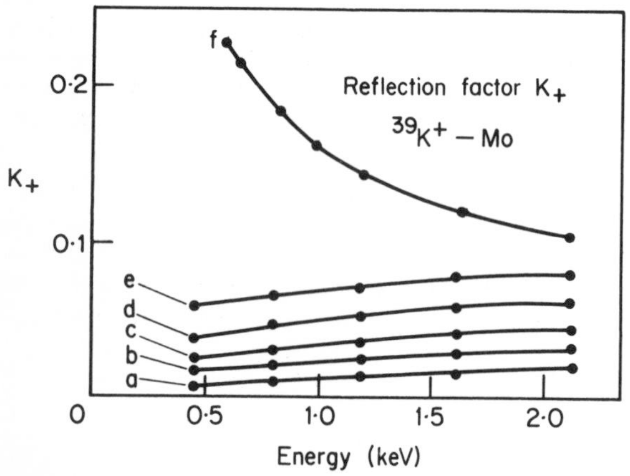

Fig. 4. 11 Change in secondary emission coefficient with surface contamination for $_{39}K^+$ ions on molybdenum. Curves a-f represent data for surfaces successively cleaned by heating from the untreated (a) to the pure (f) state. (Ref. 4. 22)

face conditions, the value of K_+ increasing by a factor of 4 at lower energies for the clean surface and Brunnée proposed that the difference in results could be attributed to complicated interactions between the ion and the random surface of sorbed gas and base metal atoms. This explanation is confirmed by experiments of Ploch[54] who obtained curves for reflection of lithium ions from degassed and non-degassed molybdenum showing that reflection coefficients decreased as ion energy increased for the degassed surface, but increased with ion energy on a non-degassed surface. (See Fig. 4. 12).

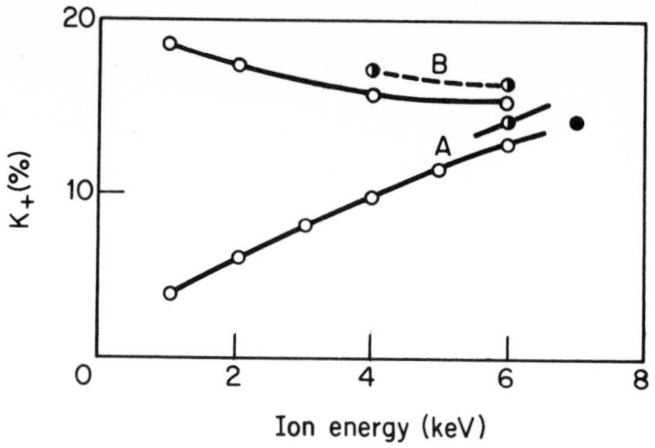

Fig. 4. 12 Change in secondary emission coefficient with surface contamination for Li^+ ions on molybdenum. A: contaminated surface; B: outgassed surface. (Ref. 4. 54)

Arifov et al[55] have also demonstrated the decrease in reflection coefficient with increase in ion energy for W, Ta, Mo, Ti and Ni targets bombarded by alkali ions. The targets were all well baked at their maximum temperatures before the experiments and the measurements were made with targets at 300°K in a vacuum of 10^{-7} Torr, so again the surfaces were probably clean. In further work Arifov and Khadzhimukhamedov[56] have studied reflection on Ta, Mo and Ni targets held at 1500°K using their double modulation technique described in Chapter 3 and have been able to distinguish three components of the secondary emission; K_s the scattering coefficient (identical to ρ), K_e, the coefficient for evaporated ions, and K_d, the coefficient for ions which diffuse out from the target material. Table 4. 8 summarises the results giving the main trend of each component and the total yield K_Σ as a function of ion energy. It is clear from the table that the scattering coefficient K_s decreases as the ion energy increases in all cases. The change in coefficients K_s, K_e, K_d and K_Σ with ion energy is illustrated in Fig. 4. 13 for Cs^+ ions on tungsten surfaces at 1500° [57]. These curves are identical in form for Na^+, K^+ and Rb^+ bombardment of tungsten and show that the true reflection coefficient K_s decreases rapidly to 600 eV and then more slowly to 1 keV whilst K_e and K_d increase gradually to saturation values at 1 keV. The parameter K_d is probably similar to the coefficient observed by Riddoch and Leck[58] who found that tungsten ribbon, when heated after a period of ion bombardment, produced a burst of positive ions of the alkali impurities present in the tung-

TABLE 4. 8

Variation of secondary emission coefficients K_s (scattered), K_e (evaporated), K_d (diffused) and K_Σ (total) with energy for various ion-target combinations. (Ref. 4. 56)

Ion	Target	Increasing Parameters	Decreasing Parameters	Constant
K	Ta	E K_d	K_s K_e K_Σ	
K	Ni	low energy E K_d K_e	K_s	K_Σ
		high energy E K_d	K_s K_e	K_Σ
Rb	Mo	low energy E K_d K_e	K_s K_Σ	
		high energy E K_d	K_s K_e K_Σ	
Na	Ta	E	K_s = K_Σ	

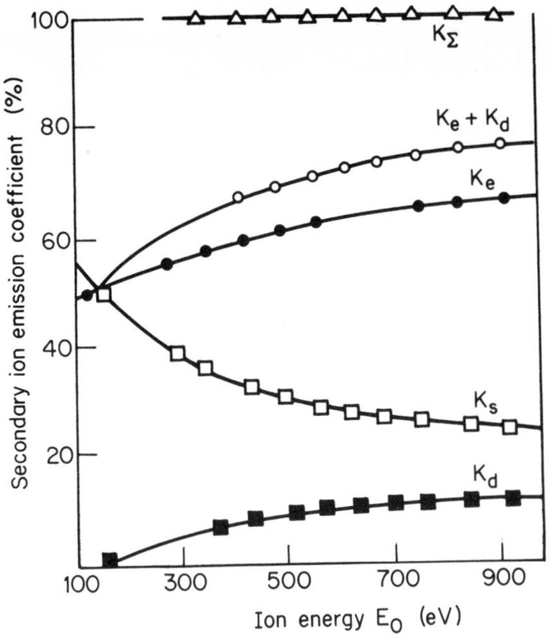

Fig. 4.13 Typical variation of coefficients K_s(□) K_e(●) K_d (□) and K_Σ(Δ) with ion energy for bombardment of tungsten. Case shown is for Cs^+ ions, but curves for Na^+, K^+ and Rb^+ are very similar. (Refs. 4.3 and 4.57)

sten material. The bombardment was assumed to uncover fresh layers of impurity atoms by sputtering away the surface and a steady increase in magnitude of the ionic emission with energy was observed for a given total ion bombardment.

At very low energies the scattering coefficient K_s ($= \rho$) was seen to go through a maximum at about 44 eV (K_s max = 95%) for Na^+ and K^+ bombardment of tungsten[59] indicating that the nature of the interaction had changed. Arifov et al proposed that the ion was interacting with a group of target atoms at these low energies, an idea that was substantiated by the further observation that Cs^+ was also scattered from nickel (which is impossible on a two atom collision basis), the scattering coefficient for Cs^+ exhibiting a sharp maximum of 90% at 42 eV and then rapidly decreasing to zero at 200 eV. Maximum energies of ejected ions were found to be a smaller fraction of the incident ion energy at these very low ion energies which was assumed to be due to the influence of the binding energy on the ejection process.

The general conclusion to be drawn from the above discussion is that at higher energies (greater than 1 keV) reflection coefficients are independent of incident ion energy whilst, at lower energies, they remain independent for noble gas bombardment, but increase with decreasing energy for bombardment by alkali ions. At extremely low energies the nature of the interaction apparently changes from a two-atom collision to a multiple atom interaction.

4.6.2 Dependence on ion and target species of ρ and K_+

The composition of the total secondary ion emission K_Σ was shown by Arifov et al[60 61] to depend strictly on the ion-target parameters as indicated in Table 4.9. Case 1 in the table corresponds to bombardment of tungsten at 1800°K by K^+ ions and it was clear from the double modulation technique that the three distinct secondary ion emission coefficients discussed in the previous section were of order $K_s \sim 30\%$, $K_e \sim 40\%$ and $K_d \sim 10\%$ for 840 eV ion bombardment. An experiment with Cs^+ ions on a heated nickel target (corresponding to case 4 in table 4.9) showed that only evaporation of sorbed incident Cs atoms as ions (86%) and desorption of diffused atoms (14%) contributed to the ion emission whilst for Ba^+ on molybdenum corresponding to case 6 the ion emission was extremely small and comprised diffusion from the bulk[62].

Brunnée has studied reflection of alkali ions from well-degassed molybdenum targets and has found that the coefficient decreases as ion mass increases as indicated in Fig. 4.14. By comparing secondary emission by isotopic pairs of ions (Li^6-Li^7, K^{39}-K^{41},

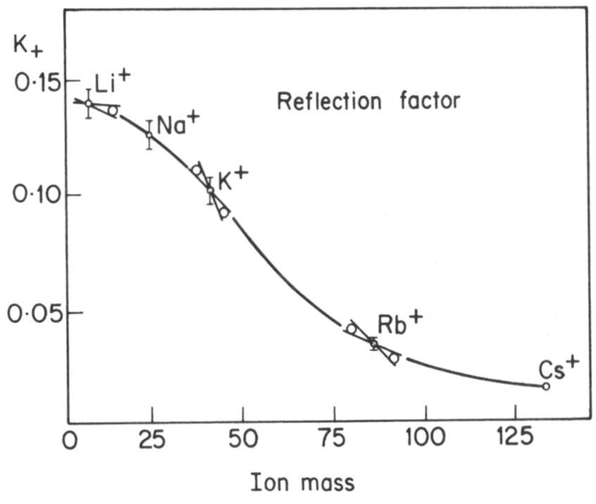

Fig. 4.14 Variation of ion reflection coefficient K_+ with ion mass for a molybdenum surface. (Ref. 4.22)

TABLE 4.9

Parameters governing the composition of the secondary ion emission coefficient K_Σ (Ref. 4.3).

Mass Relation Ion Target	Ionization potential	Work function	Temperature	Composition of secondary ion current
1 $M_1 < M_2$	$V_i < \phi$		$T \geqslant 1200$°K	$K_\Sigma = K_s + K_e + K_d$
2 $M_1 < M_2$	$V_i < \phi$		$T < 1200$°K	$K_\Sigma = K_s$
3 $M_1 < M_2$	$V_i > \phi$		T any value	$K_\Sigma = K_s$
4 $M_1 > M_2$	$V_i < \phi$		$T < 1200$°K	$K_\Sigma = 0$
5 $M_1 > M_2$	$V_i < \phi$		$T \geqslant 1200$°K	$K_\Sigma = K_e + K_d$
6 $M_1 > M_2$	$V_i > \phi$		T any value	$K_\Sigma = 0$

Rb^{85}-Rb^{87}) Brunnée has been able to calculate dK_+/dM for ions having the same electronic structure but different masses and has shown that the dK_+/dM values compare favourably with those on the K_+-M curve of Fig. 4. 14. Brunnée concluded that the change in emission coefficient was, therefore, mainly due to the mass of the bombarding ion rather than differences in electronic structure and that the process could be described to a first approximation by interaction of hard-spheres of equal radius, the ion colliding with several target atoms.

Results of Arifov et al for bombardment of targets by lighter ions ($M_1 < M_2$) and by heavier ions ($M_1 > M_2$) indicated that there were two distinct secondary emission processes (as discussed later in Section 4. 11), both mechanisms being described by single collisions between the incident ion and target atom. The change in reflection coefficient with ion mass, M_1, found by Arifov and Khadzhimukhamedov[55] was rather complicated: for energies less than 400 eV K_s increased with M_1 whilst, for ion energies greater than 1 keV, K_s decreased as M_1 increased, as observed by Brunnée[22]. (See Fig. 4. 15). Arifov et al

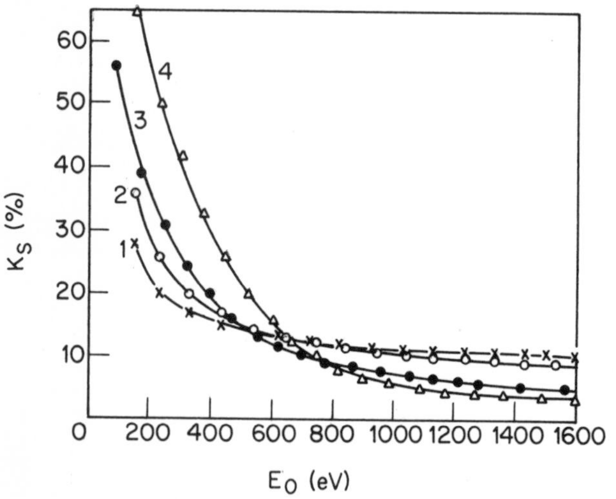

Fig. 4. 15 Variation of ion emission coefficient K_s with energy for various ions on a molybdenum surface at 300°K. × Na^+, ○ K^+, ● Rb^+, Δ Cs^+. (Ref. 4. 55)

explained that this cross-over of curves at 600-700 eV reflected the reduction in collision cross-section of target atoms which preferentially allowed the smaller light ions to penetrate into the target lattice rather than undergo scattering. However, for heated molybdenum targets no cross-over in the curves

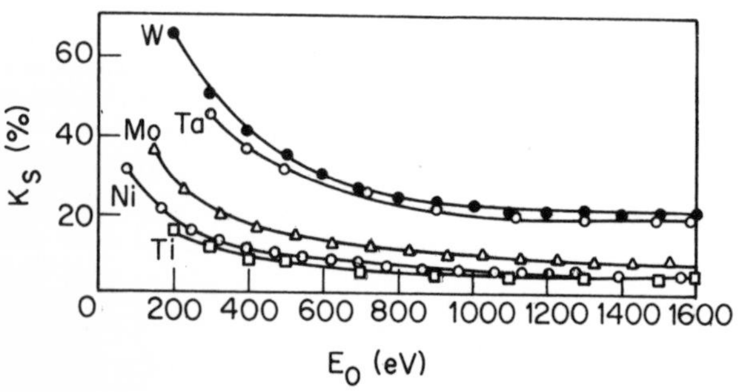

Fig. 4. 16 Variation of ion emission coefficient K_s with ion energy for potassium ion bombardment of various targets at 300°K. ● W, ○ Ta, Δ Mo, ○ Ni, □ Ti. (Ref. 4. 55)

occurred and K_s was found to decrease as M_1 increased at all energies studied (200-1600 eV).

The effect of target mass on yield for Na^+ bombardment is shown in Fig. 4. 16 and it is clear that K_s increases with target mass M_2. Thus, Arifov et al have shown that, apart from the low energy results on 300°K molybdenum targets, the secondary emission coefficient K_s is a direct function of the ratio M_2/M_1.

The decrease in K_+ with increase in ion mass was also found for noble gas bombardment of tungsten by Petrov and Dorozhkin.[53] This decrease was not observed by Fogel et al[50], however, who found an increase in the reflection coefficient with ion mass for 10-40 keV bombardment of Mo by H^+, He^+, Ne^+, A^+, Kr^+ and O^+ ions. However, the targets used by Fogel et al were shown to be contaminated and their results show therefore that the interaction with contaminant adsorbed atoms must be of a different nature to that occurring at clean surfaces.

4. 7 SECONDARY EMISSION COEFFICIENT R

4. 7. 1 Energy dependence

The early research of Healea et al[13 68] correctly predicted the trend of the secondary emission curve showing it to increase linearly with the ion energy in the range 200-1600 eV for noble gas bombardment of gas-covered nickel. Hagstrum[1] has found the same linear relationship for He^+ ions on clean tungsten, but values of the coefficient R were some two orders of magnitude lower than those of Healea et al.

At higher energies (10-40 keV) Fogel et al[50 69] found that the coefficient R continued to increase with incident ion energy for H^+, He^+, Ne^+, A^+, Kr^+, and O^+ bombardment of molybdenum although there was evidence that the H^+ and He^+ curves had passed through maxima and were decreasing again at 10 keV. Walther and Hintenberger[70] observed a maximum at 1. 6 ± 0. 4 keV for Ne^+, A^+, Kr^+ and Xe^+ bombardment,

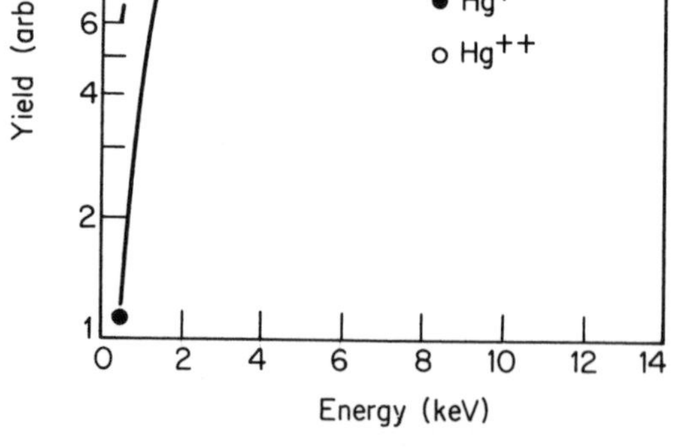

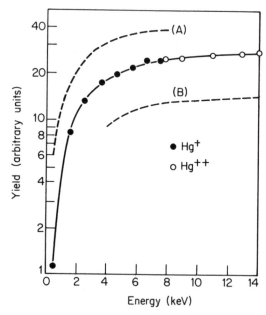

Fig. 4. 17 Yield of tantalum ions as a function of incident mercury ion energy during bombardment of a tantalum target ● Hg^+, ○ Hg^{++}. Broken curves show trend of sputtering curve for tungsten bombarded by N_2^+(A) and tantalum bombarded by Hg^+(B). Relative position of curves on vertical ordinate have no significance. (Ref. 4. 37)

but in this experiment the detector looked at emission only in a direction normal to the surface for bombardment at 45° so that the complete emission picture was not clear from their results. For mercury ion bombardment of tantalum McHugh and Sheffield[37] observed that the yield of tantalum ions increased quite sharply with incident ion energy in the region 0.3-2 keV (Fig. 4.17) and then proceeded to approach a maximum value at approximately 8 keV. As the tantalum ion yield was the major contributor to secondary emission it was assumed by McHugh et al to indicate the trend of the total secondary emission coefficient.

The foregoing discussion indicates clearly that, whereas the reflection coefficient tends to a constant value at high energies, the secondary emission coefficient increases and only at very high energies (10 keV or more) is there any evidence that the R-E curve is approaching a maximum value.

4.7.2 Dependence of R on ion and target species

The secondary emission coefficient has been shown by several workers to increase with target mass, which is to be expected as the coefficients K or ρ which contribute to the coefficient R have also been found to increase with target mass in our earlier discussion (4.6.2.). Ploch[54] has found for 2 keV Li^+ bombardment that R_{Pt} ($\simeq$ 23.5%) > R_{Mo} ($\simeq$ 18%) whilst, for hydrogen bombardment, Gehrtsen[71] has found $R_{Pt} > R_{Ag} > R_{Ni} \simeq R_{Cu}$ and $R_{Al} > R_{Mg} > R_{Be}$ and Eremeev et al [49, 72, 73] have shown that R_W ($\simeq$ 20.5%) > R_{Ta} ($\simeq$ 19.8%) for 2-6 keV K^+ bombardment.

The effect of increasing the mass of the incident ion is in general to increase the magnitude of the secondary emission coefficient. Panin[74] has shown that R values for bombardment of molybdenum and zirconium by atomic, molecular and triatomic hydrogen ions having the same velocity, increase almost exactly in the ratio 1:2:3, respectively. A similar situation was observed by Petrov[75] for bombardment of tantalum by hydrogen ions. McHugh and Sheffield[37] have presented data for bombardment of tantalum by various ions at 8.4 keV showing that Ta^+ yields increase with ion mass in the manner shown in Fig. 4.18. Leland and Olson[76] found an almost linear increase in the yield of Al^+ ions with incident ion mass during bombardment of aluminium by N_1^+, N_2^+, CO^+, Al^+, CO_2^+ and Kr^+ ions at 100 keV.

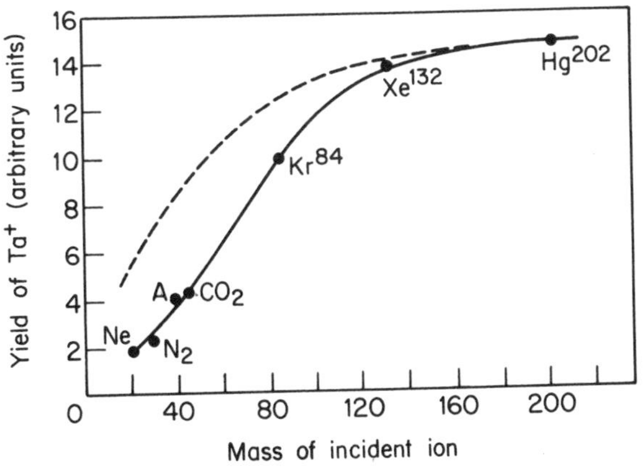

Fig. 4.18 Yield of tantalum ions as a function of incident ion mass during 8.4 keV bombardment of a tantalum target at 1300°C. Broken curve shows variation of maximum energy transfer coefficient with ion mass. (Ref. 4.37)

Walther and Hintenberger[70] observed that in the energy range 4 keV ⩽ E ⩽ 30 keV the secondary emission coefficients for bombardment of gold, copper and graphite targets varied in the manner $R_{Xe} > R_{Kr} > R_A > R_{Ne} > R_{He}$ when particles ejected in the normal direction to the target surface were detected, the incident bombardment being at 45°. This trend is the reverse of that found for ion reflection coefficients, ρ, and it is interesting that Walther et al found that the above inequality was violated for measurements with the detector set at 45° where a large contribution of specularly reflected ions would be expected to be produced.

The dependence of R on ion-target combination is thus not as clear as the dependence of ρ and it appears, from data available, that R increases both with target and ion mass whilst ρ increases with the target mass, but is inversely related to ion mass.

4.8 DEPENDENCE OF IONIC EMMISION COEFFICIENTS ON INCIDENT ION CHARGE

Very little data is available on reflection of neutral atoms at a surface. Medved et al[77, 78] have bombarded a flashed molybdenum target with 0.5-2.5 keV argon and neon atoms and observed the secondary and tertiary electron currents produced by the incident and reflected beam. In an alternative experiment Medved has determined the energy transfer of the primary and secondary beam particles to uncleaned platinum disc thermocouples, the second thermocouple aligned in the direction of specular reflection only. Medved concluded from his results that, whereas 0.02% of 750 eV argon ions would be reflected from a tungsten surface (according to Hagstrum[1]) and probably less than this fraction would be reflected from a molybdenum surface, no less than 20% of the neutral argon atoms appeared to be reflected from molybdenum.

Flaks[79, 80] has studied the effect of ion charge on the secondary emission coefficient R for potassium ions bombarding gas-covered platinum surfaces. Yields for K^+ K^{++} and K^{+++} at 20 keV were found to be 49%, 62% and 81%, respectively, indicating that the electronic configuration does play an important part in the reflection process, at least for dirty surfaces. However, Fogel et al[69] have found that reflection coefficients ρ for positive and negative hydrogen atomic ions at 22 keV were of approximately the same magnitude; $\rho'_{H^+} \simeq 1.56\%$, $\rho'_{H^-} \simeq 2.03\%$ and secondary emission coefficients were almost identical; $R_{H^+} \simeq 0.44\%$, $R_{H^-} \simeq 0.45\%$.

Arifov et al[81] have also found that the scattering coefficient-energy curve is identical for neutral and ionic sodium bombardment of tantalum the neutral K_S^0 coefficient decreasing as energy increased in the range 200-1000 eV and reaching a constant value of ~ 18% at 800 eV.

4.9 DEPENDENCE OF IONIC EMISSION COEFFICIENTS ON ANGLE OF INCIDENCE

Early investigations of the scattering of ions from dirty surfaces [82-88, 42] have shown that both R and ρ increase with the angle of incidence of the ion beam θ (measured from the target normal). Fig. 4.19 shows the variation of R with α ($\alpha = 90 - \theta$) for various

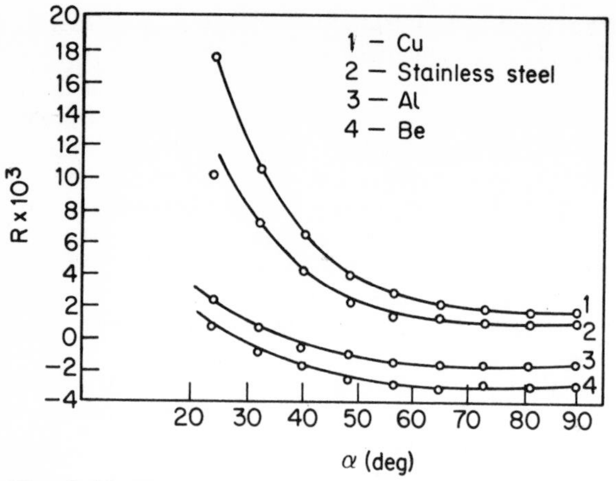

Fig. 4.19 Variation of secondary emission coefficient R with angle of incidence of 50 keV proton beam. (Ref. 4.42)

targets bombarded by 50 keV protons obtained by Mitropan et al[42] and it is clear that yields increase rapidly as grazing incidence is approached. Furthermore, it has been noted in many cases that a sizeable fraction of secondary ions are emitted in the specular reflection direction, although there is evidence that the reflection angle (i.e. the angle with respect to the target normal) decreases as the incident ion energy increases for bombarding energies greater than 30 eV.[82, 83, 85-87].

4.10. SINGLE CRYSTAL STUDIES

Very little data on ionic emission from single crystal targets has been presented in the literature and all the work so far considered deals with ions of very high energy (10-100 keV). Nelson and Thompson[89] have bombarded a (110) plane of a copper monocrystal which could be rotated around an axis parallel to the the ⟨110⟩ direction with 50 keV H^+ He^+ Ne^+ and Xe^+ ions. It was seen that, for a given angle of incidence, θ, the magnitude of the secondary ion current passed through several minima, these minima occurring when the beam direction was parallel to low index planes or low index directions. Table 4.10 summarises their results.

TABLE 4.10

Directions in which secondary emission currents are a minimum for 50 keV H^+, He^+, Ne^+, or, Xe^+ bombardment of a (110) copper surface rotated about an axis parallel to the ⟨110⟩ direction. (Ref. 4.89)

Angle of incidence	Beam parallel to plane		Beam parallel to direction
30°	(111) (100)		
45°	(111)		⟨100⟩
60°	(100)	(110)	⟨110⟩

The presence of these minima were proposed as direct evidence for the phenomenon of 'channelling' where the incoming ion can see a clear path between adjacent planes of atoms or a hollow well in the surface in a given low index direction. Hence the ion penetrates the target material too far to contribute to secondary emission processes. A fuller discussion of this phenomenon is presented in Chapter 5.

Fluit et al[90] have also observed the depression in the secondary yields for bombardment of a copper (100) surface, rotated about an ⟨001⟩ direction, by 5, 10 and 15 keV A^+ ions. The secondary current comprises neutral argon atoms in this case, but the minima still corresponded to the low index channelling direction ⟨110⟩ (see Fig. 4.20).

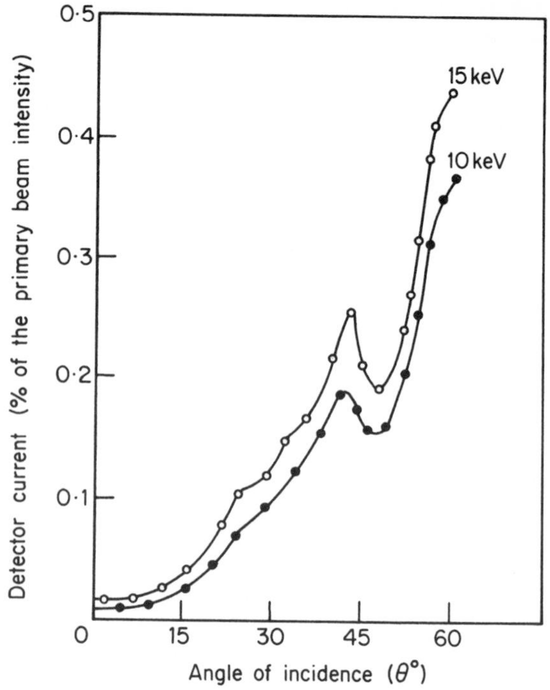

Fig. 4.20 Variation of secondary emission with angle of incidence of A^+ ions for a (100) copper surface rotated about a ⟨001⟩ direction. (Ref. 4.90)

4.11 EJECTED IONS; ENERGIES AND SPATIAL DISTRIBUTIONS

A thorough investigation of the ejection energies of secondary ions can throw much light onto the mechanisms governing the collision process. Bradley[27] has bombarded molybdenum, tantalum and platinum targets with 0-1 keV rare gas ions and has estimated from the shift in secondary spectra on a mass spectrometer that ejection energies were of the order 3-7 eV whilst Honig[28] found the ejection energies of Ge^+ ions during bombardment of germanium by 400 eV Kr^+ ions were in the range 0-20 eV with a most probable energy of 2 eV. A similar result was obtained by Kirchner and Benninghoven[91] for 2 keV Hg^+ bombardment of aluminium and dural, who found that the most probable ejection energies of Al^+ ions were 5 eV with a long high energy tail in the distribution extending beyond 100 eV.

Veksler[92] has expressed the opinion that the energies obtained above would be distorted by the transmission factor of the detecting mass spectrometer. His results for 900-2150 eV Cs^+ ion bombardment of molybdenum and tantalum allowed for this transmission error and indicated distributions of width 30-35 eV for secondary Mo^+ ions and 35-50 eV for Ta^+; values far in excess of those obtained by Bradley and Honig. In later work Veksler[21] has shown that the energies of the ejected ions increased with the incident ion energy for both Rb^+ and Cs^+ bombardment of heated molybdenum targets; most probable ejection energies for Cs^+ bombardment being approximately 6 eV and 12

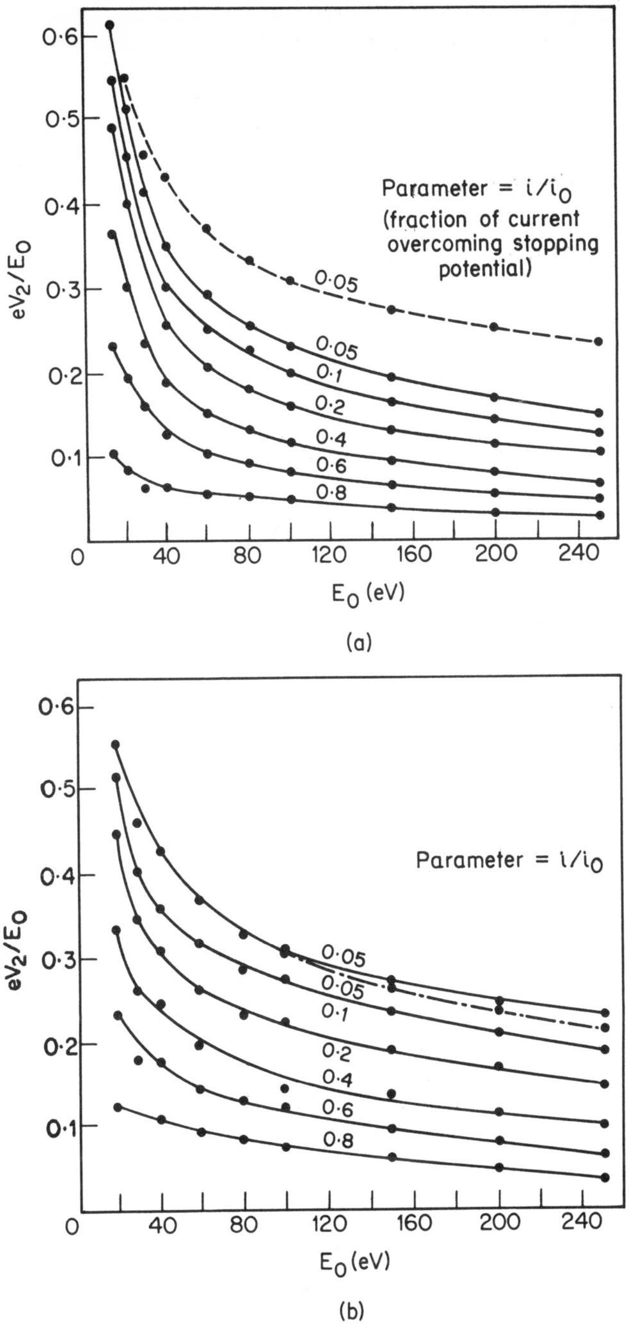

Fig. 4.21 Distribution of ejected ion energies for ion bombardment of molybdenum at 40 eV and 100 eV energy, (a) $C_s{}^+$ ions (broken curve; $R_b{}^+$ ions) (b) Rb^+ ions (broken curve; results not corrected for thermal ionization) (Ref. 4.21)

eV for incident ion energies of 40 eV and 100 eV, respectively (see Figs. 4.21 a and b). Stanton[93] has also found that most probable ejection energies were generally in the range 5 to 10 eV, for He^+, Ne^+, A^+, Kr^+, Xe^+, N_2^+, O_2^+, CO^+ and air ions bombarding stainless steel, beryllium, brass, lead and tin targets.

Arifov et al[63-67, 94] have carried out some very useful and interesting experiments using their double modulation technique (described in Chapter 3). For Na^+ bombarding tantalum ($M_1 < M_2$) their results indicate a cosine distribution of ejected ions regardless of the target temperature and the angle and energy of the incident particles. A calculation of the process based on the collision of an ion with a single target atom has been presented by Arifov et al[64] showing that the maximum energy of the scattered ions E_β at scattering angle β is given by:

$$E_\beta = E_0 \frac{(M_1 - M_2)^2}{M_1^2\left[\cos\beta + \left\{\left(\frac{M_2}{M_1}\right)^2 - \sin^2\beta\right\}^{1/2}\right]^2} \qquad 4.11$$

When $M_1 > M_2$ however the root term in the above expression becomes negative unless $\sin\beta < \frac{M_2}{M_1}$ so that the scattered ions can only leave the target at angles less than a maximum value:

$$\beta_{max} = \sin^{-1}(M_2/M_1) \qquad 4.12$$

Experiments by Arifov et al[67] for Cs^+ and Rb^+ ions on molybdenum have confirmed the existence of this limiting angle β_{max} most conclusively. For Cs^+ on molybdenum a large group of secondary ions appeared, but only when the incidence angle of the primary beam was increased to a value large enough so that ions deflected through the limiting 'β' could escape from the surface. The limiting angle was found to be 50° whilst the theory predicts an angle of 46°30′. The angle was seen to be independent of primary ion energy and target temperature and was similar to that ejected at the maximum angle were seen to be 75 eV which again compares well with the calculated value of 79 eV. A similar correlation between experimental results and theoretical predictions was found for Cs^+ ions on nickel where the measured limiting angle was seen to be approximately 32°.

The above process is thus clearly one of elastic collision by an incoming ion with an individual atom of the target for ions of mass $M_1 > M_2$. However, Arifov et al also observed a second group of reflected particles which possessed a much lower energy (1-2 eV) and were ejected in a cosine distribution. The distribution was relatively independent of incident ion energy and target temperature and was similar to that obtained by bombarding a heavy target with light ions[94]. Arifov proposed that these low-energy secondaries were produced by actually sputtering off atoms from an electro-positive coating on the molybdenum surface (i.e. a species for which $V_i < \phi$ so that emission would be of an ionic nature) and was able to add weight to this hypothesis by demonstrating that the emission was a strong function of the incident ion current. Bradley et al[32] have also shown that the secondary ions produced during bombardment of Pt by 300 eV Xe^+ originated from an adsorbed layer of xenon gas on the platinum surface, as the energies of these secondary particles (approximately 1 eV) were not commensurate with estimated reflection energies.

Veksler[92] and Petrov[75, 95] had earlier attempted to explain scattering from molybdenum by Cs^+ ions on the basis of the collision of the Cs^+ ion simultaneously with two, or more, molybdenum atoms. Similar arguments were put forward by Brunnée[22] and Arifov et al[59] who proposed that the collisions were influenced by the atomic binding energies. Arifov[3] has calculated an effective mass for such a collision (see section 4.14 equation 4.30).

$$M_e = \frac{M_2\left(1.385 + \frac{3E_c}{E_0}\right)}{1 - \frac{3E_cM_2}{E_0M_1}} \qquad 4.13$$

where E_c is the displacement energy of a target atom and E_0 the incident ion energy. The M_e-E_0 curve has a maximum at $E_0 \sim 40$ eV at which energy the experimental scattering coefficient was also seen to reach a maximum[59]. There is, at first sight, an apparent anomaly here as there is some confirmation for the sputtering adsorbed gas model and also the effective mass model of the process. A solution of this problem is provided by Veksler[21] who demonstrated that the scattering coefficient is critically dependent on target contamination. For clean (heated) molybdenum the K_s-E_0 curve passed through a maximum at about 40 eV as predicted by Arifov whilst, for contaminated molybdenum, the K_s-E_0 curve resembled a sputtering yield-energy pattern as if the adsorbed cesium were sputtered off as ions. It is reasonable to suppose therefore that the dependence of K_s on the ion current density observed by Arifov et al[53] only applied to contaminated surfaces (indeed the model depends on this contamination!) whilst the effective mass treatment is applicable under clean target conditions.

For $M_1 < M_2$ a cosine distribution of ejected atoms is generally found to be produced[63-5, 94, 96, 97] and the mechanics of the collision is shown to obey equation 4.11 which is derived on the assumption that ions collide with individual target atoms.

Datz and Snoek[98] have been able to mass analyse the ejected secondaries and confirmed that the collisions were predominantly bi-particle although the fact that the secondary argon ion peak had a shoulder on its high energy flank indicated that there were some multiple collisions occuring (e.g. for A^+ -Cu and a scattering angle of 70° the energy after 1 collision is equal to 0.40 E_0 whereas the energy after two 35° collisions is equal to 0.64 E_0 i.e. argon ions ejected after multiple collisions will have higher energies). The secondary spectra obtained by these workers included peaks corresponding to multiple charged species of both the incident and target atoms. Scattering from a (100) monocrystalline copper surface was found to produce two distinct secondary argon ion peaks, one corresponding to collisions with Cu^{63} and the other with Cu^{65}.

Parilis and Turaev[99] have also shown that the energy spectra of secondary ions obtained by Molchanov and Shoshka[100] for 25 keV A^+ ions bombarding copper and by Arifov et al[101] for 0.7 keV Rb^+ on tantalum could be described by single and multiple binary collision processes, the most probable energy at a scattering angle β (resulting from a single ion-atom collision) being given by the expression

$$E_m(\beta) = \frac{E_0}{(1+\mu)^2}\left(\cos\beta \pm \sqrt{(\mu^2 - \sin^2\beta)}\right)^2 \qquad 4.14$$

where E_0 was the incident ion energy and $\mu = M_2/M_1$. A similar correlation between the predicted angular distribution of secondary ions and the experimental values was obtained by Arifov et al[67] for 0.7 keV Cs^+ ions on molybdenum and by Mashkova et al[102] for 30 keV A^+ ions on graphite.

Further confirmation of the free particle collision theory is given by comparing the predicted maximum energies of the ejected ions from the equation for two atom collisions derived by Brunnée[22] and Eremeev et al[48, 82]

$$E_{2\max} = \frac{M_2 - M_1}{M_2 + M_1} E_0 = \nu E_0 \qquad 4.15$$

Table 4.11 gives the theoretical and experimental values for ν and a reasonable agreement between the two is observed.

TABLE 4.11

Comparison of experimental and theoretical values of the maximum fraction of incident ion energy retained by secondary ions on the basis of isolated two-atom collisions.

Target	Ion	Experi-mental	Ref	Theoretical $(M_2 - M_1)/(M_2 + M_1)$
Mo	Li	0.90	22	0.88
	Na	0.50	22	0.61
	K	0.32	22	0.40
	Rb	0.12	22	0.06
Ta	Li	0.82	48, 82	0.92
	K	0.60	48, 82	0.64
	Cs	0.13	92	0.16

Panin[96] has carried out a thorough analysis of the energies of ions ejected from molybdenum and beryllium targets during bombardment by H_1^+, H_2^+, Ne^+, N_1^+, N_2^+, O_1^+, O_2^+, CO^+, A^+ and A^{2+} ions and concluded from his results that the collisions could be considered as being between two free atoms. The most probable energy of the secondary A^+ ions for A^+—Mo bombardment were shown to increase linearly with incident ion energy maintaining a ratio $E_1/E_0 = 0.41$ and the results indicated multiply charged ion species up to A^{5+} in the secondary spectrum. For bombardments with ions of mass less than four percent of the target mass calculations indicated that ejection energies from 0.975 E_0 to 0.986 E_0 should be possible on a single atom-atom collision basis and these were in fact observed. However, the distribution in secondary energies for these very light ions indicated that most ions had suffered multiple collisions before ejection. Finally, for bombardments of ions with mass greater than the target, Panin found different energy spectra which could be described by ejection of ionized target species after multiple collisions within the target. It is worth noting that the results of Panin for complex ion bombardment (N_2^+ and O_2^+) indicated that the molecules dissociated on impact and reacted as if they were single ions with half the incident energy. Similarly results for A^{2+} bombardment were identical to those for A^+ with the same incident energy.

We can thus summarise the ion emission mechanism as being basically concerned with collision of the incoming and target atom as if they were free particles[22, 48, 82, 96, 98, 99]. For $M_1 < M_2$ however Datz et al[98] and Parilis et al[99] have shown that two or more two-particle collisions occur. For $M_1 > M_2$ a secondary interaction can be explained by assigning an effective mass to the target atom;[3] i.e. a factor which takes account of the fact that it is not completely isolated from its neighbours.

4.12 INELASTIC COLLISIONS

Work discussed so far in this chapter indicates that secondary ions are produced principally as a result of binary collisions where the target atom can be treated as if it were isolated from the target lattice.

At low ion energies (0—5 eV) it has been seen that this simple treatment is invalid and the binding energy of target atoms becomes important[3]. We now look at high energy (> 10 keV) results and find that, whilst the simple binary or multiple atom collisions are still occurring, they cannot account for the total energy loss of the ion. In this energy regime a proportion of the ion energy is used in inelastic processes; causing charge stripping of both the incident ion beam and the target atoms.

Snoek et al[103] have carried out an energy analysis of the secondary ions ejected during the bombardment of a (110) copper target and also a copper vapour target, by 40, 60 and 90 keV argon ions and have calculated a weighted mean inelastic energy loss $\overline{Q}$. $\overline{Q}$ was seen to increase linearly with the scattering angle in the centre of mass system to a maximum value which was higher for higher energies. The maximum occurred at smaller scattering angles for bombardment at higher energies and the curves for the gaseous target were almost identical to those for the solid. The average number of missing electrons in the ejected species was however found to be much less for the solid target than for the gaseous one and Snoek et al proposed that the interaction was the same, but some Auger, or, resonance neutralization process occurred at the surface of the solid, thus reducing the charges on the ejected species.

Mashkova et al[104, 105] have carried out a similar experiment with 30 keV A^+ ions on the (100) and (114) faces of copper and found evidence in the ejected energy spectra of some inelastic interactions. The spectrum of energies predicted on the basis of collisions between isolated atoms is illustrated in Fig. 4.22 and the agreement with the experimental distribution is seen to be reasonable.

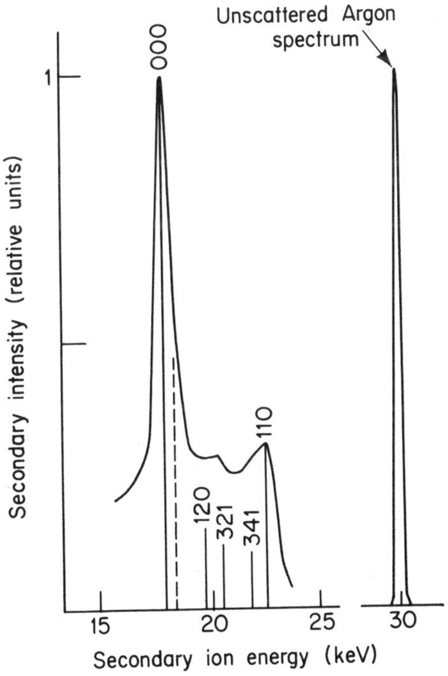

Fig. 4.22 Comparison of experimental ejected ion energy values with those anticipated from isolated two-atom collision events for 30 keV A^+ bombardment of a (100) copper target at 30° incidence angle and scattered through 50°. Broken lines refer to A^+-^{63}Cu collision. (Ref. 4.105)

Dahl and Magyar[106] have made a careful analysis of secondary ion energies produced when a (100) aluminium target, slightly contaminated with oxygen, was bombarded with 50 keV A^+ ions. The spectrum of ejected energies showed a broad continuum on which sharp peaks, which Dahl et al showed were due to single two-atom collisions, were superimposed. The continuum was shown to be due to multiple collisions. From an analysis of the collisions contributing to the sharp peaks the inelastic energy loss Q was calculated and plotted as a function of the distance of closest approach r_0 (obtained by Everhart et al[107] using a Bohr screened coulomb potential) for collisions leading to ejection of Al^{2+}, Al^{3+} and A^{2+} species. Q values obtained from the expression

$$Q\,(E_0\,E_2\,\phi) = \frac{2M_1}{M_2}\,(E_0E_2)^{1/2}\cos\phi - \frac{M_1+M_2}{M_2}\,E_2 - \frac{M_1-M_2}{M_2}\,E_0 \qquad 4.16$$

or

$$Q\,(E_0, E_1, \psi) = 2\left(\frac{M_2E_0E_2}{M_1}\right)^{1/2}\cos\psi - \frac{M_1+M_2}{M_1}\cdot E_1 \qquad 4.17$$

where E_0 = incident ion energy, E_2 = scattered particle energy, E_1 = recoil particle energy, ϕ = scattering angle, ψ = recoil angle and M_1, M_2 are ion and target masses, respectively, were found to be approximately equal for all species at 450 eV for $0.12 < r_0 < 0.18$ Å increasing for lower values of r_0. These results were of the same order as Morgan and Everhart[108] for A^+ –A gaseous target collisions. Detailed investigation of the ejected energy spectra by Dahl et al[106] led them to the conclusion that the inelastic energy is lost in a single collision process.

4.13. EFFECTS OF TARGET TEMPERATURE ON IONIC YIELD

The principal effect of varying the target temperature in most apparatus will, unfortunately, be confused by the change in surface cleanliness. Bradley[27] has shown that the temperature is an important factor, the yield of secondary ions from molybdenum decreasing by a factor of ten as the temperature was raised from 20-1000°C. These curves are distinctly different from those for neutral atom ejection (i.e.

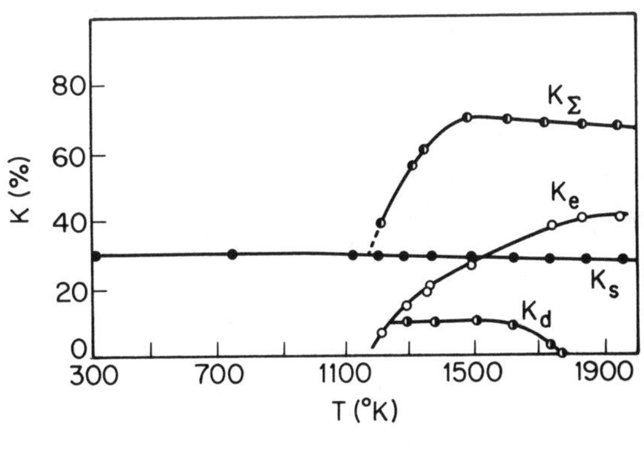

Fig. 4.23 Variation of coefficients K_s(●), K_e(○), K_d(◑), and K_Σ(◐), with target temperature for 560 eV K^+ bombardment of tungsten. (Refs. 4.3 and 4.57)

sputtering, see Chapter 7) where the yield is not such a critical function of the temperature. Eremeev et al[49, 72] have observed a sudden rise in the secondary ion function at a temperature near 800°K for 3 keV K^+ bombardment of tungsten and this trend is also seen by Arifov et al[62] at 1100°K for 560 eV K^+ bombardment of tungsten. Results obtained by Arifov et al[57] illustrating the variation of the coefficients K_s, K_e, K_d and K_Σ with temperature for 560 eV K^+ ions on tungsten are presented in Fig. 4.23. It is clear that the true reflection coefficient K_s $(= \rho)$ is nearly independent of temperature over the range 300 to 1900°K, a slight decrease occurring above 1500°K. This pattern for K_s as a function of temperature was also observed for Na^+, Rb^+ and Cs^+ ions on tungsten.

From Fig. 4.23 it is clear that the rise observed by Eremeev et al may be explained by the increase in the fraction of thermally evaporated primary ions (K_e) and ions diffused from the bulk (K_d).

At higher temperatures (above 1200°K) Petrov[109], Arifov et al[62] and Eremeev[49, 72] have all found yields from tungsten, tantalum and molybdenum to be nearly independent of target temperature for ion energies from 0.1 to 20 keV.

4.14 THEORETICAL TREATMENTS OF IONIC EMISSION

Very few theoretical treatments of ionic emission have appeared in the literature. According to Langmuir[110] and others the ratio, ε, of ions to atoms leaving a surface of work function ϕ is given by

$$\varepsilon = \exp\{(\phi - V_i)\, e/kT\} \qquad 4.18$$

where V_i is the ionization potential of the atoms, K Boltzmann's constant, T the target temperature in °K and e the electronic charge. However, in all practical cases (ϕ-Vi) ~ −3 to −4 volts so that $\varepsilon = 10^{-54}$ which is far less than the measured values of 10^{-2} to 10^{-4}. At the high temperatures used by Arifov et al[57] however ε becomes of the order 1-10% and equation 4.18 describes the ion emission contributing to the coefficients K_e and K_d fairly satisfactory. Thus the Langmuir equation describes ionic emission of those atoms which have completely accommodated with the surface (i.e. sorbed ions diffusing out or impurity atoms evaporating as ions, or completely accommodated atoms of the bombarding gas leaving the surface) and does not account for the secondary ion component resulting from scattering at the surface.

A comprehensive theoretical treatment of secondary ion emission has been presented by von Roos[112] who used a Born approximation to obtain the interaction cross-section, the potential being assumed to be of the form

$$V(r) = \frac{Z\text{eff}}{r} \exp\left(-\frac{r}{r_0}\right) \qquad 4.19$$

which, according to Vapnik et al[113], is not valid for low ion energies. Von Roos neglected the binding energy of lattice atoms so that the theory applies mainly for cases where $M_1 < M_2$. By employing a free-path collision model the reflection process can be described by a Boltzmann equation:

$$\frac{dN(r, v, t)}{dt} = n\sigma_s(V)\, VN(r, v, t) + n \int dV'\, f(V', V)\, V'\sigma_s(V')\, N(r, V', t). \qquad 4.20$$

which represents the time rate of change of the distribution function N(r, V) of incident ions moving among the free lattice atoms. The equations are solved with several simplifying assumptions to yield.

$$\rho = \rho_0(\mu) - \rho_1(\mu).\ \frac{Mr_0^2}{h^2} \cdot E_0 \qquad 4.21$$

$\rho_0(\mu)$ is a function dependent on the mass ratio $\mu = M_2/M_1$, likewise $\rho_1(\mu)$, which is a complex integral, and r_0 is a screening radius and is an adjustable parameter for fitting the expression to experimental results. This theoretical treatment was shown to be in good agreement with the higher energy (greater than 2 keV) results of Brunée[22] for Li^+, Na^+ and K^+ ion bombardment of molybdenum, although the actual predicted magnitudes were 3-4 times too large. The energy distribution of ejected ions was, however, predicted reasonably well and the equation above confirms the experimentally observed decrease in ρ as E_0 increases.

An alternative treatment by Vapnik et al[113] tackles the collision cross section calculations in a different manner, but is otherwise basically the same. It was predicted by these workers, however, that $\rho(E)$ would remain constant as the incident ion energy, E_0, increased due to their assumption that the scattering cross-section was spherically symmetric, i.e. collisions were between hard spheres.

In chapter 10 of Arifov's book[3] Parilis and Gurvich showed that the hard sphere treatment could be extended to cover low energy interactions and the resulting expressions adequately described the variation in the effective mass of the target atoms with ion energy which was observed experimentally. They have assumed that the interactions of all neighbouring atoms with the one under consideration can be expressed by a modification of the single-atom interaction energy U(R) to $U_i[f(R), \alpha_i] + U(R)$. Such a limitation is possible provided $U(R) \gg U(R_i)$ and the Lagrangian can therefore be written

$$L = \frac{1}{2} \cdot M_0 \dot{R}^2 - U(R) - U_i[f(R), \alpha_i] \qquad 4.22$$

where $M_0 = M_1M_2/(M_1 + M_2)$. The scattering angle θ is given by $\theta = 2\pi - \phi_0$ where

$$\phi_0 = \int_{R_0}^{\infty} \frac{M/R^2\, dR}{[\{E_R - U(R) - U_i(f(R), \alpha_i)\}2M_0 - M^2/R^2]^{1/2}}$$

(see chapter 2) 4.23

where $M = M_0\, p\, v_0$, p is the impact parameter, v_0 the incident ion velocity, R_0 the distance of closest approach of colliding atoms and E_R the energy of the relative motion between the colliding particles. Parilis et al further assumed that the atom is situated in a potential well of depth ε where ε takes into account the total energy required to move the atom to an interstitial position and is larger than the binding energy ($\varepsilon \sim 20 - 30$ eV). Equating $-\varepsilon$ to $U_i[f(R), \alpha_i]$ equation 4.23 becomes:

$$\phi_0 = \int_{R_0}^{\infty} \frac{M/R^2 dR}{[\{\varepsilon + E_R - U(R)\}2M_0 - M^2/R^2]^{1/2}} \qquad 4.24$$

This expression can be made identical to the conventional isolated two atom collision scattering angle relation by introducing

(1) An effective mass

$$m_\epsilon = m_0(1 + \varepsilon/E_R) \qquad 4.25$$

(2) an effective momentum

$$M_\epsilon = m_\epsilon p v_0 \qquad 4.26$$

and (3) an effective energy

$$E_\epsilon = E_0(1 + \varepsilon/E_R) \qquad 4.27$$

The scattering angle may then be determined from

$$\phi_0 = \int_{R_0}^{\infty} \frac{dR/R^2}{\left(1 - \frac{U(R)}{E_\epsilon} - \frac{p^2}{R^2}\right)^{1/2}} \qquad 4.28$$

The differential scattering cross-section in the laboratory coordinate system is given by

$$d\sigma = \tfrac{1}{2}\pi a^2 \left[2\frac{m_1}{m_{2\epsilon}} \cdot \cos\beta + \frac{1 + (m_1/m_{2\epsilon})^2 \cos 2\beta}{[1 - (m_1/m_{2\epsilon})^2 \sin^2\beta]^{1/2}} \right] \sin\beta \, d\beta \quad (m_1 > m_2)$$

$$= \tfrac{1}{2}\pi a^2 \cdot \frac{1 + (m_1/m_{2\epsilon})^2 \cos 2\beta}{[1 - (m_1/m_{2\epsilon})^2 \sin^2\beta]^{1/2}} \cdot 2\sin\beta . d\beta \quad (m_1 < m_2) \qquad 4.29$$

where

$$m_{2\epsilon} = \frac{m_2\,(1 + (\varepsilon/E_R))}{1 - (m_2\varepsilon/m_1 E_R)} \qquad 4.30$$

and the energy of the scattered particle is determined by

$$E_1 = E_R \frac{(m_1 - m_{2\epsilon})^2}{m_1^2\,[\cos\beta - \{(m_{2\epsilon}/m_1)^2 - \sin^2\beta\}^{1/2}]^2} \qquad 4.31$$

Thus, from equation 4.30 Parilis et al were able to show that the effective mass of the target increased as the ion energy decreased. At $E_R = m_1\varepsilon/m_2$ m_ϵ changes from $+\infty$ to $-\infty$ and at lower energies it increases from $-\infty$ to zero as $E_R \to 0$. The effect of this change on the scattering coefficient is an increase at very low energies going through a maximum as the energy increases and a decrease as the ion energy increases further. This is qualitatively borne out by experiment[59], but, for quantitive comparison of scattering coefficients, a more realistic interaction potential must be used.

Parilis et al have considered that an ion is reflected if it is scattered through an angle $\geq \frac{1}{2}\pi$ (for normal incidence), so that the total collision cross-section for the process is πp_0^2 where p_0 is the impact parameter corresponding to a scattering angle $\frac{1}{2}\pi$. As seen in Chapter 2 a scattering angle $\frac{1}{2}\pi$ corresponds to an angle $\theta = \cos^{-1}(-m_1/m_2)$ in the centre of mass system. Hence, from classical collision considerations (equation 4.28)

$$\int_R^{\infty} \frac{p_0\, dR}{R^2\left[1 - \frac{V(R)}{E_R} - (\frac{p_0}{R})^2\right]^{1/2}} = \frac{\pi - \cos^{-1}(-m_1/m_2)}{2} \qquad 4.32$$

Using a Firsov potential

$$V(R) = \frac{Z_1 Z_2 e^2}{R} X \left[\psi(Z_1, Z_2), \frac{R}{a}\right] \qquad 4.33$$

where Z_1, Z_2 are atomic numbers of colliding atoms, R the interatomic distance, X the screening function in the Thoma-Fermi potential, $a = (9\pi^2/128)^{1/3} \times (h^2/4\pi^2 me^2) = 4.7 \times 10^{-9}$ cm. and $\psi(Z_1, Z_2) = (Z_1^{1/2} + Z_2^{1/2})^{1/3}$, Parilis et al have solved equation 4.32 numerically to obtain the variation of σ_0 with ion energy. Fig. 4.24 illustrates this function which is

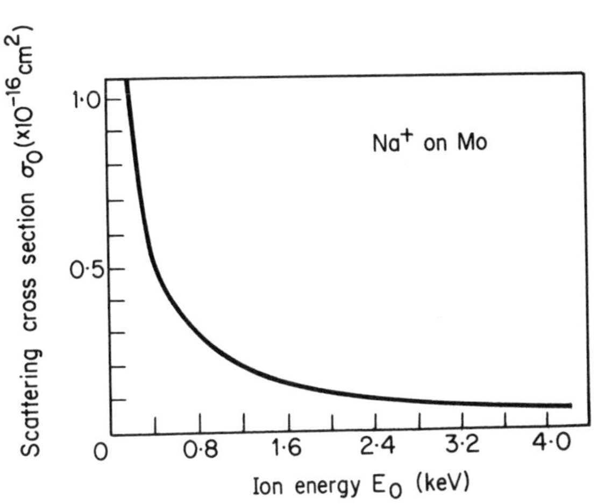

Fig. 4.24 Theoretical variation of scattering cross-section σ_0 with ion energy for Na^+ ions on molybdenum. (Ref. 4.3)

seen to decrease rapidly at first, and then gradually for $E_0 > 2.4$ keV. The scattering coefficient was estimated from the σ_0 values using the approximate expression

$$K_{sc} \simeq \sigma_0 . N . \lambda_\epsilon \qquad 4.34$$

where N is the number of target atoms /cc and λ_ϵ the effective depth from which secondary ions can be emitted, obtained by curve fitting. Figs. 4.25a and b compare experimental values obtained by Arifov et al[3 114 115] with the theoretical curves assuming that λ_ϵ has a fixed value equal to three lattice constants. The theory is seen to give good agreement with experimental values, but is low at higher energies which, Parilis et al suggest, indicates that there is in fact an increase in λ_ϵ with energy; this would be expected from ion range data discussed in Chapter 5.

The theories so far described consider the relatively simple situation of two-particle elastic collisions and derive expressions for scattering coefficients of the incident ions. It is clear from experimental work discussed in this chapter that not all ionic emission is representative of the incident species which indicates that inelastic collisions are occurring and should be considered in theoretical treatments of the process. This is especially true at high ion energies where a large fraction of the incident particles penetrate the

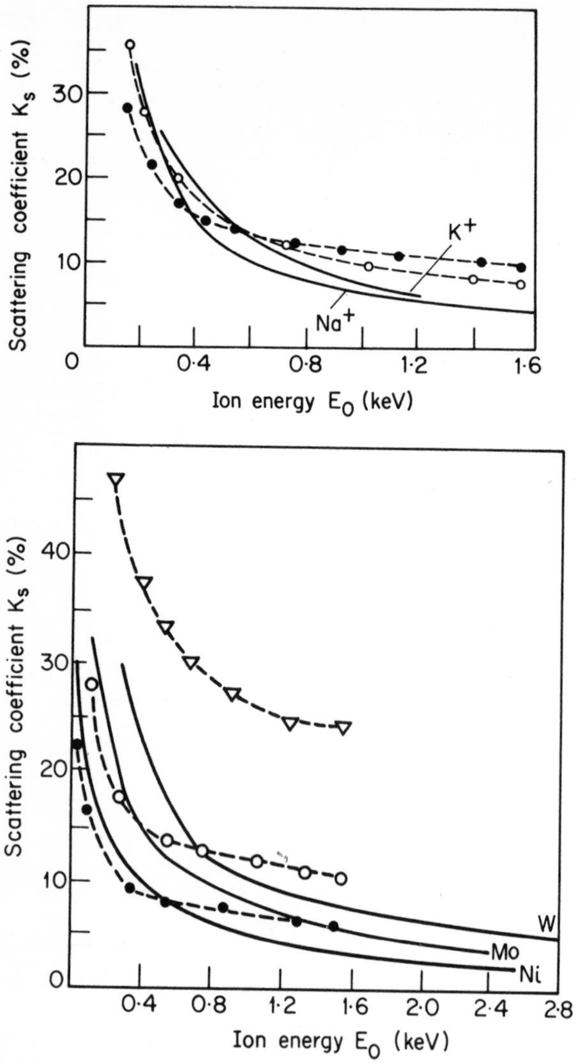

Fig. 4. 25 Comparison of theoretical (continuous curves) and experimental (broken curves) values of the scattering coefficient K_S

(a) Na^+(●) and K^+(○) bombardment of molybdenum

(b) Na^+ bombardment of tungsten (▽), molybdenum (○) and nickel (●).

(Ref. 4. 3)

target lattice and cannot be considered to interact with individual atoms in a scattering event. A theory considering these inelastic processes has been presented by Kaminsky[116] who proposed that the number of particles ejected in an ionized state is governed by the charge-changing collisions between energetic recoil atoms and the quasi-stationary lattice atoms. Simplified expressions for the electron capture (σ_c) and electron loss (σ_L) cross-sections in such interactions have been derived by Bohr and Lindhard[117] as follows

$$\sigma_c = \pi a_0^2 Z_1^2 Z_2^{1/3} (V_0/V)^3 \tag{4.35}$$

$$\sigma_L = \pi a_0^2 Z_2^2 Z_1^{1/3} (V_0/V^*)^3 \tag{4.36}$$

where a_0 (=0. 52 × 10^{-8} cm) is the Bohr radius, Z_1 the effective charge on the moving ion Z_2 the effective charge on the ion at rest V_0 (= e^2/h = 2. 19 × 10^8 cm./sec) is the velocity of an electron in the ground state of a hydrogen atom, V^* is the orbital velocity of the outer electron in the ground state of the lattice ion core and is approximately equal to V the velocity of the recoil ion.

The equilibrium fractions of singly charged (N_i) and neutral (N_0) particles can be written in terms of these cross-sections

$$\left(\frac{N_0}{N}\right)_\infty = \frac{\sigma_c^{10}}{\sigma_c^{10} + \sigma_L^{01}} \tag{4.37}$$

and

$$\left(\frac{N_i}{N}\right)_\infty = \frac{\sigma_L^{01}}{\sigma_L^{01} + \sigma_c^{10}} \tag{4.38}$$

where $N = N_0 + N_i$ and the upper indices indicate the transition of the singly charged ion to a neutral (10) or the inverse process (01).

Applying the above expressions to the case of 40 keV copper atoms recoiling in a copper lattice Kaminsky found $(N_i/N_0)_\infty \simeq 20\%$ which is in reasonable agreement with the experimental value of the ion-atom ejection coefficient. Thus we conclude that at these high ion energies the ionic emission process is governed more by inelastic collision processes and is no longer a simple isolated two atom scattering process.

REFERENCES

1. Hagstrum, H. D. (1961) Phys. Rev. **123**, 758
2. Kaminsky, M. (1964) Atomic and Ionic Impact Phenomena on Metal Surfaces. Springer-Verlag, Berlin
3. Arifov, U. A. (1961) 'Vzaimodeistvie atomnykh chastits s poverkhnost'yu metalla'. Tashkent, UzSSR English translation 'Interaction of Atomic Particles with the Surface of a Metal' (1963) U.S. Joint Publications Research Service Translation AEC-tr-6089. New York
4. Klein, A. L. (1925) Phys. Rev. **26**, 800
5. Arnold, F. C. and Beckett, C. (1938) Proc. Roy. Soc. A. **168**, 103
6. Sloane, R. H. and Press, R. (1938) Proc. Roy. Soc. A **168**, 284
7. Sloane, R. H. and Love, H. M. (1947) Nature **159**, 302
8. Arnot, F. L. and Milligan, J. C. (1936) Proc. Roy. Soc. A **156**, 538
9. Chaudri, R. M. and Khan, A. W. (1947) Nature **159**, 202
10. Oliphant, M. L. E. (1928) Proc. Camb. Phil. Soc. **24**, 451
11. Koch, J. (1936) Zeits. f. Physik **100**, 685
12. Paetow, H. and Walcher, W. (1938) Zeits. f. Physik **110**, 69
13. Healea, M. and Houtermans, C. (1940) Phys. Rev. **58**, 608
14. Mayer, H. (1933) Phil. Mag. **16**, 597
15. Sporn, H. (1939) Zeits. f. Physik **112**, 278
16. Stuart, R. V. and Wehner, G. K. (1960) Phys. Rev. Letters **4**, 409
17. Fluit, J. M., Friedman, L., Eck, J. van, Snoek, C. and Kistemaker, J. (1962) Proc. Fifth Internatl. Conf. on Ionization Phenomena in Gases Munich (1961), 131. North Holland Publishing Co. Amsterdam
18. Kistemaker, J. and Snoek, C., (1962) Le Bombardment Ionique, Colloques International du Centre National de la Recherche Scientifique No. **113**, 51 Bellevue Paris Dec. (1962)
19. Snoek, C., Weg. J. van der and Rol, P. K. (1964) Physica Letters **30**, 341
20. Veksler, V. I. (1963) Fiz. tver. tela **5**, 2737 English translation in Soviet Physics—Solid State (1964) **5**, 2003
21. Veksler, V. I. (1962) Zh. eksper. i teor. fiz. **42**, 325 English translation in Soviet Physics—J.E.T.P. (1962) **15**, 222
22. Brunnée, C. (1957) Zeits. f. Physik **147**, 161
23. Böhmer, H. and Lüscher, E. (1963) Physics Letters **5**, 240
24. Sternberg, D. (1957) Ph. D. Thesis, Univ. of Columbia, U.S.A.
25. Shekhter, Sh. Sh. (1937) Zh. eksper. i teor. fiz. **7**, 750
26. Castaing, R. and Slodzian, G. (1962) J. de Microscopie **1**, 395
27. Bradley, R. C. (1959) J. Appl. Phys. 30, 1
28. Honig, R. E. (1958) J. Appl. Phys. 29, 549
29. Honig, R. E. (1961) Proc. Mass Spectrometry Conf. Oxford
30. Pitzer, K. S. and Clementi, E. (1959) J. Am. Chem. Soc. **81**, 4477
31. Honig, R. E. (1961) Proc. Fifth Internatl. Conf. on Ionization Phenomena in Gases Munich 1961, 118. North Holland Publishing Co. Amsterdam
32. Bradley, R. C. Arking, A. and Beers, D. S. (1960) J. Chem Phys. **33**, 764
33. Bradley, R. C. and Ruedl, E. (1962) Proc. Fifth Internatl. Conf. on Ionization Phenomena in Gases Munich 1961, 150. North Holland Publishing Co. Amsterdam
34. Bradley, R. C. and Ruedl, E. (1962) J. Appl. Phys. **33**, 880
35. Ruedl, E. and Bradley, R. C. (1962) J. Phys. Chem. Solids **23**, 885
36. Langmuir, I. (1918) J. Am. Chem. Soc. **40**, 1361
37. McHugh, J. A. and Sheffield, J. C. (1964) J. Appl. Phys. **35**, 512
38. Hagstrum, H. D. (1953) Phys. Rev. **91**, 543
39. Fogel, Ya, M., Slabospitskii, R. P. and Karnaukhov, I. M. (1960) Zh. tekhn. fiz. (SSSR) **30**, 824, English translation in Soviet Physics—Tech. Phys. (1960) **5**, 777
40. Veksler, V. I. and Shuppe, G. N. (1953) Zh. tekhn. fiz. (SSSR) **23**, 1573
41. Mitropan, I. M. and Gumeniuk, V. S. (1957) Zh. eksper. i teor. fiz. SSSR **32**, 214. English translation in Soviet Physics—J.E.T.P. (1957) **5**, 157
42. Mitropan, I. M. and Gumeniuk, V. S. (1958) Zh. eksper. i teor fiz. SSSR **34**, 235. English translation in Soviet Physics—J.E.T.P. (1958) **7**, 162
43. Krohn, V. E. (1962) J. Appl. Phys. **33**, 3525
44. Arifov, U. A. and Tashkhanova, D. A. (1960) Izv. Akad. Nauk SSSR ser. fiz. **24**, 6664. English translation in Bull. Acad Sci (USSR) Physics Series (1961), 673
45. Arifov, U. A. and Tashkhanova, D. A. (1960) Izv. Akad. Nauk UzSSR ser. fiz-mat. nauk **2**, 61
46. Abroyan, I. A. and Lavrov, V. P. (1962) Fiz. tver. tela **4**, 3254 English translation in Soviet Physics—Solid State (1963) **4**, 2382
47. Kerr, J.T. (1963) Corning Glass Works (USA) Report L-143, January 23rd
48. Eremeev, M. A. (1951) Dokl. Akad. Nauk SSSR **79**, 775
49. Eremeev, M. A. and Shestukhina, V. V. (1952) Zh. tekhn. fiz. **22**, 1262
50. Fogel, Ya. M., Slabospitskii, R. P. and Rastrepin, A. B. (1960) Zh. tekhn. fiz. **30**, 824. English translation in Soviet Physics—Tech. Phys. (1960) **5**, 58
51. Batanov, G. M. (1962) Fiz. tver. tela. **4**, 1778. English translation in Soviet Physics—Solid State (1963) **4**, 1306
52. Batanov, G. M. (1961) Fiz. tver. tela. **3**, 642. English translation in Soviet Physics—Solid State (1961) **3**, 471
53. Petrov, N. N. and Dorozhkin, A. A. (1961) Fiz. tver. tela. **3**, 53. English translation in Soviet Physics—Solid State (1961) **3**, 38
54. Ploch, W. (1951) Zeits. f. Physik **130**, 174
55. Arifov, U. A. and Khadzhimukhamedov, Kh. Kh. (1962) Izv. Akad. Nauk. SSSR ser. fiz. **26**, 1426. English translation in Bull. Acad. Sci. USSR Physics Series (1963) **26**, 1450
56. Arifov, U. A. and Khadzhimukhamedov, Kh. Kh. (1962) Izv. Akad. Nauk SSSR ser. fiz. **26**, 1422. English translation in Bull. Acad. Sci. USSR Physics Series (1963) **26**, 1446
57. Arifov, U. A. and Khadzhimukhamedov, Kh. Kh. (1959) Izv. Akad. Nauk Uz SSR ser. fiz-mat. nauk **2**, 47
58. Riddoch, A. and Leck, J. H. (1958) Proc. Phys. Soc. **72**, 467
59. Arifov, U. A., Ayukhanov, A. Kh. and Gruich, D. D. (1960) Izv. Akad. Nauk SSSR Ser. fiz. **24**, 710 English translation in Bull. Acad. Sci. USSR Physics Series (1961) **24**, 716
60. Arifov, U. A., Ayukhanov, A. Kh., Starodubtsev, S. V. and Khadzhimukhamedov, Kh. Kh. (1959) Dokl. Akad. Nauk (SSSR) **124**, 60 English translation in Soviet Physics—Doklady (1959) **4**, 86

61. Arifov, U. A., Ayukhanov, A. Kh., Starodubtsev, S. V. and Khadzhimukhamedov, Kh. Kh. (1958) Izv. Akad. Nauk UzSSR ser. fiz-mat. nauk **5**, 15

62. Arifov, U. A. and Ayukhanov, A. Kh. (1956) Izv. Akad. Nauk SSSR ser. fiz. **20**, 1165. English translation in Bull. Acad Sci USSR Physics Series (1957) **20**, 1057

63. Arifov, U. A., Ayukhanov, A. Kh. and Starodubtsev, S. V. (1954) Zh. eksper. i teor. fiz. **26**, 714

64. Arifov, U. A. and Ayukhanov, A. Kh. (1954) Zh. eksper. i teor. fiz. **27**, 87

65. Arifov, U. A. and Ayukhanov, A. Kh. (1951) Dokl. Akad. Nauk. Uz. SSR **4**, 12

66. Arifov, U. A., Ayukhanov, A. Kh. and Starodubtsev, S. V. (1957) Zh. eksper. i teor. fiz. **33**, 845. English translation in Soviet Physics—J.E.T.P. (1957) **6**, 653

67. Arifov, U. A., Ayukhanov, A. Kh. and Aliev, A. A. (1962) Izv. Akad. Nauk SSSR ser. fiz. **26**, 1440. English translation in Bull. Acad. Sci. USSR Physics Series (1962) **26**, 1465

68. Healea, M. and Chaffee, E. H. (1936) Phys. Rev. **49**, 925

69. Fogel, Ya. M., Slabospitskii, R. P. and Karnaukhov, I. M. (1960) Zh. tekhn. fiz. SSSR **30**, 824. English translation in Soviet Physics—Tech. Phys. (1961) **5**, 777

70. Walther, V. and Hintenberger, H. (1963) Z. Naturforsch. **18a**, 343

71. Gehrtsen, Chr. (1930) Zeits f. Physik **31**, 948

72. Eremeev, M. A. and Shestukhina, V. V. (1952) Zh. tekhn. fiz. **22**, 1268

73. Eremeev, M. A. (1951) Dokl. Akad. Nauk (SSSR) **79**, 775

74. Panin, B. V. (1961) Zh. eksper. i. teor. fiz. **41**, 3. English translation in Soviet Physics—J.E.T.P. (1962) **14**, 1

75. Petrov, N. N. (1960) Fiz. tver. tela. **2**, 940. English translation in Soviet Physics—Solid State (1960) **2**, 857

76. Leland, W. T. and Olson, R. (1960) Proc. Atomic and Molecular Beams Conference Denver, Colorado, 293

77. Medved, D. B. (1963) J. Appl. Phys. **34**, 3142

78. Comeaux, A. and Medved, D. B. (1963) Proc. 23rd Physical Electronics Conf. March

79. Flaks, I. P. (1955) Zh. tekhn. fiz. (SSSR) **25**, 2463

80. Flaks, I. P. (1955) Zh. tekhn. fiz. (SSSR) **25**, 2467

81. Arifov, U. A., Flyants, N. N. and Ayukhanov, A. Kh. (1961) Dokl. Akad. Nauk UzSSR, **10**

82. Eremeev, M. A. and Zubchaninov, M. V. (1942) Zh. eksper. i teor. fiz. SSSR **12**, 358

83. Gurney, R. W. (1928) Phys. Rev. **32**, 467

84. Longacre, A. (1934) Phys. Rev. **46**, 407

85. Read, G. E. (1928) Phys. Rev. **31**, 629

86. Sawyer, R. B. (1930) Phys. Rev. **35**, 124

87. Sawyer, R. B. (1930) Phys. Rev. **35**, 1090

88. Woodcock, K. S. (1931) Phys. Rev. **38**, 1696

89. Nelson, R. S. and Thompson, M. W. (1963) AERE-Report No. R. 4262

90. Fluit, J. M., Kistemaker, J. and Snoek, C. (1964) Physica **30**, 870

91. Kirchner, F. and Benninghoven, A. (1964) Physics Letters **8**, 193

92. Veksler, V. I. (1960) Zh. eksper. i. teor. fiz. SSSR **38**, 324 English translation in Soviet Physics—J.E.T.P. (1960) **11**, 235

93. Stanton, H. E. (1960) J. Appl. Phys. **31**, 678

94. Arifov, U. A., Ayukhanov, A. Kh. and Aliev, A. A. (1961) Izv. Akad. Nauk UzSSR ser. fiz. -mat. nauk **6**, 57

95. Petrov, N. N. (1960) Fiz. tver. tela. **2**, 940. English translation in Soviet Physics—Solid State (1960) **2**, 857

96. Panin, B. V. (1962) Zh. eksper. i teor. fiz. SSSR **42**, 313 English translation in Soviet Physics—J.E.T.P. (1962) **15**, 215

97. Walther, V. and Hintenberger, H. (1962) Z. Naturforsch. **17a**, 694

98. Datz, S. and Snoek, C. (1964) Phys. Rev. **134A**, 347

99. Parilis, E. S. and Turaev, N. Yu. (1965) Dokl. Akad. Nauk SSSR **161**, 84 English translation in Soviet Physics—Doklady (1965), **10**, 212

100. Molchanov, V. A. and Shoshka V. (1964) Dokl. Akad. Nauk SSSR **155**, 70 English translation in Soviet Physics—Doklady (1964) **9**, 209

101. Arifov, U. A., Ayukhanov, A. Kh. and Aliev, A. A. (1964) Izv. Akad. Nauk UzSSSR ser. fiz. -mat. nauk 4

102. Mashkova, E. S. and Molchanov, V. A. (1962) Dokl. Akad. Nauk SSSR **146**, 585. English translation in Soviet Physics—Doklady (1962) **7**, 829

103. Snoek, C. Weg. W. F. Van der, Geballe, R. and Rol, P. K. (1965) F. O. M. Laboratory Report Amsterdam

104. Mashkova, E. S. and Molchanov, V. A. (1965) Zh. Tekhn. Fiz. **35**, 1321 English translation in Soviet Phys.—Techn. Phys. (1966) **10**, 449

105. Mashkova, E. S., Molchanov, V. A., Parilis, E. S. and Turaev, N. Yu (1965) Physics Letters **18**, 7

106. Dahl, P. and Magyar, J. (1965) Phys. Rev. **140A**, 1420

107. Everhart, E., Stone, G. and Carbone, R. J. (1955) Phys. Rev. **99**, 1287

108. Morgan, G. H. and Everhart, E. (1962) Phys. Rev. **128**, 667

109. Petrov, N. N. (1960) Fiz. tver. tela. **2**, 949 English translation in Soviet Phys.-Solid State (1960) **2**, 865

110. Kingdon, K. H. and Langmuir, I. (1923) Phys. Rev. **21**, 380

111. Zemel, J. (1958) J. Chem. Phys. **28**, 410

112. Roos, O. Von (1957) Zeits. f. Physik **147**, 184

113. Vapnik, V. N., Gurvich, L. G. and Zinov'ev, N. V. (1960) Izv. Akad. Nauk SSSR Ser. fiz. **24**, 685 English translation in Bull. Acad. Sci. USSR Physics Series (1960) **24**, 692

114. Arifov, U. A. and Khadzhimukhamedov, Kh. Kh. (1960) Izv. Akad. Nauk. UzSSR Ser. fiz. -mat. nauk **2**, 61

115. Arifov, U. A. and Khadzhimukhamedov, Kh. Kh. (1961) Izv. Akad. Nauk UzSSR Ser. fiz. -mat. nauk **5**, (1961)

116. Kaminsky, M. (1964) Argonne National Lab. Report

117. Bohr, N. and Lindhard, J, (1954) Kgl. Danske Videnskab Selskab Mat-fys Medd **28**, 1

118. Hagstrum, H. D. (1960) Phys. Rev. **119**, 940

119. Hagstrum, H. D. (1956) Phys. Rev. **104**, 672

CHAPTER 5

The Penetration of Ions

As we have seen in previous discussion, an energetic ion on collision with a solid surface has a high probability of electron capture and neutralisation. In the following we shall generally assume that this uncharged state is maintained by the incident particle during its subsequent progress through the solid. This assumption is open to criticism when the particle velocity becomes comparable to the electron orbital velocities of the particle or the struck lattice atoms. For the time being however we shall assume that the collisions are purely elastic and can therefore be treated by the methods developed in the earlier part of Chapter 2. In some practical cases the particle energy will exceed A. Kev (the approximate criterion for the onset of excitation and ionisation losses) and therefore to allow comparison of data from these experiments, with theory, a short discussion on the effects of inelastic collisions will also be given.

If we wish to consider the motion of the incident particle after its first impact with the macroscopic surface, we may assume that interactions with the lattice atoms are via isolated two body collisions only, and the trajectory of the particle is determined by the collision parameters at each isolated impact. Thus, a particle incident at some arbitrary surface point, in a given direction, may suffer a collision with a lattice atom at, or close to, the surface. The particle will suffer energy loss and be deflected into a new trajectory according to the magnitude of its initial energy and the value of the impact parameter for the collision. It may then travel some distance before encountering another lattice atom and again suffer energy loss and deflection from the original direction. In this way, via a succession of elastic collisions, the incident particle will slow down until it no longer possesses sufficient kinetic energy to surmount the potential energy barriers offered by the lattice atoms. In the remainder of this discussion we shall assume that when an incident atom has slowed down to an energy of 25eV it becomes 'frozen' into the lattice, either as an interstitial, a lattice, or a foreign substitutional atom. The choice of 25eV is based on criteria which will be developed in greater detail in the discussion of radiation damage, and it is sufficient to accept here that this energy is of the order of magnitude of the dynamic potentials offered to a moving atom by the surrounding lattice.

Clearly one may start the primary from any surface point, with a spatial distribution of incident directions, and the collisions made by any primary ion moving through the lattice will be entirely different from those of any other primaries. Consequently it cannot be expected that all primaries will become frozen into the lattice at precisely the same depth below the surface and, it must be anticipated that some penetration distribution function will result, such that from a known incident number of primaries with a defined energy and direction of incidence, a specific fraction will penetrate a known distance below the surface. Recently, experiments[1] have been conducted which determine the form of this penetration function for a number of different incident atoms, or various target materials over a wide range of energy, and it is a primary aim of the present discussion to investigate if these observed penetration functions can be predicted theoretically. The primary atoms, in coming to rest in the lattice lose their energy via a succession of elastic collisions in which energy is transferred to virtually stationary lattice atoms and eventually dissipated in the form of heat or stored potential energy of the lattice. The energies which bind the lattice, are as regards dynamic displacements, only of the order of 25eV and it is evident that because of collisions between the primary and lattice atoms, some of these latter may be removed from their normal positions, thus radiation damage has occurred. If sufficient energy is transferred to surface (or para surface) atoms, it may result in their removal from the solid and constitute sputtering. Whilst these two topics are the subjects of discussion in later chapters we must bear them in mind in the present analysis, since it is clear that damage of the interior or recession of the surface, both resulting in non-normally placed lattice atoms could have large effects on the trajectories of primary particles i.e. two particles starting with exactly the same incidence parameters but separated in time may not experience the same subsequent interactions with the lattice since the former would cause lattice rearrangement. To date no theoretical evaluations of penetration functions have considered these effects and in the following we must therefore ignore them in a first approximation.

A further influence upon the trajectory of the primaries will be the primaries which have been previously 'locked' in the lattice. If the earlier primaries have been stopped in non-normal lattice positions, or if the size of the primary differs markedly from a lattice atom although it is located at a normal site, the scattering of later primaries will differ markedly from a primary free lattice. Such effects of sorbed primaries upon the penetration function of subsequent atoms have been reported experimentally and certainly exist. Again however, theoretical calculations have not been able to include such effects realistically and so in the simple treatment presented here we ignore their influence. A further effect which we may mention, but exclude from consideration, is the possibility of knocking on of trapped atoms by later primaries. This will influence the penetration distribution, and has, in fact been experimentally observed to do so.

It may be argued that such effects will not assume importance until large numbers of primaries have entered the lattice, but this is not acceptable since the extent of radiation damage to a lattice may considerably exceed the primary path as a result of the long range particle and energy transmission processes such as channelling[2,3,4,5] and focusing which we shall consider in this and subsequent discussion. Moreover the effects of annealing out damage produced in the lattice will also be of some importance in realistic penetration analyses, but again this is difficult to treat in a straightforward manner and will not be considered. Despite these oversimplifications in ignoring events correlated with the primary collision sequence however, we may anticipate that a theoretical evaluation of penetration distances or ranges will be of value in assessing the general properties of the particle stopping process. Indeed we will see that even more restrictive assumptions are necessary to arrive at tractable solutions for penetration parameters, and it turns out that these restrictions still allow an adequate representation of the real problem.

Initially, therefore, we shall survey the theoretical background to penetration problems and compare the results with those obtained experimentally and by studies using computer techniques to simulate the collisions between primaries and a lattice. This latter technique is currently of very great value in penetration phenomenon analysis since it can be used to bridge the gap between theory and experiment and show in what respects theoretical treatments can be improved to give better representation of the actual processes occurring. The computer analyses have in fact gone further than this and predicted effects which should have been observed experimentally and later shown to exist, thus testifying to their utility.

In order to investigate the properties of penetration functions we must first define the parameters in which we shall be interested. Clearly we are not concerned with the path and subsequent resting point of one incident primary only, but in the statistics of these parameters when counted over a large or infinite number of primary histories. For definition purposes however it is convenient to consider a typical trajectory of one primary (although as we have seen no one primary can really be considered typical, because of the infinite variety of trajectories) and to discuss parameters associated with this trajectory and final resting point.

5.2 RANGE QUANTITIES

In figure 5.1 the paths of two typical primaries are shown to illustrate the point about the diversity of individual trajectories. The two primaries have been assumed to enter the solid at two slightly different points and it is apparent that this fact alone has accounted for their subsequently different flight paths. In this connection it should be pointed out that all theoretical, and to date computer, analyses assume collisions with an ideal atomically plane surface, devoid of any imperfections, and in which the interatomic spacing is identical with that within the bulk of a perfect lattice. It is evident that such conditions are almost impossible to duplicate experimentally.

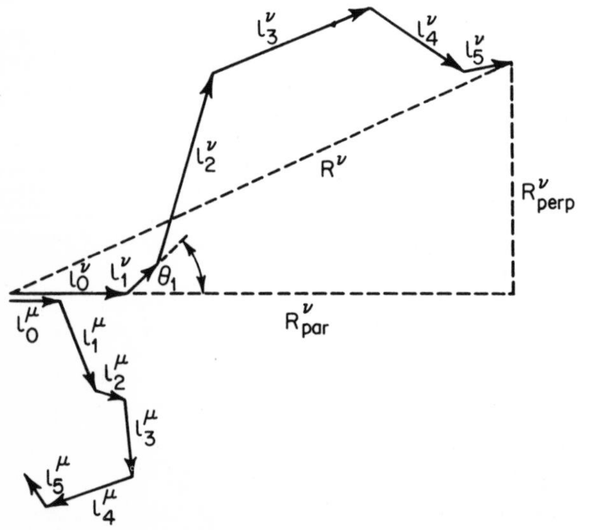

Fig. 5.1 The paths of two primary atoms broken up into linear segments.

From Fig. 5.1 if we consider the path of the νth atom, made-up of a number of approximately linear segments between collisions with lattice atoms, then the total path length is given by

$$L^{(\nu)} = l_0^{(\nu)} + l_1^{(\nu)} + l_2^{(\nu)} + \ldots . \; l_n^{(\nu)} \qquad 5.1$$

where the sum is terminated in the nth flight path at which the primary becomes trapped in the lattice. The actual paths $l_0(\nu)\ldots\ldots l_n(\nu)$ will not, of course, be exactly linear, since the moving primary will always be influenced by lattice forces. However, for convenience we represent these paths as linear, with directional changes only at impacts between the primary and a lattice atom. This essentially regards the primary lattice atoms as hard elastic spheres and this representation, as we shall see, is most useful in range determinations.

The average total path over the distribution is thus

$$\overline{L} = \frac{1}{N}\sum_{\nu=1}^{\nu=N} L^{(\nu)} \qquad 5.2$$

for a number N of incident primaries (which may be conceptually infinite, in which case 5.2 passes into an integral form).

The vector range $R^{(\nu)}$ is the distance from the initial point of entry of the primary to its final resting point, and is generally used to denote merely the magnitude of this distance independent of the angular displacement. If $F(\underline{r})d\underline{r}$ is the normalised spatial distribution of final resting positions, then the average vector range is given by

$$R = \frac{1}{N}\sum_{\nu=1}^{\nu=N} R^{(\nu)} = \int rF(\underline{r})d\underline{r} \qquad 5.3$$

Normalisation is achieved by requiring the total number of trapped atoms to equal the total number incident N (less any which may escape through the boundaries of the solid).

The penetration $R_{par}{}^{(\nu)}$ is the projection of the vector distance to the final resting position onto the original direction of the motion. Thus

$$R_{par} = \underline{r} \cdot \underline{v_0}/v_0 \qquad 5.4$$

where $\underline{v_0}$ is the initial velocity vector.

Thus the average penetration

$$\overline{R}_{par} = \int \underline{r} \cdot \underline{v_0}/v_0 \cdot F(\underline{r})d\underline{r} \qquad 5.5$$

The spread in stopping points perpendicular to the initial direction of motion R_{perp} is obtained similarly to R_{par} but through resolution in a direction perpendicular to this latter, $\overline{R}_{perp}$ is also obtained similarly. In this latter determination, the particular axis chosen will be unimportant for $F(\underline{r})d\underline{r}$ has azimuthal symmetry about the axis determined by $\underline{v_0}/v_0$.

In many experimental range determinations, the measured parameters are concerned with penetration parallel to the initial velocity vector and the projected R_{par} and R_{perp} are of considerable importance. We are therefore concerned also with the projected distribution function f(x)dx where the x direction is assumed to coincide with the initial direction of motion i.e. the velocity vector.

This distribution function may be evaluated from F(r) dr through resolution in the x direction.

Other parameters of significance will be the median range R_m such that half the primaries are slowed down within this range and defined thus

$$\int_0^{R_m} F(r)dr = 1/2, \qquad 5.6$$

from which median values are immediately obtainable.

The mean squares of the quantities R, R_{par}, R_{perp} (viz R^2, R^2_{par}, R^2_{perp}) will also be relevant since these will be typical of the deviations from the average values, i.e. they will indicate the probable spread in values of the appropriate ranges or the skewness of the distribution of ranges. Higher order powers of the range quantities may also be of importance and should be mentioned, whilst the most probable ranges, R_{mp}; $R_{par.\,mp}$; $R_{perp.\,mp}$., will indicate the spatial positions where most primaries are brought to rest.

Thus $R_{m.\,p}$ is defined by

$$\frac{\delta}{\delta r}(F(r)) = 0 \qquad 5.7$$

and

$$\frac{\delta^2}{\delta r^2}(F(r)) \text{ should be negative.}$$

Similar values for the most probable projected ranges follow from this definition. If the number of collisions in a given life history is $N_c^{(\nu)}$ then the average number of collisions over all N primaries is

$$\overline{N}_c = \frac{1}{N}\sum_{\nu=1}^{N} N_c^{(\nu)} \qquad 5.8$$

$\overline{N}_c$ has a finite value, only if the primaries are considered to be lost from the incident flux when their kinetic energy has fallen below a certain finite value (25eV for example) rather than to zero energy; this latter condition generally requiring an infinite number of collisions. Finally the energy transfer spectrum f(T)dT, the average number of struck atoms which receive energies in the range $T \rightarrow T + \delta T$ will also be a useful parameter of some value.

From this point several different methods of evaluation of the above parameters are possible and in the following we will discuss these various solutions to the problem. Most analytical calculations, to date, however, have been unable to take into account the correct arrangement of the lattice atoms in the solid, although several important exceptions may be found in the investigations of Thompson and Nelson, [2,3] Lehmann and Leibfried[4] and Lindhard.[5] These calculations will be discussed shortly, but considerable simplification of the analysis is achieved if we assume, as have most previous analyses, that the real solid lattice arrangement can be replaced by a random array of atoms with a density chosen to represent, as closely as possible, the real lattice. This randomisation is achieved by introduction of the mean free path concept.

5.3 THE MEAN FREE PATH ASSUMPTION

In the classical kinetic theory of gases,[6] one of the most useful concepts is the mean free path, or the average distance between interatomic collisions which the atoms can travel in essentially unperturbed motion. In gaseous mechanics the assumption of collision free flights is readily justified in view of the large distances between atoms compared with the extent of the (important) interatomic forces. When one considers collisions of a fast primary with a solid lattice one is on much less firm ground, since as we have already argued, although each collision is essentially an isolated two body process, both before and after collision, the primary is moving in the fields of force of many lattice atoms. Indeed calculations which ignore this real interaction between the primary, and as we shall show subsequently, the lattice, miss many of the important features of penetration. Nevertheless as a first approximation we will treat the solid as a highly compressed gas and allow it the appropriate properties. Several factors which we have ignored, in fact, tend to make randomisation of the lattice acceptable. Thus radiation damage to the lattice will destroy much of the initial lattice order, whilst thermal oscillation and zero point motion of the atoms will have a similar effect.

From simple kinetic theory considerations, it is easily shown that the average uninterrupted path between collisions of a 'marked' primary atom and other atoms, is given by

$$\lambda(E) = \frac{1}{n.\,\sigma(E)} \qquad 5.9$$

where $\lambda(E)$ is the mean free path between collisions at the primary energy E, n* is the atomic density and $\sigma(E)$ is a cross section for interatomic collisions. If the atoms are assumed to be hard elastic spheres of radius R_0, then, as seen in Chapter 2 the cross section for elastic collisions $\sigma(E)$ is simply given by

$$\sigma(E) = \pi\, 4R_0^2 = \pi r_0^2 \qquad 5.10$$

where r_0 is the distance of closest approach of the atomic centres in a collision.

The probability of a path of length between l and $l + \delta l$ at an energy E is also readily derived to be

$$P.(l)dl = \frac{1}{\lambda(E)} \exp\left[-l/\lambda(E)\right]dl \qquad 5.11$$

With these equations it is possible to evaluation the parameters shown in Figure 5.1 and discussed in 5.2 in terms of the primary mean free path $\lambda(E_0)$ at the initial energy of the primary (E_0) and we shall illustrate this shortly. It is often more convenient to consider the collisions in terms of the cross section σ_c or even the differential cross section $d\sigma(T)_c$ for a specific energy transfer T, and it is this approach, originally used by Bohr[7] and more recently by Lindhard and others,[8,9] which we shall discuss first.

5.4 THE SPECIFIC ENERGY LOSS METHOD

In Figure 5.1 the trajectory of a typical primary is shown, broken up into segments, each of which corre-

---

* n will be chosen in randomised model so that the correct solid density is preserved.

sponds to a collision between the primary and a target atom. In this respect there is a resemblance to the actual trajectory of a primary in a real lattice in that the overall trajectory is made up of a succession of isolated encounters with lattice atoms, each contributing something to the final deflection. With the mean free path assumption, one can go to the extreme and consider that the primary loses energy continuously along its path. Thus if we consider the average over an infinite number of primaries, the average energy loss of these per unit path length is given by $T_{AV}X$ (average number of collisions/unit path length), where T_{AV} = average energy loss per collision.

The average number of collisions/unit length is given simply by $1/\lambda(E_0)$ whilst the average energy loss T_{AV} is given by

$$\frac{1}{\sigma}\int_0^{T_m} T d\sigma(T)_c \qquad 5.12$$

i.e. the normalised integral over all possible values of the energy loss, with σ the total collision cross section and $d\sigma(T)$ the differential collision cross section for energy transfer T. The rate of energy loss/unit path is thus given by

$$\frac{1}{\lambda \cdot \sigma}\int_0^{T_m} T d\sigma(T)_c = n\int_0^{T_m} T d\sigma(T)_c \qquad 5.13$$

and this is known as the 'Specific energy loss'. The energy loss in a path length $d\bar{L}$ is thus given by

$$dE = d\bar{L}\cdot n\int_0^{T_m} T d\sigma(T)_c \,;\therefore \frac{dE}{d\bar{L}} = n\int_0^{T_m} T d\sigma(T)_c \qquad 5.14.1$$

which we can also write as the 'stopping power' S, where the stopping power $S = n\sigma$ and where σ is the total stopping cross section. Thus the rate of energy loss at an energy $E' = n\sigma(E') = \frac{dE'}{dL}$ and integration shows, that for an initial energy E_0, the average total path length $\bar{L}$ is given by

$$\int d\bar{L} = \bar{L} = \int_0^{E_0} \frac{dE'}{dE'/d\bar{L}} = \frac{1}{n}\int_0^{E} dE'/\sigma(E') \qquad 5.14.2$$

if the primaries are assumed to slow down to rest before trapping occurs.

One may also deduce the range straggling, or the average square fluctuation in range, since the average square fluctuation in energy loss

$$(\overline{\Delta E^2}) = n\Omega^2 d\bar{L} \qquad 5.15.1.$$

where

$$\Omega^2 = \int_0^{T_m} T^2 d\sigma(T) \qquad 5.15.2$$

is proportional to the average square energy loss per collision. Thus there may be an average square error in $\bar{L}$ at each energy loss given by

$$(\Delta\bar{L}^2) = (\Delta E^2)\left(\frac{\partial \bar{L}}{\partial E}\right)^2 = n\Omega^2 d\bar{L}\left(\frac{d\bar{L}}{dE}\right)^2$$
$$= n\Omega^2 dE\left(\frac{d\bar{L}}{dE}\right)^3 \qquad 5.15.3$$

and thus the average square fluctuation in the total path is given by

$$(\Delta\bar{L}^2) = \frac{1}{n^2}\int_0^E \frac{dE'\,\Omega^2(E')}{\sigma^3(E')} \qquad 5.15.4$$

As simple examples of the use of these equations, we may consider the values of $\bar{L}$ for collisions between hard spheres the cross section of which is a) independent of energy and b) a simple function of energy

(a) If the hard sphere radius is energy independent, the total energy transfer collision cross section $\sigma(E')$ is simply

$$\int_0^{E'} \frac{T\,.\,4\pi R_0^2\,dt}{E'} = E'\,.\,2\pi R_0^2 \qquad 5.16$$

and $\bar{L} = \infty$ because of the lower limit of zero in the integral. Thus, $\bar{L}$ can be rendered finite, only by introduction of a lower limiting real energy transfer.

(b) If we assume that the interatomic potential is of the Bohr type

$$V(r) = \frac{A}{r}\exp\left(-\frac{r}{a}\right)$$

then as we have seen earlier, this potential may be approximated by an inverse power potential

$$V(r) = \frac{c}{r^s}.$$

By matching both potential and the slope of the potential at an interatomic spacing r_0 it is, as we have shown in Equation 2.46 readily seen that

$$V(r_0) = \frac{c}{r_0(1 + r_0/a)} \qquad 5.17.1$$

where r_0 is the distance of closest approach in a head-on collision at the energy E_R^1. Bohr[7] reasoned that in many cases of high energy bombardment the distance r_0 would be of order a, and the interatomic potential then reduces to $V(r_0) \simeq c/r_0^2$.

r_0 may now be taken as twice the radii of the collision partners, assuming that these are now hard spheres, with a radius varying with energy through the relation

$$V(r_0) = E_R' = \frac{E'}{2} = \frac{c}{r_0^2} \qquad 5.17.2$$

for primary and struck atoms of equal mass

Thus

$$r_0 = \left(\frac{2c}{E'}\right)^{1/2}$$

and

$$\sigma(E') = \int_0^{E'} \frac{T\,.\,2\pi c}{(E')^2}\,dT = \pi c \qquad 5.17.3$$

Hence

$$\bar{L} = \frac{E}{n\pi c} \qquad 5.17.4$$

For a general mass ratio A, with $C = Z_1Z_2e^2a_2$ one further deduces

$$\overline{L} = \left\{\frac{1 + A}{2A} \cdot \frac{1}{n\pi Z_1 Z_2 e^2 a_2}\right\} \cdot E_0 \qquad 5.17.5$$

It is interesting to observe that the mean free path at an energy E_0

$$\lambda(E_0) = \frac{1}{n\pi(r_0)^2} = \frac{E_0}{2n\pi c} \qquad 5.17.6$$

Thus the average range is just twice the primary mean free path at the incident energy.

In this case it is also deduced that

$$(\Delta\overline{L}^2) = \frac{E_0^2}{3n^2\pi^2c^2} \qquad 5.17.7$$

Bohr[7] has shown that such expression are obeyed quite accurately for the range of heavy primaries in light substances (e.g. fission fragments in hydrogen gas).

Both Bohr[7] and Nielsen[9] have made similar calculations to that in the above example for the case $s = 2$, but have not used the intermediate step of the hard sphere approximation to obtain the differential cross section. Thus the differential cross for energy transfer $d\sigma(T)_c$ may be deduced from the scattering law from an inverse r^2 potential (which is somewhat different from that from a hard sphere). For the r^{-2} potential, the scattering angle is related to p via the relation,

$$\phi = \pi\left\{1 - \left(1 + \left(\frac{p}{p_c}\right)^2\right)^{-1/2}\right\} \qquad 5.18.1$$

where $p_c = \frac{b \cdot a}{e}$ and $\overline{L}$ may be calculated to be

$$\overline{L} = \frac{5}{32\pi n a_0} \cdot \frac{(Z_1^{2/3} + Z_2^{2/3})^{1/2}}{Z_1 Z_2 e} \cdot \frac{1 + A}{A} \cdot E \qquad 5.18.2$$

It is often assumed that the distribution functions for ranges $F(r)dr$, $f(\overline{L})d\overline{L}$ obey Gaussian distributions about the mean values, although experiments have recently revealed the innaccuracy of this assumption. Nevertheless, assumption of such a distribution does reveal the value of the parameters $\overline{L}$ and $(\Delta\overline{L}^2)$.

A Gaussian distribution of path lengths L may be expressed as

$$f(\overline{L})d\overline{L} = \frac{1}{\sqrt{2\pi}} \frac{1}{(\Delta\overline{L}^2)^{1/2}} \exp - \left\{\frac{L - \overline{L}}{2\Delta\overline{L}^2}\right\} \qquad 5.19$$

involving both the average path length and the mean square fluctuation in this function. Comparison between this assumed, and other more realistic or experimentally determined functions will later show the value of these range parameters.

The second example b) given here is just one of a class of hard-sphere models described by Holmes[10] as consistent. This implies that the mean free path assumption is used in such a way that it is energy dependent via the relation

$$\lambda(E) = \frac{1}{n\pi r_0^2}$$

r_0 itself is energy dependent through the relation $V(r_0) = E_R$. In the example r_0 was evaluated through the intermediate step of matching the Bohr potential to the inverse power potential c/r^s and assuming $s = 2$. In general s will vary considerably with energy as a primary slows down by collision and one must be prepared for different results for path lengths than the simple value deduced. Lindhard, Scharff and Schiøtt[8,11] have used this method to deduce range relations, when the interatomic potential has been assumed to be represented by the power law $V(r) = c/r^s$ or by a screened form of the Thomas-Fermi[12] type $V(r) = \frac{c}{r}\phi\left(\frac{r}{a}\right)$. The effects of inelastic losses have also been included in this evaluation, as we shall now show.

For an interatomic potential of the inverse power type

$$V(r) = \frac{c}{r^s}; \qquad 5.20.1$$

with

$$C = \frac{Z_1 Z_2 e^2 a_s^{s-1}}{s} \qquad 5.20.2$$

and

$$a_s = 0.8843\, a_0 Z^{-1/3} \qquad 5.20.3$$

these authors have shown that the differential cross section for elastic collision transfer of energy T is given by

$$d\sigma_n = \frac{C_n}{T_m^{1-1/s}} \frac{dT}{T^{1+1/s}} \text{ for } s \geqslant 1 \qquad 5.20.4$$

with

$$T_m = \gamma E_0 = \frac{4M_1M_2}{(M_1 + M_2)^2} \cdot E_0 \qquad 5.20.5$$

C_n is connected to the stopping cross section σ by the relation

$$C_n = \frac{\pi}{s}\left[b^2 a_s^{2s-2} \cdot \frac{3s - 1}{8s^2}\right]^{1/s} \cdot T_m$$

$$= \left\{1 - \frac{1}{s}\right\}\sigma_n, \text{ and } b = \frac{Z_1 Z_2 e^2}{E_R} \qquad 5.20.7$$

It is generally found convenient to introduce scaling parameters

$$\rho = \overline{L}\left\{n \cdot 4\pi a^2 \frac{M_1 M_2}{(M_1 + M_2)^2}\right\} \qquad 5.21.1$$

and

$$\varepsilon = E\left\{\frac{aM_2}{Z_1 Z_2 e^2 (M_1 + M_2)}\right\} \qquad 5.21.2$$

for range and energy, and with this notation, one obtains a universal differential cross section for scattering from a power law potential

$$d\sigma = \pi a^2 \frac{d\varepsilon}{2t^{3/2}} \lambda_s t^{1/2-1/s},$$

with

$$t^{1/2} = \varepsilon\left(\frac{T}{T_m}\right)^{1/2}$$

and

$$0.3 \leqslant \lambda_s \leqslant 1 \qquad 5.22.2$$

For a Thomas-Fermi potential

$$d\sigma = \pi a^2 \frac{dt}{t^{2/3}} \cdot f(t^{1/2}) \qquad 5.23.1$$

where the function $f(t^{1/2})$ has been evaluated numerically by the authors. The stopping power for elastic collisions dE/dL can then be rewritten in terms of

$$\frac{d\varepsilon}{d\rho} = \int_0^{\varepsilon^2} \frac{dt}{t^{3/2}} \cdot f(t^{1/2}) \frac{1}{\varepsilon} \qquad 5.24$$

and this can again be evaluated numerically for the Thomas-Fermi function and for a general inverse power function. The result for $s = 2$ can be easily evaluated analytically as we essentially showed in example b) above, and the results of calculations of $d\varepsilon/d\rho$ from the Thomas-Fermi potential and the inverse r^2 potential are compared in Figure 5.2 plotted as a function of $\varepsilon^{1/2}$ (representative of the primary velocity). Clearly the r^{-2} potential gives values of $d\varepsilon/d\rho$ which are energy independent whilst the Thomas-Fermi potential gives values both above and below this depending upon the primary energy.

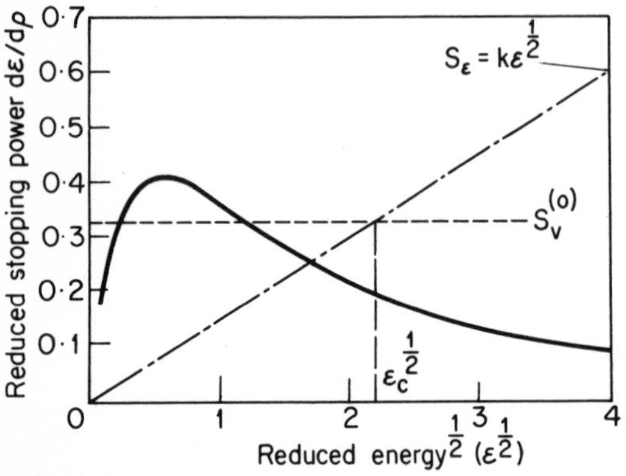

Fig. 5.2 Reduced stopping power as a function of reduced energy for elastic collisions assuming a Thomas-Fermi interatomic potential (———) and an r^{-2} interatomic potential (- - - - -) and for inelastic collisions with the parameter $k = 0.15$ (· — · — · — ·) (viz. Ref. 5.8)

At high energies, where the primary velocity compares in magnitude to the electron orbital velocities, some account must be taken of inelastic collisions.

As we have seen Lindhard and Scharff[11] have proposed that at primary velocities $v < v_0 Z_1^{-2/3}$ the stopping power is directly velocity dependent and one can then express

$$\left\{\frac{d\varepsilon}{d\rho}\right\}_{inelastic} = k\varepsilon^{1/2} \qquad 5.25.1$$

with

$$k = \xi_e \cdot \frac{0.0793\, Z_1^{1/2} Z_2^{1/2} (A_1 + A_2)^{3/2}}{(Z_1^{2/3} + Z_2^{2/3})^{3/4} A_1^{3/2} A_2^{1/2}}$$

and

$$\xi_e \cong Z_1^{1/6} \qquad 5.25.2$$

Except for values of $Z_1 \ll Z_2$ it is easily shown that k is less than unity and generally of order 0.1 to 0.2. Thus, for purposes of comparison, the stopping power for $k = 0.15$ is included in Figure 5.2 for inelastic losses. Clearly elastic losses dominate until ε is of the order of ε_c but as pointed out by Lindhard et al,[8,11] the values of $(d\varepsilon/d\rho)$ elastic, derivable from the Thomas-Fermi potential are probably erroneous for values of ε less than 10^{-2} since the Thomas Fermi potential is probably a poor approximation for large impact parameters, which for $\varepsilon < 10^{-2}$ corresponds to $p \gtrsim 100a$. By means of these stopping power formulae and use of the numerical data shown in Figure 5.2 it is a straightforward matter to now calculate the range relationships as a function of primary energy.

If, initially we consider elastic collisions only, we see that

$$\bar{\rho} = \int_0^{\varepsilon} \frac{d\varepsilon}{\left|\frac{d\varepsilon}{d\rho}\right|_{elastic}} \qquad 5.26$$

and the range ρ is a function of ε only for all primary and target masses.

Using the curves in Figure 5.2 for $\frac{d\varepsilon}{d\rho}$ as a function of ε, values of $\bar{\rho}$ as a function of ε are readily computed numerically, and these are shown in Figure 5.3 for the Thomas-Fermi potential and the r^{-2} approximation. This latter is a straight line corresponding to $\bar{\rho} = 3.06\,\varepsilon$ an expression already deduced by Bohr[7] and Neilsen[9]. The Thomas-Fermi potential leads to $\bar{\rho}$ values above this line at low ε values where the effective potential becomes dependent upon distance to a power of r numerically greater than —2.

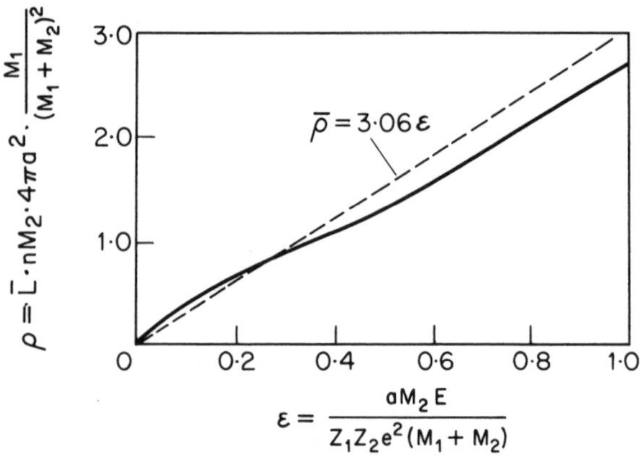

Fig. 5.3 Reduced Range-Energy plots derived assuming a Thomas-Fermi Potential (———) or an r^{-2} interatomic potential (- - - -) (viz. Ref. 5.8 and 5.11)

At higher energies, the stopping power, evident from Figure 5.2 increases above the r^{-2} stopping and so the range-energy falls below the $\bar{\rho} = 3.06\,\varepsilon$ line, whilst at still higher energies scattering becomes of the Rutherford (r^{-1}) type and the range again rises above the straight line. This behaviour is clear in Figure 5.3.

The Thomas-Fermi $\bar{\rho}/\varepsilon$ plot must be expected to be adequate at intermediate energies, but not at very low ε values (10^{-2}) or at higher energies where inelastic losses will become predominant.

If we allow for inelastic losses at intermediate energies $(v \lesssim v_0 Z_1^{-2/3})$ and assume a reduced stopping cross power proportional to $\varepsilon^{1/2}$ the differential cross section due to elastic and inelastic losses may be written

$$\frac{d\varepsilon}{d\rho} = \frac{d\varepsilon}{d\rho}_{elastic} + k\varepsilon^{1/2} \qquad 5.28$$

This relation may be now used to evaluate the range $\bar{\rho}$ inserting $\frac{d\varepsilon}{d\rho}$ for $|\frac{d\varepsilon}{d\rho}|$ elastic in Equation 5.26 and since, in general, $0 < k < 0.5$ the appropriate $\bar{\rho}/\varepsilon$ relations may be computed numerically for typical values of k. This is shown in Figs. 5.4a, b also, for k values of 0.05, 0.1, 0.2 and 0.4, from which it is evident that the effect of inelastic collisions are important even at moderately low ε values. The general effect of even small k values is to depress the $\bar{\rho}/\varepsilon$ curve below the $\bar{\rho} = 3.06\varepsilon$ line.

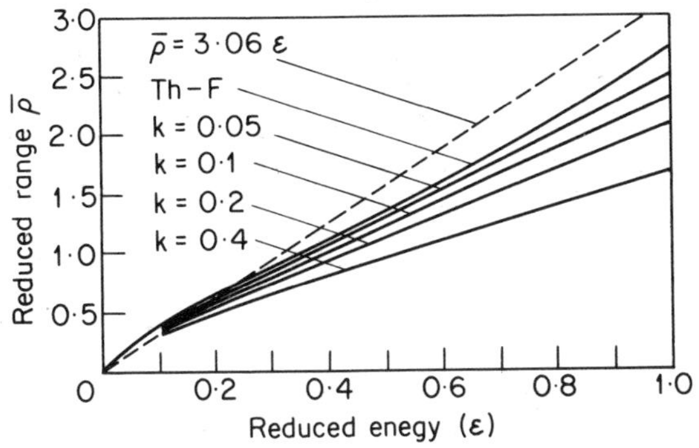

Fig. 5.4a Reduced range-energy plots assuming elastic collisions and a Thomas-Fermi interatomic potential (Curve Th-F), an r^{-2} interatomic potential (— — — —) and for a Thomas-Fermi interatomic potential including inelastic losses for various values of the parameter k. (viz. Ref 5.8)

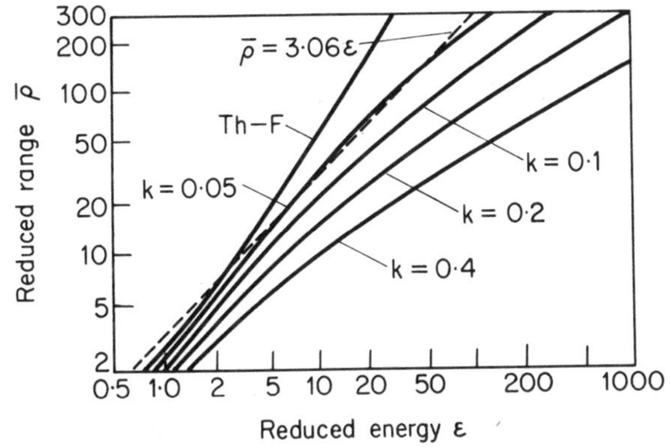

Fig. 5.4b Reduced range-energy plots as in Fig. 5.4a continued to higher ε values

Thus it is possible, in a given experimental determination of $\{\bar{L}/E\}$ to compare the observations with a variety of theoretical $\bar{\rho}/\varepsilon$ curves and determine the k value which give the best fit; hence to determine the importance of inelastic collisions. Lindhard and Scharff 11, 8 have pointed out that such derivations are based on the assumptions that elastic and inelastic losses are separable events. As a first approximation this is probably true but one must expect some correlation between the two types of loss mechanism which may affect higher powers of the range because of cross terms in stopping power evaluations. The mean square straggling in range may also be computed from Equations 5.15.4, 5.22.2 and is given for nuclear stopping only, and the inverse r^s power potential by

$$\left(\frac{\Delta\rho}{\rho}\right)^2 = \left(\frac{\Delta R}{R}\right)^2 = \frac{s-1}{s(2s-1)} \text{ with } \gamma = \frac{4M_1M_2}{(M_1+M_2)^2}. \qquad 5.29$$

Thus the relative straggling at low energies where electronic stopping should be relatively unimportant, is independent of the range itself. Equation 5.29 also indicates that the relative square straggling is almost independent of s between 2 and 3 and

$$\left(\frac{\Delta R}{R}\right)^2 \simeq \gamma/6 \qquad 5.30$$

For the Thomas-Fermi potential, Equation 5.24 must be used to determine the straggling and the contribution of electronic stopping is assessed by using Equation 5.28. This leads to curves for the relative straggling as in Figure 5.5a and the absolute straggling as in Figure 5.5b. Clearly the absolute straggling reaches a maximum value determined by electronic stopping processes alone, as these processes become dominating, and the relative straggling falls.

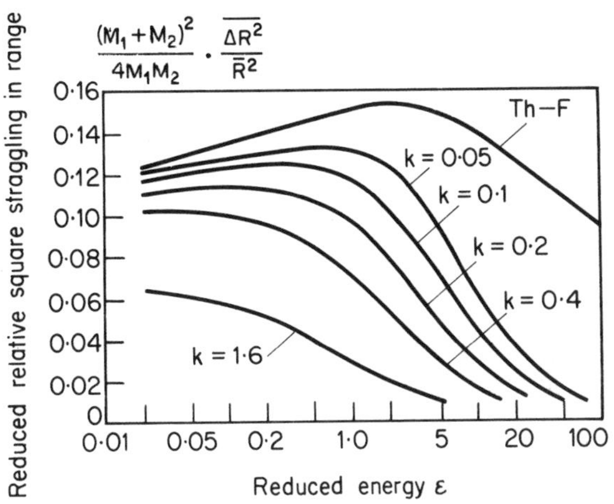

Fig. 5.5a Reduced Relative Square straggling in range as a function of reduced energy for a Thomas-Fermi interatomic potential assuming elastic collisions, and assuming an inelastic contribution with various values of the parameter k. (viz. Ref 5.8)

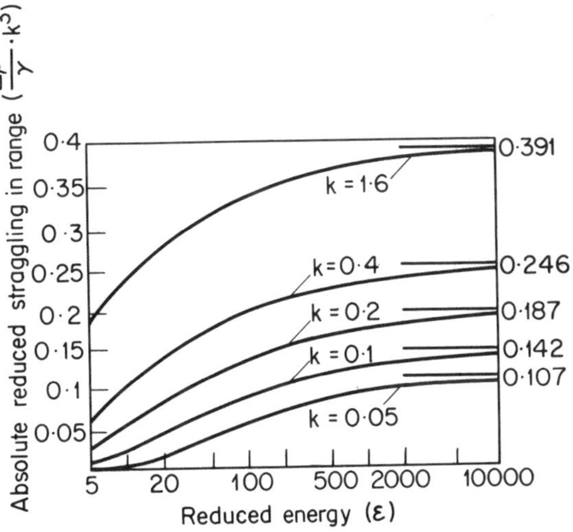

Fig. 5.5b Absolute reduced range straggling as a function of reduced energy for a Thomas-Fermi interatomic potential and assuming an inelastic contribution with various values of the parameter k. (viz. Ref. 5.8)

In order to further explore this question of powers (or moments) of the range $\bar{L}$ we must consider the range distribution $f(L, E)dL$ which specifies the probability of primaries with initial energy E reaching path lengths between L and $L + \sigma L$ from the initial starting point at the lattice surface.

Clearly $f(L, E)dL$ is subject to the normalisation

$$\int_0^{L_{max}} f(L, E)dL = 1$$

and average values of the mth power (or moment) of the range are derivable from

$$< \overline{L}^m > = \int_0^{L_{max}} L^m . f(L, E)dL \qquad 5.31$$

We may now derive a defining equation for $f(L, E)$ from the mean free path assumption as follows.

Suppose that the primary, has at a given instant, an energy E and moves a distance δL. There is then a probability for an energy transfer T in this path length given by $n\delta L\delta\sigma_{n,e}$ where the suffixes (n,e) show that the total energy transfer T is composed of loss in elastic collisions T_n and inelastic excitational collisions $\sum_i T_{ei}$ (the summation is necessary for the individual atomic electrons i). If this collision occurs, the primary energy is reduced to $E - T = E - T_n - \sum_i T_{ei}$ and the primary then has a probability $f(L - \delta L, E - T_n - \sum_i T_{ei})$ of reaching the range L.

Multiplication by the collision probability thus gives the contribution of this collision to the probability of attaining the range L. This probability is then summed over all energy transfers to find the probability for the range L. However, a collision may not occur in the path δL, for which a probability $1 - n\delta L \int d\sigma(T)$ exists, and such primaries then have a probability of arriving at the range L, given by $\{1 - n\delta L \int d\sigma(T)\}$ $\{1 - n\delta L \int d\sigma(T)\} f(L - \delta L, E)$.

On thus obtains, for the total probability of finding primaries with a range L, $f(L, E)$ equal to the summation of these individual probabilities, i.e.

$$f(L, E) = \int n\delta L d\sigma(T) f\left(L - \delta L, E - T_n - \sum_i T_{ei}\right)$$

$$+ (1 - n\delta L \int d\sigma(T)) f(L - \delta L, E) \qquad 5.32.1$$

If it is assumed the inelastic losses are small compared to elastic losses and separable from these, accuracy is still maintained by rewriting Equation 5.32.1 as

$$\frac{\partial f(L, E)}{\partial L} = n \int d\sigma_n \{f(L, E - T_n) - f(L, E)\}$$

$$- n\sigma_e \frac{d}{dE} f(L, E)$$

In the limit where

$$\delta L \to 0 \qquad 5.32.2$$

One can now, in principle at least obtain the moments of the range, by multiplication of the equation with L^m and integration by parts. This leads immediately to

$$m < \overline{L^{m-1}}(E) > = n \int d\sigma(T)$$

$$\{< L^m(E) > - < L^m \left(E - T_n - \sum_i T_{ei}\right) > \qquad 5.33.1$$

The average range, with $m = 1$, is thus given by

$$1 = n \int d\sigma(T) \left\{\overline{L}(E) - \overline{L}\left(E - T_n - \sum_i T_{ei}\right)\right\}$$

One method of solving this equation is by a series expansion of $\overline{L}(E - T_n - \sum_i T_{ei})$ in powers of $T_n + \sum_i Te_i$ which at first sight would appear to be poor since for equal primary and struck atom masses T can range from 0 to E itself. However, with a Thomas-Fermi type potential the elastic collision cross sections favour small energy transfers, so that the expansion may be justified for such a case.

If one takes only first order terms in the expansion of $\overline{L}(E, T)$ one obtains

$$1 = n \int d\sigma(T) \left\{\overline{L}(E) - \overline{L}(E) - \frac{Td\overline{L}(E)}{dE}\right\} \qquad 5.33.3$$

and if one denotes the value of $\overline{L}(E, T)$ obtained by this approximation as $\overline{L}_1(E)$. Then

$$\frac{d\overline{L}_1(E)}{dE} = \frac{1}{n\sigma(T)(E)}$$

and hence

$$\overline{L}_1(E) = \int_0^E \frac{dE'}{n\sigma(E')} \qquad 5.33.4$$

which is just the expression for $\overline{L}(E)$ given earlier. If second order terms are included in the expansion of $\overline{L}(E - T)$ it is readily deduced that, the second approximation $\overline{L}_2(E)$ is given by

$$\overline{L}_2(E) = \frac{1}{n} \int_0^E \frac{dE'}{\sigma(E')} \times$$

$$\left\{1 + \frac{\Omega^2(E')}{2} \frac{d}{dE'} \left(\frac{1}{\sigma(E')}\right)\right\} \qquad 5.34.1$$

Higher order moments of the range may be evaluated allowing values of $m = 2, 3, \ldots$ and if one requires the average square fluctuation in range $\overline{\Delta L^2(E)}$ which is evidently equal to $\overline{L^2(E)} - \overline{L(E)}^2$ the value $m = 2$ leads, for a first approximation to

$$\overline{\Delta L_1^2} = \frac{1}{n^2} \int_0^{E'} \frac{dE'\Omega^2(E')}{\sigma^3(E')} \qquad 5.35.1$$

and including second order terms

$$\overline{\Delta L_2^2} = \frac{1}{n^2} \int_0^E \frac{dE'\Omega^2(E')}{\sigma^3(E')} \times$$

$$\left\{1 + \left[\frac{K(E')}{\Omega^2(E')\sigma(E')} - \frac{5\Omega^2(E')}{2\sigma^2(E')}\right] \frac{d\sigma(E')}{dE'} + \frac{1}{2\sigma(E')} \cdot \frac{d\Omega^2(E')}{dE'}\right\} \qquad 5.35.2$$

where

$$K(E') = \int_0^E T^3 \, d\sigma(E') \qquad 5.35.3$$

In order to evaluate the accuracy of these approximations, Lindhard et al[8] have computed $\overline{L}_1$, $\overline{L}_2$, $\overline{\Delta L_1^2}$, $\overline{\Delta L_2^2}$ for the inverse power potential r^{-s} with

$s = 3/2$, 2 and 3 for the cases where the mass ratio's (defined by $\gamma = 4M_1M_2/(M_1 + M_2)^2$ are small and equal to unity respectively, and compared these with exact values of $\overline{L}$ and $\overline{\Delta L^2}$. These latter can be readily deduced for the inverse power potentials (i.e. equation 5.33.3 is soluble exactly) and are given in the papers by these authors.[8] Tables 5.1, a, b, show the results of this evaluation and it is clear that, just for these potentials, even the first approximations are good, and therefore may be used confidently as in Figure 5.3 to compare with experimental data.

TABLE 5.1a. (Ref. 5.8.).

Comparison of first and second approximation of expansion in γ, for power law scattering. Results for average range and range straggling.

s	$\overline{L}_2/\overline{L}_1$	$(\overline{\Delta R^2})_2/(\overline{\Delta R^2})_1$
3/2	$1 + \gamma/24$	$1 + \gamma.0.10$
2	1	$1 + \gamma/6$
3	$1 - \gamma/15$	$1 + \gamma.0.14$

TABLE 5.1b. (Ref. 5.8.).

Comparison of first and second approximation with exact formula when $\gamma = 1$. Average ranges and range straggling for power law scattering.

s	$\overline{L}/\overline{L}_1$	$\overline{L}/\overline{L}_2$	$(\overline{\Delta R^2})/(\overline{\Delta R^2})_1$	$(\overline{\Delta R^2})/(\overline{\Delta R^2})_2$
3/2	1.053	1.01	1.03	0.94
2	1	1	1.20	1.03
3	0.904	0.97	1.26	1.10

There still remains the question however of the real utility of these values for comparison with experimental observations. This question arises since many experiments measure, not the total primary flight paths, but the projection of these parallel to the initial direction of injection) i.e. $\overline{x}$ and f(x)dx are the observables. It is thus desirable to know the relation between $\overline{L}$ and $\overline{x}$ and higher moments.

One may derive an integral equation for the projected range probabilities in a quite analogous manner to that used in the deduction of Equation 5.32 with the result that

$$\frac{\partial}{\partial x} f(x, E) = \int d\sigma_{n,e} \{-f(x, E) + f(x, (E-T)\cos\theta)\} \qquad 5.36.1$$

where $\cos\theta$ is the cosine of the scattering angle between the path L and the x direction in the laboratory system and is given in terms of our earlier definition $\underline{L} \cdot \underline{v}_0/v_0$.

One deduces, for the average projected range R_{par}

$$1 = n \int d\sigma_{n,e}\{R_{par}(E) - R_{par}((E - T)\cos\theta)\}$$

Approximate solutions of this equation can be effected, if we assume for example that $T \ll E$ for all collisions, this means that $M_1 \gg M_2$ or $M_1 \ll M_2$. Equation 5.36.2 then becomes

$$1 = n\left\{\overline{R}_{par_1}(E) \int d\sigma_{n,e}(1 - \cos\theta) + \frac{d\overline{R}_{par_1}(E)}{dE} \int T d\sigma_{n,e} \cos\theta\right\} \qquad 5.36.3$$

For $\cos\theta \simeq 0$ this equation is identical to that for $\overline{L}$. One can now introduce a transport mean free path λ_{tr} and transport stopping cross section σ_{tr} such that

$$1/\lambda_{tr} = n \int d\sigma_{n,e}(1 - \cos\theta) \qquad 5.36.4$$

and

$$\sigma_{tr} = \int d\sigma_{n,e} T \cos\theta \qquad 5.36.5$$

and deduce

$$1 = \overline{R}_{par_1}(E)/\lambda_{tr} + \frac{d\overline{R}_{par_1}(E)}{dE} \cdot n\sigma_{tr}(E) \qquad 5.36.6$$

which has the solution

$$\overline{R}_{par_1}(E) = \int_0^E \frac{dE'}{n\sigma_{tr}(E')} \exp \times \int_E^{E'} \frac{dE''}{\lambda_{tr}(E'')n\sigma_{tr}(E'')} \qquad 5.36.7$$

For low values of $A = M_2/M_1$, $\cos\theta$ is always small and one may approximate $\cos\theta$ by $1 - \theta^2/2$. Thus equation 5.36.7 can be evaluated for $\overline{R}_{par_1}(E)$ through use of Figure 5.4 to obtain $d\sigma$ for various values of k. The difference between $\overline{L}$ and $\overline{R}_{par_1}$, may then be plotted as in Figure 5.6a as a function of

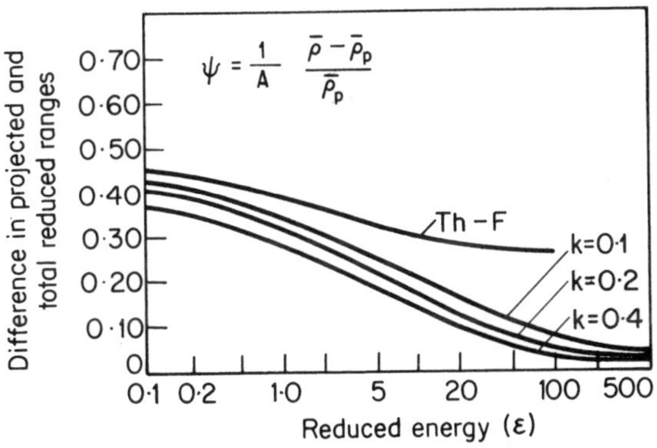

Fig. 5.6a Fractional differences between projected (ρ_p) and total (ρ) reduced ranges as a function of the reduced energy to first order in the mass ratio $A = M_2/M_1$, for inelastic stopping with various values of the parameter k. (viz. Ref 5.8)

primary energy. For larger values of A ($\gtrsim 1$) the accuracy of the results is less certain since θ may adopt large values, but an estimate of the corrections required on $\overline{L}$, to obtain $\overline{R}_{par_1}$, may be obtained and these are shown in Figure 5.6b. It is apparent that $\overline{L}$ and $\overline{R}_{par_1}$ show maximum deviation for low primary energies, which may be anticipated heuristically since many angular deflections will be large. In all cases the projected range $\overline{R}_{par_1}$, is considerably less than the actual path length, and such corrections must be applied before many experimental comparisons are valid.

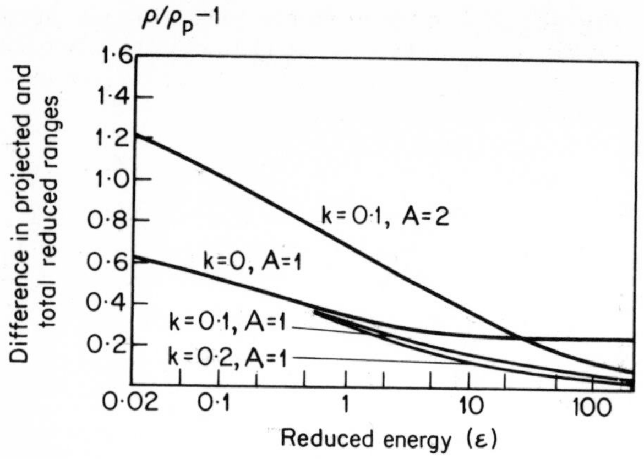

Fig. 5.6b Fractional differences between projected (ρ_p) and total (ρ) reduced ranges as a function of the reduced energy as in Fig. 5.6.a for larger values of the mass ratio $A = A_2/A_1$

For the special case of inverse power potentials it can be shown[8] that for s = 2

$$\frac{\overline{L}}{\overline{R}_{par_1}} = \tfrac{1}{4}\left\{-1 - 3A + (5+A)\frac{(1+A)}{2A^{1/2}}\cos^{-1}\times \frac{1-A}{1+A}\right\} \simeq 1 + \frac{A}{3} \text{ for all A.} \qquad 5.37.1$$

whilst for small A but any value of s

$$\frac{\overline{L}}{\overline{R}_{par_1}} \simeq 1 + \frac{As^2}{4(2s-1)} \qquad 5.37.2$$

Finally, higher moments of $\overline{R}_{par_1}$, and similarly of $\overline{R}_{perp_1}$ may be deduced in an analogous manner. It is sufficient here to summarize the results for the first order of approximation to the projected straggling compared to the overall path straggling.

$$\frac{\overline{\Delta L^2}}{\overline{\Delta R^2}_{par_1}}$$

and to the projected path,

$$\frac{\overline{\Delta R^2}_{par_1}}{\overline{R^2}_{par_1}}$$

in table 5.2.

TABLE 5.2. (Ref. 5.8.).

Straggling in projected range for power law scattering and A = 1.

s	3/2	2	3
$\overline{\Delta R^2}/\overline{\Delta R_p^2}$	1.25	1.33	1.38
$\overline{\Delta R_p^2}/\overline{R_p^2}$	0.204	0.275	0.341

In this section we have been concerned mainly with results of investigations at Copenhagen and Aarhus and it should be pointed out that this survey has been very superficial. For a fuller discussion of the present and many other questions associated with range problems the reader is referred to the publications by Bohr,[7] Lindhard and others,[8,11] some already cited and others in the series 'Notes on Atomic Collisions'

Although we have discussed the range concepts and moments of these in some detail and obtained useful range energy data we have not yet deduced a probable form for the range distribution, although the treatment here assumes to a first order approximation, the Gaussian distribution mentioned earlier. However, many experimental observations have revealed a range distribution differing considerably from the Gaussian type. In order to investigate this distribution problem further, we must turn to an alternative treatment of range problems which has been extensively used by investigators at the Oak Ridge National Laboratory.[10,13,14,15]

5.5. THE CONSISTENT HARD SPHERE METHOD

In this method, the primary and lattice atoms are supposed to act as hard spheres, with radii defined from the energy conditions.

$$V(2R_0) = E_R = \frac{A}{1+A} \cdot E \qquad 5.38$$

The radius R_0 is then connected directly with the primary energy, and, as the primary slows down via elastic collisions, the radii vary accordingly. In the specific energy loss method, the differential energy transfer cross section is generally deduced from the assumed form for the interatomic potential directly, rather than by assumption of a hard sphere radius derived from the potential. Thus, for an inverse r^2 potential, the Lindhard[8,11] et al. differential cross section derived directly from this potential is

$$\pi/2 \; \frac{Z_1Z_2e^2\,a_1}{E_R}\left(\frac{5}{32}\right)^{1/2}\frac{T_m{}^{1/2}}{T^{3/2}} \qquad 5.20.8$$

whereas if the colliding atoms are assumed to have hard sphere radii defined from the closest approach distance the differential cross section turns out to be

$$\pi/2 \; \frac{Z_1Z_2e^2a_1}{E_R} \cdot \frac{1}{T_m} \qquad 5.39$$

In the earlier example (b) the latter method of determination of $d\sigma(T)$ was used to simplify calculations, however the former is more correct, but both lead to similar values for the mean path, differing by a numerical factor of about 1.6.

In the consistent hard sphere method,[10,13] the distance of closest approach is always allowed to define a hard sphere radius R with the differential cross section $d\sigma = \pi \,.\, 4R^2/T_m$ and the mean free path $= 1/n\sigma = 1/4n\pi R^2$ without further use of the interatomic potential for exact determination of these.

We have seen earlier that the hard sphere assumption in many cases is a quite adequate approximation, particularly for large energy transfers and small impact parameters. Thus one may expect this method to be quite representative of a primary moving in a lattice of similar atomic weight. In fact, the following analysis was originally developed by Leibfried and

Holmes[13] for studies of a primary moving in a lattice of similar atoms. (Radiation damage processes.)

If we return to the representation of the path of a given primary as shown in Figure 5.1. then the total path of this is $L^{\nu} = l_0^{\nu} + l_1^{\nu} + \ldots\ldots l_n^{\nu}$. In this the primary with an initial energy E_0 is assumed to travel a distance l_0^{ν} without collision then after the first collision, it continues for a distance l_1^{ν} with a reduced energy E_1. After the next collision the energy is further reduced to E_2 and this process of energy degradation continues until E is reduced to zero (or some arbitrary low enrgy). Clearly the average value of the first path, is $\int P(l_0)dl_0 \cdot l_0$

$$= \int l_0 \exp\left\{-\frac{l_0}{\lambda(E_0)}\right\}\frac{dl_0}{\lambda(E_0)} = \lambda(E_0) \quad 5.40$$

The average path at the energy E^1, is descrived by a similar relation, but one must multiply by the probability that the primary possesses energy in the range E_1 to $E_1 + \delta E_1$ after the first collision.

Thus the average path after the first collision is

$$\int \lambda(E_1)\, g(E_0, E_1)\, dE_1 \qquad 5.41.1$$

(i.e. the summation over all average paths at the energy E_1 multiplied by the probability of finding the primary at this energy) with $g(E_0, E_1)$ etc. defined, as earlier, as the probability of finding a primary of energy E_0 in the energy interval E_1 to $E_1 + \delta E$, after collision. Similarly the average path after the second collision is

$$\iint g(E_0, E_1)\, dE_1 \cdot \lambda(E_2)\, g(E_1, E_2)\, dE_2 \qquad 5.41.2$$

and so the total average path length $\bar{L}$, is simply given by

$$\bar{L} = \lambda(E_0) + \int \lambda(E_1)\, g(E_0, E_1)\, dE_1 + \iint g(E_0, E_1)\, dE_1\, \lambda(E_2)\, g(E_1, E_2)\, dE_2 + \ldots\ldots \qquad 5.41.3$$

where the integrations are to be taken over the allowed energy range (αE_1 to E_1 for unequal masses) and the sum continues to an infinite number of collisions.

Using this relation one can readily calculate the total average path $\bar{L}$ for appropriate values of $\lambda(\varepsilon)$ and $g(E, \varepsilon)$ where ε is the primary energy after any collision with an initial energy E. As an example we can again take the interatomic potential represented by an inverse r^2 form ($V(r) = c/r^2$) and as before $(2R)^2 = 2c/E$. If this is taken as twice the hard sphere radius then $\lambda(\varepsilon) = \frac{\varepsilon}{\pi 2cn}$, and, as we have seen earlier, for the hard sphere approximation, $g(E, \varepsilon)\, d\varepsilon = \frac{d\varepsilon}{E}$.

Using these values in Equation 5.41.3 it is readily deduced that $L(E_0) = \frac{E_0}{n\pi C}$ as found previously.

It is plain that both methods of deduction of L therefore give correct answers for the hard sphere approximation.

In order to apply Equation 5.41.3 for more realistic interatomic potentials it is convenient to generalize this Equation further.

If $g_{\nu}(E_0, E_z)$ is the probability distribution function for finding primaries of initial energy E_0 between energies of E_z and $E_z + \delta E_z$ after z collisions, then clearly

$$g_{\nu}(E_0, E_z) = \underset{z\ \text{terms}}{\iiint} g(E_0, E_1) \cdot g(E_1, E_2) \ldots\ldots g(E_{z-1}, E_z)\, dE_1 \ldots\ldots dE_{z-1} \qquad 5.43.1$$

For the hard sphere approximation, with

$$g(E_{z-1}, E_z) = \frac{1}{E_{z-1}} \qquad 5.43.2$$

the integral of Equation 5.43.1 is readily evaluated to give

$$g_z(E_0, E_z) = \frac{1}{E_0} \cdot \frac{1}{\underline{|z-1}}\left\{\log e \frac{E_0}{E_z}\right\}^{z-1} \qquad 5.43.3$$

Thus, the average total path $\bar{L}$, may be re-written as

$$\bar{L} = \lambda(E_0) + \sum_{z=1}^{\infty} \int g(E_0, E_1) \ldots\ldots g(E_{z-1}, E_z)\lambda(E_z)\, dE_0 \ldots\ldots dE_z \qquad 5.44.1$$

or with the abbreviations $g_z(E_0, E_z)$

$$\bar{L} = \lambda(E_0) + \sum_{z=1}^{\infty} \int_0^{E_0} g_z(E_0, E_z)\lambda(E_z)\, dE_z \qquad 5.44.2$$

Thus

$$\bar{L} = \lambda(E_0) + \sum_{z=1}^{\infty} \int_0^{E_0} \frac{1}{E_0 \underline{|z-1}} \left\{\log e \frac{E_0}{E_z}\right\}^{z-1} \lambda(E_z)\, dE_z \qquad 5.44.3$$

Performing the sum over all z, the final result is

$$\bar{L}(E_0) = \lambda(E_0) + \int_0^{E_0} \lambda(\Sigma)\frac{d\Sigma}{\Sigma} \qquad 5.44.4$$

Also, since

$$(L_{\nu})^2 = (l_0^{\nu} + l_1^{\nu} + l_2^{\nu} + \ldots\ldots l_n^{\nu})^2 \qquad 5.45.1$$

Then

$$(L^{\nu})^2 = \sum_{m,n=0}^{\infty} l_m^{\nu} l_n^{\nu} \qquad 5.45.2$$

and

$$L^2 = \sum_{m,n=0}^{\infty} \langle l_m l_n \rangle_{AV} = \sum_{m} \langle l_m^2 \rangle_{AV} + 2\sum_{n>m} \langle l_m l_n \rangle_{AV} \qquad 5.45.3$$

Since

$$\langle l_m^2 \rangle_{AV} = \int_0^{\infty} l_m^2 \exp\left(-\frac{l_m}{\lambda_m}\right) dl_m = 2\lambda_m^2$$

and similarly

$$\langle l_m l_n \rangle_{AV} = \lambda_m \lambda_n \quad 5.45.4$$

Then

$$\overline{L^2} = 2\left\{\sum_m \lambda_m^2 + \sum_{m>n} \lambda_m \lambda_n\right\} \quad 5.45.5$$

The two terms on the right hand side of this equation may be deduced in a similar way to the evaluation of $\overline{L}$, with the final result.

$$\overline{L^2} = (\overline{L})^2 + \lambda^2(E_0) + 2\int_0^{E_0} \lambda^2(\Sigma)\frac{d\Sigma}{\Sigma} \quad 5.45.6$$

It is more difficult to obtain $\overline{R}_{AV}$, $\overline{R}_{par}$ etc. since these contain the directional dependence of the paths also, but Leibfried and Holmes[13] have shown how these and higher order averages can be calculated for cases where the primaries are isotropically spatially distributed, or confined to a given direction of incidence. The quantity of greatest interest in penetration problems is probably $\overline{R}_{par}$ and it is instructive to evaluate this, for a uni-directional incident primary distribution, using Leibfried and Holmes'[13] arguments. The total average projected path $\overline{R}_{par}$ is made up of the projection of all the individual paths along the incident direction, i.e.

$$R_{par_\nu} = l_0^\nu + l_1^\nu \cdot \underline{v}_0/v_0 + l_2^\nu \cdot \underline{v}_0/v_0 + \ldots\ldots \quad 5.46$$

When averaged over all primaries, the l_n^ν's will contribute just the average value of (λ_n) projected on to the original direction of motion. For hard spheres, the scattering is assumed to be azimuthally symmetric about the collision direction, and so the average n^{th} path λ_n when projected upon the $n-1^{th}$ direction contributes $\lambda_n \cos\theta_n$ where θ_n is the scattering angle in the Laboratory system. Thus the average contribution of the nth path projected upon the initial direction of motion will be obtained by multiplying λ_n by the product of the cosines of all previous scattering angles.

i.e.

$$\lambda_{n_{par}} = \lambda_n \cos\theta_n \cos\theta_{n-1}\ldots\ldots\cos\theta_1 \quad 5.47$$

For the equal mass case,

$$\cos\theta_n = \left(\frac{E_n}{E_{n-1}}\right)^{1/2} \quad 5.48.1$$

thus

$$\cos\theta_n \cos\theta_{n-1}\ldots\ldots\cos\theta_1 = (E_n/E_0)^{1/2} \quad 5.48.2$$

In analogy to Equation 5.41.3 for $\overline{L}$ one thus obtains

$$\overline{R}_{par} = \lambda(E_0) + \int_0^{E_0} g(E_0, E_1)\lambda(E_1)\left\{\frac{E_1}{E_0}\right\}^{1/2} dE_1$$

$$+ \int_0^{E_0}\int_0^{E_1} g(E_0, E_1)dE_1 g(E_1, E_2)\lambda(E_2)\left\{\frac{E_2}{E_0}\right\}^{1/2} dE_2$$

$$+ \ldots\ldots \quad 5.49.1$$

with a quite similar result to Equation 5.44.4

$$\overline{R}_{par} = \lambda(E_0) + \frac{1}{E_0^{1/2}}\int_0^{E_0} \lambda(\Sigma)\frac{d\Sigma}{\Sigma^{1/2}} \quad 5.49.2$$

$\langle R_{par}^2\rangle_{AV}$ can be deduced in an analogous way.

For the inverse r^2 potential matched to the hard sphere radius R one obtains

$$\overline{R}_{par} = \frac{5}{6}\frac{E_0}{n\pi C} = \frac{5}{6}\overline{L} = \frac{5}{3}\lambda(E_0) \quad 5.50.1$$

This result may be compared with the Lindhard et al[8] result for $\overline{L}/\overline{R}_{par_1} = 4/3$ for A = 1. c.f. Equation 5.37.1 which gives $\overline{L}/\overline{R}_{par} = 4/3$. Obviously the exact treatment without intermediate use of the hard sphere assumption gives results quite close to those using this model.

As a further example one may consider the use of a realistic potential such as the Bohr form

$$V(r) = \frac{Z_1^2 e^2/a}{r/a}\exp(-r/a)$$

for equal primary and target masses. One then deduces the hard sphere radius

$$2R(\Sigma) \text{ from } \Sigma = E_B \cdot \frac{a}{2R(\Sigma)}\exp\left[-\frac{2R(E_0)}{a}\right] \quad 5.51$$

with $E_B = 2Z_1^2 e^2/a$ and the mean free path at the energy Σ becomes

$$\lambda(\Sigma) = \frac{1}{n\pi}[2R(\Sigma)]^2 \quad 5.52$$

One may evaluate $\overline{L}$, $\overline{L^2}$ through use of the integrals

$$\int_0^E \lambda(\Sigma)\frac{d\Sigma}{\Sigma} = \int_{r_0(E)}^{\infty} \frac{1}{n\pi r^2}\left\{\frac{1}{r} + \frac{1}{a}\right\}dr$$

$$= \lambda(E)\left\{\frac{1}{2} + \frac{r_0(E)}{a}\right\} \quad 5.53.1$$

and

$$\int_0^E \lambda^2(\Sigma)\frac{d\Sigma}{\Sigma} = \int_{r_0(E)}^{\infty}\left(\frac{1}{n\pi r^2}\right)^2\left(\frac{1}{r} + \frac{1}{a}\right)dr$$

$$= \lambda^2(E)\left\{\frac{1}{4} + \frac{1}{3}\frac{r_0(E)}{a}\right\}$$

where

$$r \equiv r_0(\Sigma) = 2R(\Sigma) \quad 5.53.2$$

From which it is seen that

$$\overline{L} = \lambda(E_0)\left\{\frac{3}{2} + \frac{r_0(E_0)}{a}\right\} \quad 5.53.3$$

$$\overline{L^2} = \lambda^2(E_0)\left\{\frac{3}{2} + \frac{2}{3}\frac{r_0(E_0)}{a}\right\} + (\overline{L})^2 \quad 5.53.4$$

These results have been expressed in terms of the first mean free path $\lambda(E_0)$ for simplicity and are clearly different from the inverse r^2 potential values, and show the relative importance of the first free path and succeeding ones. Evalutaion of $\overline{R}_{par}$ and $\overline{R}^2_{par}$ is less straightforward but the results

$$\overline{R}_{par} \simeq \lambda(E_0)\left\{3 - \frac{8a}{r_0(E_0)} + \frac{56a^2}{r_0^2(E_0)} - \ldots\ldots\right\} \qquad 5.54.1$$

$$\overline{R}^2_{par} \simeq \lambda^2(E_0)\left\{\frac{7}{2} + \frac{2r_0(E_0)}{a} + \frac{16a}{5r_0(E_0)} + \ldots\ldots\right\} \qquad 5.54.2$$

can be deduced.

Normalised values of $\overline{L}, \overline{L}^2, \overline{R}_{par}, \overline{R}^2_{par}$ are plotted in Figure 5.7 as a function of E/E_B, $\overline{L}$ etc. are normalised to L_a the mean free path for

$$r_0 = a\left(\text{i.e.} = \frac{1}{n\pi a^2}\right)$$

and thus corresponds with $A = 1$, to the ρ etc. presented in Figures 5.4, 5.5 whilst E/E_B is again for $A = 1$, identical to σ of those Figures. Thus direct comparison of Figure 5.7 and the earlier Figures 5.4, 5.5 for the Thomas-Fermi potential are possible in the overlapping range. It is seen that the Bohr potential with the hard sphere approximation consistently gives higher values of $\overline{L}$ etc. than does the Thomas-Fermi potential at low primary energies. This is a result of the fact that the Thomas Fermi potential is much larger than the Bohr potential for $r_0 \gg a$ which has a tendency to reduce the free paths. At very low E values, however, one can expect that neither representation will be very accurate, although both give order of magnitude values for the interesting ranges.

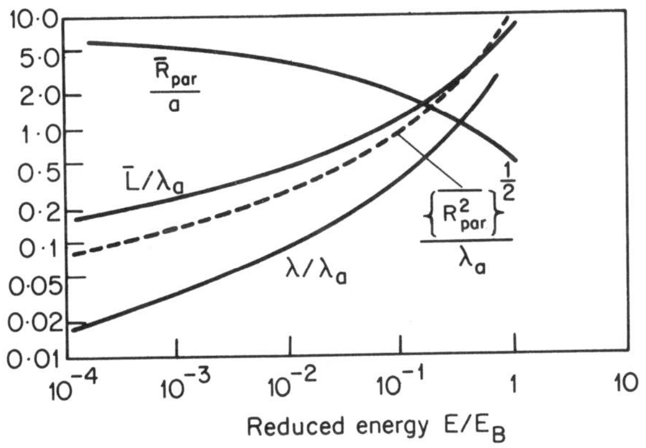

Fig. 5.7 Dependence of the characteristic range averages on reduced energy E/E_B for the hard sphere approximation to the Bohr interatomic potential. λ_a is the mean free-path $= \dfrac{1}{n\pi a^2}$ and $E_B = 2Z^2e^2/a$. Equal mass primary and target atoms are assumed. (viz. Ref. 5.13)

Whilst this approach can give values of average ranges and the range straggling (from $\langle \Delta R^2_{par}\rangle = \overline{R}^2_{par} - \overline{R}_{par}$) which gives information about the form of the range distribution curves f(R)dR it is still difficult to obtain this distribution formally. In order to do this, Leibfried,[14] has developed an elegant mathematical extension of the consistent hard sphere model, namely the operator method.

5.6 THE OPERATOR METHOD

If one considers the integral

$$\int_0^E g(E, \Sigma)f(\Sigma)d\Sigma \qquad 5.55.1$$

then one can express this as $g\,.\,f(\Sigma)$ where g is the integral operator defined through

$$g\,.\,f(\Sigma) = \int_0^E g(E, \Sigma)f(\Sigma)d\Sigma \qquad 5.55.2$$

$g_\nu f(\Sigma)$ is then equivalent to $g^\nu f(\Sigma)$ and implies that the operator is applied ν times i.e.

$$g_\nu f(\Sigma) = g^\nu f(\Sigma) = \underset{\nu\ \text{terms}}{\iiint} g(E, \Sigma_1)f(\Sigma_1)$$

$$g(\Sigma_1\Sigma_2)f(\Sigma_2)\ldots\ldots d\Sigma_1 d\Sigma_2 \ldots\ldots d\Sigma_\nu \qquad 5.55.3$$

Using this notation, Leibfried[14] has shown that the interesting range quantities may be written as

$$\overline{L} = \lambda(E_0) + \int_0^{E_0} \sum_{\nu=1}^{\infty} g_\nu(E_0, \Sigma)\lambda(\Sigma)d\Sigma \qquad 5.56.1$$

$$= \lambda(E_0) + g\,.\,\lambda(E_0) + g^2\,.\,\lambda(E_0)$$

$$+ \ldots\ldots g^\nu\,.\,\lambda(E_0)$$

$$= \frac{1}{1-g}\,.\,[\lambda(E_0)] \qquad 5.56.2$$

for the equal mass case.

$$\overline{R}_{par} = \frac{1}{E_0^{1/2}}\,.\,\frac{1}{1-g}\,.\,[E_0^{1/2}\,.\,\lambda(E_0)] \qquad 5.57.1$$

$$\overline{L}^2 = \frac{2}{1-g}\,.\left\{\lambda(E_0)\,.\,\frac{1}{1-g}[\lambda(E_0)]\right\}$$

$$= \frac{2}{1-g}\,.\,[\lambda(E_0)\,.\,\overline{L}] \qquad 5.57.2$$

$$\overline{R}^2_{par} = 2\left\{\frac{2/3}{1-G} + \frac{1/3}{1-g}\right\}.\,[\lambda(E_0)\langle\overline{R}_{par}\rangle] \qquad 5.57.3$$

where G is an operator given by

$$G(E, \Sigma) = g(E, \Sigma)\,.\,\frac{1}{2}\left\{\frac{3\Sigma}{E} - 1\right\} \qquad 5.57.4$$

This operator method essentially provides a shorthand notation for writing down the interesting range averages formally. We should note also that Korchovei, Gika and Greku,[16] have independently formulated a very similar treatment for the penetration function of energetic primaries in an isotropic solid with identical results to those of Leibfried.[14] However, in order to evaluate these range parameters in terms of known quantities it is necessary to carry through the implicit operations. Leibfried[14] has shown how this may be accomplished for the parameters in the above equations and as an example we consider the evaluation of $\overline{L}$.

If $g(E, \Sigma)$ has the form

$$g(E, \Sigma) = \frac{h(\Sigma/E)}{E} \qquad 5.58.1$$

which is clearly true for hard sphere scattering where $g(E, \Sigma) = 1/E$ and $h(\Sigma/E) = 1$ then it is readily shown that all powers are 'eigenfunctions.'

i.e.

$$g \cdot E^n = \int_0^E h(E, \Sigma) \frac{\Sigma^n d\Sigma}{E} = \alpha_n E^n \qquad 5.58.2$$

with

$$\alpha_n = \int_0^1 h(\eta)\eta^n d\eta \qquad 5.58.3$$

For the case $h(E, \Sigma) = 1$ it is readily seen that $g \cdot E^n = \frac{E^n}{n+1}$. Further, all powers are eigenfunctions to $\frac{1}{1-g}$ i.e.

$$\frac{1}{1-g} \cdot E^n = \frac{1}{1-\alpha_n} \cdot E^n \qquad 5.59.1$$

which is readily proved by a series expansion of $(1-g)^{-1}$, and in the case $h(E, \Sigma) = 1$, one obtains

$$\frac{1}{1-g} \cdot E^n = \frac{n+1}{n} \cdot E^n \qquad 5.59.2$$

The operation $\frac{1}{1-g} \cdot f(E)$ may be rewritten as

$$\left(1 + \frac{g}{1-g}\right) \cdot f(E)$$

or

$$f(E) + \int_0^E S(E, \Sigma) f(\Sigma) d\Sigma \qquad 5.60.1$$

where the kernel $S(E, \Sigma)$ is obtained from the operation $\frac{g}{1-g}$ and

$$\left(\frac{g}{1-g}\right) \cdot E^n = \frac{\alpha_n}{1-\alpha_n} \cdot E^n \qquad 5.60.2$$

For the hard sphere case $(h(E, \Sigma) = 1)$, $\frac{g}{1-g} \cdot E^n$ is clearly $\frac{1}{n} E^n$. Since

$$\frac{E^n}{n} = \int_0^E \Sigma^n \frac{d\Sigma}{\Sigma},$$

it is therefore plain that in this case $S(E, \Sigma) = 1/\Sigma$ and consequently

$$\frac{1}{1-g} f(E) = f(E) + \int_0^E \frac{1}{\Sigma} f(\Sigma) d\Sigma \qquad 5.60.3$$

If we require the average path $\overline{L}$ then this is given at an energy E_0 by

$$\overline{L} = \frac{1}{1-g} \cdot \lambda(E_0) \qquad 5.61.1$$

where we have seen previously that $\lambda(\Sigma) = \frac{\Sigma}{2n\pi C}$.

We are therefore interested in the case where $f(\Sigma) = \lambda(\Sigma) \propto \Sigma$. Thus

$$\overline{L} = \lambda(E_0) + \int_0^E \frac{1}{\Sigma} \frac{\Sigma d\Sigma}{2n\pi C} \qquad 5.61.2$$

from Equation 5.60.3 or $\overline{L} = 2\lambda(E_0)$ the result already derived in Equations 5.17.6 and 5.41.3.

Values for the other range parameters may be derived in an analogous manner. One of the most useful properties of the operator method is that is can be used with facility for the unequal mass case. Under such circumstances it is difficult to determine parameters such as $\overline{R}_{par}$ using the methods of 5.5 since the $\cos\theta_n$ terms are no longer simply given by

$$\left\{\frac{E_n}{E_{n-1}}\right\}^{1/2}$$

but by

$$\cos\theta_n = \frac{1}{2}\left\{(1+A)\left(\frac{E_n}{E_{n-1}}\right)^{1/2} + (1-A)\left\{\frac{E_{n-1}}{E_n}\right\}^{1/2}\right\} \qquad 5.62$$

where A is the mass ratio.

However $\cos\theta_n$ may be written as $C(E, \Sigma)$ and thus, in the operator notation

$$\overline{R}_{par} = \frac{1}{1-g_c} \lambda(E_0) \qquad 5.63.1$$

with

$$g_c = g(E, \Sigma) \cdot C(E, \Sigma) \qquad 5.63.2$$

Since $C(E, \Sigma)$ is a function of Σ/E only, the problem is therefore soluble by the methods used above.

In view of the simplification introduced by the operator notation it is opportune to enquire whether their use enables calculation of the range distribution function, which has so far eluded our analysis.

Using the operator notation, it is a straightforward matter to show that the total path distribution can be expressed by the relation

$$g \cdot f(L, E) = \hat{f}(L - l_0, E) \qquad 5.64.1$$

where $f(L, E)$ is the total path distribution for primary energies E, and $\hat{f}(L - l_0, E)$ is the path distribution after the first free path. This relation is easily obtained by the probability considerations leading to Equation 5.32. It is further evident that

$$\{g\langle\overline{L^m}\rangle\}_E = \{\langle\overline{L - l_0}\rangle^m\} \qquad 5.64.2$$

and Leibfried has shown that this leads to a relation for the average m^{th} power of the total path, namely

$$\langle\overline{L^m}\rangle = \underline{|m}\left\{\frac{1}{1-g} \cdot \lambda\right\}^m \qquad 5.64.3$$

where the index m indicates that the operation $(1-g)^{-1}$ is applied m times. This leads to results for $m = 1, 2$ identical to those given in Equations 5.44.1 and 5.45.6.

The powers $\langle \overline{L^m} \rangle$ of course, give information about the form of the distribution function in that they describe the average path, path straggling etc., however it is equally interesting to deduce the actual form of the distribution. This may be achieved as follows. The Fourier Transform of the path distribution function, $f(L, E)$ may be obtained from

$$\tilde{f}(k, E) = \int_{-\infty}^{\infty} \exp(ikL) f(L, E)\, dL \qquad 5.65.1$$

or the distribution itself from the inverse transform

$$f(L, E) = \int_{-\infty}^{\infty} \exp(ikL) \tilde{f}(k, E) \frac{dk}{2\pi} \qquad 5.65.2$$

This Equation can be expressed in a series expansion of kL/i from which it appears that

$$\tilde{f}(k, E) = \int_{-\infty}^{\infty} \sum_{m=0}^{\infty} \left(\frac{kL}{i}\right)^m \frac{1}{\underline{|m}} \cdot f(L, E)\, dL \qquad 5.65.3$$

Clearly terms such as

$$\int_{-\infty}^{\infty} L^m f(L, E)\, dL$$

are just the averages $\langle \overline{L^m} \rangle$ and it is easily seen therefore substituting for each term in Equation 5.65.3.

$$f(L, E) = \int_{-\infty}^{\infty} \frac{dk}{2\pi} \exp(ikL) \times$$

$$\sum_{m=0}^{\infty} \frac{\langle L^m \rangle (\Sigma) k^m}{\underline{|m} \cdot i^m} \qquad 5.65.4$$

The value of knowing $\langle \overline{L^m} \rangle$, which are plainly the mth derivatives of the Fourier Transform of the $f(L, E)$ in the operator notation, now becomes apparent, since the values of $\langle \overline{L^m} \rangle$ may be evaluated from Equation 5.64.3 substituted into Equation 5.65.4 and the integration performed.

Taking the hard sphere case as an example where $\lambda(E)$ is proportional to E then $\langle \overline{L^n} \rangle = \underline{|n+1} \cdot \lambda^n(E)$. Performing the sum of Equation 5.65.4 the result

$$f(L, E) = \int_{-\infty}^{\infty} \frac{dk}{2\pi} \exp(ikL) \times$$

$$\frac{1}{(1 + i\lambda k)^2} = \frac{L \exp(-L/\lambda)}{\lambda^2} \qquad 5.66.1$$

is readily obtained.

In the more general case of $\lambda(E) \propto E^{\mu}$ one obtains

$$\langle \overline{L^n} \rangle = \lambda^n \frac{\underline{|n + 1/\mu}}{\underline{|1/\mu}} \qquad 5.66.2$$

and

$$f(L, E) = \left(\frac{L}{\lambda}\right)^{1/\mu} \exp\left(-\frac{L}{\lambda}\right) \cdot \frac{1}{\lambda \underline{|1/\mu}} \qquad 5.66.3$$

Holmes[10] has evaluated this distribution for the case where $\lambda(E) \propto E^{1/2}$ thus

$$f(L, E)_{1/2} = \frac{L^2}{2\lambda^3} \exp\left(-\frac{L}{\lambda}\right) \qquad 5.66.4$$

and compared the result with a computer evaluation of the distribution function. We will discuss the $E^{1/2}$ case and computer studies shortly, but it is pertinent to show the results in Figure 5.8 and observe the close agreement. Leibfried[14] has also obtained the form of the distribution function when the primary is assumed to come to rest at an energy E_d in the lattice (i.e. $\lambda(E_d)$ goes to zero at E_d) and in this case

$$f(L, E) = \frac{\exp}{\lambda^2}\left(-\frac{L}{\lambda^2}\right)\left\{L\left(1 - \frac{\lambda_d}{\lambda}\right) + \lambda_D\right\}$$

for $\mu = 1$, i.e. 5.67

hard sphere scattering $\lambda(E) = \lambda, \lambda(E_D) = \lambda_D$. The result is patently less than that at which cut off is assumed at zero energy (Equation 5.66.1 since $L > \lambda$ and is of course anticipated to be so.

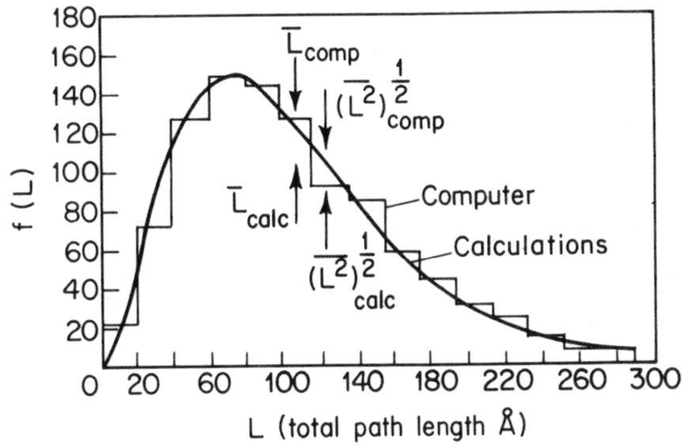

Fig. 5.8 The distribution in path lengths, a comparison of computer calculations with the theoretical expression

$$F(L) = \frac{L^2 \exp(-L/\lambda_0)}{2\lambda_0^3}$$

derived assuming $\lambda(E_0) \propto E_0^{1/2}$ (as for 5 keV Cu primaries in Cu) (viz. Ref. 5.10 and Equn. 5.70)

In the examples discussed so far, the hard sphere model has been applied throughout, without reference to the actual interatomic potential, i.e. the mean free path at energy E has been assumed to be $E/2\pi nC$ which is obtained assuming an inverse r^2 potential.

If one attempts to use a realistic potential, such as the Bohr potential then the equivalent hard sphere radius at an energy E, must be obtained from $E = E_B \frac{a}{2r_0} \exp\left(-\frac{r_0}{a}\right)$ which clearly leads to complex relations for $\lambda(E)$ and hence, in the operator notation for $\overline{R}_{par}$, etc.

In view of the simplicity, which we have seen, obtains for $\lambda(E)$ with the form E^{μ} it is useful to investigate whether such behaviour can be reproduced by matching of a simpler potential to the Bohr potential.

We have seen in Chapter 2 that a matching potential of the form $V_m(r) = C/r^s$ is often used to simulate the Bohr potential. It was shown that the best matching is obtained by fitting both the potential and its first derivative at the distance of closest approach r_0. If this distance r_0 is supposed to be twice the hard sphere radius, then it turns out that at the energy E_0.

$$s(E_0) = 1 + \frac{r_0(E_0)}{a} \qquad 5.68$$

At any energy below E_0 say E, a hard sphere radius may be then defined from

$$\frac{A}{1+A} \cdot E = \frac{C}{r_0(E)^{s(E_0)}}$$

for a mass ratio A. Thus the mean free path at the energy E is simply $\frac{1}{n\pi r_0^2(E)}$ which is seen to be

$$\lambda(E) = \frac{1}{n\pi} \cdot \left[\frac{A}{(1+A)C}\right]^{2/s(E_0)} . E^{2/s(E_0)} \qquad 5.69$$

The evaluation of $\overline{L}$, $\langle \overline{L}^2 \rangle$, ... $\langle \overline{L}^m \rangle$ is therefore straightforward from Equation 5.64.3 and hence f(L, E) is also derivable. The values of $\lambda(E)$ should be quite accurate in the initial energy range ($E \simeq E_0$) where the contribution to range quantities is greatest. As the primary slows down, the mean free path will deviate further from its correct value, since s has been determined at E_0 only, although clearly s is itself a function of E.

As an example, one may consider 5 kev copper primaries slowing down in copper ($Z_1 \sim 50$) where it is found that $r_0(E_0) \simeq 3a$ and $s(E_0) \simeq 4$. In this case $\lambda(E) \propto E^{1/2}$ and the distribution function is

$$f(L, E) = \frac{L^2}{2\lambda_0^3} \exp\left(-\frac{L}{\lambda_0}\right) \qquad 5.70$$

and, as shown in Figure 5.8 this agrees with exact (computer) evaluations.

Another matching potential $V_m(r) = A\left(\frac{a}{r} - 1\right)$ for $r < a$, which was seen in chapter 2 to give excellent agreement to the Bohr potential, may also be considered.

In this case

$$g_m(E, \Sigma) = \frac{\pi r_0^2}{4T_m} \times$$

$$\left\{\frac{(1 + r_0/a)(1 + r_0/2a)}{(1 + r_0/a)\left(\frac{E - \Sigma}{T_m}\right) + (r_0/2a)^2}\right\}^2 \qquad 5.71$$

and range quantities may be evaluated using the methods outlined above. According to Holmes,[10] these calculations give good agreement with exact calculations.

In order to evaluate the higher order averages and $\overline{R}_{par}$ for the general mass ratio condition and so specify the distribution function more accurately, Leibfried[15] has shown that it is more convenient to generalise the operator $g_c f$ of Equation 5.55.2 still further. Thus

$$g(m)(E_1, \Sigma) = \frac{P_m(\cos\theta)}{(1-\alpha)E_1} \qquad 5.72$$

for the unequal mass hard sphere case, where P_m are the Legendre polynomials of order m and cos θ is a function of E and Σ, through Equation 5.48.1.

Thus

$$g(m)f(E_1) = \int_{\alpha E_1}^{E_1} \frac{P_m(\cos\theta)}{(1-\alpha)E_1} f(\Sigma)d\Sigma \qquad 5.73$$

g_c is clearly just the case g(1).

With this notation, it is readily proved, via the method of Complex integration, that

$$\overline{R}_{par} = \frac{1}{1 - g(1)} \cdot \lambda(E) \qquad 5.74.1$$

which may be compared with the results of Equation 5.57.1

$$\overline{R}^2_{par} = 2\left\{\frac{1/3}{1 - g^{(0)}} + \frac{2/3}{1 - g^{(2)}}\right\}\lambda \cdot \overline{R}_{par} \qquad 5.74.2$$

and

$$\overline{R}^2_{perp} = 2\left\{\frac{1/3}{1 - g^{(0)}} - \frac{1/3}{1 - g^{(2)}}\right\}\lambda \cdot \overline{R}_{par} \qquad 5.74.3$$

with somewhat more complicated forms for the higher powers. For a power dependence of $\lambda(E)$ upon E, i.e. $\lambda(E) \propto E^{\mu}(=E^{2/s})$ the results are obtained directly, since as with the simple function, g, powers of E are eigenfunctions of all the operators. i.e.

$$g(m)E^{\mu} = \alpha_{\mu}^{(m)}E^{\mu} \qquad 5.75.1$$

with

$$\alpha_{\mu}^{(m)} = \frac{1}{1-\alpha}\int_{\alpha}^{1} P_m(\eta)\eta^{2\mu+1}\, d\eta$$

$$\text{and } \alpha = \left(\frac{1-A}{1+A}\right)^2 \qquad 5.75.2$$

Thus

$$\frac{1}{1 - g(m)} \cdot E^{\mu} = \frac{1}{1 - \alpha_{\mu}^{m}} \cdot E^{\mu} \qquad 5.75.3$$

and

$$\overline{R}_{par} = \frac{1}{1 - \alpha_{\mu}^{(1)}}\lambda(E_0) \qquad 5.75.4$$

and other averages are expressed equally simply.

Table 5.3 shows values of $\alpha_{\mu}^{(m)}$ for arbitrary μ. For equal masses and the hard sphere case where $\lambda(E) = CE$ it is readily seen that $\overline{R}_{par} = \frac{5}{3}\lambda(E_0)$ which is exactly the result obtained in Equation 5.50.1. The general utility of this method, in the simple results to which it leads are therefore self evident. However, as pointed out by Leibfried,[15] only averages of the power of the projected ranges can, as yet, be computed. The actual form of the projected range distribution has not been evaluated. Nevertheless, the averages of the powers do give useful information about the form of the distribution, since the 1st power gives the average range, the second power, gives the straggling, from $\langle \overline{R}^2_{par} \rangle - \langle \overline{R}_{par} \rangle^2$ and the third power gives the skewness, or asymmetry of the distribution.

$$\langle \overline{R}^3_{par} \rangle - \langle \overline{R}_{par} \rangle^3 - 3\langle \overline{R}_{par} \rangle\{\langle \overline{R}^2_{par} \rangle - \langle \overline{R}_{par} \rangle^2\} \qquad 5.76$$

TABLE 5.3. (Ref. 5.15).

Values of $\alpha_\mu{}^m$ and $\dfrac{1}{1-\alpha_\mu{}^m}$ for m = 0, 1, 2, 3.

m	0	1	2	3
$\alpha_\mu{}^{(m)}$	$\dfrac{1}{\mu+1}$	$\dfrac{2}{2\mu+3}$	$\dfrac{2\mu+1}{2(\mu+1)(\mu+2)}$	$\dfrac{4\mu}{(2\mu+3)(2\mu+5)}$
$\dfrac{1}{1.-\alpha_\mu{}^{(m)}}$	$\dfrac{1+\mu}{\mu}$	$\dfrac{2\mu+3}{2\mu+1}$	$\dfrac{(\mu+1)(\mu+2)}{\mu^2+2\mu+3/2}$	$\dfrac{(2\mu+3)(2\mu+5)}{4\mu^2+12\mu+15}$

A possible method of obtaining the distribution function $f(R_{par}, E)$ is to assume that the total path distribution is made up of the first path distribution $f(l_0, E)$ and the distribution after the first path (collision). One therefore sees that

$$f(R_{par}, E) = \int_0^\infty f(l_0, E)dl_0 f_1(R_{par} - l_0, E) \qquad 5.77.1$$

The first path may be taken as distributed exponentially, and one may make an intelligent guess about the subsequent path distribution. Thus

$$f(l_0, E) = \frac{1}{\lambda(E_0)} \exp\left(-\frac{l_0}{\lambda(E_0)}\right) dl_0 \qquad 5.77.2$$

and one may postulate, for example, that

$$f_1(R_{par}, E) = \frac{1}{a+b} \times \begin{cases} \exp \dfrac{(-R_{par} - C)}{a} & \text{for } R_{par} > C \\ \exp \dfrac{(R_{par} - C)}{b} & \text{for } R_{par} \leqslant C \end{cases} \qquad 5.77.3$$

Using this assumed distribution, Leibfried[15] shows that

$$f(R_{par}, E) = \frac{1}{a+b}\left\{\exp\frac{(-R_{par} - C)}{\Lambda}\right\} \times \frac{\Lambda/a + \Lambda/b}{\left(\frac{\Lambda}{a} - 1\right)\left(\frac{\Lambda}{b} + 1\right)} - \left\{\exp - \frac{(R_{par} - C)}{a}\right\}\frac{1}{\frac{\Lambda}{a} - 1}$$

$$\text{for } R_{par} > C \qquad 5.77.4$$

$$= \frac{1}{a+b}\,\frac{\exp\left\{\dfrac{R_{par} - C}{b}\right\}}{\Lambda/b + 1} \quad \text{for } R_{par} \leqslant C$$

with four unknown constants, a, b, c and Λ replacing λ for generality. These constants may be determined from the first three powers of the averages. It turns out that, for a particular but arbitrary dependence of $\lambda(E)$ upon E of the form $\lambda(E) \propto E^{0.91}$ (which is determined from the initial energy E_0, i.e. $2/s = 0.91$) the agreement between the predicted distribution function from Equation 5.77.4 with values of the constants determined from the averages of the powers of the ranges, and a computer evaluation is very good, viz. Figure 5.9.

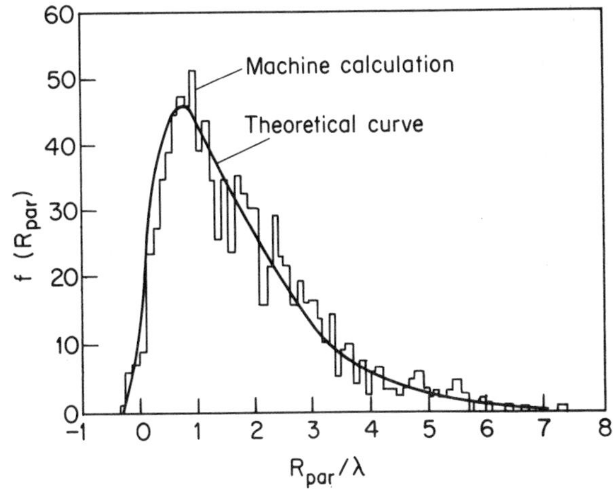

Fig. 5.9 Representation of the distribution $f(R_{par})$ according to equation 5.77.4 compared with a machine calculation. Matching is effected using the averages $\overline{R_{par}}, \overline{R^2{}_{par}}, \overline{R^3{}_{par}}$ with $\Lambda = 1.16\lambda, a = 0.637\lambda, b = 0.097\lambda, c = 0.$ (viz. Ref. 5.15)

A further method of obtaining the range moments has been described by Baroody[17,18] using adaptations of transport theory as applied to problems of neutron slowing down in nuclear reactors. Baroody's most recent work[18] on this problem seems to offer a concise method of determining range moments for arbitrary scattering functions and the technique is worthy of some discussion.

5.7 TRANSPORT THEORY

Basically the method adopted by Baroody[17] is described in texts on neutron slowing down theory as the application of transport theory and, in particular the Boltzmann transport equation.[19,20]

If one considers a plane source of primary ions of energy E_0 starting perpendicularly to the plane $x = 0$ in an infinite medium, then due to scattering processes, only a certain number $N(x, \mu, E)dEd\mu$ per unit volume will be moving at angles to the x direction between $\cos^{-1}\mu$ and $\cos^{-1}(\mu + \delta\mu)$ i.e. μ is the direction cosine of the ion motion with respect to the axis) and with energies between E and $E + \delta E$ at the plane at x.

If v is the velocity of these ions, then the number of collisions made by the ions per unit volume is

$N(x, \mu, E)dEd\mu \frac{v}{\lambda(E)}$ where $\lambda(E)$ is the ion mean free path at the energy E. Thus the model is essentially concerned with a random array of immobile target atoms, i.e. the gas model.

$N(x, \mu, E)\frac{v}{\lambda(E)}$ is now rewritten as $\psi(x, \mu, E)$ the collision density and $\lambda(E)\psi(x, \mu, E)$ is the flux of ions across unit area. Since these ions are moving in a direction at $\cos^{-1}\mu$ with respect to the x axis, there will be a net flux of ions leaving unit volume of

$\mu\lambda(E)\frac{d\psi}{dx}$ in the appropriate energy and angle range (the term μ arises since these ions cross a plane perpendicular to x at an angle $\cos^{-1}\mu$). At the same time, through scattering processes, other ions within the unit volume under consideration, will enter the energy and angular limits δE, $\delta\mu$ from other energies and angles of motion, and the total collision density of ions entering the considered region is just

$$\frac{(A+1)^2}{4A}\int dE'\int d\mu' f(\Omega, E, \Omega', E')\psi(x, \mu', E') \qquad 5.78.1$$

where $\psi(x, \mu', E')$ is the collision density at energy E' and angle $\cos^{-1}\mu'$ and $f(\Omega, E, \Omega', E')$ describes the fraction of ions in this energy and angle range which enter the considered range at E and $\cos^{-1}\mu$. Integration is over all allowed energies E' and angles described by Ω', the unit vector in the direction of motion $\cos^{-1}\mu'$.

One can now set up a balance for the rate of loss of ions by collision from the energy and angle limits at E and μ i.e.

$$\psi(x, \mu, E) + \mu\lambda(E)\frac{d\psi}{dx}(x, \mu, E)$$

against the rate of gain of ions

$$\frac{(A+1)^2}{4A}\int dE'\int d\mu' f(\Omega, E, \Omega', E')\psi(x, \mu', E')$$

$$+\ \delta(\mu-1)\delta(x)\delta(E-E_0)$$

The second term in this sum represents ions emerging from the source at $x = 0$, $E = E_0$ and $\mu = 1$ (i.e. $\cos^{-1}\mu = 0$) and is a product of Dirac Delta functions which are zero everywhere except at $x = 0$, $E = E_0$, $\mu = 1$.

One finally arrives at the time independent form of the Boltzmann equation

$$\mu\lambda(E)\frac{d\psi}{dx} + \psi = \frac{(A+1)^2}{4A}\int dE'\int d\mu' f(\Omega, E, \Omega', E')$$

$$\psi(x', \mu', E') + \delta(\mu-1)\delta(x)\delta(E-E_0) \qquad 5.78.2$$

Methods of solution of this form of the transport equation have been reviewed by, Marshak,[21] Tait,[22] Davison,[23] and in many texts on neutron reactions.[19,20] A particularly straightforward solution may be obtained when scattering is assumed isotropic in the centre of mass system, in which case the cosine of the angle between the initial and scattered ion directions is, as we have seen, simply given by

$$w = \Omega . \Omega' = \frac{1}{2}\left[(1+A)\left(\frac{E}{E'}\right)^{1/2} + (1-A)\left(\frac{E'}{E}\right)^{1/2}\right]$$

and the function $f(\Omega, E, \Omega', E')$ which is just $g(E, E')$ defined earlier, is given by

$$f(\Omega, E, \Omega', E') = \frac{(A+1)^2}{4A\pi}\cdot\frac{v}{v'^2}\,\delta\left[\Omega . \Omega' - \frac{1}{2}\left[(1+A)\left(\frac{E}{E'}\right)^{1/2} + (1-A)\left(\frac{E'}{E}\right)^{1/2}\right]\right] \qquad 5.79$$

where the Delta function again indicates zero scattering probability into angles other than those defined by w above.

One now expands $\psi(x, \mu, E)$ as a Legendre polynomial viz.

$$\psi(x, \mu, E) = \frac{1}{4\pi}\sum_{l=0}^{l=\infty}(2l+1)\psi_n(x, E)P_l(\mu) \qquad 5.80$$

where the functions $\psi_n(x, E)$ are independent of angle and $P_l(\mu)$ depends only upon the scattering angle. The values of $P_0(\mu)$, $P_1(\mu)$, $P_2(\mu)$ are simply 0, 1 and ½ $(3\mu^2 - 1)$ respectively and higher order terms are readily deduced from the Legendre series.

Multiplying equation 5.78.2 throughout by $P_l(\mu)$ and integrating over allowed μ values from −1 to +1, one obtains

$$\frac{l+1}{2l+1}\frac{\partial\psi_{l+1}(x, E)}{\partial x} + \frac{1}{2l+1}\frac{\partial\psi_{l-1}}{\partial x} + \frac{1}{\lambda(E)}\psi_l(x, E)$$

$$= \iint\psi(x, E, E')d\mu' dE'\int f'(\Omega, E, \Omega', E')P_l(\mu)d\mu$$

$$+\ S_n(x, E) \qquad 5.81$$

where $S_n(x, E)$ is the integral

$$\int_{-1}^{+1}P_l(\mu)\delta(x)\delta(\mu-1)\delta(E-E_0)d\mu$$

The above equation follows from the property of Legendre Polynomials that

$$\int_{-1}^{+1}P_l(\mu)P_n(\mu)d\mu = 0 \text{ if } n \neq l$$

$$= \frac{2}{2l+1}\text{ if } n = l \qquad 5.82$$

If one now defines the moment

$$\psi_{nl}(E) = -\int_{-\infty}^{\infty}\frac{x^n dx}{\lfloor n}\int_{-1}^{1}P_l(\mu)\psi(x, \mu, E)d\mu \qquad 5.83$$

then equation 5.81 may be multiplied throughout by x^m and integrated from $-\infty$ to ∞ to give

$$-\frac{(l+1)}{2l+1}\psi_{n-1,l+1}(E) - \frac{1}{2l+1}\psi_{n-1,l+1}(E)$$

$$+\ \frac{1}{\lambda(E)}\psi_{nl}(E) = \frac{(1-\alpha)^{-1}}{\lambda(E)}\int_E^{E/\alpha}\psi_{nl}(E')P_l(w)\frac{dE'}{E'}$$

$$+\ \frac{1}{\lambda(E)}E_0\delta_{no}\delta(E-E_0) \qquad 5.84$$

where

$$\alpha = \left(\frac{1-A}{1+A}\right)^2$$

The first term on the right hand side of the above equation arises as follows. Expanding $f'(\Omega, E, \Omega', E')$ as a Legendre polynomial in terms of the scattering angle w at a collision, we have.

$$f'(\Omega, E, \Omega', E') = \frac{1}{4\pi} \sum_{l=0}^{\infty} (2l + 1) f_l(E, E') P_l(w)$$

5.85

Using this expansion and the corresponding expansion for $\psi(x, E, E')$ it is then found that

$$\iint \psi(x, E, E') d\mu' dE' \int f'(\Omega, E, \Omega', E') P_l(\mu) d\mu$$

reduces to $\int \psi_l(x, E) f_l(E, E') dE'$. Multiplication by $P_l(w)$ and integration over w between the limits -1 to $+1$ then leads to

$$\int_{-1}^{1} f(E, E') P_l(w) \psi_l(x, E, E') dE'$$

and finally multiplication by x^n and integration over $-\infty$ to ∞ for isotropic scattering gives

$$\frac{(1-\alpha)^{-1}}{\lambda(E)} \int_E^{E/\alpha} \psi_{nl}(E') P_l(w) \frac{dE'}{E'}$$

Letting $\psi_{nl}(E) = M_{nl}$, it is clear that the moments are defined by the equation.

$$M_{nl} = \left\{ \frac{\lambda(E)}{2l + 1} \right\} \left\{ (l + 1) M_{n-1,\, l+1} + l M_{n-1,l+1} \right\}$$
$$+ \frac{1}{1-\alpha} \int_E^{E/\alpha} M_{nl}(E') P_l(w) \frac{dE'}{E'} + E_0 \delta_{no} \delta(E - E_0)$$

5.86

It is further apparent that the range moments are given by

$$\langle x^n \rangle = \underline{|n} \cdot \frac{M_{no}}{M_{oo}}, \text{ i.e. } l = 0 \qquad 5.87$$

In the case of equal primary and target atom masses M_{oo} is given by the solution to

$$M_{ol} = \int_x^1 M_{ol}(y') P_l(w) \frac{dy'}{y'} + \delta(y - 1) \text{ for } l = 0$$

where

$$y = \frac{E}{E_0}, \; w = \left(\frac{y}{y'}\right)^{1/2}$$

and is of the form

$$M_{oo} \propto \Sigma C y^q \qquad 5.88$$

The values of q are most readily determined by insertion of trial solutions into equation 5.88.

M_{no} can then be solved by an exactly analogous process, by assuming a series summation solution, and in doing this it is found convenient to rewrite the equation for M_{nl} in terms of the lethargy $u = \log_e y$. Again for the case of equal masses, and a mean free path $\lambda(E)$ which is proportional to E^k, one deduces a solution for the mean ion projected range at an energy $E < E_0$ of

$$\langle x(E) \rangle =$$
$$\left\{ \frac{(2k-1)y^{k+1/2} + (2k+3) + (2k+1)y^{k+1} \cdot \delta(x-1)}{(2k+1)(1 + x\delta(x-1))} \right\} \lambda(E_0)$$

5.89

When ions have slowed to zero energy, the mean projected range is

$$\bar{R}_{par} = \frac{2k+3}{2k+1} \cdot \lambda(E_0) \qquad 5.90$$

which assumes values of $3\lambda(E_0)$, $2\lambda(E_0)$, $\frac{5}{3}\lambda(E_0)$ for k values of, 1, $\frac{1}{2}$ and 0. We should note that the final value of $\frac{5}{3}\lambda(E_0)$ agrees with the value derived earlier using Holmes and Leibfried's[13] method for an essentially constant mean free path independent of energy $k = 0$. The total mean path length $\bar{L}$ may be obtained with equal facility, and higher range moments may also be evaluated with slightly greater complexity.

Solution of the moments equation for unequal masses is more difficult and requires use of Laplace transformation and the methods of complex integration to arrive at a tractable solution. In the interests of brevity, these computations are not reproduced here and the reader is referred to the paper by Baroody[17] for a fuller account. This author[18] has also considered the effects of using non-isotropic scattering functions, such as those suggested by Lindhard et al[8] for scattering from inverse power potentials, and has shown that an inverse 4th power potential leads to much closer correspondence for the projected path and the mean square projected path with results derived from isotropic scattering than does scattering from an inverse 2nd power potential.

We thus see, that by making some assumptions about the form of the interatomic potential, and the scattering process, we have been able to derive the interesting parameters in range determinations, namely averages of the powers of the total path length and the projected path length, and the distribution functions for these paths. Such methods are expected to be reliable where the actual form of the interatomic potential can be closely evaluated (for example from elasticity data) and are therefore best suited to collisions between atoms of similar mass. Although several forms of the interatomic potential have been proposed (c.f. Chapter 2) no methods have, as yet been devised to test their validity for grossly unequal mass cases. Indeed comparison of experimental ion bombardment studies and theoretical models may allow prediction of this interatomic potential.

5.8 THE DIFFUSION MODEL

This model which is basically that used in the calculations of the slowing down of neutrons in heavy reactor materials,[19, 20] is one approximation to the Boltzmann transport equation and is therefore of optimum applicability in the case of very light atoms passing through heavy target materials. In view of the completeness of the treatment of neutron slowing down theory, given for example in Glasstone and Edlund[20] it is necessary here to summarize only the salient features.

The incident ions are again assumed to slow down via collisions with the target atoms and their migration is considered to be represented by the methods of classical diffusion theory modified to account for the non isotropy of the primary scattering i.e. the transport of primaries is a result of concentration gradients of these. Solution of the diffusion equations is then possible, with the general result that the distribution function $f(R_{par}, E)$ has the form

$$f(R_{par}, E) = \int \frac{s(x^1)dx^1}{\sqrt{4\pi\tau}} \exp - \left(\frac{R_{par} - x^1}{4\tau}\right)^2 \qquad 5.91$$

which is simply the statement that the probability of reaching the projected path R_{par} is equal to the convolution of the possibilities for the path x^1 and of the remaining path $R_{par} - x^1$. The second term in the integral is a consequence of the assumed diffusion mechanism, where primaries are assumed to come to rest when their energy falls below E_d. Thus the quantity τ, the 'Fermi age' in reactor theory, is related to the average squared flight distance from a source point at energy E_0, to a resting point at energy E_d. Thus

$$\tau(E_0, E_d) = \frac{1}{3\xi(1 - \bar{\mu}_0)} \int_{E_d}^{E_0} \lambda^2(\epsilon) \frac{d\epsilon}{E_0} \qquad 5.92$$

ξ is the average logarithmic energy decrement per primary collision, which is seen from equation 5.43.2. to be

$$\int_{\alpha E_0}^{E_0} \frac{\log_e \epsilon/Ed.\, g(E_0, \epsilon)d\epsilon}{\int_{\alpha E_0}^{E_0} g(E_0, \epsilon)d\epsilon} = 1 + \frac{\alpha \log_e \alpha}{1 - \alpha} \qquad 5.93$$

and $\bar{\mu}_0$ is the average cosine of the scattering angle in the L system (non isotropy in this system), which is readily seen from Equation 5.48.1 to be given by

$$\bar{\mu}_0 = \frac{2}{3} A \qquad 5.94$$

When $A \gg 1$, where scattering is approximately isotropic in the L system, also, the result of equation 5.91 is identical with that of normal diffusion theory. The first term, which describes the first path distribution function, may conveniently be assumed to be of the exponential form described by Equation 5.40. However one must include in this term, other sources to account for the boundary condition at the macroscopic surface. One such condition would be that $f(R_{par} = 0, E_0) = 0$ for primaries incident externally at the surface, but an improvement is expected if it is required that $f(R_{par}, E_0)$ should vanish at some extrapolated distance outside the surface, i.e. allowing finite $f(R_{par} = 0, E_0)$

This latter condition may be expressed as

$$f\left(-\frac{2}{3}\frac{\lambda(E_0)}{1 - \bar{\mu}_0}, E_0\right) = 0 \qquad 5.95$$

This condition is energy dependent, since $\lambda(E_0)$ is itself energy dependent. In order to simplify matters, a convenient average, such as the logarithmic average, may be chosen for λ
i.e.

$$\bar{\lambda} = \frac{1}{\log_e E_0/E_d} \int_{E_d}^{E_0} \lambda(\epsilon) \frac{d\epsilon}{E_0} \qquad 5.96$$

and this value may then be used in Equation 5.91 in place of $\lambda(E_0)$.

Holmes[10] has compared the result of this model for the calculated case of 1 Kev helium ions incident on Aluminium, with computer calculations assuming a hard sphere and a Bohr potential interaction. Figure 5.10 shows the result of this comparison and it is evident that the hard sphere approximation is better in this case. Reasons for this will be discussed later.

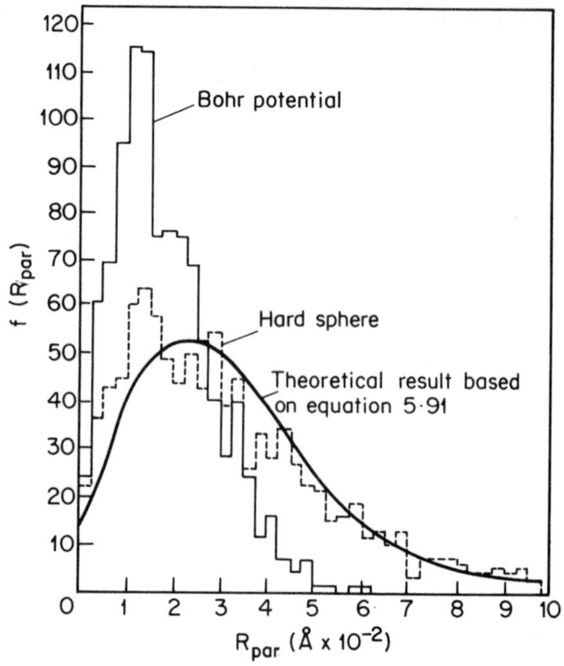

Fig. 5.10 A comparison of the distribution of ranges $f(R_{par})$ calculated using the Bohr potential and the hard sphere model on a computer and using the diffusion model of equation 5.91 for 1000 eV He^4 on Al. (viz. Ref. 5.10)

In view of the fact that experimental measurements of the range-energy relations are available, it is worth noting that, in principle, it is possible to adduce approximately the interatomic potential from these data.

If we consider that the random lattice model and the assumption of hard sphere collisions are adequate, then the average projected range $\bar{R}_{par}$ is given from Equation 5.49.2 as

$$\bar{R}_{par} = \lambda(E_0) + \frac{1}{E_0^{1/2}} \int_0^{E_0} \lambda(\epsilon) \frac{d\epsilon}{\epsilon^{1/2}} \qquad 5.49.2$$

for a primary energy E_0, and equal masses for the primary and target atoms.

If $\bar{R}_{par}$ is measured experimentally as a function $h(E_0)$ of the energy. The one has

$$h(E_0) = \lambda(E_0) + \frac{1}{E_0^{1/2}} \int_0^{E_0} \lambda(E_0) \frac{dE}{E^{1/2}} \qquad 5.97.1$$

Differentiation with respect to E_0 and substitution of the value of the integral from the above equation, then leads to

$$\frac{dh(E_0)}{dE_0} = \frac{d\lambda(E_0)}{dE_0} + \frac{1}{E_0}\left\{\frac{3\lambda(E_0) - h(E_0)}{2}\right\} \qquad 5.97.2$$

i.e.

$$E_0h'(E_0) + \tfrac{1}{2}h(E_0) = E_0\lambda'(E_0) + \tfrac{3}{2}\lambda(E_0) \qquad 5.97.3$$

where $h'(E_0)$, $\lambda'(E_0)$ are the first differentials with respect to E. This differential equation is readily solved for $\lambda(E_0)$ in terms of $h(E_0)$ as

$$\lambda(E_0) = \frac{1}{E_0^{3/2}} \int_0^{E_0} \frac{E_0 d}{dE}\left[E_0^{1/2} h(E_0)\right] dE_0 \qquad 5.97.4$$

Thus experimental measurement of $h(E_0)$ as a function of E_0, leads finally to $\lambda(E_0)$. However $\lambda(E_0)$ in the hard sphere approximation, is given by $\frac{1}{n\pi r^2}$ 5.98

i.e.

$$r = \frac{1}{\sqrt{n\pi}} \frac{1}{\sqrt{\lambda(E_0)}}$$

Consequently the functional dependence of r upon E may be deduced and since $V(r) = E_R$ the function V(r) itself.

Since the above analysis is limited to the equal mass case, the only applicable and currently available measurements of projected ranges are for Na^{24} in Al^{27}.

In this case Corkhill and Carter [24] have shown that the range data predicts an interatomic potential of the form r^{-4} for 0.17 Å-0.36 Å. One may anticipate that further measurements will be available soon, and a fuller determination of the interatomic potential should become possible in these cases.[25] Any such interpretations on these lines should be treated cautiously, however, in view of the known differences in scattering from hard sphere and realistic potentials.

Summary

In this section we have evaluated the dependence of the interesting range parameters upon primary energy and investigated probable forms of the distributed functions. An important restriction on all these calculations however has been the fact that lattice randomisation was assumed, and thus the chance of a primary making a collision was essentially that chance of finding target atoms in spatially isotropic distribution. Real solid crystal lattices, of course, consists of rows and planes of atoms in well defined positions, and the atomic spatial distribution is far from isotropic. This lattice symmetry may be expected to influence the collision sequence of a given primary, resulting in range parameters and distributions differing markedly from those analysed to date.

The effects of lattice symmetry were first realised during computer studies of primary ranges by Robinson et al[26,27,28] and by Beeler and Besco.[29] Subsequently experimental work has confirmed the presence of range abnormalities due to lattice effects and several theoretical analyses have been recently reported. In order to preserve continuity of presentation the analytical evaluations of ranges assuming a real lattice are considered in the following section, although, as stated, these were undertaken largely as a result of the machine calculations to be discussed later. Therefore points made here regarding the influence of crystal structure will be emphasised later also, since it was in the machine calculations that their significance was first realised and assessed.

5.9 RANGES IN REAL LATTICES

5.9.1 Since, as we saw in Chapter 1, a real lattice consists of a regular atomic arrangement we should expect this lattice regularity to exert some considerable influence upon the history of a primary atom.

To date the most profound effect of crystal structure has been the observation of extremely long primary histories where the primary was injected into the lattice in certain crystal directions at defined positions on a lattice plane. These histories (observable in computer calculations and experimental investigations) have been termed 'channelled events', since it was discovered that, primaries suffering these long histories moved, for the majority of their trajectory in channels in the crystal structure, which were regions of low force concentration.

To understand how these channels exist let us consider briefly a hypothetical cubic lattice with atoms situated at each cube corner. Each plane parallel to a cube face contains a square array of lattice atoms as shown in Figure 5.11. If one considers one array

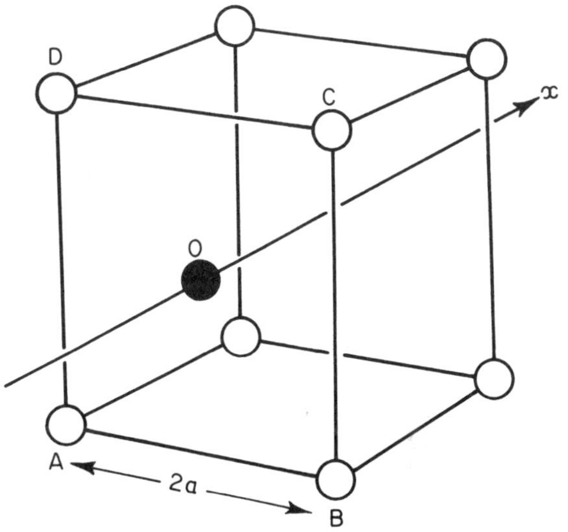

Fig. 5.11 Schematic representation of the path of an atom moving along the centre line on which is a 'channel' in a simple cubic arrangement of atoms

of four atoms A, B, C, D, and an axis perpendicular to this plane through the centre O, of the array ABCD, then the potential O due to A, B, C and D will be $\sum_A^D V(a\sqrt{2})$ with 2a as the interatomic spacing and the potential due to an atom = V(r). The Force on a primary at O, will be zero since the forces at opposite ends of the diagonal are equal, but oppositely directed. A small displacement of the primary from O, in the ABCD plane will result in a net force acting upon the primary, in such a direction that for repulsive forces, decreasing with increasing atomic separation, the atom will tend to return to O. If one considers the situation along the line Ox, then the force on a primary at a given position on Ox fluctuates periodically with x (going from zero at a plane, back to zero midway between planes) and is always directed along Ox. Thus it is readily seen that a primary started along Ox always travels along Ox, since it can only lose energy in the Ox direction. Similarly atoms started at a small distance from Ox will perform some form of periodic motion about Ox with an asymptotic tendency to travel along Ox. It is therefore conceived that such directions in the lattice may act as channels, along which primaries will travel large distances. The reason that the distances of travel will be large is that since the distances of approach of the primary and lattice atoms are always large ($=\frac{1}{\sqrt{2}}$x atomic spacing) only small energy transfers will occur, compared to a random sequence of collisions where, in a head on collision, all primary energy may be dissipated (for the equal mass case).

It is appreciated that this case is hypothetical, but consideration of real lattices leads to basically similar atomic configurations which can cause channelled trajectories as we shall presently show.

Three analytical calculations on channelling events have so far been reported. One by Lehmann and Leibfried[4] is applicable specifically to the case of medium mass primaries in a target of the same material, started with energy of the order of 10 kev.

The others by Nelson and Thompson[2, 3] and Lindhard[5] are more applicable to the case of quite energetic (100 kev) light primaries (protons) in heavier targets. Both employ the same calculational approach, the use of the impulse approximation, to describe the interactions between the primary and target atoms, and both lead to similar conclusions. However, there are certain differences which make it necessary to consider both treatments here. Undoubtedly, neither investigation fully describes the phenomenon and further publications are undoubtedly imminent.

We consider first the Lehmann-Leibfried[4] analysis.

In this treatment the authors have assumed either of the two forms for the interatomic potential.

(a) Bohr potential

$$V_B(r) = \frac{A_B \cdot a_B}{r} \exp(-r/a_B)$$

(b) Born-Mayer Potential

$$V_{BM}(r) = A_{BM} \exp(-r/a_{BM})^{31}$$

The values of the constants A_B, a_B, A_{BM}, a_{BM} may be derived from elasticity data[32] and are taken as respectively $A_B = 99.43$ kev; $a_B = 0.1218$ Å; $A_{BM} = 22.5$ kev; $a_{BM} = 0.197$ Å. The Bohr potential (a) was used largely in order for comparison with computer results, since, at the separation distances considered in this analysis, it is insufficiently strong, and moreover since its range of applicability when employing the impulse approximation is quite restricted (viz. Chapter 2 section 2.9)

In order to comprehend more clearly the motion of a primary in a channel, the ⟨110⟩ channel in the f.c.c. copper lattice is chosen. This channel is bordered by four atomic ⟨110⟩ rows as shown in Figures 5.12a and 5.12b. Here, since the x axis is a symmetry axis, forces at Ox vanish perpendicularly to Ox and have only a component along Ox. Thus as outlined before initial motion along Ox is maintained, energy losses occurring through weak interactions of the primary with the surrounding chains.

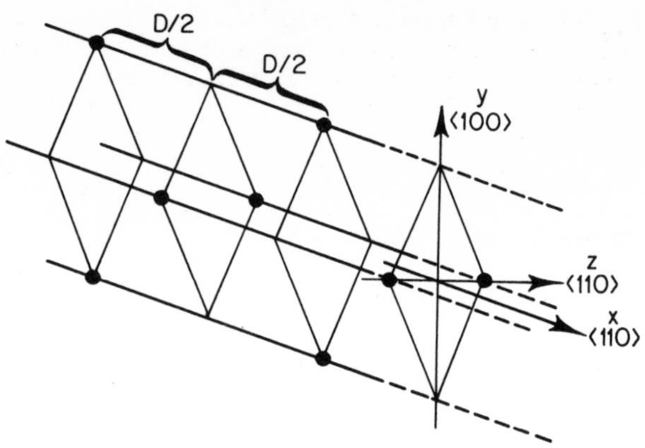

Fig. 5.12a Isometric view of a ⟨110⟩ channel bordered by four ⟨110⟩ atomic chains. The x, y and z axis are shown

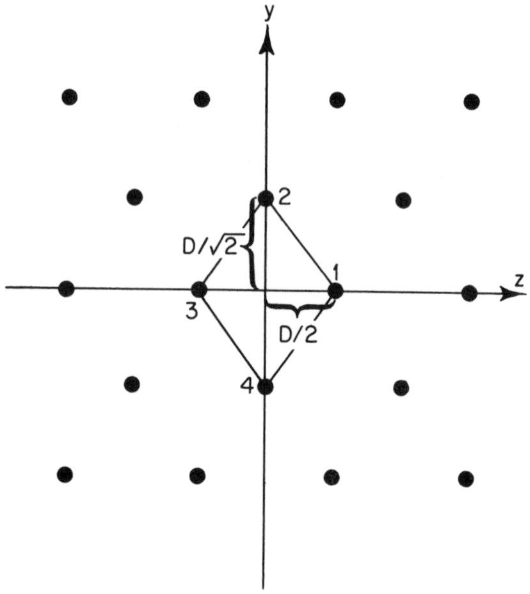

Fig. 5.12b Sectional view showing the intersections of ⟨110⟩ chains with a {110} plane

Since the Bohr and Born Mayer potentials decrease rapidly with increasing separation it is necessary only to consider the influence of the four surrounding ⟨110⟩ rows, more distant chains may be ignored.

Further, since the impact parameters are large (order of 10a) primaries moving near the channel axis experience only glancing collisions with the lattice atoms and perform a wave like oscillation about the axis. Because of the glancing nature of the collisions it is generally legitimate to apply the impulse approximation to a collision (the actual limits of validity of this approximation are discussed subsequently). In this approximation the struck lattice atoms are assumed to remain stationary during the interaction, which implies that the potential $\phi(x, y, z)$ close to the Ox axis defined in figure 5.12 is static with time, but periodic in x.

For small deviations from Ox, the potential may be expanded in powers of y and z (Oy and Ox were also defined in Figure 5.12a) thus

$$\phi(x, y, z) = \phi_0(x) + \phi_y(x).y + \phi_z(x)z + \tfrac{1}{2}\{\phi_{yy}(x).y^2 + 2\phi_{yz}(x).yz + \phi_{zz}(x)z^2\} \quad 5.99.1$$

where ϕ_y, ϕ_z are the first differentials of the potential at x with respect to y and z respectively.

ϕ_{yy}, etc. are second differentials etc., and are effectively coefficients to the powers of y and z. If we define an axis of symmetry (such as Ox) as one in which, for equal positive and negative, y or z values, the potentials $\phi(x, y, z)$ and $\phi(x, -y, -z)$ are equal. Thus, all odd powers in the expansion of Equation 5.99.1 vanish and further, ignoring powers above the second, an approximate form for $\phi(x, y, z)$ is given by

$$\phi(x, y, z) = \phi_0(x) + \tfrac{1}{2}\{\phi_{yy}(x)y^2 + \phi_{zz}(x)z^2\} \qquad 5.99.2$$

The Equations of motion then become

$$M\ddot{x}(t) = -\frac{\partial\phi}{\partial x} \simeq \frac{\partial\phi_0(x)}{\partial x} \qquad 5.100.1$$

$$M\ddot{y}(t) = -\frac{\partial\phi}{\partial y} \cong -\phi_{yy}(x).y \qquad 5.100.2$$

$$M\ddot{z}(t) = -\frac{\partial\phi}{\partial y} \cong -\phi_{zz}(x).z \qquad 5.100.3$$

With $\ddot{x}$, $\ddot{y}$ and $\ddot{z}$ the 2nd spatial derivatives with respect to time and M the primary mass. The first of these trajectory equations may be solved exactly to $M\dot{x}^2(t) + \phi_0(x) = \text{Const.}$ 5.101.1
for the conservation of energy along the x axis.

If the energy losses are considered small in a first approximation then $\phi_0(x)$ may be ignored and equation 5.101.1 shows that the axial velocity $\dot{x}$ is a constant equal to v.

Equations 5.100.2 and 5.100.3 may then be transformed into x dependent only i.e.

$$\ddot{y}(x) = -\frac{\phi_{yy}(x).y}{2E};\ \ddot{z}(x) = -\frac{\phi_{zz}(x).z}{2E}$$

with

$$E = \tfrac{1}{2}Mv^2 \qquad 5.101.2$$

If the wavelength of the expected path is large compared with the period P of the channel structure (P = D in Figure 5.12a for the ⟨110⟩ channel) then the fluctuations of ϕ_{yy} over a period will be small and ϕ_{yy} may be replaced by its average over one period. Thus

$$\overline{\phi}_{yy} = \frac{1}{P}\int_0^P \phi_{yy}(x)dx;\ \ddot{y} = -\frac{\overline{\phi}_{yy}.y}{2E},\ \ddot{z} = -\frac{\overline{\phi}_{zz}.z}{2E} \qquad 5.102.1$$

Solution of these latter equations lead to the expected oscillatory equations of motion

$$y(x) = \exp\left\{\pm i\left(\frac{\overline{\phi}_{yy}}{2E}\right)^{1/2}.x\right\}$$
$$z(x) = \exp\left\{\pm i\left(\frac{\overline{\phi}_{zz}}{2E}\right)^{1/2}.x\right\} \qquad 5.102.2$$

The trajectory is sinusoidal, if the coefficients $\overline{\phi}$ are positive with the primary always returning to the axis. If either coefficient is negative the path will expand exponentially in that plane. In the example of the ⟨110⟩ channel in coppper it turns out that $\overline{\phi}_{yy}$ ⟨0 and $\overline{\phi}_{zz}$⟩0 which may be referred to as semi-stability.

This allows one to define a second type of axis, in which the averages of the first potential derivatives $\overline{\phi}_y, \overline{\phi}_z$ over a period vanish although the potential derivatives ϕ_y, ϕ_z at any given position do not. Thus

$\overline{\phi}(y, z) = \frac{1}{P}\int_0^P \phi(x, y, z)dx$ and expanding the average potential $\overline{\phi}_{y,z} = \overline{\phi}_0 + \overline{\phi}_y.y + \overline{\phi}_z.z + \tfrac{1}{2}\{\overline{\phi}_{yy}.y^2 + \overline{\phi}_{yz}.yz + \overline{\phi}_{zz}.z^2\} + \ldots.$ 5.103.1

Hence on the axes of average zero first potential derivative

$$\overline{\phi}(y, z) = \overline{\phi}_0 + \tfrac{1}{2}\left\{\overline{\phi}_{yy}.y^2 + \overline{\phi}_{zz}.z^2\right\} \qquad 5.103.2$$

which are force free $\left(\frac{\partial\overline{\phi}_y}{\partial x} = 0\right)$ in the average, and the axes y, z are chosen to render $\overline{\phi}_{yz} = 0$

Along this axis, the equations of motion become

$$M\ddot{x} = 0;\ dx/dt = v$$

$$M\ddot{y}(t) = -\overline{\phi}_{yy}.y^2 \text{ or } \ddot{y}(x) = -\overline{\phi}_{yy}.y/2E$$

$$M\ddot{z}(t) = -\overline{\phi}_{zz}.z^2 \text{ or } \ddot{z}(x) = -\overline{\phi}_{zz}.z/2E \qquad 5.104.1$$

The solution of these equations requires a knowledge of the positional (x) dependence of E and thus of the rate of energy loss or stopping power, $\left(-\frac{dE}{dx}\right)$. We shall return to this question shortly, but for the present examine the number and position of the axes along which $\overline{\phi}_y, \overline{\phi}_z$ are vanishing. Since potentials (1) and (2) above decrease very rapidly with distance then it is readily seen that the potential at any point in a plane will be largely dependent upon the potentials

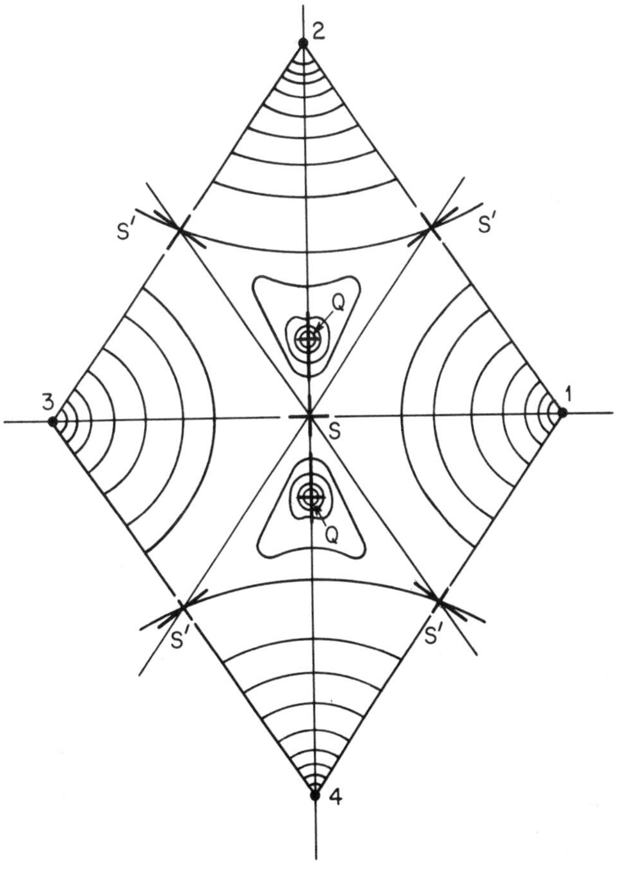

Fig. 5.13 Contours of equal average potential, $\Phi(y, z)$ = constant. The S, S′ and Q axis are shown. (viz. Ref. 5.4)

of the atoms closest to the point in question. Similarly the potential due to a row of atoms will exhibit a similar behaviour with increasing distance from the chain as that due to a single atom. Thus one may define channels along which the potential is due to the nearest rows to the channel and axes along which the average potential is zero. Inspection of Figure 5.13 then shows that three types of such axis exist. The axis S is determined by the potentials of all four atoms 1, 2, 3, 4, but the effects of 1 and 3 dominate. The axes S^1 are determined almost wholly by atom rows such as 1 and 2, whilst axes Q are determined by the rows 1, 2 and 3. Detailed consideration shows that the Q axes are those along which the primary motion is most stable, and it is clear that, for this particular plane, such axes occur in pairs. We will thus confine our attention for the present, to a discussion of these Q axes. In order to determine the primary trajectory along these axes, it is necessary to know (a) the potential variation in the channel and (b) the energy loss along the channel. We consider the potential variation first.

The potential at any point within a ⟨110⟩Q channel is determined by the superposition of the potentials due to all atoms in chains surrounding the channel. Consider the potential at a point x along the channel, due to a chain of atoms parallel to the x axis (Q axis), a perpendicular distance ρ from the point under consideration, where the interaction potential is given by V(r). This is given by

$$\Phi(x, \rho) = \sum_{m=-\infty}^{m=\infty} V\sqrt{(x - mP)^2 + \rho^2} \qquad 5.105.1$$

where m is integral

This may be replaced by a Fourier series e.g.

$$\Phi(x, \rho) = \sum_{\mu=-\infty}^{\infty} \Phi(\rho) \exp\left(i\frac{2\pi}{P}\mu x\right) = \Phi_0(\rho) + 2\sum_{\mu=1}^{\infty} \Phi_\mu(\rho)\frac{\cos 2\pi\mu x}{P} \qquad 5.105.2$$

with

$$\Phi_\mu(\rho) = \Phi_\mu(-\rho) = \frac{2}{P}\int_0^\infty V\sqrt{x^2 + \rho^2} \,.\, \cos\frac{2\pi}{P}\,.\,\mu x dx \qquad 5.105.3$$

This identity is readily deduced by noting that

$$\Phi_\mu(\rho) = \frac{1}{P}\int_0^P \Phi(x, \rho)\cos\frac{2\pi}{P}.\ \mu x dx$$

$$\therefore\ \Phi_\mu(\rho) = \frac{1}{P}\int_0^P \{V(x^2 + \rho^2)^{1/2} + V[(x - P)^2] + \rho^2]^{1/2} + \ldots\ldots V[x - mP)^2 + \rho^2]^{1/2}\}\cos\frac{2\pi\mu x.\,dx}{P}$$

$$+\{V[(x + P)^2 + \rho^2]^{1/2} + \ldots\ldots V[(x + mP)^2 + \rho^2]^{1/2}\}\cos\frac{2\pi\mu x.\,dx}{P} \qquad 5.105.3a$$

$\cos\frac{2\pi\mu x}{P}$ may be equally readily written as

$\cos\frac{2\pi\mu}{P}(x - mP)$

or $\cos\frac{2\pi\mu}{P}(x + mP)$ from which is seen

$$P\Phi_\mu(\rho) = \int_0^P V(\sqrt{z^2 + \rho^2})\cos\frac{2\pi\mu z}{P}\,.\,dz$$

$$\int_P^{2P} V(\sqrt{z^2 + \rho^2})\cos\frac{2\pi\mu z}{P}\,.\,dz + \int_{2P}^{3P}\ldots\ldots + \int_{-P}^{-2P}\ldots\ldots \qquad 5.105.3b$$

with $z = x - mp$.

i.e.

$$\Phi\mu(\rho) = 2/P\int_0^\infty V(\sqrt{z^2 + \rho^2})\cos\frac{2\pi\mu z}{P}\,.\,dz$$

For the Bohr potential it is readily shown (Ref. Leibfried and Lehmann[30]) that

$$\Phi_\mu(\rho) = 2A_B\rho/P\,\frac{1}{\beta_\mu}K_0\{\beta_\mu\rho/a_B\} \text{ with } \beta_\mu^2 = 1 + \frac{(2\pi\mu a_B)^2}{P} \qquad 5.106.1$$

and K_0 is the modified Hankel function discussed in Chapter 2. For the Born-Mayer potential

$$\Phi_\mu(\rho) = 2A_{BM}\frac{\rho}{P}\frac{1}{\beta_\mu}K_1\{\beta_\mu\rho/a_{BM}\} \qquad 5.106.2$$

The potentials due to one chain averaged over x are $\Phi_0(\rho)$ which for potentials (1) and (2) are

$$\Phi_0(\rho) = \frac{2A_B a_B}{P}K_0(\rho/a_B) \simeq \frac{2A_B a_B}{P}\left\{\frac{\pi a_B}{2\rho}\right\}^{1/2} \times \exp(-\rho/a_B) \qquad 5.107.1$$

$$\Phi_0(\rho) = \frac{2A_{BM}\rho}{P}K_1(\rho/a_{BM}) \simeq \frac{2A_{BM}\rho}{P}\left\{\frac{\pi a_{BM}}{2\rho}\right\}^{1/2} \times \exp(-\rho/a_{BM})$$

i.e. for primaries close to the Q axis 5.107.2

Since the coefficients β_μ increase with μ, the exponential decrease of the potential for the higher order terms of the Fourier series is even larger than in the above equations.

Thus the periodic variation of the potentials, for large ρ is suppressed and the potential is adequately expressed by the first few terms of the Fourier expansion. Considering, initially, only the average potential, then along the direction Q in Figure 5.13 the potential is that due to the surrounding chains, i.e.

$$\Phi(y, z) = \sum_{i=1}^{4}\Phi_0(\rho_i) \qquad 5.108.1$$

where y_i and z_i are the coordinates of each chain relative to the S axis.

i.e.

$$\rho_i^2 = (y - y_i)^2 + (z - z_i)^2$$

The position of Q, which is equally spaced between the atoms 1 and 3 (i.e. z = 0) is given by the minimum of

$$\overline{\Phi}_0(y, 0) = \Phi(l_2 - y) + 2\Phi_0(\sqrt{l_1^2 + y^2}) \qquad 5.109.1$$

and l_1, l_2 are defined in Figure 5.14 due to chains

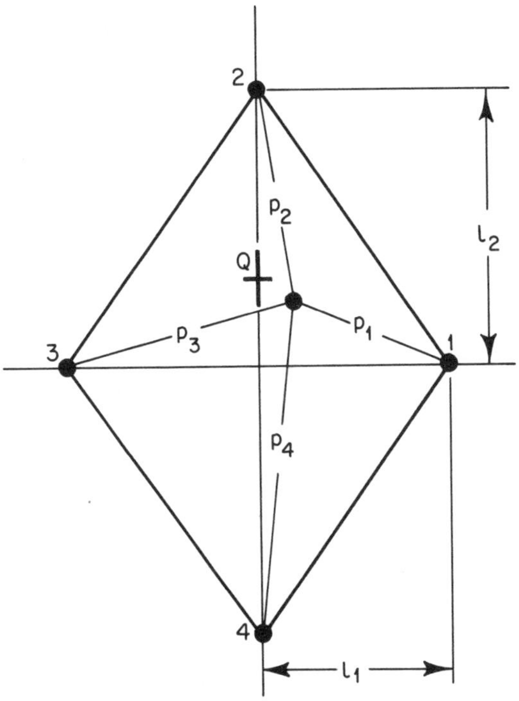

Fig. 5.14 Evaluation of $\overline{\Phi}$ in a ⟨110⟩ channel at a point near the Q axis. (viz. Ref. 5.4)

1, 2 and 3. Substitution of the potentials in Equations 5.109.1 leads to y values of Q, relative to S axis, given by

$$y_Q = \pm\ 0.160D \quad \text{Bohr potential} \qquad 5.109.2$$

$$y_Q = \pm\ 0.140D \quad \text{Born-Mayer potential} \qquad 5.109.3$$

Having located the Q axis, one may now consider this as the channel x axis, and expand the average potential about this axis in powers of y and z, as in equation 5.103.2

Thus

$$\overline{\Phi}(y, z) = \Phi(Q) + \tfrac{1}{2}\Phi_{yy}(Q).\, y^2 + \tfrac{1}{2}\Phi_{zz}(Q).\, z^2 \qquad 5.110.1$$

The variation of the potential parallel to the x axis may be assessed by computing the first term of the Fourier expansion in Equation 5.105.2. Thus, for the ⟨110⟩ channel, the potential due to the rows 1, 2 and 3, at a position Q" close to the origin is given by

$$\Phi(x, Q") = 3\Phi_S(l) + 6\sum_{\mu=1}^{\infty} \Phi_\mu(l) \cos\frac{2\pi\mu x}{D} \qquad 5.111.1$$

where l is the distance between the Q" axis and each chain of 1, 2 and 3 atoms and $l = 3D/4\sqrt{2}$ and the variation in Φ along the channel, $\delta\Phi \simeq 12\Phi_1(l)$ i.e.

$$\delta\Phi \cong 24\,\frac{A_B a_B}{D}\, K_0\left(\frac{1}{a_B}\sqrt{1 + \left(\frac{2\pi a_B}{D}\right)^2}\,\right)$$

for the Bohr potential 5.112.2

$$\delta\Phi \cong \frac{24A_{BM}a_{BM}\ l}{a_{BM}D\sqrt{1 + \left(\dfrac{2\pi a_{BM}}{D}\right)^2}}\ K_1\left(\frac{1}{a_{BM}}\sqrt{1 + \frac{(2\pi a_{BM})^2}{D}}\right)$$

for the Born-Mayer potential 5.112.3

Substitution for the values of K_0 and K_1 lead to

$$\delta\Phi \simeq 0.62 \text{ eV for Bohr potential} \qquad 5.112.4$$

$$\simeq 58 \text{ eV for Born-Mayer potential} \qquad 5.112.5$$

Which, since these are small compared with the initial primary energy allows one, in a first approximation, to neglect energy losses along a channel.

The path of the primary projected on to the y, z plane, is given by Equations 5.104.

If the coefficients $\overline{\Phi}_{yy}$ and $\overline{\Phi}_{zz}$ were equal the path in the y, z plane would be elliptical with Q as the centre (motion under perpendicular restoring forces). For $\overline{\Phi}_{yy} \neq \overline{\Phi}_{zz}$ the motion is a complicated Lissajous figure, but may be separated into y and z and z components each of which has a wave like nature, with wavelengths given from Equations 5.102.1 and

TABLE 5.4. (Part 1) (Ref. 5.4.).

Channel direction	⟨110⟩	⟨100⟩	⟨112⟩	⟨103⟩	⟨111⟩
Number N_c of channels	12	6	24	24	8
Channel area f (f/D^2)*	$1/\sqrt{2}$	1/2	$1/\sqrt{6}$	$1/\sqrt{10}$	$1/\sqrt{12}$
Period P of channel structure (P/D)	1	$\sqrt{2}$	$\sqrt{3}$	$\sqrt{5}$	$\sqrt{6}$
Position of the axis	0.140 (BM)			0.341 (BM)	
(Y_Q/D)	0.160 (B)			0.330 (B)	
Distance l† between chains and Q-axis (l/D)	0.57 (1x), 0.52 (2x) (BM); 0.55 (1x), 0.53 (2x) (B)	½	$\frac{1}{2}\sqrt{11/12}$	0.366 (1x), 0.408 (2x), 0.578 (2x) (BM)†; 0.38 (1x), 0.40 (2x) (B)	⅓

* The channel area f has been chosen as the unit cell in the yz plane (cf. Fig. 5.17). D is the Distance between nearest neighbours in the lattice.

† In this case the contribution of the 3rd. nearest neighbours to Q with distance 0.758 D (indicated in Fig. 5.17) can be neglected.

TABLE 5.4. (Part 2).

Bohr Potential

$\bar{\Phi}_{yy} \cdot D^2/A \cdot 10^4$	6.16	6.26	12.7	57.5	72.7
$\lambda_y \cdot \frac{1}{D}\sqrt{\frac{kev}{E}}$	35.7	35.6	25.0	11.8	10.5
$\bar{\phi}_{zz} \cdot D/A \cdot 10^4$	4.16	6.26	3.66	6.25	72.7
$\lambda_z \cdot \frac{1}{D}\sqrt{\frac{kev}{E}}$	43.4	35.6	46.7	35.7	10.5
$\delta\phi^{(*)}$ (ev)	0.62	0.98	1.60	9.40	35.0
E_c (ev)	2.12	1.58	13.8	39.3	54.3
$E_{MA}^{(\dagger)}$ (ev)	20	40	60	4×10^2	1.2×10^3
$E_{QM}^{(\dagger)}$ (ev)	1.6×10^2	6×10^2	1.2×10^3	4×10^4	4×10^5

(*) First Fourier coefficient of ϕ: In the Q axis (equidistant to the three bordering rows) for the ⟨110⟩ and ⟨103⟩ case, and in the symmetry axis for the three other cases.

(†) In the Q axis for the ⟨110⟩ and ⟨103⟩ case, and in the symmetry axis for the three other cases.

TABLE 5.4. (Part 3).

Born-Mayer Potential

$\bar{\phi}_{yy} \cdot D^2/A \cdot 10^2$	3.9	13.4	22.6	44.0	34.4
$\lambda_y \cdot \frac{1}{D}\sqrt{\frac{kev}{E}}$	9.5	5.1	3.95	2.83	3.20
$\bar{\phi}_{zz} \cdot D^2/A \cdot 10^2$	15.5	13.4	4.8	1.35	34.4
$\lambda_z \cdot \frac{1}{D}\sqrt{\frac{kev}{E}}$	4.8	5.1	8.57	16.2	3.20
$\delta\phi^{(*)}$ (ev)	58.2	116	154	389	802
E_c (ev)	174	77	192	625	585
$E_{MA}^{(\dagger)}$ (ev)	2.5×10^3	2.7×10^3	3.15×10^3	9×10^3	13.5×10^3
$E_{QM}^{(\dagger)}$ (ev)	3.5×10^6	4.5×10^6	7.7×10^6	4.5×10^7 $(7.0 \times 10^5)^{(\ddagger)}$	1.4×10^8

(*) First Fourier coefficient of ϕ: In the Q axis (equidistant to the three bordering rows) for the ⟨110⟩ and ⟨103⟩ case, and in the symmetry axis for the three other cases.

(†) In the Q axis for the ⟨110⟩ and ⟨103⟩ case, and in the symmetry axis for the three other cases.

(‡) For the two additional rows included in the calculation of Y_Q.

5.102.2 i.e.

$$\lambda_y = 2\pi \frac{\sqrt{2E}}{\sqrt{\Phi_{yy}}}$$

and

$$\lambda_z = 2\pi \frac{\sqrt{2E}}{\sqrt{\Phi_{zz}}} \qquad 5.113$$

Values of λ_y, λ_z are thus calculable from the values of Φ which are readily deduced for potentials (1) and (2). Table 5.4 indicates normalised values of λ for this channel and for other important channels in the f.c.c. structure. Other data of interest including Φ_{yy}, channels area, $\delta\Phi$ etc. for these channels, already defined, or defined in the table are also presented. The values of λ are clearly many times larger than the lattice period P for energies in the interesting range $\gtrsim 5$ Kev.

If the wavelengths become shorter and of the order of the period of the chain (lower initial energies for example), then the averaging of $\overline{\Phi}$ is no longer permitted and the periodic variation of the potential must be considered i.e. the primary then experiences sharp angular changes at each collision. One may obtain a rough estimate of the minimum energy E_c which a primary must possess in order to use the above analysis, by choosing E_c such that for the ⟨110⟩ channel, $\lambda_y \approx D$, $\lambda_z \approx 2D$. The reasons for these choices of λ are explained directly from Figure 5.15 which shows sections in the Oy and Oz plane for the ⟨110⟩ channel. It then turns out that

$$E_{c,y} \simeq D^2 \overline{\Phi}_{yy}/8\pi^2 \simeq 0.78\text{eV Bohr potential} \quad 5.114.1$$

$$\simeq 11\text{eV Born-Mayer potential} \quad 5.114.2$$

$$E_{c,y} \simeq D^2 \overline{\Phi}_{yy}/8\pi^2 \simeq 2.12\text{ eV Bohr potential} \quad 5.114.3$$

$$\simeq 174\text{eV Born-Mayer potential} \quad 5.114.4$$

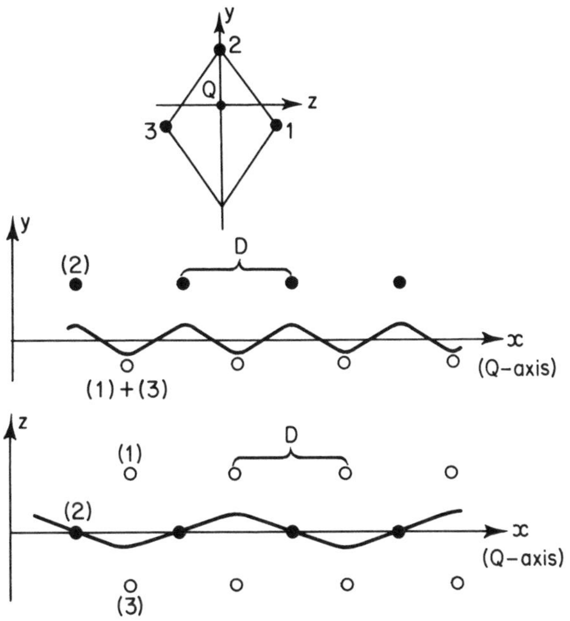

Fig. 5.15 Representation of the projected trajectory of an ion in a ⟨110⟩ channel near the Q axis illustrating the wavelength of the ion. (viz. Ref. 5.4)

On the other hand, as shown in Chapter 2 Section 2.9, classical mechanical impulse approximation considerations using the impulse approximation are only accurate for primary energies above a lower limit $E_{M.A}$ and below an upper limit $E_{Q.M}$. For the Bohr potential this gives limits of applicability $20\text{eV} \lesssim E \lesssim 160\text{eV}$ and for the Born-Mayer potential $2500\text{eV} \lesssim E \lesssim 3.5 \times 10^6\text{eV}$.

Clearly the Bohr potential imposes very serious restrictions, and, as pointed out by Lehmann and Leibfried[4, 30] can properly only be used for qualitative comparison with machine calculations.

We should also mention that the potential due to a chain at a position just off the channel axis, as described by $\Phi_0(\rho)$ may be closely approximated by the logarithmic expansion from Equation 5.107,

$$\Phi_0(\rho) \simeq \Phi_0(\rho_c) \exp - \left(\frac{\rho - \rho_c}{a^1}\right) \quad 5.115$$

since $\rho \cong \rho_c$ where ρ_c = chain to channel axis distance and a′ is determined from the logarithmic derivative of Φ_0 at $\rho = \rho_c$. Whilst this analysis indicates the essentially wavelike nature of the primary trajectory, it is incomplete in as much as the primary is assumed to retain its initial energy indefinitely, losing no energy at each impulsive encounter with lattice atoms.

In fact the lattice atoms are not rigidly fixed in space during an encounter with the primary and this must therefore be continuously reduced in energy, which will lead to a damping effect on the oscillatory trajectory.

The momentum transfer p, from a primary moving initially along the ξ axis with an energy E, to a stationary atom mass m, is given as in Equation 2.58 by

$$p = \sqrt{\frac{2M_1}{E}}\Psi(b) \quad 5.116.1$$

where

$$\psi(b) = \int_0^{\infty} \frac{b\,d\xi}{(b^2+\xi^2)^{1/2}} \left\{-\frac{\partial}{\partial r} V\,(b^2+\xi^2)^{1/2}\right\} = \int_b^{\infty} \frac{b\,dr}{(r^2-b^2)^{1/2}} \frac{\partial}{\partial r} V(r) \quad 5.116.2$$

where b = impact parameter and r the instantaneous atom separation. The energy loss is then

$$\Delta E = p^2/_2M_2 = \frac{M_1}{M_2 E}\psi^2(b) \quad 5.117.1$$

For the Bohr and the Born-Mayer potentials it may be shown,[30] as in Chapter 2, that

$$\psi(b) = AK_1(b/a)$$

and

$$\psi(b) = \frac{Ab}{a} K_0(b/a) \quad 5.116.3$$

respectively, which may be evaluated numerically for appropriate values of b/a.

In order to determine b, for a given impact, we note that the trajectory of the primary is approximately straight (and the true path may be replaced by its tangent at the distance of closest approach. Thus in figure 5.16, it is seen to be related to the distance of closest approach r in the plane containing the target atoms, by the identity

$$b = |\underline{l} - \underline{r}|\,.\cos\alpha \quad 5.118$$

with l and α as defined in Figure 5.16 and u is the primary direction of motion (along the ξ axis). For large impact parameters (ξ axis and Q axis almost coincident)

$$\sin\alpha \simeq \alpha \simeq \frac{u\,.(\underline{l}-\underline{r})}{|\underline{l}-\underline{r}|} = \frac{\underline{r}'\,.(\underline{l}-\underline{r})}{|\underline{l}-\underline{r}|} \simeq \frac{\underline{r}'\,.\underline{l}}{\underline{l}} \quad 5.119.1$$

with $r^2 = y^2 + z^2$ and $(r')^2 = (dy/dx)^2 + (dz/dx)^2$

and since $\cos \alpha \simeq 1 - \alpha^2/2$ one obtains

$$b \simeq l \left\{ 1 - \frac{\underline{r}.\underline{l}}{l^2} + \frac{1}{2l^2}\left[r^2 + \frac{(rl)^2}{l^2} - (\underline{r}'.\underline{l})^2 \right] \right\} \qquad 5.116.4$$

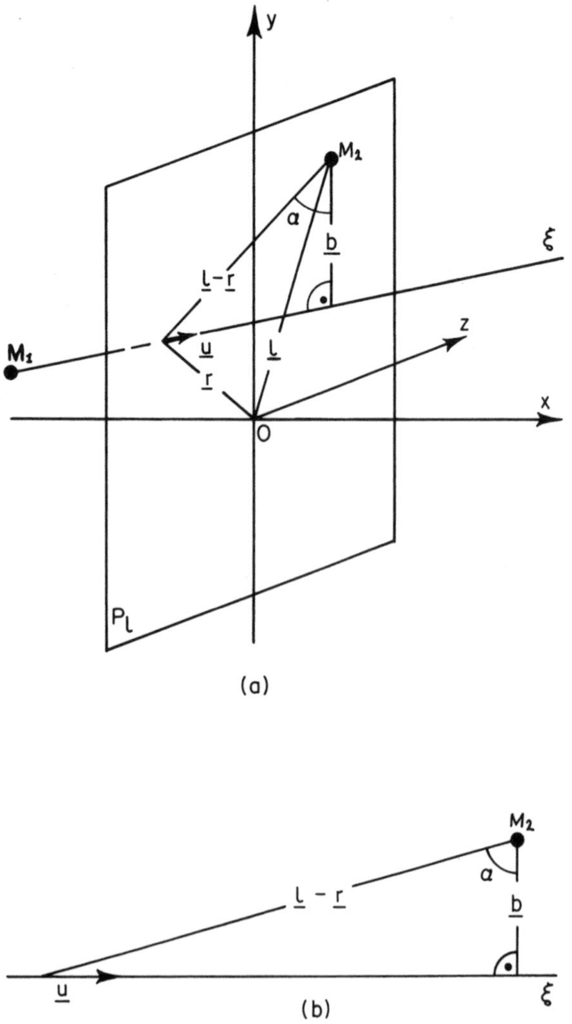

Fig. 5.16 Geometry of a collision between an ion (mass M_1) and a target atom (mass M_2) in a channel. (viz. Ref. 5.4)

neglecting higher than second order terms in $\underline{r}$ and $\underline{r}'$. The energy loss ΔE may be obtained in an analogous way through

$$\Delta E \simeq \frac{M_1}{M_2 E}\left\{ \psi^2(l) + \left.\frac{d\psi^2(b)}{db}\right|_{b=l} (b-l) + \left.\frac{d^2\psi^2(b)}{db^2}\right|_{b=l} (b-l)^2 \right\} \qquad 5.117.2$$

Since b depends upon $\underline{r}$, $\underline{r}'$ and $\underline{l}$ only, one can write this in functional form.

$$\Delta E = \frac{M_1}{M_2 E} F(\underline{r}, \underline{r}', \underline{l}) \qquad 5.117.3$$

where $\underline{r}'$, and $\underline{l}$ are to be evaluated at the x position at which the energy is transferred. Specifically

$$\Delta E = \frac{M_1}{M_2 E}\left\{ \psi^2(l) + \left.\frac{d\psi^2(b)}{db}\right|_{b=l} \frac{1}{2l} \right\} r^2 + \frac{(\underline{rl})^2}{l^2} - 2(\underline{rl}) - (\underline{r}'.\underline{l})^2 + \left.\frac{d^2\psi^2(b)}{db^2}\right|_{b=l} \frac{(\underline{rl})^2}{2l^2} \Big\} \qquad 5.117.4$$

In the momentum approximation the energy losses are additive and one may calculate the energy loss per period,

$$\epsilon = \sum_{i=1}^{Np} \Delta E(x_i; \underline{r}(x_i); \underline{r}'(x_i); \underline{l}(x_i)) \qquad 5.120$$

with $x_i \ldots x_{N_p}$ are the x positions of the atoms of one chain in one period. Since the energy may vary only slowly with x, one may define an average energy loss per unit length (stopping power)

$$-\frac{dE(x)}{dx} = \frac{\varepsilon(x)}{P} \qquad 5.121$$

Thus, from equation 5.120

$$\frac{\varepsilon(x)}{P} = \frac{1}{E(x)} \frac{M_1}{M_2} \sum_{i=1}^{N_p} \frac{1}{P} \cdot F(\underline{r}(x); \underline{r}'(x); \underline{l}_i) \qquad 5.122.1$$

$$= \frac{1}{E(x)} \cdot \frac{M_1}{M_2} G(\underline{r}, \underline{r}') \qquad 5.122.2$$

where $G(\underline{r}, \underline{r}')$ is a determined function from

$$\frac{d^2\psi^2(b)}{db^2}; \frac{d\psi^2(b)}{db} \text{ and } (b - l)$$

and $(b - l)^2$ from Equations 5.116.2 and 5.116.4

One now has equations which determine the trajectory and energy loss completely, viz:

$$\ddot{y}(x) = -\overline{\Phi}_{yy} \cdot y(x) / 2E(x) \qquad 5.123.1$$

$$\ddot{z}(x) = -\overline{\Phi}_{zz} \cdot z(x)/2E(x) \qquad 5.123.2$$

and

$$\frac{-dE(x)}{dx} = \frac{1}{E(x)} \frac{M_1}{M_2} \cdot G\{y(x); z(x); y'(x); z'(x)\} \qquad 5.123.3$$

Evaluation of G from Equations 5.116.2, 5.116.4 show that this contains only linear and quadratic terms in r and r', and since the channel Q axis is conveniently chosen to be symmetrical with respect to z, G may be expanded, in terms of its Q axis derivatives as

$$G = G_0 + G_y \cdot y + \tfrac{1}{2} G_{yy} \cdot y^2 + \tfrac{1}{2} G_{zz} \cdot z^2 + \tfrac{1}{2} G_{y'y'} \cdot (y')^2 + \tfrac{1}{2} G_{z'z'} \cdot (z')^2 \qquad 5.124$$

G may be evaluated numerically for given values of y, z, y', and z' (i.e. position and angle in the target atom plane) and the co-efficients G_0 etc. determined. The data for the five major channels in the Copper are given in Table 5.5 whilst Figure 5.17 shows the atom configurations in these channels.

TABLE 5.5. (Part 1) (Ref. 5.4.)

Channel	⟨110⟩	⟨100⟩	⟨112⟩	⟨103⟩	⟨111⟩
Bohr Potential					
$G_0 \cdot D/A^2$	7.78×10^{-11}	3.45×10^{-10}	7.28×10^{-10}	2.04×10^{-8}	2.52×10^{-7}
$L_0 \cdot \frac{1}{D}\frac{(\text{kev})^2}{E^2}$	6.55×10^5	1.47×10^5	6.98×10^4	2.48×10^3	2.02×10^2
$G_{yy} \cdot D^3/A^2$	3.62×10^{-8}	3.20×10^{-7}	1.01×10^{-6}	3.52×10^{-5}	2.43×10^{-4}
$G_{zz} \cdot D^3/A^2$	1.07×10^{-7}	3.20×10^{-7}	3.41×10^{-7}	3.88×10^{-7}	2.43×10^{-4}
$\gamma \cdot 10^2$	5.55	3.38	4.77	17.3	11.3
$\frac{a^2\pi}{4f_Q} \cdot 10^2$	0.50	0.37	0.44	1.13	1.23
$\tilde{E}$ (ev)	1.05	2.5	4.85	37.4	87.6

TABLE 5.5. (Part 2).

Born-Mayer Potential

$G_0 \cdot D/A^2$	3.20×10^{-5}	6.30×10^{-5}	8.34×10^{-5}	4.10×10^{-4}	1.54×10^{-3}
$L_0 \cdot \frac{1}{D}\frac{(\text{kev})^2}{E^2}$	31.0	15.7	11.85	2.41	0.64
$G_{yy} \cdot D^3/A^2$	3.55×10^{-3}	1.64×10^{-2}	3.35×10^{-1}	1.87×10^{-1}	3.21×10^{-1}
$G_{zz} \cdot D^3/A^2$	1.44×10^{-2}	1.64×10^{-2}	9.92×10^{-3}	7.34×10^{-3}	3.21×10^{-1}
$\gamma \cdot 10^2$	19.8	12.04	17.55	110.0	52.0
$\frac{a^2\pi}{4f_Q} \cdot 10^2$	1.31	0.93	1.14	2.95	3.22
E (eV)	286	299	510	3590	1830

TABLE 5.5. (Part 3).

E keV	L_{HS}/D	L_0^{110}/D	L_0^{100}/D	L_0^{112}/D	L_0^{103}/D	L_0^{111}/D
1	2.6	—	—	—	—	—
5	7.9	775	392	296	—	—
10	16.8	3100	1570	1185	241	—
15	31.5	6980	3530	2660	541	144
20	57.8	12400	6280	4740	963	256

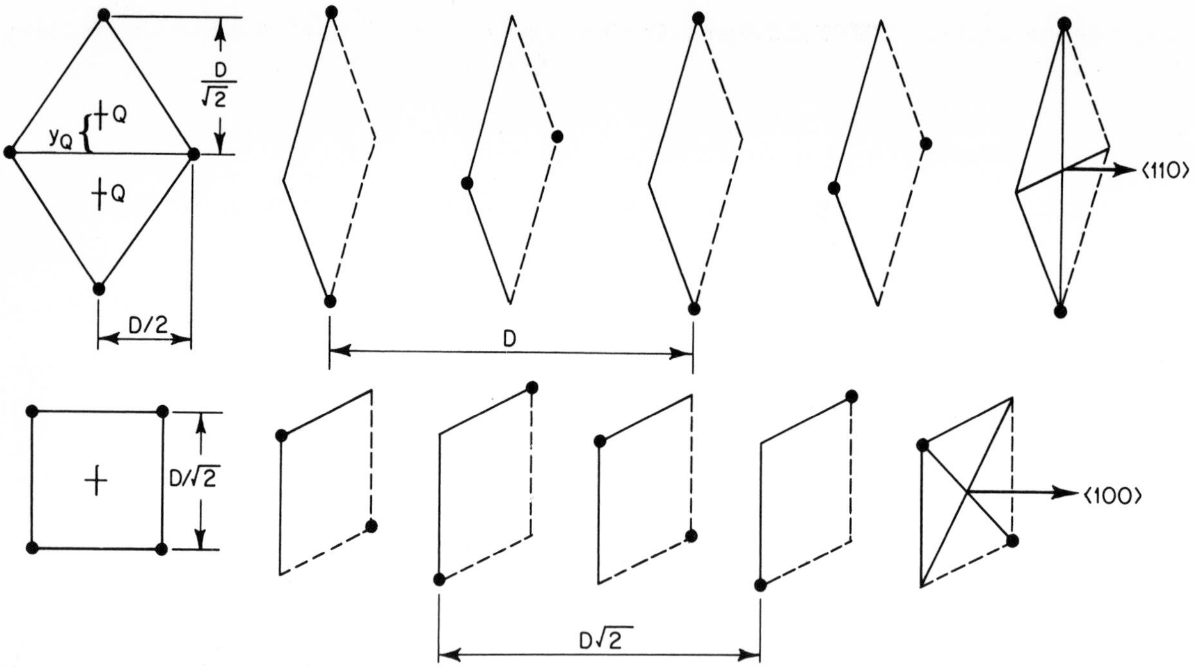

Fig. 5. 17 (Part 1) Structure of the ⟨110⟩ and ⟨100⟩ channels in an f. c. c. lattice

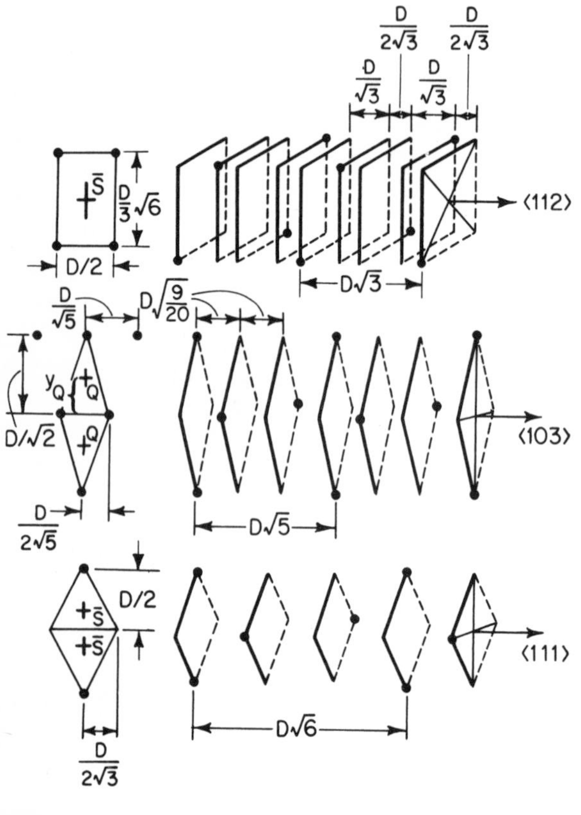

Fig. 5. 17 (Part 2) Structure of the ⟨112⟩, ⟨103⟩ and ⟨111⟩ channels in an f.c.c. lattice

The maximum range will clearly be for a particle incident directly along the Q axis ($y = z = y' = z' = 0$) and one thus obtains, for this range from Equation 5. 123. 3

$$\frac{-dE(x)}{dx} = \frac{G_0}{E(x)} \cdot \frac{M_1}{M_2} \qquad 5.125.1$$

with the solution

$$E_0^2 - E^2(x) = \frac{M_1}{M_2} \cdot 2G_0 \cdot x \qquad 5.125.2$$

for a primary of initial energy E_0 at $x = 0$.

The maximum range L_0 is obtained by setting $E(L_0) = 0$, thus

$$L_0 = \frac{M_2}{M_1} \frac{1}{2G_0} \cdot E_0^2 \qquad 5.125.3$$

This expression is not quite accurate since, as the primary slows down, the impulse approximation loses validity, and Andersen & Sigmund[33] suggest that, since the channel border atoms can move during the primary passage, the energy losses may be weaker than the momentum approximation values. Allowing for atomic motion essentially leads to an energy loss δE proportional to E^{-n}, where $n < 1$ & hence to a range which varies less rapidly than E^2. As we shall see later such a behaviour has been observed experimentally. However the orders of magnitude of L_0 are, as seen from Table 5. 5 extremely large. Table 5. 5 shows the L_0 values compared with the mean free path derived from the isotropic lattice assumption, which as seen from Equation 5. 44. 4 is adequately representative of primary ranges in the isotropic case. Clearly the channelling phenomena can lead to much deeper penetrations than can be expected for a random lattice.

5. 9. 2 Range Distributions

In addition to the maximum primary ranges, it is interesting to know the distribution in primary ranges. As seen from Equation 5. 125. 1 a primary initially incident along the channel axis has a well defined range. In the same way primaries incident at some other point on the channel will also have a range uniquely determined by their starting conditions. If we assume a uniform density of primary incident over the channel section, at normal incidence, then for a given primary

$$E(0) = E_0;\ y = y_0;\ z = z_0;\ y'(0) = z'(0) = 0$$

with a uniform distribution of positions y_0, z_0.

The distribution of ranges for primaries starting very close to the channel axis, i.e. . those primaries with range close to the maximum (axis) range, may be determined by expanding over the channel section, at normal incidence, then for a given primary

$$L(y_0, z_0) = L_0 - L_{yy} \cdot y_0^2/2 - L_{zz} \cdot z_0^2/2 \qquad 5.126$$

Linear terms in z_0 vanish for symmetry reasons, and terms linear in y_0 drop out since y(x) is essentially oscillatory with x (where the channel axis coincides with an axis of symmetry for the channel plane (as in ⟨100⟩, ⟨112⟩, ⟨111⟩ channels) terms linear in y_0, z_0 must vanish for symmetry reasons anyway) Equation 5.126 illustrates that for ranges $L(y_0, z_0)$ near the maximum, the range is constant for primaries started on the surface at any point $(y_0 z_0)$ on an ellipse of major and minor axes

$$\frac{\sqrt{L_{yy}}}{[2(L(y_0, z_0) - L_0]^{1/2}} \text{ and } \frac{\sqrt{L_{zz}}}{[2(L(y_0, z_0) - L_0]^{1/2}}$$

Thus the probability of finding ranges between $L (= L(y_0, z_0))$ and L_0, is simple the ratio of area within this ellipse defining the range L, to the surface area A_Q belonging to one axis. Values of A_Q in terms of the area A of the plane in question are given in Table 5.5

$$f(L) = \frac{1}{A_Q} \frac{2\pi}{(L_{yy}L_{zz})^{1/2}} (L_0 - L)$$

$$= \frac{2\pi}{A_Q} \left\{ \frac{L_0}{L_{yy}} \cdot \frac{L_0}{L_{zz}} \right\}^{1/2} \{1 - L/L_0\} \qquad 5.127$$

To evaluate this it is necessary to calculate the coefficients L_{yy}, L_{zz} which since the y_0 and z_0 components are independent, may be determined from initial conditions with $y_0 = o$ or $z_0 = o$ in turn. We consider this for motion in the Oy plane (z = o) since the y component has linear terms for the energy loss and is therefore more general.

For this motion, entirely in the Oy plane, Equations 5.102.1 and 5.123.3 become

$$\ddot{y}(x) = -\overline{\Phi}_{yy} \cdot y/2E(x) \qquad 5.128.1$$

$$-\frac{dE(x)}{dx} = \frac{M_1}{M_2} \left\{ G_0 + G_y \cdot y + G_{yy} \cdot \frac{y^2}{2} + G_{y'y'} \cdot \frac{(y')^2}{2} \right\} \frac{1}{E(x)} \qquad 5.128.2$$

If one assumes, as a first approximation, no energy losses in determining the trajectories, then Equations 5.128.1 and 5.128.2 solve to

$$y(x) = y_0 \cos 2\pi x/\lambda(\overset{2}{E_0}) \qquad 5.128.3$$

$$E_0^2 - E^2(x) = \frac{2M_1}{M_2} \int_0^x \{G_0 + G_y y(x) + G_{yy} \cdot y^2/_2 + G_{y'y'} \cdot \frac{y'^2}{2} \Big\} dx \qquad 5.128.3$$

For large initial primary energy, the range is large and contains many wavelengths, one may average the y's over one wavelength λ using equation 5.128.3 and treat these as x independent. Thus

$$\bar{y} = 0; \bar{y}^2 = y_0^2/_2; \overline{y'^2} = \left[\frac{2\pi y_0}{\lambda_0}\right]^2 \Big/ 2 \qquad 5.129$$

Thus the range L, given by E (x = L) = 0, follows from

$$E_0^2 = L \cdot \frac{M_1}{M_2} \{2G_0 + y_0^2/_2(G_{yy} + G_{y'y'}(2\pi/\lambda_0)^2)\} \qquad 5.130.1$$

Using Equation 5.125.3 for L_0, it is deduced that

$$L(y_0, 0) = L_0 \left\{1 - \frac{(G_{yy} + G_{y'y'}(2\pi/\lambda_0)^2)}{2G_0} \times y_0^2/2\right\} \qquad 5.130.2$$

and thus

$$\frac{d^2L}{dy^2} = L_{yy}$$

is given by

$$L_{yy} = L_0 \left\{ \frac{G_{yy} + G_{y'y'}(2\pi/\lambda_0)^2}{2G_0} \right\} \qquad 5.130.3$$

If on the other hand, energy losses are not discounted, these Equations 5.128.1 and 5.128.2 may not be solved independently. Intuitively, if the energy losses are small (e.g. $-\frac{dE}{dx} \ll E/\lambda$) then the trajectories will have the character of a damped oscillatory motion. Thus one may anticipate a solution to Equation 5.128.1 of the form $y(x) = Y(x) \cos \phi(x)$ 5.131.1 where Y(x) is a slowly varying function of x. Inserting this trial solution into Equation 5.128.1 gives the result

$$\left\{Y''(x) - Y'(x)\phi'^2 + \frac{\overline{\Phi}_{yy}}{2E} \cdot Y(x)\right\} \cos \phi(x)$$

$$= \{2Y'(x)\Phi' + Y(x)\Phi''\} \sin \phi(x) \qquad 5.131.2$$

For the assumed form to be a solution, the coefficients of cos ϕ(x) and sin ϕ(x) in Equation 5.131.2 must vanish separately. Thus for slowly varying Y(x); $Y''(x) \to 0$ and may be neglected and thus

$$\phi'^2 = \overline{\Phi}_{yy}/2E; \; 2Y'\phi' + Y\phi'' = 0 \text{ or}$$

$$\frac{1}{Y} d^2(Y^2\phi') = 0 \qquad 5.132.1$$

Consequently $Y^2\phi' =$ constant

$$= Y^2 \left\{\frac{\overline{\Phi}_{yy}}{2E}\right\}^{1/2} = Y_0^2 \left\{\overline{\Phi}_{yy}/2E_0\right\}^{1/2} \qquad 5.132.2$$

Thus

$$Y^2 = Y_0^2 \left\{\frac{E}{E_0}\right\}^{1/2} = y_0^2 \left\{\frac{E}{E_0}\right\}^{1/2}$$

since

$$y_0(x = 0) = Y_0(x = 0) \qquad 5.132.3$$

To solve Equation 5.128.2 we may again average over one wavelength $\lambda = \frac{2\pi}{\phi'}$ and in view of the slow variation of Y(x) neglect $Y'^2(x)$ in comparison to $y'^2(x)$. Thus

$$-E\frac{dE}{dx} = \frac{M_1}{M_2}\left\{G_0 + G_{yy}\frac{Y^2}{4} + G_{y'y'}\frac{Y^2}{4}\left(\frac{2\pi}{\lambda}\right)^2\right\} \qquad 5.133.1$$

According to Equation 5.125.2 and 5.125.3

$$E_x = E_0\left\{1 - \frac{x}{L_0}\right\}^{1/2} \qquad 5.133.2$$

Thus

$$Y^2(x) = y_0^2(1 - x/L_0)^{1/4} \qquad 5.133.3$$

Equation 5.133.1 may then be integrated and by assuming $E(x = L) = 0$ and the range $L(y_0, 0) \cong L_0$ then

$$L(y_0, 0) = L_0\left\{1 - \left[\frac{4G_{yy}/5 + 4G_{y'y'}(2\pi/\lambda_0)^2}{2G_0}\right]\frac{y_0^2}{2}\right\} \qquad 5.134$$

Clearly very similar to Equation 5.130.2 where the energy loss inclusion is seen to alter the coefficients $G_{yy}, G_{y'y'}$. $L(0, z_0)$ may be obtained in a quite analogous manner, with the result that the range distribution function f(L) is expressed by

$$f(L) = \frac{2\pi}{f_Q}\cdot\left[\frac{2G_0(1 - L/L_0)}{\left\{\frac{4G_{yy}}{5} + \frac{4G_{y'y'}\bar{\Phi}_{yy}}{2E_0}\right\}\left\{\frac{4G_{zz}}{5} + \frac{4G_{z'z'}\bar{\Phi}_{z'z'}}{2E_0}\right\}}\right]^{1/2} \qquad 5.135.1$$

$$\simeq \frac{5\pi}{f_Q}\frac{G_0}{(G_{yy}G_{zz})^{1/2}}(1 - L/L_0) = \gamma(1 - L/L_0) \qquad 5.135.2$$

For a given channel, the coefficients G_0, G_{yy}, G_{zz} are determinable constants as given in Table 5.5. Thus the range distribution for the primaries near the channel decreases linearly. This distribution is shown in Figure 5.18 for the ⟨100⟩ channel where it is compared with machine computations[34] of ⟨100⟩ channelled events for various forms adopted for the Born-Mayer potential. It is clear that the theoretical curve is close to the tail of the B computed curve. This (b) curve in fact is that computed for an assumed potential which agrees most closely with that used in the present analysis.

5.9.3 Thermal and other effects

In the preceding discussion it has been assumed that the lattice atoms are at rest in the appropriate positions. Of course the atoms are in fact oscillating about mean positions due to the finite temperature of the lattice, and this can be expected to increase the energy loss of the primaries. The distance between the atoms of the channel bordering chains will have a distribution $g(l - \bar{l})$ about the average distance $\bar{l}$ to the channel axis, depending upon the target temperature.

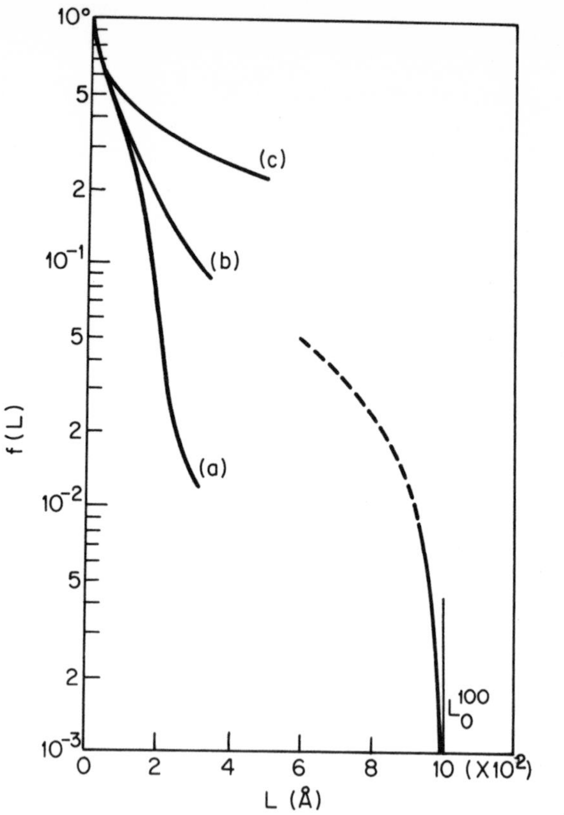

Fig. 5.18 Comparison of the range distributions for 5 keV Cu primaries slowing down in the ⟨100⟩ channel in Cu. The curve L_0^{100} is calculated from equation 5.135.2

Thus the primaries will have a distribution about an average maximum range L_0. Since, for a single collision, the energy loss is given by $-\Delta E^2 = 2\psi^2(l)$ (for equal primary and target atom masses) and a primary on the channel axis ($l = b$), then the energy E_n after N collisions is given by

$$E_n^2 = E_0^2 - \sum_{\nu=1}^{N} 2\psi^2(l) \qquad 5.136.1$$

Thus after many collisions, where the average number of collisions is $\bar{N}$ leading to the average maximum range $\bar{L}_0$, where $E_n^2 \to 0$ then one may average over $\psi^2(l)$ and obtain

$$E_0^2 = \bar{N}\cdot 2\overline{\psi^2}(l) \qquad 5.136.2$$

Thus the formulae for a static lattice may be applied replacing $\psi^2(l)$ by the average $\overline{\psi^2}(l)$ taking acount of the lattice vibrations. It may be assumed that the distribution $g(l - \bar{l})$ is Gaussian, i.e.

$$g(l - \bar{l}) = \sqrt{\frac{\alpha}{\pi}}\exp[-\alpha(l - \bar{l})^2] \qquad 5.137$$

where α is temperature dependent. Since $\bar{l} \gg \alpha$ Equation 5.116.3 indicates that $\psi^2(l)$ behaves as $\exp(-2l/a)$. Thus

$$\overline{\psi^2}(l) = \int_{-\infty}^{\infty}\psi^2(\bar{l})g(l - \bar{l})dl =$$

$$\int_{-\infty}^{\infty}\psi^2(\bar{l})\exp\left[-\frac{2(l - \bar{l})}{a}\right]g(l - \bar{l})dl =$$

$$\psi^2(\bar{l})\int_{-\infty}^{\infty}\exp\left[-\frac{2(l - \bar{l})}{a}\right]\sqrt{\frac{\alpha}{\pi}}\exp[(l - \bar{l})^2\cdot\alpha]\,dl$$

$$= \psi^2(\bar{l}) \exp\left(\frac{1}{\alpha a^2}\right) \qquad 5.138$$

Approximate formulae for α as a function of temperature T may be given (Ref. Leibfried[4, 30] and Lehmann[32])

$$\frac{1}{\alpha} \simeq \frac{D^2}{10^2} \cdot \frac{T}{T_m} \text{ for } T \geqslant \Theta_D$$

$$\frac{1}{\alpha} \simeq \frac{D^2}{10^2} \cdot \frac{\Theta_D}{4T_m} \text{ for } T \simeq 0°K$$

where Θ_D is the Debye temperature[35] and T_m the melting temperature.

$$\text{Thus for } T \gtrsim \Theta_D;\ \psi^2(l) \cong \psi^2(\bar{l}) \exp\left(\frac{T}{T_m}\ \frac{D^2}{100a^2}\right) \qquad 5.139$$

and consequently all ranges are reduced by the exponential factor $\exp\left[\frac{1}{\alpha a^2}\right]$ which increases rapidly with increasing temperature. Between target temperatures of 0°K and the melting point 1370°K the range is decreased in the ratio $1 : \exp\left[1 - \frac{\Theta_D}{4T_m}\right] \cdot \frac{D^2}{100a^2}$.

Ranges for primaries started close to the axis are obtained equally readily, replacing ϕ by $\phi \exp \frac{1}{4\alpha a^2}$ and ψ^2 by $\psi^2 \exp \frac{1}{\alpha a^2}$ whilst in the range distribution only L_0 is changed to $\bar{L}_0$.

Other factors which influence the ranges are the initial angle of incidence and the primary energy distribution. It may be readily shown that for angles deviating from the normal by more than 1°, the preceding analyses are invalidated. For closely specified angles however, the general effect is to reduce the ranges without modifying the distribution functions. Slight variations in the primary energy may however lead to quite noticeable changes in these distributions. We may note also how an experimental study of the most penetrating primaries may lead to a knowledge of the interatomic potential at distances corresponding to half the lattice spacing in a channel.

Equation 5.125.3 shows how the maximum range L_0 depends upon G_0, which, as shown by Equation 5.122.2 for $r = 0$ and $l = b$ is closely related to $\psi^2(b)$. If L_0 is measured for different channel axes, in the same target, say the ⟨100⟩, ⟨112⟩ and ⟨111⟩ channels in copper where the channel axes are also axes of symmetry, then the maximum ranges are L_0^{hkl}, and for three channels are directly related to the values of $\psi(l)_{hkl}$ for these channels, where l_{hkl} are easily obtained. From the three values of $\psi(l)_{hkl}$ obtained, one may obtain information about the potential as follows.

From Equation 5.116.2

$$\psi(l) = \int_{\infty}^{\infty} \frac{l\,dr}{(r^2 - l^2)^{1/2}} \left\{\frac{-\partial V(r)}{\partial r}\right\} \qquad 5.140.1$$

which is an Abel Integral equation for $\frac{\partial V(r)}{\partial r}$ with the solution (see Equation 2.70 of Chapter 2.)

$$\frac{\partial V(r)}{\partial r} = \frac{2}{\pi r} \int_r^{\infty} \frac{l\,dl}{(r^2 - l^2)^{1/2}} \frac{d\psi(l)}{dl} \qquad 5.140.2$$

From the three values of $\psi(l)_{hkl}$ obtained from L_0^{hkl} data one may then obtain information about the general trend of the $\psi(l)/l$ curve, hence $\frac{d\psi(l)}{dl}$ and finally therefore $\frac{\partial V(r)}{\partial r}$ and V(r).

For example if $\psi(l)$ is a rapidly decreasing function of l, Equation 5.140.2 may be replaced by

$$V(r) = \frac{2}{\pi} \int_r^{\infty} \frac{dl\,\psi(l)}{(l^2 - r^2)^{1/2}} \qquad 5.141$$

If $\psi(l)$ and $\frac{d\psi(l)}{dl}$ are determined for one value of l, then one may assume, for rapidly decreasing $\psi(l)$ that

$$\psi(\eta) = \psi(l) + \psi'(l)(\eta - l) \qquad 5.142$$

for $l \leqslant \eta \leqslant l'$ where $l' - l = -\psi(l)/\psi'(l)$ and zero for $\eta > l'$ i.e. $\psi(l)$ is a linear function of l up to a cut off at l′. Then one obtains from Equation 5.141.

$$V(l) = \frac{4\sqrt{2}}{3\pi} [\psi(l)]^{3/2}/(-\psi'(l))^{1/2} \qquad 5.143$$

Which from values of $\psi(l)$ and $\psi'(l)$ lead to the potential at l.

The primary distribution function (L) near L_0 can also be used to obtain information about the potential. Since, for example for the ⟨100⟩ channel

$$G_{yy} = G_{zz} = 6\frac{d\psi^2}{l\,dl} + 2\frac{d^2\psi^2}{dl^2}$$

the slope of the final range distribution (which from Equation 5.135.2 equals $\frac{5\pi}{f_Q} \frac{G_0}{(G_{yy}G_{zz})^{1/2}}$) gives a relation between the first and second derivatives of $\psi^2(l)$. Clearly, similar information may be obtained from other channels and with this knowledge, the form of $\psi(l)$ and hence V(l) may be specified more closely.

It should be pointed out however, that whilst this method is useful in principle, the experiments would have to be carefully controlled for primary energy spread and incident angle to determine the L_0's and $\psi(L)$'s accurately enough to be useful.

Finally we should note that whilst the above treatment is valid for an essentially collimated primary ion beam, a different situation will exist for a distribution of primaries started isotropically in space (as may be anticipated to occur in radiation damage effects where the struck particles are approximately isotropically distributed).

Consider, for example, primaries incident isotropically into the ⟨100⟩ channel. If a primary starts in the Oyx plane on the channel axis with a small angular deviation θ then since the motion is oscillatory, of the form $y_x = y_0 \sin 2\pi x/\lambda$ the primary may be considered to have started at a position y_0 given by $\theta = dy/dx(x = 0) = 2\pi y_0/\lambda$. The fraction of angles which lead to ranges between L and L_0 is thus given by the fraction of the primaries entering the solid angle

$\pi\theta^2$ i.e. $\theta^2/4$ multiplied by twice the number of available channels, since the primary can start in either the positive or negative x direction. Thus the probability for ranges between L and L_0 for isotropic primaries is

$$f_i(L) = \frac{\theta^2}{4} \cdot 2N_c = 2N_c\pi^2 y_0^2/\lambda^2$$

For a symmetric channel $f(L) = \pi y_0^2/f_Q$.

Thus

$$f_i(L) = 2\pi N_c f_Q f(L)/\lambda^2 = \pi N_c (D/\lambda)^2 f(L) \qquad 5.144$$

for the ⟨100⟩ channel. Since D/λ is very small, the distribution $f_i(L)$ is considerably less than f(L), but even though small, the long range primaries may be expected to contribute a significant amount to range averages, and exert considerable influence on radiation damage processes.

5.9.4.

An alternative, very similar, calculation of channelled events has been given by Nelson and Thompson[2,3], for high energy protons (=70kev) incident on gold targets. In view of the comprehensive treatment given to the Lehmann-Leibfried[4] analysis, it is necessary only to discuss briefly the differences apparent in this alternative method.

Even though for 70kev protons the energy losses are dominated by inelastic transfers to electrons, the angular changes at each collision are so small (because of the low electron mass) as to render a channelling mechanism by this mechanism impossible. Thus any channelling process must be due to elastic collisions with the atoms in the chains defining the channel.

If the Bohr interatomic potential

$$V(r) = \frac{Z_1 Z_2 e^2}{r} \exp(-r/a)$$

is assumed, then the momentum transfer to a stationary atom, with an impact parameter b, is given from Equation 5.116.2 specialised to the Bohr potential. i.e.

$$p = \frac{2Z_1Z_2e^2}{a\left(\frac{2E}{M_1}\right)^{1/2}} \frac{2b}{a} \int_0^\infty \frac{1 + [(b/a)^2 + (x/a)^2]^{1/2}}{[(b/a)^2 + (x/a)^2]^{3/2}} \times$$

$$\exp\{-[(b/a)^2 + (x/a)^2]^{1/2}\}dx \qquad 5.145$$

which may be evaluated numerically as a function of b/a i.e. $\gamma(b/a)$. If the primary is moving in a channel between lattice planes (which in this case define a channel) of period D_{hkl} at a distance y from the channel axis and at an angle ϕ to the channel axis then for zero assumed energy loss

$$\phi = \frac{dy}{dx} = \frac{dy}{dt}/2E/M_1$$

i.e. E = constant.

Each collision with an atom distance b_r from the axis, causes a change $\Delta\phi_r$ in the primary direction given by $\Delta\phi_r = -p_y/\sqrt{2E/M_1}$ where p_y is given by Equation 5.145 for $b = b_r - y$. Thus, after N collisions in the period D_{hkl} the total angular defection is given by

$$\frac{d\phi}{dt} = \frac{2Z_1Z_2e^2}{D_{hkl}a\sqrt{2EM}} \sum_1^N \left\{\frac{b_r - y}{a}\right\}\gamma\left\{\frac{b_r - y}{a}\right\} \qquad 5.146$$

since in a time interval $dt = D_{hkl}/\sqrt{2E/M_1}$ the primary moves a distance D_{hkl}. Thus, since

$$\frac{d\phi}{dt} = \frac{d^2y}{dt^2}/\sqrt{2E/M_1}$$

Then

$$M_1\frac{d^2y}{dt^2} = -\frac{2Z_1Z_2e^2}{D_{hkl}\cdot a}\sum_1^N\left\{\frac{b_r - y}{a}\right\}\gamma\left\{\frac{b_r - y}{a}\right\} = -F(y) \qquad 5.147$$

where F(y) is an effective restoring force on the primary. Thus the primary may be assumed to be moving in an effective potential well defined by

$$V(y) = \int_0^y F(y)dy \qquad 5.148.1$$

The primary then oscillates about the channel axis with an amplitude given by equating the kinetic energy of the transverse motion at y = 0 to $V(y_0)$ i.e.

$$V(y_0) = E_\phi \phi_0^2 \qquad 5.148.2$$

Nelson and Thompson[2,3] have calculated V(y) for protons in the ⟨110⟩ channel in gold where Oy is the narrowest direction perpendicular to the channel and $b_r = 1.4$Å with the result shown in Figure 5.19.

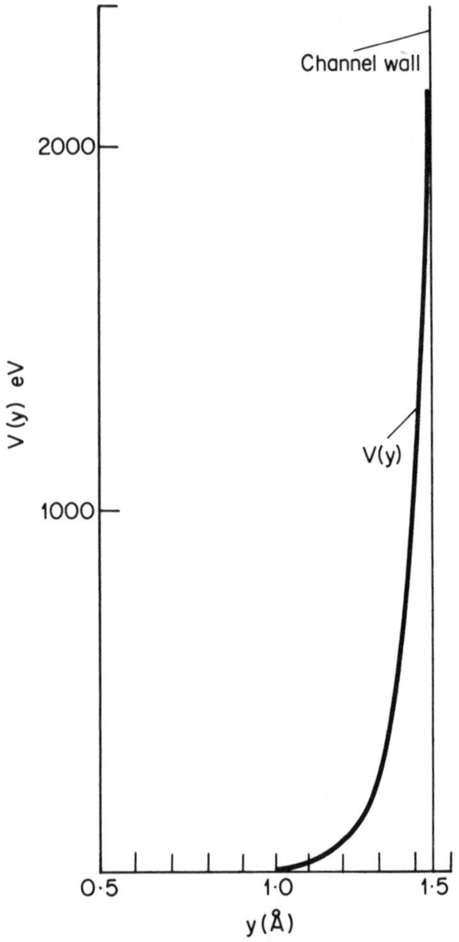

Fig. 5.19 The variation of the transverse potential V(y) experienced by protons in the Au ⟨110⟩ channel as a function of distance from the channel axis (y). (viz. Refs. 5.2 and 5.3)

The potential is almost zero until y ~ 1.0 Å when a rapid increase occurs. Thus the potential is effectively in the form of a square function as opposed to the approximately harmonic behaviour for the Cu-Cu case. If Equation 5.148.2 is used to calculate y_0 as a function of ϕ_0 for various energies, curves such as Figure 5.20 are obtained showing only slight energy dependence in the range 10 → 100kev. Thus the primary follows a zig-zag trajectory as shown in Figure 5.21 with a wavelength $\lambda = 4y_0/\phi_0$. Figure 5.20 shows that the distance of closest approach to a channel wall r_0, is roughly energy independent and equal to about 0.1 → 0.2Å. The condition for a channel to operate efficiently is therefore $b_r > r_0 \cdot b_r$ is 1.4Å for the channel between {110} planes, 1.15Å for ⟨110⟩ channels and 1.00Å for ⟨100⟩ channels. Thus all may be expected to channel primaries effectively although the latter may be restricted.

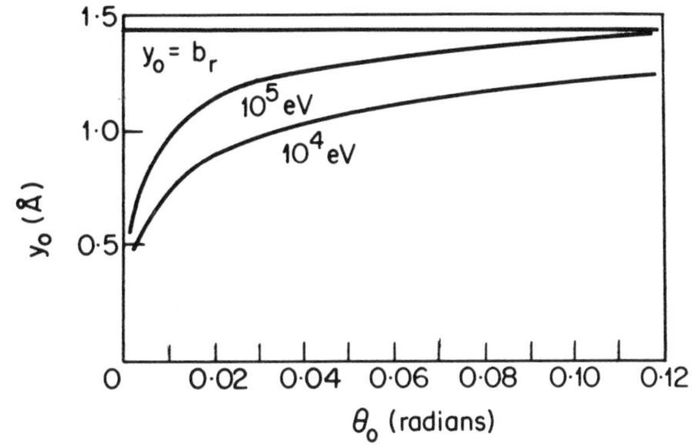

Fig. 5.20 Minimum distance of approach of 10^4 eV and 10^5 eV protons in an Au ⟨110⟩ channel as a function of the starting angle ϕ_0 from the channel axis. (viz. Refs. 5.2 and 5.3)

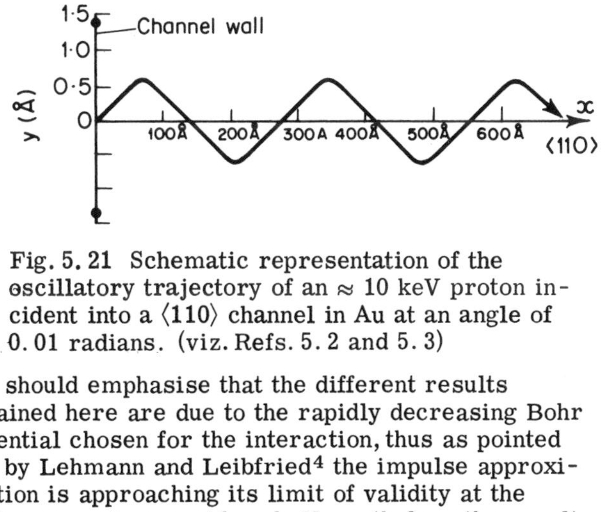

Fig. 5.21 Schematic representation of the oscillatory trajectory of an ≈ 10 keV proton incident into a ⟨110⟩ channel in Au at an angle of 0.01 radians. (viz. Refs. 5.2 and 5.3)

We should emphasise that the different results obtained here are due to the rapidly decreasing Bohr potential chosen for the interaction, thus as pointed out by Lehmann and Leibfried[4] the impulse approximation is approaching its limit of validity at the higher energies considered. Nevertheless the results confirm the oscillatory nature to be expected for a primary nearer a channel axis.

Lindhard[5] has also given a similar, but more precise and elegant treatment of the channelling process which is again particularly relevant to the high energy region. He introduces the concept of 'strings' of atoms with which the moving ion interacts rather than individual atomic collisions and derives a continuum average potential barrier due to a string over which an ion must escape to leave the channel. The Thomas-Fermi potential is used throughout the calculations, and it is shown that, because of these barrier considerations, only ions moving in certain well defined angular directions given by

$$\psi < \sqrt{\frac{2Z_1Z_2e^2}{E \cdot d}}$$

for an ion of energy E and interatomic separation d can be channelled at a particular energy. Interplanar channelling is then found to be of secondary importance. This treatment is very useful in explaining some of the recently observed angular effects involved in proton and fission fragment penetration and nuclear reaction yield and the interested reader is referred to Lindhard's[5] paper for further details.

5.10 Machine Calculations.

5.10.1 In view of the difficulties in making range calculations analytically with exact forms for the interatomic potential, it has been necessary, as we have seen in paragraphs 5.3-5.7 to make simplifying assumptions in the calculations, e.g. the hard sphere scattering approximation. Because of this fact it is difficult to compare approximate range observations with theoretical results and deduce probable forms of the interatomic potentials. Realising this, groups at Oak Ridge and the General Electric Laboratories initiated computer studies of the flight path of an energetic ion colliding with a solid lattice, in which the primary ion was allowed to interact with the simulated lattice through classical force laws, the equations of motion were solved for each collision and the trajectory of the ion followed. In the preliminary computations of Oen, Holmes and Robinson,[27, 28, 36, 37] the form of the assumed force laws at a collision could be varied so that the accuracy of the analytical calculations could be checked, whilst the force law which gave best agreement with experimental results could also be deduced. In the later work of Robinson and Oen,[26, 34] and of Beeler and Besco,[29] the effects of lattice structure upon range phenomena were investigated, and it was as a result of these that the phenomena of channelling or super ranges were first predicted.

In order to be able to appreciate the results of these computations it is necessary to give a brief outline of the computational methods used by the various investigators. The preliminary calculations by the Oak Ridge group assumed a randomised array of atoms for their target, just as the earlier analytical calculations, which the work was designed to evaluate, ignoring lattice symmetry and preserving only the correct atom density. We will therefore consider first the Random Lattice Model.

5.10.2 Random Lattice Calculations

In these computations by Oen, Holmes and Robinson[27, 36], and Robinson and Oen[28, 37], the correct atom density was preserved, but the exactness of lattice atom positions were neglected. The collision probability for a primary to strike a target atom was therefore assessed using a Mean Free path type of assumption, and it was further assumed that the primary interacted with one target atom at a time (reasonably so above an energy of ≈100 eV as we saw in Chapter 2.) This was achieved computationally by restricting the impact parameter for a given primary lattice atom collision to values less than one-half the nearest neighbour distance ($2R_c$) in the real lattice. This corresponded to effectively cutting off the interatomic potential at R_c, but only in the sense that the primary was not allowed to interact with the target atom if the impact parameter was $>R_c$. However for impact parameters less than R_c, the potential was assumed to extend to infinity and the scattering angle at the collision was calculated using this and further assuming that the primary atom was incident from infinity upon the target atom (i.e. the angular deflection corresponded to the angle between the asymptotes to the trajectory).

The deflection angle in the C.M. system for a given collision was then calculated from

$$\theta = \pi - 2p\int_0^{u_0} \frac{du}{\left\{1 - \frac{V(u)}{E_R} - p^2u^2\right\}^{1/2}} \qquad 5.149$$

and the corresponding L system deflection angle ϕ and the transferred energy T, from Equations 2. 8a., 2.10b.

The assumed interatomic potential was generally taken as the Bohr screened potential

$$V(r) = \frac{E_B}{2}\,\frac{\exp(-r/a)}{r/a}$$

with

$$E_B = 2Z_1Z_2e^2/a$$

and

$$a = ka_H[Z_1^{2/3} + Z_2^{2/3}]^{-1/2} \qquad 5.150$$

a_H is the first Bohr radius and a numerical factor k was included to assess the effects of varying the screening distance. Some calculations were also made using the Firsov factor[38] in a Thomas-Fermi type screened potential, whilst use of the hard sphere approximation with

$$V_{HS}(r) \begin{array}{l} = 0 \;\; ; r > r_0 \\ = \infty \;\; ; r \leqslant r_0 \end{array}$$

enabled comparison of the computations with analytical expressions. The effective hard sphere radius r_0 was found by matching to the Bohr potential at the distance of the closest approach i.e.

$$\frac{A}{1 + A}\cdot E = \frac{E_B}{2}\exp(-r_0/a)/r_0/a$$

Whilst the details of each collision could be solved using the above, it was necessary also to deduce the collision frequency, so that the path of the primary could be followed collision by collision. To estimate this collision probability, Oen, Holmes and Robinson, made use of the following free flight model. The lattice is assumed to consist of a cubic array of touching spheres of radii R_c as shown in Figure 5.22 and the average free flight $\bar{l}_{ff}$ is then the average of the distances in the voids between the spheres, and may be evaluated as follows. The radii R_c define the effective spheres of influence of each atom, but if the hard sphere approximation is used, the actual collision radii are $R_0 = \frac{1}{2}r_0$ which are necessarily less than R_c, to ensure a collision. If it is supposed that a given primary begins its history on the surface of a sphere radius R_c, there is then a probability of collision $P = R_0^2/R_c^2$ of colliding with the assumed hard sphere located at the same position.

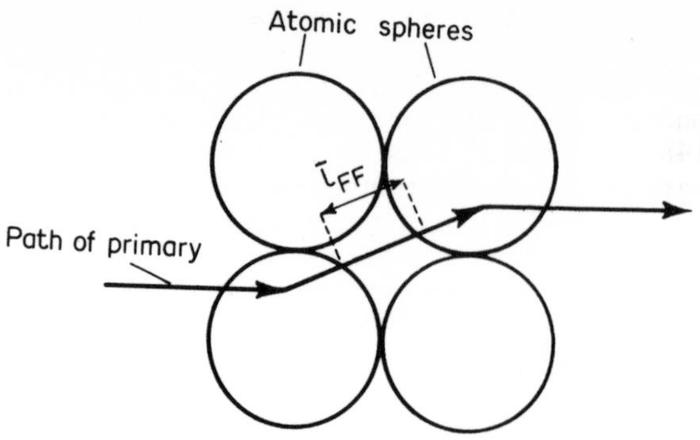

Fig. 5. 22 Path of primary atom showing a typical 'free flight' $\bar{l}_{FF}$ used in the random solid model of Oen et al and Robinson et al. (viz. Refs. 5.27 and 5.36)

For a set of may primaries of the same initial energy, the average distance travelled by those which make hits on the hard sphere is

$$\bar{d}_c = \int_0^{r_0}\{(R_c^2 - p^2)^{1/2} - (r_0^2 - p^2)\}\frac{2pdp}{r_0^2} \qquad 5.151.1$$

where p is the impact parameter on the hard sphere. Thus

$$\bar{d}_c = \tfrac{2}{3}\frac{R_c}{P}\{1 - P^{3/2} - (1 - P)^{3/2}\} \qquad 5.151.2$$

In addition some primaries starting from R_c, miss the inner hard sphere, and travel an average distance, within the sphere of influence

$$\bar{d}_1 = \int_{R_0}^{R_c}\frac{[R_c^2 - p^2]^{1/2}}{R_c^2 - r_0^2}\,2pdp = \tfrac{4}{3}[R_c^2 - R_0^2]^{1/2} \qquad 5.152.1$$

and an average distance $\bar{l}_{ff}$ before attempting the next collision. Thus the average distance without a first collision is

$$\bar{d} = \bar{d}_1 + \bar{l}_{ff} = \tfrac{4}{3}[R_c^2 - R_0^2]^{1/2} + \bar{l}_{ff} \qquad 5.153$$

and these primaries then attempt a second, and further collisions, with probabilities identical to the first. Thus the effective mean free path can be obtained from the recursion relation.

$$\lambda_{mc} = P\bar{d}_c + (1 - P)(\bar{d} + \lambda_{mc}) \qquad 5.154.1$$

$$\lambda_{mc} = \bar{d}_c + \frac{1 - P}{P}\bar{d} \qquad 5.154.2$$

This is in fact a mean free path relating to the first path before any collisions have been made and in order to obtain a true collision free path one must add a quantity $R_c(1 - P)^{1/2} + \bar{l}_{ff}$ since after the first collision the origin of reference is no longer the imaginary sphere radius R_c but at the surface of the hard sphere radius R_0.

The final result is thus

$$\lambda_{mc} = R_c(1 - P)^{1/2} + \bar{d}_c + \bar{l}_{ff} + \frac{(1 - P)}{P}\bar{d} \qquad 5.154.3$$

By requiring this λ_{mc} to be identical to the analytical hard sphere mean free path $\lambda = \frac{1}{n\pi R_c^2}$ it is finally deduced that

$$\bar{l}_{ff} = \frac{1}{n\pi R_c^2} - \tfrac{4}{3}R_c \qquad 5.155$$

Using these parameters, the range parameters were then evaluated as follows, using an IBM 7090 computer. Monte Carlo methods, based upon the use of random numbers[39] were used to generate the histories of a large number of primaries (about 1000) for various assumed forms of the interatomic potential and for an isotropic distribution of primaries. Thus for each attempted collision between a primary and lattice atom, impact parameters p were selected from the distribution.

$$P_1(pdp) = \frac{2\pi pdp}{R_c^2}; 0 \leq p \leq R_c$$
$$= 0 \text{ otherwise} \qquad 5.156.1$$

and an azimuthal angle was selected from

$$P_2\{\theta d\theta\} = \frac{d\theta}{2\pi}; 0 \leq \theta \leq 2\pi \qquad 5.156.2$$

at each collision the C. M. deflection-angle was evaluated from Equation 5.149 by the computer by numerical quadrature (except for the hard sphere approximation where the scattering angle is known simply from Equation 2.14a) together with the energy transfer and the L system deflection angle. Since the primary was assumed to move along its asymptotic trajectory before and after collision, it was necessary, in order to deduce the directional change, to locate the intersection of the asymptotes at the collision. Ideally this requires evaluation of the displacement integral of the trajectory

$$\tau = \int_{1/R_c}^{u} \frac{du}{u^2\left\{1 - \frac{V(u)}{E_R} - p^2u^2\right\}^{1/2}} \qquad 5.157.1$$

where $\frac{\tau}{1+A}$ is the distance moved by the primary from the start of the interaction to the deflection point, but an increase in computing speed was obtained using the hard sphere approximation. Thus

$$\tau = (R_c^2 - p^2)^{1/2} - (R_0^2 - p^2)^{1/2} \qquad 5.157.2$$

where R_0 is the distance of closest approach in the actual orbit. The error in using this approximation was found to be small.

After evaluating the intersection of the L system asymptotes at a given collision, the new direction of primary motion was deduced, and collision with a further target atom explored. The distances travelled, equal to segments of each asymptote plus the free flight distances were stored in the memory of the computer. The collision sequences were followed through for many primaries until each had lost sufficient energy to become trapped in the lattice (this was usually effected by selecting $E_d = 25$ eV) or until it escapes from the lattice. This allows simulation of external irradiation as used in most experimental range determinations, or internal irradiation of the solid which occurs during radiation damage processes. Information such as average path lengths $\bar{L}$, $\langle L^2\rangle$, $\bar{R}_{par}$, $\bar{R}$, $\langle R^2\rangle$ etc. and the distribution of final resting positions were thus obtained for sets of about 1000 primaries, with accuracies of ±3%. No information was obtained upon the fate of struck atoms nor was the influence of the damaged lattice upon subsequent primary histories explored. In view of the randomisation procedure, these were hardly possible. The results of these computations were as follows.

Initially it was desirable to test the validity of the hard sphere approximation used to obtain range parameters as in paragraphs 5.2, 5.5. To do this the analytical calculations were modified slightly to account for the finite primary energy at trapping (=25 eV), but except at low primary incident energies this modification was unimportant. The comparison of the averages of three parameters, $\langle R^2\rangle$, $\bar{R}_{par}$ and $\langle R^2_{perp}\rangle$ for the hard sphere approximation is shown in Figure 5.23 in terms of the reduced range and energy introduced in Figure 5.3. The Bohr energy E_B and the mean free path λ_a for several primary ion/target atom combinations are given in Table 5.6. The effect of increasing the constant k in the screening length is also shown to decrease the range as expected since this hardens the potential at a given separation. It is clear that the machine and analytical calculations agree closely, except at low primary energies. The reasons for this departure are apparently that (1) The finite size of the hard spheres shortens the machine mean free path (compared to $\frac{1}{n\pi R_{HS}^2}$ by a length which is of the order of R_{HS}. For high energies the correction is negligible since $\lambda_{mc} \gg$ Radius of the hard spheres, but this is no longer true at low primary energies (2) The first effective mean free path of the primary is shorter by the length $R_c + \bar{l}_{ff}$ than the analytical mean free path. This correction is again unimportant for high energies, where the ranges are large, but is of consequence at lower primary energies. (3) The analytical and machine calculations are universal, only if the same ratio of E_d/E_B is used. E_B depends upon the atomic species considered (c.f. Table 5.6) and also upon the value of k assumed. Thus a universal curve is not expected unless E_d is modified so that E_d/E_B is maintained constant. To illustrate this E_d/E_B has been varied from 1.257×10^{-4} to 1.257×10^{-5}, corresponding to changing E_d from 25 eV to 2.5 eV for the Cu-Cu, k = 1.0 case, in figure 5.24. The expected increase in range occurs as E_d is decreased.
Since the hard sphere results matched so well, it is expected that machine results using a Bohr optential will also fall upon a universal curve, and this expectancy is confirmed by the results shown in Figure 5.25. Only at the lower energies do systematic variations occur, for the same reasons discussed in (3) above. However, when comparison is made of the magnitudes of the range quantities, obtained from machine calculations using the Bohr potential with the hard sphere approximation and with analytical results using Equation 5.44 etc. it is found that penetrations in the hard sphere approximation are from 10% to 80% too high. This may be expected since the stopping power calculated from the Bohr potential is significantly larger than that using the hard sphere approximation (c.f. Chapter 2 Figure 2.6). The spread $\langle R^2_{perp}\rangle^{1/2}$ is similar for both calculations.

This indicates that the hard sphere approximation, used

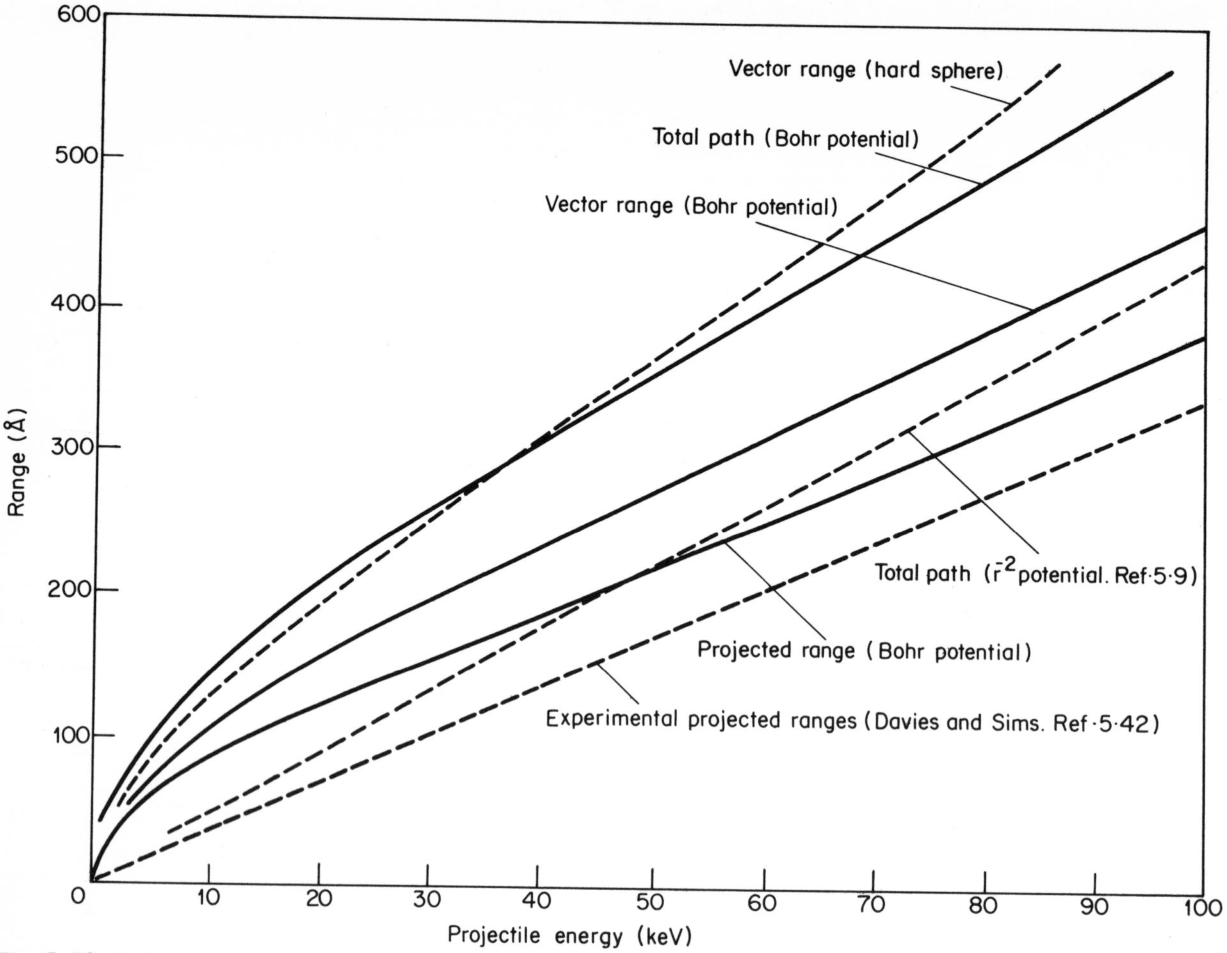

Fig. 5. 23 Total path, vector range and projected range for Cu atoms slowing down in Cu under a Bohr interatomic potential (k = 1). Results for hard sphere and r^{-2} approximations are shown for comparison in addition to experimental data by Davies & Sims (Ref. 5. 42). Curves derived assuming random model of Cu. (viz. Refs. 5. 27, 5. 36)

TABLE 5. 6. (Ref. 5. 36)

Ion	Target	E_B(keV)	$\frac{M_1 + M_2}{2M_2} E_B$(keV)	λ_a(Å)	$\frac{(M_1 + M_2)^2}{4M_1M_2} \lambda_a$(Å)
Na^{24}	Al	25.187	23.796	197.67	198.35
K^{42}	Al	47.806	61.113	238.69	250.570
Rb^{86}	Al	106.76	223.53	313.88	431.68
Xe^{133}	Al	170.07	504.22	373.89	666.69
Cu	Cu	198.86	198.86	253.45	253.45
Ag	Ag	613.57	613.57	505.08	505.08
Au	Au	2060.98	2060.98	709.97	709.97

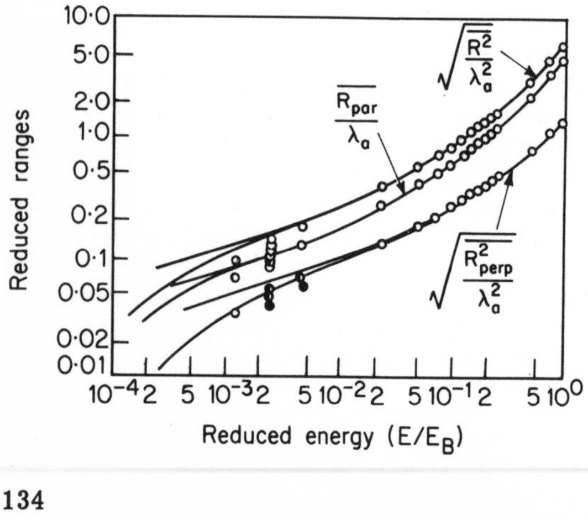

Fig. 5. 24 Comparison, using the hard sphere approximation, between computer and analytical ranges (viz. Ref. 5. 13)
Lower Solid lines of merging pairs are analytical for k = 1. 0, $E_F/E_B = 1.257 \times 10^{-4}$
Upper Solid lines of merging pairs are analytical for k = 1. 0, $E_F/E_B = 1.257 \times 10^{-5}$
○ are computer points for Cu—Cu, k = 1. 0 and $E_F/E_B = 1.257 \times 10^{-4}$
● are computer points for Cu—Cu, k = 1. 5 and $E_F/E_B = 1.257 \times 10^{-4}$
◐ are computer points for Au—Au, k = 1. 0 and $E_F/E_B = 1.257 \times 10^{-4}$
E_F is the energy at which primaries are assumed to be stopped. (viz. Ref. 5. 36).

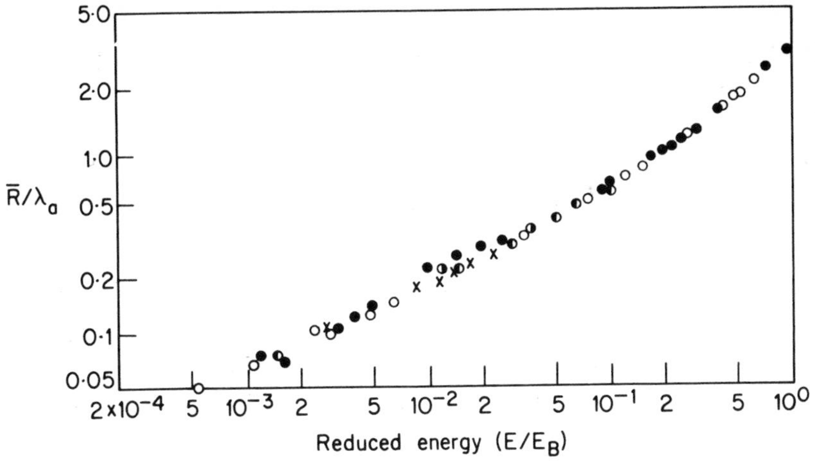

Fig. 5. 25 Comparison of computer calculations of the mean Range $\bar{R}/\lambda_a$ as a function of reduced primary energy E/E_B for equal mass primary and target atoms on a Universal plot

●, k = 1. 0;
○, k = 1. 3, Cu-Cu;
◑, k = 1. 5,
◐, k = 1. 87, Ag-Ag;
×, k = 2. 34, Au-Au.

(viz. Ref. 5. 36)

in Paragraphs 5. 5 is really only useful in predicting orders of magnitude of the range quantities and exploring the effects of parameter variation (such as the mass ratio). However this conclusion does not detract from the value of these calculations in elucidating the methods of analysis. In view of the close approximation of the matching potential $V(r) = A(r/a - 1)$ to the exact Bohr potential discussed in Chapter 2 and in Paragraph 5. 6 it is anticipated that range evaluations using this method will approximate more closely the machine results for the Bohr potential. Such calculations are currently in progress by the Oak Ridge group and should prove valuable. However it is also necessary to discuss whether the Bohr potential itself accurately represents the true interatomic potential. Thus Oen et al, [27,36] have compared the machine computations for primary ranges of Copper atoms in Copper, Gold atoms in gold and Silver atoms in silver, with the experimental values observed by Van Lint et al[40] which we shall discuss more fully later. The parameter k was varied and as shown in Figures 5. 26 best agreement was found for

$k_{Cu} = 1.15$

$k_{Ag} = 1.68$

$k_{Au} = 2.34$

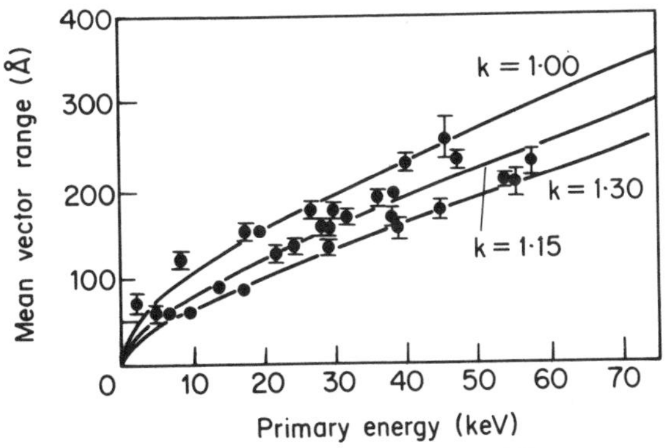

Fig. 5. 26 Computer calculations of the mean vector ranges for Cu in Cu as a function of primary energy using the Bohr potential. The points are the experimental data of van Lint et al (Ref. 5. 40) for Cu^{62} in Cu. (viz. Ref. 5. 36)

It thus appears that, to achieve agreement between experiment and predictions from a Bohr potential, the parameters k should increase with increasing atomic weight. This in itself indicates that the Bohr potential may not be a good approximation to the actual interatomic potential. Further it is suggested that for primary energies different to those used in Figure 5. 26 different values of k would have to be used to allow agreement, again mitigating against the validity of the Bohr potential.

The machine calculations were also compared with the experimental range determinations of Davies et al, [41, 42] for some alkali metal and inert gas ions in Aluminium (These and other experimental results will be discussed fully later) in an attempt to further investigate the applicability of the Bohr potential. The machine calculations of the unequal primary and target atom mass cases of interest are shown in

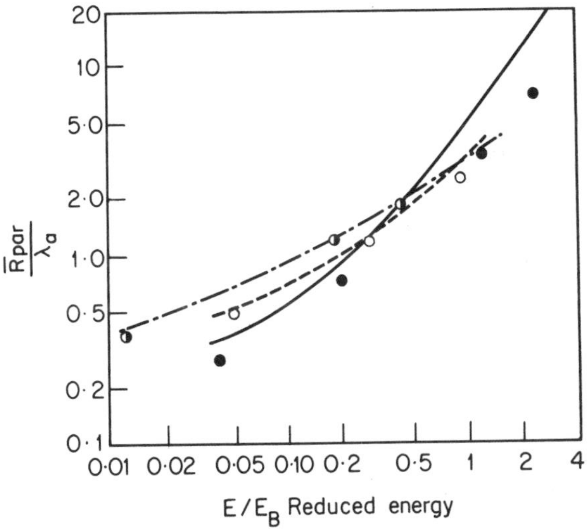

Fig. 5. 27 Comparison of projected range—reduced energy data obtained from computer and analytical calculations (from equation 5. 75. 4) for unequal masses. Curves are analytical
◑ Cs^{137} ions incident on Al
○ Rb^{86} ions incident on Al
● Na^{24} ions incident on Al
(viz. Refs. 5. 10 and 5. 36)

Figure 5. 27 for the projected penetration $\bar{R}_{par}$. Scaling factors $\frac{(M_1 + M_2)^2}{4M_1M_2}\lambda_a$ and $\frac{M_1 + M_2}{2M_1}$. E_B are introduced to account for the unequal masses and this figure 5. 27 corresponds to the ρ/ϵ plot in Figure 5. 3, but it is apparent that the figure shows non universality. Universality does obtain with respect to the adjustable parameter k however for each mass ratio, and thus for each of the curves in Figure 5.27 it is possible to construct calculated ranges as a function of the primary energy and observe the effect of varying k over the whole energy range. Thus in Figure 5.28 the median penetration

$$\left(\text{where } \int_0^{R_{par}\,(\text{median})} f(R_{par})dR_{par} = {}^1\!/_2\right)$$

deduced from the machine calculations and from Davies and Sims[42] experimental observations for Na^{24} in Al^{27} are plotted together. The agreement is rather poor for k = 1.0 but an improvement is obtained by normalizing the experimental data for k = 1.10. Similar behaviour was found for the various primary-target atom combinations tested and the deviations at low energy between experiment and computation must be regarded as evidence against the reality of the Bohr potential. At higher energies, where the agreement is better, no account was taken of ionisation losses and so the proximity of the results may also be fortuitous.

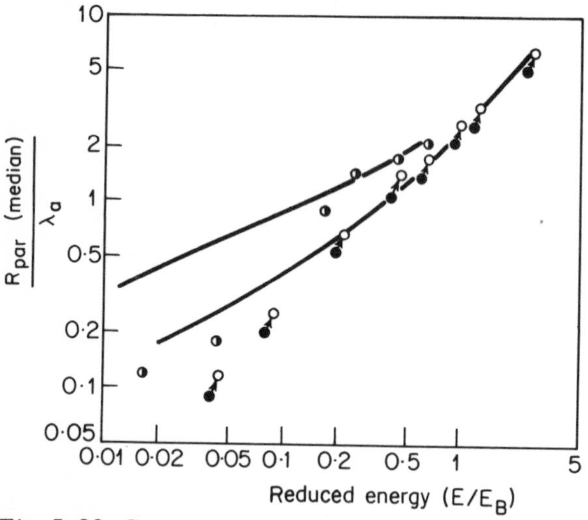

Fig. 5.28 Comparison of median projected ranges as a function of reduced ion energy for Na^{24} and Cs^{137} ions incident on Al from experimental data (points Ref 5.1) and computer evaluation (curves).

● Na^{24}; ○ Na^{24}, adjusted for k = 1.1

◑ Cs^{137} adjusted for k = 1.414. (viz. Refs 5.10 and 5.36).

Oen and Robinson[34] subsequently extended these calculations for a Thomas-Fermi interatomic potential with the Firsov[38] screening function for various values of the target atom—primary ion mass ratio A and introduced the Lindhard-Scharff[11] scaling factor 1 + A/3 viz. equation 5.37.1 to bring the results for different mass ratios into more nearly equal coincidence. These authors showed that the stopping power of the target was larger at smaller energies for the Thomas-Fermi potential than for the Bohr potential, since the former is a stronger potential at larger separations. It is therefore not surprising to find that the median ranges predicted by Thomas-Fermi calculations were also smaller than corresponding values for the Bohr potential at low primary energies, and this behaviour is displayed in the curves of Figure 5.29. It was found that the available experimental data falls between the Bohr and the Thomas-Fermi predictions, but at high energies both calculations lead to too large ranges—Oen and Robinson[34] suggest

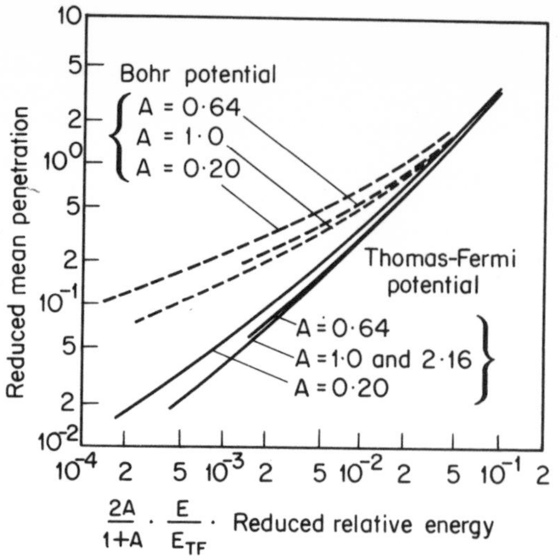

Fig. 5.29 Computer calculations of the mean projected range as a function of the reduced energy for various values of the mass ratio A using the Thomas-Fermi and the Bohr Potentials. (viz. Ref. 5.34).

that the latter result is due to neglect of electronic stopping, and that the former results implies that neither the Bohr, nor the Thomas-Fermi potentials are accurately typical of the target atom-primary ion potentials. At this stage however, the authors were well aware of the channelling process, which leads to higher ranges than predicted by random target atom models, so that experimental results typical of a quasi-random structure (i.e. an amorphous target) should be closer to the Thomas-Fermi potential results than the Bohr potential calculations. In fact, comparison of experimental results for 10 kev X_e^{+133} ions in amorphous WO_3 with the Thomas-Fermi calculations showed remarkably good agreement, suggesting that in random targests at least, this should be the better potential. It may be that a composite Thomas-Fermi-Bohr potential or some similar combination will eventually prove to be the most acceptable. This potential may give better agreement with experiment since for low energies (large impact parameters) the Bohr potential is too low, shown by too large ranges at low energies on Figure 5.26 and the Thomas-Fermi potential is allowed to dominate these. Whilst at higher energies, where the Bohr potential appears to be adequate, this is allowed to dominate.

Finally, the machine calculations give information about the range distribution functions. This is one region of superiority over the analytical calculations, since only for total path distribution functions, can theoretical methods be used with facility. In order to test the machine calculations for reliability in such evaluations, comparison was made with the total path distribution for the case where $\lambda(E_0) \propto E_0^{1/2}$ (i.e. an inverse r^4 potential) with the results shown earlier in Figure 5.8 which, as we saw, were remarkably good. The machine evaluated distribution function, or histogram as it is for 1000 primaries, was then compared, assuming the Bohr potential, with experimental distribution functions measured by Davies and Sims.[42] One such comparison is shown in Figure 5.30 for 60 keV Na^{24} in Aluminium, and these curves, as is typical of all others, although of similar form, show some distinct differences in detail. These are (1) the calculated distributions are less "skewed" than the experimental. This may be seen from the values $\bar{R}_{par}$ and $\langle R\rangle_{median}$ the ratio of which gives a measure of the "skewness". (2) Exponential tails of the distribution, observed in many cases by Davies and Sims,[42] are not found in the machine results.

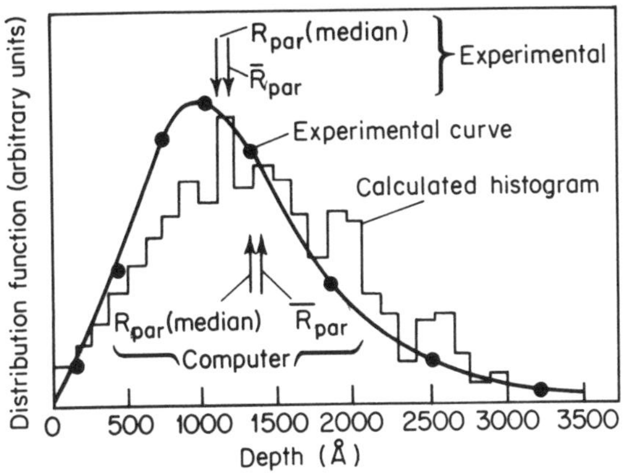

Fig. 5. 30 Comparison of experimental (Ref. 5. 42) data and computer calculations of the projected range distribution for 60 keV Na^{24} ions incident on Al. (viz. Refs. 5, 10 and 5. 36)

The skewness is not improved by adjustment of the parameter k and we shall return to a further discussion of this behaviour later. To some extent however the exponential tail to the distribution, is characteristic of the influence of the first flight free paths, as is obtained for example with the hard sphere or diffusion models shown in Figure 5. 10.

Once again the inadequacy of the Bohr potential is apparent, and is the result of the too large weighting given to small angle (large impact parameter) collisions, which tend to slowly turn the primary direction from the incident direction.

This behaviour of the Bohr potential can also be seen by observing the perpendicular spread of the incident primaries via the ratio $\{\langle \overline{R}^2_{perp}\rangle / \langle \overline{R}^2_{par}\rangle\}^{1/2}$ and, comparing with the hard sphere case, Figure 5. 31 shows that, at all energies, the Bohr potential gives a more rounded distribution as opposed to the forward peaked hard sphere distribution. This is the result of turning the primary by the large impact parameter collisions of the Bohr potential which are complete misses in a hard sphere approximation.

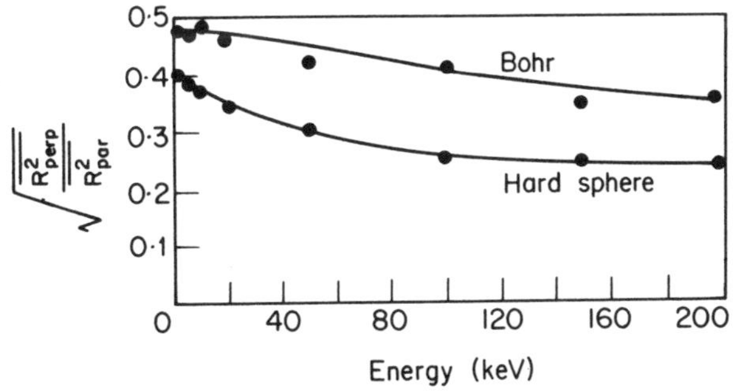

Fig. 5. 31 Variation of the spread in atom stopping points $(\sqrt{\overline{R}^2_{perp}/\overline{R}^2_{par}})$ as a function of energy. (viz. 5. 10, 5. 27 and 5. 36)

It thus appears that analytical calculations using the hard sphere approximation may be of some value, although, as mentioned earlier, matching via comparison of stopping powers rather than closest approach hard sphere radii may be preferable. This latter comparison is effected by taking the stopping power $\frac{-dE}{dx}$ $(=\epsilon)$ for the assumed potential $= n\int T d\sigma$

$$= 2\pi n \int_{\text{all } p} T p\, dp \qquad 5.158$$

and equating this to the hard sphere stopping power

$$-\left|\frac{dE}{dL}\right|_{HS} = \int_0^{\alpha E_0} \frac{T \cdot \pi r_m^2 dT}{(1-\alpha)E_0}$$

Thus

$$2\pi n \int_{\text{all } p} T p\, dp = \tfrac{1}{2}(1-\alpha)E_0 n \pi r_m^2 \qquad 5.159$$

where r_m is the appropriate stopping power matching radius. Oen, Robinson and Holmes[43] have calculated r_m as a function of the primary energy E_0 from equation 5. 159 and computed data for the differential cross section for the Bohr potential. Using these values of r_m the analytical expression deduced by Holmes and Leibfried[13] (equation 5. 49. 2) connecting $\overline{R}_{par}$ and E_0 was used to evaluate $\overline{R}_{par}$ as a function of E_0 for Cu atoms in a Cu target.

Thus in Figure 5. 32 the exact machine calculations for the Bohr potential are compared with analytical hard sphere calculations using the closest approach distance approximation using equation 2. 24 and the above approximation. Clearly the latter is much superior.

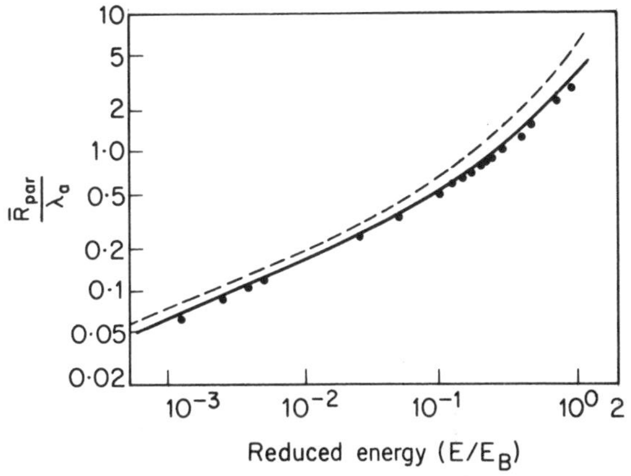

Fig. 5. 32 Comparison of projected range-reduced energy deduced by various methods
• points obtained from computer using Bohr potential
Dashed curve obtained from computer using Hard sphere approximation matched to Bohr potential at distance of closest approach
Full curve obtained from computer using Hard sphere approximation matched to Bohr potential via stopping power. (viz. Refs. 5. 10, 5. 43)

However this improvement in analytical techniques still does not lead to a better potential than the Bohr potential, it merely approximates this more closely. One may anticipate that, when a more precise potential is found, the stopping power approximation may be used very usefully.

Van Lint et al[40] have also made machine calculations on primary ranges using the Bohr potential, but assuming the screening radius a to be given by the Thomas-Fermi function. The range-energy data produced by these calculations are very similar to those described by Oen Holmes and Robinson and Robinson and Oen differing in magnitude only because of the introduction of a different value for a. However Van Lint et al[40] have also produced useful information on the change in the range-energy relation as the atomic mass ratio $A = M_2/M_1$ is varied, thereby extending the data of Figure 5.25. Variations of A from 0.05 to 20 have the effects on range-energy data shown in Figure 5.33 and, as expected, the vector

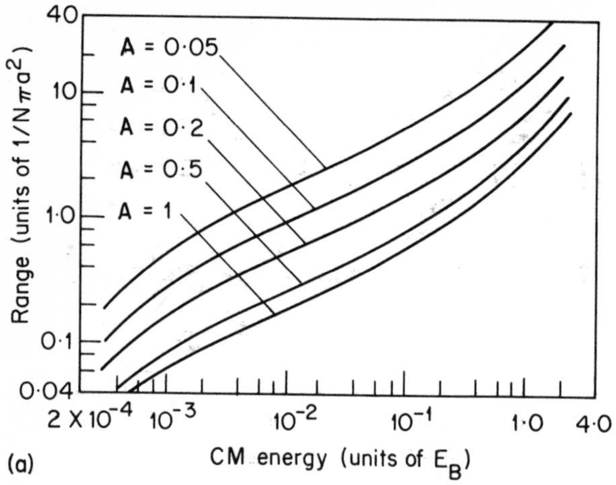

Fig. 5.33a Vector range vs energy, $A = M_2/M_1$, $E_B = Z_1Z_2e^2/a$. (viz. Ref. 5.40)

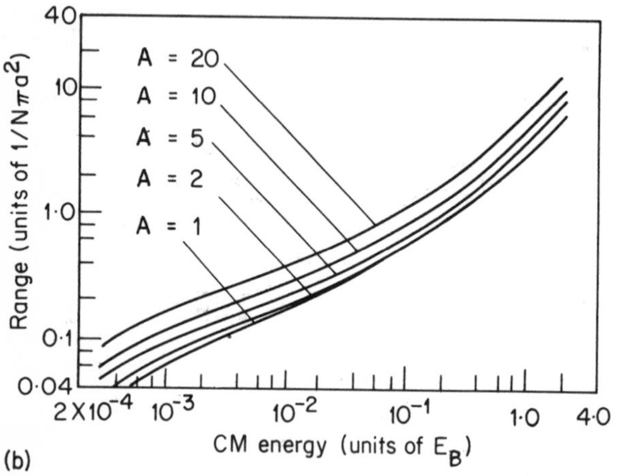

Fig. 5.33b Vector range vs energy, $A = M_2/M_1$, $E_B = Z_1Z_2e^2/a$. (viz. Ref. 5.40)

range minimises for $A = 1$, where energy losses are most efficient. Similarly the ratio of total to projected range as a function of primary energy for various mass ratios also provides useful information about the collision histories. Figures 5.34 show these data, again for A between 0.05 and 20, and qualitative expectations are once again confirmed. Thus total and projected ranges become more closely equal as A decreases, at any primary energy, since scattering is preferential in the forward direction for low A ratios. It is also apparent that the projected and total ranges are most closely equal for very low or very high primary energies and diverge, according to the mass ratio at intermediate energies. This is also expected since, at low energies, only about one collision is involved, whilst at high energies the scattering is due to an inverse r potential and is strongly forward peaked. Notwithstanding this qualitative utility however this data must be regarded with similar reservations to that of Robinson and Oen since this also will require a variable 'a' to fit the experimental curves.

However criticisms on these grounds of the Bohr potential have so far been assumed to be valid because this potential is itself inadequate in describing atomic interactions. On the other hand it may be that the basic model used in computations was also inaccurate, e.g. the process of lattice randomisation is inadmissable, and it is this that leads to differences between experimental and computed range data. Realising this possibility Robinson and co-workers[26,28] and Beeler and Besco[29] undertook further computations using a model of the target which preserves the correct lattice symmetry, and it is to this approach that we now turn our attention. It will be seen that this 'lattice model' leads to a much better agreement with experimental data, particularly with the work on single crystals, as one should expect since the real state of affairs is more closely approximated.

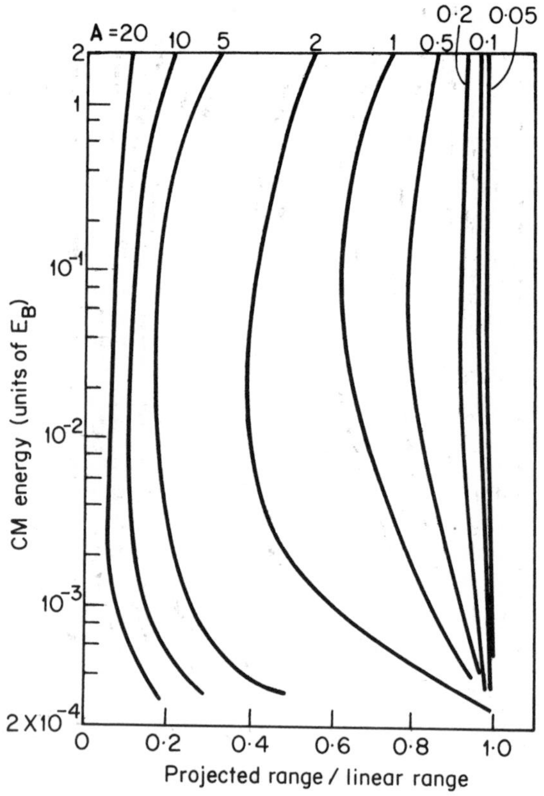

Fig. 5.34 Projected range/linear range vs energy, $A = M_2/M_1$, $E_B = Z_1Z_2e^2/a$. (viz. Ref. 5.40)

5.10.3 The Lattice Model

In this model Robinson and Oen[26,28] instead of assuming that the target atoms were randomly distributed spatially, the lattice atoms were allowed to reside at their normal positions. Thus the concept of a collision free path was unnecessary since at each collision the deflection angles were deduced, as in the random model, and thus the position of the next impact was immediately defined from the atomic array. Energy transfers, were also deduced as in the previous section, but flight distances made use of the known crystal dimensions as well as the distances travelled during collisions. In the calculations of Robinson and Oen[28] the histories of Copper atoms slowing down in a copper lattice were followed until either (a) The primary energy fell below 25 eV (b) the primary escaped from the crystal boundaries or (c) the number of collisions made by the primary exceeded a given preset number (250 generally). This latter criterion was necessary because of the channelling events which we will discuss shortly.

In order to assess the effects of crystal structure variation, three models of the copper lattice were assumed. One, the normal f.c.c. structure with correct atomic dimensions and the others, "b.c.c." and "diamond" copper the dimensions of which were evaluated assuming the same nearest neighbour distance as in f.c.c. copper. The appropriate lattice constants for these three structures as given in Table 5.7. To

TABLE 5.7. (Ref. 5.28).

Crystallographic properties of 'copper' targets. Nearest neighbour distance 2.5562 Å.

	fcc	bcc	diamond
Coordination number	12	8	4
Lattice constant (Å)	3.6150	2.9516	5.9032
Relative density	1.0000	0.9186	0.4593

determine the effects of variation of primary mass, calculations were made with $M_1 = 190.62$ ($A = 1/3$) and $M_1 = 21.18$ ($A = 3$). Further realism was introduced into the programme by allowing lattice thermal vibrations. Each atom was allowed to vibrate spherically symmetrically about its lattice site, independent of its neighbours, with a specified root mean square amplitude. The distribution of amplitudes was chosen as the triangular approximation to a Gaussian:

$$\begin{aligned} P(\rho) &= (2\pi)^{-1/2} \exp \; -\frac{\rho^2}{2} \\ &\simeq \frac{1}{\sqrt{6}} - \frac{|\rho|}{6} \text{ for } -\sqrt{6} \leqslant \rho \leqslant \sqrt{6} \\ &\cong 0 \text{ for } \sqrt{6} \leqslant \rho \leqslant \infty \end{aligned} \qquad 5.160$$

where ρ is the radial displacement of an atom from the lattice site in units of r.m.s. amplitude, $P(\rho)$ is the probability distribution function for displacements between ρ and $\rho + \delta\rho$. Specifically, r.m.s. amplitudes of 0.05Å and 0.20Å, representative of the approximate behaviour of Copper at 0°K and at the melting point respectively (Ref. Lehmann and Leibfried[4]), were studied.

Two types of computation were performed, for different initial primary distributions. (1) A distribution of primary directions isotropic about a lattice site in an infinite crystal, and useful for radiation damage applications. (2) A distribution of primary positions over the symmetry element of a particular crystallographic surface of a semi-infinite crystal; corresponding to external ion bombardment by a beam of particles on a specific crystal face.

Probably of equal significance to the assumption of lattice reality were the assumed forms for the interatomic potential. In view of the limited success of the Bohr potential in the random model calculations, and the too rapid decline of this potential with interatomic separation, calculations were also made for a Born-Mayer potential. This exhibits better behaviour for large separations but is insufficiently strong for close encounters. However it was expected that use of both potentials would allow investigation of their relative merits.

Thus the Bohr potential for the Cu-Cu case was of the form

$$\phi_B(r) = C_B(a_B/r) \exp(-r/a_B)$$

with C_B and a_B defined as previously, and the Born-Mayer potential.

$$\phi_{BM}(r) = C_{BM} \exp(-r/a_{BM})$$

The constants, a_B, C_B, a_{BM} and C_{BM} were derived from elasticity data and are as given in table 5.8, a_{BM} and

TABLE 5.8. (Ref. 5.28).

Interatomic potential parameters for Cu-Cu interactions.

Potential	Coefficient, C (keV)	Screening length, a (Å)
Bohr	99.4	0.1218
Born-Mayer	22.5	0.1966

C_{BM} are values corresponding to those used by Gibson et al[44] in extensive radiation damage simulation studies which will be discussed in the following Chapter. In fact the potential actually used in the computer was in the form

$$V(r) = \begin{cases} \phi(r) - \delta \,.\, \phi(R_c) & \text{for } 0 \leqslant r \leqslant R_c \\ 0 & \text{for } R_c < r < \infty \end{cases} \qquad 5.161$$

which corresponded to cutting off the potential $V(r)$ at $r = R_c$ (half the nearest neighbour distance) as in the random calculations. δ assumed the values 0 (where the potential was termed truncated) and thus at $r = R_c$ the potential fell as a step function from $\phi(R_c)$ to zero, or 1, in which the potential $V(r)$ was always less than the real potential $\phi(r)$, but ensured that the potential fell smoothly to zero (termed as eroded) at $r = R_c$.

This treatment of the potential, in which the atoms are essentially surrounded by spheres of force of finite radius R_c leads to peculiarities in the model. Firstly, force free voids, possibly interconnecting, will exist in the crystal. If a primary enters such a system of connecting voids there is a possibility of passage along this channel for extremely large distances, which in fact is observed to occur. Secondly the model is found to be very sensitive to details of the assumed potential i.e. whether eroded or truncated. In the eroded case, as the impact parameter approaches R_c, the C.M. scattering angle approaches zero smoothly, but the stopping power is less than if the potential had not been cut off. With the truncated potentials however, as the impact parameter becomes large, the distance of closest approach reaches R_c before p, and hard sphere scattering takes place off the edge (step function) of the potential. For impact parameters, p, in the range

$$\left\{1 - (1 + A)\frac{\phi(R_c)}{AE}\right\}^{1/2} < p/R_c < 1$$

the stopping power is greater than would be the case for a continuous potential, whilst for primary energies less than $(1 + A)\frac{\phi(R_c)}{A}$ hard sphere scattering occurs for all values of the impact parameter p. (Further discussion of scattering from truncated potentials has been given by Lehmann and Leibfried (2.32) and was mentioned in Chapter 2). This hard sphere scattering is found to lead to an interesting effect in the computations which will be discussed shortly.

At this point we may consider the differences between the assumed model with its force free voids and a real lattice structure. In the latter, no voids will occur, but the regions most remote from lattice positions, which correspond to the voids, will be of low force concentration and therefore computed results with total voids may be expected to simulate qualitatively at least the actual results. Indeed as was seen in the earlier theoretical evaluation, use of real potentials still leads to the observation of channelling events.

In an effort to remove the voids and duplicate more closely the real structure, Robinson and Oen[28] considered several types of truncation for the Born-Mayer potential of Table 5.9. In the first (potential 1) truncation is effected at 50% of the nearest neighbour distance, whilst potential II is truncated at 53% of the nearest neighbour distance in the f.c.c. structure, thus preventing connected voids. Table 5.9 shows these potentials, along with potentials III and IV which prevented inter-connecting voids in the hypothetical b.c.c. and dia Cu structure respectively. We will see that elimination of connecting voids does give gross quantitative variations in the penetration phenomena, but the observed effects are maintained qualitatively. Thus comparison of the present model with experimental data should be reasonably fruitful. As an illustration of the position of the voids, figure 5.35 shows the (001) face for an f.c.c. Cu crystal, where the connecting voids are semi-pincushion cross section. Other more complex void configurations occur for different crystal directions, as was seen in the earlier theoretical discussion of channelling.

TABLE 5.9. (Ref. 5.28).

Designations of various truncated and eroded potentials.

Potential	R_c(Å)	$\phi(R_c)$ (eV)
Truncated Bohr	1.2781	0.26
Truncated Born-Mayer		
I	1.2781	33.83
II	1.3556	22.80
III	1.3914	19.01
IV	2.2137	0.29
Eroded Born-Mayer	1.2781	33.83

In order to facilitate discussion of the results of the calculations Robinson and Oen[28] found it convenient to introduce the concept of crystal "transparency". Qualitatively it is easy to see from visual examination of a crystal model (ball and spoke), that the structure is more optically transparent when viewed in certain directions than when viewed in other directions. Quantitatively one can express the transparency ρ_{hkl} as the number of ⟨hkl⟩ rows passing through unit areas of an (hkl) plane, the lower the value, the more transparent is the structure, i.e. more effectively force free space exists between atomic rows. Table 5.10 shows ρ_{hkl} values for some of

TABLE 5.10 (Ref. 5.28).

The most open directions of fcc, bcc, and dia 'Cu'.

fcc	⟨hkl⟩ bcc	dia	Row density ρ_{hkl} (Å^{-2})
...	...	011	0.162
...	111	111	0.199
011	...	...	0.217
...	001	001	0.230
...	...	112	0.282
001	...	...	0.306
...	011	...	0.324
...	...	013	0.363
112	...	...	0.375
...	113	113	0.380
...	...	123	0.429
013	...	...	0.484
...	...	114	0.487
...	133	133	0.500
...	012	012	0.513
111	...	...	0.530
...	...	233	0.538
...	112	...	0.562
123	...	...	0.572

the most open directions considered in the three copper structures.

Initial assessment of the lattice model was made by comparing the results of an initially spatially isotropic distribution of primaries slowing down under a Bohr potential interaction in a lattice model, and a random model calculation. Table 5.11 shows the results of the study, where $\bar{l}$ the mean distance between collisions, $\bar{R}_{par}$ and $\{(\langle \bar{R}^2_{par} \rangle)^{1/2}/\bar{R}_{par}\}$ are compared. The close correspondence between the values of $\bar{l}$ indicates the reliability of the free flight distance chosen for the random calculations. However $\bar{R}_{par}$ is not in as close agreement as appears in Table 5.11 since about 1% of the primaries which have very long ranges are omitted. This suggests that the real lattice arrangement can lead to some very long trajectories, and this is borne out by the lattice values of $\{[\langle \bar{R}^2_{par} \rangle]^{1/2}/\bar{R}_{par}\}$ which measures the increased skewness of the distribution towards longer paths. It is seen that the lattice model already provides a closer agreement with the experimental observations mentioned earlier.

TABLE 5.11. (Ref. 5.28).

Comparison of lattice and random models. Initially isotropic Cu atoms slowing down to 25 eV in fcc Cu. Truncated Bohr potential; static lattice.

Initial primary energy (keV)		1	5	10
$\langle l \rangle$ (Å)	Lattice	2.14	2.20	2.24
	Random	2.08	2.18	2.21
$\bar{R}$ par(Å)	Lattice	31.7	59.1	79.7
	Random	27.9	58.8	79.9
$\overline{(\bar{R}^2 par)}^{1/2} / (\bar{R}_{par})$	Lattice	1.44	1.35	1.31
	Random	1.20	1.20	1.19

maries which made more than 250 collisions were evaluated as shown in Table 5.12. From this table it is evident, from the isotropic distribution results alone, that the biggest contribution to the longest ranges is from primaries eventually moving in ⟨011⟩ directions. For primaries started in open (transparent) directions it is clear that those with the longest range remain in these directions. This is clear evidence that the lattice effectively "channels" the primaries, i.e. some primaries are constrained by large numbers of glancing collisions to move in regions of low potential (e.g. near the centre of the cell formed by two equally spaced ⟨001⟩ rows in the example of Figure 5.35) surrounded by relatively closely packed atomic rows. This concept is confirmed by study of Figure 5.35 which shows the positions Ox on a [001] face at which some eventually channelled ⟨001⟩ normally incident copper 1 kev primaries entered the lattice. Those primaries which made glancing collisions at the surface continued to do so and moved solely along the initial ⟨001⟩ direction. Other primaries making closer collisions with the channel boundary atoms were removed from the channel and some eventually channelled in other directions. It is notable that in the isotropic direction distribution case, most channelled primaries enter ⟨011⟩ directions the most transparent direction (i.e. lowest ρ_{hkl} in Table 5.10).

When an attempt was made to obtain statistical information on primary distributions using the Bohr potential, it was found that the number of channelled histories was so great as to render machine time prohibitively large. This is undoubtedly due to the weakness of the Bohr potential at large separations. Consequently, for this case, only observations were made upon the general characteristics of some individual

TABLE 5.12. (Ref. 5.28).

Average directions of trajectories involving >250 collisions. 1- to 10-keV Cu slowing down in fcc Cu. Truncated Bohr potential. Static lattice.

Initial primary directions	Isotropic	⟨011⟩	⟨001⟩	⟨111⟩
Total number of primaries	5056	5836	6968	6207
Fraction > 250 collisions	0.011	0.789	0.601	0.226
Number of long trajectories analyzed for direction	56	2145	1875	1227
Fraction of long trajectories with average direction near				
⟨011⟩	0.77	0.997	0.005	0.035
⟨001⟩	0.05	0.000	0.990	0.003
⟨112⟩	0.05	0.002	0.002	0.014
⟨013⟩	0.02	0.000	0.001	0.003
⟨111⟩	0.02	0.000	0.000	0.937
⟨123⟩	0.04	0.000	0.000	0.001
Other	0.05	0.001	0.002	0.007

In view of these results it was evident that the crystal symmetry allowed deep penetration of a small fraction of even isotropically distributed primaries, and it was therefore necessary to study which lattice direction was most responsible for this. Consequently the histories of many primaries were studied, using the isotropic direction and the position distributions for the primaries, and the fractions of the primaries and the results of these observations provided interesting insight into the behaviour of the primaries, Figures 5.36a and 5.36b show the histories of several Copper 1 kev primaries projected in the ⟨001⟩ and ⟨011⟩ directions, the primaries move both in the plane of the figures and perpendicular to this, the projected motions in the [001] and [011] plane are shown. It is clear that the ⟨001⟩ channel events are

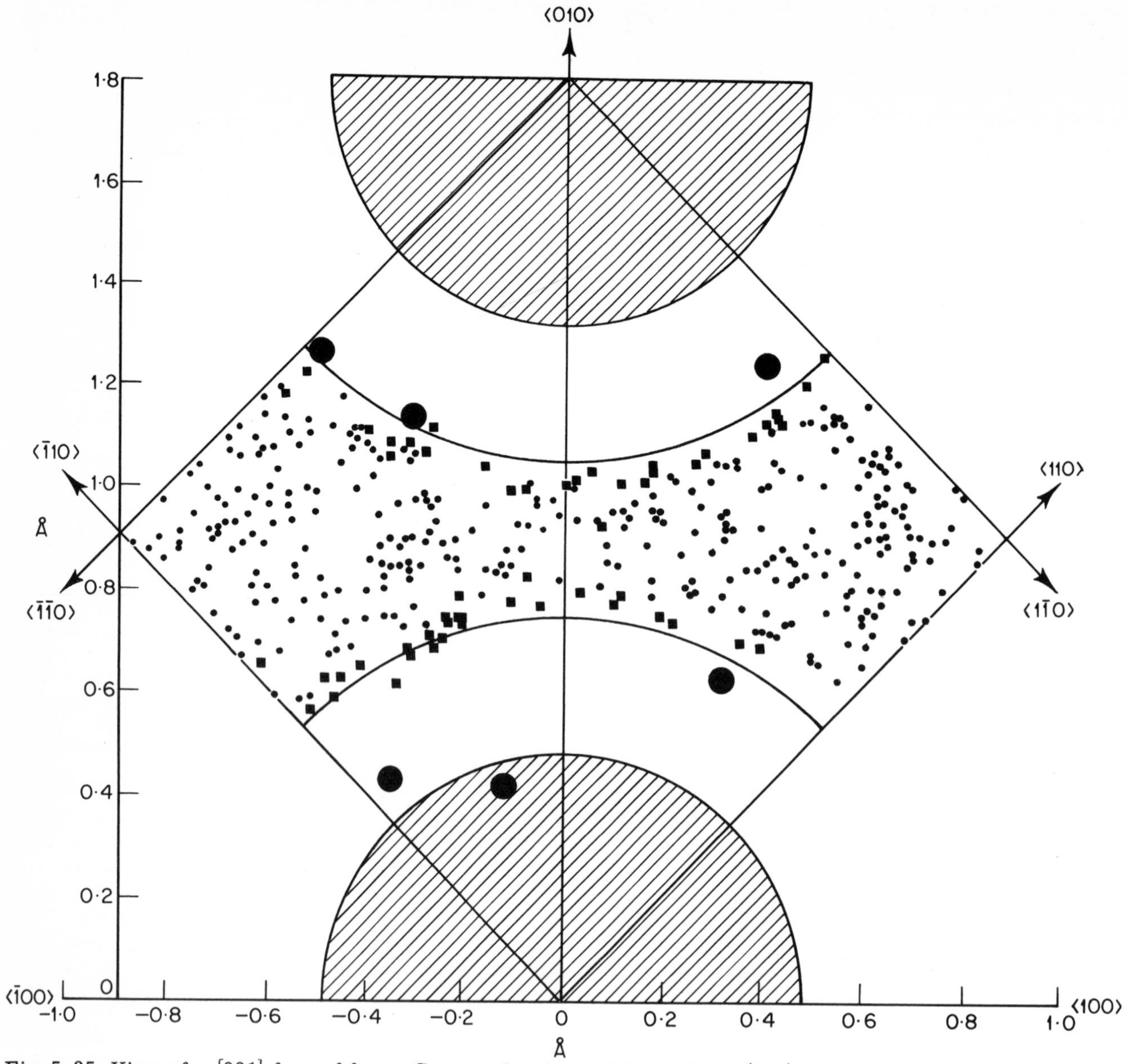

Fig. 5.35 View of a {001} face of f.c.c. Copper showing points at which ⟨001⟩ channelled 1 keV Cu primaries enter the channels. The larger filled circles show the entry points of primaries which become channelled in other directions. The shaded circles show the location of target atoms, their radii represent the distance of closest approach in a head on collision at 1 keV. The larger radii circles represent the impact parameter for transfer of 10 eV at 1 keV. A truncated Bohr potential in a static lattice is assumed. (viz. Ref. 5.28)

stable (restricted to a single channel) and have shapes related to the symmetry of the crystal. Thus the lower left event in Figure 5.35a was confined almost completely to the plane in which it started, the (110) which is a mirror plane of the crystal. The upper right event was less restricted however since it started in an (010) plane which is unoccupied by atoms. The (011) events in Figure 5.36b are less stable than the (001) events, and the latter are confined to two neighbouring channels. It should be noted, as in the earlier theoretical treatment, that ⟨ 001⟩ channels occur in pairs, the axes lying in the triangular region where the three nearest atomic potential interaction spheres come together. It is also found that, in addition to the motion around the channel axis, the trajectories have a component which tends to carry them around a neighbouring close packed row. Thus the primaries tend to drift readily from one channel to another and it is quite easy to imagine a 'macro-channel' motion where the trajectory spirals around a close packed row and is constrained by a hexagonal array of outer rows.

When the Born-Mayer truncated potential 1 was used, another interesting phenomenon was observed. In this case it appeared that many of the primaries which made many collisions, and were confined to channels, did not travel large distances along the channels. This behaviour was observed when the primary was moving in a direction nearly perpendicular to the direction of the nearest neighbour bonds of the crystal (⟨011⟩ in f.c.c. and ⟨ 111⟩ in b.c.c. and dia. Cu). Thus the most prominent channels in which this reduction in range or trapping occurred was eroded at half the nearest neighbour distance, or cut off at 53% of the nearest neighbour distance. This suggested that the phenomenon was an artifact of the potential used and examination of some trajectories showed that trapping occurred when the primary energy had fallen to below ≃ 100eV and it then made hard sphere collisions off the edges of two neighbouring atoms, with small energy loss at each collision. It then was

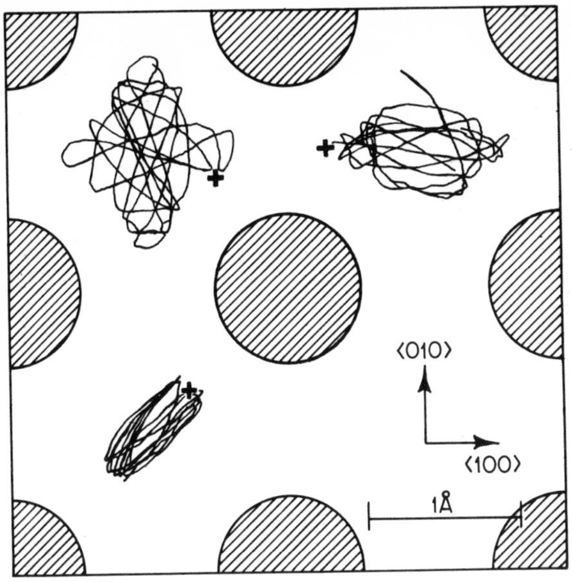

Fig. 5. 36a Projection of some ⟨001⟩ channel trajectories onto the {001} surface of f.c.c. Cu. for 1 keV Cu slowing down according to the truncated Bohr potential. The points of entry of primaries are indicated by crosses. Each primary penetrated approximately 300 Å into the crystal in the trajectories shown (250 collisions) (viz. Ref. 5. 28)

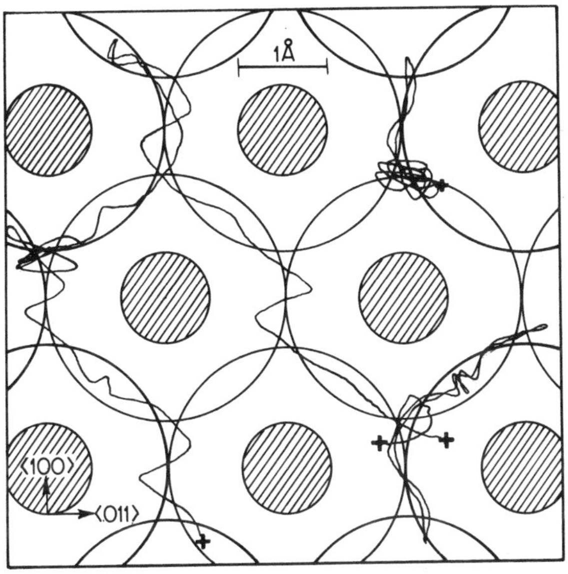

Fig. 5. 36b Projection of some ⟨01$\bar{1}$⟩ channel trajectories on to the {01$\bar{1}$} surface of f.c.c. Cu for 1 keV Cu slowing down according to the truncated Bohr potential. (viz. Ref. 5. 28)

compelled to move in the plane of the nearest neighbour bond making a succession of collisions with each atom in turn. The sequence is illustrated in Figure 5.37. Although a component of motion perpendicular to the plane of the figure could eventually remove the primary, if sufficiently high, the effect would still result in a net range reduction.

As Robinson and Oen[28] point out, this result is a consequence of the form of potential adopted, but it does illustrate the subtle effects the lattice can exert upon the primary motion.

Results of greater interest for experimental comparison were obtained by studying the penetration distribution functions for primaries slowing down in the various structures, and observing the influence of

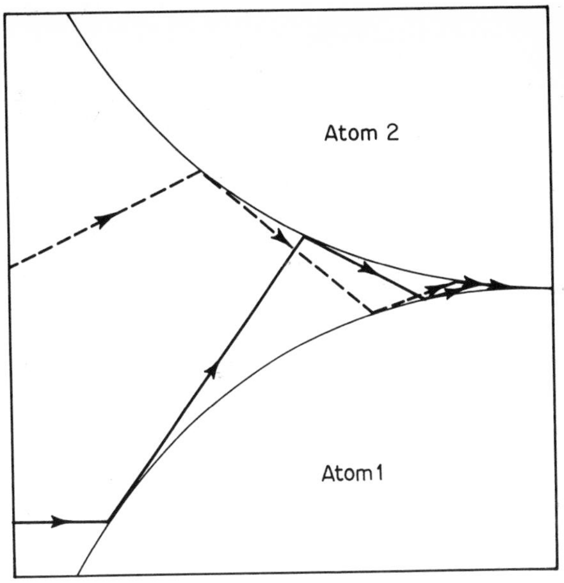

Fig. 5. 37 Schematic representation of the trapping of a primary by a succession of hard sphere collisions with nearest neighbours. A mass ratio of 1 is assumed. (viz. Ref. 5. 28)

effective variations of the primary energy, and mass, and target temperature. The differential penetration probability function f(L, E)dL as defined earlier was obtained from the computations, but for comparison with experimental data it is more convenient to evaluate the integral penetration function defined as

$$\int_{L}^{L_{max}} f(L, E)dL$$

This function describes the total probability of finding primaries between the range L and the maximum L_{max} and is clearly (1 or 100%) at L = 0 for primaries which remain trapped in the lattice. Integral probability distribution functions are plotted for 5kev Copper primaries slowing down via Born-Mayer potential 1 in f.c.c. Copper in Figures 38a-e for the most important channel directions and the isotropic case. Figure 5.38a illustrates the results for 5kev normal Copper slowing down in a lattice free from thermal vibrations (denoted as static) and Figures 5.38c and 5.38d show the effects of decreasing the primary mass ($A = 1/3$), again for a static lattice.

The effects of introducing lattice vibrations at 0°K are shown in Figure 5.38e.

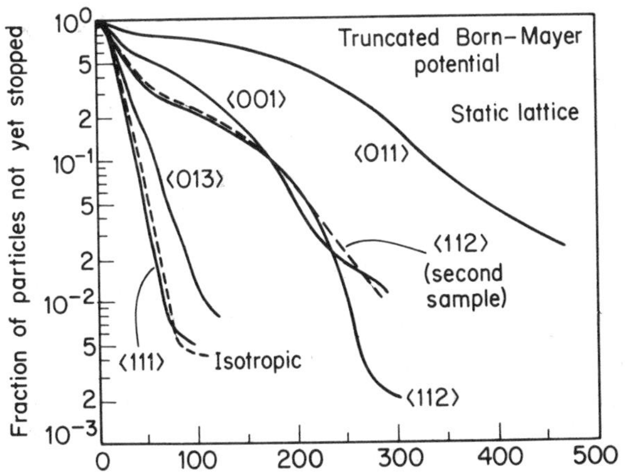

Fig. 5. 38a Distribution of Penetration Depths; 5-keV Cu slowing down to 25 eV in Cu; (A = 1). The truncated Born-Mayer Potential I is assumed for a static lattice. (viz. Ref. 5. 28)

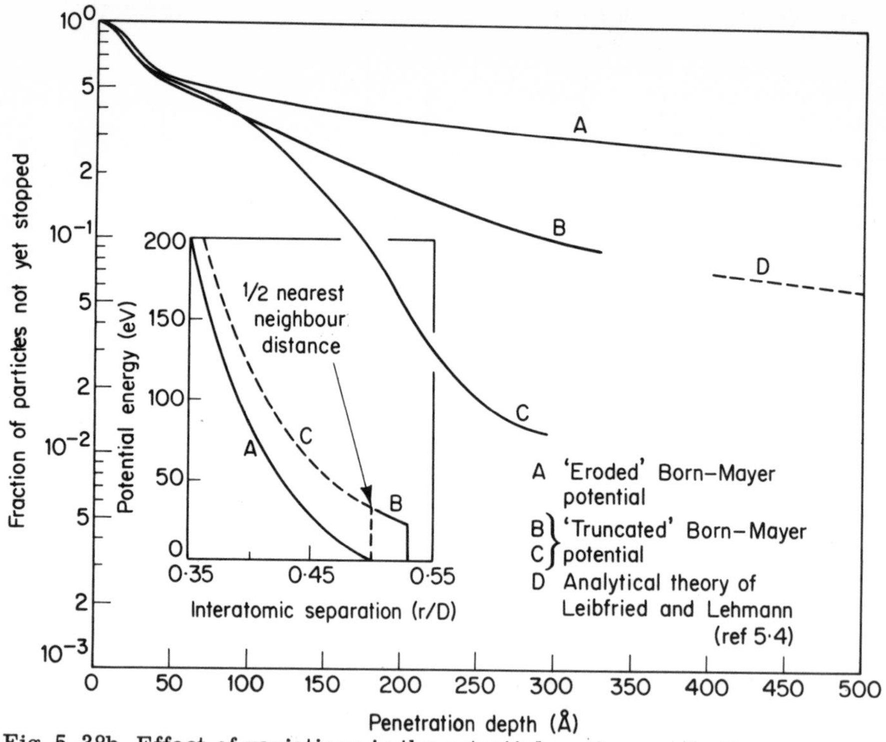

Fig. 5. 38b Effect of variations in the potential on the penetration distribution. 5-keV Cu → Cu.⟨001⟩ incidence. Inset shows the potential energy functions. (viz. Ref. 5. 28)

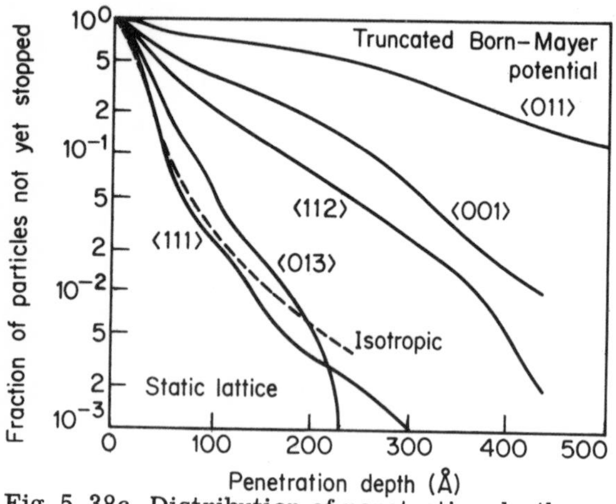

Fig. 5. 38c Distribution of penetration depths, 5-keV 'Light Cu' → Cu (A = 3). (viz. Ref. 5. 28)

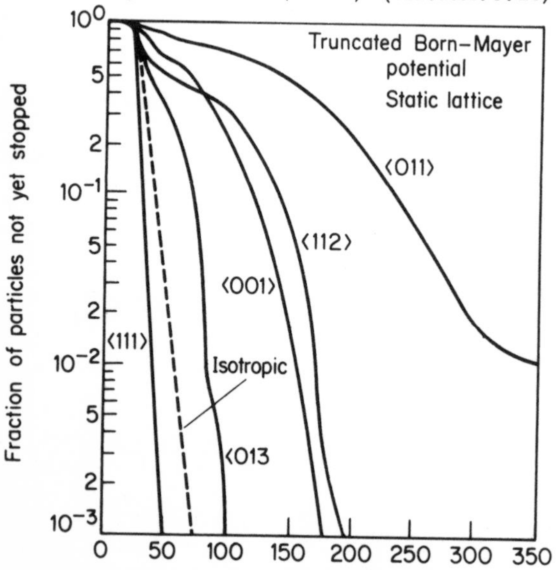

Fig. 5. 38d Distribution of penetration depths, 5 keV 'Heavy Cu' → Cu (A = 3). (viz. Ref. 5. 28)

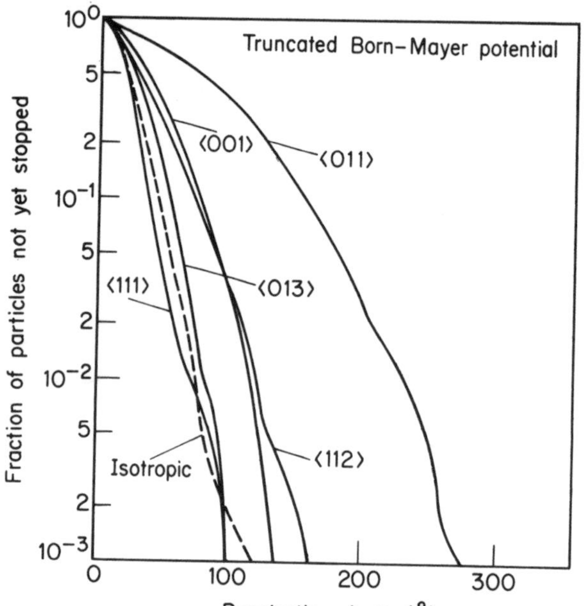

Fig. 5. 38c Effect of a large thermal vibration amplitude on the penetration distributions of 5-keV Cu → Cu (A = 1). Rms lattice vibrational amplitude = 0. 20 Å (corresponding to a temperature of ~ 1350°K). This figure should be compared with 5. 38a. (viz. Ref. 5. 28)

The general conclusions from these curves are

1. the accuracy of the calculations is high, evident from the reproducibility of two independent ⟨ 112⟩ curves in Figure 5. 38a. Only at the largest penetrations, are the two independent samples somewhat different because of the small numbers of primaries involved. The statistics of very many analyses shows a Poisson error distribution.

2. The ⟨ 011⟩ penetrations are greatest, independent of the primary mass or target temperature. The ⟨ 001⟩ and ⟨ 112⟩ penetrations are intermediate and the ⟨ 013⟩ and ⟨ 111⟩ are least, differing only slightly

from isotropic distributions. It should be pointed out that averaging over the various ⟨ hkl⟩ curves will not give the isotropic distributions since these latter all originate from the lattice sites, rather than distributed around lattice sites positionally.

3. The general disposition of the distribution (except for the crossing of ⟨ 001⟩ and ⟨ 112⟩ curves is as expected from the transparency considerations of Table 5.10.

4. The dispersion of the distributions is greatest for 'light' primaries (A = 3) and least for 'heavy' primaries (smaller penetration depths for $A = \frac{1}{3}$).

5. The effect of increasing the vibrational amplitude of the lattice atoms is to decrease the primary range.

The median penetrations (defined from

$$\int_0^\infty Rf(R)dR = \tfrac{1}{2})$$

are listed in Table 5.13 and taken from the curves in Figures 5.38a to 5.38e.

TABLE 5.13. (Ref. 5.28).

Effects of mass ratio and of thermal vibration amplitude on the penetration of 5-keV"Cu" into fcc Cu. Truncated Born-Mayer potential I.

Median penetrations (Å)

Initial primary direction	Mass ratio effect (static lattice) A = 3	A = 1	A = 1/3	Thermal effect (A = 1) rms = 0.05 Å	rms = 0.20 Å
⟨011⟩	235	191	145	174	77
⟨001⟩	69	59	65	49	34
⟨112⟩	38	29	52	31	27
⟨013⟩	28	24	34	24	24
⟨111⟩	20	19	24	18	17
Isotropic	19	19	28	19	20

All these results clearly confirm the theoretical predictions, at least qualitatively of Equations 5.138, 5.139 and Table 5.10.

The crossing of the ⟨ 001⟩ and ⟨ 112⟩ characteristics in fact is again found to be a result of the truncation at 50% of the nearest neighbour distance. For eroded or 53% nearest neighbour truncation the effect may be eliminated, as shown in Figure 5.38b.

Clearly the eroded potential leads to larger penetrations because of the weaker interactions involved and similar arguments apply to the decreased penetrations when truncation at 50% or 53% nearest neighbour separation is used. In this Figure the analytical results of Equations 5.135 are also shown, extrapolated beyond the region of real applicability. It is clear however that the 53% Born-Mayer truncated potential results agree most closely with the analytical values. This must be expected since this corresponds most closely to the analytical potential used.

The nature of the distribution functions may be emphasized by replotting as differential penetration probabilities as in Figure 5.39 for just two particular cases. It is immediately apparent that the isotropic

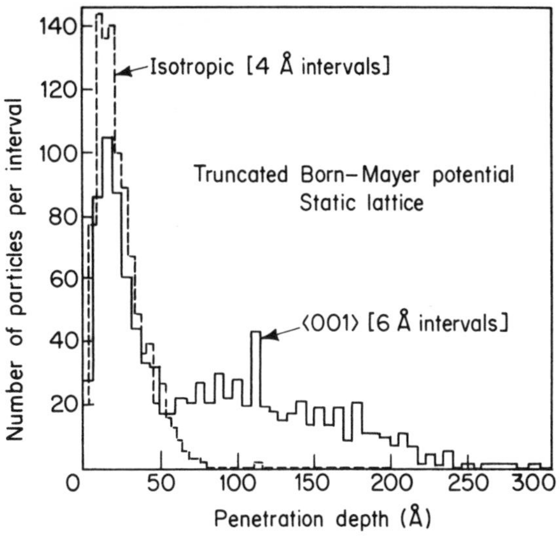

Fig. 5.39 Differential penetration distributions for initially isotropic and initially ⟨001⟩ 5 keV Cu primaries slowing down to 25 eV in f.c.c. Cu. (viz. Ref. 5.28)

distribution is unimodal, but the ⟨ 001⟩ histogram is bimodal. The first peak of the ⟨ 001⟩ roughly coincides with the isotropic distribution but the second occurs at considerably deeper penetration. This illustrates the nature of the channelling where the larger fraction of primaries is unaffected by lattice symmetry, but a small proportion are channelled. The smaller fraction can exert considerable influence upon the averages of the range quantities however.

When the effects of crystal structure are examined, further lattice effects are exposed. Figure 5.40

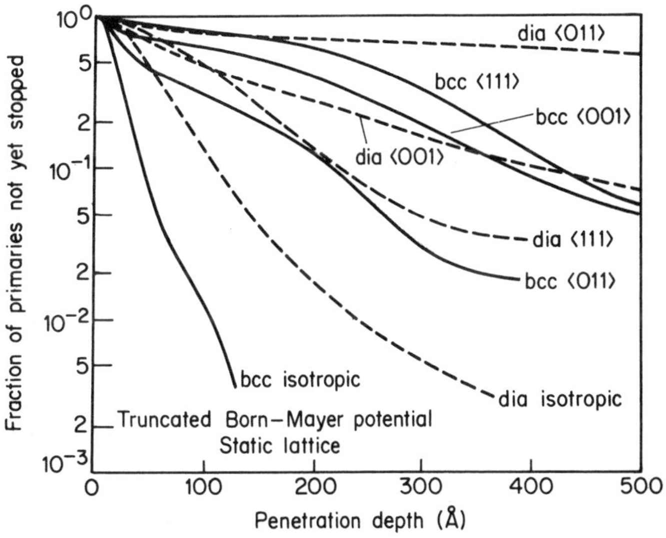

Fig. 5.40 Integral penetration distributions for 5 keV Cu atoms slowing down to 25 eV in b.c.c. and dia. 'Cu'. Truncated Born-Mayer Potential I, Static lattice. (viz. Ref. 5.28)

shows the integral penetration distribution for b.c.c. and dia Copper with incident 5keV copper primaries. The penetration depths are in increasing order from f.c.c. to b.c.c. and dia, as is expected from the relative densities. However closer studies, show that the penetration increases are even larger than expected from the density decrease, as evidenced in Figure 5.41 where the median penetration is given as a function of primary energy. There is definite evidence of a structural effect.

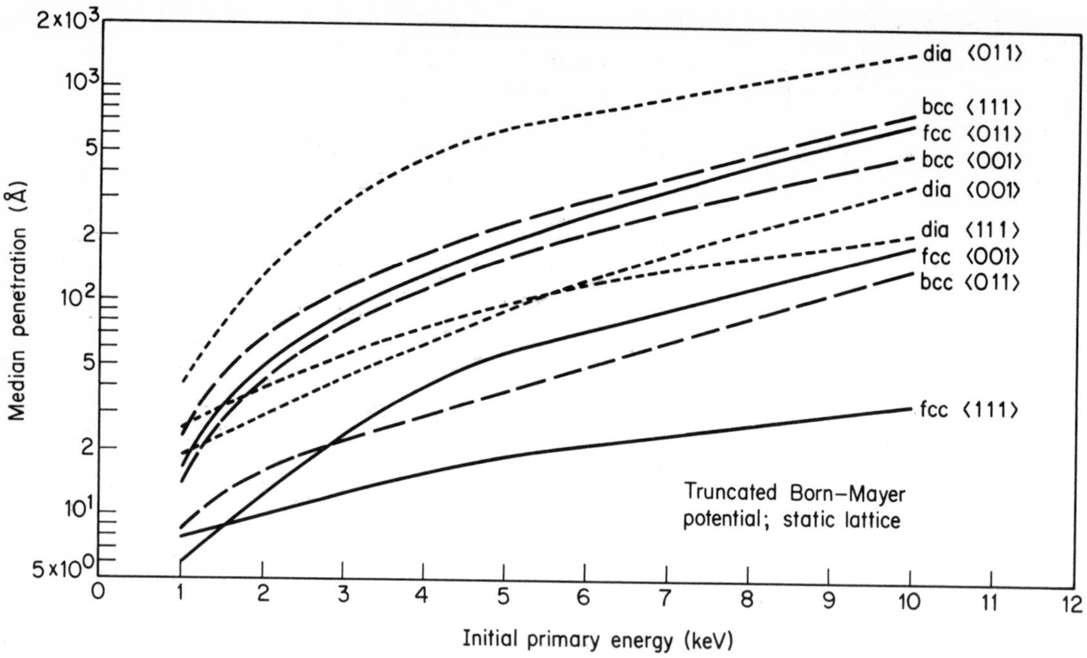

Fig. 5. 41 Median projected ranges of Cu primaries slowing down to 25 eV in 'Cu', as functions of the initial direction, the type of crystal and the initial primary energy. (viz. Ref. 5. 28)

When comparisons are made of median penetrations into the three copper structures, as in Table 5. 13 with the transparency values of ρ_{hkl} there is the expected increase of median penetration with increasing transparency. Exceptions may be found in the cases of the ⟨001⟩ and ⟨111⟩ dia directions. The transparencies of the ⟨001⟩ and ⟨111⟩ directions in dia and b.c.c. copper are the same, so that similar penetrations should be expected. However the discrepancy may be understood when it is realised that the spacing between atoms in the rows bordering the channels, in a direction parallel to the channels, is larger in dia than b.c.c. copper. Thus more primaries may 'leak' out of certain dia channels than from a corresponding b.c.c. channel. Another lattice influence, which in this case tends to reduce penetrations.

The reduction in range with increased lattice vibration amplitudes (higher temperatures) is also in, at least qualitative, accord with the theoretical predictions.[41]

Other information derived from these computations included the probability of an incident primary re-emerging from the plane of incidence and the indications were that light primaries had a higher escape probability, particularly from a more open structure such as dia Copper. There was a slight decrease in escape probability with increasing primary energy. Representative values of escape probabilities are given in Table 5. 14 but it must be remembered that those primaries which have energies less than 25ev are not counted in these studies, so that experimentally determined escape or reflection probabilities may be substantially larger (c.f. Chapter 4).
Finally, in view of the analytic results of section 5. 9 where it was seen that the final distribution of primary energies gives information about the interatomic potential, (and thus about the scattering properties of this potential), the machine data on these final energy distributions are interesting. It was observed that, using potential B-M-I. the final primary energies were distributed uniformly below 25eV. This is not surprising when analysis shows that hard sphere scattering only takes place off the cut edge of this potential below about 67eV. For potential B-M. II. the energy distribution increases near 25eV, since forward scattering is more important here, as the potential is not cut off until lower energies. These results illustrate how an analysis of experimental data may allow deduction of the potential at small separation distances.

TABLE 5. 14 (Ref. 5. 28).

Probability of primaries escaping from targets.

(a) 5-keV light "Cu" in fcc Cu (A = 3); truncated Born-Mayer potential I; static lattice.

Initial primary direction	Percent primaries escaping
⟨111⟩	11. 3
⟨013⟩	8. 7
⟨112⟩	8. 2
⟨001⟩	5. 4
⟨011⟩	3. 4

(b) ⟨001⟩ incident Cu in dia "Cu" (A = 1); truncated Born-Mayer potential I; static lattice.

Initial primary energy (keV)	Percent primaries escaping
1. 0	1. 8
2. 5	2. 0
5. 0	1. 1
7. 5	0. 5
10. 0	0. 6

Of similar importance is the distribution of energies of the secondary, target atoms, and Table 5. 15 shows the results of the computation for 5keV primaries in f.c.c. and dia. Copper. In the f.c.c. case, primaries moving in channel directions produce many more lower energy secondaries than does an iso-

TABLE 5.15. (Ref. 5.28).

Production of secondaries by 5 keV Cu atoms in dia "Cu." Truncated Born-Mayer potential I. Static lattice.

Initial primary direction	Secondaries produced per primary with energies (eV)[a] > 25		> 50		> 100		> 250	
	A	B	A	B	A	B	A	B
⟨011⟩	8.6	8.7	5.4	5.4	3.0	3.0	1.4	1.4
⟨111⟩	7.0	9.1	4.7	6.7	2.9	4.6	1.5	2.7
⟨001⟩	8.8	8.8	6.0	6.1	3.8	3.9	2.1	2.1
Isotropic[b]	6.5	6.8	4.9	5.2	3.3	3.7	2.0	2.3

[a] Precision of tabular values is about ± 0.1.

[b] Primaries originated from A sites.

tropic primary distribution, due to the lower energy transfers involved in the glancing collisions. This fact may be of some importance in the radiation damage effects, which will be discussed in the next Chapter. In the dia. case similar effects occur and two groups of secondaries may be distinguished, 'A' secondaries which originate from one of the interpenetrating f.c.c. sublattices of which the dia structure is formed and 'B' secondaries from the other sublattices. The excess of 'B' secondaries no doubt occurs because of the choice of an 'A' type surface from which the primaries originated. Similar effects will be seen in the subsequent discussion of calculations for the binary BeO structure.

To sum up these calculations, we may observe that the lattice model predicts many effects which are missed by the randomisation procedure. In view of the sensitivity of the calculations to apparently minor changes in the assumptions of the interatomic potential, it is unwise, as pointed out by Robinson and Oen,[28] at this stage to attempt a quantitative comparison with experimental data. However, the computations give good qualitative agreement with the somewhat restricted theoretical treatment and indicate the increased skewness of penetrations as observed experimentally. Further comparison of this data will be deferred until after presentation of the experimental results.

We continue this survey of machine computational methods by examining the results obtained recently by Beeler and Besco.[29, 45–49] These authors have studied the interactions between energetic primary atoms and several hypothetical and real binary structures of Beryllium Oxide. The original aim of this work was to assess the nature of the damage to the BeO structure itself, but information was also obtained on the fate of the primary and of Be and O atoms which move through the lattice.

In view of the rather complete description given of the machine calculations of Oen and Robinson we shall not give a full account of the computational technique of Beeler and Besco. In fact the methods of analysis were similar to those already described and differed only in the details we describe now.

The primary and target atoms were allowed to interact via a screened Bohr potential extending to infinity around each atom (i.e. no cut off). Thus

$$V(r) = \frac{Z_1 Z_2 e^2}{r} \exp(-r/a)$$

with $a = ka_0(Z_1^{2/3} + Z_2^{2/3})^{-1/2}$

and k chosen as an adjustable parameter for the particular primary/target atom combination under consideration. The method of choosing k was unusual, in that the k values obtained by Oen et al in the random model calculations for Cu,Cu: Ag,Ag: and Au,Au: interactions were plotted against $(Z_1^{2/3} + Z_2^{2/3})^{1/2}$ with a resulting straight line. Values of k for a given primary/target combination were then obtained from the graph using suitable values of Z_1 and Z_2, except where the k value appeared to fall below unity, when k was arbitrarily assumed to be 1. The scattering angle was computed assuming a hard sphere collision with a radius dependent upon the impact parameter and the relative energy of motion i.e.

$$V(r_0) = E_R(1 - p^2/r_0^2) \qquad 5.162$$

As we have seen in Chapter 2 this leads to a scattering law which is probably better than that for a hard sphere with a radius defined only by the distance of closest approach in a head on collision ($p = 0$).

Another unique feature of the programme was that the current damage state of the crystal was assumed during the history of a given atom. To do this each collision was analysed and the fate of both partners followed, treating the particle which emerged with greatest velocity from the collision first. Thus the primary could displace target atoms, leading to lattice damage, which when stored in the computer memory could lead to changes in its own history and those of subsequent primaries. The energy required to displace a target atom from a normal lattice position was taken to be about twice the sublimation energy for a solid of those atoms, but whether the struck atom actually escaped from the lattice site depended upon its ejection direction i.e. if it was ejected between two surrounding atoms it would have a high escape probability. These questions will be discussed in greater detail in Chapter 6 and are of interest here only in that they indicate how greater reality in the collision process was achieved. Radiation induced annealing of damage, during a history, was also considered by allowing association of an interstitial and a vacancy, via collision of a primary or target atom with the interstitial. On the other hand a primary was not allowed to collide with a vacancy.

Computations were made assuming the collisions of

(a) Iodine[127] and Krypton[84] atoms with an assumed two dimensional array of Be and O atoms arranged on a square planar array, in the incident energy range 1-50keV[29]

(b) Iodine and Krypton atoms with a real BeO Wurtzite lattice in the incident energy range 0.5-50keV[46].

(c) 2 keV Beryllium and 6 keV Oxygen atoms with a real BeO lattice[45].

(d) 2 keV Iron and Copper atoms with lattice of Iron and Copper respectively[47, 48, 49].

(e) Krypton atoms with certain directions of aluminium and tungsten targets[45].

In most cases the angle of incidence on the crystal surface was a variable parameter.

The results of the computations could be divided into two groups. Those describing the damage state of the target after bombardment, to which we shall return in Chapter 6 and those describing the primary penetration functions, which are of immediate interest and to which we shall, at present, confine our attention.

The initial results[29] of Krypton and Iodine bombardment of square planar BeO with the incident angle variable about the normal direction, led to the immediate observation of extremely deep penetration for normal incidence and 45°. The authors naturally interpreted this as a channelling phenomenon and as evidence of this show a typical trajectory of a 1 keV Iodine atom incident mid way between rows at an angle of 10°, which is reproduced in Figure 5.42. This is clearly of a damped oscillatory nature, as expected from the analytical results of section 5.9. Further the penetration depth and energy loss per unit length (stopping power) were observed to be functions of the azimuthal incidence angle and the position of entry between rows. Figures 5.43a and 5.43b exhibit the expected nature of these results according to the earlier analysis. The reduced penetration for 45° incidence must be expected since the inter row spacing is only $1/\sqrt{2}$ that for normal incidence.

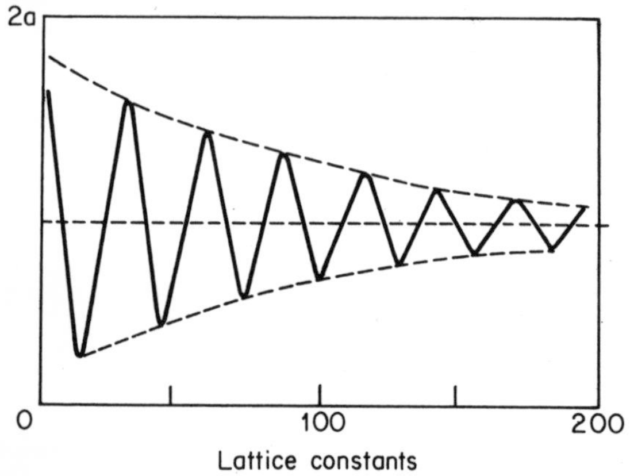

Fig. 5.42 Focused trajectory of a 1 keV I^{127} atom injected at 10° to the surface normal to a BeO square array of atoms, showing the damped oscillatory nature of the path. Atom injected midway between rows of spacing a. (viz. Ref. 5.29)

These computations must be largely of academic interest however because of the oversimplification introduced into the assumed lattice structure but they do exhibit the details of the channelling events. Moreover, it was noted that the primaries which became channelled events caused very little target damage, supporting the view that the low energy transfers to struck atoms result in fewer displacements.

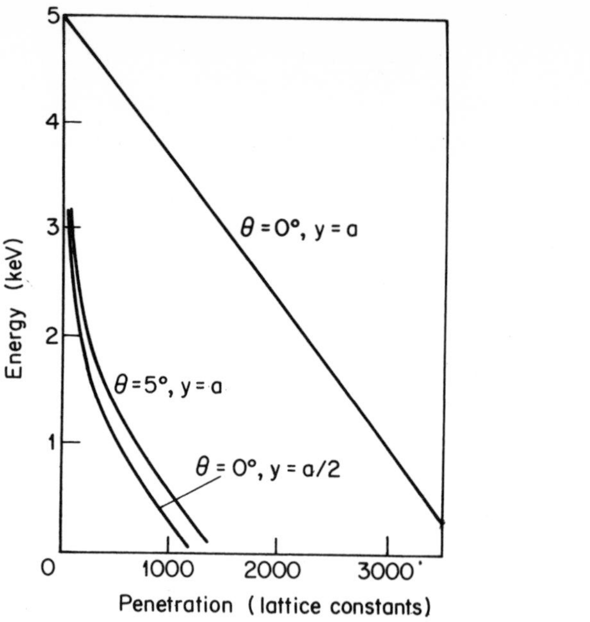

Fig. 5.43a Penetration depth as a function of primary iodine atom energy for atoms incident on a square planar array of BeO at different distances from a row of atoms (y), and different incidence angles to the normal (θ). (viz. Ref. 5.29)

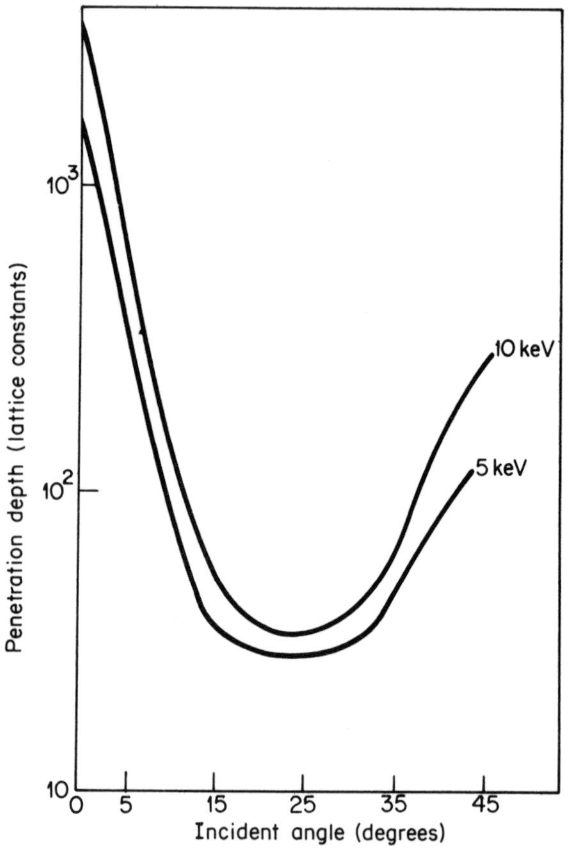

Fig. 5.43b The penetration depth of 5 keV and 10 keV I primaries into square planar BeO incident mid way between atomic rows and at various angles of incidence to the normal. (viz. Ref. 5.29)

When the work was extended[46] to include the real wurtzite structure (WL) of BeO the deeply penetrating components were still evident however, as Figure 5.44 indicates for 50 keV Kr bombardment of this structure. Once again the magnitude of the penetration must be regarded circumspectly, since although as

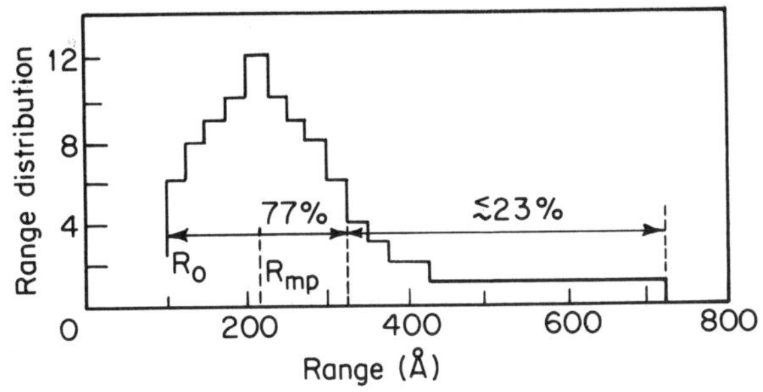

Fig. 5.44 Computed range distribution for 50 keV Kr ions incident on a Wurtzite structure BeO lattice. The tail in fact extends to 3300 Å and indicates the presence of channelling. (viz. Refs. 5.45, 5.46)

the authors point out, force free voids are eliminated, the weakness of the Bohr potential undoubtedly assists in achieving very large penetrations. A stronger potential was in fact observed to reduce the penetration considerably. Nevertheless the deeply penetrating component is evident in Figure 5.44 although smaller than for the square planar lattice case. In the WL structure the channels were observed to be surrounded by a hexagonal array of Be and O atoms, the exact nature of which we shall discuss presently, but again the tendency to drift between adjacent channels was evident (as in some of the Cu-Cu results described earlier), showing the importance of crystal structure. The reduction in damage caused by channelled atoms was again notable.

Computations [47, 48, 49] on the slowing down of Copper 2keV atoms in f.c.c. Copper and Iron 2keV atoms in b.c.c. Iron also confirmed the reality of the channelling events. Initially, the stopping powers for these atoms directed along the axes of the ⟨100⟩, ⟨110⟩ and ⟨111⟩ channels in iron and the ⟨110⟩ and ⟨100⟩ channels in copper, were deduced and are shown in Table 5.16. The order of increase of these is in accordance

TABLE 5.16. (Ref. 5.47).

Comparative Stopping Power along channel directions

Iron (B.C.C.) k = 1.00		
⟨100⟩	0.43	eV/Å
⟨110⟩	1.12	eV/Å
⟨111⟩	1.80	eV/Å
Copper (F.C.C.) k = 1.15		
⟨110⟩	1.57	eV/Å
⟨100⟩	2.52	eV/Å

with the ρ_{hkl} values given in Table 5.10 except for the high stopping power of ⟨111⟩ iron, which is presumably related to the correct interatomic distances used for this case, rather than the hypothetical values in the b.c.c. Copper examples. The magnitude of the stopping power is of order 1.OeV/Å whereas, the stopping power of a random array may be calculated from Equation 5.44.4 to be about 200 eV/Å for Cu. in Cu (hard sphere collisions). Thus the ranges of atoms in channels should be considerably larger than in an isotropic lattice. However only a very few primaries in a given experiment will start exactly on a channel axis or at normal surface incidence. Thus the effect of varying the angle of incidence of an iron atom into a ⟨100⟩ iron channel is of importance, although at this stage the results must still be expressed qualitatively. It was observed that 2 keV iron normally incident into a ⟨100⟩ iron channel followed an almost completely straight trajectory. When the incidence angle was changed to 5° (from the axis) the trajectory approximated a helix with a narrow amplitude in the channel, in neither of these cases were target atoms displaced. For 10° and 15° incident angles the path still followed a helical form although the projected path length was shortened and displaced atoms occurred at the channel walls. At higher incident angles, channel trajectories along ⟨100⟩ did not develop and in some cases primaries were deflected into ⟨110⟩ channels, whilst the damage production was increased for the non channelled events. These results are in qualitative agreements with the predictions of section 5.9 and must be expected in view of the increased stopping power at non channel axial incidence as shown in Figure 5.45. Similar results

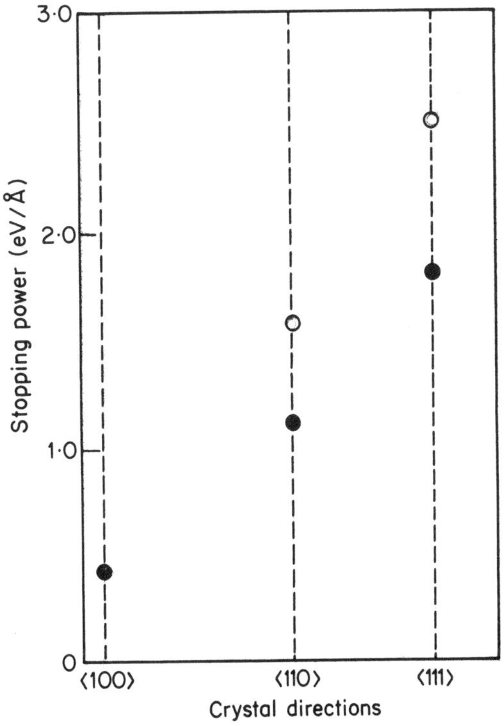

Fig. 5.45 Comparison of stopping powers of 2 KeV Fe and Cu atoms moving in channels in their own host lattices. • - Fe; ○ — Cu. (viz. Ref. 5.47)

were obtained in more detailed study[45] of the trajectories of Be and O atoms passing through a real simulated BeO lattice. In order to appreciate these results we consider briefly the structure of BeO assumed as shown in Figures 5.46a, b.c. The wurtzite BeO structure consists of Be and O atoms arranged in projected hexagonal form in planes parallel to the basal plane A in Figure 5, 146a. Hatched circles represent beryllium atoms and open circles oxygen atoms in this diagram, and all atoms labelled with the same integer lie uniformly spaced in lines parallel to the basal planes. With this structure one can obtain channels formed by atoms from two adjacent basal planes, the cross section of such a channel is shown in Figure 5.46b. The axis of this channel is in the plane defined by the line PQ in Figure 5.46c which defines the hexagonal projection of the BeO array on a basal plane. Clearly the channel under consideration does not possess rotational symmetry, as have those discussed previously. Two types of calculation were performed, in which primary atoms of Be or O, were injected into a channel at various angles ϕ with respect to the

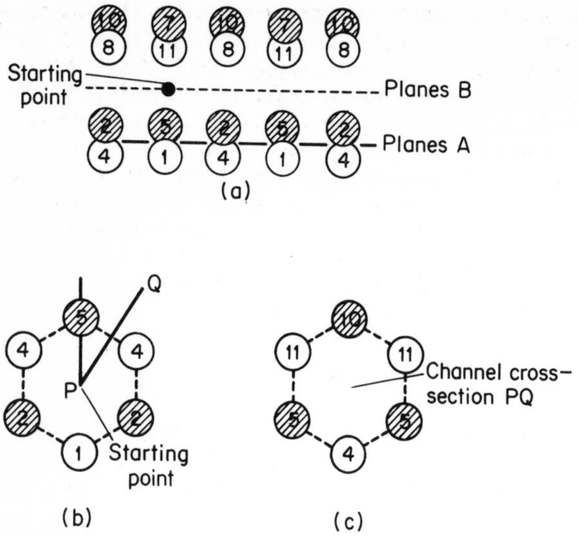

Fig. 5.46 The structure of channels in the Wurtzite structure of BeO (a) Definition of planes B and A and an atom starting position in plane B. (b) Atom starting point in plane A. (c) Cross section of the channel core for the tunnel direction PQ ($\phi = 0$). (viz. Ref. 5.45)

symmetry axis PQ (between 0° and 30°), starting from positions in the basal plane A (point P) or midway between basal planes (in plane B). Primary atoms of 6keV Oxygen started in the B plane (already on the channel axis and termed O_B atoms) channelled for angles ϕ ranging from 0 to about 15°, as is evident from Figure 5.47a which shows the maximum primary range as a function of ϕ. Above an azimuthal angle of $\approx 15°$, the range is constant and typical of an isotropic range value. Oxygen atoms started in plane A (O_A atoms) on the other hand have a shorter range since their initial deflection was found to be downwards from the basal Plane A into a channel, below and to the left of one in which an O_B atom was started. The initial interaction was stronger and dissipated considerable O_A energy causing range reduction for channelled events ($\phi \lesssim 15°$). Similarly the minimum ranges (for $\phi > 15°$) were smaller for O_A than for O_B atoms since again O_A atoms experience an initial hard collision with either atoms 4 or 5 which causes considerable energy losses. The impact parameter for O_B atoms for these azimuthal angles is about 3 times that for O_A atoms and thus the initial energy losses are much reduced.

When 2keV beryllium primaries were initiated in planes A and B (B_A and B_B atoms respectively) the range/azimuthal angle characteristics shown in Figure 5.47b were obtained, of comparable form to those for $R \mid \phi$ in Figure 5.47a. The more gradual decline of range with angle ϕ indicates the greater probability of Be channelling than O channelling, a result of the fact that the interaction potential is weaker for Be than for O atoms.

Channelling events were also recorded[45] for Krypton primaries moving in the ⟨100⟩ direction in tungsten and in Aluminium. Once again the general effects of channelling were evident and it was noted, as expected, that hardening the assumed interatomic potential (increasing k from 1.5 to 1.85) reduced channelling event probabilities and ranges. Increased primary energies of course resulted in greater channelling.

Damage production during Be and O bombardment of BeO was again found to be much reduced by channelled trajectories, exact results depending upon the

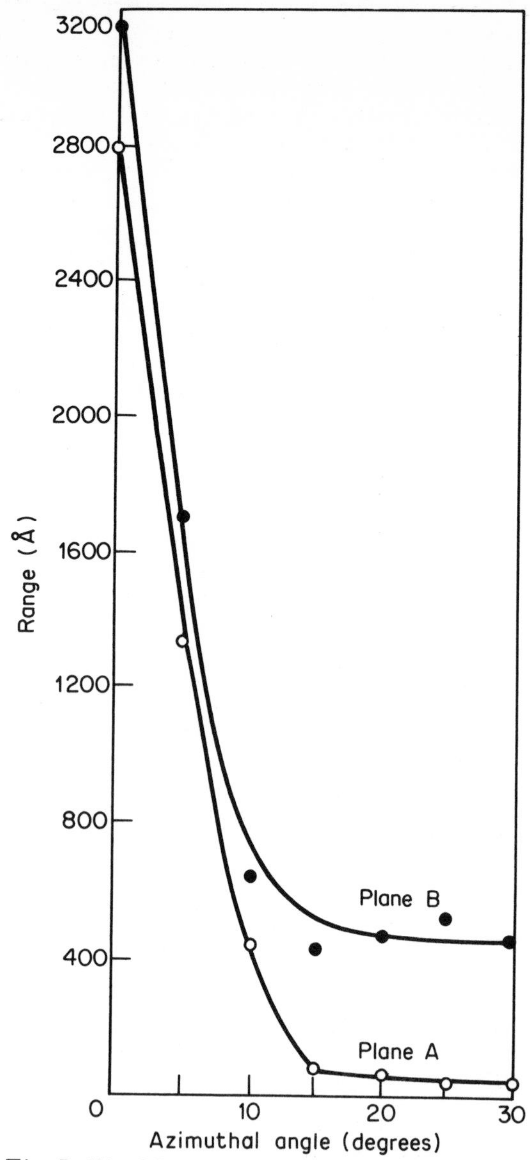

Fig. 5.47a Maximum ranges of 6 keV O atoms in a Wurtzite structure BeO lattice as a function of starting angle. (viz. Ref. 5.45)

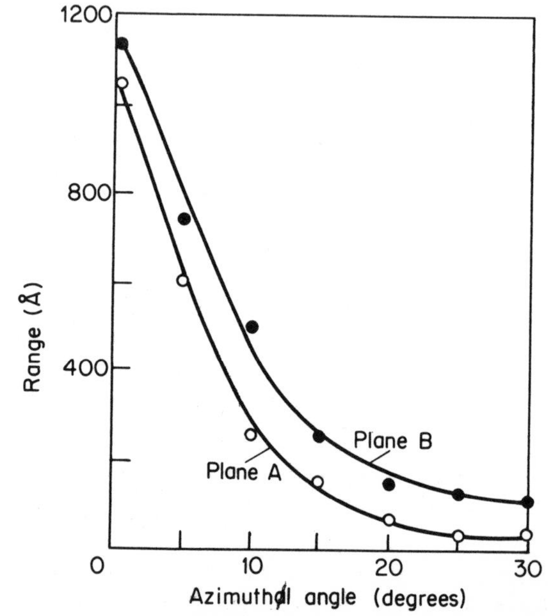

Fig. 5.47b Maximum ranges of 2 keV Be atoms in a Wurtzite structure BeO lattice as a function of starting angle. (viz. Ref. 5.45)

primary atom and starting plane, but reductions of as much as 50% of that due to a normal primary (non channelled) were evident. Similar paths were described by the Be and O primaries in channels, as those described by Robinson and Oen[28] for Copper, (Figure 5.36) but because of the lack of channel symmetry, the actual paths were a little more complex. No channel interchange was observed as with 50keV Krypton in BeO but it was observed that vacancies in the channel boundary atoms could result in the termination of a channel event if the primary was incident on the vacancy. This phenomena is of a similar nature to that of 'leakage' out of ⟨001⟩ and ⟨111⟩ channels in dia. Copper and once again shows the effect that lattice effects can impose upon the penetration. Indeed, it can be easily imagined that interstitials in a channel border, or within the channel itself may cause channel interruption and blockage. Thus it seems desirable that further studies should be made of the influence of the damage state of the crystal upon the penetration functions, and that these effects should be borne in mind in carrying out and interpreting experimental results. It is interesting to note that such processes which reduce channelling events begin to return the crystal to its effectively random state. We must therefore regard the merits of the earlier analytical and machine computation as being not too unrealistic, particularly if the results of experimental studies of amorphous, polycrystalline or heavily damaged materials are under review. We may also note that Erginsoy, Vineyard and Shimizu[50] have recently computed the energy losses of 1keV iron atoms injected along simulated ⟨100⟩ and ⟨111⟩ channels in iron using composite Bohr-Born Mayer type of potential. These authors found the interesting result that for accurately channelled atoms, the time rate of energy loss was constant. This suggests that the effective channel stopping power $-\left|\frac{dE}{dx}\right|$ is proportional to $E^{-1/2}$, or that the maximum channel range R is proportional to $E_0^{\,3/2}$. It is evident that this is a different result from that deduced by Lehmann and Leibfried[4] but, as we shall see later, this is just the form of channelled range/energy dependence which has been found experimentally.

Finally Harrison, Leeds and Gay[51] have examined a computer simulation of Cu atom ranges in a real Cu lattice. In a preliminary study with a 30 atom crystallite, in which interaction of the primary with all the target atoms was allowed, Gay & Harrison[52] found that scattering angles in the n-body model were considerably different than in the binary model as used by Robinson and Oen and this suggested that the co-operative effects may be important in range problems

Thus in Harrison, Leeds and Gay's work[51], as the primary atom moved through a crystallite, as it approached the end faces of a crystallite two further planes of atoms were placed in front of the moving atoms, so that the trajectory could be followed through many collisions (a maximum range of about 1000Å was investigated before the programme was terminated). A Born-Mayer potential of the type used by Gibson, Goland, Milgram and Vineyard[44] was employed and primary ion energies up to 10keV were investigated.

The first important result deduced by these authors,[51] for atoms started at various positions on a [110] surface plane showed that inclusion of the n-body interactions, considerably enhanced the possibility of long range events and that channel events could occupy up to 70% of a surface symmetry cell for ion energies above 3keV. This is believed to be a result of the diminution of scattering angles by the n-body interactions. It was also found that primary ions started on the <110> channel axis obeyed a range/energy relation of the form Range $\propto$ (Energy)$^{3/2}$ for energies below 1keV, as also found above by Erginsoy et al[50] with Fe atoms, and thus the stopping power was proportional to (Energy)$^{-1/2}$ on the axis. More surprisingly, for ions started anywhere in the surface section appropriate to channelled events the stopping power was related to energy in the manner

$$-\left|\frac{dE}{dn}\right| = AE^{-1/2} + B$$

where A & B were functions of the starting positions. Integration over all starting positions then gave an approximately linear range/energy relation up to 3keV.

Information on the oscillatory motion of channelled ions was also obtained and suggests that this oscillatory motion is more complex than the binary collision models predict.

As these authors point out,[51] this step in including n-body collisions and Erginsoy et al's[50] similar calculations already lead to somewhat improved agreement with experiment, and we may anticipate that even more sophisticated models, allowing for example for inelastic energy losses, will produce even better results.

Summary

Undoubtedly these methods are of great value in that they allow an amenable method of assessing experimental results. Thus the assumed forms of the interatomic potential may be varied to obtain optimum agreement with experimental data and hence information about the actual interatomic potential may be deduced. The earlier computations, using a randomised lattice model are of undoubted value in that the accuracy of analytical approximations may be assessed, and a large fraction of experimental results on amorphous and to some extent polycrystalline materials reproduced. However the introduction of reality to the assumed lattice model in later computations has led to a better understanding of experimental results and illustrated the various processes, such as channelling, and lattice damage which may influence penetration phenomena. The computer method provides a convenient link between the theoretical approach with its limiting assumptions and the experimental approach with the inexplicable data.

5.11 EXPERIMENTAL RANGE MEASUREMENTS

5.11.1. Many experimental determinations of ranges of higher energy ions in gases have been made, due primarily to the ease with which such measurements may be performed e.g. particle tracks may be readily identified by the ionization in the wake of the primary as in Cloud or Bubble chambers. Similar determinations may be performed when the stopping medium is a photographic emulsion, again because of the relative ease with which the trajectory is identified by the development of the activated silver grains when the ion energy is high. For low ion energies, range measurements in solids are considerably more difficult both because the trajectory is confined to a spatially small extent of the stopping medium and because electronic excitation processes which identify the trajectory are absent. Consequently, until very recently, only a very few range measurements of low energy primaries in solids were available, and these of dubious validity. The situation has improved lately however with the introduction of more sophisticated techniques which have allowed measurements of ranges and associated parameters in a number of target materials. Some of these methods allow measurement of the range or projected range in a wide variety of targets, whilst other methods allow complete determination of the range distribution in a restricted number of materials. Undoubtedly these techniques and others will eventually allow a detailed analysis of the range parameters in all materials.

In the following we shall outline these experimental techniques, present the data obtained and discuss these in comparison with the earlier theoretical and computed results. There are essentially six methods of range determination, which involve:

(a) Injection of a collimated primary ion beam into the target and subsequent irradiation of the latter with either photons, low energy electrons or medium energy protons. A study of the change in reflectance for photons, the stopping power of electrons and the scattering of protons then allows deduction of parameters such as the average projected range, but generally not of complete determination of the range distribution. Furthermore the range may not be determined unequivocally since damage to the lattice itself may result in changes ascribed to the primaries only.

(b) Injection of energetic γ rays into a target which undergo photo-nuclear reactions resulting in the production of fast neutrons and radioactive recoil atoms of the target material. Counting of the number of atoms recoiling out of the target and the number remaining within the target allows measurement of a parameter related to the average range. This method is restricted to materials with disintegration products which have measurable half lives and, more seriously, generally only allows deductions of ranges of primary atoms in targets composed of similar atoms.

(c) Injection of a collimated primary beam into thin targets and observation of the number of primaries transmitted through the foil. Target foil thicknesses may be varied but it is very difficult to produce extremely thin foils of sufficient uniformity for low energy studies.

(d) Injection of a collimated beam of radioactive primaries which disintegrate with α particle emission. By a study of the energy spectrum of the α particles emerging from the target, and the known stopping power of the target for α particles, the energy spectrum may be converted to a depth distribution of primary ranges.

(e) Injection of a collimated primary beam of radioactive ions into a target. These primary decay with γ ray emission which may be converted in the K shells of the primary atoms to electrons of known ejection energy. These electrons, in escaping from the target lose energy, and a study of the electron momentum spectrum can be used to estimate the primary penetration depth.

(f) Injection of a collimated primary beam into a target and subsequent sectioning of the target parallel to the surface with measurement of the number of primaries trapped within each section. Sectioning techniques include the use of a stack of thin sections which may be separated later, gradual etching of the surface with appropriate chemical etchants, electrochemical processes, and sputtering of the surface by low energy ion bombardment. These methods allow complete determination of the range distributions but suffer many restrictions on the nature of the primary ion and the target materials.

These limitations will be discussed subsequently when a full appraisal of these techniques will be given.

We now consider these methods in more detail although generally only the basic principles of the methods will be discussed. The methods of ion production are discussed further in Chapter 9 whilst original papers should be consulted for many technical details.

(a) Exploration of property changes

(1) If a solid, transparent to optical radiation, is composed of parallel layers of material of different refractive index, then the reflectance of the solid is found to vary with the wavelengths of incident radiation in a manner characteristic of the refractive index variation with depth. When glass, quartz or vitreous silica are bombarded with primary ions in the energy range from about 1-60 KeV, the primaries are stopped within a relatively short distance from the surface and cause considerable damage to the target. This primary occlusion and target damage results in refractive index changes of the surface layers, and Hines[53] has utilised the method to determine inert gas ion ranges in these materials.

After bombardment with H_2^+, D_2^+, He^+, Ne^+, A^+, Kr^+ or Xe^+ ions, the change in the reflectance of the glass, quartz or vitreous silica with incident optical wavelength was studied. Theory shows that the form of the reflectance/reciprocal wavelength curve depends upon the depth over which the refractive index is altered and upon the change in the refractive index. For example quite distinctive changes in shape are observed, if it is assumed that the altered refractive index is constant to some depth d (the extent of the damage) and then typical of the unbombarded solid for the remainder of the depth. Alternatively the refractive index may be assumed to change in two or more depth step functions, but theoretical analysis of these situations becomes complex. Hines[53] found that the experimentally observed reflectance/reciprocal wavelength curve, could be interpreted by the former refractive index change, which allowed values for the depth of damage production d and the refractive index change to be determined. Both the values of d and the refractive index change $\frac{\Delta n}{n}$ were observed to vary with the total ion flux received by the target, but in the cases of H_2^+, D_2^+, He^+, Ne^+, and A^+, d and $\frac{\Delta n}{n}$ reached saturation values after small total bombardments, whilst d appeared to increase slowly with Kr^+ and Xe^+ bombardment. For the lighter gas ions, the initial variations of d before a constant value was achieved, were probably due to the fact that the hypothetical refractive index changes with depth were initially unrepresentative, but became more accurate after larger bombardments.

It was necessary to allow for effects due to contamination of the surface by background gases during bombardment (the experiments were conducted at pressures of about 10^{-5} torr). After application of this correction the depths d shown in Table 5.17 for the various incident ions were deduced, whilst Figure 5.48 shows a typical depth d versus incident ion

TABLE 5.17. (Ref. 5.53)

Ion ranges in Quartz and Vitreous Silica

Ion	Ion energy E(keV)	Effective layer depth (microns)	(Representative of Range)
H_2^+	14.6	0.171 ± 0.009	
H_2^+	19.9	0.235 ± 0.012	
H_2^+	32.6	0.338 ± 0.017	
D_2^+	12.8	0.219 ± 0.011	
D_2^+	18.8	0.290 ± 0.015	
D_2^+	29.6	0.400 ± 0.020	
He^+	7.5	0.091 ± 0.005	
He^+	15.1	0.191 ± 0.010	
He^+	23.5	0.272 ± 0.014	
Ne^+	38.3	0.074 ± 0.004	
Ne^+	43.9	0.085 ± 0.004	
Ne^+	51.8	0.095 ± 0.005	
A^+	22.9	0.060 ± 0.003	
A^+	38.4	0.070 ± 0.003	
A^+	59.0	0.100 ± 0.005	
Kr^+	20.3	0.050 ± 0.005	
Kr^+	39.7	0.060 ± 0.006	
Kr^+	59.0	0.067 ± 0.004	
Xe^+	20.3	0.047 ± 0.010	
Xe^+	39.4	0.053 ± 0.005	
Xe^+	59.0	0.058 ± 0.006	
He^+	7.5	0.091 ± 0.005	
Ne^+	38.3	0.074 ± 0.004	

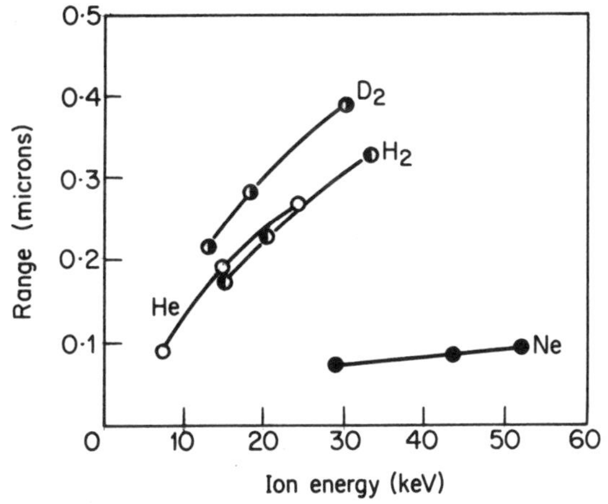

Fig. 5.48 Range of H_2^+, D_2^+, He^+ and Ne^+ ions in quartz as a function of energy. (viz. Ref. 5.53)

energy plot for H_2^+ and D_2^+ which must be viewed cautiously since it is well known that the molecular ions dissociate on striking a solid surface and proceed with half the original energy. Further the exact relationship between the depth d, calculated assuming a uniform change in refractive index over this depth, and any real ion range quantity, for example the average projected range is not clear. Hines[53] suggested that d and $\overline{R}_{par}$ are almost equal, and it is probable that the values of d are better than order of magnitude approximations to $\overline{R}_{par}$ at least. It was found that above 10 keV, H^+, D^+ and He^+ ions lost the major fraction of their energy through ionisation processes, whereas at this energy the heavier ions lost energy primarily through elastic collisions as anticipated theoretically. The slow increase of apparent penetration depth of Kr and Xe indicates the inadequacy of the simplifications in the analysis of the data and probably illustrates that knock-on silicon and oxygen atoms contribute to the damage extent. This argument is supported by the fact that in glass, quartz and vitreous silica, the magnitudes and signs of the refractive index changes differ considerably, indicating that it is indeed lattice damage which contributes to the observations rather than just the primary stopped atoms. The extent of the lattice rearrangement is probably not appreciably greater than the ion ranges however, and thus the data may be used at least as range indicators. It was also found that the normal reflectance of an umbombarded sample could be restored by heating the bombarded material to 600°C-700°C, presumbably annealing out the damage.

(a) (2) Numerous investigations have shown that prolonged ion bombardment causes deterioration in the luminescence of phosphor surfaces. This is a consequence of the rearrangement of the phosphor structure by the energetic primaries, and Young[54] has shown how this luminescence degradation can be used to give information about primary ion ranges in phosphors.

A ZnS-Ag phosphor was initially bombarded with primary ions of H^+, H_2^+, He^+, Ne^+, N_2^+ and A^+ of energy between 1 KeV and 25 KeV, and the luminescence of the phosphor was then studied by irradiating the damaged phosphor with electrons of energy variable between 1 and 25 KeV and recording the light output photoelectronically. The luminescence after ion bombardment was then compared with that of an unirradiated sample and the percentage degradation evaluated. The type of information obtained is shown in Figure 5.49 for the luminescence change after H_2^+

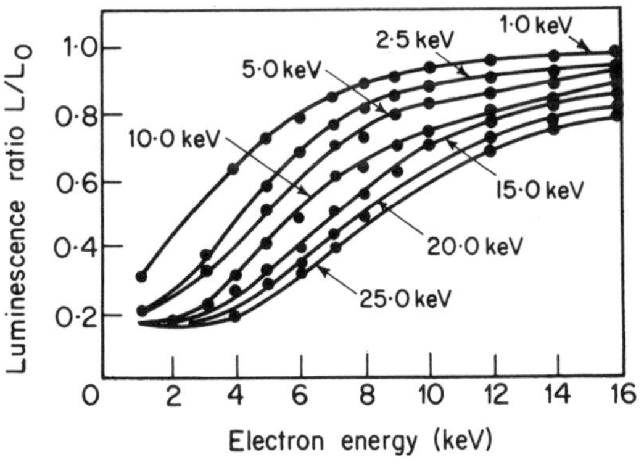

Fig. 5.49 The luminescence degradation produced by 2×10^{-7} Coulombs of H_2^+ ions (of energies indicated) bombarding a ZnS phosphor. (viz. Ref. 5.54)

ion bombardment at various ion energies. It is clear that a marked degradation occurs, which is apparently constant for low electron exploring energies, but suddenly increases at a particular electron energy. The constant luminescence change region is supposed to be associated with electrons which penetrate only the damaged surface layers of the phosphor (i.e. low energy electrons) whilst the upward break occurs just as electrons start penetrating beyond the damaged layer to virgin phosphor with a consequent increase of luminescence, typical of the undamaged layer. Clearly the luminescence degradation ratio approaches unity when the electron energy is high and the light excitation takes place almost entirely beyond the damaged surface layer, in virgin phosphor. The electron energy which just results in the upward break can then be used to deduce the extent of the damage through knowledge of the electron range/ energy relation. Young[54] used the Thomson[55]-Whiddington[56] law

$$x = \frac{E_{el}^2}{b} \qquad 5.163$$

where b is a known constant, x is the depth of electron penetration at an energy E_{el}, and hence evaluated from curves such as Figure 5.49, the damage depth/ primary ion energy relation. Again the damage depth was interpreted as indicating the ion range, but exactly which parameter should be used is not clear since of course the ranges are distributed. Nevertheless, the data does, again, show order of magnitudes for range quantities. Figure 5.50 shows a range/ energy plot for H_2^+ ions and Table 5.18 the data for the other ions. It was observed that the luminescence degradation and hence ion range decreased with increasing ion mass for the ions Ne^+, N_2^+ and A^+, as expected theoretically, but the opposite was true for the low mass primaries. This latter behaviour was interpreted as evidence of the dominance of ionization losses for the lighter ions which caused less lattice rearrangement for lighter primaries and therefore less degradation.

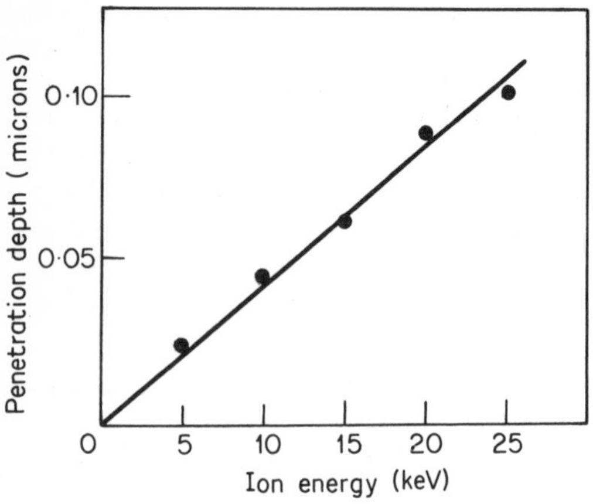

Fig. 5.50 Penetration depth—ion energy data for H_2^+ ion in ZnS phosphor deduced from Fig. 5.49. (viz. Ref. 5.54).

TABLE 5.18. (Ref. 5.54).

Ion energy 20 keV.

Ranges of several ions in ZnS-Ag phosphor

Positive ion	Calculated range in microns.
H^+	0.16
H_2^+	0.08
He^+	0.18
Ne^+	0.11
N_2^+	0.05
A^+	0.05

It was also observed that the luminescence degradation could be stored by annealing the phosphor at 600°C, i.e. the damage state was removed, just as was the case for the reflectance properties of quartz. This annealing behaviour will be discussed further in Chapter 6. Another common feature of this method and that of reflectance measurement is the limitation to certain materials only, i.e. to luminescent and optically transparent substances respectively.

Heinz, Gyorgy and Ohl[57] have used a somewhat similar technique to determine the ranges of 30 keV He^+ ions in silver. These authors observed that the ions with energies in excess of about 200 eV, incident upon the surface of a silicon crystal resulted in marked changes in the electrical properties of the silicon. In particular the breakdown voltage of a reverse biased junction formed from a platinum point and the bombarded silicon was found to be considerably larger (more negative) than that obtained with an unbombarded surface. This effect was used to detect the passage of 30 keV He^+ ions through silver films vacuum deposited upon a silicon surface. After deposition of a known thickness of silver (measured interferometrically) and bombardment by He^+ ions, the silver was removed, and the reverse breakdown voltage compared with that of an unbombarded surface. The film thickness was progressively increased until no change in reverse breakdown voltage occurred and this was taken to represent the range of the 30 keV ions (the 200 ev necessary for voltage change was considered to constitute a small error in the assignation of the range). In this way the range of 30 keV He^+ ions in silver was determined to be 2480 ± 250Å. It is clear however that the range measured is not an accurate specification of any particular range parameter, but tends to represent the maximum range to which a sufficient number of ions can penetrate to be observable. A rather different technique enabled the maximum ion range of 30 keV He^+ ions to be determined to be of the order of 6000Å but again the same criticism of the exact nature of which range was determined must be applied.

(a) (3) A third method of target irradiation after ion bombardment has been described by Powers and Whaling,[58] who studied the penetration of Ne^+, N^+, Ar^+, Kr^+, and Xe^+ ions with energies between 30 keV and 500 keV into Be, B, C and Al targets. After injection of primary ions into the target, protons of variable energy (E_{10}) were caused to strike the target at a given angle of incidence (ϕ_1) to the target normal and those protons which recoiled from the target due to collisions with target atoms or embedded primaries, at an angle ϕ_2 and with a fixed energy (E_{20}) were analysed and counted in a magnetic spectrometer.

If primary atoms are located at a perpendicular depth s below the surface, then the incident proton energy at this depth is

$$E_{1s} = E_{10} - \int_{x = s/\cos\phi_1}^{x = o} \left(\frac{dE}{dx}\right) dx \qquad 5.164.1$$

where $-\dfrac{dE}{dx}$ is the rate of loss of proton energy with depth in the target material. (stopping power)

If the proton is then scattered elastically through a laboratory angle ϕ_L by the stopped primary atom, then the energy of the recoil proton is given from Equation 2.11a as $E_{2s} = \alpha E_{1s}$ where

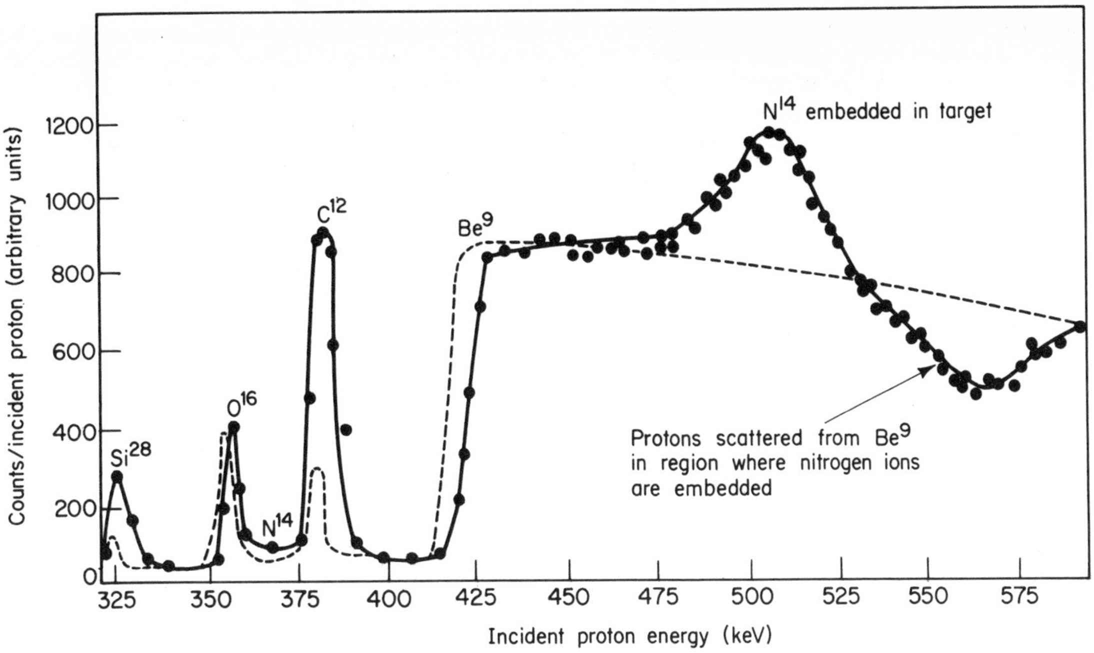

Fig. 5.51 The number of protons scattered at a laboratory angle of 129° with energy 287.6 keV as a function of the energy of the incident protons on a Be target. The dashed curve was measured before, and the full curve after bombardment of the target with 39000 microcoulombs/cm^2 of 400 keV N^+ ions. The symbols indicate the incident proton energies at which protons scattered from Si^{28}, O^{16}, N^{14}, C^{12} and Be^9 on the target surface would be detected in the spectrometer. (viz. Ref. 5.58)

$$\alpha^{1/2} = \frac{M_p \cos\phi_L}{M_p + M_1} + \left\{\left(\frac{M_p \cos\phi_L}{M_p + M_1}\right)^2 + \left(\frac{M_1 - M_p}{M_1 + M_p}\right)\right\}^{1/2}$$

M_p is the proton mass, M_1 the stopped primary atom mass and $\phi_L = \phi_1 + \phi_2$ as defined from the bombardment-collection geometry. The primary then returns to the surface, suffering an energy loss in passage, and emerges with an energy E_{20} which is readily shown to be given by

$$E_{20} - \alpha E_{10} - \alpha \int_{s/\cos\phi_1}^{0} \left|\frac{dE}{dx}\right| dn - \int_0^{s/\cos\phi_2} \left|\frac{dE}{dx}\right| dn \qquad 5.146.2$$

The stopping power $-\dfrac{dE}{dx}$ may be readily estimated theoretically or determined experimentally for an unbombarded target and since ϕ_1, ϕ_2, E_{20}, were fixed experimentally, Equation 5.164.2 gives an explicit relation between E_{10}, M_1 and s. Thus as the primary energy E_{10}, was varied recoiling protons were recorder from atoms, M_1, at various depths s. Although Equation 5.164.2 contains M_1 and s, since M_1 for both parent material and stopped primaries are known, the values of s are determinable. Figure 5.51 shows the result of a proton energy scan for an unbombarded Be target and a target after irradiation with 400 keV N^+ ions.

Several peaks occur at low energies which are readily identified as impurity adsorbed surface atoms of Si, O and C, whilst the continuum commencing at 415 keV is readily associated with a target of mass 9 (Be) with s increasing from O. After bombardment with N_{14}^+ ions, the surface adsorbed gas atom peaks change because of accumulation effects, but, what is more important, the continuum changes markedly with a broad peak at about 507 keV. This must be associated with N^{14} atoms trapped during bombardment. After making corrections for proton energy loss in the surface contaminant layers and changes in stopping power because of trapped primary atoms values of the primary range and the range straggling may be determined from curves such as those in Figure 5.51

In evaluating the range straggling parameter (defined by these authors as the difference in penetrations at 50% maximum concentrations of the trapped atoms) corrections must be made for the finite instrumental energy resolution and the proton energy straggling.

Clearly this technique gives values of the projected mean range and the projected range straggling and these quantities are enumerated for the ions and targets cited earlier, in Table 5.19. Since the measured range parameters are projected values along the target normal Powers and Whaling[58] have corrected the data to path length values using the Lindhard-Scharff[11, 8] equation

$$\frac{\langle R\rangle}{\langle Rpar\rangle} \simeq 1 + \frac{M_1}{3M_2}$$

The results using this correction are plotted in Figure 5.52 and compared with the Nielsen[9] normalised range-energy (ρ/ϵ) and Lindhard-Scharff[8, 11] equations, excepting the Ne^+ and N^+ data which do not satisfy the $M_1 \gg M_2$ requirement for the correction factors. The experimental data is consistently 20% below the theoretical predictions which may be interpreted as either an inadequacy in the theoretical analysis because of an erroneous assumption of the Thomas-Fermi potential or in comparing the experimental data with a theoretical curve assuming elastic collisions only. In view of the high energies involved there must certainly be a correction for inelastic collisions, and in order to account for this effect one of the curves of Figure 5.5 should really be compared with the experimental data. The curve of Figure 5.5 which should be used corresponds to the appropriate value of k in Equation 5.25.2 for the desired values of M_2 and M_1 and a typical comparison of the corrected curve for Xe in Be is shown in Figure 5.53. Clearly the agreement is improved indicating that in this case at least the Thomas-Fermi potential is adequate.

TABLE 5. 19 (Ref. 5. 58).

Experimental values of the range and range straggling. The uncertainties listed are probable errors. When no uncertainty is listed, the probable error is less than 1%.

Ion and target	Ion energy (keV)	Range (μg/cm²)	Range straggling (μg/cm²)	Ion and target	Ion energy (keV)	Range (μg/cm²)	Range straggling (μg/cm²)
Xe in Be	32. 4 ± 9. 4	4. 3 ± 1. 2	4. 4 ± 1. 1		300. 0	55. 6 ± 3. 9	26. 1 ± 3. 3
	100. 3	9. 4 ± 1. 0	6. 0 ± 1. 1		500. 3	86. 6 ± 5. 8	22. 9 ± 8. 0
	200. 5	17. 3 ± 1. 2	10. 1 ± 1. 3	Ar in C	49. 9	10. 4 ± 2. 7	7. 5 ± 1. 5
	300. 8	24. 0 ± 1. 8	12. 1 ± 1. 7		100. 0	18. 1 ± 2. 6	13. 4 ± 1. 5
	401. 0	32. 0 ± 2. 0	21. 3 ± 1. 8		201. 0	36. 7 ± 4. 1	19. 6 ± 2. 2
	501. 3	41. 1 ± 5. 1	19. 3 ± 1. 9		300. 0	49. 2 ± 4. 0	20. 0 ± 4. 4
Xe in Al	50. 1	4. 3 ± 0. 9	4. 4 ± 1. 5		400. 0	64. 6 ± 7. 4	28. 9 ± 8. 1
	100. 3	7. 7 ± 1. 4	11. 3 ± 1. 5		500. 0	86. 0 ± 5. 9	27. 2 ± 5. 6
	200. 5	15. 2 ± 2. 0	17. 7 ± 2. 0	Ne in Be	45. 2 ± 2. 7	14. 1 ± 2. 9	12. 3 ± 2. 1
	300. 8	22. 8 ± 2. 8	30. 9 ± 3. 3		95. 7 ± 2. 5	41. 7 ± 3. 4	19. 8 ± 3. 0
	401. 0	36. 6 ± 3. 3	33. 7 ± 3. 2		194. 6 ± 3. 5	72. 7 ± 6. 5	33. 9 ± 3. 9
	501. 3	43. 7 ± 4. 9	30. 3 ± 6. 0		296. 6 ± 3. 6	108. 9 ± 4. 2	. . .
Kr in Be	45. 9 ± 3. 0	5. 8 ± 1. 0	3. 9 ± 1. 3		393. 7 ± 5. 5	134. 1 ± 10. 7	41. 9 ± 9. 9
	96. 0 ± 3. 2	10. 6 ± 1. 5	8. 7 ± 1. 1		490. 5 ± 7. 4	155. 1 ± 9. 9	42. 0 ± 6. 7
	196. 2 ± 3. 6	23. 4 ± 2. 3	16. 6 ± 2. 0	Ne in C	50. 1	17. 9 ± 2. 1	17. 4 ± 2. 9
	295. 6 ± 4. 2	35. 5 ± 3. 7	21. 1 ± 3. 4		99. 6 ± 1. 1	38. 3 ± 2. 7	15. 4 ± 4. 7
	395. 6 ± 5. 0	48. 2 ± 4. 4	28. 4 ± 4. 6		200. 2	75. 2 ± 4. 1	24. 2 ± 6. 8
	495. 6 ± 5. 8	60. 7 ± 4. 0	26. 4 ± 6. 2		299. 7	100. 4 ± 7. 0	30. 2 ± 12. 5
Kr in Al	50. 1	5. 0 ± 1. 4	6. 9 ± 2. 1		400. 5	127. 3 ± 8. 2	40. 3 ± 10. 8
	100. 3	9. 1 ± 2. 2	15. 3 ± 1. 8		500. 6	143. 7 ± 9. 5	31. 1 ± 10. 7
	200. 5	19. 2 ± 1. 7	19. 0 ± 3. 1	N in Be	48. 3 ± 1. 3	23. 8 ± 2. 3	11. 0 ± 1. 8
	300. 8	35. 2 ± 4. 0	28. 5 ± 3. 9		97. 5 ± 1. 9	40. 9 ± 2. 6	12. 5 ± 3. 5
	401. 0	47. 4 ± 6. 4	38. 9 ± 6. 5		195. 5 ± 3. 6	76. 5 ± 4. 5	23. 2 ± 5. 6
	501. 3	56. 1 ± 7. 6	45. 2 ± 8. 9		291. 3 ± 6. 3	103. 1 ± 5. 8	23. 1 ± 5. 5
Ar in Be	48. 5 ± 1. 0	8. 7 ± 2. 2	8. 2 ± 1. 2		385. 9 ± 9. 6	127. 6 ± 5. 3	23. 7 ± 6. 2
	98. 6 ± 1. 4	18. 5 ± 2. 0	14. 2 ± 1. 7		492. 3 ± 7. 6	151. 2 ± 6. 1	17. 0 ± 5. 7
	198. 8 ± 2. 1	36. 0 ± 3. 3	21. 0 ± 2. 5	N in C	49. 9	24. 0 ± 3. 6	14. 3 ± 3. 9
	298. 0 ± 3. 3	56. 7 ± 4. 0	25. 7 ± 3. 7		99. 7 ± 1. 1	43. 4 ± 3. 2	20. 9 ± 6. 0
	396. 9 ± 4. 3	72. 8 ± 5. 0	30. 9 ± 4. 5		199. 6	75. 7 ± 6. 7	31. 5 ± 11. 4
	500. 2	97. 3 ± 6. 5	37. 8 ± 5. 0		300. 0	100. 9 ± 5. 8	30. 1 ± 12. 2
Ar in B^{10}	44. 7 ± 3. 0	8. 2 ± 2	. . .	N in Al	46. 7 ± 2. 1	30. 8 ± 10. 0	39. 9 ± 10. 8
	99. 6 ± 1. 1	15. 9 ± 2. 0	12. 4 ± 2. 4		100. 1	74. 0 ± 8. 3	22. 2 ± 10. 1
	300. 2	50. 0 ± 3. 9	22. 9 ± 2. 7		200. 2	114. 1 ± 12. 8	44. 1 ± 12. 5
	500. 2	82. 4 ± 7. 3	26. 7 ± 8. 7		296. 2 ± 3. 6	156. 1 ± 14. 2	62. 9 ± 16. 0
Ar in B	49. 6 ± 0. 6	9. 2 ± 2	. . .		400. 5	198. 7 ± 15. 1	42. 8 ± 14. 6
	100. 2	19. 0 ± 1. 7	11. 4 ± 1. 4		497. 4 ± 5. 4	218. 5 ± 16. 8	57. 2 ± 16. 8
	249. 5	44. 6 ± 2. 8	17. 2 ± 2. 5				

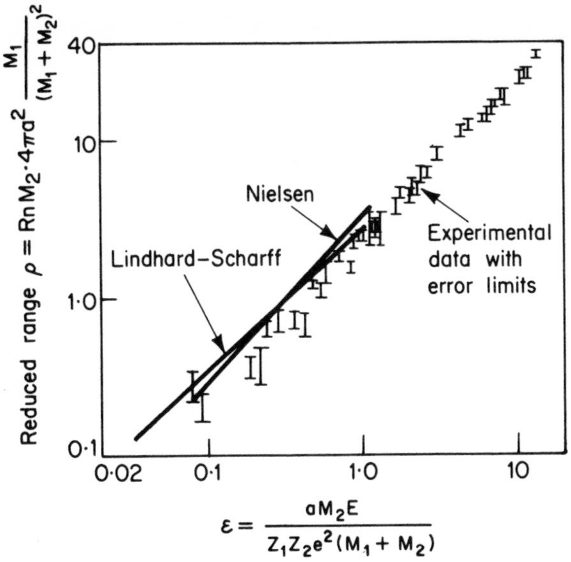

Fig. 5. 52 Experimental reduced range-energy data deduced from curves such as in Fig. 5. 51 for A, Kr and Xe in Be. The experimental projected ranges are multiplied by the factor 1 + A/3 to convert to total path lengths, and are compared with the Nielsen and Lindhand-Scharff theoretical predictions. (viz. Ref. 5. 58)

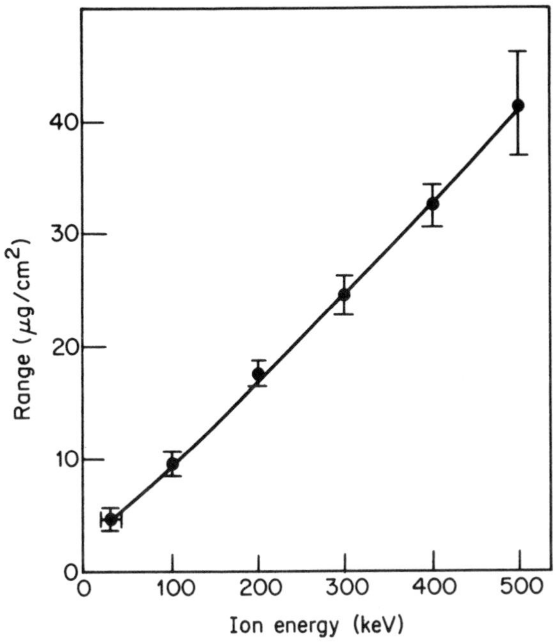

Fig. 5. 53 Total Range—ion energy data for Xe^+ ions in Be. The curve is theoretical (Ref. 5. 8) including both elastic and inelastic stopping with the value of k appropriate to Xe in Be. The experimental data points are corrected by the factor 1 + A/3. (viz. Ref. 5. 58)

For Ne^+ and N^+ ions the energy losses are predominantly electronic (about ten times greater than elastic losses) and comparison of the stopping powers obtained experimentally with theoretical values obtained from the Lindhard-Scharff[8, 11] estimates are within the experimental accuracy. It should be noted that the primary ion doses were in the range 4×10^{14}-6×10^{15} ions/sq. cm. and that no observable changes in the range distribution due to the influence of trapped primaries occurred.

(a) (4) Guseva, Inoptkin and Tsytko[59] have explored the primary ion penetration distribution after injection of Si^{30} of energies between 10 and 30 keV into Ta and Cu targets. After injection of the primaries the targets were subjected to proton bombardment and these reacted with the trapped silicon to produce γ radiation of 940 keV energy. If the target atoms are located at some depth within the target then the γ energy is attenuated on emergence from the target, and thus the energy spectrum of the emitted γ rays will reflect the depth distribution of the primaries. A typical γ ray energy spectrum for 10 keV Si^{30} in Ta is shown in Figure 5. 54 and from a knowledge of

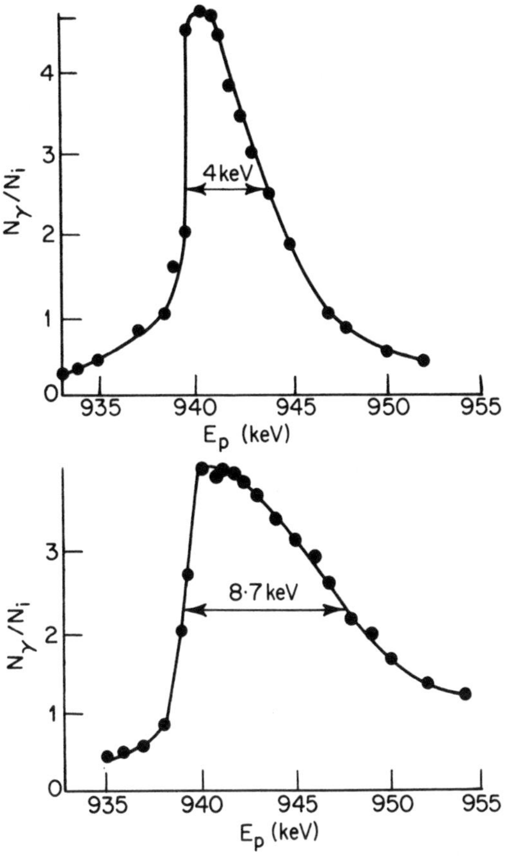

Fig. 5. 54 Relative yield of gamma radiation from the $Si^{30}(p, \gamma)p^{31}$ reaction; resonance at 940 keV; upper curve Si^{30} on tantalum backing; lower curve Si^{30} on copper backing. Initial ion energy = 25 keV. (viz. Ref. 5. 59)

the characteristic γ ray loss, this may be replotted as a primary range distribution as in Figure 5. 55. Since the silicon ion mass is considerably less than the Tantalum atom mass, the progress of the primary should be described quite well by the neutron stopping calculations leading to Equation 5. 92. Consequently the theoretical distribution for this combination is also plotted in Figure 5. 55 and the curves are normalised at one point (marked A). The theoretical and experimental results agree very closely and the stopping of primary atoms close to and at the surface is notable. This is clearly a result of considerable primary back scattering. Moreover the half widths of the distribution, defined theoretically by Equation 5. 92 when compared are also in excellent agreement i.e. $W_{1/2\ exp} = 30\ \mu g/cm^2$; $W_{1/2\ theor} = 31\ \mu g/cm^2$.

Phillips and Read[60] and Barker and Phillips[61] have used a similar method to determine range-energy data for 0. 4-6. 4 MeV N_{15}^+ ions in Ni, Au & Ag, which, of course is mainly in the inelastic collision range. The $N_{15}{}^+$ ions were injected into the respective materials and then the loaded targets bombarded by vari-

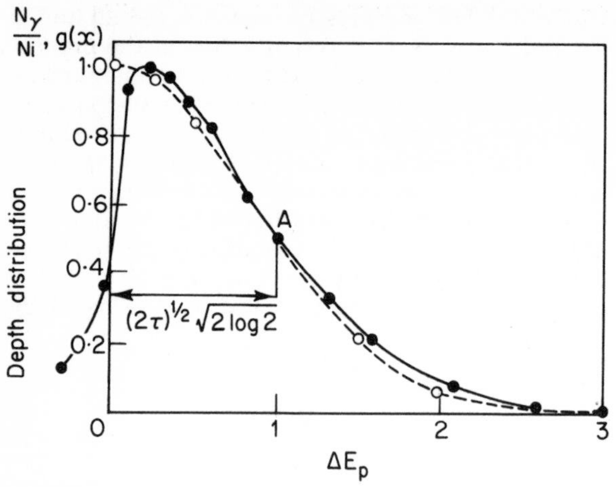

Fig. 5. 55 Depth distribution of Si^{30}, 25 keV ions in Tantalum. Solid curve is experimental. Dashed curve is theoretical deduced from diffusion slowing down model. (viz. Ref. 5. 59)

able energy protons. At 898 keV the protons give rise to the $^{15}N(p, \alpha\gamma)^{12}C$ reaction with emission of 4.43 MeV γ rays which were detected. However, because of the proton energy loss in reaching the trapped N^{15}, the resonance will occur at an energy E_r where

$E_r - R_p \left|\frac{dE}{dx}\right|_{protons} = 898$ keV and R_p is the most probable N_{15} range and $-\left|\frac{dE}{dx}\right|_{protons}$ the proton stopping cross section.

Measurement of E_r (and the spread around E_r) thus gave R_p and the straggling for the N_{15}^+ ions. From the range-energy data, the stopping cross sections— $\left|\frac{dE}{dx}\right|_{^{15}N}$ were calculated for the three target materials and to a first approximation were proportional to $E^{1/2}$, as suggested by the Lindhard-Scharff[8, 11] equation. At low energies, the slight discrepancy was attributed to elastic collision effects, but the constant of proportionality ξ in the Lindhard-Scharff[8, 11] analysis was found to increase from 1.4 for Ni, to 2.1 for Ag and 2.4 for Au. suggesting the inadequacy of the statistical model for predicting inelastic losses in detail.

These authors[61] were also able to show that diffusion effects and target loading were not important at these energies.

These methods of using a radiation probe to determine the effects of target irradiation have certainly not yet been fully exploited. Certain disadvantages are immediately obvious however. For example photon exploration is limited to materials which have photon penetration depths much greater than the damaged layer depth. This damage itself may also confuse interpretation of range data, since the probe may interact more with the damaged target than the trapped atoms.

(a) (5) One probe method, used by McCaldin and Widmer[62] however, should not disturb the ion penetration function. In this work, Cs^+ and Na^+ ions were injected into intrinsic or p type silicon. The depth of Cs or Na penetration was estimated by diffusion of phosphorus around the bombarded area to form a field effect transistor. Observation of the capacitance of the altered layer led to a value for the ion range of about 1000 Å and it was observed that penetration was much greater if ions were incident along a ⟨100⟩ direction of the silicon than along the ⟨110⟩ direction. Na^+ and Cs^+ ions showed the same effects but the ion ranges were larger for incident Na^+. This is a direct, although qualitative, observation of the channelling phenomenon, and finds quantitative support in measurements by Davies et al[63] described on page 194. Since the experiments were conducted at target temperatures of 400°C there may be some reservations about the possibility of diffusion and indeed a temperature dependence of range was observed between 400°C and 700°C.

Nevertheless, the method appears to be worth further investigation to see if range probability functions can also be deduced.

(b) Recoil Methods

This method has been used extensively by workers at the General Dynamics laboratories, notably Schmitt and Van Lint[40, 64-70] and by several other investigators. Bremsstrahlung γ-rays of a known energy spectrum were produced by interaction of an energetic electron beam (2-45 MeV) with a platinum converter foil. These γ-rays were then allowed to strike sandwiches of alternating aluminium catcher foils and foils of target material. The γ-rays then underwent photo nuclear reactions in the target foils creating neutrons and recoiling energetic radioactive nuclei. These reactions occur uniformly throughout the target foils and the recoil nuclei then moved through the target foils losing energy by elastic and inelastic collisions.

A certain fraction of the recoils escaped from the target foils and were trapped in the catcher foils. It may be shown that the ratio of the number of nuclei trapped in the catcher foils to those remaining embedded in the target foils i.e. $f = \frac{\text{Constant}}{t} R(E)$

where t is the target foil thickness and R(E) is the recoil range at the energy E. Exactly which range parameter is measured by this ratio has been the subject of some discussion by the investigators and by Leibfried and Holmes.[13] According to the former, the range measured is the mean path length whilst the latter interpret the measurements as revealing $[\langle R^2(E)\rangle]^{1/2}$ where E is the average recoil energy. We adopt the connotation employed by Van Lint et al,[40, 64-70] but remember the uncertainty of interpretation. The mean energy of the recoiling atoms is also necessary in determining range-energy relations and again the values of the recoil energies are open to doubt. The method of evaluating mean energies is to assume a form for the Bremsstrahlung γ-ray spectrum, and, from a knowledge of the photonuclear reactions involved, deduce the mean recoil energies. If the assumed spectrum (taken to be a Schiff spectrum)[71] is in error, average recoil energies will be of doubtful validity. However we may expect that both sources of error will not invalidate at least qualitative discussion of the range-energy data.

The number of recoil atoms trapped in the target and catcher foils were counted by disassembling the foil stack and measuring the ratio of the activities of these foils after given intervals. Most of the recoil nuclei decay via positron or negatron emission and these are passed through Aluminium converters producing γ-rays which were counted with Na I (Te) crystal counters. Targets of C, Ti, V, Cr, Fe, Co, Ni, Cu, Zn, Ge, Zr, Mo, Rh, Pd, Ag, Cd, Sn, Gd, Ta, Pt, Au,

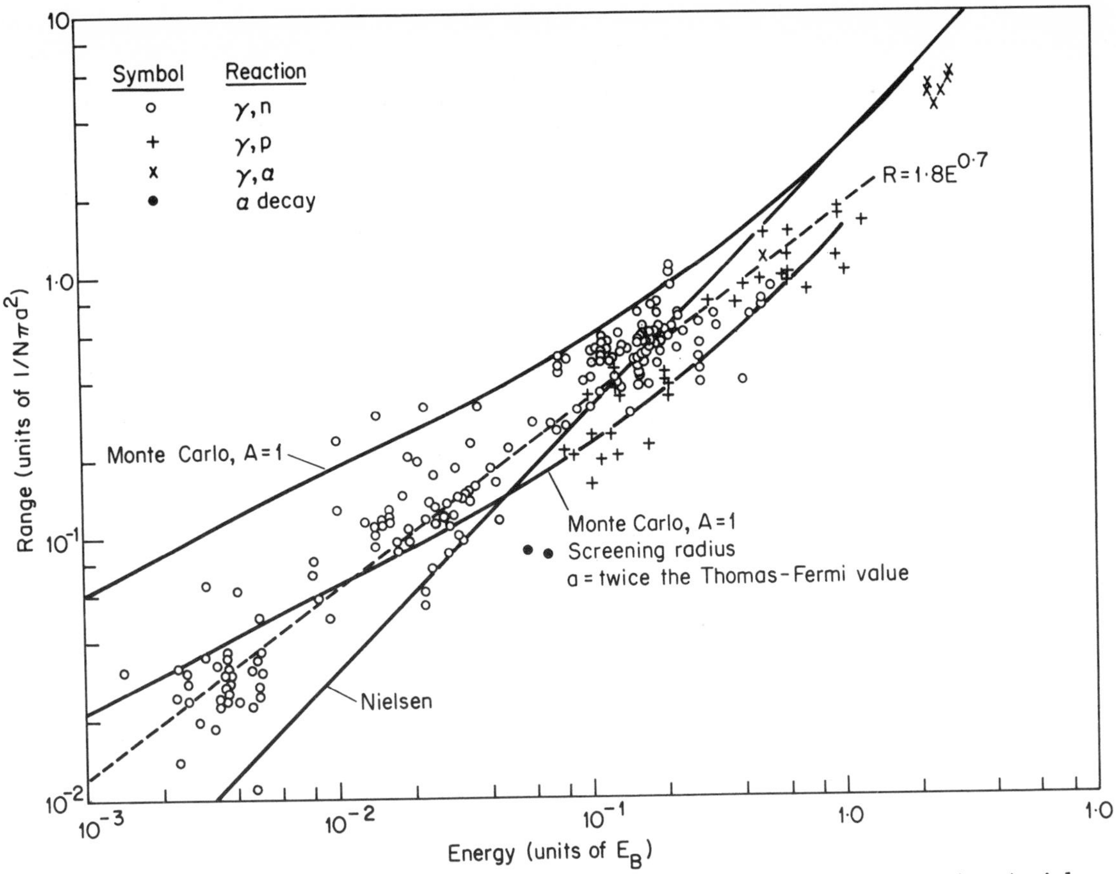

Fig. 5.56 Experimental-range energy data for primary atoms in their own target material as listed in the text according to Ref. 5.40. The nuclear reactions leading to the primary recoils are indicated.

Pb, Te, U, prepared from bulk material were irradiated as described above. The irradiations were performed in atmosphere, but check experiments indicated that any air entrapped between foils had no influence. Corrections were also applied for background activity induced in the foils by natural radioactivity, by reactions which involved electrons passing through the platinum converter and striking the targets, and by active material transplanted from the target to the catcher foils during the intimate contact. The effect of reduction of the activity ratio because of recoiling atoms, reflecting from, rather than entering the catcher foils was also investigated and the necessary corrections applied. Alloyed targets of Cu-Au were also studied in an attempt to study recoil ranges in essentially the non-parent material, whilst a number of experiments were conducted with evaporated thin films of variable thickness of Copper to investigate the distribution of recoil ranges.

The range-energy data for the bulk material targets enumerated above, are plotted in Figure 5.56 on a reduced range-energy graph, where they are compared with the Nielsen[9] range formula and with machine results assuming a Bohr potential with different screening radii. There is evidently a wide scatter in results but a best fit relation $R \propto E^{0.87}$ was found. Range/energy plots for gold, copper and silver were also compared with the theoretical range estimates of Holmes and Leibfried[13] (equation 5.49.2 and Figure 5.7) assuming the Bohr potential and an adjustable screening radius. It was found (as shown in Figure 5.57 for the case of silver), that it was necessary to adjust the screening radius for each target in order to obtain agreement with experimental results. Thus if the screening radius was taken to be $k\,a_B$, where a_B is the Bohr screening radius, k had the values 1.7, 2.0 and 3.0 for Cu, Ag and Au respectively. We should note that Oen, Holmes and Robinson,[27, 36] using machine computations with a Bohr potential derived corresponding k values of 1.15, 1.68 and 2.34 for best agreement with the Van Lint et al data.[40, 64-70] Clearly the different values arise from the differences obtained in machine and theoretical esti-

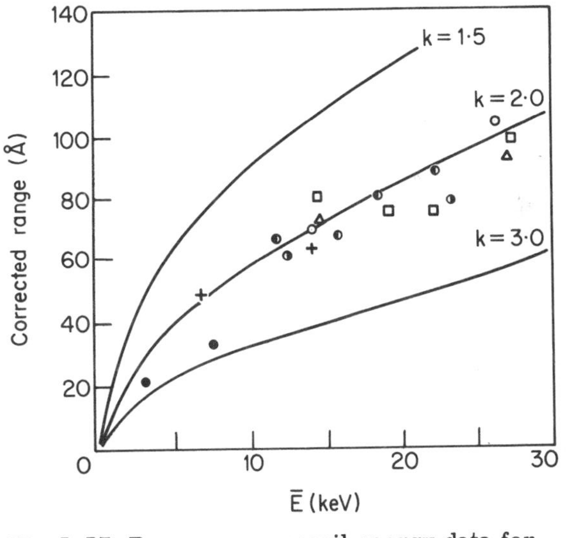

Fig. 5.57 Range-mean recoil energy data for Silver atoms in a Silver target. Solid lines are computer results for a Bohr potential with variable screening radius parameter k. Data points were obtained for various incident Bremsstrahlung energies as follows.

● 11.0 MeV; +13.1 MeV; ◐ 16.8 MeV; ◑ 17.4 MeV ○ 20.6 MeV; △23.6 MeV; □25.8 MeV. (viz. Ref. 5.40 and 5.65)

TABLE 5. 20. (Ref. 5. 40)

Alloy Foil Data

Recoil Atom	Target Material	w	$R_c(\frac{\mu g}{cm^2})$	E_R(keV)
Cu^{64}	90% Cu-10% Au	0	11. 1	35. 6
		180	9. 1	17. 0
	10% Cu-90% Au	0	142. 0	50. 6
		180	224. 0	25. 0
		0-180	169	37. 7
	100% Cu	0	16. 7	35. 6
		180	13. 9	17. 0
		0	18. 2	50. 6
		180	14. 5	25. 0
		0-180	17. 0	37. 7
Au^{196}	90% Cu-10% Au	0	2. 94	10. 5
		180	2. 11	5. 37
	10% Cu-90% Au	0	7. 36	11. 4
		180	6. 20	5. 87
	100% Au	0	3. 94	10. 5
		180	3. 27	5. 37
		0	4. 81	11. 4
		180	3. 83	5. 87

w is the recoil angle, E_R the recoil energy and R_c the measured range corrected for centre of mass solid angle effects

mates of range. Range measurements in Cu-Au alloy containing different concentrations of Cu and Au, in Cu: Au ratios of 1:9 and 9:1, showed interesting features which are summarised in Table 5. 20. Cu recoils appeared to possess surprisingly large ranges in the gold rich alloy, possibly because of errors introduced in evaluating the range data where corrections for range projections are required, which are inadequate for Cu scattering from the heavier Gold. The large ranges of Gold in gold-rich alloys was thought to be due to experimental errors.

In order to understand the thin film results and how these may be used to evaluate range distributions, we should investigate how the ranges are determined by the theoretical equation given earlier ($f = \frac{c}{t} . R(E)$) and how this must be modified for thin targets.

If a thick target is considered initially, with thickness $t \gg R$ (the range of the recoil nuclei), then a γ ray of energy k is assumed incident in the Z direction (target normal) which collides with and is absorbed by a nucleus of mass A + 1. This results in the emission of a nucleon of momentum Pu at an angle $\pi - \theta$ to the Z direction in the C.M. system and a recoiling nucleus of momentum P in the laboratory system.

Then

$$P_z = P_n \cos\theta + k \qquad 5.165.1$$

$$P_\perp = P_n \sin\theta \qquad 5.165.2$$

Thus

$$P = \sqrt{P_n^2 + 2\,k P_n \cos\theta + k^2} \approx P_n + k\cos\theta + \frac{k^2}{2P_n}\sin^2\theta \qquad 5.165.3$$

assuming k/P_n is small.

The direction of motion of the recoil atom in the laboratory system ϕ_L, is correspondingly given by

$$\cos\phi_L = \frac{P_n\cos\theta + k}{P} \approx \cos\theta + \frac{k^2}{P_n}\sin^2\theta - \frac{3}{2}\frac{k^2}{P_n{}^2}\sin^2\theta\cos\theta \qquad 5.165.4$$

which can be inverted to give

$$\cos\theta \simeq \cos\phi_L - \frac{k}{P_n}\sin^2\phi_L - \frac{1}{2}\frac{k^2}{P_n{}^2}\sin^2\phi_L\cos\phi_L \qquad 5.165.5$$

If a simplifying assumption is made initially that recoils are generated uniformly throughout the thickness of the target at a rate n_f/unit volume and that the recoils are isotropically spatially distributed, then, at a depth x within the target, in a depth interval δx, $n_f\delta x$ recoils are produced. Of these a fraction $\frac{n_f \sin\theta\delta\theta}{2}$ move back towards the surface in the solid angle defined by the angles $\theta \to \theta + \delta\theta$. Only those recoils for which $x \leqslant R\cos\theta$ will emerge from the surface for a well defined range R, so that total num-

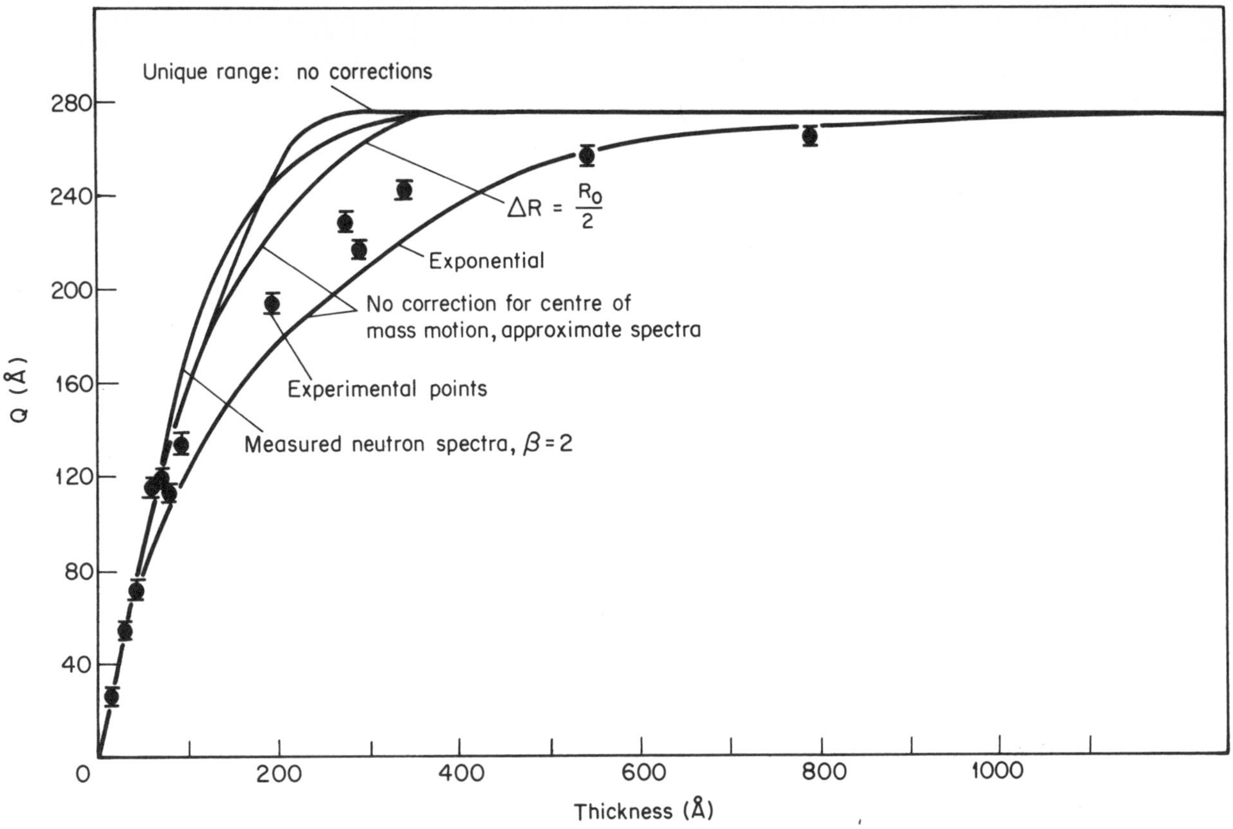

Fig. 5. 58 Copper thin-film data: 0 deg. Recoil fraction (represented by Q) as a function of film thickness. Various theoretical curves for unique and exponentially disturbed ranges are shown. (viz. Ref. 5. 40)

ber of recoils emerging from the target and entering the catcher foil will be given by

$$n_c = \int_0^R n_f dx \int_0^{\cos^{-1}(x/R)} \frac{\sin\theta d\theta}{2} = \frac{R}{4} \cdot n_f \qquad 5.166$$

Thus the fraction f of the recoils emerging from the target to those produced in the target ($=n_f \cdot t$) is given by

$$f = R/4t \qquad 5.167.1$$

If N_c is the number of recoils trapped in the Catcher and N_f the number retained in the target

$$f = \frac{N_c}{N_c + N_f} = R/4t \qquad 5.167.2$$

or generally, since

$$N_f \gg N_c, \frac{N_c}{N_f} = f = R/4t \qquad 5.167.3$$

For a thin foil, where $R > t$ the integration can be performed throughout the foil rather than to a depth R only, and the ratio

$$f = \frac{N_c}{N_c + N_f}$$

leads to definition of a length

$$Q = 2t(1 - t/2R) \text{ for } t < R \qquad 5.168.1$$
$$Q = R \text{ for } t > R$$

and

$$f = \frac{Q}{4t} \text{ for all t} \qquad 5.168.2$$

If the range is not sharply defined, but has a probability P(r) of range r, then the integration is equally straightforward. Van Lint and Wyatt[40] have evaluated Q for range distributions, either uniform between $R_0 - \Delta R_0$ and $R_0 + \Delta R_0$ and zero elsewhere, or exponentially distributed i.e.

$$P(r)dr = \frac{1}{R_0} \exp(-r/R_0)dr$$

The results of these calculations are plotted in Figure 5. 58 together with the experimentally observed Q/t behaviour.

There is a source of error in these calculations which is the assumption of isotropy of recoil atom emission since a unique recoil energy with a unique range is assumed. This error can be accounted for, by introducing into the integration, the dependence of the recoil angle upon the recoil energy and therefore the range. Thus one may assume that the range R for a recoil of momentum P may be expressed as an expansion about the nucleon momentum P_u, i.e.

$$R(P) = R_0(P_u) + \frac{dR}{dP}(P - P_u) \qquad 5.169$$

and the fraction of recoils escaping is then

$$f = \frac{1}{4\pi t} \oint d\Omega R(P(\phi_L)) \cos\phi_L$$

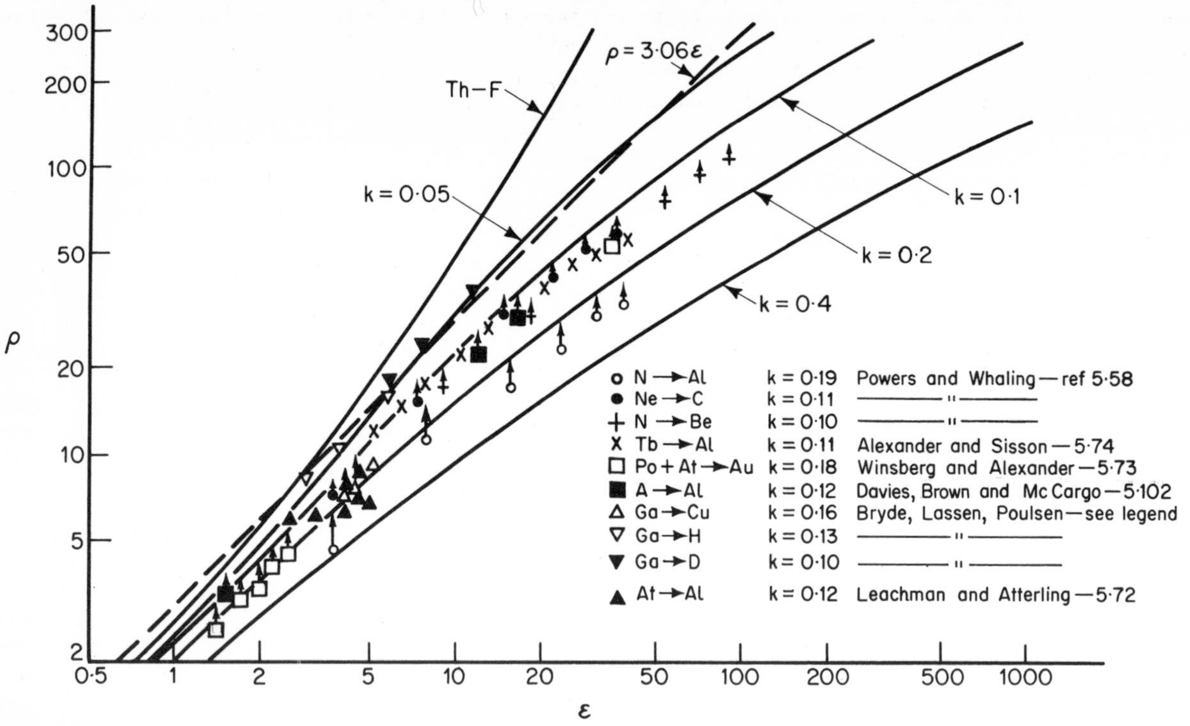

Fig. 5. 59 Comparison of Experimental and Theoretical Range-Energy data accord to Ref. 5. 8. The data of Bryde, L, Lassen. N.O, and Poulsen, N.O.R., is contained in Mat. Fys. Medd. Dan Vid. Selsk 33, 8, 1962.

Transforming this integral via Equations 5. 165, 169 leads to

$$f = \frac{c}{4t} \cdot R \qquad 5.170$$

where C is a calculable constant.

For thin targets similar modifications to the simple theory can be made, and these corrections are also shown in Figure 5. 58. Clearly the experimental points indicate a range distribution but the exact form of this is not yet calculable nor meaningful since the exact structure of the films is unknown.

Other measurements on recoil atom ranges after nuclear disintegration have been made by Leachman and Atterling[72] who investigated At^{203} and At^{205} recoils in Aluminium. Winsberg and Alexander[73] and Alexander and Sisson[74] who studied Tb^{149} recoils of energies of between 4 and 30 MeV in Al and At and Po recoils in Al and Au at energies of 3. 5-13 MeV, and Harvey, Wade and Donovan[75] observed ranges of At^{205} and At^{207} recoils of rather poorly defined energies between 400 and 900 keV in Bismuth. Finally Baulch and Duncan[76] determined the ranges of α particle recoils in H_2, A and air. These measurements [72, 73, 74] employed initially incident protons or heavy ions to induce the nuclear reaction and collected the recoils in Aluminium catcher foils. The results of these studies are collected together in Figures 5. 59 where they will be subsequently compared with theoretical data. Porile[77] has employed a similar technique to determine the range of Ga atoms recoiling from (α, γ), (p, γ) and (d, γ) reactions in α particle, proton and deuteron bombarded Cu and Zn. It was found that for Ga atom energies between 0. 1 MeV and 1. 0 MeV a linear range-energy equation $R(\mu g/cm^2) = 0.193\ E$ (KeV) fitted the experimental data in both materials and that this relation was close to the Lindhard et al[8, 11] universal range-energy expression for an electronic stopping parameter $k = 0.16$.

Chasman, Jones and Ristinen[78] have also determined the magnitude of the inelastic losses of 20-100 keV Ge^{72} atoms recoiling in Ge following neutron irradiation by observing the line broadening in the energy spectrum of internal conversion electrons from decay of the O^+ excited state in Ge^{72} due to the inelastic loss. In this energy range it was found that the inelastic loss incurred from 3% to 20% of the total energy loss and was in extremely good agreement with the Lindhard et al[8, 11] prediction for a Thomas-Fermi potential.

(c) Transmission Methods

This method is theoretically applicable to study of a wide range of target materials and primary particles. Unfortunately it is difficult to produce self supporting films of sufficient thinness to determine the transmission of low energy primaries. Further it is difficult to detect the transmitted primaries with sufficient sensitivity. Therefore the only measurements of any value, using this method, have been performed using thin Aluminium films evaporated on to substrates of phosphor materials which luminesce when bombarded by energetic primaries, somewhat thicker self supporting films of Aluminium oxide and Carbon through which primaries passed and were detected by an electron multiplier, and Aluminium, Gold and Copper foils supported on a quartz substrate which suffered changes in reflectivity after deuteron bombardment.

Young[79] has described measurements of the transmission of H^+, H_2^+ and He^+ ions through Al films using a modification of the technique described in a. 2. When energetic ions bombard a ZnS phosphor the observed luminescence is a characteristic function of the ion energy, commencing at a minimum energy as observed earlier for electrons. If a thin film of Al is deposited upon the phosphor then luminescence is again observed but commencing at an energy determined by the film thickness. Above the minimum energy, the luminescence/energy curves are identical for different film thickness, shifted only on the energy scale, and, after corrections are made, identical to the luminescence curve for an unaluminised sample. This clearly indicates that the energy defect between the curve for a film of given thickness and for an unaluminised sample is indicative of the energy loss of the ions for that film thickness. Thus it is a straightforward matter to deduce a range energy relation for each ion, although again the exact range parameter is unspecified. It is possible to confirm the energy defect by measuring the luminescence/energy curves over a wide energy range, not only at the "cut-in" energy, but it was necessary to ensure low primary fluxes since damage to the phosphor lattice results in luminosity degradation. Young[79] found that the range/energy relation for the three ions mentioned above was adequately expressed over a primary energy of range of 1 keV to 25 keV by $R = kE^{0.83}$, with $k = 2.0$ Å/keV for H^+, 1.5 for H_2^+ and 2.1 for He^+ with E expressed in keV and R in Angstroms. This result may be contrasted with the Form $R = CE^{0.87}$ deduced by Van Lint et al.[40]

Since the H_2^+ ion was expected to dissociate upon entering the Al, the observation that the H_2^+ ion range was greater than that of an H^+ ion of half the energy, was unusual and without explanation.

On the other hand, Hines[80] used an extension of the method described earlier[53] to study Deuteron ion ranges in Al, Cu and Au, wherein the deuteron passed through thin evaporated foils of these materials before striking a quartz substrate. The quartz suffered changes in optical reflectivity due to the deuterons passing through the film and causing damage and by assuming a Gaussian range distribution, it was possible to correlate the reflection coefficient changes with the energy of the deuterons passing through the metals and into the quartz and hence determine the median deuteron range from 5 keV to 27 keV in the above metals. The resulting range/energy curves are shown in Figure 5.60 and it is interesting to note

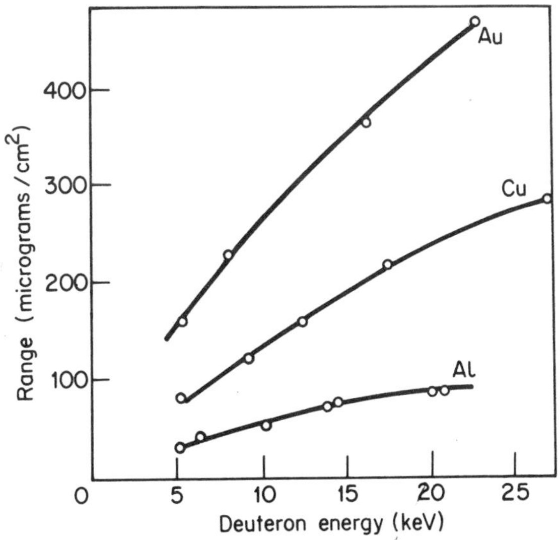

Fig. 5.60 Ranges of deuterons in Al, Cu and Au. The bombarding species were D_2^+, but since this dissociates into two D atoms at the surfaces, each with half the D_2 energy, it is this latter energy which is used. (viz. Ref. 5.80)

that the range of a D_2^+ ion was, within experimental accuracy, equal to the range of a D^+ ion of half the energy (i.e. the D_2^+ ion dissociates). Furthermore the range determined by this method for 15 keV deuterons in Al was within 5% of twice the value reported by Young[79] for 7.5 keV protons.

We should note that in this energy range, all collisions will be almost entirely inelastic and the curvature of ranges in Figure 5.60 is therefore expected.

The range of energetic Cs^{137} ions in Germanium has also been measured by the transmission method by Davies et al.[81] This technique relies on the type of experiment explained more fully under method f) and although appropriate to the present discussion, a description of these measurements is deferred until later to facilitate analysis. Van Winjgaarden and Duckworth[82] have made a more direct measurement of primary ranges of H, He and Ar ions with energies from 4 to 30 keV in Aluminium oxide and Carbon films, by measuring the energy loss of ions transmitted through these films. Mass and energy analysed primary ions were injected into a target film about 200 Å thick and the energy spectrum of the charged fraction of transmitted primaries was measured using an electrostatic analyser and an electron multiplier for primary detection. By varying the angle between the primary beam and the normal to the film, the effective film thickness $t' = t/\cos\theta$ could be changed, and by varying the angular position ϕ of the primary ion collector system with respect to the incident primary direction, the angular spread of the transmitted primaries was observable.

A typical set of results for 17.5 keV H_1^+ ions transmitted directly through an Al_2O_3 film of variable effective thickness is shown in Figure 5.61. The peak shape at 17.5 keV is first measured with the film absent, and shows a sharp peak at 17.5 keV (E_0). The film is then introduced and the energy spectrum determined at various incidence angles, as the effective film thickness is increased, the shape of the spectrum changes, broadening from that typical of the instrument resolution to one typical of the variable energy losses of the primary beam. Simultaneously the energy at which the maximum number of primaries are transmitted falls i.e. the peak shifts on the energy scale.

It is reasonable to assume that the shift in the energy at the peak, ΔE_0, is the most probable energy loss suffered by the primaries, at an average energy $E_0 - \frac{\Delta E_0}{2} = \overline{E}$. If this is the case, then the stopping power $- \frac{dE}{dx} . N$ should be constant at a given primary energy, for films of variable effective thickness. Thus the stopping power $N\Delta E_0/t/\cos\theta$ was determined for different average primary energies $\overline{E}$, for different film angular orientations. The results are shown in Table 5.21 for H^+ in Al_2O_3 and the agreement indicates that the method measures stopping power accurately. Thus stopping power/energy relations were determined for H and He in Al_2O_3 and Carbon with the results

$$S = 4.3 \times 10^{-15} E^{0.45} \text{ eV cm}^2 \text{ for H in } Al_2O_3$$

$$S = 3.5 \times 10^{-15} E^{0.41} \text{ eV cm}^2 \text{ for H in Carbon.}$$

$$S = 4.6 \times 10^{-15} E^{0.44} \text{ eV cm}^2 \text{ for H in } Al_2O_3$$

$$S = 4.0 \times 10^{-15} E^{0.40} \text{ eV cm}^2 \text{ for He in Carbon.}$$

Since, in the energy range used, the light primary ions lose energy by inelastic collisions almost exclusively, one expects, from Equation 5.25.1 a stopping power

TABLE 5. 21. (Ref. 5. 82)

Relative insensitiveness of $\Delta E/t^1$ to the film thicknesses employed

$\bar{E}$, keV	$t^1 = 205$ Å ($\theta = 2.5°$)	$t^1 = 278$ Å ($\theta = 42.5°$)	$t^1 = 383$ Å ($\theta = 57.5°$)	$t^1 = 536$ Å ($\theta = 67.5°$)
	$\Delta E_0/t^1$(eV/Å)			
30	16. 3	17. 1	16. 7	17. 2
20	13. 8	14. 4	14. 2	14. 4
15	12. 1	12. 7	12. 5	12. 6
10	10. 3	10. 6	10. 7	
5	7. 4	7. 5		

dependent upon the power 0. 5 of the energy. This is approximated quite well by the observed dependence and suggested that reasons for the discrepancies are the influence of elastic collisions and basic innaccuracies in the theoretical equation.

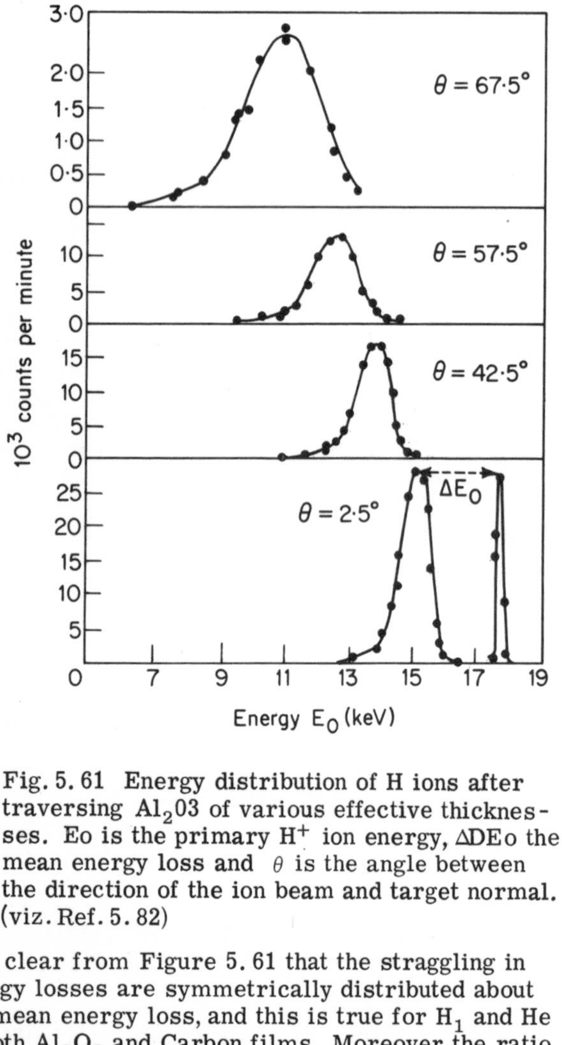

Fig. 5. 61 Energy distribution of H ions after traversing $Al_2 03$ of various effective thicknesses. Eo is the primary H^+ ion energy, ΔDEo the mean energy loss and θ is the angle between the direction of the ion beam and target normal. (viz. Ref. 5. 82)

It is clear from Figure 5. 61 that the straggling in energy losses are symmetrically distributed about the mean energy loss, and this is true for H_1 and He in both Al_2O_3 and Carbon films. Moreover the ratio $E_{1/2}/\Delta E_0$ where $E_{1/2}$ is the width at half maximum of the energy spectrum, is also found to be a constant for a given film independent of film thickness. This is again expected from the results of Figure 5. 5a where, when electronic stopping dominates, the relative range straggling approaches a constant value. On the other hand, when A^{40} was used as the primary species, considerable asymmetry of the energy spectrum was observed, presumably due to the wide angle scattering resulting from elastic collisions, and the consequent widening of the spectrum of primaries able to reach the collector. Further evidence of this was obtained by observing the angular spread of the emerging primaries. In the case of H and He^4 very little scattering from the initial primary direction was observed, but the angular distribution of scattered A^{40} primaries was very broad. This corresponds to preferential forward scattering expected with inelastic losses (Rutherford scattering) and more isotropic scattering with elastic collisions.

One other significant result of these observations was that the emerging primary beam, contained, in addition to the positive ions, neutral species and negative ions, the relative percentages of which varied with primary energy. However the energy spectrum of the transmitted particles appeared to be charge independent, an important result since it indicated the absence of effects of charge exchange which may be exerted upon ranges, at least when averaged over many primary collisions.

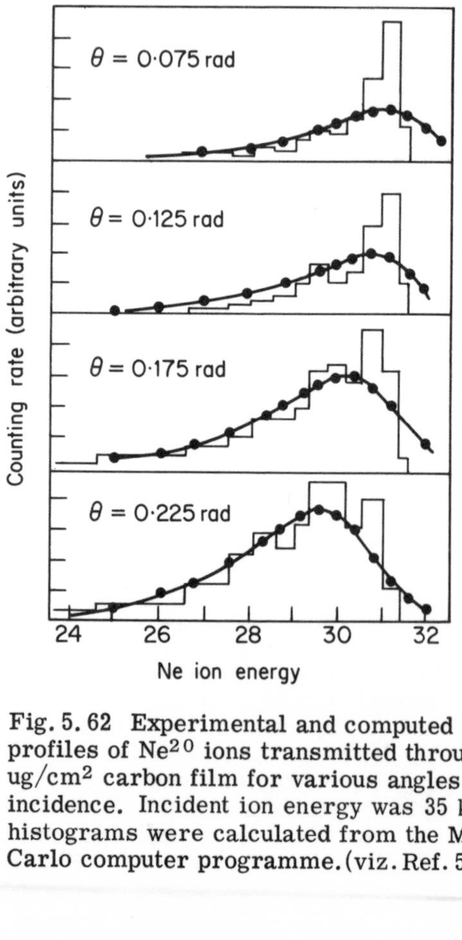

Fig. 5. 62 Experimental and computed energy profiles of Ne^{20} ions transmitted through 3. 36 ug/cm² carbon film for various angles of ion incidence. Incident ion energy was 35 keV. The histograms were calculated from the Monte Carlo computer programme. (viz. Ref. 5. 83)

Ormrod and Duckworth[83] subsequently extended these measurements to the investigation of electronic stopping of Li^6, Li^7, Be^9, B^{11}, C^{12}, N^{14}, O^{16}, F^{19}, Ne^{20}, Ne^{23} and Mg^{24} in Carbon films at primary energies between 10 and 140 keV. The transmitted primary ion spectra were determined at various transmission angles ϕ and the total collision cross sections S_0 from the shift in the spectral peak. As shown in Figure 5. 62 for Ne^{20} primaries, the energy spread in the transmitted primaries is considerably larger than with H^1 and He^4 ions. This must be expected since the heavier primaries lose considerable energy through elastic nuclear collisions. In order to determine the magnitude of the elastic losses, a Monte Carlo computer programme was employed to determine the energies and angular emission properties of a simulated Ne^{20} beam striking a Carbon target. The elastic collisions were assumed to be hard sphere and inelastic losses were included by assuming an energy loss proportional to the path length between collisions. The constant of proportionality was adjusted to achieve agreement between the low energy tails and the peaks of experimental and calculated energy spectra at all transmission angles. The computer programme then gave the amount of energy lost in the elastic collisions when the spectra were matched, and thus the nuclear stopping cross section σ_ν was deduced by division by the foil thickness. Finally the electronic stopping cross section σ_e was deduced by subtraction of the calculated σ_ν from the observed total cross section σ_0. For Ne the inelastic cross section/primary energy relation was found to be $\sigma_e = k \,.\, E^p$ where $p = 0.47$ and $k = 3.8$, again confirming the $E^{0.5}$ inelastic collision dependence.

The electronic stopping cross sections for the other primary ions were deduced as follows. Equation 5. 18. 2 shows that for an inverse r^2 interatomic potential, the ratio of the nuclear stopping cross sections of primaries of masses M_A and M_B in Carbon (mass 12) is given by

$$\frac{\sigma_{\nu A}}{\sigma_{\nu A}} = \frac{M_B + 12}{M_A + 12} \cdot \frac{a_A}{a_B} \cdot \frac{M_A Z_A}{M_B Z_B} \qquad 5.171$$

provided that the parameter

$$\frac{a}{b} = \frac{a_0 m_0 v^2}{2Z_{p\to 1} Z_{r\to 2} e^2 \{Z_{p\to 1}^{2/3} + Z_{r\to 2}^{2/3}\}^{1/2}} \text{ is a constant.}$$

Thus from the nuclear stopping cross section σ_ν for Ne at a given energy the nuclear stopping cross section for any other primary ion at other energies may be deduced.

Finally, from the total observed cross section at these energies, the inelastic cross section/energy relations may be deduced by subtraction. These relations were all found to have the form $\sigma_e = k \,.\, E^p$ (as for Ne) where p lies between 0. 40 and 0. 50, (again confirming the $E^{0.5}$ predicted behaviour) as shown in Table 5. 22. For low primary masses (H^1 and He^4) and high primary energies the values of σ_ν are small since electronic stopping is almost completely dominant.

These results were compared with theoretical data in two ways. Firstly, as seen from Equation 5. 25. 1 the electronic stopping cross sections for two isotopes of the same primary ion should be equal for equal velocity ions. This was confirmed by plotting the electronic stopping cross sections of Li^6 and Li^7 against velocity, as in Figure 5. 63. The agreement is remarkably precise. Secondly, equation 5. 25. 2 indicates that the electronic stopping cross section should depend upon the primary atomic number via

$$\sigma_e \propto \xi_e [Z_1^{2/3} + Z_2^{2/3}]^{-3/2} \,.\, v \,.\, Z_1$$

(Z_1 and Z_2 referring to the primary and target atoms respectively).

Where ξ_e is a constant between 1 and 2 which may vary as $Z_1^{1/6}$. The predicted dependence of σ_e upon Z_1 for $\xi_e = 1.2$ and $Z_1^{1/6}$ is shown in Figure 5. 64 together with the experimentally observed relation. It is apparent that the experimental measurements lie within the predicted ξ_e limits of 1 and 2, but the $Z_1^{1/6}$ dependence is apparently wrong. In fact there is a periodic dependence of σ_e upon Z_1 i.e. upon the filling of electron shells.

TABLE 5. 22. (Ref. 5. 83).

Electronic stopping cross sections in carbon for various atoms—coefficients and exponents in the empirical relationship $\sigma_e = kE^p$ eV-cm²/atom.

Atom	k × 10¹⁵	p	Energy interval (keV)
H^1	3. 3	0. 40	10-25
He^4	3. 7	0. 43	10-80
Li^6	3. 0	0. 45	20-70
Li^7	3. 0	0. 43	15-70
Be^9	3. 3	0. 48	12-130
B^{11}	4. 4	0. 47	12-140
C^{12}	5. 9	0. 43	12-140
N^{14}	6. 2	0. 44	15-140
O^{16}	6. 2	0. 42	20-140
F^{19}	4. 9	0. 45	20-140
Ne^{20}	3. 8	0. 47	20-140
Na^{23}	2. 9	0. 48	20-70
Mg^{24}	2. 5	0. 50	20-130

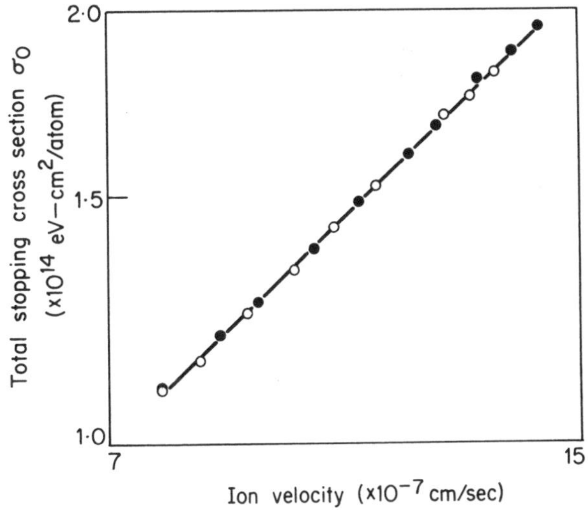

Fig. 5. 63 Total stopping cross section for Li ions in Carbon films as a function of ion velocity
● Li^6
○ Li^7

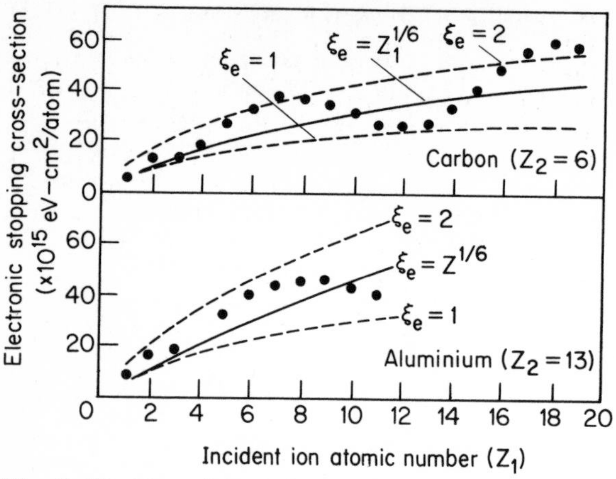

Fig. 5. 64 Experimental electronic stopping cross sections (points) as a function of the incident ion atomic number (at constant velocity = 9×10^7 cm/sec) for carbon and aluminium targets. The curves are theoretical for ξe values of 1, 2 and $Z_2{}^{1/6}$ (viz. Ref. 5. 84)

This dependence may be anticipated since the Thomas-Fermi statistical model of the atom upon which the theoretical stopping cross sections are based is not expected to display effects due to the electronic periodicity.

However one should expect the outer electrons to contribute significantly to the stopping and hence a periodicity with Z as observed.

This periodicity was further confirmed when the above studies were extended[84] to include measurements of electronic stopping cross sections of 10-150 keV ions of atomic number $\leqslant 19$ in C and Al films. Once again a stopping power of the form $\sigma_e \propto E^{0.5}$ was observed, but the constant of proportionality was not adequately described by the Lindhard-Scarff parameter and marked maxima and minima occurred at Z_1 values of 8, 18 and 3 and 12 respectively. In addition an odd effect was observed when stopping powers of singly and doubly charged ions of the same energy (for P^{31} and Cl^{35} but not A^{40}) were compared. It was found that the doubly charged, lower mass, ions had slightly larger than expected cross sections and again this must be ascribed to inadequacies in the simple theory.

The importance of these results is evident, since although obtained at low energies, the dominant losses are inelastic, and hence useful information is gained about these processes. In view of such results as displayed Figure 5. 64 further experiments on inelastic processes are desirable to elucidate the exact dependence upon nuclear charge and mass and primary energy.

Poskanzer[85] has used the transmission technique to determine Ne^{22} penetration functions in Aluminium at high energies. Primary Ne^{22} ions of energies between 1 and 3 MeV were injected into stacked thin Al foils (150 μg/cm^2 thick) which were subsequently sectioned, melted separately in a vacuum system and the quantity of Ne^{22} retained in each foil determined mass spectrometrically. Because of the relatively large foil thicknesses, the resolution of the penetration functions was rather poor, but allowed measurement of average projected ranges and estimation of range straggling. The mean range/energy data are summarised in Table 5. 23 and the range straggling appeared to be constant at energies between 1 and

TABLE 5. 23. (Ref. 5. 85)

Mean Projected Ranges of Ne^{22} in Al(in μg/cm^2)

Energy MeV)	Projected Range
1. 0	350
2. 0	540
2. 8	670

30 MeV. This latter effect is again in agreement with the predictions of Figure 5. 6 where the electronic stopping, which clearly dominates at these high energies, leads to constant range straggling. The mean range/energy data fit an expression $\langle R \rangle \propto E^{0.6}$ again indicating the electronic stopping effects. Finally, Nelson and Thompson,[2,3] have used the transmission technique to illustrate, qualitatively, the existence of channelling events in gold. 75 keV protons were injected at an angle of 35° to the surface normal into a thin (4000 Å) gold target. The foil was then rotated about the normal direction (which was a ⟨111⟩ direction) and any protons transmitted through the film were collected by a biassed electrode. As the foil was rotated, maxima were observed in the transmitted ion current at angles corresponding to ions incident in ⟨110⟩ directions, as shown in Figure 5. 65. This indicated the presence of preferential channelling events in ⟨110⟩ directions. Since the foil was thick, ions heavier than He could not penetrate, but it was observed, during bombardment with these ions, that the maxima gradually disappeared. Subsequent bombardment with protons revealed no maxima, suggesting that the heavier Helium ions blocked the channels, or introduced damage into the crystal, also leading to channel blockage.

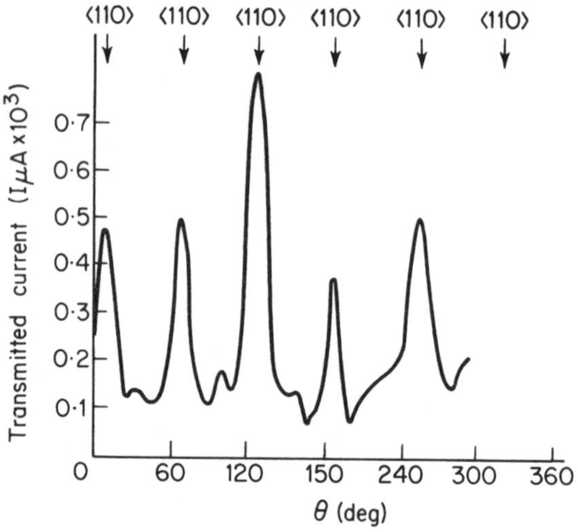

Fig. 5. 65 The transmission of 75 keV protons through a gold crystal. Electrode current I for a constant $I_0 = 0.4$ μA, as a function of θ, the angular position of the target foil. The foil was rotated about its normal which coincided with the ⟨ 111⟩ axes, and the beam was incident at 35° to the normal. (viz. Ref. 5. 2)

Further evidence of channelled events, was obtained when protons, Ne^+ and Xe^+ ions reflected from a Copper surface were studied as a function of the direction of ion incidence. Because of the possibility of an unknown secondary electron emission contribution the results were largely qualitative. However, it was quite clear that for ion incidence directions corresponding to ⟨110⟩, ⟨100⟩ and ⟨121⟩ directions the reflected ion spectra exhibited pronounced minima. Similar results were obtained with proton, Neon and Xenon ion bombardment, but more and better defined minima were observed with protons.

The logical interpretation of these latter results, as suggested by Nelson and Thompson,[2,3] is that, when ions were incident in directions where the probability of channelling was high, {⟨100⟩, ⟨100⟩, ⟨121⟩}, these penetrated relatively deeply into the copper and the probability of re-emergence due to large angle scattering events was reduced. Because the interatomic potential increases in the sequence H^+, Ne^+, Xe^+ the effective channel cross sections decrease with increasing ion mass, hence the channelling probabilities (and the number of possible channels) decreases as the ion is varied from H^+ through to Xe^+.

(d) α Particle re-emission

When a beam of radioactive ions is injected into a target, they come to rest with a range distribution typical of the primary/target combination. If the primaries are α particle emitters, then these particles escape through the bombarded surfaces with energies degraded below the emission energy according to the depth of material through which α particles penetrate and the energy spectrum will characterise the penetration depth spectrum. Domeij et al[86] have used this method to determine the range of $Radon^{222}$ ions of energies between 70 and 210 keV in Aluminium, Silver, Gold and Tungsten polycrystalline targets.

If a primary ion is trapped at a distance x below the bombarded surface, and emits an α particle with energy E_0, then the energy of this particle when recorded by a detector, is given by $E = E_0 + \varepsilon - (\rho x + S)$.

Where ε is the energy contributed by the finite energy resolution of the detector, ρ is the energy loss of the α particle per unit depth within the target, and S is the straggling in the α particle energy loss.

If the average value of the detected energy E, is E_c, and the straggling in the α particle energy loss is uniformly distributed about zero.

Then the average energy measured E_c, is given by $E_c = E_0 + \bar{\varepsilon} - \rho\langle\bar{R}_{par}\rangle$. $E_0 + \bar{\varepsilon}$ is the mean detected energy for an α source in a target of zero thickness. Thus $\langle\bar{R}_{par}\rangle = (F_L - E_L) \cdot 1/\rho$, where $F_L = E_0 + \bar{\varepsilon}$ which can be determined using a standard α source of known emission energy.

In principle, a complete determination of the range distribution is possible, but tedious since $\bar{\varepsilon}$ must be known for each E value. Thus only $\langle\bar{R}_{par}\rangle$ was measured accurately in these studies, although observation of the deepest penetration was made because of the importance in interpretation of channelled events. The primaries trapped with deep penetrations were observed to decrease exponentially with distance.

The total primary ion bombardments of the targets were kept below $10^{13}/cm^2$ in order to minimise damage to the targets and to obviate any influences upon primary ranges which trapped atoms may cause and the ion energy spread was within 0.1%. The resulting emitted α particle spectra were examined by a solid state surface barrier detector with a resolution of 25-30 keV for 6 MeV α particles.

Values of ρ for α particles in Al, Ag, Au and W were assumed from the data of Whaling [87] and an independent check for Al was made using thin targets.

A typical α particle energy spectrum for 210 keV Rn^{222} in Al is shown in Figures 5.66a and 5.66b and the resulting mean ranges and half thickness of the most penetrating exponential tail in Al, Ag, W and Au are compared with the more accurate data deduced from studies described in the following section and listed in Table 5.24. In Figure 5.66 increasing channel number corresponds to increasing α particle energy (1 channel ≅ 2 keV α particle energy interval with zero α energy at channel-3000).

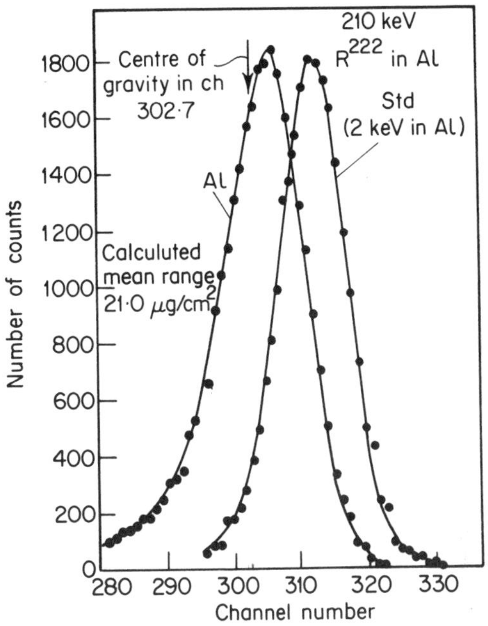

Fig. 5.66a α-spectrum from 210 keV Rn^{222} in Al (linear scale). (viz. Ref. 5.86)

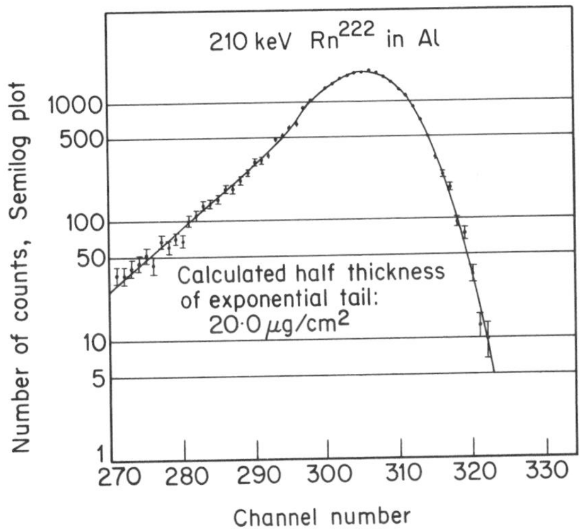

Fig. 5.66b α-spectrum from 210 keV Rn^{222} in Al (logarithmic scale). (viz. Ref. 5.86)

Table 5.24 indicates that the agreement is quite satisfactory, in view of the several sources of error inherent in the method, and the marked difference in the mean ranges in Au and W is certainly an experimental fact which cannot be attributed solely to atomic weight differences of the targets. The explanation probably lies in a channelling mechanism which will be discussed in greater detail later.

The results indicate that the method may find application to a wide variety of target materials, but the primary ions are restricted to α emitters. The low energy limit (≃ 20 keV) of these primaries is also

TABLE 5. 24. (Ref. 5. 86)

Range of Rn^{222} in various solids.

Target	Energy (keV)	Mean range ($\mu g/cm^2$) Ref. 5. 86	Mean range ($\mu g/cm^2$) Peeling method Ref. 5. 88	Half-thickness of tail ($\mu g/cm^2$) Ref. 5. 86	Half-thickness of tail ($\mu g/cm^2$) Peeling method Ref. 5. 88
Al	133	20. 5 ± 2. 5	15. 5 ± 2. 5	11. 5 ± 4. 5	17 ± 3
	210	21. 0 ± 2. 5	21. 5 ± 3. 5	20. 0 ± 2. 0	17 ± 3
Ag	133	29. 5 ± 5. 0		27. 5 ± 4. 5	
W	70	85 ± 15		99 ± 15	
	80		116 ± 20		113 ± 15
	133	121 ± 27	152 ± 25	142 ± 20	134 ± 15
	210	137 ± 21		158 ± 17	
Au	133	34 ± 8		38 ± 8	

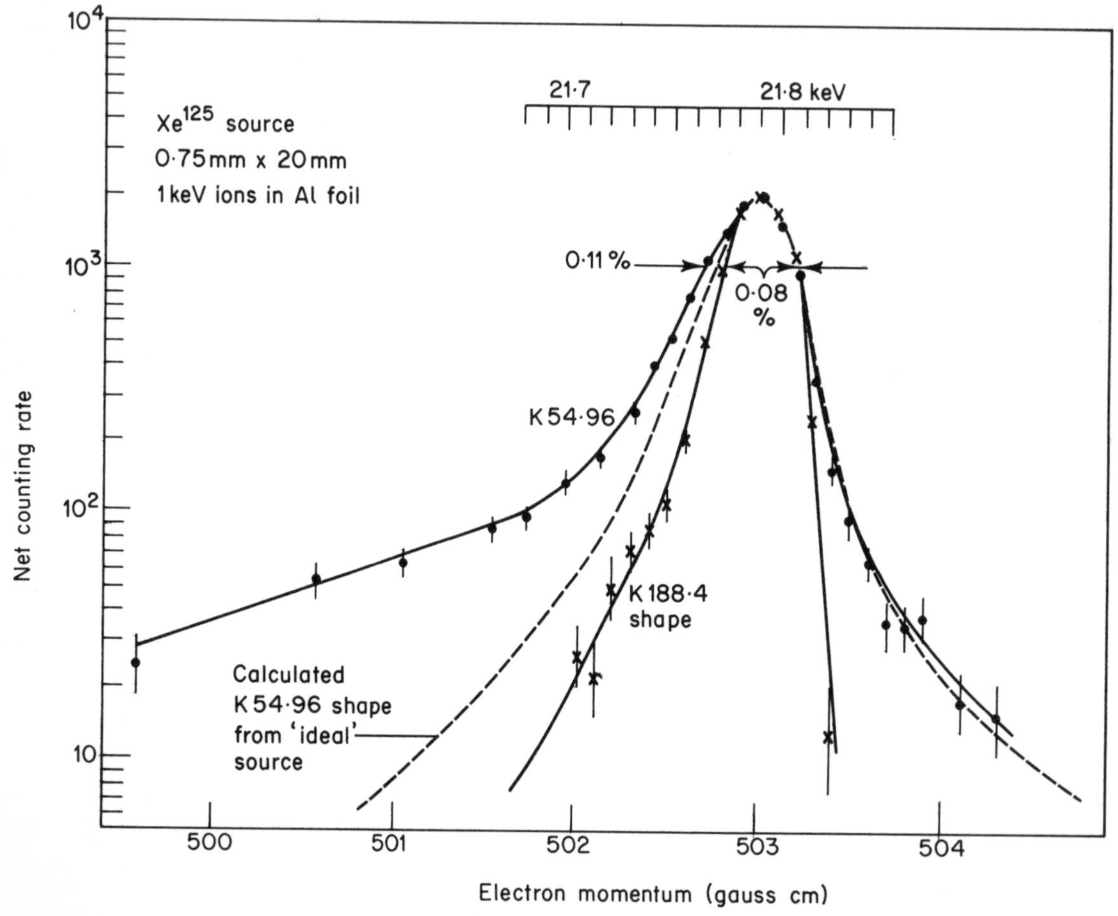

Fig. 5. 67 Comparison of the shapes of the K 54. 96 and K 188. 4 conversion lines from the thinnest Xe^{125} source studied in this work (1 keV ions in Al). In plotting the K 188. 4 line data, the momentum values are divided by a factor of 2. 83 so that the peak shapes can be compared meaningfully. The total natural width for K conversion lines at $Z = 53$ is $\Gamma_K \simeq 13$ eV. The dashed line shows the shape which might be expected for the K 54. 96 keV line from a very thin source. It was obtained by folding a Lorentz factor of width $\Gamma = 11.2$ eV into the K 188.4 shape so as to allow for the larger natural width contribution to the lower energy line shape. (viz. Ref. 5. 89)

rather high due to the uncertainty in resolving the small α energy degradation in passing through thin surface layers.

(e) Electron re-emission

A method, very similar in principle to that described above, has been used by Bergstrom et al[88, 89] and Graham et al[90, 91] to study the ranges of Xe ions in Al, Be, Ni, Zr, Ta and Au. Xe^{125} ions injected into targets of these materials, subsequently decayed to I^{125} via γ ray emission which in turn caused ejection of electrons at mean kinetic energies of 21.8 keV and 155.2 keV (corresponding γ energies were 54.96 keV and 188.4 keV). Since the primaries are embedded within the target the electrons lose energy in escaping to the surface, typical of the penetration depth of the primary involved.

Figure 5.67 illustrates the momentum profile of electrons emitted from Xe^{125} ions embedded at 1 keV in Al. Since the 155.2 keV electron energy losses are very small the curve labelled K188.4 may be regarded as a standard "thin" source (i.e. since penetration depths of Xe into Al at 1 keV are small the penetration depth may be regarded as zero). The corresponding K54.96 momentum curve may then be calculated theoretically from the K188.4 curve, and compared with the experimentally determined spectrum. The curves in Figure 5.67 are normalised to the same maximum and high energy tail (which is readily accounted for by natural line width in the electronic momentum spectrum). However the enhanced low energy tail, evident in the experimental results must be interpreted as broadening due to electron energy loss in passage through the target. This belief is confirmed by increasing the ion bombardment energy, and as the penetration depth increases, the low energy tail becomes more pronounced, viz Figure 5.68a. Changing the target material also, as may be expected, also causes changes in the low momentum tail, by comparison with a standard spectrum shape (5 keV Xe^{125} in Al), as shown in Figure 5.68b. This behaviour is typical of both conversion lines. It appears that the low atomic number targets exhibit line shapes, closest to the standard, and an interpretation of this would be that the primary range in these materials is well defined and little distortion of the electron momentum spectrum occurs. This view will be supported by later evidence.

This technique may be used to actually determine[90, 91] penetration depths or functions, as follows. In addition to the momentum spectrum from a bombarded sample, the electron spectra may be measured from such a sample, upon which variable thicknesses of known metal have been condensed. Thus in Figure 5.69a the momentum spectra for Al bombarded with 1 keV Xe^+ ions, Al coated with ~300 Å of gold after bombardment and bulk Au bombarded with 5 keV ions are compared. Since the penetration of gold by 5 keV, Xe^+ ions is known to have an average at about 300 Å

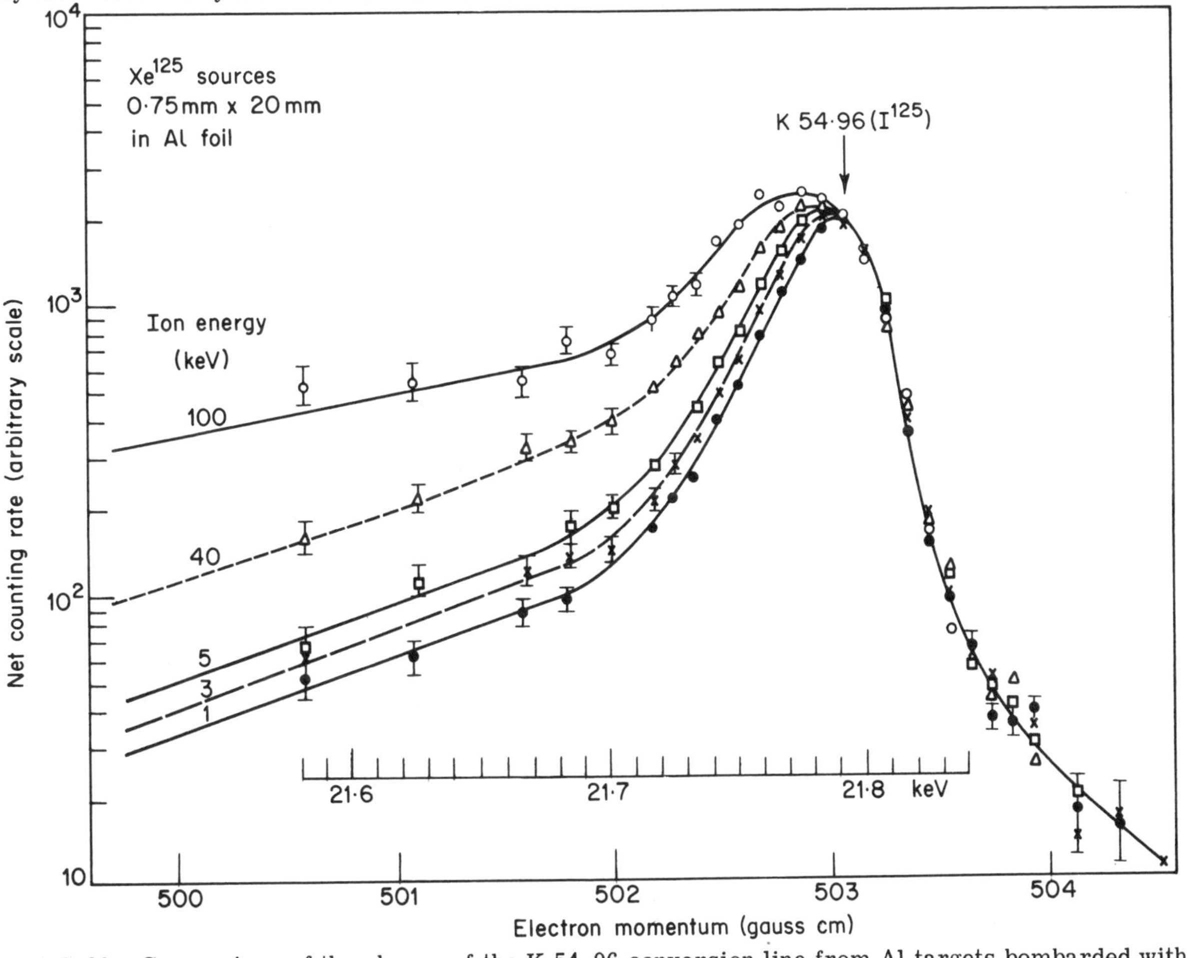

Fig. 5.68a Comparison of the shapes of the K 54.96 conversion line from Al targets bombarded with Xe^{125} ions of different energies. The counting-rate scales have been adjusted to match the high-energy tails, which have a common shape due to natural width. The source dimensions were defined by a machined slot of 0.75 mm by 20 mm in the 0.8 mm-thick Cu mask. Each mask was drilled to fit on the dowel pins of the standard source holder in the β-spectrometer. By this method the radial position of the slots for successive sources were identical, i.e. ± 0.05 mm. The width of the Xe^{125} deposit in the target was normally ~ 1 mm. (viz. Ref. 5.89)

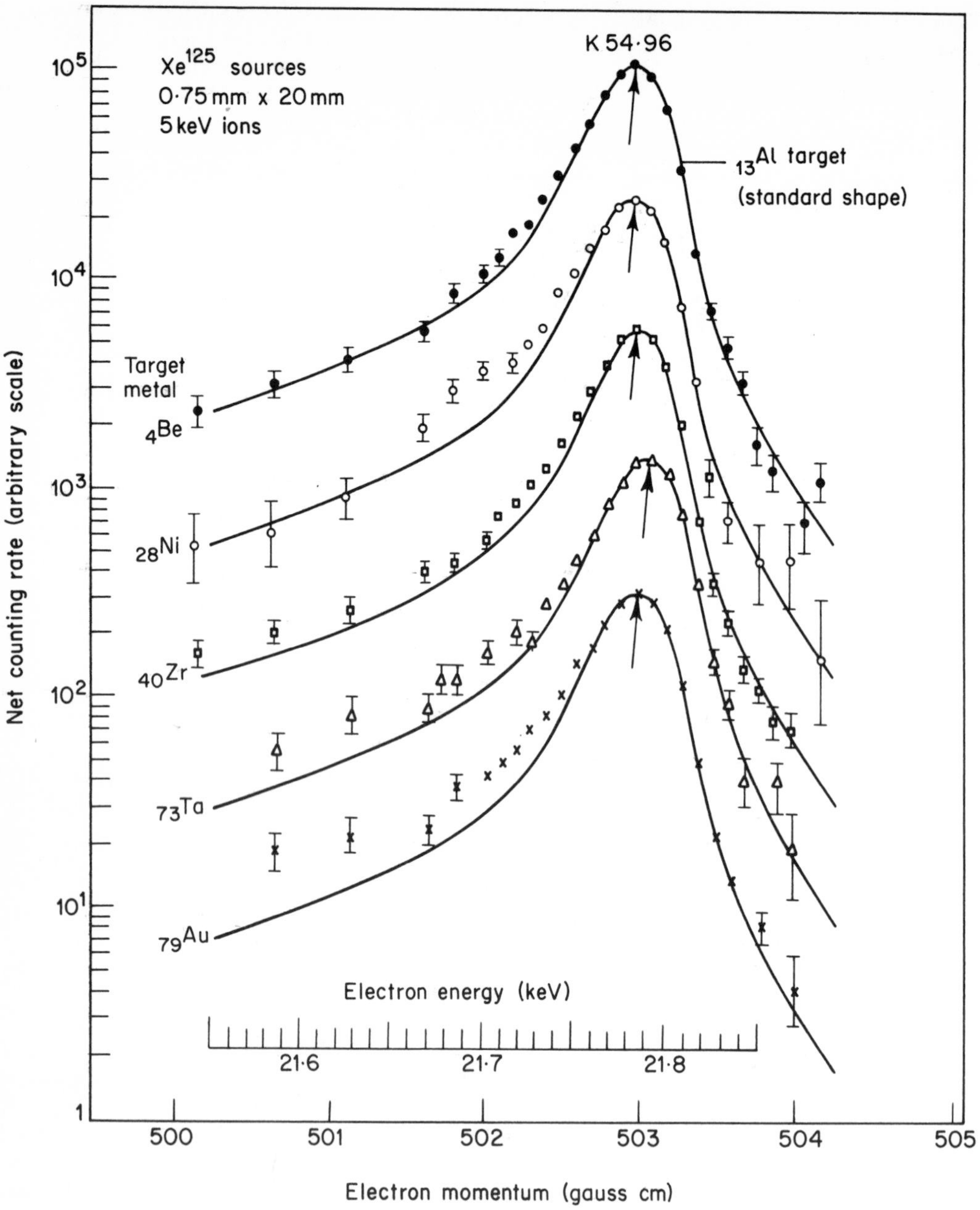

Fig.5.68b Comparison of the shapes of the K 54. 96 conversion line from various metal targets which have been bombarded with 5 keV Xe^{125}ions. For convenience in comparison, the line shape from the Al target has been used as the standard shape. The sources were mounted as described in fig. 2. The displacement of the line position in Ta is believed to be real but is not fully understood.(viz. Ref. 5. 89)

(see subsequent data), then if this range were single valued, the spectra for the evaporated gold and solid gold targets would be expected to be identical. Clearly the spectra are different, indicating that there is a considerable range spread in Au. These observations may be made more quantitative by noting, for example, the reduction in the number of electrons emerging from the targets at a given energy, as the target is coated with films of varying thickness. Thus if the magnitude of the K54. 96 and K188. 4 lines, corresponding to the peaks in the conversion spectrum are followed after 3 keV Xe^{125} bombardment of the Aluminium target, as increasing thicknesses of Al or Au are deposited upon the surface, the results of Figure 5. 69c are obtained. From these curves, the normalised peak counting rate may be plotted as a function of the mean depth of the Xe^{125} atoms. The latter values are obtained by adding the known mean range of Xe^{125} (obtained from other studies to be described shortly) at 3 keV to the thickness of coating applied to the target. These plots have the form shown in Figure 5. 69d and are clearly exponential in character although the Al absorber graph shows some curvature.

To a first approximation, the conversion electrons will lose energy at a uniform rate (constant stopping power) as they pass through the target and absorber, and so the number of electrons which are recorded at the peak of the momentum spectrum corresponds to those which travel the distance $\bar{x}$, to the surface without collision, i.e. $N = N_0 \exp(-x/\lambda)$ where λ is a mean free path for electron collisions. Clearly Figure 5. 69d reproduces this behaviour quite well and enables values of λ and N_0 to be calculated. Thus measurement of the relative peak reduction and knowledge of λ enables $\bar{x}$ to be determined for a given primary energy, and hence the actual penetration depth as a function of energy. In fact the range $\bar{x}$ measured in these experiments is not the arithmetic mean range $< \bar{R} >$ but an 'exponential range given by

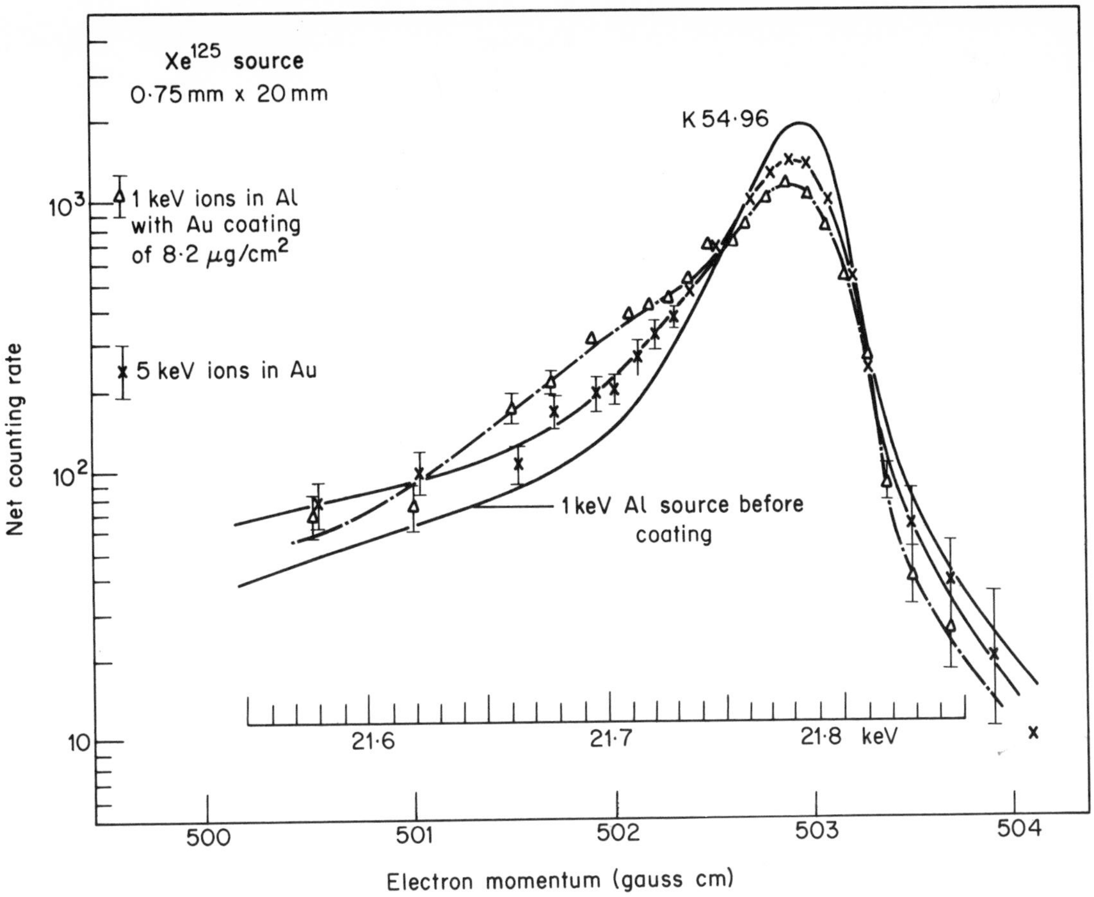

Fig. 5. 69a Comparison of the K 54.96 line shape from a Au-coated Al target (8. 2 μg/cm² of Au, fig. 5) with that from a Au target bombarded with 5 keV Xe^{125}ions. The mean depth of the Xe^{125} atoms are comparable. The difference in shapes is due to the difference in depth distributions of the Xe^{125} atoms. (viz. Ref. 5. 89)

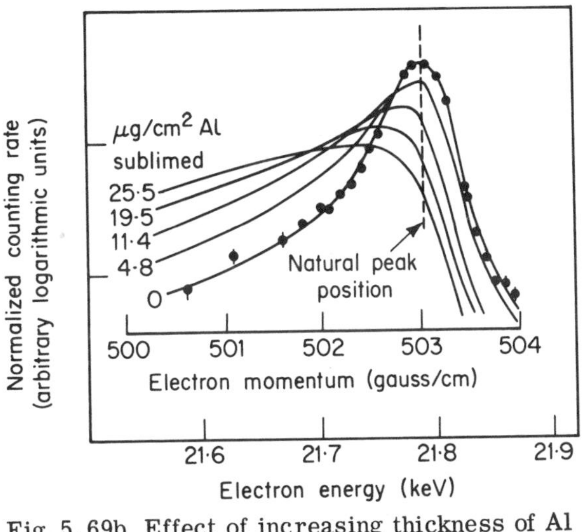

Fig. 5. 69b Effect of increasing thickness of Al absorber on K 54. 96 conversion line shape after injection of 3 keV Xe^{125}ions. (viz. Ref. 5. 90 and 5. 91)

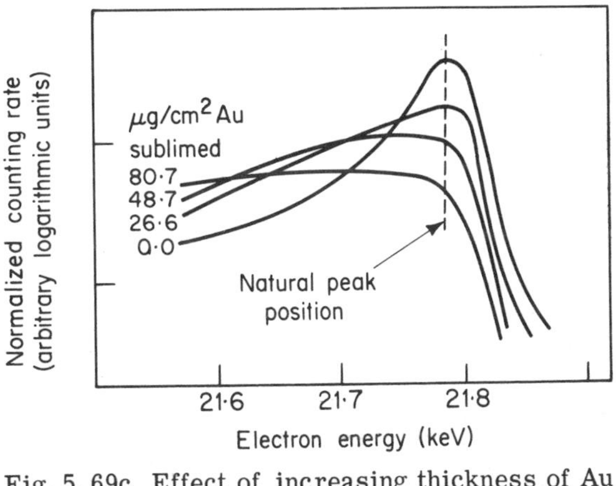

Fig. 5. 69c Effect of increasing thickness of Au absorber on K 54. 96 conversion line shape after injection of 3 keV Xe^{125}ions into W substrate. (viz. Ref. 5. 90 and 5. 91)

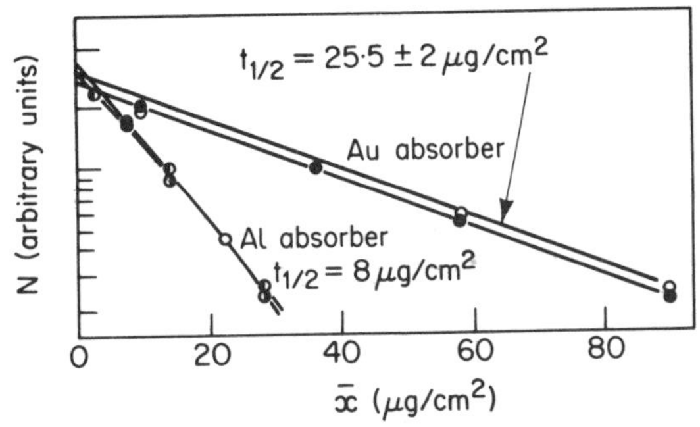

Fig. 5. 69d Calibration of N, the normalized counting rate at the natural peak position of the K 54. 96 line against the mean "exponential" depth of the Xe^{125} atoms $(\bar{x})$. (viz. Ref. 5. 91)

TABLE 5. 25. (Ref. 5. 91).

Mean range of accelerated Xe^{125} ions in metals.

Metal	Measured range* (in $\mu g/cm^2$)	Xe^{125} injection energy (in keV): 1	5	20	40
Al	$\overline{R}$	1. 4 ± 0. 2	3. 1 ± 0. 2	6. 0 ± 0. 6	10 ± 0. 6
	$\bar{x}$	2. 3 ± 0. 5	3. 3 ± 0. 5	5. 8 ± 0. 8	8. 0 ± 1. 0
W	$\overline{R}$	7 ± 3	15 ± 2	42 ± 3	73 ± 5
	$\bar{x}$	7. 7 ± 2. 5	11. 5 ± 2. 5	24 ± 3	33 ± 3
Au	$\bar{x}$	4	8 ± 4	15 ± 2. 5	23 ± 3

* $\overline{R}$ is the true mean range deduced from the electrolytic peeling method (Davies, Brown and McCargo 1963, Ref. 5. 102; McCargo, Davies and Brown 1963, Ref. 5. 101; $\bar{x}$ is the mean "exponential" range deduced using the β-spectroscopic method described in (Ref. 5. 91)

$$\frac{1}{\rho} \int_0^\infty f(x) \exp(-x/\lambda)\, dx$$

where f(x) is the fraction of primaries stopped at a distance x below the surface, and P is the total number of stopped primaries. However if the primary range distributions are narrow compared to λ as is expected for Xe^{125} in Al and W, $\overline{R}$ and $\bar{x}$ may be expected to be approximately equal. The distributions of Xe in Al and W have been measured by other, more direct methods, which we shall discuss later and from these known distributions, values of $\bar{x}$ may be calculated. Theoretical $\bar{x}$ values for 20 and 40 keV Xe ions in tungsten (using the measured values of λ) are $23\mu g/cm^2$ and $33\mu g/cm^2$ which compare extremely favourably with the experimentally determined $\bar{x}$ values shown in Table 5. 25. Moreover, the experimental $\bar{x}$ values also compare favourably with values of $\overline{R}$ determined by the alternative method which determines penetration functions, and is also seen by examination of Table 5. 25.

This method offers potential use for a wide range of target materials, which is often impossible by other techniques, but for the present does not allow deduction of range distributions.

(f) Sectioning Methods

This final method has been the one most widely used to date to determine primary ranges and range distributions, and has consequently given the most successful data for comparison with theory. Basically the technique consists of injection of a collimated monoenergetic primary ion beam into a target, subsequent sectioning of the target parallel to the macroscopic surface and determination of either the number of primaries trapped in each section or remaining within the unsectioned material. The following four methods of sectioning have been employed. 1.) A stack of thin foils were clamped together and subsequent separation provided thin sections, within each of which the number of trapped primaries was evaluated. 2) After bombardment of a thick target, thin layers were removed from the surface mechanically with a grinding or abrasion tool. 3) Thin layers were removed by chemical or electrochemical etching and 4) The surface was slowly eroded away by bombardment with a second ion species and knowledge of the target sputtering rate enabled the thickness of the section to be determined.

The number of trapped primaries in methods 1), 2) and 3) was determined by using a primary beam of radioactive atoms and subsequent measurements of the activity of the sections or the remaining unsectioned material. The same technique has been used in method 4), but in addition, since this is a gas phase technique, the number of primaries released during erosion (or remaining after erosion) was also measured by recording with a mass spectrometer.

Methods (1) and (2) are worthy only of brief discussion since they both suffer from severe drawbacks. It is difficult to produce uniform thin self supporting foils (as noted in connections with method (c) and consequently only one range determination (of 40 KeV Xe^+ ions in Formvar films) has been reported by Thulin[92]. Mechanical sectioning has been used by Bartholomew and La Padula[93] for Kr^+ ions in Al with anomalously large observed penetrations. This may be ascribed to activity deposited upon the unsectioned material by the grinding instrument, or because of uneven grinding of specific areas of the surface. Technological advances in the production of thin films and cleavage techniques may render these methods more useful in the future however.

Method (3) has been used by Bredov and Okuneva,[94, 95, 96] who utilised the chemical etching technique to study Cs^{134} ranges in Germanium, Bartholomew and La Padula[97] who studied Kr^+ ion ranges in Mo and most extensively by Davies and co-workers[1, 41] using a two stage electrochemical etching technique to study the ranges of many ions in Al, Au, W and Ge. Bredov and Okuneva[94] measured the residual activity of Cs^{134} after etching a Ge target in H_2O_2 for various times. The rate of etching was determined by etching an unbombarded sample and measuring the rate of dissolution of the Germanium. The results of these studies will be presented subsequently in comparison with similar data obtained by Davies et al[81]. This comparison shows that the former measurements exhibit anomalously large penetrations, probably due, as pointed out by Davies et al[81], to non uniform etching by the solvent and to an inhibited etching rate of the bombarded Germanium compared with the standard unirradiated sample. Nevertheless the results are valuable in pointing out the sources of error which may arise with the direct chemical etching technique.

Bartholomew and La Padula[97] measured extremely high penetrations ($> 10^4$Å) of very low energy (< 30 eV) Kr^+ ions in Mo using the chemical stripping technique, and ascribed their anomalous ranges to a radiation enhanced diffusion process due to the high ion flux used. However, as we shall see in Chapter 8 a preferred explanation is that the ions were actually trapped beneath sputtered layers.

Realising these difficulties Davies and his collaborators[1, 41, 98] developed a two stage etching technique which consisted of initially converting a thin surface layer of the target to a compound which could be subsequently dissolved chemically without attacking the underlying target substrate. The initial conversion was achieved, for Aluminium targets, by electrochemical anodisation at constant voltage in an aqueous solution of ammonium citrate at 25°C. (the target serving as anode). It was found that this treatment, if carried through for a specified time, converted uniform thin layers of the surface Aluminium to Aluminium oxide. The thickness of these layers was intimately related to the applied voltage via the relation $t = 11.1\ (V + 1.8)$ Å, so that film thicknesses, as small as 37Å were readily produced at low applied voltages. This relation also included a correction due to the fact that the conversion of Al to Al_2O_3 is not 100% efficient and some Al was lost into the electrolyte.

After anodisation, the Al_2O_3 layers were removed completely by immersion in a phosphoric acid-chromium trioxide solution maintained at 90°C which, it was shown, did not attack the underlying unconverted Al.

The first use[41] of this method of target stripping was in a determination of the ranges of radioactive alkali metal ions in Al. These ions, evaporated from suspensions on a suitable cathode, were accelerated to energies between 2 and 50 keV and bombarded the aluminium targets which were generally preanodised to ensure a plane uniform surface. After bombardment the targets were removed from the vacuum system and the target activity measured. The targets were then anodised at the voltage required to produce the desired layer thickness and this layer subsequently removed by the stripping procedure described. The residual target activity was then measured and the difference in activity compared with that introduced into the solvent. The two activity measurements agreed very closely and in view of the much simpler determination of residual target activity this technique was subsequently employed only. Further layers of target were successively removed and the diminution of target activity determined after each section. Since the thickness of each section was accurately known it was then a simple matter to deduce the residual activity/thickness removed distribution. If n_x atoms were trapped at a distance x from the surface, then the residual activity after stripping a depth x from initial surface, was proportional to $\int_x^\infty n_x dx$ i.e. proportional to the number of primaries trapped beyond a penetration x. A plot of residual activity against depth removed therefore gave the 'integral' range distribution of primaries.

If N was the total number of primaries stopped in the target between x = o and ∞ then the activity difference between the unstripped target and that stripped to a depth x,

$$= N - \int_x^\infty n_x dx$$

$$= \int_o^x n_x dx. \text{ Thus } \frac{d}{dx}\left\{\int_o^x n_x dx\right\} = \frac{d}{dx}\left\{N - \int_x^\infty n_x dx\right\}$$

$$= \frac{-d}{dx}\left\{\int_x^\infty n_x dx\right\} = n_x$$

and a plot of the differential of the residual activity with respect to depth removed against the depth removed hence gives the number of primaries stopped at the depth x i.e. the differential range curve which is shown in Figure 5.70a for 50 keV C_s^{137} ions and integral range curves for C_s^{137} ion energies between 2 and 50 keV are reproduced in Figure 5.70b. It

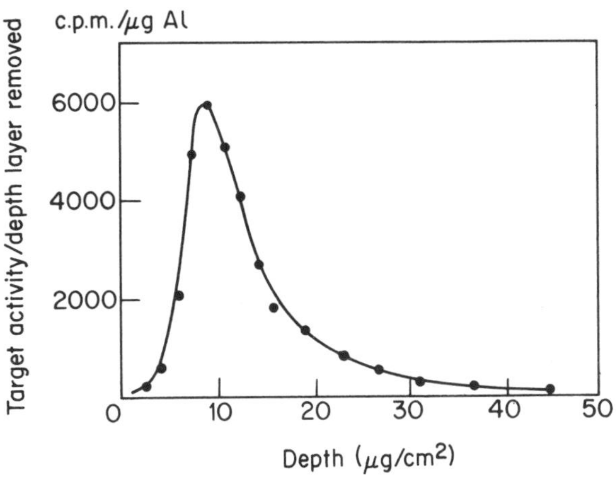

Fig. 5.70a Depth of penetration of 50-keV Cs^{137} ions in aluminium. (Differential)

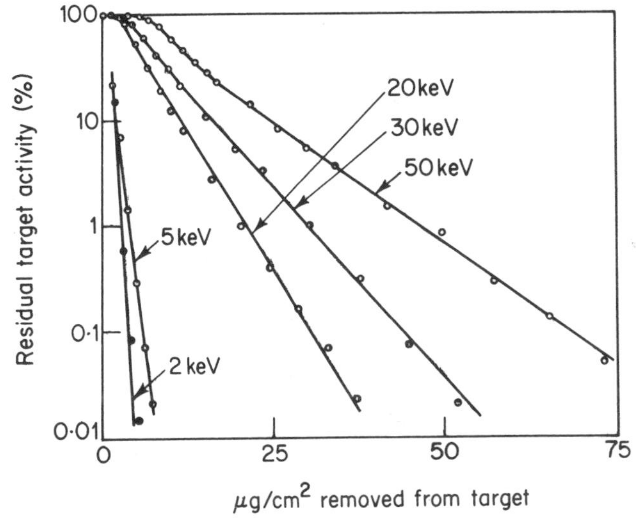

Fig. 5.70b Distribution curves for Cs^{137} ions of various energies in aluminum. (Integral) viz. (Ref. 5.41)

should be noted that the thickness of the first layer removed is assumed to be 20 Å larger than as measured because of the oxide layer always present upon the Aluminium during bombardment. The total number of ions striking the targets in these studies were of the order of $10^{14}/cm^2$ and therefore some radiation damage to the target may have been anticipated. However trapped primaries were expected to exert little effect on the paths of subsequent atoms, whilst erosion of the surface by bombardment would not be anticipated to influence the range distribution. Nevertheless, Davies et al[41] explored the possibility of such effects by increasing the bombardment dose by a factor of ten with no observed changes in the range distribution. However this negative result cannot be interpreted as illustrating unequivocally the absence of the above effects, since the total bombardment of the targets may have been sufficient to reach a saturation damage state where further bombardment increases could be of no consequence. Indeed, as we shall see later, these authors and others have shown that primary doses of the magnitude used above can lead to severe alteration of the range functions.

Similar results were observed after primary ion bombardment with Na^{24}, K^{42} and Rb^{86} and typical differential range curves for 30keV ions are shown in Figure 5.71a. Integral range curves for Na^{24} are also shown in Figure 5.71b. This figure is included here, only to preserve the historical continuity with which the range measurements were developed. In fact later work by McCargo et al[99] showed these data to be in error because of the effects of large bombardment doses.

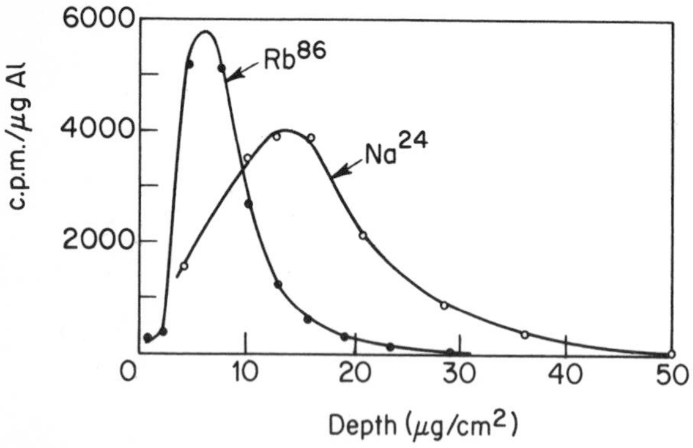

Fig. 5.71a Depth of penetration of 30-kev Rb^{86} and Na^{24}ions in aluminum. (Differential). (viz. Ref. 5.41)

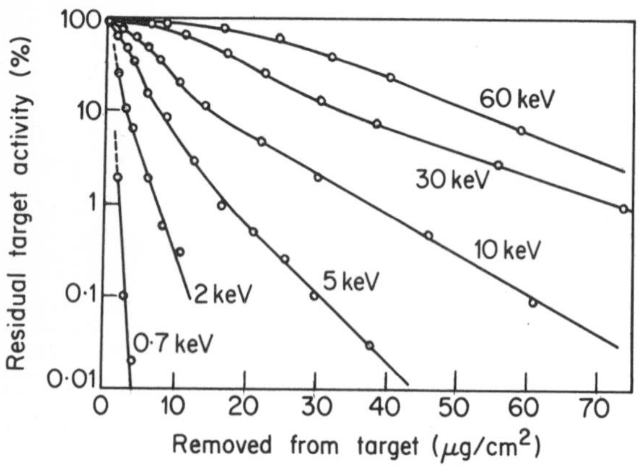

Fig. 5.71b Distribution curves of residual target activities for Na^{24}ions of various energies in aluminum. (Integral).(viz. Ref. 5.42)

Nevertheless, at higher energies in particular, the data of Figure 5.70 is useful in that it indicates the range magnitudes and their variation with energy.

It is clear, from the integral range curves, that an exponential long range portion exists, which leads to asymmetry in the differential range curves and considerable differences between the most probable range R_p (where the differential curve has a maximum) and the median R_m defined as the range where 50% of the primaries have been stopped.

Values of R_p, R_m and the half thickness $X_{1/2}$ of the exponential tails are enumerated in Table 5.26 and it should be noted that these values are all projected range parallel to the initial primary direction (normal to the target surface). The differential range distributions for Na^{24} indicate considerable primary stopping at and near to the target surface, an artifact not observed with heavier primaries. This is clearly a result of the near equality of the primary and target atoms for light primaries (as noted in Chapter 2) which gives considerable large angle deflections at the first collisions and stopping of the primaries close to the surface.

Comparison of the results in table 5.26 with the simple stopping formulae of equations 5.17 indicates that for the intermediate energies, the range-energy relations are linear functions. However the absolute magnitudes of the measured and theoretical ranges are different, due no doubt to the fact that the theoretical ranges are total values whilst the experimental ranges are projected values. For the light Na^{24} ions, with considerable back scattering, the projected ranges will be considerably smaller than the absolute values, but for the Cs^{137} ions the agreements should be, and is, closer. This discrepancy will be investigated in more detail when discussing the results of inert gas ion bombardment as will the deviation from range-energy linearity at high energies, which probably arises from electronic stopping processes. The exponential tails are also larger than may be expected on theoretical grounds, even allowing for non isotropic scattering, and although the Aluminium samples used were polycrystalline, must be ascribed to channelling events. In order to investigate the agreement between the experimental observations and a more realistic theoretical treatment, Davies et al[41] developed a Monte Carlo machine calculation of primary trajectories, similar to that of Oen, Holmes and Robinson[27, 36] assuming however, isotropic C.M. scattering and that the energy loss per collision is exactly half the maximum energy loss. This treatment necessitates assumption of a mean free path λ^0 at the initial primary energy E_0 and subsequent comparison of the computed results with the experimental data allows deduction of an optimum value for λ^0.

This Monte Carlo calculation gives a range probability distribution increasing to a maximum and a final exponential tail with a half thickness equal to the initial mean free path. This result may be anticipated from the theoretical deductions of Equation 5.17 which assumed a mean free path directly dependent upon primary energy as used in the Monte Carlo evaluation. Thus from the simple Nielsen stopping power formula

$$-\frac{dE}{dR} = 1.68\,\frac{M_1}{(M_1+M_2)M_2}\cdot\frac{Z_1Z_2}{(Z_1^{2/3}+Z_2^{2/3})^{1/2}} \qquad 5.173.1$$

then approximately

$$\frac{-dE}{dR} = T_{AV}\cdot\frac{E_o}{\lambda_o} \qquad 5.173.2$$

where T_{AV} is the average energy loss per collision. If T_{AV} is assumed to be

$$\frac{T_{max}}{2} = \frac{2M_1M_2}{(M_1+M_2)^2}$$

then one deduces

$$\lambda_o = 1.19\,\frac{M_2^2}{M_1+M_2}\,\frac{[Z_1^{2/3}+Z_2^{2/3}]^{1/2}}{Z_1Z_2}\cdot E_0 \qquad 5.173.3$$

From the Monte Carlo calculations it turns out that the range parameters R_p, R_m, and R_{AV} are simply constant multipliers k_p, k_m and $\bar{k}$ larger than the first mean free path. The calculated values of these constants for several Alkali metal ions in Aluminium are

TABLE 5. 26. (Ref. 5. 42)

Projected range of alkali metal ions in aluminium and Range per unit Energy values.

Ion	Energy (keV)	R_P ($\mu g/cm^2$)	R_M ($\mu g/cm^2$)	$X_{1/2}$ ($\mu g/cm^2$)	$\frac{R_P}{E}$(exptl)	$\frac{R_P}{E}$(calc)	$\frac{R_M}{E}$(exptl)	$\frac{R_M}{E}$(calc)
Na^{24}	0.7	—	0.4 ± .2	0.4 ± .1				
	1.0	—	0.5 ± .2	0.7 ± .1	0.36	0.27	0.59	0.47
	2.0	0.7 ± .3	1.1 ± .2	1.6	For E = 0.7 → 10 keV			
	5.0	1.6 ± .4	3.0	3.6				
	10.5	3.9 ± .4	6.2	8.3				
	15.0	—	7.8	9.0				
	24	9.8	12.0	—				
	30	13.1	15.0	15.5				
	60	26	29.5	16				
K^{42}	2	—	0.6_5 ± .2	0.6_7 ± .1				
	30	6.8	9.0	9.2	0.23	0.18	0.30	0.27
Rb^{86}	30	6.6	8.1	5.4	0.22	0.11	0.27	0.14
Cs^{137}	2	—	0.6 ± .3	0.4 ± .1				
	5	—	0.9 ± .3	0.6 ± .1	0.19	0.09	0.25	0.10
	20	4.0 ± .4	4.8	2.9	For E = 2.0 → 30 keV			
	30	5.7 ± .4	7.4	4.0				
	50	9.5	11.3	6.5				

Note: The estimated experimental error is ±6% except where otherwise noted.
R_P is the most probable range, R_M is the median range and $X_{1/2}$, the half thickness of the exponential tails.

enumerated in Table 5. 27. Thus multiplying the derived values of λ^0 in Equation 5. 173. 3 by the appropriate constants should give theoretical range magnitudes which may be compared with experimental data. Range per unit energy values obtained by both methods are given in Table 5. 26. for Na^{24}, K^{42}, Rb^{86} and Cs^{137} and whilst agreement is not very good, orders of magnitude are consistent.

TABLE 5. 27 (Ref. 5. 42).

k-Factors for various mass ratios.

Mass ratio	Ion	k_P	k_M	$\bar{k}$
0.889	Na^{24} in Al^{27}	0.70	1.23	1.50
1.556	K^{42} in Al^{27}	1.00	1.49	1.79
3.185	Rb^{86} in Al^{27}	1.75	2.21	2.55
5.074	Cs^{137} in Al^{27}	2.70	3.10	3.46

This comparison may be taken further, and since for example $R_m = K_m \lambda$ and λ is proportional to $M_2^2/M_1 + M_2$ a dependence of the range R_m upon M_1 and M_2 of the form

$$R_m \propto k_m \frac{M_2^2}{M_1 + M_2} \qquad 5.174$$

should be observed experimentally.

In order to investigate the validity of this approximation, Davies, McIntyre and Sims[98] performed simultaneous range determinations on the Na^{22} and Na^{24} isotopes, where electronic stopping effects would be expected to have similar results and the scattering laws would be almost identical.

The Na^{22+}, and Na^{24+} ions were injected simultaneously into the Aluminium targets, and the activities present in uniformly stripped Al layers were counted. The stripped layers were then allowed to stand for 1 week so that the Na^{24} activity decayed completely, and the remaining Na^{22} activity was determined. The initial Na^{24} activity was determined by difference, and the Na^{22} and Na^{24} contents in successive thin layers finally evaluated. The results of three separate range determinations are shown in Table 5. 28 from which it is clear that the Na^{22} has a

TABLE 5. 28 (Ref. 5. 98).

Median range (R) of 24-keV sodium ions in aluminum (in $\mu g/cm^2$).

Run No.	R_{22}	R_{24}	R_{22}/R_{24}
1	13.6_8	13.4_4	1.018
2	13.0_2	12.7_3	1.023
3	13.0_6	12.8_8	1.018 ± 0.004

higher mean range, but it was also observed that a considerably larger number of Na^{22} primaries were stopped close to the surface, presumably due to the greater back scattering for these primaries. The higher mean range of the Na^{22} primaries is a consequence of the higher mean free paths of these ions, which may be appreciated by a simple argument, as follows. At a given energy E, the distance of closest approach between primary and target atoms in a head on collision, is given, assuming a Coulomb repulsion, by $E_R = V(r)$

$$\text{i.e.}\quad r^2 = \frac{Z_1 Z_2 e^2}{E}\left\{\frac{M_1}{M_2} + 1\right\} \qquad 5.175$$

Thus, as M_1 and Z_1 decrease, r also decreases and the mean free path $= 1/_{n\pi r^2}$ increases. From the experimentally determined R_m values for Na^{22} and Na^{24}, the range ratio was determined to be 1.018, ± 0.5% whereas the k_m ratio, of 0.979 determined by the Monte Carlo method, multiplied by the ratio $\left(\frac{24+27}{22+27} = \frac{\lambda_{22}}{\lambda_{24}}\right)$ of 1.041, gives 1.019. Clearly the agreement is good, indicating that the assumptions in the Monte Carlo calculation are sufficiently valid to be able to compare primary ions of similar mass. However as shown in Table 5.26 the assumptions of isotropic scattering and constant energy loss are not valid for all the primary ions.

Davies and his collaborators[100-104] at Chalk River and Stockholm subsequently improved the ion bombardment apparatus by inclusion of an isotope separator stage, and measured the range of A^{41}, Kr^{85}, Xe^{133} and Rn^{222} in polycrystalline Al and W. These data are of importance since they allow comparison of ranges of primary ions of similar mass but very different chemical reactivity (i.e. A^{41}, and K^{42}, Xe^{133} and Cs^{137}) in the same target, and of the same primary ions in targets of different atomic mass. The same stripping technique was used for Al as previously described and W was anodised and stripped using a method described by Knutsen[105] and McCargo, Davies and Brown[101]. A^{41} energies between 0.7 keV and 2.25 MeV, Kr^{85} energies from 2 to 600 keV, Xe^{133} energies between 0.5 keV and 240 keV and Rn^{222} energies of 2-450 keV and total ion fluxes of about 10^{10} atoms cm^2 were used. Integral and differential range rata for the penetration of the four primary ion species in Al are summarised in Figures 5.72-5.75 a and b and of A^{41}, Kr^{85} and Rn^{222} in W in Figures 5.76, 5.77, 5.78 a and b. Values of $\bar{R}_{par}$, $\bar{R}_m$, $\bar{R}_{mp}$, $X_{1/2}$ and $W_{1/2}$ (the peak width at half maximum of the differential curves) are summarised in Tables 5.29-5.36. The differential range curves of Ar^{41} and Xe^{133} in Al are also compared with the earlier data for K^{42} and Cs^{137} in Al and with Monte Carlo calculations assuming isotropic scattering in Figures 5.78 and 5.79.

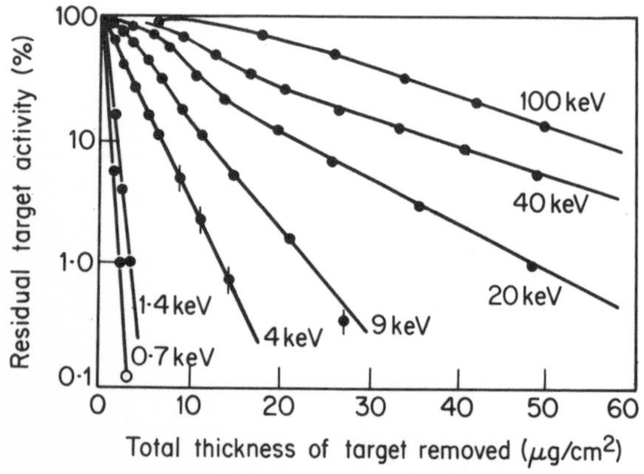

Fig. 5.72a Integral range distribution curves for A^{41} ions in polycrystalline Al; ion energies 0.7 →100 keV. (viz. Ref. 5.102)

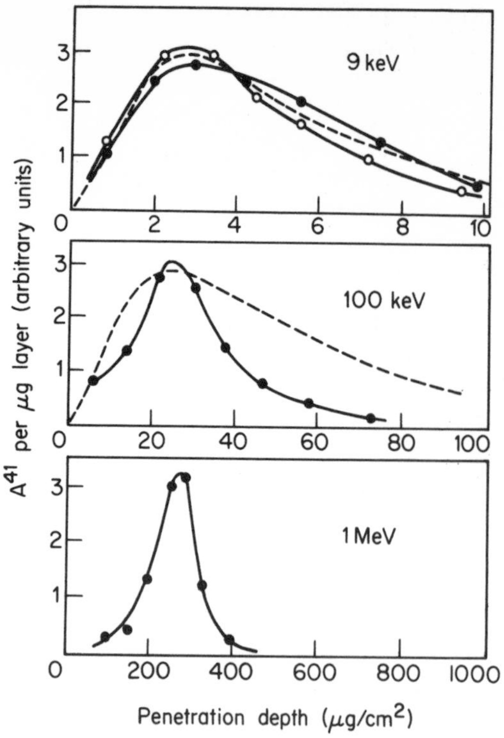

Fig. 5.72b Differential range distributions of 9keV, 100 keV and 1MeV A^{41}ions in polycrystalline Al ● are points for 10 keV K^{42}ions. The dashed curves are obtained by a Monte-Carlo computer calculation. viz.(Ref. 5.102)

General features of these curves are

(1) In Aluminium

(a) At low energies the ranges of Kr, Xe and Rn increase linearly with energy, but less quickly at higher energies. A(and K) show a linear increase at all energies however.

The A peak shape becomes narrower and peaked towards higher ranges with increasing ion energy, but this behaviour is not observed with, for example, the heavier Xe ion. A simple explanation of this observation lies in the fact that for Xe, (primary mass ≫ target mass) scattering takes place in a screened Coulomb field up to energies of about 500 keV, the interaction potential is thus approximately inverse r^2 and is consequently approximately isotropic at all energies studied. However, A^{41} with a much weaker interaction potential, approaches the target atoms more closely at higher energies, and the scattering is non isotropic (larger back scattering), thus the peak shape deviates markedly from the Monte Carlo predictions as shown in Figure 5.72. Similar reasoning applies to the Na^{24} primary ion also. Inelastic electron losses at higher energies for these lighter ions exert a similar influence on the distribution curve shape. It should be noted that A^{41} and K^{42}, Xe^{133} and Cs^{137} ions have almost identical ranges at high energies, showing that chemical reactivity exerts little influence on penetration phenomena. However discrepancies arise at lower energies probably due, according to Davies et al, to the larger ion fluxes employed in the earlier work on K^{42} and Cs^{137}, which lead to distortions in the penetration function due to 'the saturation' phenomenon. This phenomenon although discounted earlier is probably significant when higher resolution is used, and as a result of these observations, Brown and Davies[103]

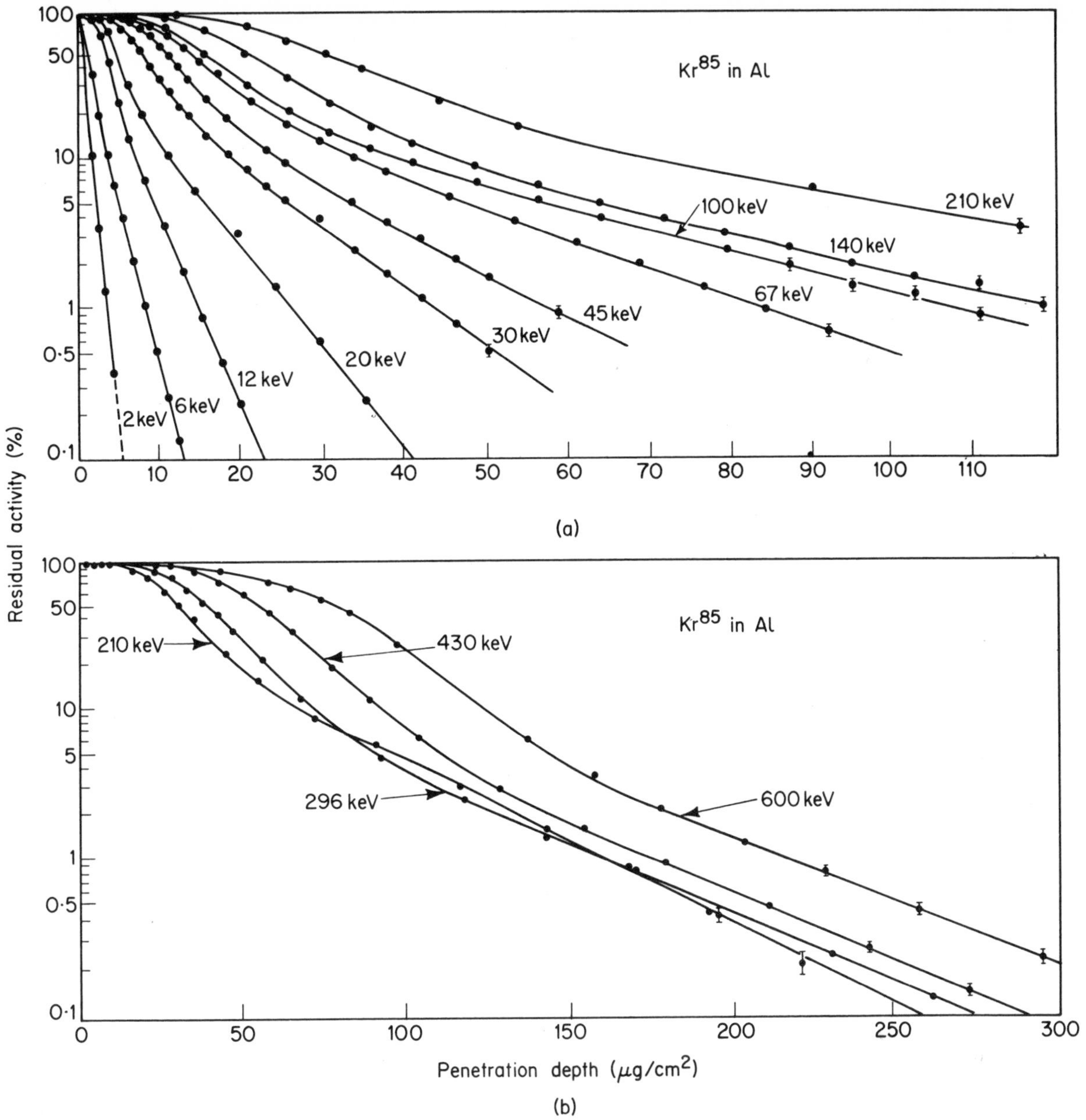

Fig. 5.73a Integral range-distributions for Kr^{85} in Al. (a) 2-210 keV (b) 210-600 keV. (viz. Ref. 5.100)

investigated the saturation effects more closely. Their observations will be discussed shortly.

(b) The half thickness $X_{1/2}$ of the exponential tails for all primary ions increases roughly linearly with energy at low energy but approach constant values at higher energies. These exponential tails, at high energies are associated with energy losses in inelastic collisions and channelling events which are necessarily low rate of energy loss events.

Thus one could expect the half thickness of the tails to remain roughly constant at high energies (as observed), as predicted by Figures 5.2 and 5.6 and Equations 5.35 but the magnitude of the range increases (again as observed).

(c) The relative peak width $W_{1/2}/\overline{R}_{m.p}$ decreases with increasing energy. Again this must be anticipated since $\overline{R}_{par}$ increases with energy, but since electronic stopping dominates at high energies, $W_{1/2}$ remains roughly constant. This results in the three ranges $\overline{R}_{par}$, $\overline{R}_{m.p}$ becoming roughly equal at the higher energies.

(2) In Tungsten

(a) Whereas range distributions in Al were accurately reproducible in successive experiments upon the same sample and with different samples, considerable variations in the ranges were observed for all primary ions in tungsten targets. Extensive tests showed that this variability was not a result of changes in bombardment conditions such as the total primary flux, the presence of unobserved neutral primaries in the beam nor of variations in the peeling technique. It was therefore concluded that the fluctuations were indicative of target variability, which although polycrystalline, consisted, on the atomic scale, of many thousands of micro crystallites in the region of primary ion bombardment. The thickness of these crystallites however, parallel to the primary direction was smaller than the primary range, and consequently variations in grain orientation and size may be expected to influence different range determinations. This conclusion agrees with the predictions of Robinson and Oen[28] and Beeler and Besco[29], regarding the influence of crystal structure upon primary ranges and is probably indicative of the existence of channelling events in tungsten.

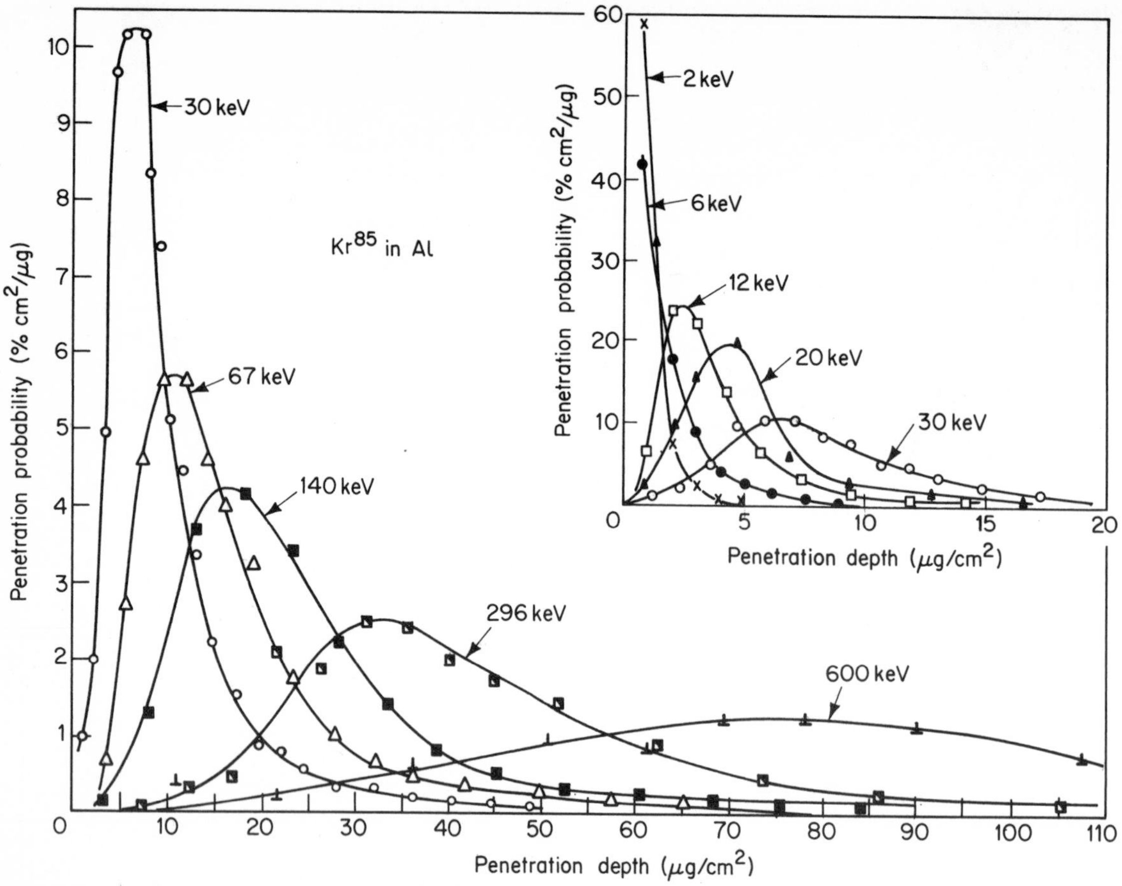

Fig. 5.73b Differential range-distributions for Kr^{85} in Al, using the same experiments as in Fig. 5.73a. Inset shows low energy results. (viz. Ref. 5.100)

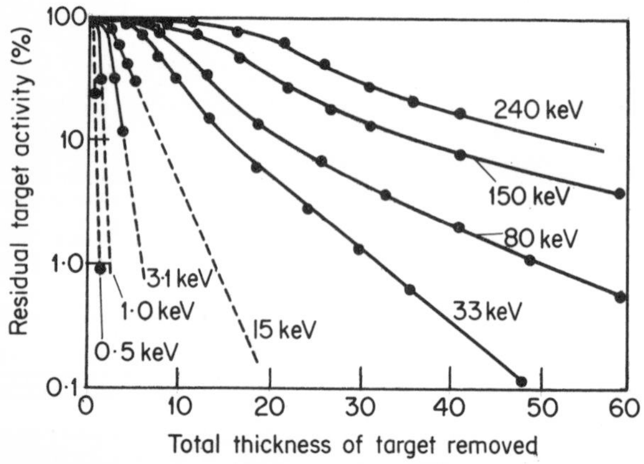

Fig. 5.74a Integral range distribution curves for Xe^{133} in polycrystalline Al. (viz. Ref. 5.102)

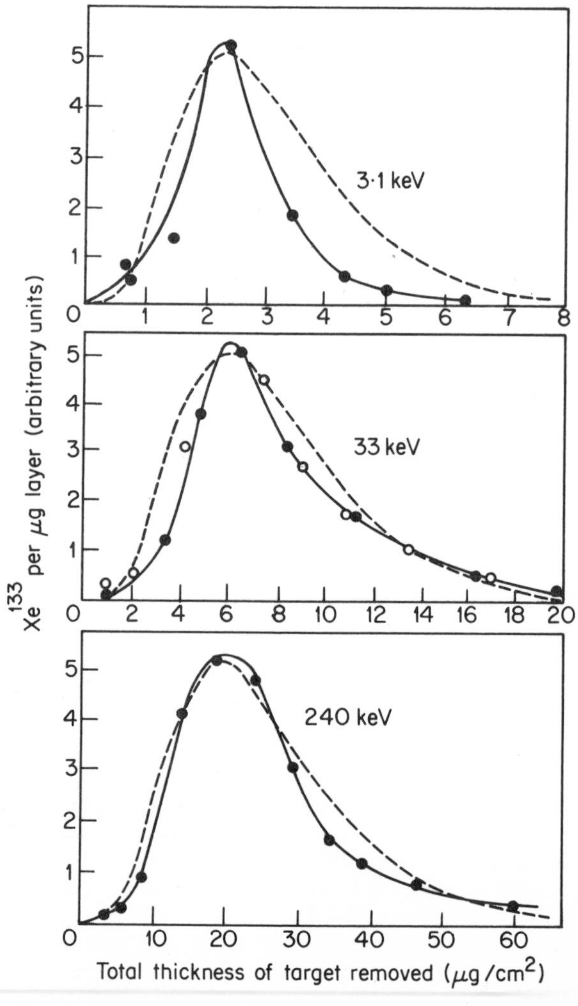

Fig. 5.74b Differential range distribution curves of Xe^{133} in polycrystalline Al (3.1, 33 and 240 keV ions) ○ are points for 35 keV C_s^{137}. Dashed curves are from Monte Carlo computer calculations (viz. Ref. 5.102)

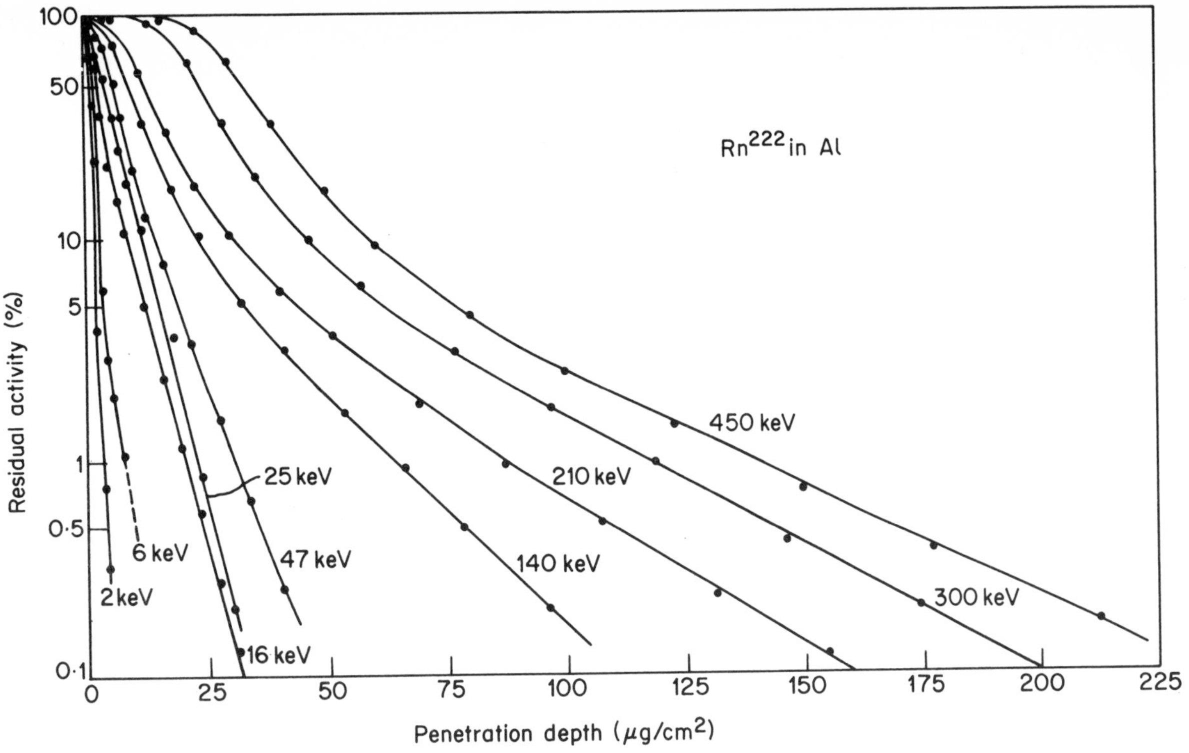

Fig. 5. 75a Integral range distributions for Rn^{222} in Al. (viz. Ref. 5. 86)

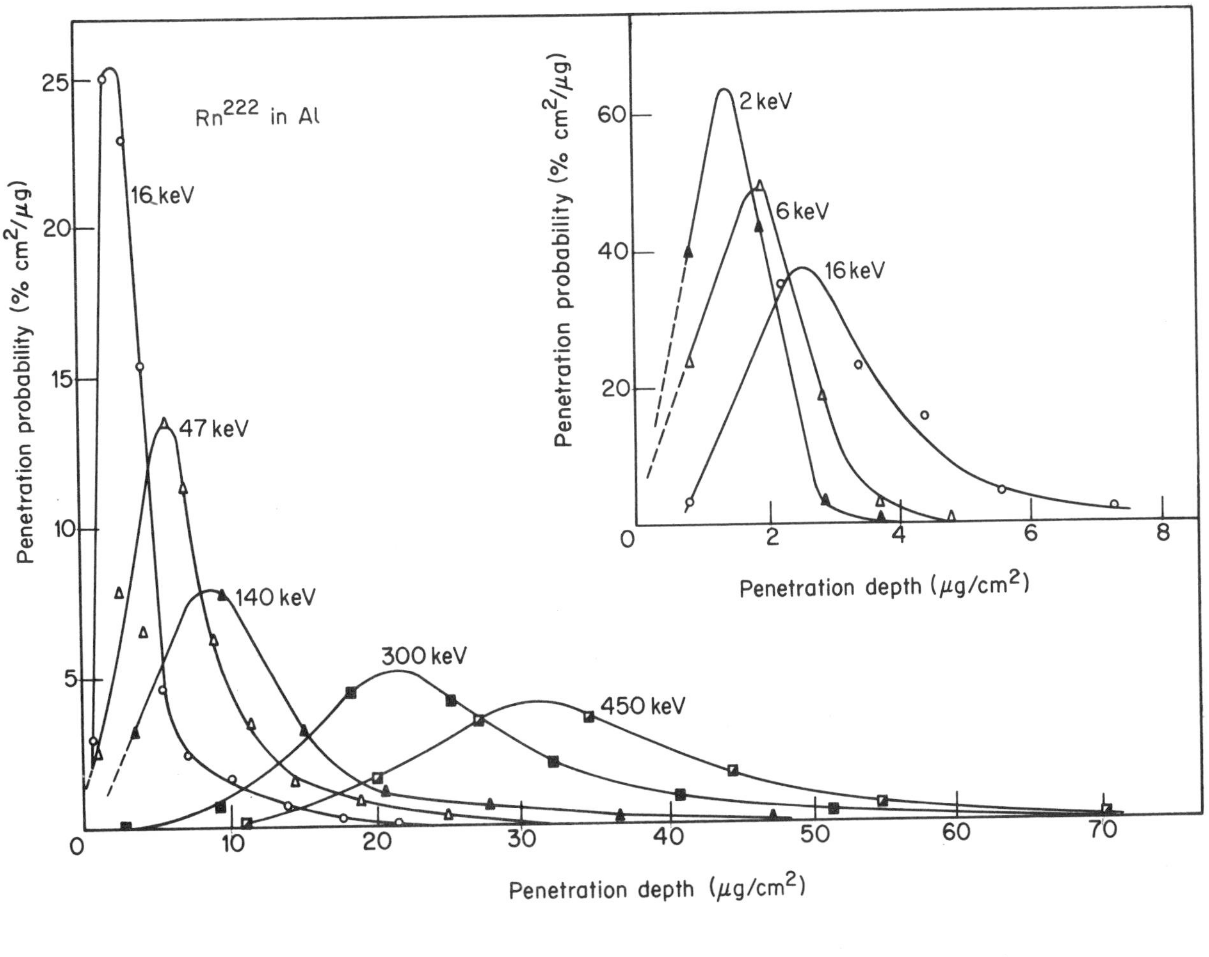

Fig. 5. 75b Differential range distributions for Rn^{222} in Al. (viz. Ref. 5. 86)

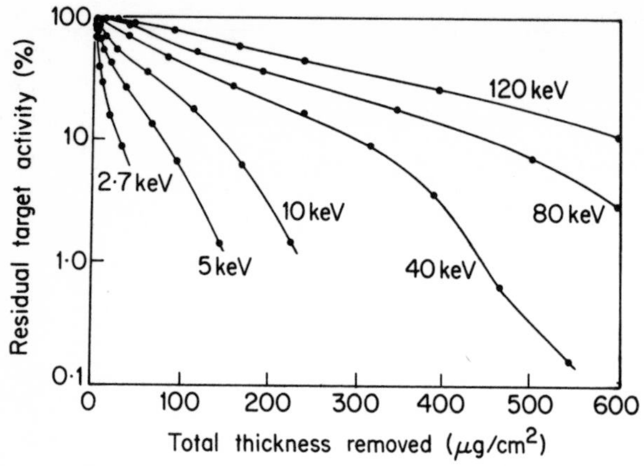

Fig. 5. 76 Integral range distribution curves for A^{41} in tungsten. (viz. Ref. 5. 101)

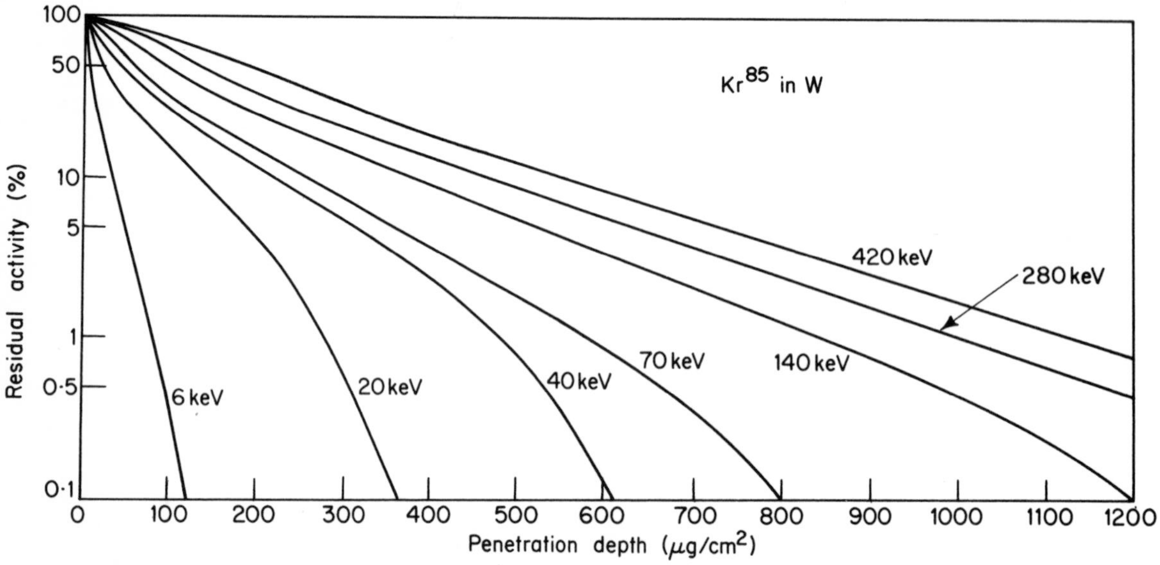

Fig. 5. 77a Integral range-distributions for Kr^{85} in W. Each curve is the average of four different runs. (viz. Ref. 5. 100)

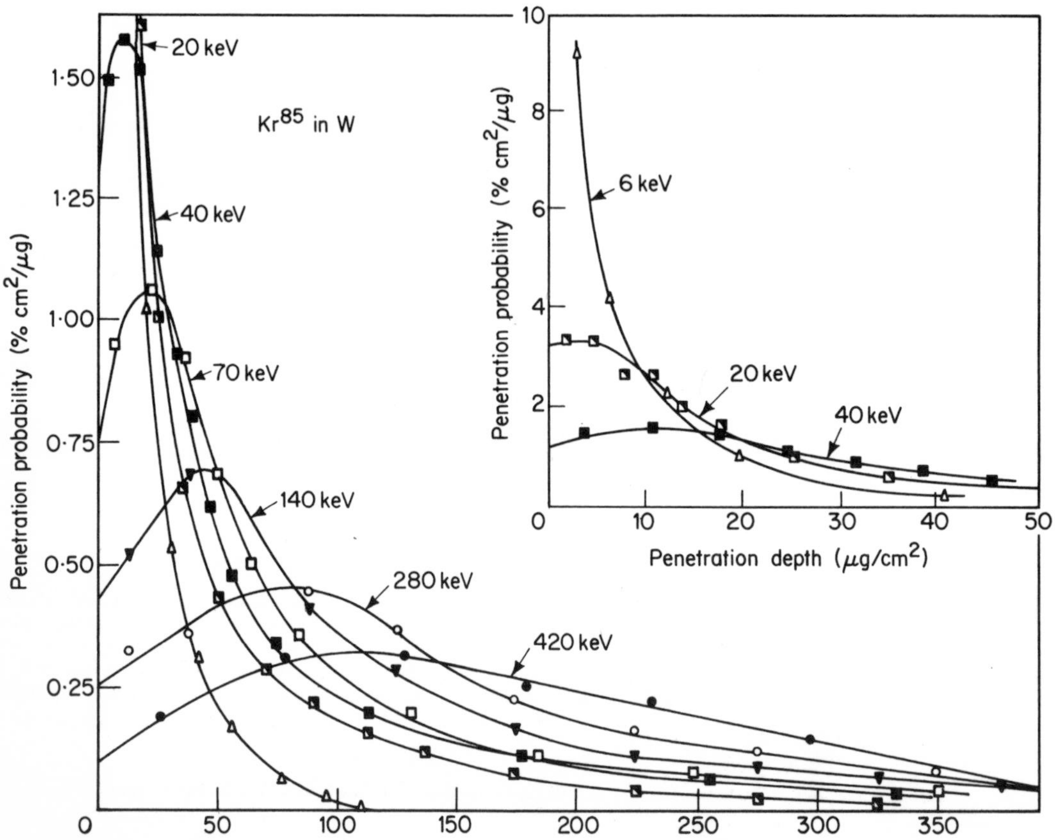

Fig. 5. 77b Differential range-distribution for Kr^{85} in W using the same experiments as in Fig. 5. 77a. Inset shows low energy results. Each curve is the average of four different runs. (viz. Ref. 5. 100)

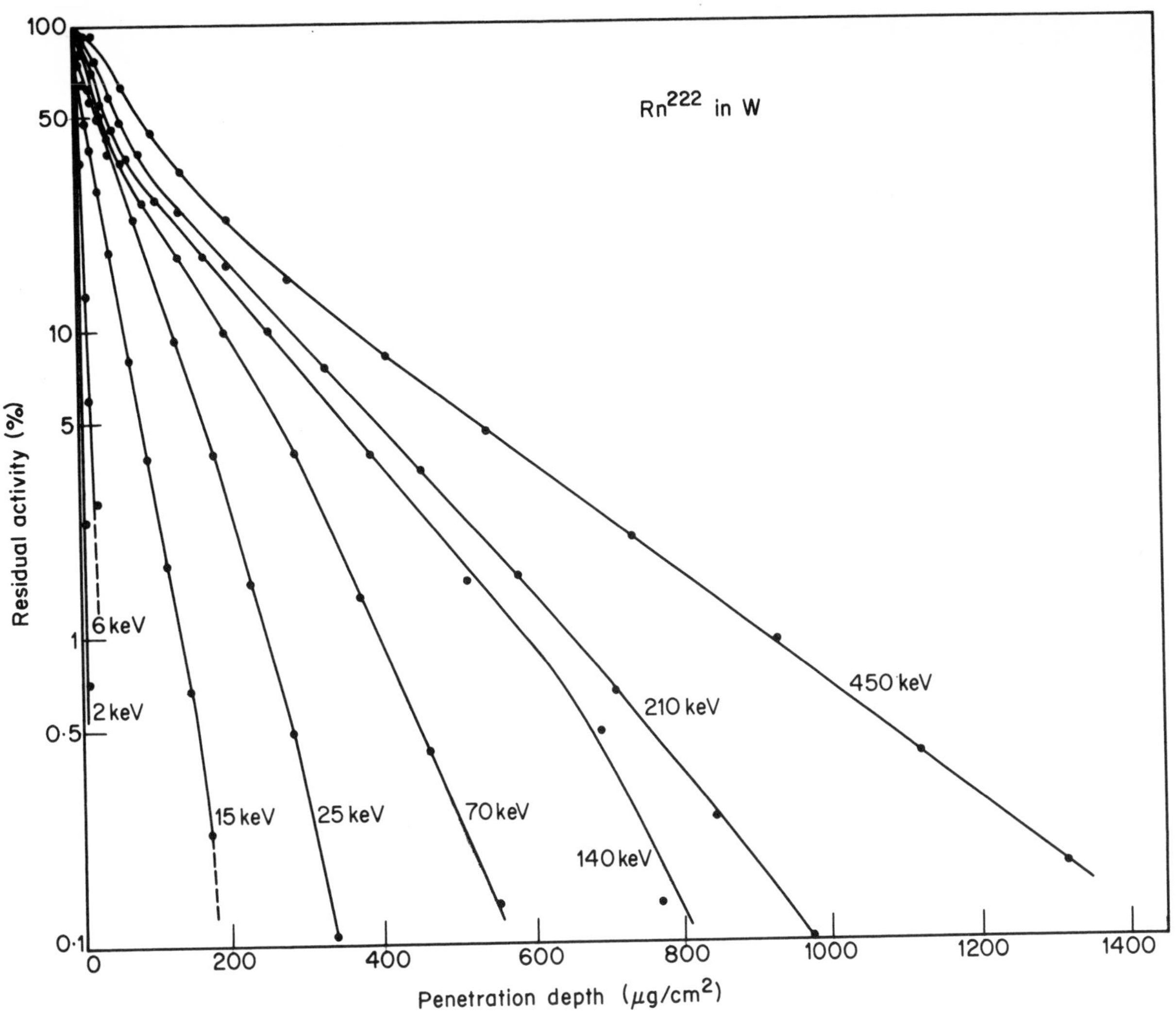

Fig. 5. 78 a Integral range distributions for Rn^{222} in W. (viz. Ref. 5. 86)

In order to obtain meaningful data for tungsten, average penetration functions were determined from four separate measurements at each energy for each ion, and these averages are reproduced in Figures 5. 76, 5. 77, 5. 78 and Tables 5. 33, 5. 34, 5. 35, 5. 36.

(b) The more penetrating tails are not exponential as in Al but resemble a Gaussian distribution, and also form a much larger proportion of the range distribution. The importance of the tails causes the ranges $\overline{R}_{par}$, $\overline{R}_{m.p}$ and $\overline{R}_m$ to be quite different, and although these values tend towards coincidence at higher energies, the convergence is not as marked as in Aluminium. Again the half thickness of the (approximately) exponential tails increases with primary energy to a limiting value at high energies, which is again indicative of the importance of electronic losses at high energies.

(c) For A^{41}, Kr^{85} and to a lesser extent for Rn^{222} and Xe^{137} there is a considerable stopping of primaries at and close to the surface, as was observed with A^{41} and Na^{24} in Aluminium. This must be again associated with back scattering of the primaries from the heavy tungsten atoms, particularly so for Kr^{85}, and leads to the broad penetration peaks observed.

A more quantitative comparison of these results will be given shortly but in view of the discrepancies noted in A^{41} and K^{42} ranges in Aluminium attributed by Davies et al to the cumulative effects of excessive primary bombardment, the subsequent detailed investigations of this phenomenon by Brown and Davies[103] are of considerable importance and are discussed now.

Brown and Davies[103] measured the range distributions in Aluminium for A^{41} and Xe^{133} primaries for four different conditions.

(1). For a low primary flux of Xe^{133} of about 10^{10} ions/cm^2.

(2). A 'saturation' experiment in which the target was bombarded simultaneously with a stable Xe isotope (Xe^{131}) and a radioactive isotope (Xe^{133}) with a total ion flux of about 6×10^{16}/cm^2, sufficient it was considered to saturate the target with ions.

(3). A 'post saturation' experiment in which the target was subjected to a short bombardment with radioactive Xe^{133} and then bombarded to saturation with stable Xe^{136}.

(4). A 'presaturation' experiment in which the target was first bombarded to saturation with a stable ion (Xe^{133} or Ar^{40}) and subsequently subjected to a short bombardment with radioactive Xe^{133} or A^{41}. Argon was not used in (2) or (3) because of the short half life of A^{41} compared to the time required to achieve saturation.

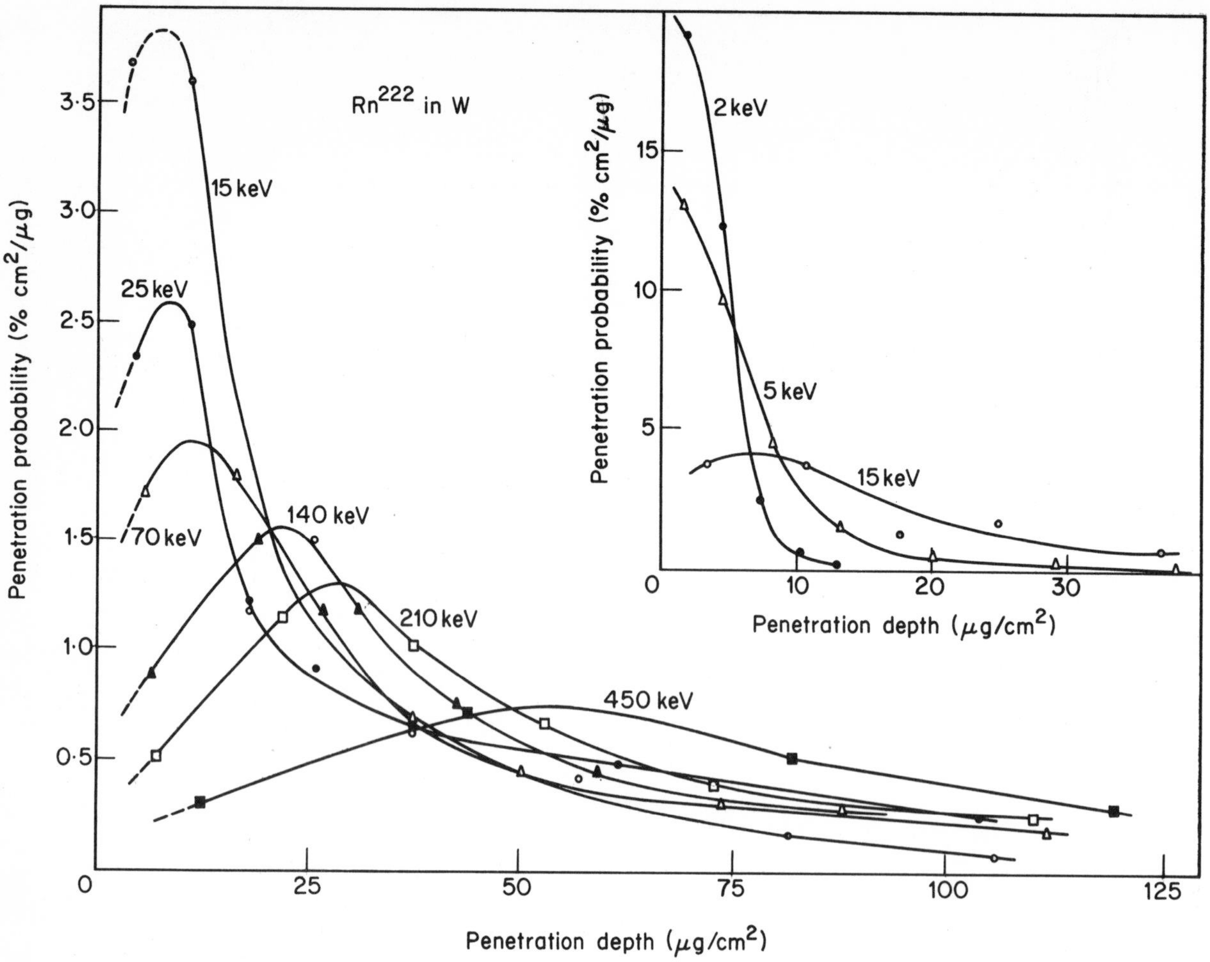

Fig. 5. 78b Differential range distributions for Rn^{222} in W. (viz. Ref. 5. 86)

TABLE 5. 29 (Ref. 5. 102).

Projected Ranges of A^{41} and K^{42} ions in aluminium (in μg/cm²).

Ion	keV	$\bar{R}_{m.p}$	$\bar{R}_m$	$\bar{R}_{par}$	$X_{1/2}$	$W_{1/2}$
A^{41}	0. 7	—	0. 4 ± 0. 2	—	0. 3 ± 0. 1	
	1. 4	—	0. 6 ± 0. 2	—	0. 5 ± 0. 1	
	4. 0	1. 6 ± 0. 3	2. 2 ± 0. 2	3. 0 ± 0. 2	2. 2 ± 0. 2	
	9. 0	3. 9 ± 0. 3	4. 7	5. 8	3. 8 ± 0. 3	
	20	6. 5	8. 2	10.$_6$	7. 8	
	30	9. 1	12.$_5$	14.$_4$	12.$_0$	
	40	9. 6	13.$_5$	18.$_2$	13.$_4$	11.$_5$
	60	15.$_0$	18.$_8$	22.$_6$	16.$_0$	17
	100	25.$_0$	27.$_8$	32.$_1$	20.$_0$	21
	180	49.$_0$	61.$_0$	—	—	—
	750	198	192	190.$_5$	17	91
	1000	262	255	252	22	101
	2250	495	480	464	23	115
K^{42}	2. 0	—	0. 6$_5$ ± 0. 2	—	0. 6$_5$ ± 0. 1	
	5. 0	—	1. 9 ± 0. 2	—	1. 6$_5$ ± 0. 2	
	10. 0	2. 7 ± 0. 4	4. 0	5. 0	3. 1	
	30	6. 8	9. 0	10.$_5$	8. 3	
	60	12.$_0$	13.$_4$	15.$_5$	11.$_0$	15
	100	23.$_0$	25.$_0$	28.$_0$	15.$_0$	23

TABLE 5. 30 (Ref. 5. 100)

Range of Kr^{85} ions in aluminum ($\mu g/cm^2$).

E(keV)	$\overline{R}_{m.p}$	$\overline{R}_m$	$\overline{R}_{par}$	$X_{1/2}$	$W_{1/2}$	$W_{1/2}/\overline{R}_{m.p}$
2	—	0. 6 ± 0. 3	1. 0 ± 0. 3	0. 6	—	—
6	—	1. 0 ± 0. 3	1. 7 ± 0. 3	1. 4	—	—
12	2. 5	3. 2	3. 9	2. 4	3. 1	1. 25
20	4. 2	4. 5	6. 0	4. 5	4. 4	1. 05
30	6. 5	8. 1	10. 2	7. 6	7. 3	1. 10
45	8. 8	11. 4	13. 6	10. 2	9. 8	1. 10
67	11. 0	14. 4	18. 0	15. 5	13. 5	1. 20
100	13. 3	16. 1	20. 6	21. 2	15. 6	1. 15
140	17	21. 5	25. 8	23. 5	19. 2	1. 15
210	25	31. 3	39. 5	27. 5	25	1. 00
296	34	40. 6	45. 8	32	33	0. 97
430	53	56. 0	60. 6	32	46	0. 87
600	80	79. 5	81. 7	35	74	0. 93

TABLE 5. 32 (Ref. 5. 88).

Range of Rn^{222} ions in aluminum ($\mu g/cm^2$).

E (keV)	$\overline{R}_{m.p}$	$\overline{R}_m$	$\overline{R}_{par}$	$X_{1/2}$	$W_{1/2}$	$W_{1/2}/\overline{R}_{m.p}$
2	(1. 3)	1. 3 ± 0. 3	1. 3 ± 0. 3	0. 7	(1. 5)	(1. 15)
6	(1. 9)	1. 8 ± 0. 3	1. 8 ± 0. 3	2. 3	(1. 8)	(0. 95)
16	2. 7	3. 4	4. 4	3. 5	3. 5	1. 30
25	3. 8	4. 8	6. 1	3. 4	3. 9	1. 03
47	6. 0	6. 6	7. 9	5. 0	5. 6	0. 94
140	8. 8	9. 8	13. 0	14. 6	10. 0	1. 14
210	11. 4	13. 0	17. 0	23. 0	12. 4	1. 09
300	21. 5	24. 5	29. 1	26. 0	15. 3	0. 71
450	31. 0	33. 2	39. 1	30. 0	21. 0	0. 68

TABLE 5. 31. (Ref. 5. 102).

Projected Ranges of Xe^{133} and Cs^{137} ions in aluminium (in $\mu g/cm^2$).

Ion	E (keV)	$\overline{R}_{m.p}$	$\overline{R}_m$	$\overline{R}_{par}$	$X_{1/2}$	$W_{1/2}$
Xe^{133}	0. 5	—	—	—	$0.1_8 \pm 0.05$	
	1. 0	—	1. 0 ± 0. 2	1. 4 ± 0. 2	$0.3_1 \pm 0.1$	
	3. 1	2. 2 ± 0. 4	2. 3 ± 0. 2	2. 7 ± 0. 2	$0.6_2 \pm 0.1$	
	5. 0	—	2. 6 ± 0. 2	3. 1 ± 0. 2	$0.8_0 \pm 0.1_5$	
	15. 0	3. 0	3. 6	4. 2	1. 9 ± 0. 3	
	33	6. 2	7. 4	9. 5	5. 2	
	45	—	8. 5	10. 3	9. 0	
	80	$10._1$	$10._6$	13.	9. 5	
	150	14	16.	21.	$20._0$	
	240	20	23.	30.	$27._0$	
Cs^{137}	2. 0	—	0. 6 ± 0. 3	—	$0.3_5 \pm 0.1$	
	5. 0	—	0. 9 ± 0. 3	—	0. 6 ± 0. 1	
	20	4. 0 ± 0. 3	6. 8	5. 2	2. 9	
	30	5. 7	7. 4	8. 1	4. 0	
	50	7. 5	9. 0	11. 2	6. 5	
	75	8. 9	10.	$12._0$	9. 0	

TABLE 5. 33 (Ref. 5. 100).

Ranges of Kr^{85} ions in tungsten ($\mu g/cm^2$)

E (keV)	$\overline{R}_{m.p}$	$\overline{R}_m$	$\overline{R}_{par}$	$X_{1/2}$
6	—	6	12. 4	15
20	3	20	46	44
40	11	39	82	92
70	23	53	100	100
140	45	88	152	144
280	80	132	199	165
420	100	187	251	180

TABLE 5. 34 (Ref. 5. 88).

Ranges of Rn^{222} ions in tungsten

E(keV)	$\bar{R}_{m.p}$	$\bar{R}_m$	$\bar{R}_{par}$	$X^{1/2}$	$W^{1/2}$	$W^{1/2}/\bar{R}_{m.p}$
2	—	2. 5	3. 1	1. 1	—	—
6	—	4. 0	6. 1	4. 8	—	—
15	7	15	26	22	—	—
25	8. 5	28	51	40	—	—
70	11. 5	32	72	71	—	—
140	21	46	96	102	43	2. 1
210	28	59	113	112	45	1. 6
450	54	89	155	166	97	1. 8

TABLE 5. 35 (Ref. 5. 101).

Range of A^{41} in tungsten* ($\mu g/cm^2$).

Energy (keV)	A^{41}/W		
	$\bar{R}_{par}$	$\bar{R}_m$	$\bar{R}_{par}/\bar{R}_m$
1. 0	—	—	—
2. 7	9. 6	5. 1	—
5. 0	29. 0	$16._0$	1.8_0
10. 0	$55._5$	$30._0$	1.8_5
20. 0	78	$46._5$	1.6_9
40	125	83	1. 51
60	140	92	1. 52
80	185	126	1. 47
100	165	115	1. 44
120	—	—	—
180	253	197	1. 28
240	—	—	—

* The estimated error is ±12% except for the low-energy measurements.

TABLE 5. 36 (Ref. 5. 101)

Range of Xe^{133} in tungsten ($\mu g/cm^2$)

Energy (keV)	Xe^{133}/W		
	$\bar{R}_{par}$	$\bar{R}_m$	$\bar{R}_{par}/\bar{R}_m$
1. 0	1. 0	0. 7	—
2. 7	3. 6	2. 3	—
5. 0	15. 0	7. 7	2.0_5
10. 0	$19._4$	$9._1$	2.1_5
20. 0	43	$20._0$	2.1_5
40	70	32	2.2_0
60	—	—	—
80	145	65	2.1_5
100	—	—	—
120	148	77	1.9_5
180	—	—	—
240	200	116	1.8_5

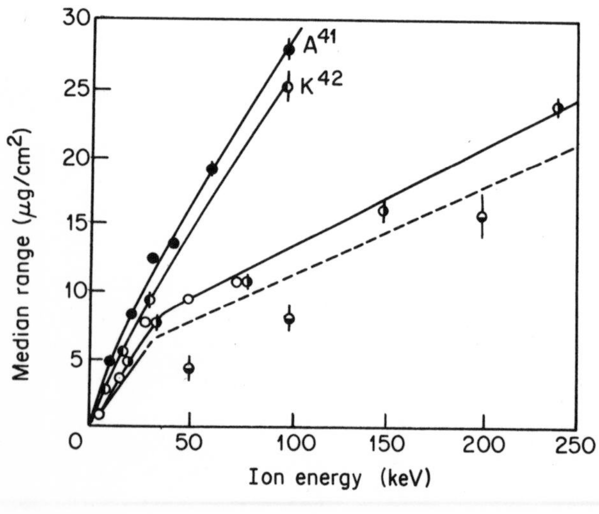

Fig. 5. 79 Comparison of median ranges $\bar{R}_m$ as a function of ion energy for A^{41} ●; K^{42} ◐; ◑ Xe^{133} and Cs^{157} O in aluminium. The crosses represent Powers and Whalings' data for the most probable range of Xe^{133} in Al (Ref. 5. 58) and the dashed curve represent Davies et als' data for this range. (viz. Ref. 5. 102)

Figures 5. 80a, 80b and 5. 80c illustrate the results of experiments 2), 3) and 4) respectively. The saturation experiment shows clearly that the distribution curve is considerably broadened during a long bombardment, peaking at lower penetration depths. The post and presaturation experiments throw some light on the reasons for this distribution change. In the postsaturation experiment, illustrated by the integral penetration functions in Figure 5. 80b the change of this function due to the presence of the trapped primaries is shown by the transition from curve C to curve A. Curve B is the actual penetration function after postsaturation bombardment, but this must be modified to curve C because of the Al sputtered from the surface during target saturation. Clearly the effect of the heavy bombardment is to cause the original primaries to be driven further into the target, i.e. a knock on phenomenon. One unexpected result of this experiment was the very small loss ($\lesssim 2\%$) of the original primaries from the target during saturation.

The results of the presaturation experiments for Xe (with two different amounts of Xe originally trapped) are shown in Figures 5. 80c. It is quite apparent that the presence of only a very small amount of gas trapped in the target leads to a marked reduction in the ranges of subsequent primaries.

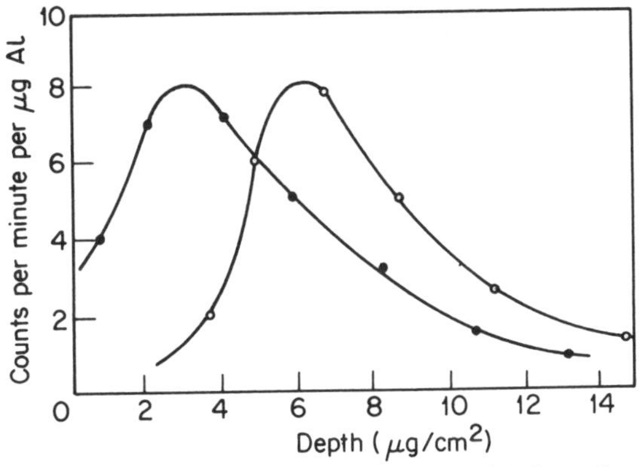

Fig. 5. 80a 30 keV Xe ions injected into polycrystalline Al, differential range curves. "Saturation" experiment ● Xe^{131} + Xe^{131m} total Xe flux of 12.5 ug/cm^2; ○ Xe^{133} total Xe flux $<10^{-5}$ ug/cm^2.(viz. Ref. 5. 103)

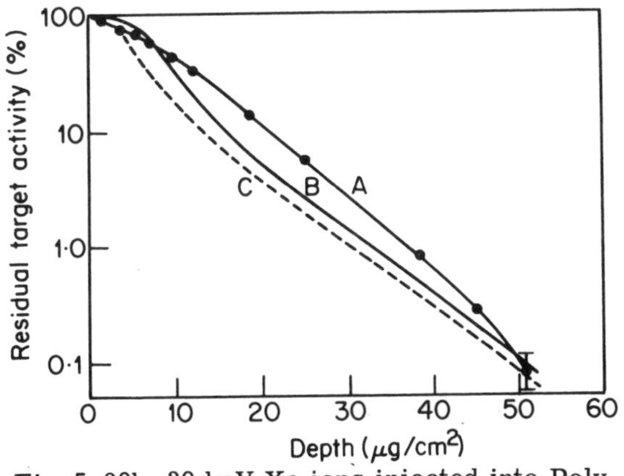

Fig. 5. 80b 30 keV Xe ions injected into Polycrystalline Ae, integral range curves. "Postsaturation" experiment. ● Xe^{133}ions injected into Al followed by bombardment with 5. 0 ug/cm^2 of 30 keV Xe^{136} full line, normal distribution of Xe^{133} for trace bombardments, dashed line is same as full line but corrected for sputtering loss of Al surface during Xe^{136} bombardment. (viz. Ref. 5. 103)

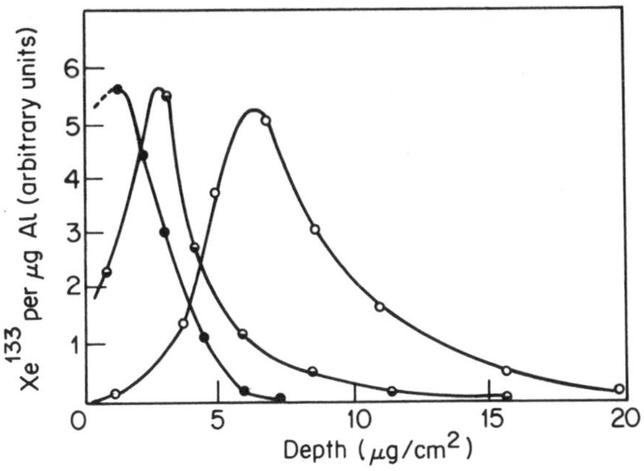

Fig. 5. 80c 30 keV Xe ions injected into polycrystalline Al, differential range curves. "Presaturation" experiment in which various quantities of 30 keV Xe^{132} bombarded the target before the Xe^{133}. ○ . No Xe^{132}; ◒ 5. 7 ug/cm^2 Xe^{132}; ● 13. 3 ug/cm^2 Xe^{132}. (viz. Ref. 5. 103)

These experiments which indicate both the knock on effect for trapped primaries and shift the initial penetration ranges to deeper values and the range reduction of later primaries, explain, at least qualitatively, the range function broadening of the saturation experiments. Brown and Davies[103] have also given a qualitative explanation of the results of the presaturation experiment. Since energy transfer is most efficient between primaries and target atoms of the same mass, then occlusion of primaries within the targets will increase the stopping power of the targets (particularly since the occluded atoms Xe and A have massess considerably greater than Al). Thus the primary range is increasingly reduced as more primaries are trapped.

Clearly these effects are of considerable importance if large primary fluxes ($> 10^{16}$ ions) are used as in the experiments of Powers and Whaling[58] and are of determining influence in the maximum numbers of primaries which may be trapped. We shall return to this question again in Chapter 8 and accept that most of the experiments conducted by Davies and his collaborators, excluding possibly some of the earlier measurements with Na^{24}, accurately reflect the penetration functions. In fact, because of this discrepancy McCargo et al[99] repeated the range measurements of Na^{24} in Aluminium at much lower total bombardment fluxes (10^{10}/cm^2) and the revised estimates are shown in Figure 5. 81a. Clearly the penetrations are considerably increased, as indicated by the two curves taken from Figure 5. 71b and used for comparison. Thus a more precise range-energy plot is as in Figure 5. 81b. Again the enhanced ranges are evident, particularly at low energies, and agreement with the Oen and Robinson[27, 36] calculated data, shown for comparison, is much improved.

In view of the results of these and several earlier experiments involving light ions bombarding heavy targets, where it was found that considerable primary stopping occurred at the target surface, this indicated that primaries would also be back scattered out of the target, leading to effective primary sticking coefficients less than unity.

Brown and Davies[103] measured the sticking factors of Xe and Ar in Al, Xe in Be, Ni, Zr, Ta, Ag, and Au and Kr in W as a function of the primary ion energy. The sticking factors were measured by evaluating the ratio of the total numbers of primary ions stopped at

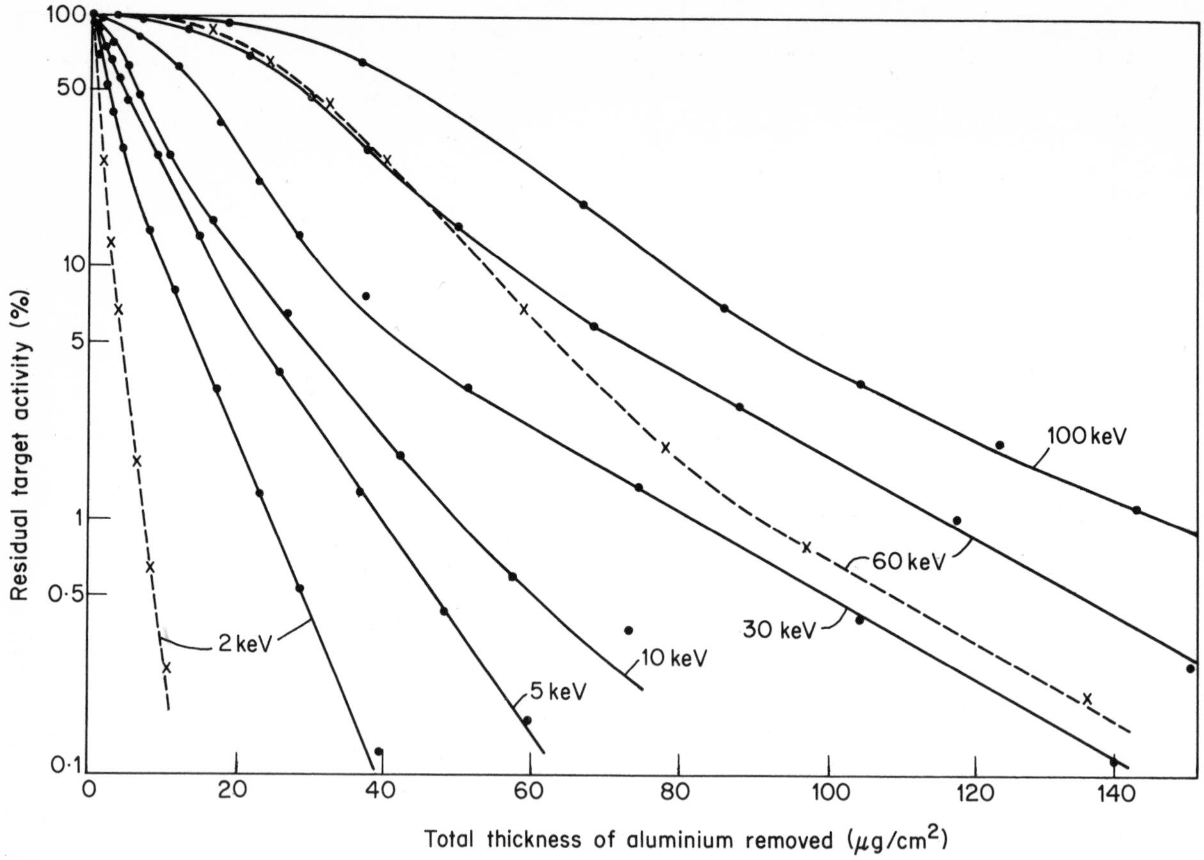

Fig. 5. 81a Integral range distributions of Na^{24}ions in aluminum: • new data, using trace bombardments; × previous work. (Ref. 5. 42) (viz. Ref. 5. 99)

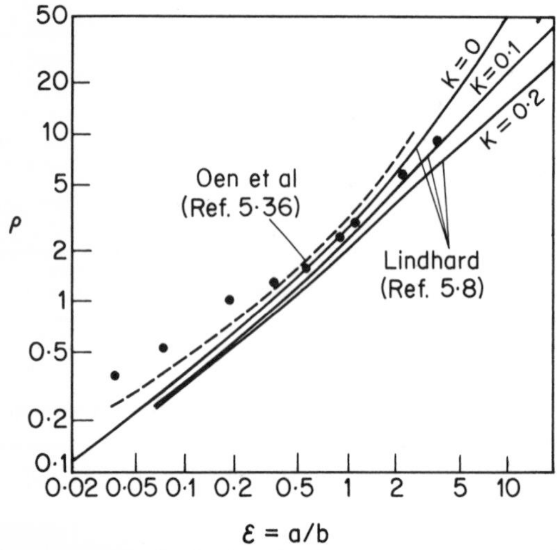

Fig. 5. 81b Comparison of the new experimental data, using trace bombardments, with various theoretical curves. For the definition of ρ and ε, see reference, 8. The appropriate value of Lindhard's electronic stopping parameter k, for Na^{24} in aluminum, is 0. 15. (viz. Ref. 5. 99)

all depths within the targets to the total measured ion flux to the targets. Unfortunately the total number of primaries which had struck the targets could not be determined accurately and so absolute values of sticking factor were evaluated by assuming that Xe ions above 5 keV incident on Al targets possessed unity sticking factor. Experimentally determined values for this combination were between 0. 97 and 1. 04, indicating the closeness of the real value to unity. Other evidence that the sticking factor is indeed unity for Xe in Al above 5 keV, was that above this energy, up to 150 keV, the measured sticking factor was unchanged.

Further, no release of Xe occurred when the Al was heated, until the melting temperature was reached. Finally, penetration function determinations, as shown earlier show no stopped primaries immediately close to the Al surface. Using this normalisation condition, sticking factor/energy curves were obtained as shown in Figure 5. 82. All these curves have common features of a low sticking coefficient up to unity at about 5 keV, and a constant value thereafter. Exceptions to this rule occur with Xe in Ag and Au targets, which as pointed out by Brown and Davies[103] do not form stable oxides and for A, Kr and Xe in W targets. This latter result is undoubtedly a result of the higher backscattering from the heavier tungsten targets. We shall return to a further discussion of these data in Chapter 8.

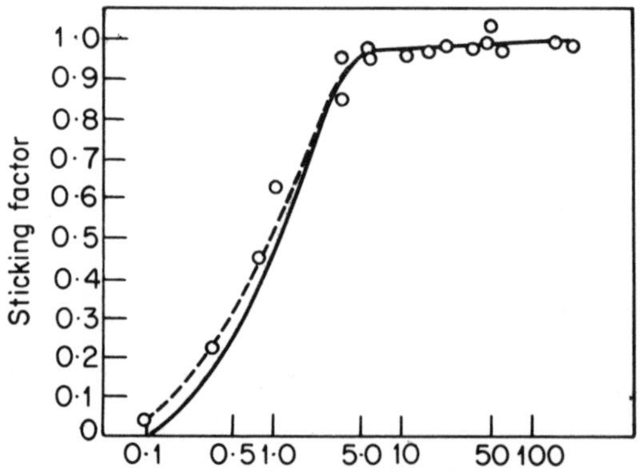

Fig. 5. 82a Sticking factor for Xe^{133} ions in Al as a function of their energy. Dashed curve is total fraction sticking, uncorrected for ~6% neutral atoms in ion beam. Full curve is corrected for presence of neutrals. (viz. Ref. 5. 103)

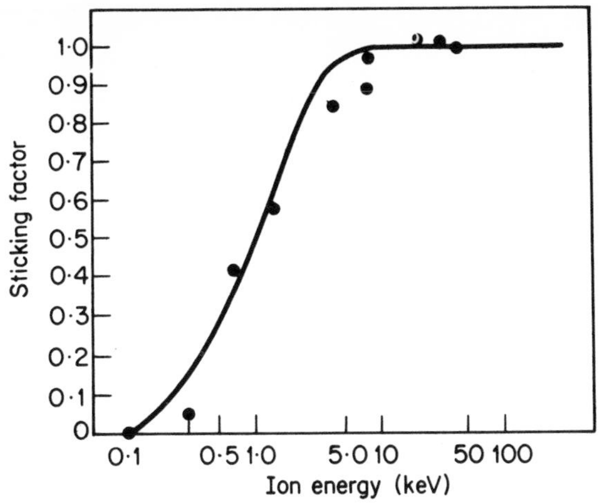

Fig. 5. 82b Sticking factor for A^{41} ions in Al as a function of their energy. ● for A^{41}; full curve for Xe^{138}. (viz. Ref. 5. 103)

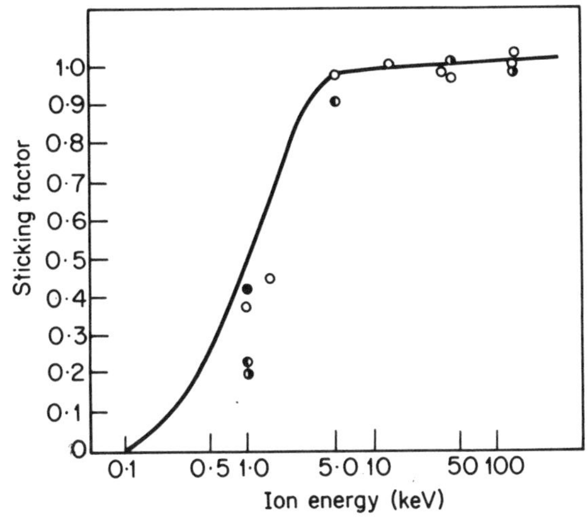

Fig. 5. 82c Sticking factor of Xe^{133} ions in various metals as a function of ion energy.
Full line Xe^{133} in Al
◐ Xe^{133} in Be; ◑ Xe^{133} in Ni; ● Xe^{133} in Zr; ○ Xe^{133} in Ta. (viz. Ref. 5. 103)

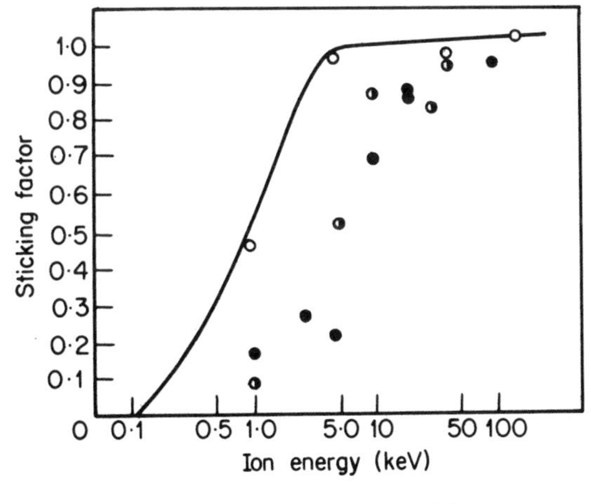

Fig. 5. 82d Sticking factor for A^{41}, Kr^{85} and Xe^{133} ions in W as a function of ion energy.
Full line, Xe^{133} in Al
○ for Xe^{133} in W
◑ for Kr^{85} in W
● for A^{41} in W
(viz. Ref. 5. 103)

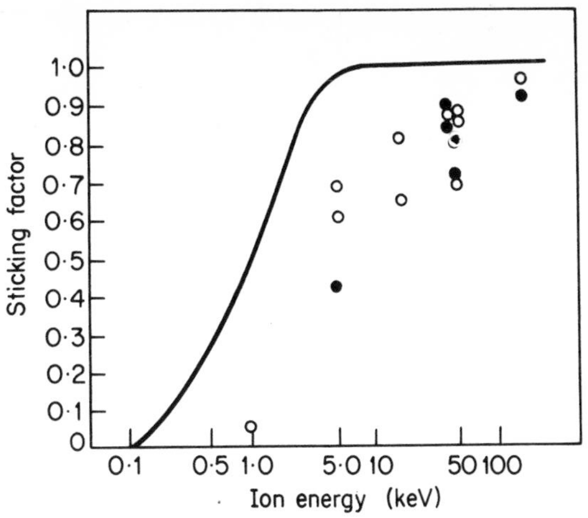

Fig. 5. 82e Sticking factor for Xe^{133} ion in Ag and Au as a function of ion energy.
Full line Xe^{133} in Al
● for Xe^{133} in Ag
○ for Xe^{133} in Au
(viz. Ref. 5. 103)

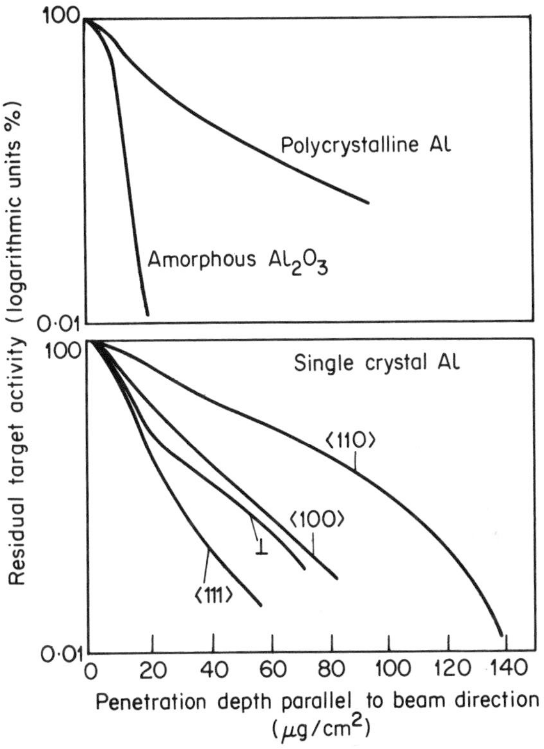

Fig. 5. 83 Integral range curves for 40 keV Kr^{85} in amorphous Al_2O_3, polycrystalline and single crystal Al illustrating the channelling phenomenon. (viz. Ref. 5. 106)

The results of the experiments on primary ranges in tungsten, strongly suggested that a channelling process such as postulated by Robinson and Oen[28], was operative. In order to investigate this possibility Piercy, Brown, Davies and McCargo[106], used the stripping technique to investigate the range distribution of Kr^{85} in polycrystalline Aluminium, amorphous Aluminium oxide and in specific directions in single crystal Aluminium. In one experiment the range distribution of 40 keV Kr^{85} ions in polycrystalline Al were determined. Various known thicknesses of Al_2O_3 were then formed upon different targets of Aluminium by the anodisation technique, and the oxidised samples bombarded. By measuring the activity before and after stripping the oxide films, the

TABLE 5.37.(Ref. 5.104).

Characteristics of range distributions in Al_2O_3.

Ion	Energy (keV)	$\overline{R}_{m.p}$ (μg/cm²)	$\overline{R}_m$ (μg/cm²)	$\overline{R}_{par}$ (μg/cm²)	W_{rms}* (μg/cm²)
Na^{24}	2	—	(1.2)	—	—
	10	3.5	3.9	4.7	2.6
	20	5.8	6.4	6.7	3.8
	40	11.5	12.4	12.7	6.5
	80	28.5	28.8	29.5	11.3
Ar^{41}	0.5	—	(1.2)	—	—
	1	—	(1.2)	—	—
	2	—	(1.5)	—	—
	5	—	(1.7)	—	—
	10	2.5	2.6	2.5	1.2
	20	6.2	5.5	5.3	2.5
	40	10.4	9.4	9.3	4.5
	80	15.4	16.3	16.6	6.8
	160	32	34.4	35.2	10.9
Kr^{85}	0.5	—	(0.6)	—	—
	1	—	(0.6)	—	—
	2	—	(1.4)	—	—
	5	—	(1.6)	—	—
	10	2.5	2.4	2.4	1.2
	20	4.2	3.8	3.7	1.7
	40	7.2	6.4	6.2	2.5
	80	11.0	11.0	10.7	4.5
	160	19.6	20.1	20.4	6.7
Xe^{125}	0.5	—	(1.3)	—	—
	1	—	(1.3)	—	—
	2	—	(0.8)	—	—
	5	—	(1.5)	—	—
	10	2.5	2.3	2.3	0.96
	20	2.3	2.5	2.6	1.4
	40	5.7	5.3	5.2	1.8
	80	8.5	8.6	8.7	2.9
	160	13.5	14.3	14.7	4.4
	Characteristics of range distributions in WO_3.				
Na^{24}	0.5	—	(2.4)	—	—
	1	—	(2.4)	—	—
	2	—	(2.4)	—	—
	5	—	3.2	3.8	3.2
	10	6	7.2	7.6	4.7
	20	14	14.9	16.3	10.2
	40	21	27.0	28.8	17.6
	80	56	58	58	33
Ar^{41}	2	—	(2.9)	—	—
	5	—	(1.5)	—	—

TABLE 5.37—continued

Characteristics of range distributions in Al_2O_3.

Ion	Energy (keV)	$\overline{R}_{m.p}$ ($\mu g/cm^2$)	$\overline{R}_m$ ($\mu g/cm^2$)	$\overline{R}_{par}$ ($\mu g/cm^2$)	W_{rms}* ($\mu g/cm^2$)
	10	—	3.9	4.4	3.3
	20	5	8.4	9.1	5.9
	40	14	16.6	17.6	10.4
	80	34	33.8	34.9	20
	160	84	71	68	34
Kr^{85}	2	—	(0.8)	—	—
	5	—	(1.0)	—	—
	10	—	2.5	2.9	2.1
	20	6.6	6.7	7.4	4.0
	40	11.7	1.27	13.5	6.2
	80	14.5	19.7	20.5	10.2
	160	38	38.0	41.0	19.5
Xe^{125}	0.5	—	(1.0)	—	—
	1	—	(1.4)	—	—
	2	—	(1.9)	—	—
	5	—	(2.9)	—	—
	10	3.2	3.5	3.5	2.1
	20	5.2	5.7	5.8	3.2
	40	9.9	10.2	10.5	4.5
	80	15.6	16.4	17.0	7.9
	160	30	28.9	28.5	13.4

* W_{rms} is the root mean square of the deviation from the mean Range $\overline{R}_{par}$

penetrating fraction of Kr^{85} for different film thicknesses was determined. Hence the penetration function was readily estimated and is shown in Figure 5.83 where it is compared to penetration in polycrystalline Al. Clearly a highly penetrating tail is observed in the polycrystalline material, due no doubt to its crystallinity. In addition Domeij et al[104] have measured the ranges of Na^{24}, A^{41}, Kr^{85}, and Xe^{125} ions of energies between 0.5 keV and 160 keV in amorphous Al_2O_3 and WO_3 using the transmission technique and in all cases found the highly penetrating component to be absent, indicating the reality but absence of channelling. Values of $\overline{R}_{m.p}$, $\overline{R}_m$ and $\overline{R}_{par}$ are tabulated in Table 5.37 at different ion energies although the low energy results ($<$ 1 keV) are thought to be unreliable due to the presence of small crystallites in the targets of the same dimensions as the ion ranges. In order to compare the data with theoretical range-energy predictions for monatomic solids the experimental ranges must be modified to accommodate the binary structure of the oxides. In a binary compound C composed of x, A atoms per y, B atoms, the range R_c is given simply by

$$\frac{R_c}{M_c} = \frac{1}{\dfrac{xM_A}{R_A} + y\dfrac{M_B}{R_B}} \qquad 5.176$$

if the stopping cross sections for the different atoms depend upon the same power of energy. In Lindhard et al's[8, 11] theory this is valid and so the ratio of the range in Al and O can be obtained theoretically, and then from the Al_2O_3 data and equation 5.176 the effective ranges in amorphous Al can be deduced. These values were deduced by Domeij et al[104] and Figures 5.84 a and b show comparisons of the experimental

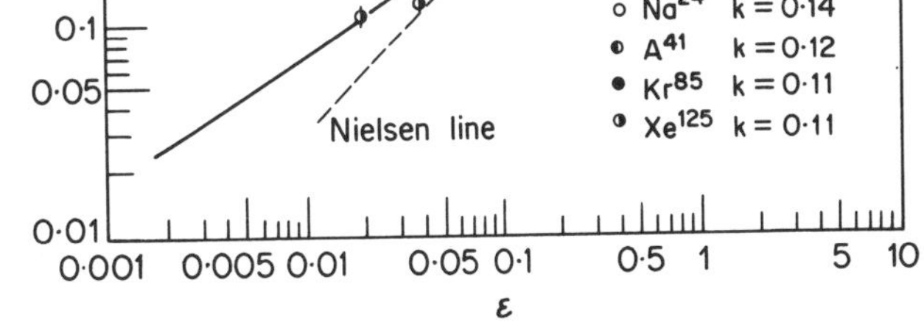

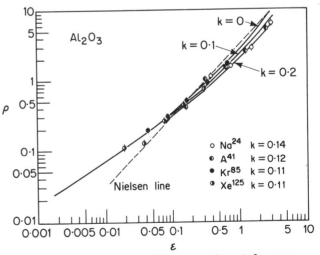

Fig. 5.84a Comparison of the experimental mean ranges in Al_2O_3 with the theoretical curves of Lindhard et al. The appropriate k value for each projectile has been calculated from equation 5.25.2. (viz. Ref. 5.104)

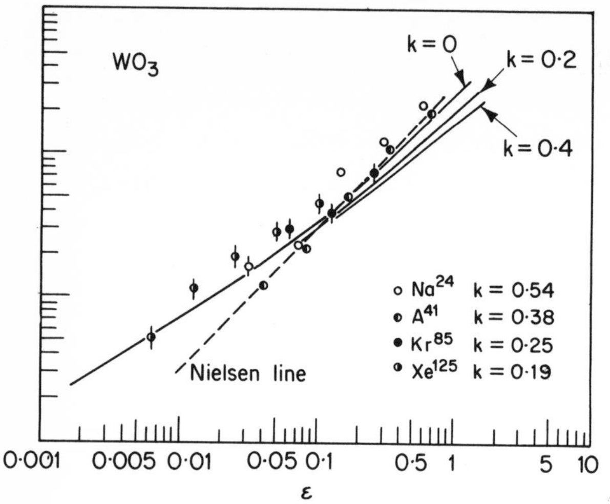

Fig. 5. 84b Comparison of the experimental mean ranges in WO_3 with the theoretical curves of Lindhard et al. The appropriate k value for each projectile has been calculated from equation 5. 25. 2. (viz. Ref. 5. 104)

range-energy data in effectively amorphous Al and W and adjusted to give mean ranges from the measured projected ranges with the Lindhard-Scharff[8] equation for several values of the electronic stopping contribution. (These are required since each projected ion demands a different k value). Clearly the agreement in the case of amorphous Al is exceptionally good at all energies whilst the slightly poorer agreement with W is readily understood in terms of the large mass difference in W & O and the adjustment required in the theoretical data because of this disparity.

The range straggling data was also found to be in good agreement with the Lindhard et al's[8, 11] predictions (equation 5.35) and suggests that this model is quite adequate for range determinations in amorphous materials. Brown et al[115] have obtained similar results of Xe^+_{125} ion ranges in amorphous Ta_2O_5 targets for ion energies between 500 eV and 100 keV and observed reasonable agreement with the Lindhard theory.

In order to investigate the channelling phenomena more thoroughly, penetration functions were determined[106] for single crystal Aluminium in which the incident beam of Kr^{85} primaries was parallel to either the ⟨110⟩, the ⟨100⟩, the ⟨111⟩ directions or at 7° to the ⟨211⟩ direction (designated normal incidence). These penetration functions are shown in Figure 5. 85 and the marked difference in range for different directions is notable. The deep penetrations are typical of channelling events and are markedly different from the results for the isotropic (amorphous) solid. The order of penetrations is ⟨110⟩, > polycrystalline, > ⟨100⟩ > normal incidence, > ⟨111⟩, which corresponds to the order predicted from the transparency considerations of Robinson and Oen.[28]

This work with single crystal Al has been extended by Piercy et al[107] who observed the penetration of a variety of ions (Na, Kr, Rb and Xe) along the main channel directions of Al. The energy dependence of the range was determined and a typical result for Kr^{85} along the ⟨110⟩ direction is shown in Figure 5. 86 at various ion energies between 20 keV and 160 keV. Changing the direction of ion incidence from a channelling direction resulted in marked, and expected, range reductions. From graphs such as those in Figure 5. 86 it was possible to deduce the minimum ranges of any fraction of ions which penetrated beyond this range. By choosing this fraction sufficiently low (10^{-4}) this range was then a measure of the maximum ion range along a channelled direction and these maximum ranges were determined as a function of the ion energy. The general shape of such maximum range/energy functions was found to be of the form $R \propto E^{\gamma}$ where γ was of order 0.75-0.80 for Kr ions between energies of 20 keV and 150 keV.

Since the simple Lehmann-Leibfried[4] channelling theory predicts a range-energy dependence of $R \propto E^2$, or an energy loss dependence $dE/dx \propto 1/E$, whilst elastic stopping predicts $R \propto E$ and $dE/dx \propto C$, and inelastic stopping $R \propto E^{1/2}$ and $dE/dx \propto E^{1/2}$, it was believed that the observed $R \propto E^{\gamma}$, resulted from simultaneous inelastic and elastic losses. The inelastic losses were therefore deduced from the Firsov atomic potential model for ions moving exactly along a channel axis, and were found to be of comparable magnitude to those lost in elastic, momentum transfer collisions. Moreover the directional dependence of this loss coincided with the sequence of increasing ion ranges with channel direction.

The mass of the incident ion was also observed to be important in determining the channelled ranges, for example ranges of 40 keV Na^+, Kr^+, Rb^+, and Xe^+, ions were in the order Na > Kr $\gtrsim$ Rb > Xe. However if the channelled part of the ranges were normalised to the same ion velocity, Kr, Rb and Xe had the same range, but Na had a considerably smaller range. Since inelastic losses predict a Range proportional to velocity the results for the heavier ions tend to confirm the importance of this mechanism, but the result for Na suggests operation of some form of efficient resonance transfer loss mechanism. Quite clearly however, the simple elastic stopping theory is inadequate, even in this relatively low energy range.

It should be pointed out however that the observed range energy relation for channelled ions is something of an experimental artifact and one is not fully justified in comparing the experimental observations with a theory such as that of Lehmann and Leibfried.[4] The theoretical predictions refer to those ions with absolute maximum ranges whereas experimental determinations refer to the fraction of ions with ranges above a certain value, i.e. these ranges are certainly not the maximum possible. In addition, when the ion ranges are extremely large the possibility of crossing dislocation planes is very high so that the imperfection of the crystal may be of determining importance in deciding the experimental ranges. For these reasons therefore the range/energy relation cannot be regarded as furnishing unequivocal evidence of the dominance of inelastic losses and showing a stopping power proportional to $(\text{energy})^{1/2}$. In order to assess the accuracy of this behaviour it will be necessary to perform experiments upon single crystals with a high degree of perfection, i.e. long coherence lengths.

We should also mention that separation of the non-channelled ions and the channelled ions was attempted by Piercy et al[107] by subtracting from the overall penetration curve, that part expected to be due to non-channelled ions from the results of the measurements in amorphous Al_2O_3.[104] This reveals, for example that 58% of 40 keV Kr^+ ions injected in the ⟨110⟩ direction experience some degree of channelling and this fraction increases with increasing ion energy. Since ions are incident uniformly over the crystal

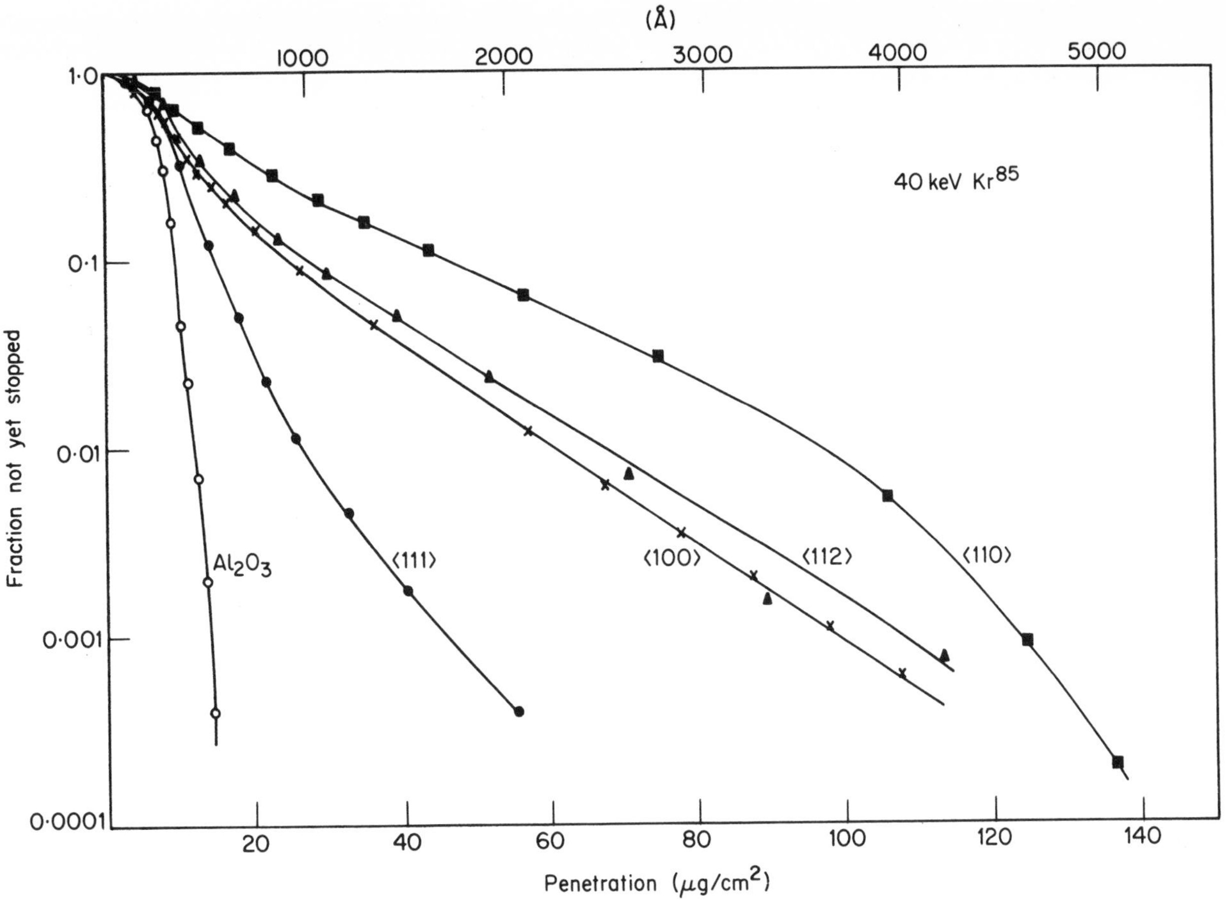

Fig. 5. 85 Penetration of 40-kev Kr^{85} ions in the principal crystallographic directions of aluminum and in amorphous Al_2O_3. Integral Ranges. (viz. Ref. 5. 107)

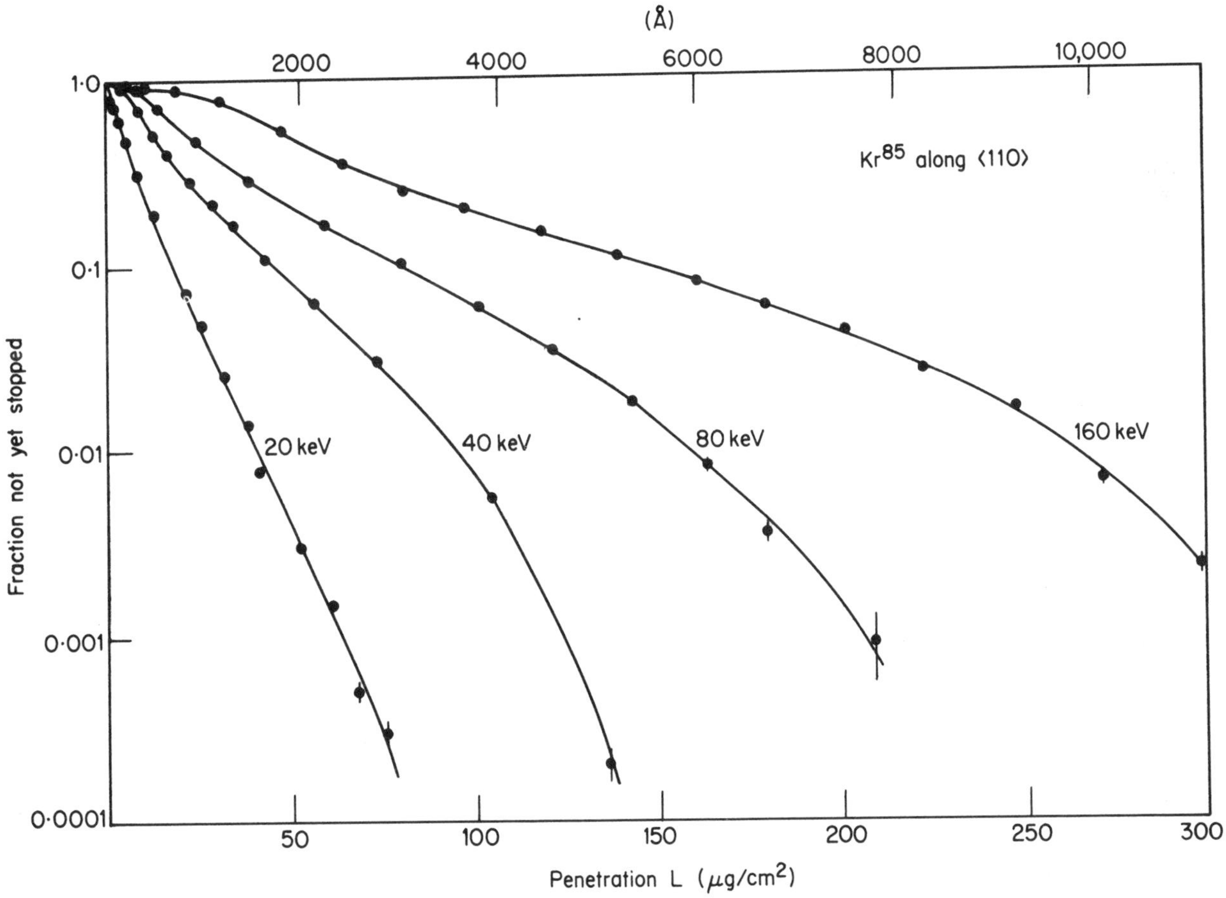

Fig. 5. 86 Penetration of Kr^{85} ions with 20, 40, 80, or 160 keV energy along the [110] direction. The statistical counting uncertainty is shown where applicable. Integral Ranges. (viz. Ref. 5. 107)

TABLE 5.38a. (Ref. 5.109).

Median penetrations [$\overline{R}_m$ ($\mu g/cm^2$)] for various bombardment parameters.

Ion	Energy (keV)	⟨111⟩	⟨100⟩	⟨110⟩	⟨112⟩	Poly	Amorphous b
Xe^{133}	1.0		~1.6			~1.0	
	5.0		13	3.4	3.8	3.5	
	20		77	21	9	5.9	
	20a	56	33	10.7	10.5		8.0
Xe^{125}	40	135	145	31	12.7	12.0	15.0
	80	195	176	55			24
	160	410	490	89			42
Kr^{85}	0.5						
	1.0		3			~1.0	
	5.0			4.6		4.7	
	20		107	27	13	11.2	
	20a		59.4				10.0
	40	176	145	31			19.0
A^{41}	40	177	170	70	44		
Na^{24}	40	377	436	95	66		39.1

a Mass separator bombardment

b See Ref. 5.104.

TABLE 5.38b. (Ref. 5.109).

Depth of penetration of 1% of ions {$R_{0.01}$ ($\mu g/cm^2$)} for various bombardment parameters.

Ion	Energy (keV)	⟨111⟩	⟨100⟩	⟨110⟩	⟨112⟩	Poly	Amorphous (b)
Xe^{133}	0.5		3.0	~1.4			
	1.0		7.2	~2.0	2.8	6.0	
	5.0		81	31.7	19	46	
	20		322	185	107	138	
	20a	263	315	157	118		19.1
Xe^{125}	40	500	590	408	218	220	32.6
	80	915	960	670			59
	160	1558	1635	1100			93
Kr^{85}	0.5		6.3		~2.4		
	1.0		15	3.9	4.2	14.8	
	5.0			50		72.5	
	20		380	223	163	230	
	20a		340				30
	40	570	592	402			43
A^{41}	40	422	453	353	305		
Na^{24}	40	880	1100	681	618		

surface, the fraction of channelled ions reflects the fraction of the surface area which accepts ions into channels, or alternatively defines the minimum impact parameters which ions must possess to become channelled. Piercy et al[107] point out that when interatomic potential data is available, the energy dependence of the fractional number of channelled atoms will give evidence of the deflection requirements for channelled sequences.

Similar results for channelled ranges of 0.25 keV to 160 keV, Na^+, A^+, Kr^+ & Xe^+ ions in single crystal tungsten have also been reported by Kornelsen et al.[108, 109, 110]

For all ion types and energies the ranges were observed to be considerably larger when the ions were injected along ⟨100⟩, ⟨111⟩, ⟨110⟩ & ⟨112⟩ directions than in amorphous WO_3 targets. For example the median penetrations along the ⟨100⟩, ⟨110⟩ & ⟨112⟩ directions for 20 keV Kr^{85+} ions were factors of 10.5, 2.7 & 1.3 respectively larger than in WO_3 targets. Tables 5.38a & 5.38b show the median ranges and the depth $R_{0.01}$ required to stop 99% of the various ions along the directions indicated above at energies between 0.5 keV and 160 keV. It is apparent that these ranges decrease in the order $\langle 100\rangle \approx \langle 111\rangle > \langle 100\rangle > \langle 112\rangle$ as predicted by the Robinson-Oen[28] channelling calculations. However the energy dependence of the $R_{0.01}$ ranges which may be taken as typical of the longest channel ranges, do not follow the $(\text{Energy})^2$ relation predicted by the Lehmann-Leibfried theory.[4] In particular the $R_{0.01}$ ranges for Xe^+ ions along the ⟨100⟩ ⟨110⟩ & ⟨112⟩ direction increase with $(\text{energy})^{1.5}$ for energies less than 5 keV as found by Erginsoy[50] from computer studies in Iron but at high ion energies ($\gtrsim$ 100 keV) the dependence tended to an $(\text{energy})^{0.5}$ form (viz Figure 5.87). As in the case of Al discussed earlier the latter result suggests the operation of wholly inelastic loss processes at high energies and that these were of some importance even down to very low energies.

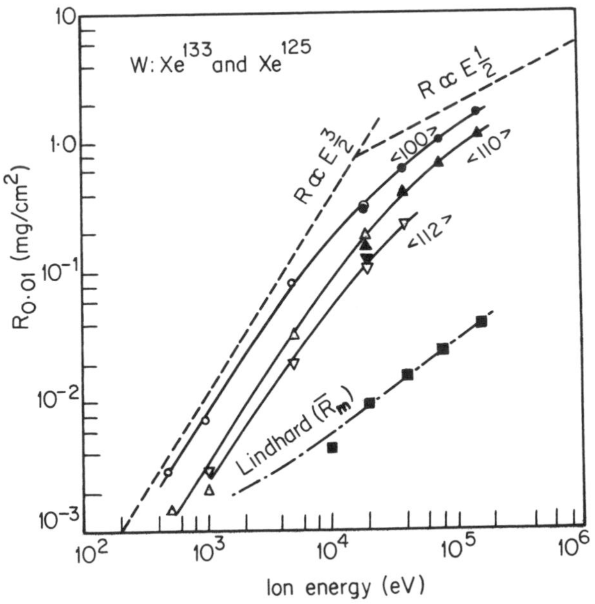

Fig. 5.87 Ranges beyond which 10^{-2}% of Xe^{125} and Xe^{133} ions are stopped in various channel directions in W single crystals, plotted as a function of ion energy. The Lindhard et al (Ref 5.8) line is theoretical for inelastic stopping and the dashed lines are assymptotic to range proportional to $(\text{Energy})^{3/2}$ and to $(\text{Energy})^{1/2}$ (viz. Ref. 5.109)

The exact behaviour of the range distribution with ion type was rather complex and did not show, as expected on the basis of lower interatomic forces with lighter projectile ions, that the lighter ions possessed the largest channelled ranges. Again it was suggested that electronic excitation processes were responsible for this behaviour.

Heating the crystal to 1200°K during bombardment showed that the channelled ion ranges were considerably reduced below the values obtained at room temperature indicating the increased stopping due to thermal vibrations of the lattice atoms, but heating of a crystal to 1200°K after Xe^+ ion bombardment at room temperature showed virtually no change in the range distribution, indicating the absence of diffusive motion at this temperature. Post bombardment heating to temperatures greater than 2000°K did indicate a change in the distribution however, showing that diffusion (and gas release) occured at these temperatures.

In addition it was found that increasing the total ion bombardment of the tungsten (from the normal trace dose of 2×10^{13} ions/cm^2 to 5×10^{14} ions/cm^2) did not materially effect the penetration probability functions suggesting that radiation damage annealed out rapidly at room temperature and did not affect the ion penetration. However at much higher ion doses, where gas trapping may become important, penetration functions may be expected to be modified.

Davies, Eriksson and Jespersgaard[111] have also studied Xe^+_{133} ions ranges in single crystal W targets at higher energies up to 1.5 MeV. In this case the distinction between the non channelled ions and the channelled ions (for instance along the ⟨100⟩ direction, becomes more apparent and instead of a tail merged into the random loss short range peak, a second, higher range peak in the distribution occurs, which can account for as many as 70% of the stopped ions. This illustrates that at higher energies the lattice is becoming quite transparent to the ions and the channelling affect is becoming predominant. These authors also obtained evidence of the interplanar channelling phenomenon suggested by Nelson and Thompson[2, 3], particularly in the [100] plane and, in measurements of the stopping powers along channel directions, found fluctuations with ion mass about the Lindhard electronic stopping power predicted curve.

Ball and Brown[112] injected 40 & 125 keV Xe^{133} & Cs^{134} ions into single crystal W & amorphous WO_3 using the stripping techniques described above to determine the ion ranges. In WO_3 there was no significant difference in the ion ranges but along the channel directions in single crystal W, the Xe^{133} ions were significantly larger than the Cs^{134} ranges (the ratio was between 1.12 & 1.20) although the median ranges were similar. Since according to the Lindhard et al statistical theory there should be no essential difference in stopping power for Xe^{133} & Cs^{134} the similar results in WO_3 & median ranges in W are understandable. The slightly higher Xe^{133} ranges along channels however, where collisions occur at glancing angles and involve low energy transfers, again suggests that the electronic stopping processes are rather more complex than described by the Lindhard et al[8, 11] treatment and further experiments on the above lines should help in assessing the true nature of this process.

Channing & Whitton[113] have also investigated the effect of target temperature on ⟨100⟩ channelling events in single crystal gold. Using a sectioning technique developed by Whitton & Davies,[114] the former workers studied the ranges of 40 keV Xe^{+}_{133} ions at 295°K and 20°K with the results shown in Figure 5.88. This graph shows that at the lower temperature, ⟨100⟩ channelled ranges are about three times greater than at room temperature, and that the superchannelling phenomenon was absent in gold. This increased channelled range with reduced temperature is in qualitative accord with the theoretical considerations which suggests that the reduced lattice vibrations lead to lower stopping powers, and of course, concur with the observations, above room temperature, in tungsten.

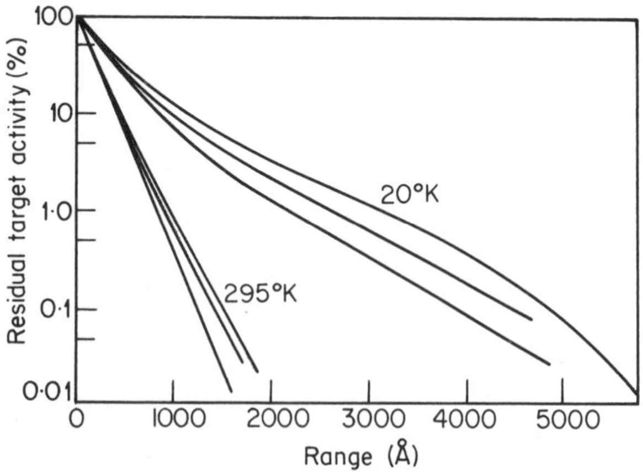

Fig. 5.88 The effect of increasing the temperature of a Au single crystal on the ranges of 40keVXe^{133} ions in the <100> channel. Integral range distributions. The results of three experiments at each temperature are shown. (viz. Ref. 5.113)

Similar temperature effects for the range of Au ions in a Au target have been reported by Brown et al[115] who observed that the channelled ranges decreased exponentially with temperature between 20°K and 300°K and as with Xe ions found these ranges to increase in the order ⟨110⟩ > ⟨100⟩ > ⟨111⟩ all being slightly larger than the corresponding Xe ion ranges. When different ions, with masses ranging from Na to Xe were injected into Au, the same anomalous diminution of the Na range was observed as in W again illustrating the effect of electronic interactions.

Kornelsen[108] & Kornelsen et al[109, 110] reported the effect upon channelling events of adsorbed gases on tungsten. It was shown that in targets which were thoroughly degassed by high temperature heating under ultra-high vacuum conditions there was considerably more evidence of channelling than in targets which had not been so treated and to which rather thick gas layers presumably adhered. Although the thickness of these layers would not have been expected to materially alter the ion range in the target itself, the observation of decreased channelling in the presence of a gas layer suggests that the primary ion directions are sufficiently re-oriented in passing through the layer to inhibit their probability of channelling. Since most experimental investigations to date which purport to depict channelled events have been conducted with essentially 'dirty' surfaces, the absolute magnitudes of the number of channelled atoms and their penetration depths must be regarded with some suspicion. A further very interesting observation has been made with these well cleaned tungsten targets in that about 0.1% of the incident ions may travel distances of the order of 1 micron or more along ⟨100⟩ directions. This phenomenon has been named superchannelling, it is observed with most primary ions at all energies and above 1 keV, Krypton ions experience this effect, although less marked penetration is observed with lighter ions. The angle of incidence of the ions into the channel was found to be critical and a 1% deviation from normality removed the effect. However thin surface oxide layers did not markedly reduce the effect nor did prebombarding and damaging the crystals with 5×10^{14} ions/cm^2 of 5 keV, Xe^+ ions. This is a truly remarkable effect since it implies a primary ion energy loss of less than 0.1 eV per collision. Explanations for it are currently tentative and suggestions range from an abnormal interstitial diffusion mechanism of the ion after essentially coming to rest, to quantum effects in which the ion is considered to be a de Broglie wave suffering Bragg reflections along the channel with reinforcements leading to long ranges. Alternatively it has been proposed that, because of its short interaction time with lattice atoms, the primary ion may become multiply charged and decrease in effective size, again leading to deep penetrations. Davies (unpublished) has shown however that the long superchannel effect exists whether ions are injected along a channel perpendicular to the surface or at a small angle to the surface, tending to support the diffusion mechanism where gas atoms wander until trapped at some centre. In addition Lutz and Sizmann (Private Communication) have performed an informative experiment in which Kr ions were injected along ⟨100⟩ W channels at −196°C, and after warming to room temperature the long 'supertail' was examined by the stripping technique to be described shortly. If, before warming however, the W was subjected to a He ion bombardment which penetrated and caused defect production beyond the stopped Kr, subsequent warming showed the absence of a supertail. This suggested that the Kr was unable to move by the interstitial mechanism at −196°C and that the vacancies induced by the bombardment prevented their further migration during warm up. This technique appears to be potentially valuable in studying diffusion processes if experiments can be conducted at variable temperatures.

Davies et al,[63] have also used the stripping technique to study Xe^{125} ranges in Si single crystals with HF as the etchant to remove the electrolytically oxidised surface layers. Typical integral range characteristics for 40 keV Xe^+ ions are shown in Figure 5.89 where the long tails again reveal the channelling behaviour.

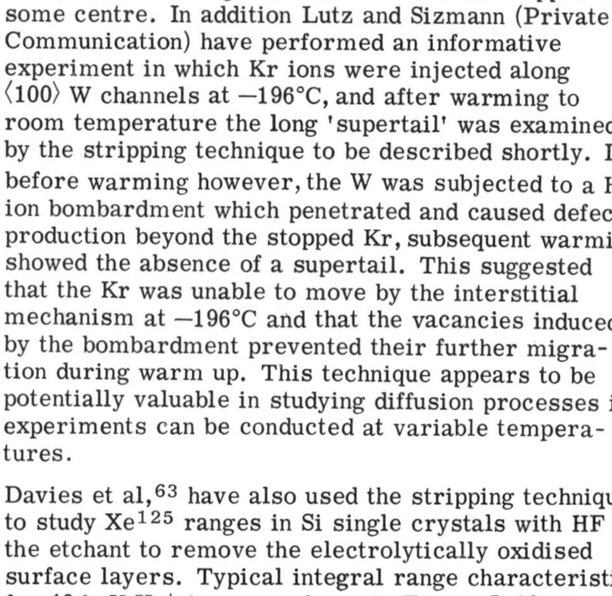

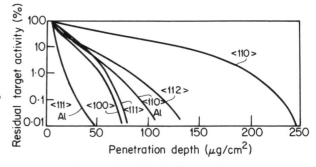

Fig. 5.89 Integral range distributions for 40 keVXe^{125} ions in Si showing channelling effects along the "open" crystal directions. Similar measurements for Al are indicated for comparison (Ref 5.107) (viz. Ref. 5.63)

The major channel directions are in the same order ⟨110⟩ > ⟨111⟩ > ⟨100⟩ as suggested by Robinson & Oen whilst the ⟨112⟩ direction also shows evidence of channelling. The channelled ion ranges are considerably larger than those in the corresponding directions in singly crystal Al (c.f. Figure 5. 85) and are presumably attributable to the more open diamond structure of Si. The maximum range of channelled ions could be inferred from extrapolation of the above curves for ion energies between 20 & 80 keV and were found not to obey an $(energy)^2$ dependence as suggested by the theoretical work of Lehmann and Leibfried[4] but a form $(energy)^{\gamma}$ where γ was of order 0. 7-0. 8. Since, as in the cases of Aluminium & Tungsten discussed earlier, an $(energy)^{0.5}$ dependence indicates the dominance of inelastic collision processes, the observed value of γ suggests operation of both inelastic and elastic processes simultaneously.

An interesting feature of the work with Silicon was the profound reduction of ion range of both the ions stopped close to the surface (unchannelled) and channelled ions when the ion dose was increased from 10^{11} ions/cm^2 to 10^{14} ions/cm^2. This result was interpreted as showing the gross effects of radiation damage inflicted by the ions, which not only blocked the channels but caused changes in the surface structure of the Silicon. Since this result is quite different to those observed in W, it is again clear that crystal structure is of determining importance in channelling phenomena.

Finally we should discuss the measurements of primary ranges in Germanium by Davies, McIntyre and Sims,[81] using the modified stripping method described for amorphous Aluminium oxide penetrations. In these measurements Germanium films of various thicknesses were deposited upon Al and bombarded by Cs^{137} ions of energies between 4 and 40 keV. The total activity of the targets was then determined and all the Germanium dissolved by an H_2O_2 etch (without attacking the underlying Al). Subsequent measurements of the Cs^{137} activity in the Aluminium then allowed evaluation of the fraction of Cs^{137} stopping in a given film thickness of Ge, and thus of the penetration functions. The results of these measurements are shown in Figure 5. 90 and are compared with those

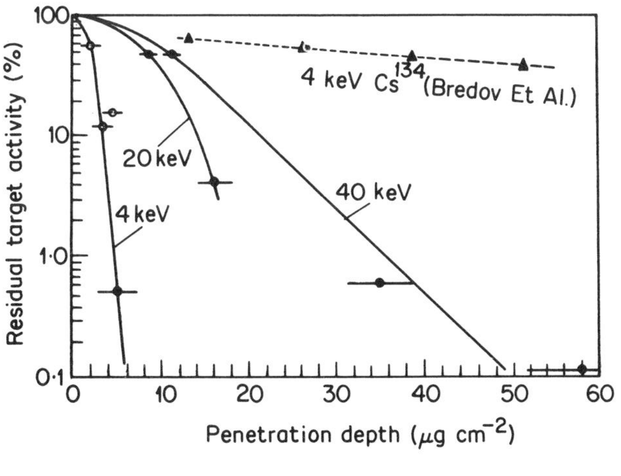

Fig. 5. 90 Depth of penetration of Cs^{137} ions in germanium as a function of energy: O using method (1); ● using method (2); ▲ Bredov's data for 4-kev Cs^{134}. Ref. 5. 94, 95, 96. Method ① involves direct etching of bombarded Ge. Method ② involves transmission through thin Ge films. (viz. Ref. 5. 81)

of Bredov and Okuneva,[94, 95, 96] and comparable studies by Davies, McIntyre and Sims[81] using a slow rate of etching of the Ge to determine penetration depths. Clearly the former technique leads to much lower penetrations of the order anticipated (when compared to Al) due it is suggested by Davies et al[81] to the uneven and diminished rate of etching of a radiation damaged Ge surface. However one must be cautious before rejecting the results of Bredov & Okuneva,[94, 95, 96] since these authors may have unwittingly, first observed the channelling phenomena. Once again it may be expected that this method will find much use in the future for target materials which may be removed from a substrate without attacking the substrate.

We finally discuss the fourth method of target sectioning, that of target erosion by secondary ion bombardment, which has been used by Burtt et al[116] and Colligon and Leck[117] for the measurement of inert gas primary distributions in polycrystalline W, Pt, and Mo and by Sizmann[118, 119, 120, 121] and his collaborators for the determination of Kr^{85} ion ranges in monocrystalline Copper & GaAs. In the former measurements,[116, 117] primary ions of Ne, A, Kr, and Xe were injected into the respective targets at energies between 0. 5 and 5 keV. The total number of ions trapped during bombardment was determined by subsequent flashing of the targets to temperatures slightly less than the melting points. This resulted in a burst of gas which was recorded on a mass spectrometer, situated in the vacuum system containing the target, tuned to the primary ion species. The quantity of gas released was readily determined by calibration of the mass spectrometer with a known gas flow rate. Alternatively trapped gas could be removed from the target, by sputtering the target with a secondary ion species. Theoretically this process slowly erodes the target surface at a known rate and trapped gas escapes as the surface recedes past the positions of the trapped atoms. The amount of gas trapped in each surface layer could be determined by determining the rate of gas release during sputtering. Unfortunately the bombardment and measurement techniques employed did not allow use of this method, and so the targets were sputtered for a known time, and then the total amount of gas remaining trapped was determined by flashing the target. Knowledge of the target sputtering rate then allowed deduction of the integral penetration function.

In order to obtain sufficient sensitivity it was necessary to use large bombardment fluxes which resulted in saturation effects as described by Brown et al.[103] Such effects were observable via the inability to trap further gas after certain total bombardments and by changes in the distribution functions. Accurate range estimates were almost impossible because of the large amount of gas it was necessary to trap and remove to achieve adequate sensitivity, i.e. resolution was sacrificed to achieve sensitivity. In view of this, only qualitative analysis of the results is possible, although estimated primary ranges were in order of magnitude agreement with other data c.f. Table 5. 39.

For light ions such as Neon, deep penetrations in Tungsten and Molybdenum were observed, whilst a heavy secondary sputtering ion appeared to cause knock on of trapped primaries to deeper penetrations.

This latter effect was observable by varying the secondary ion species and energy. The resulting penetration functions determined did not correspond exactly to expectations from known variations of sput-

TABLE 5.39.(Ref. 5.116).

Investigators	Reference	Material bombarded	Bombarding ions	Depth $\bar{R}_{par}$ ($\times 10^6$) cm
Young	5.79	Aluminium	Hydrogen (1.0 keV)	1.5
Young	5.54	Phosphor	Argon (20 keV)	0.25
Bartholomew and La Padula	5.93	Nickel	Radioactive krypton (0.15 keV)	260
Bredov and Okuneva	5.94, 95, 96	Germanium	Radioactive caesium (4 keV)	2.5
Burtt et al	5.116	Tungsten	Argon and krypton (2.7 keV)	0.63

In order to assist the comparison the penetration depths $\bar{R}_{par}$ given in this table have all been referred to an ion energy of 1.0 keV. It has been arbitrarily assumed that the depth of penetration is proportional to incident energy.

tering coefficients with ion species and energy. In the case of platinum it was impossible to obtain unequivocal results because a large amount of trapped gas was not released until the targets were fused.

Another factor which tends to render these results inaccurate is the assumption that secondary ions only release trapped gas through sputtering of the surface with attendant gas removal. It is very possible at the energies considered here that gas is released via direct energy transfer from the bombarding ions, which distorts the measured penetration distribution.

Although this data is relatively inaccurate, it appears that development of the technique particularly with a view to increasing sensitivity and resolution, will be valuable.

Lutz and Sizmann[118, 119] have achieved an increase in sensitivity by using a different measuring technique, returning to the radioactive tracer. Penetration functions were determined for Kr^{85} primaries of energies between 10 and 150 keV injected parallel to the ⟨100⟩, ⟨110⟩ and ⟨111⟩ direction in copper single crystals. After injection of about 10^{14} ions/cm^2 at a given primary energy, the target surface was slowly eroded by sputtering with a 2.5 keV stable Krypton beam and the decrease in target activity noted as a function of depth eroded, with a G.M. tube. The depth eroded required a knowledge of sputtering rates for Copper which were deduced by sputtering sufficiently large target layers to be measured by optical techniques. Integral range functions were obtained in this manner, and from these, differential distributions, most probable, median and mean ranges as a function of primary energy. Figure 5.91 shows the mean ranges as a function of ion energy for the three crystal directions. Apparently R ⟨110⟩ $\simeq$ R ⟨100⟩ > R ⟨111⟩, but errors are large (± 10%) and this tendency may be actually different. Definite highly penetrating tails are observed for each direction, however, with a marked enhancement in the ⟨110⟩ direction. Typical range results are shown in Figure 5.92 and are again evidence of the existence of channelling events, particularly so since the order of preference for long range primaries is ⟨110⟩ $\gtrsim$ ⟨100⟩ ⟨111⟩, i.e. the sequence suggested by the predictions of Robinson and Oen[28] and Leibfried and Lehmann.[4]

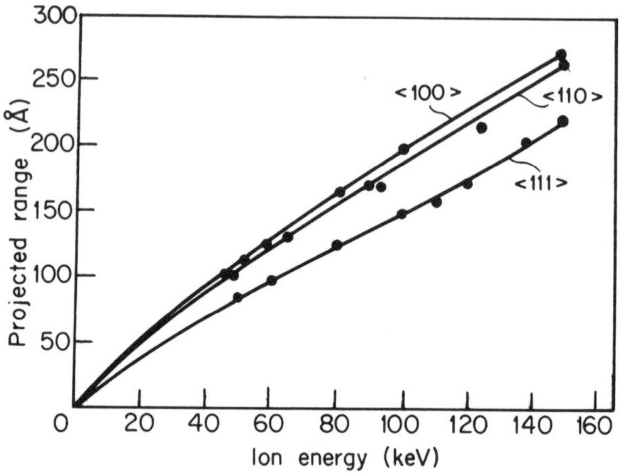

Fig. 5.91 Projected mean ranges of Kr^{85} ions in the <100>, <110> and <111> channels in Cu single crystals as a function of the ion energy. (viz. Ref. 8.119)

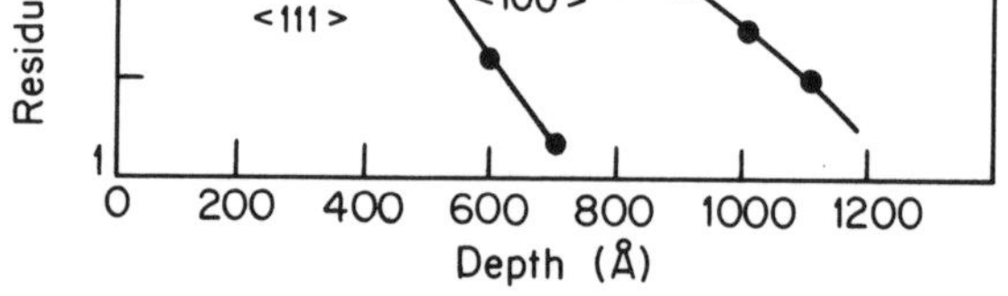

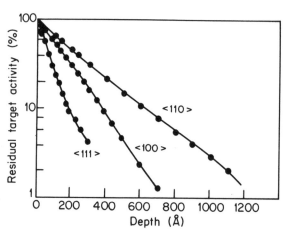

Fig. 5.92 Integral penetration functions for 26 keV Kr^{85} ions in the <110>, <100> and <111> channels in Cu single crystals. (viz. Ref. 5.119)

At energies below 50 keV, there is always a positive intercept at zero range on the penetration function curves, indicating the importance of backscattering of the Kr from the, only slightly lighter, Copper atoms. Above this energy, the first mean free path is apparently large enough to ensure always greater than zero ranges. One cannot attempt interatomic potential evaluations from this data unfortunately, since the targets were always bombarded with low energy Krypton before the tracers were used, to achieve a clean surface. This treatment certainly damages the surface, probably blocks some of the channels and generally distorts the channelling distribution. This is reflected in the smaller than expected channelled ranges. The possible effects of gas sputtering must also be borne in mind.

The ⟨111⟩ penetrations, however, may be converted to give results typical of a random target array, since these penetrations are closest to the random values. If this is done, Lutz and Sizmann[119] show that the resulting range energy data fall upon a Lindhard-Scharff[8, 11] plot at a value of k (the electronic stopping factor) close to that expected for Kr^+ ions in Cu.

It should also be remarked that subsequent work by Heinen, Lutz and Sizmann[120] who prebombarded a [110] Cu face with 10^{18} 2.9 keV Kr^+ ions/sq cm before determining the ⟨110⟩ range of 25 keV Kr^+ ions found that not only were the surface contours smoothed but that the range was considerably diminished, indicating the possible effects of channel blocking.

Pohlau, Lutz and Sizmann[121] have also employed this technique to study channelling processes in the bombardment of the III-V compound structure of Gallium Arsenide by 80 keV Kr^+ ions. As expected from transparency considerations the ranges in the ⟨110⟩ direction were considerably greater than in the ⟨111⟩ direction, for a low ion dose of $5 \times 10^{13}/cm^2$, whilst for larger doses ($\gtrsim 10^{17}$ ions/cm^2) the ranges in all directions were reduced to a common level, below either channelling direction.

Again the influence of damage processes and channel blocking is evident.

5.12 OTHER EVIDENCE FOR CHANNELLING IN CRYSTALS

In addition to the direct observations of the channelling phenomena using sectioning techniques to determine ion ranges in single crystals, a number of indirect measurements of phenomena associated with channelling have been reported, and we take this opportunity to summarise these briefly. We have already noted in Chapter 3, and earlier in this Chapter, that ion induced secondary electron emission from single crystals exhibits an angular dependence which can be directly correlated with deep penetration along channel directions, whilst sputtering studies described in Chapter 7 and ion trapping probabilities discussed in Chapter 8 exhibit minima and maxima respectively along channel areas. Lindhard[5, 122] suggested, on the basis of the channelling phenomenon that energetic protons injected into a single crystal would experience channelling according to their position of incidence on the crystal surface, and that such chanelled ions would be unable to approach lattice atoms sufficiently closely to promote nuclear reactions. To investigate this possibility Bøgh, Davies and Nielsen[123] injected protons of the appropriate energy into single crystal Si and Al and observed the emitted γ rays from the ensuing (p, γ) reactions as a function of the proton incidence angle. In both materials pronounced minima were observed in the emitted γ ray counts when the beam was incident along the ⟨100⟩ channel axes, and the angular width of these minima was of the order expected from considerations of the angle of beam incidence necessary to allow sufficiently close approach to the lattice atoms. In an analogous experiment where protons were incident upon a Cu single crystal and the neutrons emitted from the 2.8 MeV Cu^{65} (p, n) Zn^{65} reaction were observed by Thompson,[124] minima in the emitted neutron count were observed in directions corresponding to channelling between $[1\bar{1}0]$ planes and $[\bar{1}11]$ planes.

Dearnaley,[125] Dearnaley and Sattler[126] and Erginsoy, Wegner and Gibson[127] have observed reductions in the stopping power of Si to MeV protons, deuterons and α particles respectively when the ion incidence direction corresponded to low index directions or planes (channels) and Sattler and Dearnaley[126] have observed an analogous effect for protons channelled in Ge. Just as nuclear reactions may be suppressed when the distance of approach between a proton and a lattice atom is insufficiently small, it may be expected that if insufficient energy is transferred to promote inner shell electron transitions (which only occur if the interaction radius is similar to the appropriate shell radii) then the characteristic X-ray emission from lattice atoms may be suppressed. Thus Brandt et al[128] have observed that the copper L X-ray yield at 75 and 115 keV proton bombardment energies shows a well defined minimum when the direction of ion incidence is along a ⟨110⟩ channelling direction, whilst the Al K X-ray yield from 100 keV protons shows a similar suppression also along the ⟨110⟩ direction.

Since ions incident from outside a crystal experience channelling it would be anticipated that particles originating from within a crystal should be subjected to the same restrictions. Thus, if an α emitting foreign atom were to be trapped in a channel defining row of lattice atoms it would be expected that in order to escape back to the surface it would initially undergo large angle collisions with the row in order to escape, and minima would be recorded in the emitted α ray angular distribution along row directions. Such minima have been recorded by Domeij and Bjorkqist[124] along ⟨111⟩ directions following injection of 60 keV Rn^{222} α emitting ions along the ⟨111⟩ direction in tungsten. In addition Astnet et al[130] have observed that even conversion electrons emitted from a 60 keV Xe^{133} ion bombarded [100] face of tantalum exhibit minima along directions corresponding to channel directions, although the exact mechanism responsible for electronic emission suppression is not at present clear.

Gemmel and Holland[131] have also discussed the blocking effect of atom rows in the emission of protons generated by a (d, p) reaction in silicon and have simultaneously observed the channelling of protons incident from outside the crystal. Sizmann (Private communication) has reported channelling of fission fragments and Datz, Noggle and Moak[132, 133] have observed both row and interplanar channelling events for Br and I ions of energies up to 80 MeV (in the fission fragment range) in gold single crystals whilst Bøgh and Uggerhøj[134] have studied wide angle (Rutherford) scattering of 400 keV protons after injection into Tantalum, Gold or Tungsten single crystals and again observed pronounced minima in yield corresponding to channelled particles along both rows and planes. It is quite evident from these studies that the channelling phenomenon has wide physical implications, particularly in high energy particle detector applications, where the effects of crystal symmetry have been assumed negligible. Certainly further work on these topics is anticipated.

5.13 COMPARISON OF THEORETICAL AND EXPERIMENTAL RANGE DETERMINATIONS.

In sections 5.4-5.8 we have shown how ranges, range moments and distributions for primaries moving in isotropic targets may be determined assuming hard sphere interactions, and interactions involving interatomic potentials of the Bohr, the Born-Mayer and the Thomas-Fermi types. Range data were also evaluated for primaries moving in a real lattice assuming Born-Mayer and Bohr potentials. The predictions of these analyses were compared with machine results in section 5.10 and the agreement was observed to be very satisfactory. The real test of the utility of the analytical approach is of course the degree of agreement achieved when compared with experimental data. Clearly the experimental parameters most readily determined are the projected average path length, the mean square straggling and the range distribution. Some of the experimental studies have determined all these parameters, notably those of Davies and his collaborators, [41 etc] whilst others have determined, with accuracy, only the first of these parameters. These latter measurements include those of Powers and Whaling[58] and of Van Lint et al[40] and even here it is the Vector range rather than projected range which was determined. In many of the other experiments described in the previous section, the range parameters were, as shown, insufficiently well defined to permit quantitative comparison with theoretical data. Moreover in several cases, the target materials were such as to prevent unequivocal assignation of a specific target mass. In order to make quantitative comparisons we must consider the definitive measurements in more detail. The data of Davies et al, [41 etc] Poszanker,[85] Leachman and Atterling,[72] Winsberg and Alexander,[73] Guseva et al,[59] Harvey et al[75] and Van Wijngaarden and Duckworth, [82-84] give values of projected range directly whereas the measurements of Powers and Whaling,[58] Van Lint et al,[40] Baulch and Duncan,[76] and Porile[77] give vector ranges. These latter therefore must be corrected to projected values to compare with theoretical data. In the case of the measurements of Powers and Whaling[58] this conversion is readily achieved for the primary ions A, Kr and Xe through multiplication by the Lindhard-Scharff[8,11] factor $1 + \frac{1}{3}\frac{M_2}{M_1}$ since M_1 is greater than M_2 in these cases. However for Ne and N the mass ratio conditions do not obtain and the correction is not possible, as is also the case for the data of Van Lint et al.[40] These latter authors, however, have compared this total range data with Monte Carlo machine calculations assuming the Bohr interatomic potential and have shown (viz Figures 5.26, 57) that the experimental and theoretical data can only be made to concur if the screening length is allowed to vary with the primary ion mass. This tends to suggest that the Bohr function itself is inadequate in describing the interatomic potential. However these results did not account for inelastic losses which must assume importance at higher energies.

Greater success is achieved when experimental results are compared with the Thomas-Fermi potential, provided that account is taken of the inelastic losses. Thus Lindhard and Scharff and Schiøtt[11] have compared their theoretical data with a considerable amount of experimentally determined data, and with the simple Nielsen[9] formula and found both to be inadequate if only elastic collisions were considered. An example of this inadequacy is shown in Figure 5.93 for the range/energy data for Kr^{85} in Aluminium and Tungsten from the data of Davies, Domeij and Uhler[100]. However, if the Lindhard-Scharff[8,11] modification to the simple range/energy formulae, including the effects of electronic stopping is employed then the agreement between experiment and theory is much improved. Thus Figure 5.59 summarizes the available experimental data obtained with polycrystalline targets where the experimental curves are compared with the Lindhard-Scharff[11] curves for appropriate values of the electronic stopping contributions (i.e. k values appropriate to the primary to target mass ratio). Clearly the agreement is considerably improved, particularly at high energies where the inelastic losses assume importance. The experimental data in tungsten however are still too large, and this, one presumes, must be associated with the chanelling events which probably occur in this target material. At lower energies, all the Lindhard-Scharff[11] curves, including electronic stopping converge on the elastic collision universal curve, and it is quite clear that all experimental points lie above this curve, and for that matter, above the range/energy curves from the simple Nielsen[9] formula.

This suggests that the Thomas-Fermi potentials may be too strong at large separation distances (low energies) which is confirmed from the potential/atomic separation curves of Figure 2.4 of Chapter 2 where this potential is seen to be weaker than the Nielsen[9] potential (which itself gives even further reduced ranges at low primary energies).

Similarly the comparison of median ranges deduced from the Bohr potential by Robinson and Oen[27,36] with the data of McCargo et al[101] in Figure 5.94 indicates that, at low penetrations, the calculated ranges are slightly too low (i.e. the Bohr potential is too strong at large separation), but too high at high energies. This latter behaviour can be ascribed to the fact that the Oen-Robinson[27,36] calculations ignore inelastic losses at high energies. The agreement at low energies between the experimental and theoretical curves is better for the Bohr potential than the Thomas-Fermi potential, which are both of course better than the inverse r^2 potential. This again may be anticipated from the potential curves of Figure 2.4 where it is seen that at large separations the strength of the potentials is in decreasing order (1) inverse r^2 (2) Thomas-Fermi (3) Bohr. A more suitable potential at large separations would appear to be one of the Born-Mayer type and the suggestion by Holmes[10] of a combination of a Bohr and Born Mayer potential therefore appears promising, and improvement on this suggestion may be combinations of Thomas-Fermi and Born-Mayer potentials with the inclusion of inelastic stopping processes. On the other hand, Lindhard et al[11] suggest that channelling events even in polycrystals may be the reason for too high penetrations at low energy, and indeed this may well be the true reason for the lack of agreement between experimental and theoretical deductions in crystalline metals. In fact comparison of Domeij et al's[104] data of Na, A, Kr and Xe ions in amorphous Al_2O_3 and WO_3 targets with the Lindhard theoretical expression shows remarkable agreement up to energies as high as 1.5 MeV. This is a real indication that the Thomas-Fermi potential is good for essentially randomised targets and that the disagreement for single

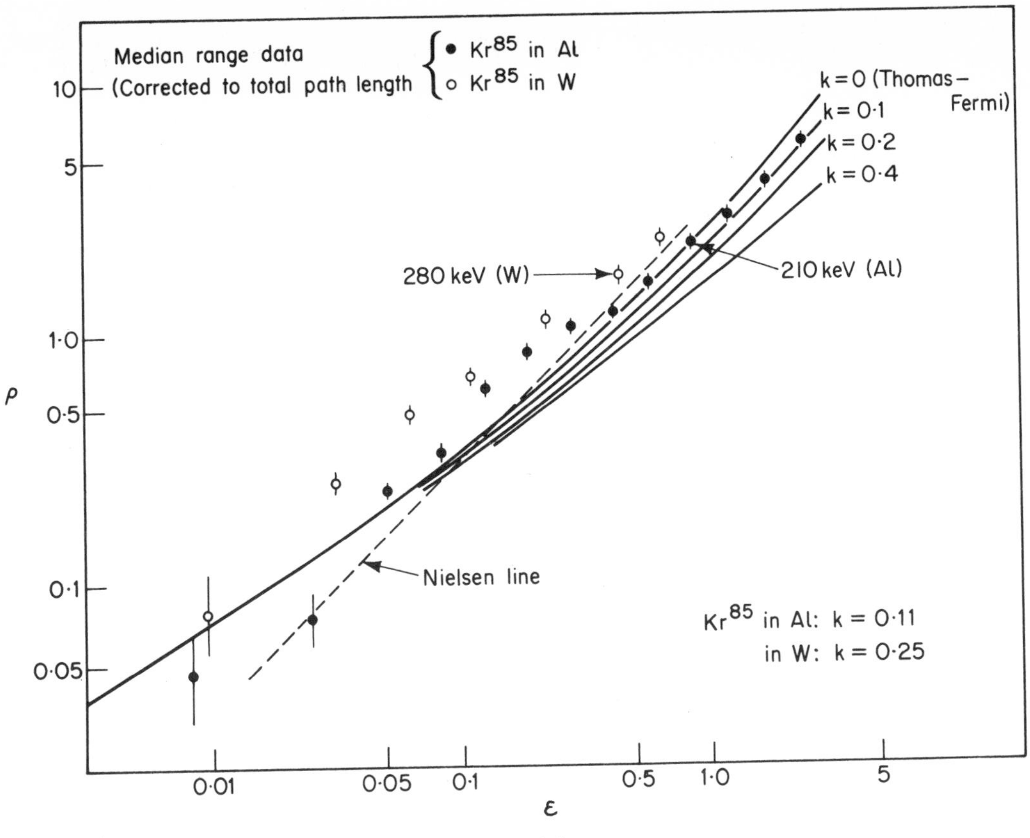

(a)

Fig. 5. 93 Lindhard plots of the measured mean ranges of Kr in Al (circles) and W (squares). (a) low energy (b) high energy. The total path length correction is obtained by multiplying by 1 + A/3. (viz. Ref. 5. 100)

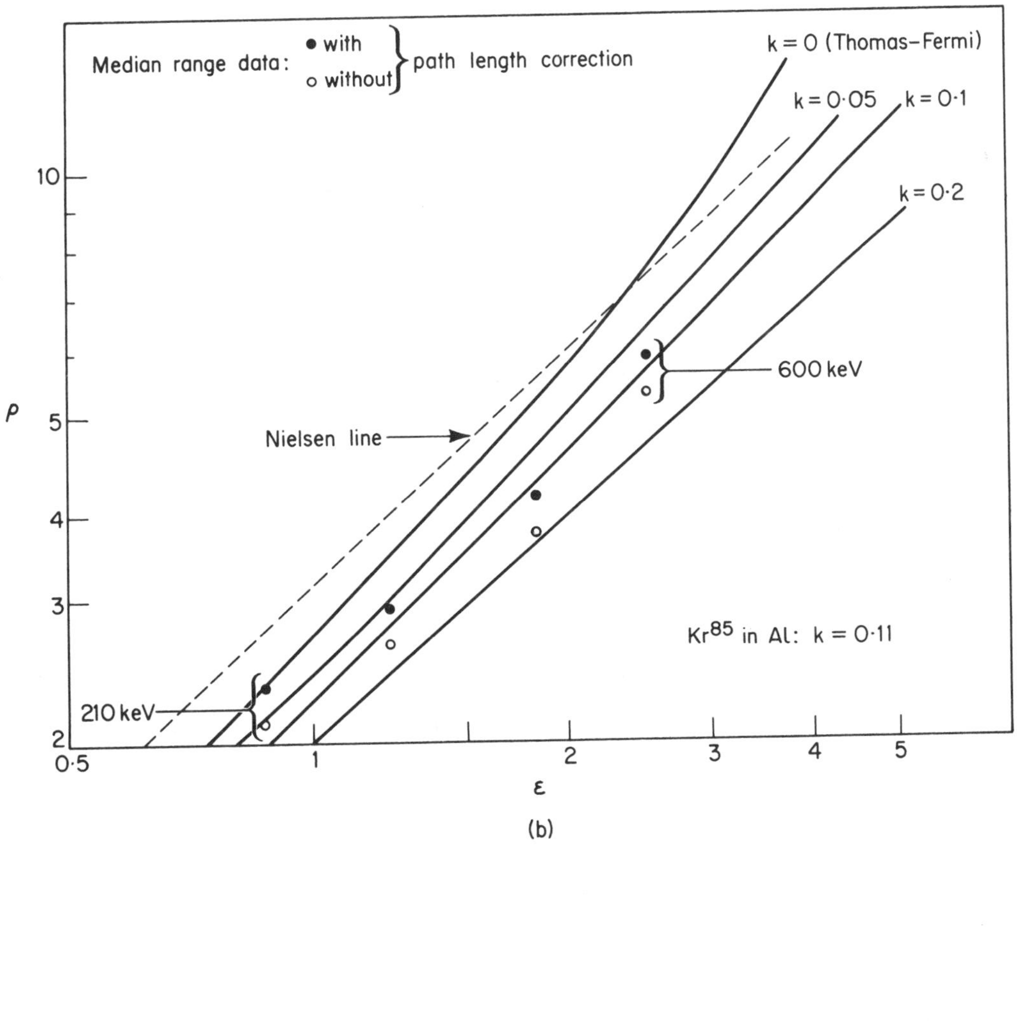

(b)

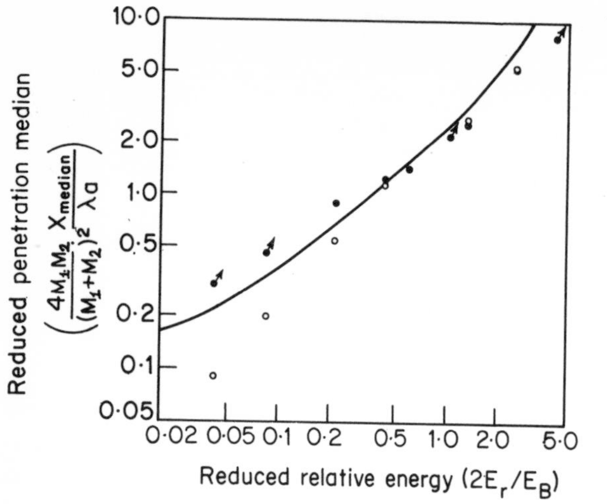

Fig. 5. 94 Comparison of experimental data for Na^{24} in aluminum with the theoretical curve of Oen et al.(Ref. 5. 36): ● new data, using trace bombardments; ○ previous work. (Ref. 5. 42) (viz. Ref. 5. 99)

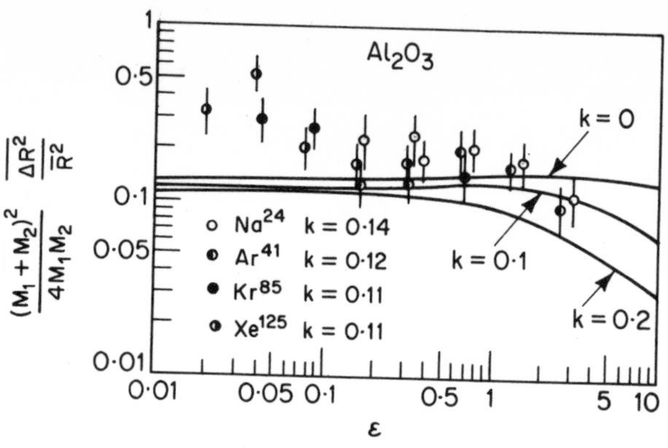

Fig. 5. 95 Comparison of the experimental relative straggling in Al_2O_3 with the theoretical curves of Lindhard et al. (Ref. 5. 8). The appropriate k value for each projectile has been calculated from equation 5. 25. 2 (viz. ref. 5. 104)

and polycrystalline targets may be entirely due to channelling processes. Domeij et al[104] have also shown that range straggling, and thus distribution functions for Al_2O_3 and WO_3 targets, are also in good agreement with the Lindhard et al[11] predictions and this further supports the value of the Thomas-Fermi potential and the theoretical calculations for randomised targets. The possibility, therefore, of determining the interatomic potential at large separations through use of these long range trajectory distributions in channelled events, assumes considerable importance. Kornelsen et al,[109] Davies et al[63] and Piercy et al[107] have evaluated the number of ions contained in the channelled tails of Xe in tungsten and other ions in Si and Al respectively as a function of energy and find that the channelled ion range follows a three halves power law of energy up to 5 keV and a half power law above this energy in the case of Xe in W. The former result indicates that the simple Lehmann-Leibfried[4] calculations may be inadequate whilst the latter result suggests that channelled ions lose energy largely through inelastic processes (which leads to an $E^{1/2}$ dependence of range) down to quite low energies. This inelastic loss mechanism may well account for the inadequacy of the Lehmann-Leibfried[4] calculations at the lower energies. A further experimental fact which reveals the inadequacy of the simple channelling theory is that channelled ranges of 40 keV ions in the ⟨100⟩ direction is seen to increase in the order A, Rb, Kr, Xe and Na. Again, inelastic losses may be a partial cause of this discrepancy. The results obtained entirely in the region of inelastic scattering i.e. those of Van Wijngaarden and Duckworth,[82] Ormerod and Duckworth[83,84] and Poskanzer,[85] show remarkably good agreement when compared with the theoretical predictions of Lindhard, Scharff and Schiøtt.[8,11] However, as pointed out earlier, there is still a need for more extensive investigation of these effects, particularly to examine the dependence of inelastic stopping on primary mass, charge and energy.

Comparison of range straggling data may be made using the Lindhard-Scharff values from table 5. 1, which employed the Thomas-Fermi potential, or the Oen-Robinson results[27,36] in Figure 5. 25 (which was shown to compare favourably with the Holmes and Leibfried[13] calculations) assuming a Bohr potential, with the data of Domeij et al[104] in Fig. 5. 95. Since the Thomas-Fermi potential is generally held to be superior, only straggling data computed from this potential are shown in Fig. 5. 95, and the agreement is satisfactory except at low energies. Oen and Robinson[34] have shown that the Bohr potential leads to larger straggling at low energies and thus, as suggested above, the Bohr potential may be superior for larger impact parameters. At higher energies the experimental behaviour must be attributed to the increased effects of electronic stopping and the Lindhard-Scharff theory therefore corresponds quite closely to the data since this indicates the tendency towards constancy of the straggling at higher energies. Lindhard, Scharff and Schiøtt[8,11] consider that further comparison is invidious since experimentally determined straggling parameters appear to be insufficiently accurate.

Considering next the range distribution we note that in this case, only theoretical predictions are available for the inverse r^2 and Bohr potential and for the specific case of very light primaries in heavy targets. In the latter case, the results of Guseva et al[59] for Si^{30} in Tantalum show good agreement with the diffusion model of stopping. For a general mass ratio as shown in Figure 5. 30 comparison of these former predictions with the experimental ranges are more skewed than results from a Bohr potential with a preponderance of deep penetrations. The deep penetrations are exponentially distributed, characteristic of the inverse r^2 potential. This experimental behaviour may be anticipated since the scattering of Na^{24} in Al should be approximately isotropic since $A_1 \approx A_2$, i.e. typical of the inverse r^2 potential. Davies and Sims[41] results indicate that the experimental distribution function deviates markedly from the predicted distribution at high primary energies. This behaviour is also observed in A^{41} in Aluminium as shown in Figures 5. 72 and is attributable to the fact that at higher energies the higher mass primaries interact with the target atoms through an unscreened potential (Rutherford scattering) and the scattering is non isotropic. Thus the higher energy experimental curves do not show the long predicted tails. In the case of Xe^{133} however, the primaries and target atoms continue to interact via the screened potential up to higher energies and the scattering tends to be isotropic. Thus the predicted and experimental curves for Xe^{133} in Al, of Figures 5. 74 agree closely. At low energies Na^{24} primaries exhibit a larger penetrating tail than predicted by the machine calculations and this must be taken as evidence of the chan-

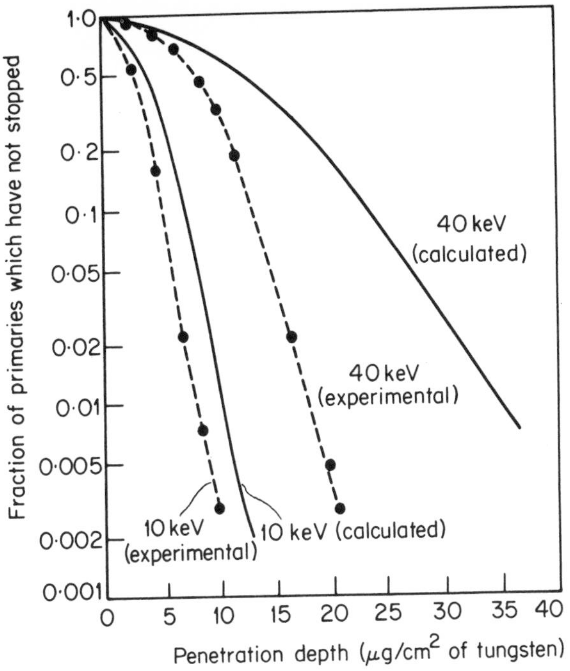

Fig. 5. 96 Comparison of computed (Thomas-Fermi potential) and experimental (ref. 5. 104) integral penetration distributions. The calculations were performed for Xe^{133} in W and the experimental data is for Xe^{125} ions in WO_3. (viz. Ref. 5. 34)

nelling events which were unequivocally observed in single crystal Aluminium. Oen and Robinson[34] have also made computer calculations of the integral range distributions of 10 keV and 40 keV Xe^{133} ions in W assuming a Thomas-Fermi potential and compared these with the experimental data of Domeij et al[104] for Xe^{125} ion ranges in WO_3 as in Fig. 5. 96. The theoretical and experimental curves are in reasonable agreement, and Oen and Robinson express the opinion that further improvement would be achieved if theoretical calculations were in fact made for amorphous WO_3. These calculations assumed a random target, neglecting channelling processes and in fact, as noted earlier, further discussion of chanelling phenomena is unproductive at the present stage of experimental knowledge and we end this chapter with the hope that both experimental and theoretical advances will soon end this state of affairs. One must be optimistic about this in view of the rapid progress made in both directions in the last five years. However the results of earlier studies which show the effects of damage and gas occlusion to the target in conditioning range distributions, must be remembered and guarded against in future work.

REFERENCES

1. Davies, J. A., Friesen, J. and McIntyre, J. D. (1960) Can. J. Chem. **38**, 1526
2. Nelson, R. S. and Thompson, M. W. (1963) Phil. Mag. **8**, 1677
3. For an important numerical correction see Nelson, R. S. and Thompson, M. W. (1964) Phil. Mag. **9**, 1069
4. Lehmann, C. and Leibfried, G. (1963) J. Appl. Phys. **34**, 2821
5. Lindhard, J. (1965) Dan. Vid. Selsk. Mat. Fys. Medd. **34**, No. 14
6. Loeb, L. B. (1961) The Kinetic Theory of Gases. Dover Publications Inc. New York. (1961) (Reprint)
7. Bohr, N. (1948) Dan. Vid. Selsk. Mat. Fys. Medd. **18**, 8
8. Lindhard, J., Scharff, M. and Schiøtt, H. E. (1963) Dan. Vid. Selsk. Mat. Fys. Medd. **33**, 3
9. Nielsen, K. O. (1955) Electromagnetically Enriched Isotopes and Mass Spectrometry. Butterworths Press. London. p. 68
10. Holmes, D. K. (1962) Radiation Damage in Solids, Vol. 1. International Atomic Energy Agency. Vienna. p. 3
11. Lindhard, J. and Scharff, M. (1961) Phys. Rev. **124**, 128
12. Gombas, P. (1956) Handbuch der Physik **36**, Springer Verlag, Berlin. p. 109
13. Holmes, D. K. and Leibfried, G. (1960) J. Appl. Phys. **31**, 1046
14. Leibfried, G. (1962) J. Appl. Phys. **33**, 1933
15. Leibfried, G. (1963) Zeits. f. Physik. **171**, 1
16. Korchovei, A., Gika, G. and Greku, D. (1962) Fiz. Tverd. Tela. **4**, 2777. English Translation in Soviet Physics. Solid State (1963) **4**, 2037
17. Baroody, E. M. (1964) J. Appl. Phys. **35**, 2074
18. Baroody, E. M. (1965) J. Appl. Phys. **36**, 3565
19. Weinberg, A. M. and Wigner, E. P. (1958) The Physical Theory of Neutron Chain Reactors. The University of Chicago Press, Chicago (1958)
20. Glasstone, S. and Edlund, M. C. (1953) The Elements of Nuclear Reactor Theory. MacMillan. London (1953)
21. Marshak, R. E. (1947) Rev. Mod. Phys. **19**, 185
22. Tait, J. H. (1956) Rep. Prog. Phys. **19**, 268
23. Davison, B. (1957) Neutron Transport Theory. Oxford University Press. Oxford (1957)
24. Corkhill, D. P. and Carter, G. (1965) Phil. Mag. **10**, 131
25. Corkhill, D. P. and Carter, G. (1964) Physics. Letters. **12**, 93
26. Robinson, M. T. and Oen, O. S. (1963) Appl. Phys. Letters **2**, 30
27. Robinson, M. T., Oen, O. S. and Holmes, D. K. (1962) Le Bombardment Ionique C.R.N.S. Colloquium at Bellevue Paris, 1962. p. 105
28. Robinson, M. T. and Oen, O. S. (1963) Phys. Rev. **132**, 2385
29. Beeler, J. R. and Besco, D. G. (1962) Radiation Damage in Solids. Vol. 1. International Atomic Energy Agency. Vienna. p. 43
30. Lehmann, C. and Leibfried, G. (1963) Zeits F. Physik. **172**, 465
31. Born, M. and Mayer, J. E. (1932) Zeits. f. Physik. **75**, 1
32. Leibfried, G. (1955) Handbuch der Physik. Vol. 7. Springer Verlag. Berlin (1955) p. 264
33. Andersen, H. H. and Sigmund, P. (1965) To be published
34. Oen, O. S. and Robinson, M. T. (1964) J. Appl. Phys. **35**, 2515
35. Debye, P. (1913) Ann. Phys. Lpz. **43**, 49
36. Oen, O. S., Holmes, D. K. and Robinson, M. T. (1963) J. Appl. Phys. **34**, 302
37. Oen, O. S. and Robinson, M. T. (1963) Bul. Amer. Phys. Soc. 8 (2) 195
38. Firsov, O. B. (1957) Zh. Eksperim i. Teor. Fiz. **33**, 696. English Trans. in Soviet. Phys.-J.E.T.P. 1958, **6**, 534
39. For a description of Monte Carlo methods see Kahn, **H.** (1954) Applications of Monte Carlo, U.S.A.E.C. Report A.E.C.U.-3259 p. 39
40. Van Lint, V. A. J. and Wyatt, M. E. Jr. (1962) United States Airforce. A.R.L. Report No. A.R.L. 62-389
41. Davies, J. A. McIntyre, J. D., Cushing, R. L. and Lounsbury, M. (1960) Can. J. Chem. **38**, 1535
42. Davies, J. A. and Sims, G. A. (1961) Can. J. Chem. **39**, 601
43. Robinson, M. T., Oen, O. S. and Holmes, D. K. (1962) Oak Ridge National Laboratory Report. ORNL-3364. p. 3
44. Gibson, J. B., Goland, A. N. Milgram, M. and Vineyard, G. H. (1960) Phys. Rev. **120**, 1229
45. Beeler, J. R. and Besco, D. G. (1963) J. Appl. Phys. **34**, 2873
46. Beeler, J. R. and Besco, D. G. (1963) Proc. Int. Conf. on Crystal Lattice Defects. Conf. Jnl. Phys. Soc. Japan. 18. Suppl. **3**, (1963) 159
47. Besco, D. G. and Beeler, J. R. Jr. (1963) Bul. Amer. Phys. Soc. 8, 339. Paper L5
48. Beeler, J. R. and Besco, D. G. (1963) Bul. Amer. Phys. Soc. 8, 339. Paper L6
49. Beeler, J. R. and Besco, D. G. (1964) Phys. Rev. 134A, 530
50. Erginsoy, C., Vineyard, G. H. and Shimizu, A. (1965) Phys. Rev. **139**, A118
51. Harrison, D. E., Leeds, R. W. and Gay, W. L. (1965) J. Appl. Phys. **36**, 3154
52. Gay, W. L. and Harrison, D. E. (1964) Phys. Rev. **135**, A1780
53. Hines, R. L. (1960) Phys. Rev. **120**, 1626
54. Young, J. R. (1955) J. Appl. Phys. **26**, 1302
55. Thomson, J. J. (1933) Conduction of Electricity through Gases. Cambridge University Press 3rd Edition. Vol. 11.
56. Whiddington, R. (1914) Proc. Roy. Soc. (London) **89**, 554
57. Heinz, O., Gyorgy, E. M. and Ohl, R. S. (1956) Rev. Sci. Inst. **27**, 43
58. Powers, D. and Whaling, W. (1962) Phys. Rev. **126**, 61
59. Guseva, M. I., Inoptkin, E. V. and Tsytko, S. P. (1959) Zh. Eksper i Teor. Fiz. **36**. Engl. Transl. in Soviet Physics, J.E.T.P. (1959) **9**, 1
60. Phillips, W. R. and Read, F. H. (1963) Proc. Phys. Soc. **81**, 1
61. Barker, P. H. and Phillips, W. R. (1965) Proc. Phys. Soc. **86**, 379
62. McCaldin, J. O. and Widmer, A. E. (1963) J. Phys. Chem. Solids **24**, 1073
63. Davies, J. A., Ball, G. C., Brown, F. and Domeij, B. (1964) Can. J. Phys. **42**, 1070
64. Schmitt, R. A. and Sharp, R. A. (1959) Phys. Rev. Letters **1**, 445
65. Van Lint, V. A. J., Schmitt, R. A. and Suffredini, C. S. (1961) Phys. Rev. **121**, 1457
66. Van Lint, V. A. J., Schmitt, R. A., Suffredini, C. S. (1961) Bul. Amer. Phys. Soc. **6**, 150, OA7

67. Van Lint, V. A. J., Schmitt, R. A. and Suffredini, C. S. (1961) Bul. Amer. Phys. Soc. **6**, 150, OA8

68.
69.
70. Vant Lint, V. A. J. and co-authors. Quarterly Status Reports from GA-1193 to GAED-2830 April 1960 to June 1962. (viz ARL report 62-389)

71. Penfold, A. S. and Leiss, J. E. (1958) Analysis of Photo Cross sections. University of Illinois (Unpublished)

72. Leachman, R. B. and Atterling, H. (1957) Arkiv. f. Fysik. **13**, 101

73. Winsberg, L. and Alexander, J. M. (1961) Phys. Rev. **121**, 518

74. Alexander, J. M. and Sisson, D. H. (1962) UCRL report UCRL-10098

75. Harvey, B. G., Wade, W. H. and Donovan, P. F. (1960) Phys. Rev. **119**, 225

76. Baulch, D. L. and Duncan, J. F. (1957) Austral J. Chem. **10**, 112

77. Porile, N. T. (1964) Phys. Rev. **135A**, 1115

78. Chasman, C., Jones, K. W. and Ristinen, R. A. (1965) Phys. Rev. Letters. **15**, 245

79. Young, J. R. (1956) J. Appl. Phys. **27**, 1

80. Hines, R. L. (1963) Phys. Rev. **132**, 701

81. Davies, J. A., McIntyre, J. D. and Sims, G. (1962) Can. J. Chem. **40**, 1605

82. Van Wijngaarden, A. and Duckworth, H. E. (1962) Can. J. Phys. **40**, 1749

83. Ormrod, J. H. and Duckworth, H. E. (1963) Can. J. Phys. **41**, 1424

84. Ormrod, J. H. McDonald, J. R. and Duckworth, H. E. (1965) Can. J. Phys. **43**, 275

85. Pozkanzer, A. M. (1963) Phys. Rev. **129**, 385

86. Domeij, B. Bergstrom, I., Davies, J. A. and Uhler, J. (1963) Arkiv f. Fysik **24**, 399

87. Whaling, W. (1958) Handbuch der Physik **34**. Springer Verlag. Berlin (1958) p. 193

88. Bergstrom, I., Davies, J. A., Domeij, B. and Uhler, J. (1963) Arkiv. f. Fysik. **24**, 389

89. Bergstrom, I., Brown, F. Davies, J. A., Geiger, J. S., Graham, R. L. and Kelly, R. (1963) Nucl. Inst. Methods **21**, 249

90. Graham, R. L., Davies, J. A. and Brown, F. (1962) Bul. Amer. Phys. Soc. Ser. 11, 7, 491

91. Graham, R. L., Brown, F., Davies, J. A. and Pringle, J. P. S. (1963) Can. J. Phys. **41**, 1686

92. Thulin, S. (1955) Arkiv. f. Fysik **9**, 107

93. Bartholomew, C. Y. and La Padula, A. R. (1960) J. Appl. Phys. **31**, 445

94. Bredov, M. M., Komareva, R. F. and Regel, A. R. (1954) Doklady Akad. Nauk. S.S.S.R. **99**, 69

95. Bredov, M. M. and Okuneva, N. M. (1957) Doklady Akad. Nauk. S.S.S.R. **113**, 795

96. Bredov, M. M., Lang, I. G. and Okuneva, N. M. (1958) Zhur. Tekh. Fiz. **28**, 252

97. Bartholomew, C. Y. and La Padula, A. R. (1964) J. Appl. Phys. **35**, 2570

98. Davies, J. A. McIntyre, J. D. and Sims, G. A. (1961) Can. J. Chem. **39**, 611

99. McCargo, M., Brown, F. and Davies, J. A. (1963) Can. J. Chem. **41**, 2309

100. Davies J. A., Domeij, B., Uhler, J. (1963) Arkiv. f. Fysik. **24**, 377

101. McCargo, M., Davies, J. A. and Brown, F. (1963) Can. J. Phys. **41**, 1231

102. Davies, J. A., Brown, F. and McCargo, M. (1963) Can. J. Phys. **41**, 829

103. Brown, F. and Davies, J. A. (1963) Can. J. Phys. **41**, 844

104. Domeij, B., Brown, F. Davies, J. A. and McCargo, M. (1964) Can. J. Phys. **42**, 1624

105. Knutsen, A. B. University of Aarhus, Denmark (Unpublished)

106. Piercy, G. R., Brown, F., Davies, J. A. and McCargo, M. (1963) Phys. Rev. Letters **10**, 399

107. Piercy, G. R., McCargo, M., Brown, F. and Davies, J. A. (1964) Can. J. Phys. **42**, 116

108. Kornelsen, E. V. (1964) Bull. of Nat. Research Council of Canada. Radio Elec. Eng. Division **14**, 34

109. Kornelsen, E. V., Brown, F., Davies, J. A. and Piercy, G. R. (1964) Phys. Rev. **136A**, 849

110. Domeij, B., Brown, F., Davies, J. A., Piercy, G. R. and Kornelsen, E. V. (1964) Phys. Rev. Letters **12**, 363

111. Davies, J. A., Eriksson, L. and Jespersgaard, P. (1965) Proc. Conf. on Electromagnetic Isotope Separators, Related Ion Accelerators and Applications to Physics. Aarhus. Denmark (1965)

112. Ball, G. C. and Brown, F. (1965) Can. J. Phys. **43**, 676

113. Channing, D. A., Whitton, J. L. (1964) Phys. Letters **13**, 27

114. Davies, J. A. and Whitton, J. (1964) J. Electrochem. Soc. **111**, 137

115. Brown, F., Ball, G. C., Channing, D. A., Howe, M., Pringle, J. P. S. and Whitton, J. L. (1965) Proc. Conf. on Electromagnetic Isotope Separators, Related Ion Accelerators and Applications to Physics. Aarhus. Denmark (1965)

116. Burtt, R. B., Colligon, J. S. and Leck, J. H. (1961) Brit. J. Appl. Phys. **12**, 396

117. Colligon, J. A. and Leck, J. H. (1961) Transactions of the 8th National Vacuum Symposium of American Vacuum Society. Pergamon Press. London (1962) p. 275

118. Lutz, H. and Sizmann, R. (1963) Phys. Letters **5**, 113

119. Lutz, H. and Sizmann, R. (1964) Z. Naturforsch. **19a**, 1079

120. Von Heinen, H., Lutz, H. and Sizmann, R. (1964) Z. Naturforsch. **19a**, 1131

121. Pohlau, C., Lutz, H., Sizmann, R. (1964) Zeits. f. Angew. Phys. **19**, 404

122. Lindhard, J. (1964) Phys. Letters **12**, 126

123. Bøgh, E., Davies, J. A. and Nielsen, K. O. Phys. Letters. **12**, 129

124. Thompson, M. W. (1964) Phys. Rev. Letters **13**, 756

125. Dearnaley, G. (1964) I.E.E. Trans. Nucl. Science. N.S. 11

126. Dearnaley, G., Sattler, A. (1964) Harwell Symposium on Atomic Collision Cascades 1964. U.K.A.E.S. Report AERE-R-4694

127. Erginsoy, C., Wegner, H. E. and Gibson, W. M. (1964) Phys. Rev. Letters **13**, 530

128. Brandt, W., Khan, J. M., Potter, D. L., Worley, R. D. and Smith, H. P. (1965) Phys. Letters **14**, 42

129. Domeij, B. and Bjorkqvist, K. (1965) Phys. Letters **14**, 127

130. Astnet, G., Bergstrom, I., Domeij, B., Eriksson, L. and Persson, A. (1965) Phys. Letters **14**, 308

131. Gemmell, D. S. and Holland, R. E. (1965) Phys. Rev. Letters **14**, 945

132. Datz, S., Noggle, T. S. and Moak, C. D. (1965) Proc. Conf. on Electromagnetic Isotope Separators, Related Ion Accelerators and Applications to Physics. Aarhus, Denmark (1965)

133. Datz, S., Noggle, T. S. and Moak, C. D. (1965) Phys. Rev. Letters **15**, 254

134. Bøgh, E. and Uggerhøj, E. (1965) Physics Letters **17**, 116

CHAPTER 6

Radiation Damage

6.1

In the previous chapter we have examined the progress of energetic primary ions passing through a solid, concentrating greatest attention upon the primary ion itself. In arriving at a final resting position within the lattice, the primary makes multiple collisions, elastic or otherwise, with the lattice atoms, and its energy is gradually degraded. This energy loss is transferred to the lattice in the form of electronic excitation when there are inelastic contributions to the loss mechanism, in kinetic energy of motion of the lattice atoms when the collisions are elastic, and possible in transmutation effects in fissile target materials. In the former case the effects will include secondary electron emission as described in Chapter 3 and the emission of electromagnetic radiation as observed by Kistemaker and Snoek[1,2] in metals (and, semiconductors and polar crystals). In the latter cases the struck atoms will be displaced from their equilibrium positions in the lattice (as determined by the interatomic forces of the surrounding atoms). If the struck atom receives sufficient energy in the collision and this is properly directed, the atom displacement will be sufficient to carry it away from the influence of the immediately surrounding atoms and a vacancy will be created at the original atom position whilst the displaced atom becomes a 'foreign' atom elsewhere in the lattice. Since these displacements occur in times short compared to those necessary to establish thermal equilibrium of the lattice atoms, the energy required to cause the displacement will be considerably different from that required for that to promote normal activated diffusion of the atom through the lattice. Similarly the initial direction of motion of the displaced atom will be important since it will be clearly easier for this atom to leave the surrounding cage of atoms if it is directed between these atoms rather than directly at a neighbouring atom. If the struck atom does not receive sufficient energy to allow its total ejection from its equilibrium position, the energy gain must be dissipated in the form of lattice heating and lattice waves (phonons).

The primary ion will therefore leave in its wake, regions of considerable lattice disturbance with some atoms removed from normal positions and others resited at non-normal positions. Because the target surface is essentially a plane of asymmetry where the atoms are subjected to binding forces from one side of the normal direction only, one would expect the displacement events to be slightly different at this plane than in the volume of the solid, and indeed ionic bombardment results in the preferential removal of surface atoms into the gas phase. This phenomenon, known as sputtering will be discussed in detail in Chapter 7, but is clearly related to the displacement processes within the interior of the solid and provides considerable proof of some of the concepts introduced in this Chapter. We shall confine ourselves, for the present, to the displacement events occurring within the solid, known collectively as Radiation Damage events, and follow the pattern adopted in the previous Chapter. Specifically, we shall describe the theoretical calculations for both an assumed isotropic random solid, and then determine the effects of lattice symmetry. Secondly we shall discuss machine calculations of damage processes, and conclude with a description of the experimental evidence of radiation effects.

Many other treatments of radiation damage in solids, notably those by Seitz and Koehler[3], Dienes and Vineyard[4], and Billington and Crawford[5] have been given, dealing comprehensively with the effects attendant on electron, photon, fission fragment and heavy charged particle bombardment of various materials. In the present analysis we shall confine ourselves to the last type of bombardment, and in particular to the low energy region of interest in this book, with greatest emphasis on the displacement processes in metals. The effects of lattice symmetry may assume dominant importance and these will be reviewed in some detail, in comparison with earlier analyses[6] which have only considered these briefly.

Since radiation damage causes atomic displacements and the production of defects in the normal undisturbed lattice it must be anticipated that damage will result in observable changes in the macroscopic properties of the bombarded solid. For example, since vacancies and impurities cause scattering of lattice waves and electrons, and in semiconductors give rise to donor and acceptor levels, one would expect observable changes in thermal and electrical conductivity of irradiated materials. Similarly, changes in optical and mechanical properties would be anticipated and these, as the other predicted effects, are, in fact, observed. In order to be able to estimate the magnitude of such damage induced processes, two characteristics of the damage must be specified. These are (1) the nature of the defects produced, and (2) the number of these defects. In the following section we will discuss the first of these in a rather qualitative way since the calculation of all except the most simple defect configurations is currently somewhat inexact. On the other hand the discussion of the rate of defect production has been the subject of quite exhaustive quantitative analysis, extended relatively recently from calculations assuming an isotropic, random target to a realistic lattice representation. The second of the above topics will consequently be treated analytically in some detail.

In order to assess the nature of radiation induced defects in solids, we shall initially discuss defects normally present in solids which result from the finite energy of the lattice atoms and their ability to migrate from normal lattice positions by thermally activated processes. Detailed discussions of the defect solid state have been given by many authors[7,8,9] and we present here only a summary of the facts necessary to understanding of radiation induced defects.

6.2 LATTICE DEFECTS

6.2.1 Point Defects

The simplest departures from perfection which may be anticipated in a perfect lattice, are atoms missing

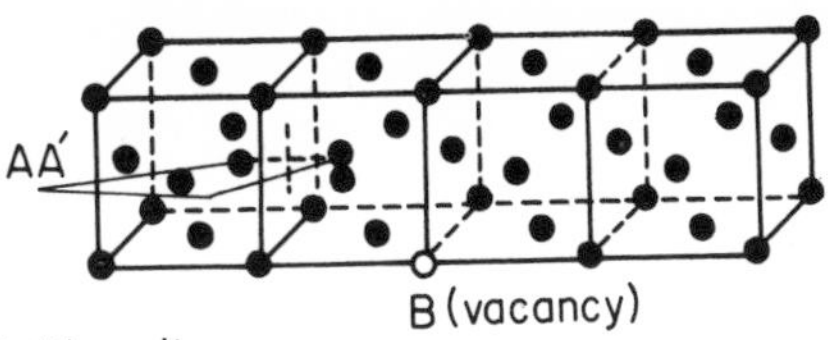

Fig. 6. 1 Vacancy and Interstitial in an F.C.C. crystal

from normal lattice positions (vacancies) and atoms residing in non-normal lattice positions (interstitials), both of which are illustrated in a representation of an f.c.c. lattice in Figure 6. 1. If atoms of a foreign substance are present in the host lattice these may be able to displace lattice atoms from their normal sites and become substitutional.

These defects in a normal structure will result in abnormal strains in the lattice and there will be a tendency for the structure to relax to the undisturbed state. Because of the finite thermal energy of the atoms, readjustment will be possible via thermally activated migration processes, and in equilibrium there will be a balance between continuous creation and destruction of defects. It is therefore of some importance to examine the energy required for migration of various types of defect. For a complete discussion of this topic the reader is referred to the text by Damask and Dienes[9], and only a short survey will be given here.

Huntington and Seitz[10] have investigated the mechanism of defect migration in copper and suggested three possible processes. These are

(1) Direct interchange of two adjacent lattice atoms.

(2) Migration of a lattice atom into an adjacent vacancy.

(3) An interstitial displaces a nearest neighbour lattice atom, the latter becoming an interstitial in the next plane.

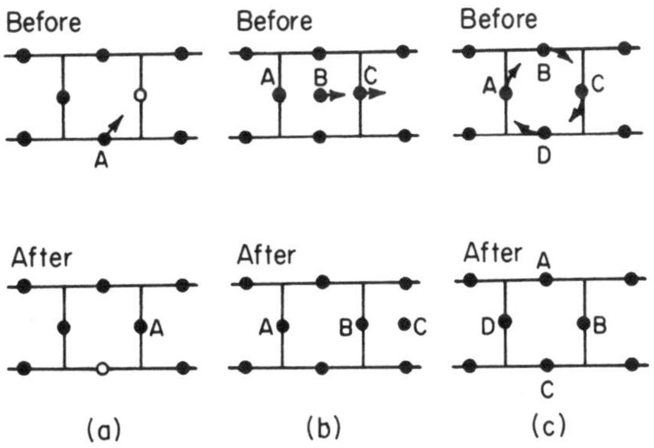

Fig. 6. 2 Possible mechanisms of self diffusion in Cu, illustrated by atomic positions before and after: (a) atom-vacancy exchange
(b) interstitialcy motion of a cubic interstitial
(c) coordinated rotation of a ring of atoms

The latter two of these processes are shown diagramatically in Figure 6. 2 with another suggested, (Zener)[11] but largely discounted (Darken)[12] mechanism of atomic rearrangement. Namely the co-ordinated rotation of a ring of three or four lattice atoms Calculations of the migration energies of the first three of the above mechanisms, taking into account the closed shell repulsion of the copper ions and the energy changes of the valence electrons, give values of

Q(direct interchange) = 10 eV

Q(vacancy mechanism)

$$= E_{1_v}f + E_{1_v}m$$
$$= (1.5 \pm 0.5\,eV) + (1.0 \pm 0.5\,eV)$$

Q(interstitialcy mechanism)

$$= E_{1_i}f + E_{1_i}m$$
$$= (4.5 \pm 1.0\,eV) + (0.16 \pm 0.10\,eV)$$

where $E_{1_v}f$ and $E_{1_v}m$ are the energies of formation of a monovacancy and migration of a monovacancy (motion of a lattice atom to annihilate a vacancy is equivalent to vacancy migration in the opposite direction) respectively and $E_{1_i}f$ and $E_{1_i}m$ are corresponding energies for the interstitial atoms. The energies of formation are those required respectively to displace a lattice atom to infinity or to add an extra atom in an interstitial position. Since the measured energy of migration (self diffusion) in Copper is about 2.05 eV (Kuper et al[13]) the most probable defect migration effect is via the vacancy process. On the other hand, it is clear that although it is difficult to form an interstitial, these are capable of easy motion through the lattice. More recent calculations by Johnson and Brown[14] suggest that the values of $E_{1_v}m$ and $E_{1_i}m$ are 0.43 and 0.05 eV respectively again indicating the higher migration probability of the interstitial once it has been formed. Huntington[10], Johnson[15,16], and Erginsoy and Vineyard[17] have evaluated an energy of migration for the vacancy in α iron to be 0.68 eV, whilst self diffusion energies have been shown experimentally[18] to be 2.6 eV, suggesting a vacancy formation of about 1.9 eV. Koehler and Leibfried[19] have also discussed the possible modes of vacancy migration in noble metals.

In addition to these simple monovacancy and single interstitial positions, several authors have shown that aggregates of vacancies and interstitials may be relatively stable, although calculations of the migration energies of such clusters are imprecise and in fact opinions differ as to the stability of various aggregates. Bartlett and Dienes[20] first suggested that two monovacancies may be bound together to form a divacancy as illustrated in Figure 6. 3a. Because of the resulting strains in this case, surrounding lattice atoms relax in the directions indicated by the arrows,

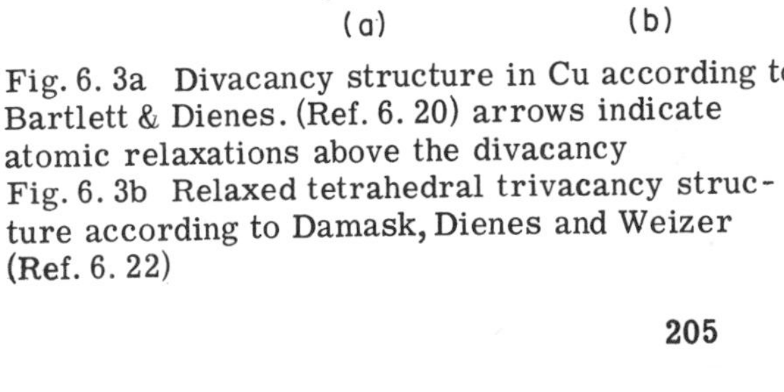

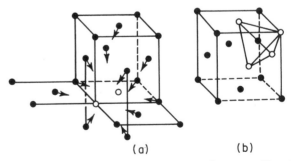

Fig. 6. 3a Divacancy structure in Cu according to Bartlett & Dienes. (Ref. 6. 20) arrows indicate atomic relaxations above the divacancy
Fig. 6. 3b Relaxed tetrahedral trivacancy structure according to Damask, Dienes and Weizer (Ref. 6. 22)

and, because of this increased relaxation it is expected that the energy of divacancy migration will be less than that of a monovacancy. Bartlett and Dienes[20] have evaluated the energy of activation for migration of such divacancies, but Lomer[21] has shown how the magnitude of this energy depends sensitively upon the assumed interatomic potential. For example the divacancy migration energy in copper was found to vary between 0. 2 eV and 1. 0 eV depending upon whether a Born-Mayer or Morse potential was used for the interatomic potential. A trivacancy structure has been suggested by Damask, Dienes and Weizer[22] and is shown in Figure 6. 3b. The migration energy of the structure in copper was calculated to be 1. 9 eV, whilst the binding energy of the aggregate was estimated to be 2. 3 eV. On the other hand Gibson et al[23] have estimated the value of this latter energy to be only 0. 5 eV, again exhibiting the disparity in predicted values. Johnson[15] has evaluated a divacancy binding energy of 0. 20 eV.

Larger vacancy aggregates have been proposed by Seeger[24] and Brinkman[25, 26] and others and evidence of these has been observed experimentally by Martin[27] et al, Barnes and Mazey[28,29], Silcox and Hirsch[30] and other investigators[31] after radiation damage, in interdiffusion measurements by Makin et al[32] and in quenching experiments by Hirsch et al[33,34] and numerous other workers. Computer calculations by Beeler and Besco[35] indicated the possibility of the formation of aggregates containing up to seven vacancies.

During ion bombardment of a target, many vacancies may be produced in a restricted region of the material. Because of the localised stresses the vacancies tend to migrate in such a direction as to reduce the stored energy of the system and this may be achieved by vacancy aggregation, (this structure having a smaller surface to volume ratio than many isolated vacancies, (viz Dienes and Vineyard[4] and Eshelby[36].) In this way depleted zones may be formed in the target, particularly at low primary energies, or towards the end of the range of a fast primary when the primary mean free path becomes comparable with the interatomic spacing and the primary collides with almost every lattice atom it passes. Experimental evidence of the existence of depleted zones[24,37] or vacancy clusters has been summarised by Gibson et al[23] and Beeler and Besco[35] have exhibited the events analytically.

Whereas the monovacancy and vacancy cluster configurations have been relatively well established theoretically and experimentally, the equilibrium position of the interstitial is open to some doubt. The interstitial in face centred cubic copper has been the subject of the most extensive investigation. At first sight it might be expected that the interstitial would reside at the cube centre, with corresponding relaxations of the surrounding atoms as shown in Figure 6. 4a and indeed Huntington[38,39] evaluated the migration energy for an interstitial in this position as lying between 0. 2 and 0. 6 eV. However Tewordt[40], Tewordt and Benneman[41,42] and Johnson and Brown[14] have shown theoretically and Gibson et al[23] confirmed via computer calculations, that this configuration is unstable and relaxes to the split interstitial configuration shown in Figure 6. 4b. In this latter two interstitials reside at close separation on the cube axis along the ⟨100⟩ direction. Benneman[42] also suggested that a ⟨111⟩ split interstitial may be metastable with respect to the ⟨100⟩ configuration, but Johnson and Brown[14] believe that the former is in fact unstable. Meechan and Brinkman[43] and Gibson et al[23] have also shown that other stable or metastable interstitial configurations may be important.

A possible configuration for an interstitial, suggested by Paneth[44], is the static crowdion in which the extra atom is considered to be squeezed into a close packed ⟨110⟩ direction with relaxation of adjacent atoms in the same row as shown in Figure 6. 4c whilst surrounding atom rows also relax outwards. However Gibson et al[23] and Johnson and Brown[14] believed that this configuration is unstable in a static lattice. Indeed calculations by Seeger et al[45] suggested, in opposition to the view held by Gibson et al[23] and Brown and Johnson[14], that the static crowdion is in fact stable in copper, but doubt has been cast upon the validity of the computational methods. Erginsoy and Vineyard[17] and Johnson[15] have also evaluated the stable interstitial configuration in α iron and shown that this is the ⟨110⟩ split interstitial which possesses an activation energy of about 0. 33 eV for migration.

Crowdion ⟨111⟩ interstitials were again found to be unstable. On the other hand there is considerable evidence that such an arrangement is at least temporarily effective during radiation damage events where an interstitial may be injected into a close packed chain where it transfers energy to the chain and the chain relaxes dynamically to an equilibrium configuration. This concept will be expanded in greater detail in a later section.

Just as vacancy clusters may be anticipated in a heavily damaged target because of the tendency to reduce the internal surface area of defects, so also interstitial clusters may be formed. Eshelby[36] and others have shown that the forces between interstitials tend to be attractive at small spacings and this leads to interstitial aggregation. Interstitial aggregates are believed to have been observed in helium ion bombardment induced damage in Aluminium and Silver by

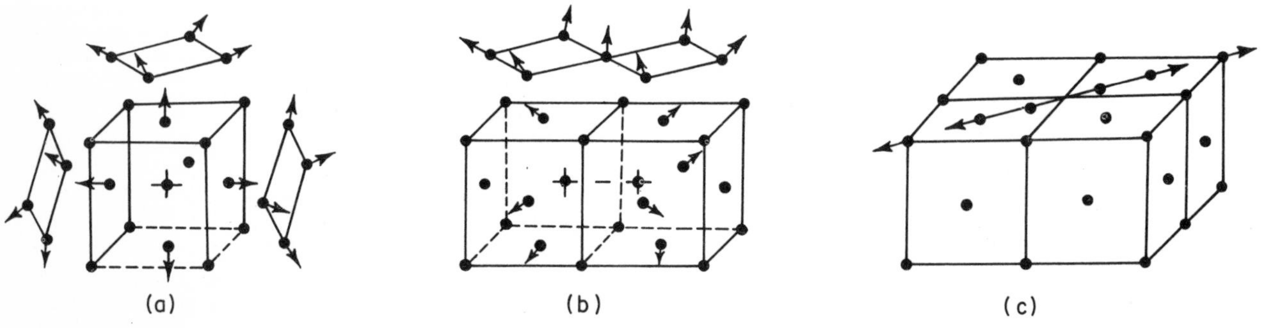

Fig. 6. 4 Possible configurations for an interstitial in Cu (a) Cubic Interstitial (b) ⟨100⟩ split interstitial (c) Crowdion (viz Ref:6. 44) The arrows indicate the approximate directions of the atomic relaxations around the defects

Barnes and his collaborators[28,29] and in other experiments[46→55]. Again these effects are expected to be important only where the primary makes multiple collisions within a small target volume. Calculations in copper and iron by Erginsoy and Vineyard[17] and Johnson[15] show that di-interstitials are bound with energies of 0.36-0.49 eV and 1.08 eV respectively. At higher energies however, the damaged regions are more confined to very localised regions where individual collisions occur and there is a greater probability of forming close spaced interstitial-vacancy pairs. In this process some of the displaced target atoms are only just removed from the normal lattice position and stabilise in the split interstitial configuration, close to the vacancy created by the displacement. This close spaced configuration is known as a close Frenkel pair and has a relatively low energy of recombination except possibly in co-valent solids. When the displaced atom is ejected to a considerable distance from the vacancy, the energy of recombination will be higher.

6.2.2 Dislocations

In addition to the simple point defects and defect aggregates already described, a number of specific extended defects are also normally present in real targets. These have been classified by Billington and Crawford[5] as (1) One and two dimensional arrangements of misplaced atoms such as line dislocations, screw dislocations, plane dislocations, grain boundaries and external surfaces, (2) Arrangements of dislocations which may be described in terms of volume defects, and which are important in plastically deformed solids, (3) Specialized defects such as stacking faults, boundaries between regions of different magnetization, etc. We discuss, initially the single line dislocation, the concept of which was first enunciated separately by Orowan[56] Taylor[57] and Polanyi[58]. If one introduces part of an extra plane of atoms into a simple cubic structure as shown in Figure 6.5a then the lattice is only strongly disturbed near the edge of this plane. The edge is known as the dislocation line and the defect is denoted as edge dislocation. Clearly this type of dislocation may be theoretically formed by making an imaginary partial cut into a lattice and shearing one side of the cut lattice relative to the other end, perpendicular to the surface as illustrated in Figure 6.5b. The dislocation line is then at the inner edge of the cut. If one side of the cut lattice is sheared parallel to the surface, as in Figure 6.5c then a different type of dislocation is formed, namely the screw dislocation. In this case the misplaced atoms will be on axial helices with the dislocation line as the axis. Much has been written about the properties of these dislocations and of their determining influence upon the mechanical and other properties of materials. It is necessary here only to summarize those features of simple dislocations which will be required later for understanding of radiation damage measurements.

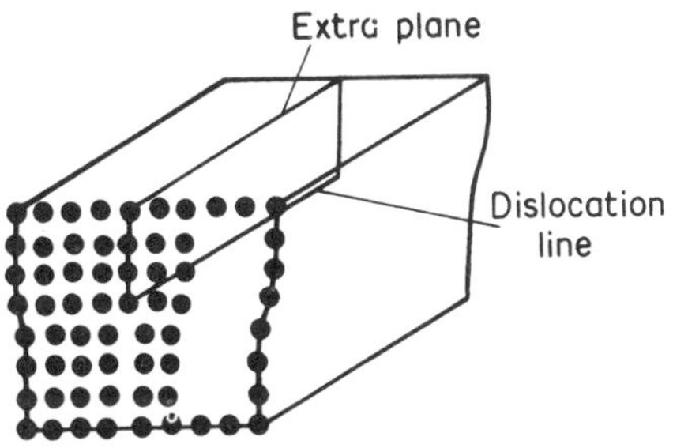

(a)

Fig. 6.5a Schematic representation of an edge dislocation with an additional plane of atoms.

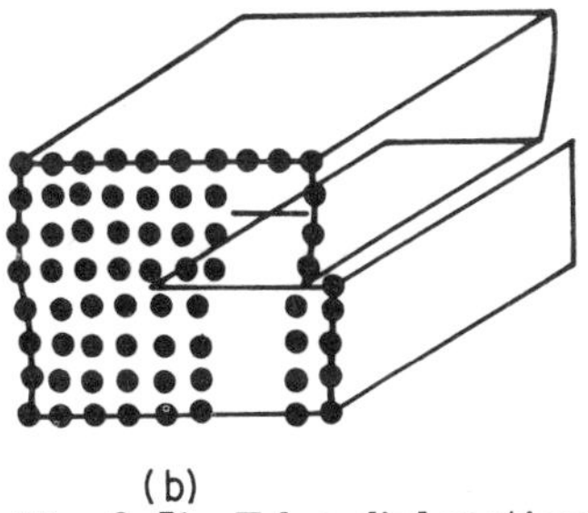
(b)

Fig. 6.5b Edge dislocation formed by a shearing stress normal to terminus of an imaginary cut.

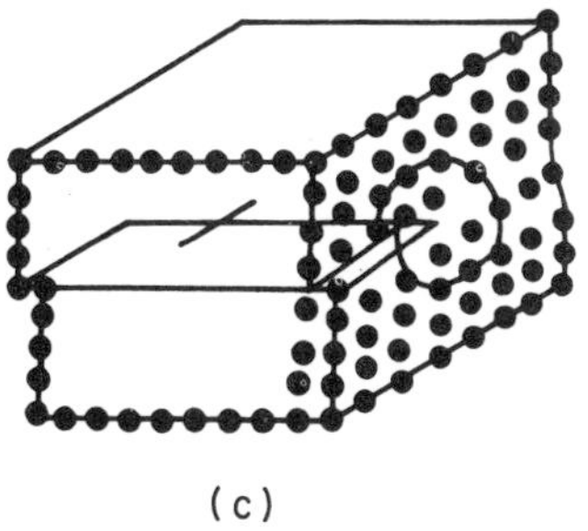
(c)

Fig. 6.5c Screw dislocation formed by a shearing stress parallel to terminus of the cut.

These are

(1) A dislocation line can never end within a crystal, either it follows a closed path or it extends to the surface.

(2) Any motion of a part or all of a dislocation line results in deformation of the lattice.

(3) The ease of motion of a dislocation depends upon the direction of attempted motion. For example the edge dislocation of Figure 6.5b is moved relatively easily, parallel to the shaded plane, which is known as the glide or slip plane. To enable motion perpendicular to this plane interstitials or vacancies must diffuse to and be captured by the plane.

(4) Because of the stress concentrations surrounding dislocations, two or more dislocations can interact with one another. A typical example of this would be the mutual attraction, and possible annihilation of a pair of partial edge dislocations forming a plane of excess interstitials or vacancies. Thus it is possible to form a raft or sheet dislocation by clustering of vacancies or interstitials as mentioned before, either from the agglomeration of mono defects or of larger clusters. The dislocation line or ring surrounds this two dimensional defect array and the formation of such a dislocation is demonstrated in Figure 6.6. This type of defect can only move by emitting vacancies or interstitials depending upon its nature and is therefore a relatively stable entity. For this reason it is termed "sessile", whereas the edge dislocation which can move easily in its glide plane is termed 'glissile'. In order to assess the magnitude of a dislocation, a system of deformation estimation, first suggested by Burger, (viz Ref. 8) is generally employed. If in Figures 6.5b and 6.5c the sheared parts of the crystals are moved a distance b (equal to the interatomic spacing in this case) then the dislocation is described by a Burgers vector strength b. It is found that the edge dislocations of opposite sign attract and lead to the partial or complete annihilation shown in Figure 6.7.

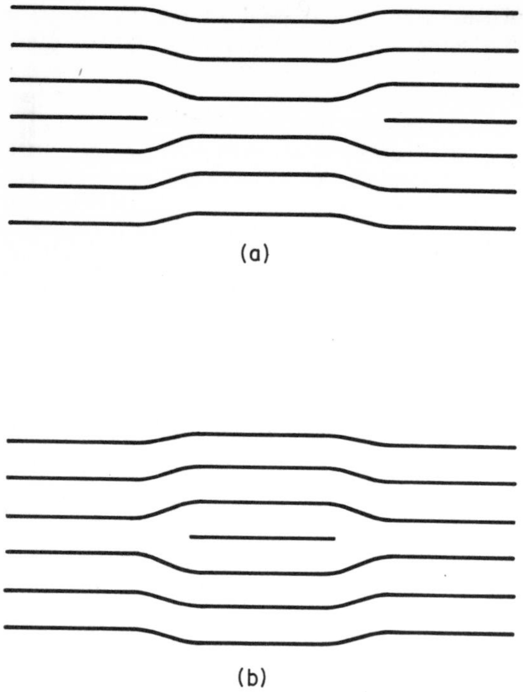

Fig. 6.6 Formation of sessile dislocation loops by aggregation of (a) vacancies and (b) interstitials, into platelets

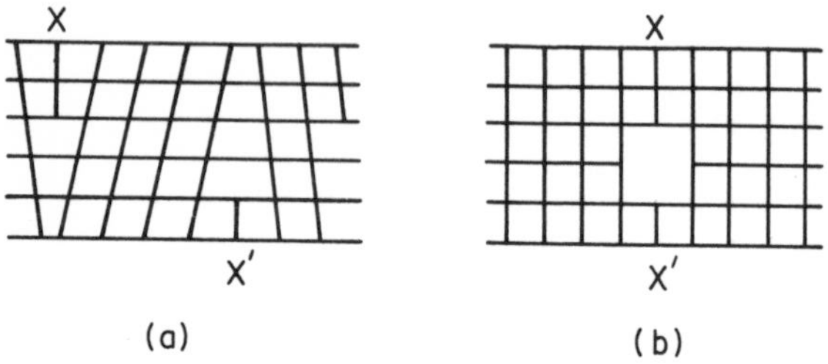

Fig. 6.7 Annihilation of two edge dislocations at x, x′ in (a) to leave vacancies perpendicular to xx′ in (b)

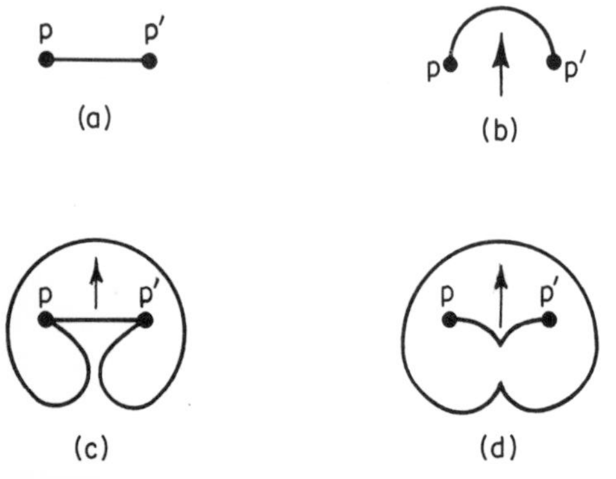

Fig. 6.8 Diagrammatic representation of the Frank-Read mechanism of dislocation generation under an applied stress (arrowed). P, P′ are the dislocation pinning points. (viz Ref. 6.59)

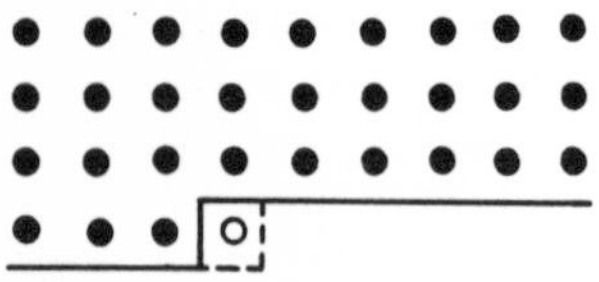

Fig. 6.9 Emission of a vacancy from a dislocation line by shifting a jog (dotted)

Another interesting feature of dislocations is the manner by which they can grow and produce further dislocations under an applied stress. The mechanism of dislocation regeneration was first enunciated by Frank and Read[59] and may be appreciated by reference to Figure 6.8. If a dislocation line is strongly pinned at its ends and a stress is applied perpendicular to this line, the line bows out, embracing further defects, then curls around the primary points and finally joins up as a circular dislocation, leaving the original dislocation free to generate further loops. More recent theories[60] of dislocation regeneration are basically similar to this model but differ in detail. Just as point defects exert mutual interaction forces, as do dislocations, it can be readily appreciated that point defects and dislocations can also interact. Generally speaking dislocations act as sinks for point defects and can absorb vacancies and interstitials. Consider an edge dislocation as shown in Figure 6.9 with the dislocation line interrupted at the position indicated and forming two levels with a jog of one atom spacing at the step discontinuity. Clearly this jog can extend to the right by emitting vacancies or absorbing interstitials, or recede to the left by emitting interstitials or absorbing vacancies. Thus the dislocation plane acts as a perfect sink and in a addition a source for both types of point defects. In equilibrium the rates of defect emission and absorption are equal. This type of dislocation motion or extension is known as 'climb' and is particularly important during the motion of a dislocation in the presence of other dislocations with which it can interact.

In addition to pure edges and screw dislocations one can imagine ones which are combinations of both, with the dislocation loop changing continuously from parallel to perpendicular to the Burgers vector. If the Burgers vector is not equal to the lattice vector (e.g. the shift is not by a multiple of lattice spacings), then the resulting structure is a partial dislocation with a stacking fault where the dislocation intersects the surface. This is illustrated in Figure 6.10a and a special form of this, the twinning mechanism is exhibited in Figure 6.10b. In this latter case the crystal is mirror imaged about the twinning plane.

These properties of dislocations have been described in very naïve terms and for more sophisticated exposition the reader is referred to the many existing texts on dislocations and defects, some of which are enumerated at the end of this Chapter. It should be clear already, however, that the presence of defects and dislocations in a solid are expected to exert dominating influence on all the physical properties of that solid. Consequently the nature of radiation induced damage should be observable by measurements of the changes in physical properties which ensue, and from a knowledge of how individual defect configurations modify these properties. Unfortunately

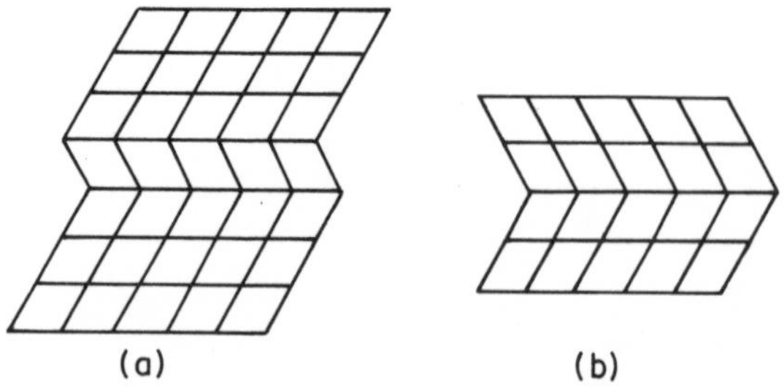

Fig. 6.10 Two types of coherent boundary condition (a) Stacking fault
(b) Twinning

it is often difficult to ascribe the change in properties to a specific type of defect produced by irradiation, since it proves difficult to distinguish between several processes which may lead to the same structure sensitive property. In the case of high energy radiation, e.g. α particle, electron, neutron and fission fragment, the experimental situation is relatively amenable to analysis after bombardment since the radiation is highly penetrating and the damage extends over large crystal volumes. The situation obtaining with low energy bombardment is more parlous, however, since the extent of the damage is small and one may expect that the property changes resulting from damage would be difficult to observe. Indeed earlier texts on radiation damage[3,4,5] have tended to ignore the effects of low energy damage because of the difficulties of experimental confirmation. Recently, however, several elegant techniques, including the field ion microscope and the transmission and reflection electron microscopes have allowed direct observation of the damage resulting from low energy primary events and these will be described in detail, later in this Chapter. Before investigating these experimental observations, however, we must consider the magnitude of the effects which we expect to encounter. We continue, therefore, with a discussion of the rates of defect production in assumed isotropic and real lattices.

6.3 Theories of the Rate of Defect Production

6.3.1.1 Many authors have investigated this problem and a number of excellent reviews[3,4,5,6,61,62] have been published. These reviews have covered the effect of damage induced by all forms of radiation whereas we are currently interested only in the damage resulting from relatively low energy, high primary mass bombardment. Nevertheless in all theories of radiation induced damage, a number of features of the displacement events are common. Detailed variations arise only because of the different energy transfers involved in collisions of differing primary particles.

The common features are (1) assumption, in general, of an isotropic, randomly distributed array of target atoms with due allowance for the correct atomic density of the target. This allows use of collision cross section and mean free path concepts as outlined in the previous Chapter. In more sophisticated estimates of defect production, due cognizance is paid to the reality of the lattice structure. (2) Assumption of a threshold energy or range of energies which, if the energy transferred to the target atom is less than those values in a collision, no displacement of the struck atom occurs. If the transferred energy lies in or above this energy range the displacement probability rises either abruptly or slowly from zero to unity. In simpler damage theory this displacement probability is assumed to be direction independent but clearly in a real lattice, atomic ejection will be easier in some directions than in others and this is accounted for in real lattice calculations. (3) Assumption that all damage events are primarily due to two body encounters between the primary particle and individual target atoms resulting in a succession of Frenkel pairs. The total damage is then obtained by addition of the individual numbers of interstitials or vacancies produced.

Such a treatment is probably quite adequate when displacement events are widely spaced, i.e. at high primary energies. However, when the primary energy is low and the interaction is with several atoms simultaneously (or the collision frequency is high) the situation is more properly represented by a 'spike' event in which a large amount of energy is deposited in a small crystal volume. The concept of spike events will be elaborated shortly.

In order to estimate the magnitude of damage events we investigate the trajectory of an incident atom passing through a target leaving damaged regions in its wake, employing the assumptions outlined above.

Suppose the primary has an energy E and collides with a target atom, imparting an energy T to the struck atom (or the primary knock-on atom (PKA) as it is known). Then if this energy T is sufficient to remove the target atom from its equilibrium lattice position, the incident atom will continue with a degraded energy E-T and the primary knock on will be ejected with an energy T^1. The energy T^1 will necessarily be less than the energy transfer T since energy will be expanded in the escape process. If $E - T$ and T^1 are both sufficiently large, the incident atom and the P.K.A. will be able to make further displacement collisions, releasing respectively more P.K.A's and secondary knock ons. For a sufficiently energetic incident particle a succession of cascades of events will ensue with a spatially distributed damage pattern, and it is the purpose of this discussion to explore the magnitude of this spatial extent. In addition to displacement events, some collisions result in inelastic losses and one must be prepared for electron excitation and ionization processes, particularly at higher primary energies. A further complication is the possibility of replacement collisions, in which the incident atom in a collision may displace the target atom, but, in doing so, lose so much energy as to be unable to move further in the lattice. It then relaxes into the lattice position previously occupied by the ejected atom. A full account of damage rates must embrace all these possibilities, and we are concerned therefore with knowing the full details of each collision. This, as we have seen in Chapters 2 and 5 involves a knowledge of the interatomic potential between the collision partners, and also a knowledge of the probabilities of displacing and replacing lattice atoms, at a collision. The information from one collision is, however, insufficient to determine the final damage state of the target and averages over many events must be sought. We are concerned therefore not with one incident particle but with a flux of particles, the collision histories of each of which may differ considerably. In order to determine the average fate and effects of these primary bombarding particles we must define some average properties of the collisions.

Suppose n bombarding particles per unit volume pass through unit area of the target per second. The flux ϕ is given by nv where v is the primary velocity, and this may be in the form of a parallel beam, an isotropic spatial distribution or somewhere between these. If the probability of collision between a primary and a lattice atom is p_c and the number of lattice atoms per unit volume is N, then the total number of collisions between primaries and target atoms per unit volume per second is given by nvp_cN. According to the nomenclature of Chapter 2 the probability of collision between a primary and a target atom is the collision cross section σ. Thus the number of collisions per unit volume per second $= N\phi\sigma$ or $\Sigma\phi$ where Σ is the macroscopic cross section. This may be appreciated by observing that the quantity $N\sigma$ is the total area presented by target atoms to the incident primary flux per unit volume. This equation may be generalised further by noting that if the primaries are distributed in energy (or velocity) then the target atoms will receive transferred energies which are also distributed. It is therefore more convenient to describe the collision in terms of a differential cross section for velocity (or energy) transfer between target atom velocities of $v_2{}^1$ and $v_2{}^1 + \delta v_2{}^1$ i.e. $d\sigma(v_1, v_2{}^1)$ where v_1 is the primary ion velocity.

The number of target atoms receiving velocities in this range is thus given by $n.v_1 N d\sigma(v_1, v_2{}^1)$ or if the primary energy is E, and the energy transfer T, the number of collisions leading to energy transfers between T and T + dT is given by

$$nv_1 N d\sigma(E, T) \qquad 6.1$$

We have seen in Chapter 2 that $d\sigma(E, T)$ is sensitively dependent upon the type of interaction potential between the primary and struck atoms, and so far for the present, all that one can say about the total number of collision events per unit volume per second, for a given primary energy E is that it is given by

$$nv_1 N \int_{\text{all } T} d\sigma(E, T) \qquad 6.2$$

$d\sigma(E, T)$ itself will be given by expressions such as those in equation 5.22 depending upon the form of the assumed interatomic potential for elastic collisions and by equations 5.25 for inelastic collisions.

It is often more convenient to express $d\sigma(E, T)$ by its equivalent form $K(E, T)dT$ as in Chapter 2 or further in terms of the impact parameter p,

$$K(E, T)dT = \pi p dp \qquad 6.3$$

Further, the differential cross section is often expressed in a normalised form by writing

$$d\sigma(E, T) = \sigma \,.\, \psi(E, T)dT \qquad 6.4$$

where σ is the total cross section for all energy transfers T at an initial energy E.

These partial and total, cross sections only describe the collision probabilities and not the probability of displacement during a collision. Since as we have seen a certain minimum energy (E_d) is required for displacement, then the total displacement cross section is given by

$$\sigma_d = \int_{T=Ed}^{T_{max}} d\sigma(E, T) \qquad 6.5$$

E_d itself is probably not a unique energy and thus one should introduce into $d\sigma(E, T)$ a probability term $p_d(T)$ which describes the probability of atomic displacement at a transferred energy T.

A number of different forms for p(T) have been proposed and these will be discussed shortly. The simplest form envisages a displacement probability of unity when T is greater than some threshold energy E_d, i.e.

$$p_d(T) = 1 \text{ for } T \geqslant Ed \qquad 6.6.1$$

and zero for transferred energies between zero and E_d, i.e.

$$p_d(T) = 0 \text{ for } T < E_d \qquad 6.6.2$$

The rate of defect production per unit volume by primaries of energy E, transferring energies in the range T to T + δT is thus

$$F_d(T) = \delta\phi N \int \psi_d(T)\delta p_d(T) d\sigma(T) \qquad 6.7$$

with $\delta\phi$ the incident flux with energy E (greater than the threshold energy E_d). Thus for all energies

$$F_d(T) = \int \phi(E)dE \,.\, N\sigma d(E)\psi_d(E, T)\delta p_d(T) \qquad 6.8$$

where $\phi(E)dE = \delta\phi$ and $\delta p_d(T)$ is the probability of displacement at transferred energies between T and T + δT.

It is clear that in order to be able to calculate this defect pair production rate we need more information on (a) the form of the differential scattering cross section which is intimately related to the interatomic potential, and (b) the displacement probability function.

6.3.1.2 The interatomic potential

In view of the lengthy discussion of Chapters 2 and 5 on this subject it is necessary only to reiterate the useful results of those chapters.

We have seen, from comparison of theoretical and experimental range data, that the most successful assumption for the interatomic potential is, for high primary energies, the Thomas-Fermi potential. At lower energies none of the potentials so far employed has reproduced the experimental data accurately, although both the Thomas-Fermi[63] and the Bohr[64] potentials give reasonable agreement, provided that in the latter case, an appropriate screening length is adopted. The Thomas-Fermi potential has not, as yet, been applied to studies of radiation damage rates, but the Bohr potential has been used in computer evaluations of defect production. The Born-Mayer[65] potential has also been used in Machine calculations, but difficulty is experienced when attempting to use both this and the Bohr potential to achieve analytical results. This difficulty arises because of the intractibility of the differential cross sections for these potentials. As we saw earlier this difficulty is largely removed if a hard sphere interaction is assumed between the collision partners, although the results are liable to be less accurate. The appropriate hard sphere radius is chosen by matching the hard sphere potential to an assumed potential at the distance of closest approach and, in this way, is caused to vary with the kinetic energy of the incident atom.

An improvement in accuracy may be anticipated by using an intermediate matching potential such as that suggested by Leibfried and Oen[66] and Lehmann and Robinson[67]. However, it turns out, as we shall see shortly, that the extent and magnitude of the damage is surprisingly insensitive to the exact form chosen for the interatomic potential. Consequently, we shall adopt the procedure of other authors and assume that the potential is adequately represented by a hard sphere interaction, even for low energy primaries, with the hard sphere radius determined from an assumed Bohr potential at the distance of closest approach. For higher energy primaries it may be necessary to use the Coulomb potential for more accurate results.

Thus for a primary of relative energy E_R

$$E_R = V(r) = \frac{Z_1 Z_2 e_2}{r} \exp(-r/a) \qquad 6.9$$

where r is the distance of closest approach in a head on collision and is twice the hard sphere radius.

After the first collision between an incident atom and lattice atom the majority of the remaining collisions are between primary, secondary, tertiary, etc. knock-ons and lattice atoms and hence the collision partner masses are equal. Consequently, a, the screening radius in equation 6.9 is given by $a = a_o/(2Z)^{1/6}$.

It is generally preferable to write a in the form $a = ka_o/(Z)^{1/6}$. In the Bohr approximation $k = \frac{1}{2}$ but Seitz and Koehler[3] have assumed $k = 1$, and Brinkman[25], that $k = 2.09$. The results of the last chapter suggest, however, that if the Bohr potential is to be used at all, the value of k must vary with the masses of the collision partners. Thus Van Lint et al[68] propose values of $k = 1.7, 2.0$ and 3.0 for Cu, Ag, and Au respectively.

As we have stated, the differential cross section for energy transfers T, in the hard sphere approximation is simple, and independent of the energy T.

At very high primary energies the partners penetrate deeply within the electron screening clouds and the interaction potential V(r) is of the Coulomb form

$$V(r) = \frac{Z_1 Z_2 e^2}{r} .$$

This form of interaction would be expected with energetic neutrons from reactor or fission sources.

According to equation 2.23 this potential leads to a differential scattering cross section proportion to $1/T^2$. Consequently one would expect that the real differential scattering cross section would be somewhere between the $1/T^0$ and $1/T^2$ limits, and in fact Dienes and Vineyard[4] suggest a differential cross section of the form

$$d\sigma \propto T^{-n} dT \qquad 6.10.1$$

where n lies between 1 and 2 for relatively energetic primary particles. (This form may be compared with the Lindhard and Scharff[69,70] equation, i.e.

$$d\sigma \propto T^{-(1+1/s)} . \, dT, \text{ where } s = 1, 2, 3 \qquad .6.10.2$$

With the hard sphere approximation, the displacement cross section is simply

$$\sigma_d = \int_{E_d}^{T_m} \frac{\pi(r)^2}{T_m} dT \; . = \pi(r)^2 \left(1 - \frac{Ed}{T_m}\right) \qquad 6.11.1$$

where r is determined from Equation 2.24 and displacement is assumed to occur at a sharp threshold E_d.

The average transferred energy $\overline{T}_d$ is

$$\frac{T_m + E_d}{2} \qquad 6.11.2$$

In the Rutherford scattering region, with

$$d\sigma = \frac{\pi b^2}{4} T_m \frac{dT}{T^2} \qquad 6.12.1$$

The total displacement cross section is

$$\left\{\sigma_D = \frac{\pi b^2}{4} \; \frac{T_m - E_d}{E_d}\right\} \qquad 6.12.2$$

and the average transferred energy $\overline{T}$ is

$$\left\{\log_e \frac{T_m}{E_d}\right\} \cdot \frac{E_d T_m}{Tm - Ed} \qquad 6.12.3$$

For the general case where $d\sigma = \frac{cdT}{T^{1+1/s}}$ with C and s constants. Then

$$\sigma_D = s \; . \; c \left\{\frac{{T_m}^{1/s} - {E_d}^{1/s}}{(T_m E_d)^{1/s}}\right\} \qquad 6.10.2$$

and

$$\overline{T}_d = \frac{T_m E_d}{s+1} \left\{\frac{{E_d}^{1/s-1} - {T_m}^{1/s-1}}{{E_d}^{1/s} - {T_m}^{1/s}}\right\} \qquad 6.10.3$$

In all cases T_m is generally considerably larger than E_d, and inserting this condition leads to simplification of the above equations. Thus for arbitrary s,

$$\sigma_D = \frac{sc}{{E_d}^{1/s}} \text{ and } \overline{T}_d = \frac{1}{s-1} \cdot \frac{{E_d}^{1/s}}{{T_m}^{1/s-1}} \qquad 6.10.4$$

The assumed form of the interatomic potential is important, not only in determining the details of such collisions, but in specifying whether the collisions may be treated as isolated two body events. The conditions necessary for such events will be that the mean free path between primary collisions should be at least equal to several interatomic distances.

From Chapter 2 we recall that the mean free path between collisions, $\lambda_c = 1/N\sigma$ and thus the displacement mean free path

$$\lambda_d = \frac{1}{N\sigma_D} \qquad 6.13.1$$

which, in the hard sphere approximation gives

$$\lambda_d = \frac{1}{N\pi(2R)^2(1 - Ed/Tm)} \qquad 6.13.2$$

If a Bohr interatomic potential with an adjustable parameter k, is assumed, then the equivalent hard sphere radius is derived from

$$2R = \frac{ka_o}{Z^{1/3}} \log_e \frac{Z^2 e^2}{2RE_R} \qquad 6.14$$

where E_R is the relative energy of the primary. One can approximate the density of target atoms N, in terms of the equivalent atomic radius of each atom r_s, through the relation

$$N = \frac{1}{\frac{4}{3}\pi {r_s}^3} \qquad 6.15$$

One thus derives

$$\lambda_d = \frac{4r_s^3}{3(2R)^2(1 - E_d/T_m)} \qquad 6.16$$

Taking the case of copper, for which Z = 29, as an example, and assuming a relative primary energy of 500 eV, (hence $\frac{E_d}{T_m} \approx 20$ for $E_d = 25$ eV), a value of r_s corresponding to 2.7 a_0 (which is the case for copper) and a value of k = 1.0, then it is readily deduced from equations 6.14 and 6.16 that $\lambda_d = 6r_s$. Other estimates of λ_d may be made, using for example the impulse approximation and determining the magnitude of the impact parameter necessary to ensure an energy transfer greater than $E_d = 25$ eV say. This treatment, given fully by Seitz and Koehler[3], leads to values of λ_d of about 2.5 r_s. Clearly, both values indicate that collisions are separable into two body events at this low primary energy, but if the energy falls below this, one must anticipate that each collision involves several target atoms.

It is not worthwhile assessing a lower energy limit for the applicability of isolated two body events, since this depends upon the assumed value of k, which is known only for Ag, Au and Cu and even then, rather inaccurately. It is readily seen that λ_d decreases sharply as k increases, because of the r^{-2} dependence of λ_d. Indeed, Brinkman[25] selected a value of k = 2.09 for Cu and arrived at a value of $\lambda_d = 0.5\ r_s$ for 300 eV Cu primaries. Although the value of k is certainly high it illustrates what Brinkman[25] assumed will occur at 300 eV, but probably starts at somewhat lower energies, namely the many body interaction or spike phenomenon. In this process the primary energy is assumed to be shared, not with one target atom, but several simultaneously, resulting in the creation of local hot spots and voids. We will return to this problem again later.

Leibfried[62] has shown that a reasonably accurate potential for copper, deduced on the basis of the primary ion ranges, discussed in Chapter 5 for small atomic separations, and from elasticity data for large separations, is given by a combination of Bohr and Born-Mayer potentials, namely

$$V(r) = E_a\left(\tfrac{1}{4} + \frac{a}{r}\right)\exp(-r/a) \qquad 6.17$$

with

$$E_a = 75 \times 10^3 \text{ eV}, a = \frac{D}{13} \approx 2 \times 10^{-9} \text{ cm}$$

(where D = nearest neighbour distance). It may be that the Bohr contribution should be replaced by a Thomas-Fermi potential but the Born-Mayer should be a reasonable representation at relatively large separations of the order of the lattice spacing, in which we are interested. We should note however that the values of E_a and a, as deduced from elasticity data, are open to some doubt, and the values chosen by Leibfried[62] correspond to those given by Huntington[38, 39].

With this potential, and use of equations 6.9 and 6.16 it is readily shown that the displacement free path is approximately equal to the lattice spacing in copper for primary energies, which are approximately equal to the displacement energy E_d. It thus appears that this potential may be used for primary energies down to the displacement energy, to predict damage effects.

The next question which naturally presents itself is, of course, the value of the displacement energy and the displacement probability at and near this energy.

6.3.1.3 *Displacement and Replacement*

We have seen, through Equation 6.7 that the displacement cross section depends upon the probability of displacement at a given primary energy and in order to accurately predict the rate of damage production it would be necessary, apparently, to know the exact dependence of this displacement probability. In a randomised array of target atoms it is conceivable that a sharp threshold for displacements exists, namely an energy E_d, below which the displacement probability p_d is zero, and above which p_d is unity, but a more realistic approach would be to assume that the displacement threshold E_d has a certain probability of lying between certain limits E_0 and E_1.

Such a procedure must be expected to be more representative in the case of a real target ensemble where ejection might be expected to be difficult along a direction containing other lattice atoms and easy along a direction between atomic rows. Thus the displacement probability may be expected to rise from zero at a primary energy E_0 to unity at an energy E_1, and remain at unity thereafter.

This is equivalent to stating that there is a variable displacement energy E_d lying between E_0 and E_1.

Thus if the probability of displacement for a lattice atom in the displacement energy range E_d to $E_d + \delta E_d$ is $\delta p(E_d)$, then this may be written in the equivalent form

$$\delta p(E_d) = f(E_d)\delta E_d \qquad 6.18$$

where $f(E_d)$ is the probability of finding the displacement threshold with a displacement probability of unity, at this energy.

Sampson, Hurwitz and Clancy[71] have assumed that the displacement probability rises linearly between limits E_0 and E_1.

i.e. $p(E_d) = 0; E < E_0$

$p(E_d) = 1; E > E_1$

$$p(E_d) = \frac{E - E_0}{E_1 - E_0}; E_0 \leqslant E \leqslant E_1 \qquad 6.19$$

The sharp threshold and the Sampson et al[71] models are illustrated in figure 6.11. Since the displacement energy must lie between E_0 and E_1, then

$$\int_{E_0}^{E_1} f(E_d)dE_d = 1$$

and $f(E_d)$ must be given by $\frac{1}{E_1 - E_0}$ for $E_0 \leqslant E_d \leqslant E_1$

and zero for any other E_d. Fein[72] has given a detailed treatment of this problem when the function $f(E_d)$.

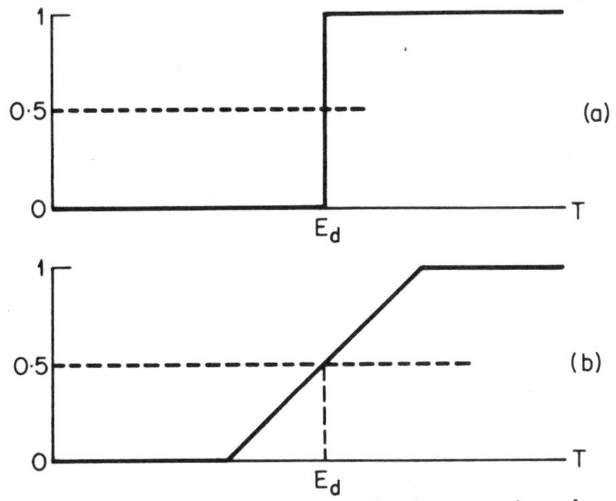

Fig. 6.11 Two forms of the displacement probability function $p(E_d)$ as a function of the energy. T transfered to the struck atom
(a) Sharp threshold at E_d
(b) Linear distributed threshold between $^2/_3\ E_d$ and $^4/_3\ E_d$ (Ref. 6.71)

has any arbitrary form, and shows that the total displacement cross section, is given by

$$\sigma_d = \int_1^a \int_y^{x_m} p(y)\, dy d\sigma(x) \qquad 6.20$$

where a, x, and y, are defined by the dimensionless parameters . $a = E_1/E_0$, $x = E/E_0$ and $y = E_d/E_0$ where E_d is a random energy between E_0 and E_1 and $x_m = E_m/E_0$ with E_m equal to the maximum energy transfer. This equation corresponds closely to the definition implicit in equation 6.5. For the hard sphere and Coulomb potentials, the displacement cross sections turn out to be

$$\sigma_s\left(1 - \frac{y_{AV}}{x_m}\right)$$

and

$$cx_m\left(\frac{1}{y_{AV}} - \frac{1}{x_m}\right) \qquad 6.21$$

respectively. Thus for large energy transfers, x_m, the results are identical to those which would have been obtained with an effective sharp threshold $E_{d_{eff}}$ given by approximately

$$E_{d_{eff}} = E_0 \exp \langle \log y \rangle_{AV} \qquad 6.22$$

where

$$\langle \log y \rangle_{AV} = \int_1^a p(y) \log_e y dy$$

As an example, the case treated by Sampson et al[71] may be used, where $E_1 = 2E_0$ then $\langle \log_e y \rangle_{AV} = \log_e a^{a/a-1} - 1$ so that

$$E_{d_{eff}} = \frac{E_0 \cdot a^{a/a-1}}{e} = 1.47E_0$$

and

$$p(E_{d_{eff}}) = 0.47 \qquad 6.23$$

This may be compared with the exact evaluation of equation 6.5 for $E_{d_{eff}}$ for the hard sphere case, which is straightforward for the Sampson et al approximation and is simply $E_{d_{eff}} = 1.5\ E_0$, close to the Fein treatment.

Lehmann[73] has also considered the effect of a distributed displacement probability function, investigating step function distributions and the linear distribution and arrived at essentially the same conclusions as outlined above. As we shall see later the defect density production is rather insensitive to the choice of probability function, for energies much greater than E_d but is dependent upon the value chosen for the effective threshold.

Seitz[74] has estimated the magnitude of E_d as follows. The energy to create an interstitial-vacancy pair via a thermally activated process is roughly $2E_c$, where E_c is the sublimation energy, and the process is reversible since it is carried out on a time scale sufficient to allow the lattice to relax. If the pair is created by a dynamic collision process, however, the surrounding lattice atoms have insufficient time to relax and the energy required for pair production should be roughly twice as large i.e. approximately $4E_c$. Since $E_c \sim$ 5-6 eV for tightly bound solids, Seitz suggested a value of 25 eV for the displacement threshold energy. More recently Huntington[39] has calculated E_c for copper using a Born-Mayer interaction potential and determined the energy required to move an atom to an interstitial position in the ⟨111⟩ direction surrounded by its three nearest neighbours as between 18.5 eV and 43 eV. The energy required for displacement in the ⟨100⟩ direction was deduced to lie between 17.5 eV and 34 eV, illustrating the necessity of a variable threshold. The range of possible values in either case results from the inadequacy of accurate specification of the screening length a.

Kohn[75] evaluated threshold energies in Germanium and obtained values below 10 eV, and again dependent upon the crystallographic direction. The lower energy required in this case undoubtedly arises because of the more open Germanium structure and illustrates again the importance of crystal structure.

A number of experimental studies of the threshold energy have been made and involve, in general, observation of damage following electron bombardment of variable energy. The choice of this technique arises since these particles penetrate the target deeply and produce uniform damage which may be observed as property changes of the target such as resistivity in metals, minority carrier lifetimes in semiconductors and saturation magnetization in Iron, occurring at, and above, the damage threshold. Thus far ion bombardment has not been utilized to determine E_d and its distribution since the damage is mainly superficial and correlation with observed property changes difficult. However the recent development of sophisticated techniques of observing surface and slightly subsurface damage, such as electron transmission and field ion microscopy and low energy electron diffraction may remedy this situation. In view of this we can only summarize a selection of data obtained via the electron bombardment technique, as in Table 6.1 which also contains the primary energy required to produce displacements for various target atoms with different primary particles and a threshold energy of 25 eV. These energies are determined from the maximum energy transfers between two colliding particles as given, for example by Equation 2.10a. From Table 6.1 it is clear that a considerable spread in threshold energies exists, depending upon the tar-

TABLE 6. 1a

Experimental Threshold Displacement Energies for various materials.

Material	Property Studied	Threshold Energy	Reference
Graphite		25 eV	D.T. Eggen (Unpublished)
Aluminium	Resistivity	32 eV	6. 178
Aluminium	Resistivity	16 ± 2 eV	6. 442
Aluminium	Resistivity	16 ± 2 eV	6. 443
Titanium	Resistivity	29 eV	6. 178
Iron	Resistivity	24 eV	6. 178
Copper	Resistivity	22 eV	6. 178
Copper (Single crystals ⟨100⟩ ⟨110⟩ directions	Resistivity	19 eV	6. 193 and 6. 197
Silver	Resistivity	28 eV	6. 178
Nickel	Resistivity	34. 5 eV	6. 430
Nickel	Resistivity	24 eV	6. 178
Gold	Resistivity	>40 eV	6. 178
Gold	Resistivity	35 eV	6. 201
Molybdenum	Resistivity	37 eV	6. 178
Platinum	Resistivity	37 eV	6. 431
Platinum	Resistivity	36 eV	6. 432
Iron in Copper	Magnetic Susceptibility	27 eV	6. 433
Copper in Cu_3Au	Resistivity	10 eV	6. 434
Germanium	Resistivity	31 eV	6. 435
Germanium	Minority Carrier Lifetime	13 eV	6. 436
Germanium	Conductivity	22. 3 eV	6. 437 and 6. 438
Germanium	Conductivity	19 eV	6. 77

Experimental Threshold Displacement Energies for various materials.

Material	Property Studied	Threshold Energy	Reference
Silicon	Minority Carrier Lifetime	12. 9 eV	6. 78
Indium Phosphide		—	—
(Indium displacements)	Minority Carrier Lifetime	6. 7 eV	6. 76
(Phosphorus displacements)	Minority Carrier Lifetime	8. 7 eV	6. 76
Indium Antimonide			
Indium Displacements	Minority Carrier Lifetime	5. 7 eV	6. 76
Antimony displacements	Minority Carrier Lifetime	6. 6 eV	6. 76
Indium Arsenide			
Indium Displacements	Minority Carrier Lifetime	6. 7 eV	6. 76
Arsenic displacements	Minority Carrier Lifetime	8. 3 eV	6. 76
Gallium Arsenide			
Gallium displacements	Minority Carrier Lifetime	9. 0 eV	6. 76
Arsenic displacements	Minority Carrier Lifetime	9. 4 eV	6. 76
Gallium arsenide	Hall Effect and Resistivity	17-18 eV	6. 202
Cadmium Sulphide			
Cadmium displacements	Fluorescence	7. 3 eV	6. 439
Sulphur displacements	Fluorescence	8. 7 eV	6. 440
Zinc Selenide	Fluorescence	10 or 8. 2 eV	6. 441

TABLE 6.1b

Energies required by various projectiles to transfer 25 eV to Copper atoms.

Projectile	Energy Required
Proton (or Neutron)	410 eV
Alpha Particle	180 eV
Copper Atom	25 eV
Xenon Atom	28 eV
Electron	492 KeV
Gamma Ray	677.5 KeV

get material temperature and lattice orientation but the assumption of an average value of $E_d = 25$ eV appears to be a logical choice.

Bauerlein[76] has also summarised the available data for threshold energies in elemental and compound semiconductors. It will be interesting to observe from further experiments, which will undoubtedly be performed in the near future, whether the directional dependence in a real lattice is important, although Brown and Augustyniak[77], Lofoerski and Rappaport[78], and Flicker, Loferski and Scott-Monck[79] have observed no such orientation dependence in Ge and Si. Indeed this lack of orientation dependence has led Wertheim[80] and Mackay and Klontz[81] to suggest that displacement in Ge operates on a somewhat different basis than in metals where the primary displaced atom takes a metastable position close to the associated vacancy. As we have seen, one choice for the limits of E_d are E_0 and $2E_0$ which correspond, in a real lattice to ejection of an atom between parallel rows and along an atomic row respectively. The value of $2E_0$ for the upper limit appears to be a logical choice, since the lattice atom will only be ejected if it can free the next lattice atom, which is itself formed with an energy E_d. Thus the displacement energy may be anticipated to be about twice the minimum energy required, i.e. $2E_0$.

It is clear that the primary ejected atom may displace a neighbouring atom, but if, after the encounter it has insufficient energy to escape from the equilibrium position of the latter, it will eventually come to rest in the site vacated i.e. the possibility of a replacement collision must be considered. This replacement probability will occur at all encounters, including those of the incident ion, and any treatment of defect production must, to be fully representative, include this effect. The condition that the primary particle will not become trapped in the lattice, i.e. make a replacement collision, is that, after collision it should retain sufficient energy to escape from the lattice site.

This energy is E_d, and so the condition for a non-replacement collision is effectively that the primary energy should be greater than $2E_d$. Similarly the primary ion will be trapped without causing a displacement if its energy is less than E_d. These assumptions form the basis of the models of radiation damage first formulated by Kinchin and Pease[82, 83].

In addition to the probabilities of replacement and displacement we must also be concerned with the energies of the primary and primary knock on, after collision. If the primary energy is E and the transferred energy T, then, according to the model of Kinchin and Pease[82], the struck atom is ejected with an energy T if $T > E_d$. Thus the lattice atom is assumed to retain all the transferred energy after collision. This is an oversimplified picture, since the lattice atom effectively resides in a potential well of depth E_d, the energy required to remove it irreversibly. Consequently, one can expect some of the transferred energy to be consumed in relaxing the lattice atom, the magnitude of which is just E_d. The energy of the ejected atom is therefore $T - E_d$, which is just the energy postulated in the damage models of Seitz and Harrison[84] and Snyder and Neufeld[85]. These models, however, ignored the possibility of a replacement collision, which is accounted for in the model of Kinchin and Pease[83]. It is not surprising, however, that estimates of defect production based on both types of model, only differ slightly, because the reduction in damage brought about by replacement collisions in one model is roughly compensated by the reduction in effective energies in the other model. Calculations by the above authors have employed a sharp threshold for displacement whereas Sampson et al[71] have adopted the Snyder and Neufeld[85] model and included a distribution function for E_d. In the following section we will use the Kinchin and Pease[82] and Snyder and Neufeld[85] models to deduce defect production rates and note the similarity of results, and briefly indicate how the distributed threshold modifies the conclusions.

6.3.2 Calculation of the Defect production density

6.3.2.1 Kinchin and Pease models

Kinchin and Pease developed their theory of defect production in two stages, the first stage[82] of which may be appreciated by reference to figure 6.12 which illustrates the energies E − T and T of the incident atom and struck atom after collision involving a primary energy E. The collision spectrum may be divided into the four regions shown according as to whether the struck atom receives an energy $T > E_d$ or $T < E_d$ and whether the incident atom retains an energy $E - T > E_d$ or $E - T < E_d$.

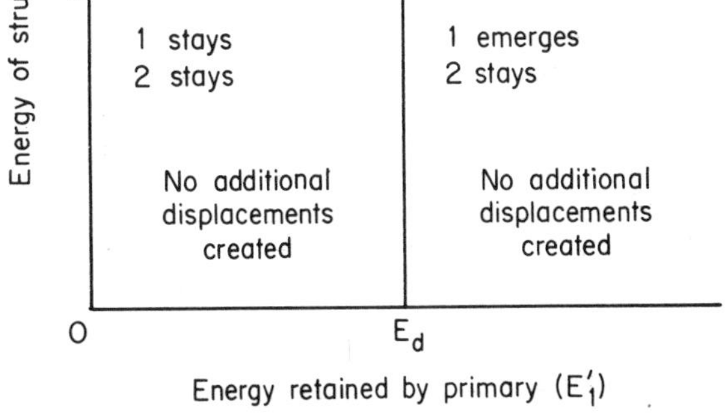

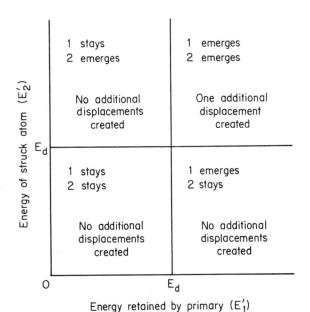

Fig. 6.12 Diagrammatic representation of the Kinchin-Pease assumptions (first model. Ref 6.82) for the creation of defects

In region (a) both energies are less than E_d after collision and so the primary atom is trapped in the lattice and forms an interstitial but not a Frenkel pair, i.e. no displacement occurs. In region (b) with $T < E_d$, and $E - T > E_d$, the incident atom is not trapped but neither is the struck atom displaced, thus no displacement. In region (c) with both $E - T > E_d$ and $T > E_d$, both struck and incident atoms emerge from the collision and one displacement occurs. In region (d) $E - T < E_d$ but $T > E_d$, thus the primary displaces the struck atom and replaces it, effectively leading to no displacement pair.

In addition to this specification of collisions, we make the following assumptions.

(1) The collisions are of the hard sphere type so that the probability of energy transfer between T and T + δT in an encounter of energy E is simply $\delta T/E$ i.e. $g(E, T) = 1/E$.

(2) All collisions are isolated two body events, in which, after a displacement event, both atoms are available to make further collisions in a cascade type process.

(3) The energies involved are below the ionization energy threshold E_i so that we may concern ourselves only with elastic collisions.

We may now assess the mean number of displaced atoms created in a cascade produced when an incident ion collides with a target atom and produces a primary knock on atom as follows. Suppose $\nu(E)$ is this number produced by a single primary knock on of initial energy E itself produced by the externally incident ion.

After the first collision of the knock on, two atoms will emerge, if $E > 2E_d$, to create additional displacements. The number of displacements expected to be produced by the primary knock on itself, including its own initial displacement, is thus $\nu(E')$ if the energy it has after collision is $E' >, E_d$, and zero if $E' < E_d$, where E' replaces $E - T$. Thus the average number of displacements produced by this atom is obtained by integrating the number of displacements expected at a given energy multiplied by the probability of acquiring this energy, over all possible displacement energies.

i.e.

$$\nu_1(E) = \int_{E_d}^{E} \frac{1}{E}\, \nu(E')dE' \qquad 6.24.1$$

The first atom displaced by the primary knock on is also expected to make $\nu(E_2')$, (where $E_2' = T$), further displacements if $E_2' > E_d$ and none if $E_2' < E_d$.

Thus the average number of displacements produced by this latter atom is given by

$$\nu_2(E) = \int_{E_d}^{E} \frac{1}{E}\, \nu(E_2)dE_2 \qquad 6.25.2$$

The average total number of displacements initiated by the primary is therefore obtained by summation of these two quantities and is clearly

$$\nu(E) = 2\int_{E_d}^{E} \frac{1}{E}\nu(E')dE' \qquad 6.24.3$$

provided that $2E_d \leqslant E \leqslant E_i$, where E_i is the Ionization Energy. If $E < 2E_d$, the collisions occur in regions (a), (b), or (d) of figure 6.12 and no displacements occur. Equation 6.24.3 is readily solved by first multiplying throughout by E and then differentiating, to obtain the differential equation.

$$\frac{E d\nu(E)}{dE} = \nu(E);\ 2E_d \leqslant E \leqslant E_i$$

i.e.

$$\nu(E) = cE. \text{ where c is a constant} \qquad 6.25.1$$

c is determined by noting that when $E = 2E_d$ only one displacement occurs and thus

$$\nu(E) = E/2E_d;\ 2E_d \leqslant E \leqslant E_i \qquad 6.25.2$$

$$\nu(E) = 1 \quad ;E_d \leqslant E \leqslant 2E_d \qquad 6.25.3$$

$$\nu(E) = 0 \quad ;E < E_d \qquad 6.25.4$$

and it may be shown

$$\nu(E) = \frac{E_i}{2E_d};\ E > E_i \qquad 6.25.5$$

$\nu(E)$ is shown as a function of E in figure 6.13 and is compared with results derived by Lehmann[73], using the same assumptions except that the displacement threshold was assumed to rise from zero at $\frac{2}{3}E_d$ to unity at 4/3 E_d (corresponding to the Sampson et al proposal).

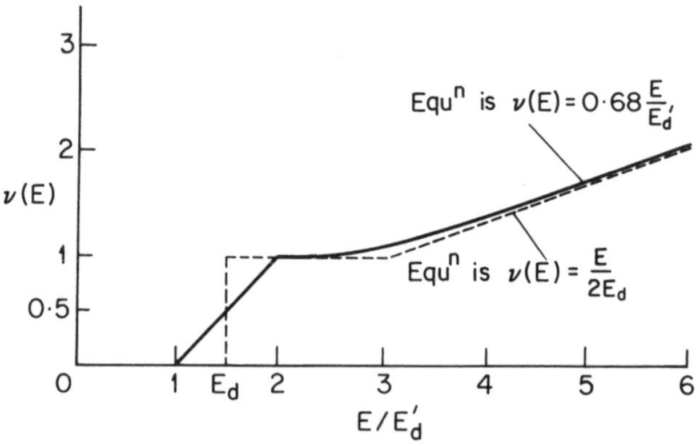

Fig. 6.13 The number of Frenkel pairs produced ($\nu(E)$) as a function of the normalised primary energy E/E_d' for a sharp threshold energy E_d (dotted curve); a linearly distributed displacement probability between $\frac{2E_d}{3}$ and $\frac{4E_d}{3}$ (full curve). E_d' is an effective threshold energy = $\frac{2}{3}E_d$.

Clearly the differences in $\nu(E)$ are only slight except in the region of E_d. Consequently experiments which involve energy transfers much in excess of E_d will not elucidate the details of the $p_d(E)$ function. It is therefore necessary to conduct experiments with this purpose in view with primary beams of well defined energy, which gives energy transfers close to the threshold region.

It is further interesting to note that the form of the relationship is not materially altered if different forms of the scattering potential (and hence displacement probability) are employed, provided that the energy is sufficiently low as to preclude Rutherford scattering. Thus Brown and Goedecke[87] have used a machine calculation, employing the Bohr potential, to study the collisions made by the primary knock on and its progeny as they slow down to rest in a simulated target. The displacement model assumed above

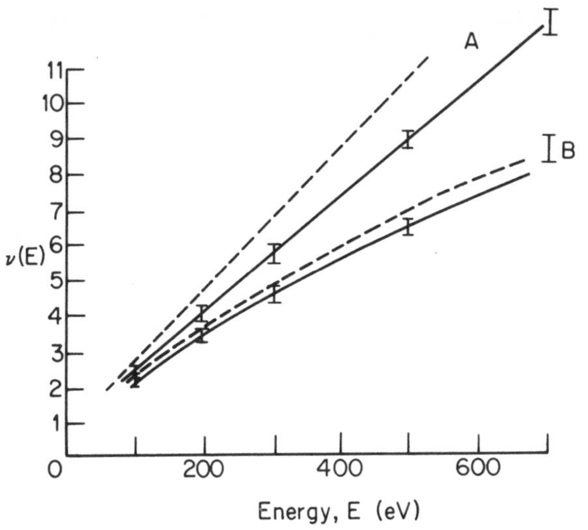

Fig. 6.14a Average number of displaced atoms, $\nu(E)$, as a function of the primary knock on energy for the Kinchin-Pease model I. obtained from a computer simulation by Brown & Goedecke. (Ref. 6.87). Solid curves employed a Bohr potential, dashed curves assumed a hard sphere interaction. Curves A are based upon unity escape probability for energies E greater than $E_d = 24$ eV. Curves B assume an escape probability of 0.8.

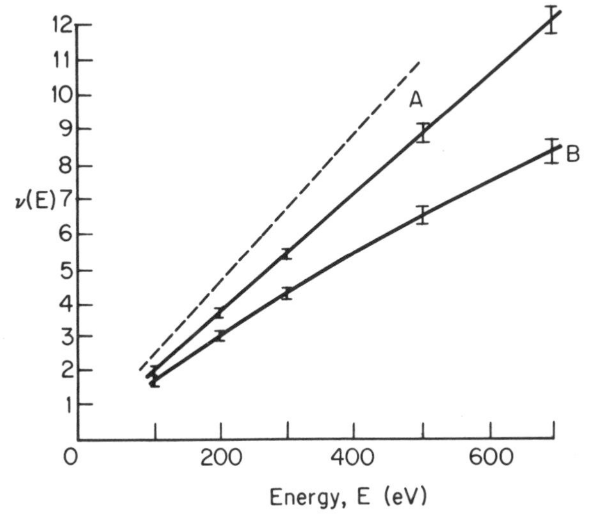

Fig. 6.14b Average number of displaced atoms, $\nu(E)$, as a function of the primary knock on energy for the Harrison-Seitz model obtained from a computer simulation by Brown and Goedecke (Ref. 6.87). Other details as in Fig. 6.14a.

was used, together with a modified model assuming $p(E_d) = 0.8$ above E_d. The results of this study are shown in figure 6.14 where the number of displaced atoms are shown as a function of the primary energy. It is evident that the use of the softer Bohr potential leads to a small reduction only in the damage production density. For the modified Kinchin-Pease model, the damage density $\nu(E)$ is related to E via the form

$$\nu(E) = \left(\frac{E}{2E_d}\right)^{0.8}$$

Lehmann[73] has also made a rather thorough investigation of defect production noting the effects of a distributed displacement probability and of different forms of the scattering probability $g(E, T)$. The results for $g(E, T) = 1/E$, the hard sphere approximation, are as already derived, whilst the calculations for a form

$$g(E, T) = \frac{\exp\left\{\dfrac{E - 2T}{2E_c}\right\}}{2\,E \sinh E/2E_c} \qquad 6.26.1$$

are

$$\nu(E) = 1\,;\; 0 \leqslant E \leqslant 2E_d \qquad 6.26.2$$

$$\nu(E) = 1 + \frac{E - 2E_d}{2E_c \sinh\,.\,E_d/E_c} = 1 + \psi(\lambda)[E/2E_d - 1];$$

$$E > 2E_d \qquad 6.26.3$$

where

$$\lambda = \frac{E_d}{E_c} \text{ and } \psi(\lambda) = \lambda/\sinh\lambda.$$

This form of the scattering law is a closer approximation to that from a real interatomic potential than is the hard sphere model, as shown by $E.\,g(E, T)$ as a function of T/E in Figure 6.15a and is more strongly peaked in the forward direction as expected with the Bohr or Born-Mayer potentials c.f. figure 2.4 of

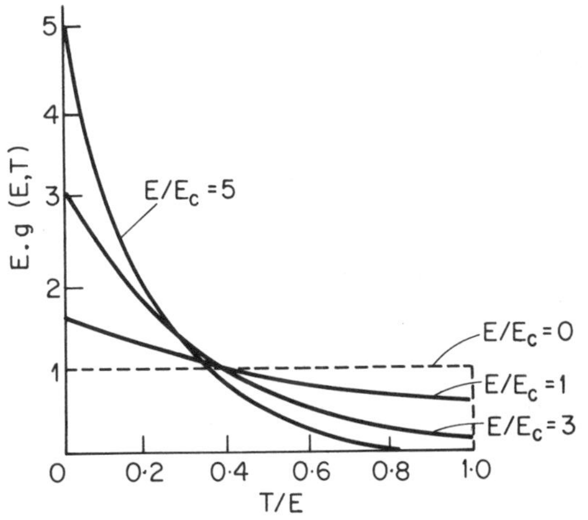

Fig. 6.15a The probability of energy transfer $g(E, T)$ as a function of the normalised energy transfer E/T for the scattering law defined in equation 6.26.1 for various values of E/E_c. (viz. Ref. 6.73.)

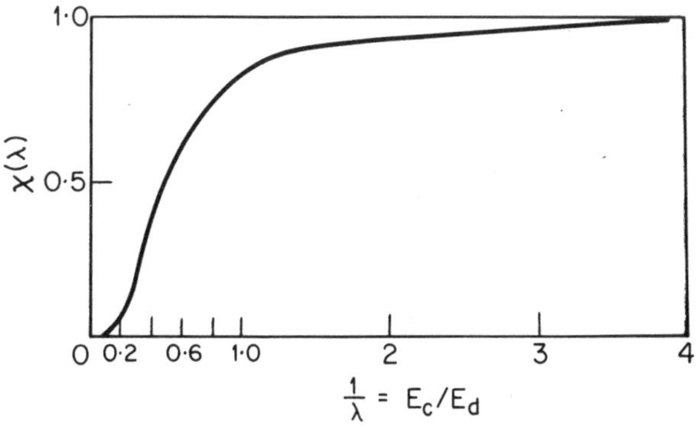

Fig. 6.15b The factor $\psi(\lambda) = \dfrac{\lambda}{\sin h\lambda}$ as a function of $\lambda\left(=\dfrac{E_d}{E_c}\right)$. (viz. Ref. 6.73.)

Chapter 2. E_c is an adjustable parameter and for $E_c \to \infty$, $\nu(E)$ is identical to that for hard sphere scattering. Figure 6.15b shows how $\psi(\lambda)$ varies with the ratio E_c/E_d and indicates that for $E_c \gtrsim 1.5E_d$; $\psi(\lambda)$ approaches unity and hence $\nu(E)$ tends to the hard sphere value. Comparison of Figure 6.15a with scattering probabilities from real potentials as in Figure 2.6 indicates that E_c will be considerably larger than E_d (for $E > 2E_d$) and so that defect density predicted by hard sphere considerations will be quite accurate for high primary energies. At lower energies however E_c is required to be smaller and thus $\psi(\lambda)$ and $\nu(E)$ are reduced below the hard sphere level. As a first approximation, therefore, the hard sphere model appears to be quite satisfactory. We may also remark that the form

$$g(E, T) = \exp\left\{\frac{E - 2T}{2E_c}\right\} / 2E \sinh E/2E_c$$

obeys the normalisation condition $\int_0^E g(E, T)\,dT = 1$ which is required for all scattering laws. We must also comment a little further upon the form of the displacement function shown in figure 6.13 and expressed by equations 6.25. This relationship corresponds to that given by Billington and Crawford(5) and Leibfried[62], but not in the region $E < 2E_d$ to that of Seitz and Koehler[3] and Dienes and Vineyard[4]. These latter authors state that $\nu(E) = 1$ for $0 < E < 2E_d$. This anomaly apparently arises from a different interpretation of displacement production.

If the primary energy E is greater than E_d, but less than $2E_d$, it can displace a target atom but not necessarily replace it. Since a target atom has been removed this may be thought of as a displacement event and $\nu(E) = 1$. If however $E < E_d$ no target atoms are ejected and apparently $\nu(E) = 0$. However the primary is imbedded in the lattice and this constitutes a displaced atom, hence $\nu(E) = 1$. Whichever scheme is adopted is largely a matter of personal definition, but the former choice appears to be somewhat more logical in that a real displacement does occur for $E > E_d$, whereas if the primary is an externally incident particle, for $E < E_d$, the damage produced is not a real lattice displacement. A final point which we have not yet discussed concerns the statistical fluctuation in the defect production density. Since the collisions are essentially statistical in nature the defect density $\nu(E)$ will also be subject to a statistical probability distribution and the mean density derived above is merely the first moment of this distribution. Put in another way this means that a large number of primary knock ons, all of energy E, will lead to different defect densities with a mean density $\bar{\nu}(E)$. Lehmann[73] has investigated the question of higher moments of $\nu(E)$ and has shown that, for the hard sphere case, there is little fluctuation about $\bar{\nu}(E)$, e.g. $\overline{\{\nu(E)\}^2} - \{\bar{\nu}(E)\}^2 = 0.15\,\bar{\nu}(E)$.

Kinchin and Pease[83] subsequently extended this model in a manner which may be appreciated by reference to the schematic energy representation of a collision in figure 6.16. In this model they retained the assumptions of replacement and displacement but defined an energy E_r, ($<E_d$) such that a struck atom receiving this energy would be displaced and replaced by the primary if the energy of this was less than E_d. This envisages that the total energy of the pair may be less to produce a replacement collision than a displacement collision, i.e. $E_r + E_d$ compared to $2E_d$.

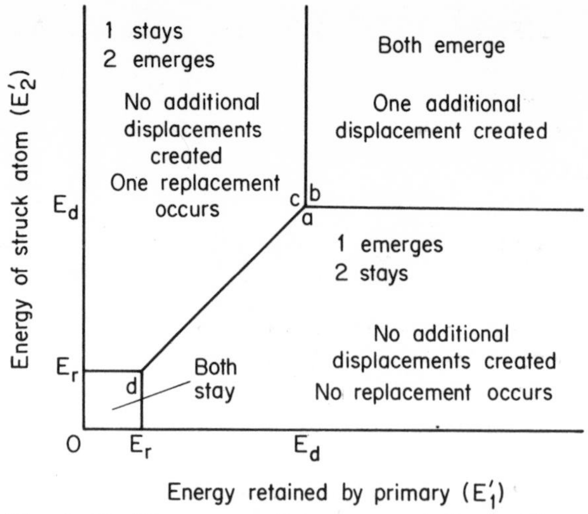

Fig. 6.16 Diagrammatic representation of the Kinchin-Pease assumptions (second model Ref. 6.83) for the creation of displacements and the occurrence of replacements.

Since $2E_d$ is still required to produce effective displacements, the average number of these will be the same as in the previous case. However, since a lower energy is required for replacement than previously, a larger number of such events must be anticipated. This number is readily deduced as follows.

Suppose $\mu(E)$ is the number of replacement events generated by a primary of energy E. If after one collision, the primary emerges with an energy E_1', and the struck atom with an energy E_2', and the probabilities of these atoms emerging at all are $p(E_1', E_2')$ and $q(E_1', E_2')$ respectively, then there also remains the probabilities that a replacement event has occurred $r(E_1', E_2')$ and that neither atom emerges.

The total number of replacement events is then calculated from the sum of (1) the average number of replacements generated at the first collision by the primary

$$= \int_0^E \frac{1}{E}\, r(E_1', E_2')\,dE_1'$$

(2) the average number of times a replacement is generated subsequently at collision of the primary with target atoms

$$= \int_0^E \frac{1}{E}\, p(E_1', E_2')\mu(E_1')\,dE_1' \qquad 6.27.1$$

for hard sphere collisions.
(3) the average number of replacements subsequently generated by the struck atom in the first collision

$$= \int_0^E \frac{1}{E}\, q(E_1', E_2')\mu(E_2')\,dE_2' \qquad 6.27.2$$

The probabilities p, q and r only have finite values in the energy regions denoted in figure 6.16. Consequently

$$\mu(E) = 0;\; E_r \geqslant E \geqslant 0 \qquad 6.27.3$$

$$\mu(E) = \frac{E - E_r}{E} + \frac{2}{E}\int_{E_r}^{E} \mu(E_1')\,dE_1';\; 2E_r \geqslant E \geqslant E_r$$

6.27.4

$$\mu(E) = \frac{1}{2} + \frac{2}{E}\int_{E/2}^{E} \mu(E_1')dE_1'; \; 2E_d \geq E \geq 2E_r$$

6.27.5

and

$$\mu(E) = \frac{E_d}{E} + \frac{2}{E}\int_{E_d}^{E} \mu(E_1')dE_1'; \; E > 2E_d \quad 6.27.6$$

These equations may be transformed to differential equations through multiplication by E and differentiation, with the results

$$E\mu'(E) = 1 + \mu(E); \; 2E_r \geq E \geq E_r \quad 6.28.1$$

$$E\mu'(E) = \tfrac{1}{2} + \mu(E) - \mu(E/2); \; 2E_d \geq E \geq 2E_r$$

6.28.2

$$E\mu'(E) = \mu(E) \quad ; E > 2E_d \quad 6.28.3$$

where

$$\mu'(E) \equiv \frac{d\mu(E)}{dE}$$

The first and third of these are immediately soluble, yielding

$$\mu(E) = E/E_r - 1; \; 2E_r \geq E \geq E_r \quad 6.29.1$$

$$\mu(E) = C(E) \quad ; E \geq 2E_d \quad 6.29.2$$

with C, an integration constant obtainable through matching with the solution of the second equation. 6.28.2

This mid-range equation can be solved by successive approximation to yield the solution

$$\mu(E) = 1.614 \log_e (E/2E_r) + 1; \; 2E_d \geq E \geq 2E_r$$

6.29.3

whence

$$\mu(E) = \frac{E}{2E_d}\{1.614 \log_e (E/2E_r) + 1\}; \; E \geq 2E_d$$

6.29.4

In the high transferred energy region, this final solution may be compared with the solution 6.25 to give the ratio of the number of atoms replaced to the number of atoms displaced.

$$\frac{\mu(E)}{\nu(E)} = 1.614 \log_e E/2E_r + 1 \quad 6.30$$

Kinchin and Pease[83] suggest that a ratio of $E_d/E_r = 10$ is not unreasonable, with the result that $\frac{\mu(E)}{\nu(E)} = 4.7$. In fact because of the logarithmic dependence of this ratio upon E_d/E_r, the replacement rate is not substantially affected by the details of the thresholds for replacement and displacement. Thus one may anticipate that whilst only a small amount of damage via displacements might be observed, other effects have occurred.

6.3.2.2 Snyder and Neufeld Model

In the early Snyder/Neufeld[85] treatment, replacement collisions were ignored, and the displacement threshold was assumed to be sharp, but the struck atom was assumed to be ejected with the difference between the transferred energy and the displacement energy. Later work[86] by these authors included the possibility of replacement and a variable ejection probability but we shall confine ourselves, for the present, to the former model.

Using these assumptions and the nomenclature of the previous section, it is readily seen that the mean displacement density $\nu(E)$ is given by the integral equation

$$\nu(E) = \int_0^E \frac{\nu(E_1')dE_1'}{E} + \int_0^{E-E_d} \frac{\nu(E_2')dE_2'}{E} \quad 6.31.1$$

This may be solved as before by multiplication with E and by differentiation with the result

$$\frac{d\nu(E)}{dE} = \frac{\nu(E - E_d)}{E} \quad 6.31.2$$

$\nu(E)$ is clearly unity for $0 < E < E_d$ and with this condition, equation 6.31.2 may be solved to

$$\nu(E) = \log_e E/E_d \quad 6.32.1$$

for $E_d \leq E \leq 2E_d$.

For $E > 2E_d$, the equation must be solved numerically and one obtains

$$\nu(E) = 0.561 \; E/E_d \quad 6.32.2$$

For energy transfers much in excess of E_d, this result differs only by about 12% from that of the Kinchin-Pease[82] model.

Snyder and Neufeld[86] extended this model to include the effects of replacement and a distributed threshold energy. As a result of the first effect, the number of displacement events is found to be reduced, in particular, for large primary energies it is found that $\nu(E) \simeq 0.35 \; E/E_d$ a reduction of 62%. The reason for the reduction in this case and not in the model of Kinchin and Pease is to be found in the fact that both Kinchin and Pease models include replacement, only differing in the energy required to produce replacement, (not displacement) collisions. Any model, such as the Snyder-Neufeld[85], which later includes replacement events must reduce the number of displacements. The results of inclusion of a distributed threshold are more difficult to assess accurately, but Sampson, Hurwitz and Clancy[71] and Fein[72] have given an approximate treatment based upon the linear threshold distribution earlier. It turns out that, at high energy transfers, the factor 0.561 in equation 6.32.2 is reduced to 0.50 and to smaller values at lower energies.

We may also note that variation of the interatomic potential in the Snyder-Neufeld model has no greater effect than it does with the Kinchin-Pease model. Thus Brown and Goedecke[87] used the Bohr potential in a machine calculation of the damage density with the Snyder-Neufeld model, and as shown in figure 6.14 achieved results very similar to those obtained with the Kinchin Pease model.

In the preceding calculations we have assumed, for simplicity that the primary ion is of the same mass as the target atoms, so that the maximum energy transfer in a collision is just the energy E of the primary ion. If, however, the primary and target atom masses differ, then the maximum energy transfer T_m is given by

$$T_m = \gamma E, \text{ where } \gamma = \frac{4M_1M_2}{(M_1 + M_2)^2}$$

Thus in all the calculations the upper limit of the integrals should in reality be γE rather than E. This has the effect of reducing all the calculated damage densities, replacing E by γE. For example the simple Kinchin Pease displacement model reduces to $\nu(E) = \gamma E/2E_d$ and other calculations are modified similarly.

It is therefore clear that a study of displacement events near the threshold, using the well-established electron bombardment techniques, or the recently developed ion bombardment techniques, will be important in deducing the exact nature of displacement and replacement events. It should be noted that the ion bombardment technique involves the observation of para surface damage and it will certainly be true that damage events at the surface will differ from those in the target interior. This arises because of the different forces experienced by surface atoms, which extend in one half infinite direction only, and may be observed in the energy dependence of the surface damage effect known as sputtering.

This subject will be described fully in the next chapter, but we may note for the present, that this surface damage effect appears to extend to energies considerably below the assumed bulk threshold energy of 25 eV.

In the preceding analysis we have tended to ignore the contribution to damage effects of energy losses in processes other than elastic collisions, assuming that to a first approximation electronic losses are negligible at primary energies less than A KeV. As we saw in Chapter 5, current investigations are casting doubt on the validity of this assumption, and, according to Lindhard et al, [88] inelastic losses are present down to the lowest energies with a half power dependence upon the energy. Consequently a fully representative description of damage production should include recognition of this energy loss process, since this effect results in energy degradation without defect production, and therefore a net reduction in $\nu(E)$ Lindhard et al[88] have shown how this loss mechanism may be incorporated into the integral equation for $\nu(E)$, by allowing an energy loss T_e to electrons in a collision. Thus equation 6. 24. 3 in the Kinchin-Pease approximation in written

$$\int d\sigma(E, T_n, T_e)dT_n dT_e\{\nu(E) - \nu(T_n) - \nu(E - T_n - T_e)\} = 0 \qquad 6.33.1$$

where T_n is the elastic collision loss.

For $T_e = 0$, this equation is identical to equation 6. 24. 3 since

$$\int d\sigma(E, T_n)\nu(E) = \sigma \cdot \nu(E) \text{ and } \frac{d\sigma(E, T_n)}{\sigma} = g(E, T_n)$$

Equation 6. 33. 1 may be expanded in T_n up to terms linear in T_n to give

$$(\sigma_e + \sigma_n)\frac{d\nu(E)}{dE} = \int_0^E d\sigma_n \nu(T) \qquad 6.33.2$$

where σ_e is the electronic stopping cross section, and was shown by Lindhard et al[88] to be proportional to $E^{1/2}$ and σ_n is the elastic collision stopping cross section.

Lindhard et al[88] have solved equation 6. 33. 2 for an inverse power interatomic potential where σ_n is proportional to E and for a Thomas-Fermi potential. The resulting expressions are somewhat complex, but indicate generally that $\nu(E)$ is reduced somewhat below the Kinchin-Pease value down to the lowest energies, but that at high energies the value of $\nu(E)$ approaches a constant value $\frac{E}{I + \text{const. } E}$, which is probably an order of magnitude higher than the simple ionization threshold model of $E_i/2E_d$.

Further development of this aspect of the damage production problem must await the presentation of a fully representative form for the interatomic potential, an experimentally justifiable specification of the energy dependence of inelastic losses, and knowledge of any coupling between elastic and inelastic processes.

We thus conclude that to a first approximation, the number of displacements in each cascade which results from a collision where the incident ion transfers an energy E to a lattice atom, is roughly $E/2E_d$. Since E_d is required for a displacement then approximately 50% of the energy of the primary knock ons is dissipated in subthreshold collisions resulting in no displacements, and the remaining 50% ($E/2E_d$) contributes to the density of the cascades. This, however, is not the whole picture, since each collision of the incident ion will, provided, that the energy transfer is greater than E_d, result in some form of a cascade.

As the primary enters the target the distance between collisions, and cascades, will be large and the damage relatively isolated. As the primary energy degrades through collision, the frequency of cascade initiation increases and the cascades overlap. At the periphery of the damage, where the primary suffers multiple collisions simultaneously the nature of the damage may change radically from that of isolated Frenkel pairs to defect aggregates produced in spike events. To determine the full nature of the damage therefore we must investigate the spatial distribution of the primary displacement events, as in the following discussion the results of which are due primarily to Holmes and Leibfried[89] Leibfried[62,90,91] and Korchovei, Gika and Greku[92].

6.3.3 The spatial distribution of primary displaced atoms

From the preceding sections we see that, in coming to rest, each incident ion creates a succession of cascades. Since each incident ion will behave differently, the resulting distribution of displaced atoms will be the average over many events. The final distribution will therefore be a statistical average over these events, and in order to ascertain this distribution we shall require the probability density of displaced atoms in all spatial regions. Each collision which produces a primary knock on of energy sufficient to generate a cascade, effectively reproduces the behaviour of the incident ion, except as regards the mass difference between the incident ion and the primary knock on, i.e. each p.k.a generated behaves as an incident ion of different mass. Thus, the incident ion generates a giant cascade, composed of subcascades induced by the p. k. a's. The spatial distribution of primary atoms which became captured in the giant cascade will therefore have similar, although not identical (because of the mass difference) characteristics to the distribution of stopped primary knock ons in each subcascade. It is considerably simpler to evaluate the spatial characteristics of these subcascades, since the p.k. a is of identical mass to the stopping atoms, with consequent simplification of scattering angle algebra, etc. Thus, in the following we evaluate the spatial distribution of stopped p. k. a's, with initial energy E in a subcascade, and use this to obtain an idea of the distribution of incident ions. Thus if the probability density of displaced atoms between radii r and r + δr from the initiation point of a subcascade is P(r)dr and the total number of displaced atoms in the cascade is $\nu(E)$ the number of displaced atoms in this spherical volume element is

$$\nu(E)p(r)dr \simeq \frac{E}{2E_d} p(r)dr$$

We then infer that the spatial distribution of displaced atoms initiated by incident ions of energy E_j at a distance R from the entry point, is given by an analogous expression $\nu(E_j)p(R)dR$.

To calculate the spatial probability distribution p(r)dr, we can employ the methods due to Holmes and Leibfried[89] and Leibfried[62,90,91] given in the previous chapter, or a closely similar, but more exhaustive treatment, given by Korchovei et al.[92] In the following we choose the former approach to illustrate the problem, and indicate the general methods of approach and refinements due to the latter authors.

If we consider a primary knock on atom generated with an energy E_0 in a vector direction u_0, then according to the ideas developed in Chapter 5, the probability of this atom moving a distance between l and $l + \delta l$ before colliding, is simply $\frac{1}{\lambda_0} \exp\left(-\frac{1}{\lambda_0}\right)dl$

where λ_0 is the mean free path at the energy E_0. Thus, since the original direction of motion and energy may be arbitrarily distributed, the probability of finding the primary in path length, angle and energy intervals of δl_0, $\delta\Omega_0$, δE_0 is

$$W_0 \delta l_0 \delta\Omega_0 \delta E_0 = \frac{\exp\left(-\frac{l_0}{\lambda_0}\right)}{\lambda_0} G(u_0, E_0)\delta l_0, \delta\Omega_0, \delta E_0 \qquad 6.34.1$$

where $d\Omega_0$ is the differential solid angle corresponding to the direction u_0; $G(u_0, E_0)$ is the angular and energy distribution function, which will be of the form $G = \delta(E - E_0)\delta(u - u_0)$* for a specific initial direction and energy and $G = \delta(E - E_0)\frac{1}{4\pi}$ for an isotropic spatial distribution. If the energy transfer at the first collision lies between E and E + δE such that the primary retains an energy between E_1 and $E_1 + \delta E_1$ and the angular displacement of this primary carries it into a solid angle $\delta\Omega_1$, then the probability of finding the primary within these path lengths, energy and angular direction limits is

$$W_1 \delta\Omega_1 \delta E_1 \delta l_1 = \frac{1}{\lambda_0} \exp\left(-\frac{1}{\lambda_0}\right) G(E_0, u_0)\delta E_1 \delta\Omega_1 \delta l_1 G(u_0, E_0, u_1, E_1) \qquad 6.34.2$$

where $G(u_0, E_0, u_1, E_1)$ is the probability of finding the primary, within the appropriate energy and direction limits and u_1 is the direction vector after the collision where the primary retains the Energy E_1.

This expression can be generalised to the nth collision such that the probability distribution after this collision with respect to the (n − 1)th is

$$\frac{1}{\lambda_n} \exp\left(-\frac{1}{\lambda_n}\right) . G(E_{n-1}, u_{n-1}, E_n, u_n)\delta E_n \delta\Omega_n \delta p_n \qquad 6.34.3$$

For a spherically symmetric potential and equal mass collision partners, the scattering angle ϕ between the direction vectors u_0 and u_1 is given unequivocally by

$$\cos\phi = u_0 . u_1 = \{E_1/E_0\}^{1/2} \qquad 6.35.1$$

and

$$u_{n-1} . u_n = \{E_n/E_{n-1}\}^{1/2} \qquad 6.35.2$$

One can thus separate the distribution function G, into the product of an angular distribution and an energy distribution. i.e.

$$G(E_0, u_0, E_1, u_1) = \frac{\delta\left(u_0 . u_1 - \left\{\frac{E_1}{E_0}\right\}^{1/2}\right)}{2\pi} . g(E_0, E_1) \qquad 6.36.1$$

where, for the hard sphere approximation, $g(E_0, E_1)$ has the simple form

$$g(E_0, E_1) = \frac{1}{E_0}, E_0 \geqslant E_1 \qquad 6.36.2$$

The distribution function for a primary of energy and direction values, E_0 and u_0, after ν collisions, is thus the product of all distribution functions in that, and preceding, collisions. i.e.

$$W_\nu = \frac{\exp(-l_0/\lambda_0)}{\lambda_0} G(u_0, E_0) \frac{\exp\left(-\frac{l_1}{\lambda_1}\right)}{\lambda_1} G(u_0, E_0, u_1, E_1) \ldots\ldots\ldots\ldots\ldots \times \frac{\exp\left(-\frac{l_\nu}{\lambda_\nu}\right)}{\lambda_\nu} G(u_{\nu-1}, E_{\nu-1}, u_\nu, E_\nu) \qquad 6.37$$

In order to be able to use this distribution to determine the actual spatial distribution of the primaries we require to know several basic properties of this former distribution.

* δ is, here, the Dirac function.

For example it is readily seen, that since u_1 is azimuthally symmetric about u_0, one must have

$$\langle u_1 \rangle_{AV} = u_0 \{E_1/E_0\}^{1/2} \qquad 6.38.1$$

Further

$$u_\nu = u_{\nu-1} \left\{\frac{E_\nu}{E_{\nu-1}}\right\}^{1/2} = u_{\nu-2} \left\{\frac{E_\nu}{E_{\nu-1}}\right\}^{1/2} \cdot \left\{\frac{E_{\nu-1}}{E_{\nu-2}}\right\}^{1/2}$$

$$\text{i.e.}\quad u_\nu = u_0 \left\{\frac{E_\nu}{E_0}\right\}^{1/2} \qquad 6.38.2$$

It may also be shown that

$$\langle u_{i_1} \cdot u_{k_1} \rangle = \frac{1}{2} \left\{ u_{i_0} u_{k_0} \left(\frac{3E_1}{E_0} - 1\right) + \delta_{ik} \left(1 - \frac{E_1}{E_0}\right) \right\} \qquad 6.38.3$$

for i, k = 1, 2, 3 or x, y, z since if u_0 is chosen in the x direction then $\langle (u_{x_1})^2 \rangle_{AV}$ must equal $(u_1 \cdot u_0)^2$, i.e.

$$\langle (u_{x_1})^2 \rangle_{AV} = \frac{E_1}{E_0} (u_{x_0})^2 = \frac{E_1}{E_0} \qquad 6.38.4$$

whilst

$$\langle (u_{y_1})^2 \rangle_{AV} = \langle (u_{z_1})^2 \rangle_{AV} = \frac{1}{2}(1 - E_1/E_0) \qquad 6.38.5$$

Finally, the energy distribution $g(E_0, E_\nu)$ after ν collisions, is given by

$$g(E_0, E_\nu) = \int g(E_0, E_1) g(E_1, E_2) \ldots\ldots g(E_{\nu-1}, E_\nu) dE_1 \ldots\ldots dE_{\nu-1} \qquad 6.39.1$$

which for hard sphere scattering, and $g(E_{\nu-1}, E_\nu) = \dfrac{1}{E_{\nu-1}}$ is simply

$$g(E_0, E_\nu) = \frac{1}{E_0 \underline{|\nu - 1}} \cdot \log_e^{\nu-1} \frac{E_0}{E_\nu}\,. \;;$$

$$E_0 \geqslant E_\nu,\ \nu = 1, 2, 3 \ldots\ldots \qquad 6.39.2$$

As shown in the previous chapter, the total path travelled $L = \sum_{\nu=0}^{\infty} l_\nu$ for an infinite number of collisions, and the vector path $r = \sum_{\nu=0}^{\infty} l_\nu \cdot u_\nu$. To be more precise, the upper limit of ν should be taken where the primary energy E falls below E_d, the capture energy, but for $E \gg E_d$, the error in taking $E_d = 0$ is small.

In order to determine the primary distribution, the quantities of interest will be average total and vector path lengths and higher order powers of the averages. As before, the average total path length

$$\langle \bar{L} \rangle = \int \frac{l_0}{\lambda_0} \exp\left(-\frac{l_0}{\lambda_0}\right) dl_0 + \iint g(E_0, E_1) \frac{l_1}{\lambda_1} \exp \left(\frac{-l_1}{\lambda_1}\right) dl, dE_1 + \ldots\ldots \qquad 6.40.1$$

which has the result given in Equation 5.44.4

$$\langle \bar{L} \rangle = \lambda(E_0) + \int_0^E \lambda(\epsilon) \frac{d\epsilon}{\epsilon}$$

where

$$\lambda(E_0) = \lambda_0 \qquad 6.40.2$$

$\langle L^2 \rangle_{AV}$ is derived with equal facility, with the result given in Equation 5.45.6. These results are not of great value, however, in determining the primary spatial distribution, since the quantities of interest will be the vector ranges, i.e. these will determine the resting place of the stopped primaries with respect to the point of primary incidence.

The values of $\langle \bar{r} \rangle_{AV}$, $\langle \overline{r^2} \rangle_{AV}$ etc. may also be deduced by the methods outlined in the previous Chapter 5 but with somewhat more difficulty, since these averages contain the scattering angles also.

The average vector path is given by

$$\langle \bar{r} \rangle_{AV} = \lambda(E_0) + \int g(u_0, E_0, u_1, E_1) \left(\frac{E_1}{E_0}\right)^{1/2} \lambda(E_1) dE_1 + \iint g(u_0, E_0, u_1, E_1) \left(\frac{E_1}{E_0}\right)^{1/2} g(u_1, E_1, u_2, E_2) \left(\frac{E_2}{E_1}\right)^{1/2} \lambda(E_2) dE_2 + \ldots\ldots\ldots\ldots \qquad 6.41.1$$

since the integrations over the l's can be evaluated to give $\lambda_0, \lambda_1, \lambda_2 \ldots$ etc in the integrals of equation 6.41.1. One thus obtains, finally

$$\langle \bar{r} \rangle_{AV} = \lambda(E_0) + \int_0^{E_0} \lambda(\epsilon) \frac{d\epsilon}{\epsilon} (\epsilon/E_0)^{1/2} \qquad 6.41.2$$

as in Equations 5.49.2 through application of Equation 5.43.3. $\langle \overline{r^2} \rangle_{AV}$ may be deduced in a manner analogous to that used to derive Equation 5.45.6 and one may quote the final result

$$\langle \overline{r^2} \rangle_{AV} = 2 \left\{ \lambda^2(E_0) + \int_0^{E_0} \lambda^2(\epsilon) \frac{d\epsilon}{\epsilon} + \frac{\lambda(E_0)}{E_0^{1/2}} \int_0^{E_0} \lambda(\epsilon) \frac{d\epsilon}{\epsilon^{1/2}} + \int_0^{E_0} \left\{ \lambda(\epsilon) \frac{d\epsilon}{\epsilon^{3/2}} \cdot \int_0^{\epsilon} \lambda(\epsilon') \frac{d\epsilon'}{(\epsilon')^{1/2}} \right\} \right\} \qquad 6.42.1$$

If the initial direction of motion is in the x direction, then, it is possible to show, after some mathematical manipulation, that

$$\langle x^2 \rangle_{AV} = \frac{\langle \overline{r^2} \rangle_{AV}}{3} + 4/3\,\gamma \qquad 6.42.2$$

$$\langle y^2 \rangle_{AV} = \langle z^2 \rangle_{AV} = \frac{\langle \overline{r^2} \rangle_{AV}}{3} - 2\gamma \qquad 6.42.3$$

where

$$\gamma = \lambda^2(E_0) + \frac{1}{4E_0^{3/4}} \int_0^{E_0} \lambda^2(\epsilon) \frac{d\epsilon}{\epsilon^{1/4}} + \frac{\lambda(E_0)}{E_0^{1/2}} \int_0^{E_0} \lambda(\epsilon) \frac{d\epsilon}{\epsilon^{1/2}} + \frac{1}{4\,E_0^{3/4}} \int_0^{E_0} \left\{ \lambda(\epsilon) \frac{d\epsilon}{\epsilon^{3/4}} \cdot \int_0^{\epsilon} \lambda(\epsilon') \frac{d\epsilon'}{(\epsilon')^{1/2}} \right\} \qquad 6.42.4$$

These relations immediately show that the distribution is broader in the initial, x, direction than in perpendicular directions. The dependence of $\langle \bar{r} \rangle_{AV}$ and $\langle \overline{r^2} \rangle_{AV}$ on E_0, may be deduced from the above relations for any given form of the interatomic potential, i.e. for a given energy dependence of $\lambda(E)$.

The variation of $\langle r \rangle_{AV}$ and $\langle \overline{r^2} \rangle_{AV}$ with E_0 for a Bohr interatomic potential are shown in Figure 5.7. Leibfried[90,91] subsequently showed how it was possible to express Equations 6.40, 41, 42 in much more concise form even in the case of unequal masses by use of the operator method as introduced in Chapter 5. Further calculations by this author[90,91] and by Korchovei et al[92] using a matrix operational method, showed how higher order averages may be obtained. In view of the elegant but protracted analysis required to arrive at the final results, it is proposed only to quote these results here. Korchovei et al[92] evaluated the third order moments of the perpendicular components of the vector ranges with the results

$$\langle y^3 \rangle_{AV} = \langle z^3 \rangle_{AV} = 0 \qquad 6.43.1$$

$$\langle x^3 \rangle_{AV} = -\tfrac{3}{4}\lambda^3(E_0) + \tfrac{3}{2}\lambda(E_0)\{\langle x^2 \rangle_{AV} - \tfrac{1}{2}\langle r^2 \rangle_{AV}\} + \tfrac{3}{4}\{\langle r^2 x \rangle_{AV}\} - \tfrac{3}{8}E_0^{-7/4}\int_0^{E_0} \epsilon^{3/4} \{\tfrac{1}{2}\lambda^3(\epsilon) + \lambda(\epsilon)(\langle x^2 \rangle_{AV}(\epsilon) - \tfrac{1}{2}\langle r^2 \rangle_{AV}(\epsilon)) + \tfrac{1}{2}\langle r^2 x \rangle_{AV}(\epsilon)\} d\epsilon \qquad 6.43.2$$

with $\langle r^2 \rangle_{AV}$ and $\langle x^2 \rangle_{AV}$ given by Equations 6.42.1, 6.42.2 and $\langle r^2 x \rangle_{AV}$ deduced from

$$\langle r^2 x \rangle_{AV} = -3\lambda^3(E_0) + \lambda(E_0)\langle r^2 \rangle_{AV} + 2\lambda(E_0)\langle x^2 \rangle_{AV} + \frac{1}{E_0^{1/2}}\int_0^{E_0} \epsilon^{-1/2}\{-3\lambda^3(\epsilon) + \lambda(\epsilon)\langle r^2 \rangle_{AV}(\epsilon) + 2\lambda(\epsilon)\langle x^2 \rangle_{AV}(\epsilon)\} d\epsilon \qquad 6.43.3$$

With these vector range moments we can obtain an approximate idea of the vector range distribution, in a similar manner as that used to derive the total path length distribution. If $f(x, y, z)$ is the distribution function for primaries stopped in a volume dxdydz at the vector range r, then the average vector range may be expressed as

$$\langle \exp(iar) \rangle_{AV} = \iiint \exp(iar)\, f(x, y, z)\, dx, dy, dz. \qquad 6.44.1$$

where a is an arbitrary vector with components ax, ay, az in the x, y, z directions. Fourier inversion then leads to

$$f(x, y, z) = (2\pi)^{-3} \iiint \langle \exp(iar) \rangle_{AV} \exp(-iar)\, da_x da_y da_z \qquad 6.44.2$$

The average $\langle \exp(iar) \rangle_{AV}$ may be expanded by a series development in $\langle x \rangle_{AV}$, $\langle y \rangle_{AV}$, $\langle z \rangle_{AV}$ and higher moments of these, with some simplifications resulting from the fact that several of the averages e.g. $\langle y \rangle_{AV}$, $\langle z \rangle_{AV}$, $\langle y^3 \rangle_{AV}$, $\langle z^3 \rangle_{AV}$ are zero.

For the present purpose it may assumed that only moments as high as third order are necessary to describe the average $\langle \exp(iar) \rangle_{AV}$ adequately, further terms contributing only a minor amount to the form of this average. In this order of approximation, one obtains

$$\langle \exp(iar) \rangle_{AV} = \exp\left\{ ia\langle x \rangle_{AV} - \tfrac{1}{2}(a_y^2 + a_z^2)\delta^2 + a_x^2\delta_x^2 - \frac{i}{2}(a_y^2 a_x + a_z^2 a_x)\gamma^3 - \frac{ia^3{}_x\psi^3}{6} \right\} \qquad 6.45.1$$

where

$$\delta^2 = \delta_y^2 = \delta_z^2 = \langle y^2 \rangle_{AV} = \langle z^2 \rangle_{AV}$$

$$\delta_x^2 = \langle x^2 \rangle_{AV} - \langle x \rangle_{AV}^2$$

$$\gamma^3 = \langle y^2 x \rangle_{AV} - \langle y^2 \rangle_{AV}\langle x \rangle_{AV}$$

$$\psi^3 = \langle x^3 \rangle_{AV} - 3\langle x^2 \rangle_{AV}\langle x \rangle_{AV} + 2\langle x \rangle_{AV}^3 \qquad 6.45.2$$

This result is then inserted into Equation 6.44.2 to obtain the primary distribution function

$$f(x, y, z) = (2\pi)^{-3/2}\, \delta_x^{-1} \,.\, \delta^{-2} \exp\left\{\left[-\frac{y^2 + z^2}{2\delta^2} - (x - \langle x \rangle_{AV})^2\right]\right\} \times \left\{\left[1 - \frac{\gamma^3}{\delta^2\delta_x^2}(x - \langle x \rangle_{AV})\right] \left[1 - \frac{y^2 + z^2}{2\delta^2}\right] + \frac{1}{6}\frac{\psi^3}{\delta^4}(x - \langle x \rangle_{AV}) \times \left[3 - \frac{(x - \langle x \rangle_{AV})^2}{\delta^2}\right]\right\} \qquad 6.46$$

If only the second order of approximation were to be employed the final term in square brackets would be omitted. The presence of this term, however, indicates that the primaries are distributed preferentially in the forward x direction, as must be expected. The distributions perpendicular to the x direction are approximately Gaussian in form and indicate that the whole distribution may be thought of as being contained within a volume formed by ellipsoids of rotation about the axes centred on the average $\langle x \rangle_{AV}$ on the x axis. There will be a slight distortion in the forward x direction which should be accentuated by inclusion of higher order moments. Finally, the number of displacements in a given volume element is obtained by multiplying $f(x, y, z)$ by the total number of displacements $\nu(E_0)$. We may note that this cigar shaped distribution is of the form predicted by the computer calculations of Oen et al[93] as described in the previous chapter. Further, the approximate centre $\langle x \rangle_{AV}$ of the giant cascade is, in view of Equation 6.41.2 roughly linearly dependent upon the primary energy. However the exact nature and extent of the distribution will depend upon the form assumed for the interatomic potential. Thus the Bohr potential will be weaker than the composite Bohr-Born-Mayer Potential of Equation 6.17 with a larger mean free path and wider region of damage. It is also evident from Equation 6.42 that, with decreasing primary energy $\langle x^2 \rangle_{AV} \simeq \langle y^2 \rangle_{AV} = \langle z^2 \rangle_{AV}$ i.e. the distribution tends towards a spherically symmetrical shape. Leibfried[62] has evaluated the variation of the damage density in the region near the centre of the cascade which involves 50% of the total damage, as a function

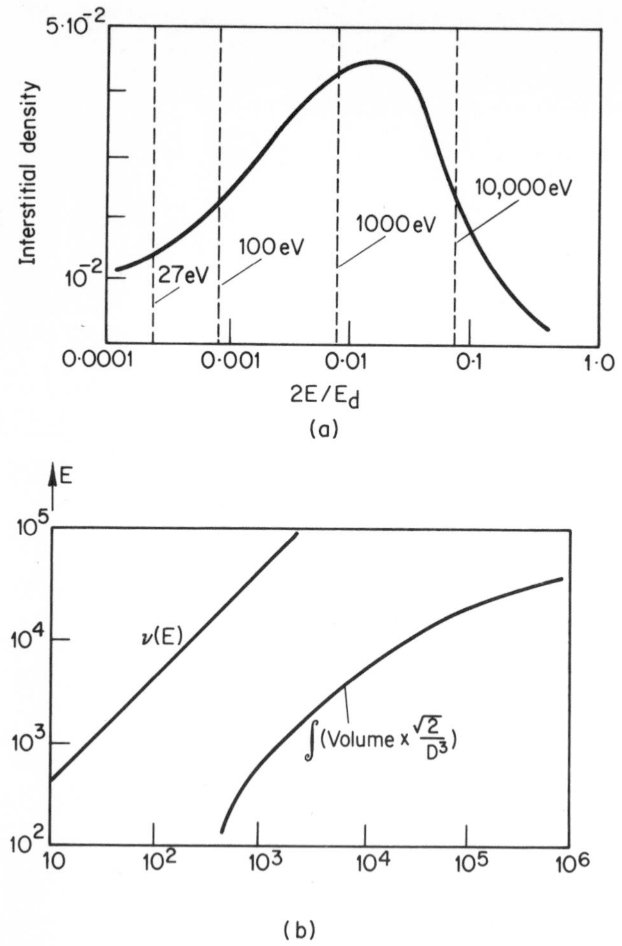

Fig. 6.17(a) Interstitial density (in atomic %) as a function of the reduced primary energy $E/2E_d$ (b) Number of Frenkel pairs (ν(E)) and volume of the cascade as a function of the primary energy E. (D = interatomic spacing) viz. Ref. 6.62.

of primary energy with the composite interatomic potential of Equation 6.17. This is shown in Figure 6.17a and it is evident that the damage density goes through a maximum for the composite potential. Since the cascade can be resolved into a number of sub-cascades, the figure indicates that above the energy for maximum damage density, the density of the sub-cascades may be higher than that of the giant cascade but when averaged out over the whole volume of the giant cascade the resulting density is reduced below the maximum. At energies at or below the optimum, each subcascade density will be lower than that of the giant cascade and to account for the total damage density at the maximum one must anticipate that the subcascades begin to overlap. This overlapping indicates that at low primary energies, the assumption of isolated two body collisions may be inadequate and the phenomenon should be more properly treated as a collective interaction (i.e. a spike). Furthermore the overlapping of cascades may lead to a reduction in overall damage because of increased probability of defect annealing.

In Figure 6.17a the total number of Frenkel pairs produced near the cascade created at 1300 eV would be about 25, ($^1/_2{}^{1300}/_{25}$), with an atomic concentration of about 5%. This region of high density would extend linearly for about 5 atomic dimensions, and clearly on an atomistic scale is a high defect density. The full extent of the cascade would extend over considerably larger distances however, and an idea of the magnitude of the damaged volume can be obtained by assuming an ellipsoidal damage region with the volume matched to the quadratic averages $\langle x^2 \rangle_{AV}$ etc. With this approximation, the increase of total damage volume and the total number of defect pairs produced increases with primary energy as shown in Figure 6.17b. The ratio of the two ordinates indicates that the average damage density will increase more rapidly with energy than a first order power law. At 1300 eV the damaged region would comprise about 1,000 atomic volumes. Both this spatial extent and the damage density will be critically dependent upon the interatomic potential and in view of the present inadequacy of our knowledge of this, we can proceed no further than the above qualitative analysis, at this stage. We should note, however, that the full extent of the damaged region may be considerably larger, but of similar order of magnitude, to the mean primary range, hence experiments described in the last Chapter which determine primary ion ranges via a change in the target structure should be accepted cautiously since these basically determine the extent of the damage.

Finally the above treatment was carried through assuming equal masses for the collision partners, so that the total cascade generated by an incident ion and a primary knock on were assumed identical. However, this is generally not the case, but a more realistic mathematical analysis presents considerable difficulties. We may content ourselves that the results given here, although of a largely qualitative nature in determining the extent of the damage in the subcascades, indicate that the total damage will be of similar nature.

In the preceding analysis it has been implicitly assumed that the target is composed of one atomic species only. This is clearly not the case in alloys and Harris[94] and Baroody[95,96] have investigated the damage production in target media composed of several components. Specific details are difficult to deduce but the general conclusions reinforce the conclusions obtained in the analysis given here, when adapted to the single atom species target.

The magnitude ν(E) of the damage, as we have seen however, is not sensitively dependent upon the assumptions of replacement and displacement, nor for that matter, upon the interatomic potential thus experimental determinations of ν(E), should allow us to assess the accuracy of the models used. It is not proposed to enter into a detailed discussion of experimental measurements in the present section, since these are considered fully in section 6.5. However, we should note, at this stage, that most experimental determinations lead to total damage rates, lower by factors between 2 and more than an order of magnitude than predicted by any of the simple theories outlined above. Moreover the anticipated linear variation of ν(E) with energy E is not observed experimentally. Instead ν(E) increases less rapidly than as the first power of E, and ionization losses cannot fully account for the discrepancy. We should also note that these experimental determinations have been carried out largely with electron, neutron and fission fragment primaries, since slow ion bombardment induced damage has only recently become amenable to analysis. However, when due allowance is made for the nature of these primaries, the deduced damage is, as stated too low.

Since such factors as replacement, a distributed threshold energy, and interaction potential, do not appear to reduce the predicted damage by a significant amount, then it appears that the discrepancy between theory and experiment must arise from a further inadequacy in the assumptions. Evidently this untenable premise is that of randomization of the target atoms. Since in a real lattice, the target atoms are located in predictable positions, then there must be a correlation between successive collisions, not a completely random sequence as hitherto assumed. In the following sections we will investigate two of these correlated effects, the focusing sequence and the channelling mechanism, and determine whether these can lead to improved agreement with experiment.

6. 3. 4. 1 Focused Collision Sequences

In a real solid, with the atoms arranged regularly, at relatively fixed lattice positions, it is readily appreciated that there exist continuous rows of atoms, interrupted only by surfaces, defects and dislocations. If it is imagined that one atom of such a row is set in motion, possibly through a collision from an incident ion or an earlier displaced atom, exactly along the axis of such a row, then this primary knock on will transfer energy to its neighbour, which will in turn collide with its next neighbour and the sequence will propagate along the row.

The energy of the moving atoms will be degraded only slowly through interaction with neighbouring rows and the sequence may progress over many lattice distances before terminating at a lattice defect. In this way one may imagine that the energy initially transferred in one region of the target may result in damage at a considerable distance from this region. Consequently the extent and magnitude of the damage may differ considerably from that calculated for a randomly distributed array of target atoms. This simple picture of a collision sequence cannot, of course, occur in practice, since the probability of the initial direction of the primary displaced atom, lying exactly along the row axis will be zero (i.e. $d(\pi p^2) = 0$, for $p = 0$). However, if the initial direction of motion makes only a small angle with the row axis, then it is easy to show that, providing certain conditions obtain, subsequent collisions along the row occur at progressively smaller angles, finally tending to zero, and the energy of the sequence becomes focused in the row axis direction. Silsbee[97] first investigated these focused collision sequences in 1957, and numerous additions and refinements have been subsequently developed. In the following we will consider the simple theory of focusing effects and discuss the developments. Not all of these developments are of direct consequence to our current study of radiation damage, but since they are of considerable importance in sputtering phenomena, the subject of the next chapter, and because no comprehensive review of focusing events has been published in the English language a rather detailed analysis will be given.

If we assume, initially,[98] that the target atoms, consist of hard impenetrable spheres, of radius r, then a typical atomic row, of initial lattice spacing D may be represented as in Figure 6. 18. If the atom to the farthest left of the diagram labelled (1) is set in motion at an angle θ_0 to the row axis with an energy E_0 it will collide with atom (2) when it reaches position C and the effective radii of atoms (1) and (2), will depend upon the energy via the relation

$$E_{0_R} = E_{0/2} = V(2r) \qquad 6.47$$

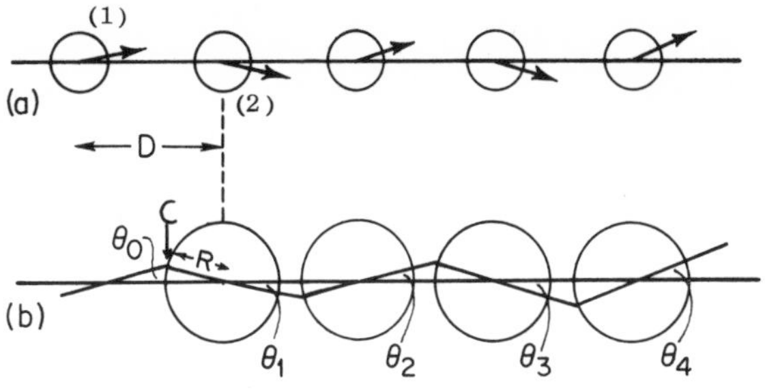

Fig. 6. 18(a) Series of collisions along a row of equidistant (spacing σ) hard spheres. (b) As in (a) but illustrating effective collision of points on hard spheres of twice the radius of (a) to determine angles of propagation of sequence.

where **V** (2r), is the real interatomic potential at the distance of closest approach 2r in a head-on collision. Since the collision partners are of equal mass, one may consider the collision as between a point and an impenetrable sphere of radius 2r(=R) as shown in Figure 6. 19.

Because energy is transferred, only along the line of centres of the spheres, the struck atom (2) moves away from its lattice position along the direction PD at an angle θ_1, to the axis, (and the atom (1), perpendicular to this direction). From the triangle OPD it is then deduced that

$$\sin\theta_1 = \sin\theta_0\,\{\alpha\cos\theta_0 - (1-\alpha^2\sin^2\theta_0)^{1/2}\} \qquad 6.48.1$$

where $\alpha = D/R$ and with the hard sphere approximation, equation 2.11b immediately reveals that the energy E_1 of the atom (2) after collision given by

$$E_1 - E_0(1 - \alpha^2\sin^2\theta_0) \qquad 6.48.2$$

since $\theta_0 + \theta_1$ is just the angle β of Chapter 2. Equation 6. 48.1 immediately shows that for $\theta_1 < \theta_0$ and both angles small, then $\alpha < 2$ i.e.

$$D < 2R \qquad 6.49$$

Thus the collsion must occur to the left of the point R/2 for this kind of collision.

Since the energy is degraded at each collision, and since the hard sphere radius inevitably increases with decreasing energy, for the interatomic potentials with which we are concerned, then subsequent collisions, between, for example the nth and (n + 1)th atoms, occur with larger radius spheres. Thus, for

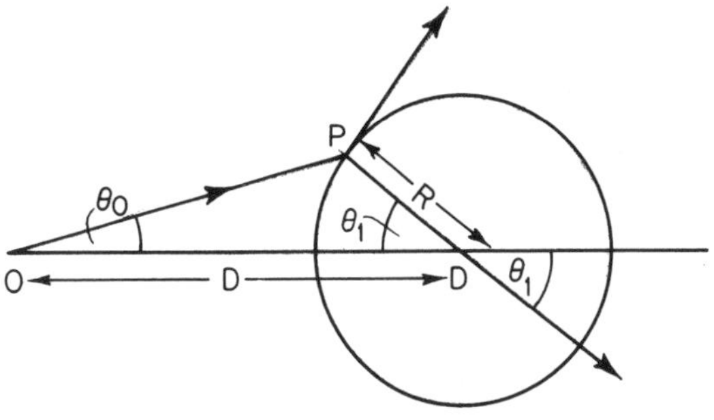

Fig. 6. 19 Enlargement on Fig. 6. 18(b) illustrating effective collision of point with hard sphere of twice the hard sphere radius of each atom in the row (R/2) to determine collision angles.

an initial collision, where the condition 6.49 is satisfied $\theta_1 < \theta_0$ and all subsequent collisions decrease the angle with which the struck atom moves away from the collision, i.e. the sequence is focused.

In the small angle approximation where $\sin\theta \to \theta \to 0$ Equation 6.48.1 shows that

$$\frac{\theta_1}{\theta_0} \simeq \frac{D}{R} - 1 \qquad 6.50$$

which further illustrates the condition for focusing $D/R < 2$. The parameter θ_1/θ_0 is usually defined as the focusing parameter λ. If the energy degredation per collision is small, then, at the nth collision $R(E_n) \simeq R(E_0)$ and $\frac{\theta_{n+1}}{\theta_n} \approx \lambda$. It is immediately seen that

$$\frac{\theta_{n+1}}{\theta_0} = \lambda^n \qquad 6.51$$

and since $\lambda < 1$, $\theta_{n+1} \to 0$ i.e. the atoms finally move along the chain axis.

Since the condition for focused collisions is that $D < 2R$ the lattice rows along which these sequences are most probable are those for which D is a minimum, i.e. the close packed directions such as the ⟨110⟩ rows in copper. It is also notable that, just for these close packed rows, the distance to neighbouring rows is rather large and thus interaction with the neighbouring rows, may be largely ignored. However, as we shall see shortly, when considering less closely packed rows, where normal focused sequences are less probable, the influence of neighbouring rows is more important and assists in the propagation of focussed events.

Thus, in the hard sphere approximation, focusing events occur when the impact point is to the left of half the equilibrium static lattice separation D, and the atoms in the surrounding rows tend to force the primary displaced atom back to its initial position. This is an energetically possible process since the primary retains very little of its initial energy in the almost head on collisions envisaged in a focused sequence. In a focused sequence it would appear, therefore, that there is no transport of matter, only of energy, except where the final atom of a sequence is permanently ejected if it is close to a surface or lattice defect. It is thus possible that this transport of energy away from the initial position of energy deposition may lead to changes in the nature of the damage pattern.

The exact details of the focusing sequence can only be evaluated by using the real interatomic potential, by considering the effects of interaction from neighbouring rows and by taking account of such lattice irregularities as thermal atomic vibrations. However, we will show later that these effects only change the details of the sequence, but not the essential concept of the mechanism. We will therefore continue, for the present, with the hard sphere assumption.

With this assumption it is evident that the maximum possible collision angle is given by

$$\sin\theta_S = R/D = 1/\alpha \qquad 6.52.1$$

However the maximum collision angle for the generation of focused sequences, is given by $\theta_1 = \theta_0$ and hence

$$\cos\theta_F = \frac{D}{2R} = \alpha/2 \qquad 6.52.2$$

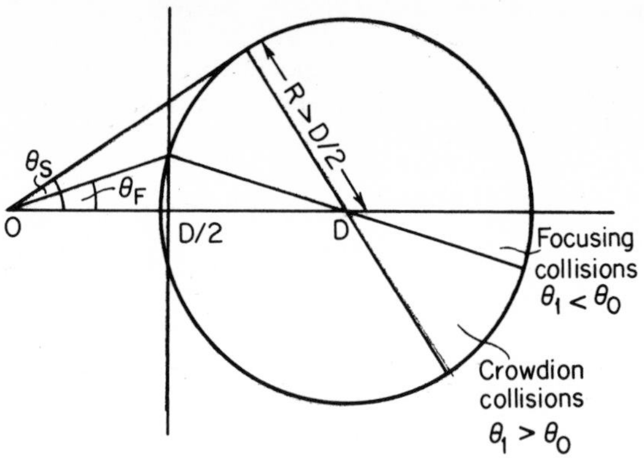

Fig. 6.20 Schematic representation of the allowed collision angles for generation of focusing or crowdion collisions.

even for the case where $R > D/2$ i.e. focused sequences are possible only for limited starting angles even though the general focusing condition is satisfied. This may be appreciated more clearly by reference to figure 6.20 where focusing collisions occur for $\theta < \theta_F$ and a second type of collision occurs for $\theta_S > \theta > \theta_F$. These latter collisions are referred to as dynamic crowdions and since collisions occur nearer to the equilibrium position of the struck atom, then there is a fair chance that the struck atom will be displaced and the primary take its place. In crowdion collisions the angle θ increases with distance along the row and so an atom is eventually ejected from the row. Crowdion collisions therefore involve the transport of the matter, in the form of interstitials, as well as energy transport. These crowdions are distinct from the static crowdions mentioned earlier in that they involve the motion of atoms in a lattice row, but are similar in so far as the lattice atoms are disturbed from their normal positions.

It is evident that the longest range sequences will obtain when α is in the region of 2 and it therefore becomes convenient to define a parameter η such that $\eta = \alpha - 2$ where

$$|\eta| \ll 1 \qquad 6.53.1$$

In the small angle approximation, expansion of Equation 6.48.1 as far as the θ_F^2 term, shows that

$$\theta_F^2 \approx -\,n \qquad 6.53.2$$

and

$$\theta_S \cong \frac{1}{\alpha} \simeq \frac{1}{2} - \eta/4 \qquad 6.53.3$$

Further the relation between the $(n+1)^{th}$ atom angle and the nth atom angle, is then deduced from Equation 6.48.1 to be

$$\theta_{n+1} = \theta_n(\alpha - 1)\left(1 + \frac{\alpha\theta_n^2}{2}\right) \qquad 6.54.1$$

Expanding, and neglecting the terms in $\eta\theta_n^2$, one has

$$\theta_{n+1} = \theta_n(1 + \eta + \theta_n^2) \qquad 6.54.2$$

Since the change in θ is small at each collision and thus

$$\theta_{n+1} \approx \theta_n + \frac{d\theta_n}{dn}$$

then,

$$\frac{d\theta_n}{dn} = \theta_n [\eta + \theta_n^2] \qquad 6.54.3$$

which is solved to

$$\theta_n^2 = \frac{\theta_0^2\, \eta \exp(2n\eta)}{\eta + \theta_0^2 - \theta_0^2 \exp(2n\eta)} \qquad 6.54.4$$

where θ_0 is the starting angle for the sequence. With the same assumptions, the energy equation 6.48.2 can be transformed to a differential equation, with the solution

$$E_n = E_0 \left(\frac{\eta + \theta_0^2 - \theta_0^2 \exp(2n\eta)}{\eta} \right)^2 \qquad 6.54.5$$

For Crowdion collisions $\theta_0{}^x > \theta_F^2$ or $\eta + \theta_0^2 >$ and one obtains a limiting number n for Crowdion collisions by setting $E_n{}^* = O$ i.e.

$$\eta + \theta_0^2 \exp\{2n^*\eta\} \qquad 6.55.1$$

This gives an upper limit n*D, for the Crowdion range, dependent upon θ_0. For focusing collisions $\eta + \theta_0^2 < O$ i.e. η is negative, which shows that for a large number of collisions $n \to \infty$ and

$$E_\infty = E_0 \left(\frac{\eta + \theta_0^2}{\eta} \right)^2 \qquad 6.55.2$$

Thus for $\theta_0 = 0$ (head on collisions) $E_\infty = 0$ whilst for $\theta_0 = \theta_F$, θ remains constant while E_n decreases exponentially to zero. It is therefore clear that with a distribution of primary atom angles, there will be a distribution of focused energies and ranges.

This energy distribution may be estimated by noting that the total probability of a primary generating a focused sequence along a ⟨110⟩ row with starting angle between θ and $\theta + \delta\theta$ is given by $W = \frac{12}{4\pi}\, \delta\Omega$. Since there are twelve equivalent ⟨110⟩ rows and $\delta\Omega$ is the solid angle enclosed by θ and $\theta + \delta\theta$. For focused sequences, θ may lie between 0 and θ_F and thus

$$\Omega = 2\pi(1 - \cos\theta_F) = -\pi\eta \qquad 6.56.1$$

Consequently the probability for focused sequences is

$$W_F = -3\eta \qquad 6.56.2$$

Further, differentiation of equation 6.54.5 indicates that the focused energy after a large number of collisions, for a uniform distribution of starting angles

$$\frac{2\pi \sin\theta \, d\theta}{2\pi(1 - \cos\theta_F)}$$

is distributed according to

$$f(E_\infty) = \frac{1}{2(E_0 E_\infty)^{1/2}} \qquad 6.57.1$$

The average focused energy is then

$$\overline{E}_\infty = E_0/_3 \qquad 6.57.2$$

This distribution indicates that a large fraction of focused sequences have a terminal energy in the neighbourhood of E_0 (e.g. 10% of focused sequences have a terminal energy within 20% of E_0).

For crowdion collisions and $\eta + \theta_0^2 > 0$ it is necessary to treat the cases $\eta > 0$ and $\eta < 0$ separately. If one requires the probability $W_c(n^*)$ for crowdion ranges greater than n*D then $\Omega_c(n^*) \simeq \pi\theta_0^2$ and

$$W_c(n^*) = 3\theta_0^2 \exp(2n^*\eta) - 1 \qquad 6.58.1$$

For $\eta < 0$ crowdion hits occur only for $\theta_0 > \theta_F$; $\Omega_c(n^*) = \pi(\theta_0^2 - \theta_F^2)$ and

$$W_c(n^*, \eta) = \frac{3}{2n^*} (1 - n^* |\eta|) \qquad 6.58.2$$

At this stage we should note that the hard sphere approximation tends to give a false impression in that it separates unequivocally crowdion sequences with energy and mass transport and focuson sequences with only energy transport. In fact the criterion for focusing in the hard sphere case, that the distance of closest approach in a head on collision should be half the static row spacing leads naturally to a non mass transfer since the struck atom does not move before the collision, which therefore takes place closer to the rest position of the moving atom than the rest position of the struck atom. With a real interatomic potential however both atoms move simultaneously and although E_F still defines the focusing condition that the distance of closest approach is one half the static row spacing, this minimum separation occurs to the right of the mid-atom position since both atoms have moved in this direction. Thus for energies of order E_F the moving atom can pass the potential saddle point and thus replace the next atom in the sequence. A lower energy E_R is therefore definable at which the moving atom just reaches the mid atom position when at the distance of closest approach, and Lehmann and Leibfried[99] have deduced the value of this replacement energy E to be about 17 eV for ⟨100⟩ Copper. It will be easier to move the struck atom in a direction away from the row axis since the interaction with subsequent atoms in the row will be reduced and it may therefore be anticipated that E_R will decrease with increasing starting angle of the sequence, Lehmann[100] has shown that E_R is reduced to 10 eV for a starting angle of 10° and even further for larger starting angles. This effect clearly reveals that even in focuson sequences, mass transport may occur with greater or less efficiency depending upon the starting energy and angle. One can therefore define three classes of collision for even the head-on case.

1. At energies $> E_F$ crowdion collisions with mass and energy transfer but no focusing.
2. At energies $> E_R$ but $< E_F$ focuson collisions with mass and energy transfer and a focusing action classed as replicons.
3. At energies $< E_R$, focuson collisions with energy transfer and focusing.

Before continuing further with the present line of reasoning to determine the range of the focused sequences (generally termed focusons for convenience) and the influence upon the damage, it is as well to investigate whether the magnitudes of the parameters we are using are reasonable. The quantity which critically determines the extent of the focusing effect is the focusing parameter λ $(= D/R - 1)$ which, as we have seen, is energy dependent. If one assumes

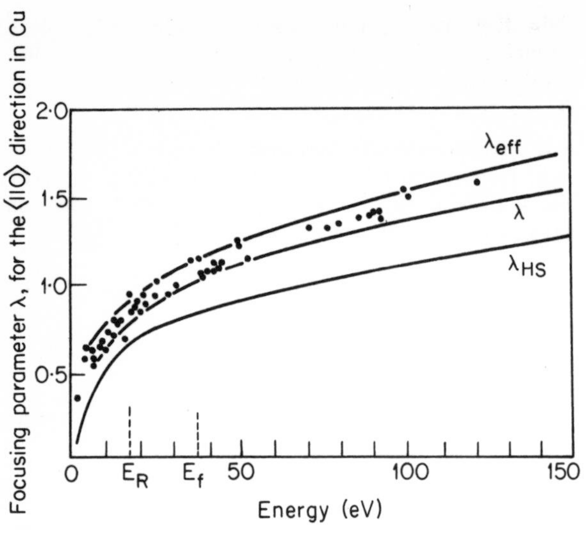

Fig. 6. 21 Focusing parameter λ in ⟨110⟩ Cu rows as a function of the energy. viz. Ref. 6. 99. Data according to Gibson et al. Ref. 6. 23. λ_{HS} derived according to hard sphere approximation (Equn. 6. 50) λ_{eff} derived according to Born-Mayer interatomic potential for initial collisions only (Equn. 6. 72. 2) λ derived according to Born-Mayer interatomic potential for a series of collisions (Equn. 6. 78).

a Born-Mayer interatomic potential for Copper of the form $V(r) = A \exp(-r/a)$ with $A = 22.5$ KeV and $a = D/13$, then the equivalent hard sphere radius is calculated from $\frac{E_0}{2} = V(R)$ at each primary energy and one can calculate λ as a function of E_0. This calculation is shown in Figure 6.21 where the results are compared with exact computer calculations of λ by Gibson et al[23] with a simulated copper lattice and the potential used above. It is immediately apparent that the hard sphere approximation underestimates the values of the focusing parameter. For example the limiting focusing energy derived from the condition $\lambda = 1, D = 2R$ is 70 eV in the hard sphere approximation but only 30 eV by exact machine calculation. It will be shown shortly how much better agreement with machine calculations can be obtained by a more realistic treatment of the collisions. Nevertheless it may be anticipated that the essential properties of focusons will not be greatly affected by the assumption of hard sphere collisions, although the number and extent of the sequences may be altered in detail.

We should also note that the theoretical curve of λ as a function of energy in Figure 6.21 was deduced for the near head on collision case. Lehmann[100] has recently shown that for large angles, λ is a function of energy and angle according to the relation

$$\lambda(E, \theta) = \lambda(E, \theta = 0)[1 + k\theta^2] \qquad 6.59$$

for starting angles up to 15°. The constant k has the value −0.15 and this shows that the focusing parameter for a focused sequence starting at a relatively large angle decreases as the sequence propagates. As we shall see later this agrees with the computer calculations of Gibson et al[23] which are also depicted in Figure 6.21.

To determine the focuson ranges we must enquire as to the mechanisms which lead to energy loss along the propagation of a sequence of hard sphere collisions.

The first mechanism, that of natural loss because of non head on collisions, has already been outlined above and it is clear that since any forward sequence eventually propagates along the row axis, the focuson range is infinite unless interrupted by a lattice defect. This treatment assumed, however, that the hard sphere radius remains unchanged as the atom energy degrades. This is a somewhat unrealistic assumption since the radius clearly changes with energy and a more complete treatment, given shortly, shows the effects of a more accurate model. Other loss mechanisms which will reduce the range to finite values are the softness of the real potential, lattice vibrations, and interaction of the focuson atoms with neighbouring rows. We shall determine the influence of the first two of these shortly when considering a more realistic treatment of focuson propagation. The third of these effects may, however, be treated in the context of the hard sphere approximation.

One may calculate the energy loss suffered by the focuson sequence due to interaction with neighbouring rows as follows. For a ⟨110⟩ type row in copper each displaced atom must pass through a square array of four nearest neighbour atoms before colliding with the next atom of the row. Thus the atom starting at the origin in figure 6.22 in the ⟨101⟩ direction decreases its separation distance to R' with the four atoms labelled 011, 110, 0$\bar{1}$1, and 1$\bar{1}$0 and may

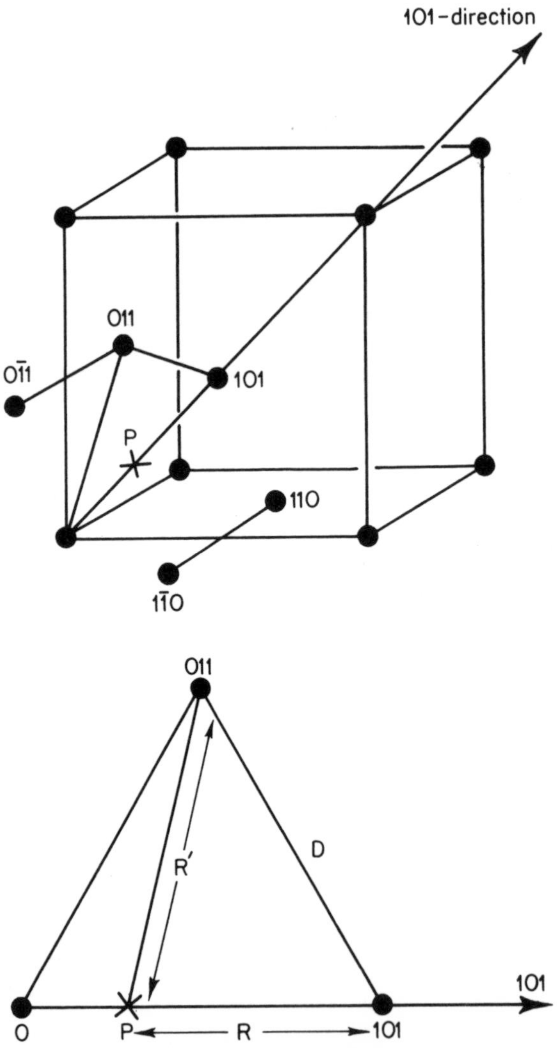

Fig. 6. 22 The interaction of an atom moving in a Cu ⟨101⟩ row with neighbouring rows to determine the energy loss (viz. Ref. 6. 99)

suffer an energy loss $\Delta E_0'$ before colliding with the next atom. The distance R', which is the same for all four atoms for a primary started exactly along the ⟨101⟩ axis, is readily calculated from figure 6.22 to be $R' = (D^2 + R^2 - RD)^{1/2}$ where P is the collision point defined by the radius R.

The energy loss $\Delta E_0'$ is thus $4\{V(R') - V(D)\}$. Since $V(R) = E_0/2$ the fractional energy loss per collision, ϵ, is given by

$$\epsilon = \frac{\Delta E_0'}{E_0} = 2\ \frac{V(R') - V(D)}{V(R)} \qquad 6.60.1$$

For the Born-Mayer potential used earlier,

$$\epsilon = 2\ \frac{\exp(-R'/a) - \exp(-D/a)}{\exp(-R/a)} \qquad 6.60.2$$

and in the limiting case for focuson collisions $\alpha = 2$ one obtains $R' = D(1 - 1/4)^{1/2} \approx D(1 - 1/8)$ and finally

$$\epsilon \approx 1.1 \times 10^{-2} \qquad 6.60.3$$

The number of collisions n_ϵ involved in the sequence, in which the energy propagated degrades eventually to zero, is therefore given by $n_\epsilon = 1/\epsilon$ which is of the order of 100 for the chosen interatomic potential. The focuson range is therefore about 100 atom spacings, but is critically dependent upon the actual interatomic potential chosen.

If $\alpha = 2 + \eta$ with small η then R does not change in the first approximation and with $R(\eta) = D/2 - D\eta/4$

$$\epsilon(\eta) = \epsilon(0)\exp\left(-\frac{D\eta}{4a}\right) = \epsilon(0)\exp(-3.25\ \eta) \qquad 6.61$$

The range therefore depends critically upon η also, (i.e. the starting angle) and decreases by a factor of 2 for $\eta = 0.2$. This situation obtains for crowdion collisions however ($\eta > 0$) and it is therefore clear that because of the interaction with neighbouring rows, the energy may be degraded in such a manner, after a very few collisions to enable the collisions to become focused. Thus the initial condition $\alpha < 2$ is not as rigid a condition for focusons as originally appeared.

Indeed, this raises the question as to whether the natural loss in energy in collisions (even without interaction with neighbouring rows) and the corresponding increase in hard sphere radius, can lead to a change from an initial crowdion like motion to a focuson type sequence.

Leibfried[62] has shown how this correlation may be given quantitative expression as follows:-

If in Equations 6.48.1 F is written for $\sin^2\theta_n$ and the Born-Mayer potential $V(R) = A\exp(-R/a)$ is used to determine α_n as a function of E_n. Then the relations

$$F_{n+1} = F_n\{\alpha_n(1 - F_n)^{1/2} - (1 - \alpha_n^2 F_n)^{1/2}\} \qquad 6.62.1$$

and

$$\alpha_{n+1} = \frac{\alpha_n}{1 - \frac{a}{D}\alpha_n \log_e(1 - \alpha_n^2 F_n)} \qquad 6.62.2$$

are readily deduced.

It is difficult to solve these recurrence formulae exactly, but since θ_n and thus F_n vary only slowly with n then

$$F_{n+1} = F(n+1) = F(n) + \frac{dF(n)}{dn} \qquad 6.63.1$$

and similar relation obtains for α_{n+1}.

With $\alpha = 2 + \eta$ equations 6.62 and 6.63 become a set of coupled differential equations

$$\frac{dF}{dn} = 2F(F + \eta) \qquad 6.63.2$$

and

$$\frac{d\eta}{dn} = -\frac{16a}{D} \cdot F \qquad 6.63.3$$

Equation 6.63.2 indicates that for $F + \eta > 0$, F_n and hence the angle θ_n increases with increasing n, which is just the condition for crowdion collisions derived earlier, generalised to any collision (i.e. $\sin^2\theta_n > -\eta$). For $F + \eta < 0$ however, the angles decrease with increasing n and focusons propagate. Equation 6.63.3 shows that η decreases continuously.

However, in order to examine whether an initial crowdion type collision with $F + \eta > 0$ transforms to a focuson sequence with $F + \eta < 0$ one requires the solution to Equations 6.63.2 and 6.63.3 in terms of n.

Exact solution is again difficult, but an idea of the general behaviour may be obtained by considering the quotient

$$\frac{dF}{d\eta} = -\frac{D}{8a}(F + \eta) \qquad 6.64.1$$

which has the solution

$$F(\eta) = \{F_0 + \eta_0 - \frac{8a}{D}\}\exp\{-\frac{D}{8a}(\eta - \eta_0)\} - \eta + \frac{8a}{D} \qquad 6.64.2$$

This equation shows how the angle θ_n (from $F_n = \sin^2\theta_n$) varies with η for a given set of initial values of F_0 and η_0, and one could insert this solution back into Equation 6.63.2 to determine F_n as a function of n. However one can obtain a qualitative picture of the events by plotting F as a function of η for given initial values of F_0 and η_0 as in figure 6.23 since η decreases continuously during a sequence (i.e. $\alpha = 2 + \eta$, and α decreases as the hard sphere radius increases), a sequence is represented by a movement from right to left on the diagram along a curve defined by the initial values of F_0 and η_0. Three regions are discernible on this diagram, one to the right of the line $F + \eta = 8a/D$ where if $F_0 + \eta_0 > 8a/D$. Equation 6.64.2 indicates that F (and hence the angle) increase to $+\infty$ as η decreases to $-\infty$ and hence crowdion type collisions obtain. A second region to the left of the line $F + \eta = 0$, where if $F_0 + \eta_0 < 0$, focusons propagate from the first collisions since $\sin^2\theta_0 < -\eta_0$.

The third region lies between these two lines where $0 < F + \eta < 8a/D$. Equation 6.64.7 indicates that for $F_0 + \eta_0 < 8a/D$, F_n increases to a maximum and crowdion collisions obtain, until $F + \eta$ becomes equal to zero, after which F decreases and the sequence

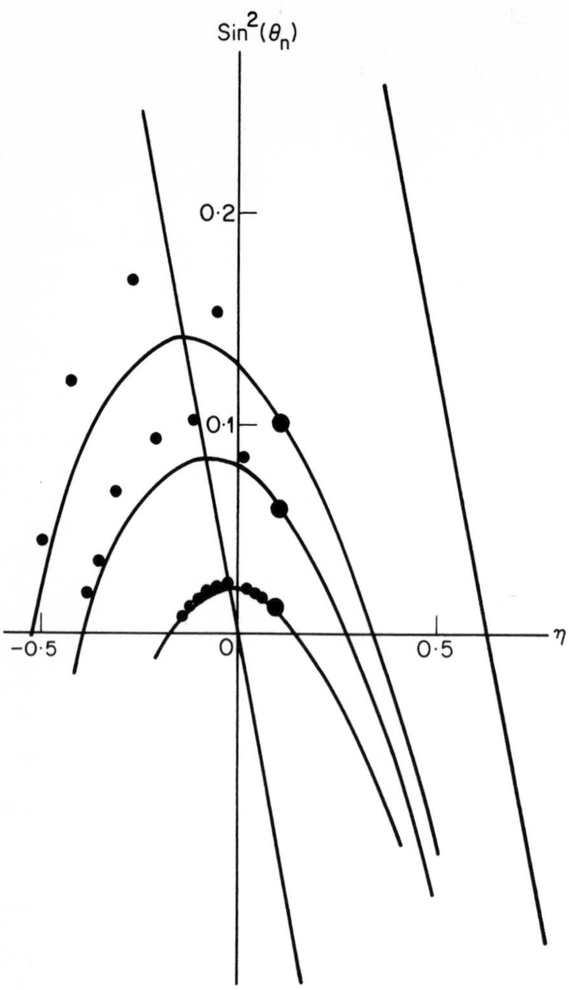

Fig. 6.23 $\sin^2\theta_n$ as a function of η, for $\eta_0 = 0.1$, $\sin^2\theta_0 = 0.1; 0.06, 0.01$ to determine ranges of operation of focusing and crowdion sequences. Full lines are approximate solutions to equn. 6.63. Points are exact solutions (viz. Ref. 6.62.)

becomes focused. This behaviour is exemplified for three initial values of $F_0 = 0.1, 0.06$ and 0.01 with $\eta_0 = 0.1$ and it is to be noted that for large F and η all curves become asymptotic to the $F + \eta = 8a/D$ line. The points on this diagram are obtained from exact numerical solution of Equation 6.63 and indicate that the approximation somewhat underestimates the region where crowdion collisions transform to focused sequences.

It thus appears that there is a region where $\alpha > 2$ when focused sequences would not normally be anticipated, but in which crowdion sequences can transform to focusons. This region is typified by the condition

$$F_0 + \eta_0 < \frac{8a}{D}$$

or

$$\sin^2\theta_0 < 8a/D + \sin^2\theta_F$$

i.e. for a given hard sphere radius, the maximum starting angle for the generation of focused sequences is increased. This can be expressed also in terms of the general condition for focusing sequences. Since, $\alpha_c < 2$ for a constant hard sphere radius and which in turn, since $\alpha_c = 2 + \eta_c$, means $\eta_c < 0$, the condition is modified with a variable hard sphere radius to give $\eta_c - 8a/D < 0$. This is essentially an energy limit for focuson propagation, and means that for the Born Mayer potential in copper, the energy limit increases by a factor of about

$$\frac{1}{\exp(-13/2)} \qquad \exp\left(\frac{-13}{2 + 8/3}\right) \simeq 5$$

i.e. the energy for crowdion-focuson collisions is about 300 eV compared to about 60-70 eV for pure focuson collisions. We should remember, however, that this energy will again depend rather critically upon the interatomic potential.

We conclude therefore, that the two types of energy degradation discussed in the above paragraphs have opposing effects. Whereas natural degradation of the energy through the collision sequence increases the probability of focuson production the interaction with neighbouring rows shortens the range.

Other effects which change the anticipated focusing effect are the use of a real potential, and lattice vibrations, and for other than the most closely packed rows, assistance rather than degradation of focusons by surrounding rows. These effects are of relatively minor importance as regards radiation damage, but are of some value in subsequent discussion, e.g. in sputtering studies. The reader interested, therefore, at this stage, only in damage events may conveniently disregard the next four sections, in which we discuss the more sophisticated treatment of focused sequences. In section 6.3.5 we again take up the question of damage production using the results already derived.

6.3.4.2 Focusing collisions with a real interatomic potential

If we assume that the potential between two colliding atoms at a separation r is given by $\Phi(r)$ then since this potential decreases rapidly with separation, the potential $\Phi(D)$ at the initial atom separation may be ignored in comparison with the potential $\Phi(R_s)$ at the distance of closest approach during the collision. We may then describe the collision between the primary displaced atom with initial velocity v_0 and energy E_0 as in Chapter 2 and an impact parameter p, and evaluate the time dependence of $x_0(t)$ and $y_0(t)$, the co-ordinates of the primary atom[99]. The origin 0 is taken as the initial rest position of the struck atom (1) and interaction with neighbouring rows is, for the present, neglected. The trajectories of primary and struck atoms are shown in figure 6.24a and it is convenient to express the problem in terms of centre of gravity co-ordinates R and relative co-ordinates r.

For equal masses m of the collision partners,

$$R = \tfrac{1}{2}(r_0 + r_1);\ r_0 = R + r/2$$

$$r = r_0 - r_1;\ r_1 = R - r/2 \qquad 6.65$$

where R, r_0 and r_1 are defined in figure 6.24.

The equations of motion are

$$M\ddot{R} = 0 \qquad 6.66.1$$

and

$$\mu\ddot{r} = -\,\partial\Phi/\partial r \qquad 6.66.2$$

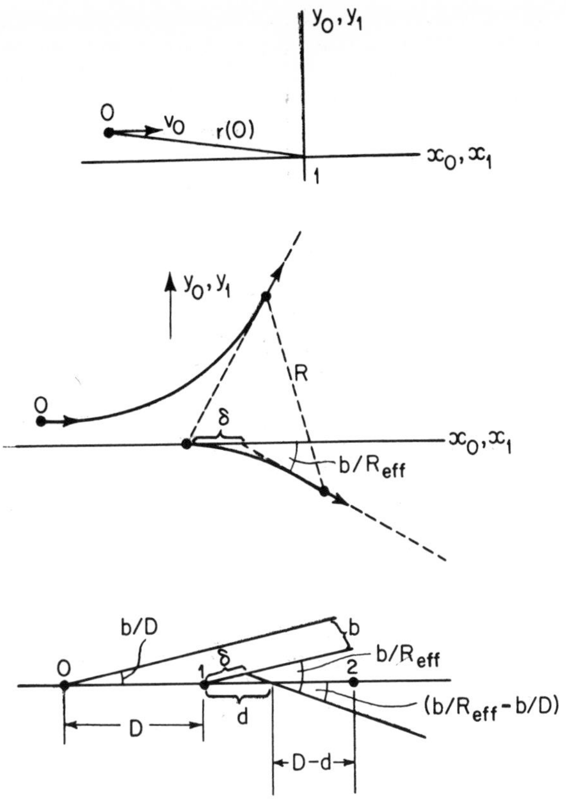

Fig. 6.24 Illustrating the displacements of atoms in a ⟨110⟩ Cu row for determination of the focusing parameter (viz. Ref. 6.99)

where M = 2m and

$$\mu = \frac{m^2}{M} = m/2 \qquad 6.66.3$$

The solution of Equation 6.66.1 is

$$R(t) = R(0) + \dot{R}(0)\,.\,t \qquad 6.67$$

where R (0) and $\dot{R}$ (0) are the values appropriate to t = 0. It is most convenient to resolve the relative cȯ-ordinates in terms of the polar co-ordinates (r, ϕ), i.e. $x = r\cos\phi$, $y = r\sin\phi$.

The equations of conservation of energy and angular momentum, then appear as in Chapter 2

$$\mu/2\,(\dot{r}^2 + r^2\dot{\phi}^2) + \Phi(r) = E_{rel} \qquad 6.68.1$$

$$\mu r^2\dot{\phi} = M_{rel} = \mu v_0 p. \qquad 6.68.2$$

where M_{rel} is the angular momentum in relative co-ordinates. Since $\Phi(r = o) = \Phi(D) \simeq o$ and if the initial starting angle is small (focuson sequences) then $\dot{\phi}(o) = 0$.

Then E_{rel}

$$= \frac{\mu v_0^2}{2} + \Phi(D) \simeq \frac{\mu v_0^2}{2} = \frac{E_0}{2} = \Phi(R) \qquad 6.69$$

Equations 6.68.1 and 6.68.2 can now be solved to

$$\dot{r}(t) = \pm v_0\left\{\frac{E_{Rel}-\Phi(r)}{E_{rel}} - \frac{p^2}{r^2}\right\}^{1/2} \simeq \pm v_0\left\{1 - \frac{\Phi(r)}{\Phi(R)} - \frac{p^2}{r^2}\right\}^{1/2}$$

6.70.1

and

$$\frac{d\phi}{dr} \simeq \frac{\dot{\phi}}{\dot{r}} = \pm \frac{p.}{r^2\left\{1 - \frac{\Phi(r)}{\Phi(R)} - \frac{p^2}{r^2}\right\}^{1/2}} \qquad 6.70.2$$

This latter equation may be integrated in two regions to give

$$\phi(r) = \phi(o) - \left\{\int_{R_s}^{r(o)} + \int_{R_s}^{r}\right\} \frac{p\,dr}{r^2\left\{\frac{E_{rel} - \Phi(r)}{\mu/2\,v_0^2} - \frac{p^2}{r^2}\right\}^{1/2}}$$

6.70.3

where R_s is the value of r(t) at which this quantity is a maximum, i.e. $\dot{r} = 0$. Since we are concerned with small angles and impact parameters, p, the integral may be expanded including only terms linear in p, to;

$$\phi(r) \cong \phi(o) - 2p\int_{R}^{r(o)} \frac{dr}{r^2\left\{1 - \frac{\Phi(r)}{\Phi(R)}\right\}^{1/2}} + p\left(\frac{1}{r} - \frac{1}{r(o)}\right)$$

6.71.1

or

$$\phi(r) \cong \pi - \frac{2p}{R_{eff}} + p/r \qquad 6.71.2$$

These operations involve splitting off an integral r(o) to r in the integrand of which the root is approximately equal to 1, and putting $\phi(o) = \pi - \frac{p}{r(o)}$ which is immediately seen to be correct from figure 6.24. R_{eff} is thus defined as

$$\frac{1}{R_{eff}} = \int_{R}^{(r_o)} \frac{dr}{r^2\left(1 - \frac{\Phi(r)}{\Phi(R)}\right)^{1/2}} \simeq \int_{R}^{\infty} \frac{dr}{r^2\left(1 - \frac{\Phi(r)}{\Phi(R)}\right)^{1/2}}$$

6.71.3

where R_s, the distance of closest approach is written, as R. In the hard sphere approximation $\Phi(r) = O$ everywhere except at r = R, and thus, $R_{eff} = R$ in this order of approximation.

It is clear, however, that for a real potential $\Phi(r)$, R_{eff} is less than the hard sphere radius R and thus the focusing parameter λ is reduced to

$$\lambda_{eff} = \frac{D}{R_{eff}} - 1 \qquad 6.72.1$$

Equation 6.71.3 may be evaluated, in principle for any potential although with some mathematical complexity. For the Born-Mayer potential $\Phi(r) = A\exp(-r/a)$, Lehmann and Leibfried[99] show that

$$\lambda_{eff} \cong \lambda_{hard\ sphere} + \frac{D}{R}\,1.39\,\frac{a}{R} - 1.36\,a^2/R^2$$

6.72.2

Again this is an energy restriction and λ_{eff} is therefore plotted as a function of E in Figure 6.21 and compared with the hard sphere approximation and the exact computer results of Gibson et al[23]. It is apparent that the order of approximation improves agreement with calculations, but now tends to underestimate the limiting focusing energy ($\lambda_{eff} = 1$ giving $E_F \simeq 25$ eV) and overestimate λ.

The reason for these discrepancies is readily found by the following argument. During a collision under a real potential, the struck particle begins to move away from the collision point before the minimum distance of approach is reached. This means that the particle (1) commences its interaction with (2) at an initial separation less than D, i.e. D–d.

Thus the focusing parameter is really

$$\lambda = \frac{D-d}{R_{eff}} - 1 \qquad 6.72.3$$

which should be applied after all except the first collision and clearly reduces λ below λ_{eff}.

The distance d is calculated as follows. Equation 6.70.2 is integrated to give

$$\int_{R_s}^{r(o)} + \int_{R_s}^{r} \frac{dr}{\left\{\frac{E_{rel} - \Phi(r)}{\mu/2\, v_0^2} - \frac{p^2}{r^2}\right\}^{1/2}} = v_0 t \qquad 6.73.1$$

or by asymptotic expansion, with neglect of terms of higher order than linear in p

$$r \simeq r(o) - 2\int_{R}^{r(o)} \frac{dr}{\left\{1 - \frac{\Phi(r)}{\Phi(R)}\right\}^{1/2}} + v_0 t \qquad 6.73.2$$

Thus

$$x = r\cos\phi \text{ and } y = r\sin\phi \simeq -p + \frac{2pr}{R_{eff}} \qquad 6.74.1$$

with the approximations $\cos\phi \to 1$, $\sin\phi \to \phi$

Use of equations 6.73.2 and 6.74.1 then leads to:-

$$x_0(t) \simeq \tfrac{1}{2}\left[-r(o) + v_0 t - r\right];$$

$$x_1(t) \simeq \left[-r(o) + v_0 t + r\right] \qquad 6.74.2$$

$$y_0(t) \simeq pr/R_{eff};\; y_1(t) \simeq p\left[1 - r/R_{eff}\right] \qquad 6.74.3$$

when the suffixes 0 and 1 refer to the atoms 0 and 1 respectively. These identifies then allow specification of the final rest position of the atom 0 after the collision, i.e. at $t = \infty$ thus

$$x_0(\infty) = r(o) - \int_{R}^{r(o)} \frac{dr}{\left(1 - \frac{\Phi(r)}{\Phi(R)}\right)^{1/2}} \simeq -$$

$$R + \int_{R}^{\infty}\left\{\frac{1}{\left[1 - \frac{\Phi(r)}{\Phi(R)}\right]^{1/2}} - 1\right\} dr \qquad 6.75.1$$

i.e.

$$x_0(\infty) = -R + \Delta \qquad 6.75.2$$

Which indicates that the final rest position of the atom 0 is shifted by a distance Δ from the corresponding position in the hard sphere approximation (-R).

Further, equation 6.74 gives the asymptotic direction along which atom (1) moves after collision, i.e. p/R_{eff} with the x_0 direction. However, this asymptote meets the x_0 direction at a distance δ from the starting point of this atom. Figure 6.24 thus indicates that this distance δ is given by

$$\delta = x_0(\infty) + R_{eff} = -R + \Delta + R_{eff} \qquad 6.76$$

This asymptotic direction then crosses the row axis direction at a distance d from the rest position of atom (1), given by

$$d = \delta . \frac{p/R_{eff}}{p/R_{eff} - p/D} = \frac{\delta}{1 - R_{eff}/D} = \frac{-R + \Delta + R_{eff}}{1 - R_{eff}/D} \qquad 6.77$$

This leads to further definition to the focusing parameter, λ the value of which may be calculated, again, for the Born-Mayer potential. It then turns out that

$$\lambda \cong \lambda_{eff} - \frac{a^2}{R^2} \cdot \frac{3.29}{1 - R/D} \qquad 6.78$$

This relation is plotted as a function of primary atom energy in Figure 6.21 and it is immediately apparent that agreement with computed values is still further improved.

Because the initial atom finally comes to rest at a position displaced by Δ from the equilibrium position, there is the possibility that mass transport may also occur in this region. The condition that the atom (0) should eventually come to rest in the atom (1) position, and thus that a defect vacancy/interstitial pair should be formed, is that the final resting position of (0) should be to the right of half the lattice spacing, i.e. beyond the saddle point of the potential due to atoms in surrounding chains. This condition clearly requires that

$$R(E_2) - \Delta = D/2 \qquad 6.79$$

where E_2 is the energy of the primary which leads to this condition. Use of the Born-Mayer potential and the results of Equation 6.75 readily leads to a value of $E_2 \simeq 17$ eV, i.e. mass transport may occur, even in essentially focusing sequences, since $E_F \simeq 35$ eV. This result also concurs with the computer calculations of Gibson et al[33] as we shall demonstrate later.

It therefore appears that use of a real interatomic potential leads to a reduced energy for focuson propagation, and we should note that Duesing and Leibfried[101], Frère[102] and Baroody[103] have reached similar conclusions using rather different calculation methods. Baroody[103], in fact, investigated the nature of the focusing sequences for a general interatomic potential of the form $\Phi(r) = \frac{B}{r^n}\exp(-r/a)$. The results confirm those obtained here and show further that the focusing parameter is essentially independent of n for $n \geq 1$. This further illustrates that for any interatomic potential the hard sphere assumption is a fairly good approximation.

We must now investigate more closely how the neighbouring rows interaction may influence the focuson propagation. As we have already seen, the influence of these neighbouring rows is relatively small, for the closed packed chains, in the hard sphere approximation, and one may anticipate a similar situation when a real potential is used. We therefore concentrate our attention upon the less closely packed chains, along which focuson propagation is less efficient and investigate the influence of the neighbouring rows on those sequences.

6.3.4.3.1. *Assisted focusing sequences*

We shall confine our attention to a study of focusing events in f.c.c. crystals, since although analogous effects are expected, and indeed are observed, in other structures, most attention has been paid to analytical investigation of the former, particularly to copper in which the assumed value of the interatomic potential has some factual basis. In this crystal the most densely packed rows are the ⟨110⟩ whilst the ⟨100⟩ and ⟨111⟩ rows are less densely packed (e.g. $D_{100} = 2D_{110}$) and are spaced more closely to neighbouring rows. Consequently, although normal focusing in ⟨100⟩ and ⟨111⟩ rows is less likely, interaction with neighbouring rows may increase possibility of these events. This may be appreciated by referring to the situation in a ⟨100⟩ row as depicted in Figure 6.25a where each

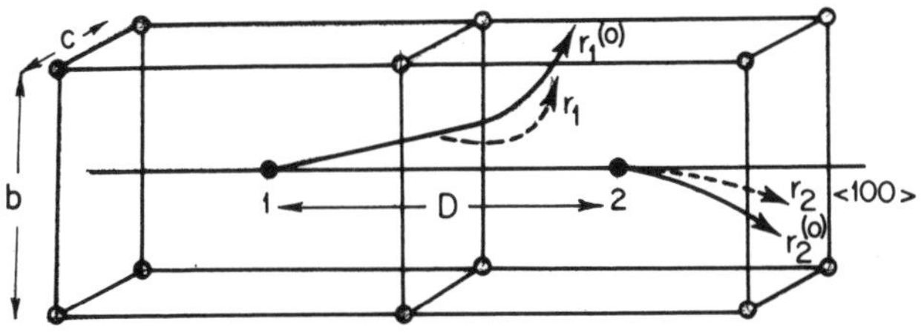

Fig. 6.25a Assisted focusing in the ⟨100⟩ direction in Cu $r_1^{(0)}$, $r_2^{(0)}$ show the paths of atoms in the absence of neighbouring row interaction r_1, r_2 show the paths of atoms influenced by these interaction forces. (viz. Ref. 6.104)

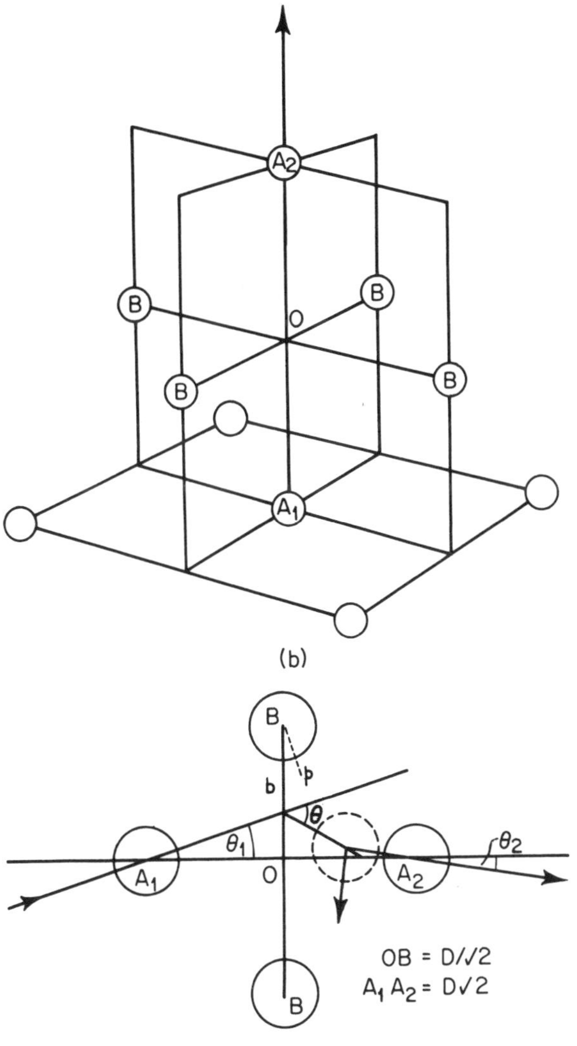

Fig. 6.25 Assisted focusing in the Au ⟨100⟩ direction (viz. Ref. 6.105)

⟨100⟩ row is surrounded by four equally spaced neighbouring rows. In the absence of these surrounding rows, if an atom was started at an angle θ_0 to the row axis, it would continue along this direction, in the hard sphere approximation, until collision with the next atom in the row. However, with the presence of surrounding rows, it is seen that a displaced atom must pass through a lens of four atoms which will tend to drive this atom back towards the axis, i.e. focus this atom, and hence reduce the collision angle. This is equivalent to increasing the hard sphere radius and assisting the propagation of a focused sequence.

In order to express this analytically[104] we must assess the decrease in angle due to the first influence of the total potential due to the neighbouring rows. In a first approximation it may be assumed that the atoms in these rows are not displaced during interaction with the primary atom, i.e. the lattice potential is considered to be due to a set of static atoms. Thus the potential acts as a perturbation on the path of the primary. If this potential is represented by $h(r_1, r_2)$ where r_1 and r_2 are the displacement positions of atoms 1 and 2, then, since the surrounding rows are considered to be rigid,

$$h(r_1, r_2) = h(r_1) + h(r_2) \qquad 6.80$$

The Lagrange function, is then given, to a first approximation, by

$$L = \frac{m\dot{r}_1^2}{2} + \frac{m\dot{r}^2}{2} + \Phi(r_1 - r_2) - h(r_1) - h(r_2) \quad 6.81$$

where $\Phi(r_1 - r_2)$ is the interatomic potential between the atoms 1, and 2 and the function $h(r_2)$, is zero before the collision since the corresponding atom (2) is assumed to remain stationary until the collision.

The rest position of atom (1) is chosen as the origin of co-ordinates; the x axis along the lattice row and the y and z axes mutually perpendicular to this. If we consider only symmetrical rows (such as the ⟨100⟩, ⟨110⟩, and ⟨111⟩) and only small angular displacements with respect to the axis, then the potential $h(r_1)$ may be expanded in y and z up to terms of second order, i.e.

$$h(r_1) = h_0(x_1) + 1/2\,(h_{yy}\, y_1^2 + h_{zz} z_1^2) \quad 6.82.1$$

Because of the symmetry of the neighbouring rows, linear terms in y and z are zero and the y and z axes are chosen so that the mixed y, z, terms vanish.

In the ⟨100⟩ and ⟨111⟩ directions, the potential $h(r_1)$ is cylindrically symmetrical, which means that the motion of the displaced atoms takes place in the plane defined by their initial directions of motion. For the ⟨110⟩ rows however, the corresponding y and z axes are ⟨1$\bar{1}$0⟩ and ⟨001⟩ in which the lattice spacings are unequal, thus the effective lenses through which the displaced atoms move are anastigmatic with different focusing effects in the Oxy and Oxz planes. The motion of a displaced atom initially directed at an angle to these planes thus becomes helical. We consider, however, in all cases, motion confined to one plane so that

$$h(r_1) = h_0(x_1) + 1/2\, h_1(x_1)\, y_1^2 \qquad 6.82.2$$

Where $h_0(x_1)$ is the potential on the axis at x_1, and $h_1(x_1)$ is the second derivative of the y component of the potential at (x_1).

An identity of analysis with that of channelling events treated in Chapter 5 may be discerned here. It was shown there that, since the lattice is periodic in D, the potential and its derivatives are also periodic in D (the lattice spacing). Thus

$$h(x, y, z) = \sum_{n=-\infty}^{\infty} \psi(x + nD, y, z) \quad 6.83.1$$

where

$$\psi(x, y, z) = \sum_{l, m = \pm 1} \Phi \left(x, y + \frac{lb}{2}, z + \frac{mc}{2}\right) =$$

$$4\,\Phi \left(x, y + \frac{b}{2}, z + \frac{c}{2}\right) \quad 6.83.2$$

= potential due to one ring of four atoms. As in Chapter 5 it is convenient to expand Equation 6.83.1 in a Fourier series, and upon insertion of the appropriate constants, $b = c = D_{110}$, $D = \sqrt{2}\,D_{110}$ for the ⟨100⟩ rows, and $c = \sqrt{2}b = \sqrt{2}D_{110}$ for the ⟨110⟩ rows and assumption of the Born Mayer potential $\Phi(r) = 22,500 \exp\left(\frac{-13r}{D_{110}}\right)$ one deduces for ⟨110⟩ rows

$$h_0(x) = 0.3519 - 0.3627 \cos\frac{2\pi x}{D_{110}} + 0.0108 \cos\frac{4\pi x}{D_{110}} + \ldots\ldots \quad 6.84.1$$

$$a^2 h_1(x) = 0.3250 - 0.1872 \cos\frac{2\pi x}{D_{110}} - 0.0100 \cos\frac{4\pi x}{D_{110}} + \ldots\ldots \quad 6.84.2$$

for ⟨100⟩ rows

$$h_0(x) = 3.486 - 4.295 \cos\frac{2\pi x}{D_{110}} + 0.894 \cos\frac{4\pi x}{D_{110}} + \ldots\ldots \quad 6.84.3$$

$$a^2 h_1(x) = 1.767 - 2.162 \cos\frac{2\pi x}{D_{110}} + 0.566 \cos\frac{4\pi x}{D_{110}} + \ldots\ldots \quad 6.84.4$$

where $h_0(x = 0) = 0$.

With the notation of the previous section, for the centre of gravity co-ordinates (R, X, and Y) and relative co-ordinates (r, x and y), the Lagrange function becomes

$$L = m\dot{R}^2 + \frac{m\dot{r}^2}{4} + \frac{mr^2\dot{\theta}^2}{4} - \Phi(r) - h(R, r, \theta) \quad 6.85.1$$

whilst, for small angles, the energy, momentum and force equations, are

$$2m\ddot{R} = -\frac{\partial h}{\partial R} \quad 6.85.2$$

$$\frac{d}{dt}\left(\frac{m}{2} r^2\dot{\theta}\right) = -\frac{\partial h}{\partial \sigma} \quad 6.85.3$$

and

$$\frac{m\ddot{r}}{2} = -\Phi'(r) - \frac{\partial h}{\partial r} \quad 6.85.3$$

The unperturbed motion is then obtained, for h = 0, as in the previous section, i.e.

$$R^0(t) = R(0) + \dot{R}(0), t \quad 6.86.1$$

$$\theta_0(r) = \theta_0(R) \mp \frac{M_{Rel}}{\sqrt{m}} \int_R^r \frac{d\rho}{\rho^2 \sqrt{\frac{E_0}{2} - \Phi(\rho)}} \quad 6.86.2$$

$$t = \pm\sqrt{\frac{m}{2}} \int_R^{r_0(t)} \frac{d\rho}{\sqrt{\frac{E_0}{2} - \Phi(\rho)}} \quad 6.86.3$$

$$r_0(t) = R + 2a \log_e \cosh\frac{v_0 t}{2a} \quad 6.86.4$$

where the suffix (o) indicates that the motion is unperturbed and R is the effective hard sphere radius. We are, of course, interested in the perturbation introduced by the potential h(r) and we may write, as a first approximation for the energy and angular momentum equations

$$2m\ddot{R}^{(1)} = -\frac{\partial h}{\partial R}^{(0)} \quad 6.85.4$$

$$\left\{\frac{d}{dt}\, m r^{(0)} r^{(1)} \theta^{(0)} + m\,\frac{(r^{(0)})^2}{2}\,\dot{\theta}^{(1)}\right\} = -\frac{\partial h^{(0)}}{\partial \sigma} \quad 6.85.5$$

Thus $\frac{\partial h}{\partial R}^{(0)}$ and $\frac{\partial h}{\partial \theta}^{(0)}$ indicates that R, r and v are inserted into $\frac{\partial h}{\partial R}$ to a zero order approximation and are thus purely time functions and $r^{(1)}$, $\theta^{(1)}$ etc., are the perturbations introduced by the row potentials.

It is a rather lengthy process to solve the above equations, for the perturbed motion, and the results derived by Leibfried and Dederichs[104] will be quoted without proof. These are

$$X^{(1)}(t) = -\frac{1}{2m} \int_{t_0}^{t} d\tau \int_{t_0}^{\tau} \left(\frac{\partial h}{\partial x_1}\right)^{(0)} d\tau^1 \quad 6.87.1$$

$$Y^{(1)}(t) = -\frac{1}{2m} \int_{t_0}^{t} d\tau \int_{t_0}^{\tau} \left(\frac{\partial h}{\partial y_1}\right)^{(0)} d\tau^1 \quad 6.87.2$$

$$\theta^{(1)}(t) = \int_{t_0}^{t} \left\{\frac{2M_{Rel}^{(1)}}{mr^{(0)\,2}} - 4\,\frac{M_{Rel}\, r^{(1)}}{mr^{(0)\,3}}\right\} d\tau \quad 6.87.3$$

$$M_{Rel}^{(1)}(t) = \int_{t_0}^{t} \left\{- \tfrac{1}{2}\left(\frac{\partial h}{\partial x_1}\right)^{(0)} r^{(0)} (\theta^{(0)} - \pi) + \tfrac{1}{2}\left(\frac{\partial h}{\partial y_1}\right)^{(0)} r^{(0)}\right\} d\tau \quad 6.87.4$$

Which indicates that the perturbations in the x and y directions are due to the force components $\left(\frac{\partial h}{\partial x_1}\right)^{(0)}$ and $\left(\frac{\partial h}{\partial y_1}\right)^{(0)}$ in these directions. The focusing parameter, defined by the ratio of asymptotic values ($t \to \infty$) of θ_1 and θ_2 of the primary displaced and struck atoms, may also be deduced with $\theta_2 = \theta_2^{(0)} + \theta_2^{(1)}$ in which $\theta_2^{(1)}$ is the perturbation introduced by the potential h(r).

For the Born-Mayer potential it is deduced finally that

$$\theta_2{}^{(1)} = \frac{1}{2E_0}\frac{p}{D}\frac{1}{R}\left\{\left(1 + 2\log_e\frac{2a}{R} - 1.36\frac{a^2}{R^2}\right)\int_0^{D-R} h_1(x).\,x(D-R-x)dx + a\left(2\log_e 2 + 0.28\frac{a}{R}\right)\int_0^{D-R} h_1(x)x\,dx - \left(1 + 2\log_e\frac{2a}{R}\right)\int_0^{D-R} h_0(x)dx + 2.18a^2h_1(D-R).(D-R) + 2a(D/R - \log_e 2)h_0(D-R)\right\} \qquad 6.88$$

which gives that part of the focusing parameter $\lambda^{(1)}$ due to the perturbation, since $\theta_1 = p/D$. Thus the focusing parameter

$$\lambda = \lambda^{(0)} + \lambda^{(1)}$$

$$\text{where } (\lambda)^0 = \frac{D}{R}\left\{1 + 2\log_e\frac{2a}{R} - \frac{a^2}{R^2}.1.36\right\} - 1 \qquad 6.89$$

is the focussing parameter for an isolated row

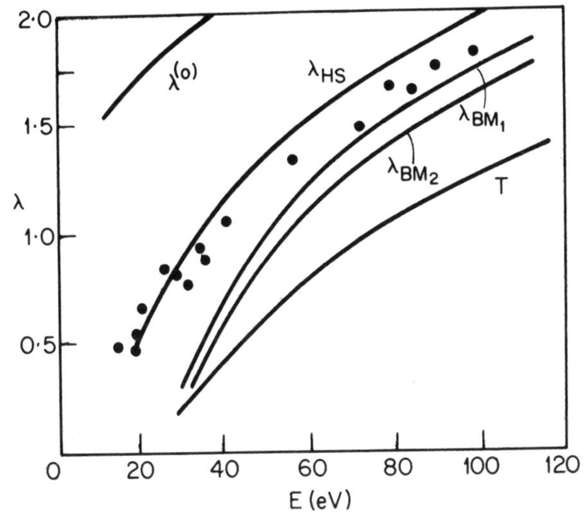

Fig. 6.26 The focusing parameter λ in the Cu ⟨100⟩ direction as a function of the energy (viz. Ref. 6.104) for assisted focusing. ● points are computer calculations by Gibson et al. (Ref. 6.23) $\lambda^{(0)}$ is calculated for an isolated row (no neighbouring row interaction). λ_{BM} is calculated from Equn. 6.89 (initial collisions). λ_{BM} is calculated from Equn. 6.89 extended to further collisions. λ_{HS} is calculated using a hard sphere approx. T is calculated according to the Impulse approx. (viz. Ref. 6.105)

λ is plotted as a function of the primary energy E_0, for the ⟨100⟩ rows in Figure 6.26 and compared with Gibson et al's[23] machine results, with an evaluation of $\lambda^{(1)}$ using a hard sphere approximation and with an impulse approximation for $\lambda^{(1)}$ derived by Nelson and Thompson[105] which we shall discuss shortly. Clearly the agreement between the asymptotic calculation of λ and the computed values are rather good, particularly in the energy region important for focusing. It also turns out that the effect of neighbouring rows in a ⟨110⟩ sequence is negligible, thus justifying our earlier assumptions, and it is also evident from Figures 6.26 and 6.21 that λ is almost identical for both the ⟨110⟩ and ⟨100⟩ rows at a given energy.

6.3.4.3.2. *Assisted focused sequences (Impulse approximation)*

Much of the difficulty in obtaining exact results for the displaced atom deviation caused by neighbouring row interaction arises because the interatomic force must be integrated over the whole trajectory. Nelson and Thompson[105] showed how an approximate, and more straightforward, assessment of the influence of the neighbouring rows could be made using an impulse approximation, and using the perturbation due to one lens of neighbouring atoms at a time.

Consider, for example the situation depicted in Figure 6.25b where the displaced atom A_1 starting in a ⟨100⟩ row in gold, in the {100} plane, must pass through the lens of four atoms B before striking the next atom A_2. For an atom started exactly along the row axis with a velocity v_0 the force of interaction between B and (A_1) directed along the radius vector is $-\frac{\partial V(r)}{\partial r}$ where V(r) is the interatomic potential. In the impulse approximation, the momentum loss by the displaced atom in passing one B atom is

$$P = \int_{-\infty}^{+\infty} -\frac{\partial V}{\partial r}\frac{p}{r}\,dt \qquad 6.90.1$$

with p as defined in Figure 6.25.c i.e. momentum loss is confined to the Oy direction only since the momentum losses on either side of Oy in the Ox direction are equal and opposite.

For a Born-Mayer potential $V(r) = A\exp(-r/a)$ the momentum loss P is given by

$$P = \frac{2Ab}{av_0}\int^{\infty}(b^2 + x^2)^{-1/2}\exp\left(-\frac{1}{a}\sqrt{b^2 + x^2}\right)dx \qquad 6.90.2$$

The integral can be evaluated numerically, but it is more convenient to suppose that the force which exists at $x = \pm c$, i.e. F_c, were to be constant within these limits and zero elsewhere, then the momentum transfer to B, would be

$$P = \frac{2A}{a}\exp\left\{-\frac{1}{a}\sqrt{b^2 + c^2}\right\}\frac{b}{\sqrt{b^2 + c^2}}.\frac{2c}{v_0} \qquad 6.90.3$$

This value of P may be compared with numerical evaluation of Equation 6.90.2 and the corresponding values of c deduced. Nelson and Thompson[105] have deduced c for $\frac{D}{\sqrt{3}} \leqslant b \leqslant \frac{D}{\sqrt{2}}$ and $\frac{D}{20} < a < D/10$ and find that c is close to D/4 for all values, thus

$$P = \frac{AD}{av_0}\exp\left[-\frac{D}{4a}\sqrt{1 + \frac{16b^2}{D^2}}\right].\frac{4b}{D\sqrt{1 + \frac{16b^2}{D^2}}} \qquad 6.90.4$$

where D is the atom spacing in the ⟨110⟩ row. For $b^2 \gg D^2/16$

$$P \simeq \frac{AD}{av_0}\exp\left[-\frac{D}{4a}\sqrt{1 + \frac{16b^2}{D^2}}\right] \qquad 6.90.5$$

Further analysis, accounting for the change in the velocity v_0 of the displaced atom and the relaxation of atom B, shows that P may be in error by as much as 30%, for energies in the focusing range. However, in view of the approximations made, this is not too serious an error to prevent further analysis.

Consider now the situation where the primary atom (A_1) starts, again in the (100) plane, but at a small angle θ_1 to the row axis. Only the two B atoms shown in Figure 6.25c influence the momentum change, and if the momentum losses to the opposing atoms are P_1, P_2 respectively the angular change in the direction of motion of atom (A_1) is given by

$$\theta = \frac{P_1 - P_2}{mv_0} \qquad 6.91.1$$

For small angles, the impact parameters on atoms, B_1 and B_2 are

$$b_1 = D/\sqrt{2}\ (1 - \theta_1) \qquad 6.92.1$$

$$b_2 = D/\sqrt{2}\ (1 + \theta_1) \qquad 6.92.2$$

and since $b = D/\sqrt{2}$

$$\theta = \theta_1 \frac{2}{3} \frac{AD^2}{a^2} \exp\left(-\frac{3D}{4a}\right). E \qquad 6.91.2$$

This indicates that the ring of atoms acts, formally, as an optical lens, of equivalent focal length f_{100}, given by

$$f_{100} = \frac{D}{\sqrt{2}} \cdot \frac{\theta_1}{\theta} = \frac{3}{2\sqrt{2}} \frac{a^2}{D} \exp\left(\frac{3D}{4a}\right). E \qquad 6.93$$

If the primary displaced atom collides with atom (A_2) and this moves away from the axis at an angle θ_2 then the focusing condition is that $\theta_1 > \theta_2$. Reference to Figure 6.25c shows that this requires the trajectory of (A_1) to cross the Ox axis to the left of the point A_2, i.e.

$$\theta > 2\theta_1 \text{ or } D\sqrt{2} > 4f_{100} \qquad 6.94$$

This latter inequality indicates that the energy E_{F100} below which focusing can occur is given by

$$E_{F100} = \frac{A}{3} \frac{D^2}{a^2} \exp(-3D/4a) \qquad 6.95$$

Further the energy loss in passing axially through the ring of four atoms is given by

$$\sigma_{F100} = \frac{4p^2}{2mE} = \frac{1}{E^2} \frac{D^2A^2}{a^2} \exp(-3D/2a) \qquad 6.96.1$$

and for focusing sequences where $E \leqslant E_{F100}$

$$\sigma_{F100} \gtrsim qa^2/D^2 \qquad 6.96.2$$

of course, the sequences can only propagate if the atom (A_1) can pass through the ring of four atoms and collide with the atom (A_2). The energy required for this is obtained by equating the initial kinetic energy in the centre of mass system to the potential energy loss in reaching the centre of the ring of B atoms. This condition, when evaluated, requires an energy

$$E_1^{100} = 5A \exp\{-D/a\sqrt{2}\} \qquad 6.97$$

We should note also, that the condition that the atom (A_1) should replace the atom (A_2) requires that the collision occurs to the right of 0, i.e. $2R \leqslant D/\sqrt{2}$ which is identical to the limit for ⟨110⟩ focused energy sequences and occurs for an energy $2A \exp -\left(\frac{D}{a\sqrt{2}}\right)$. This energy is clearly less than that required to penetrate the ring of B atoms, and thus all collision sequences, including focusons result in replacement.

As a rough estimate, one may obtain the number of replacement events due to a primary starting with the focusing energy E_{F100} from

$$n_{F100} \simeq \frac{1}{2E_{F100}} \qquad 6.98.1$$

i.e.

$$n_{F100} \simeq D^2/20a^2 \qquad 6.98.2$$

Values of E_{F100}, ϵ_{F100}, E_1^{100} and n_{F100} are enumerated in Table 6.2 for gold, with the Born-Mayer constants $A = 8 \times 10^5$ eV and $a = D/15$ deduced by Nelson and Thompson[105] and for copper with the constants $A = 22.5$ KeV and $a = D/13$. An identical treatment (with different values of b etc.) is possible for the ⟨111⟩ and ⟨110⟩ rows and the corresponding values of E_{F111} etc. are also given in Table 6.2 and it is apparent that the number of replacement events in gold is somewhat higher than in copper. We again note that the focusing energies for the ⟨100⟩ and ⟨110⟩ rows are very similar, but the energy for the ⟨111⟩ rows is considerably higher since interaction with neighbouring rows is stronger.

TABLE 6.2 (viz. Ref. 6.105)

Energy Limits and attenuation of focused collision sequences.

For Cu with $A = 2 \times 10^4$ eV, $a = D/13$; and for Au with $A = 8 \times 10^5$ eV, $a = D/15$.

crystal direction	E_F(eV) Cu	E_F(eV) Au	E_1(eV) Cu	E_1(eV) Au	ϵ_f Cu	ϵ_f Au	n_f Cu	n_f Au
⟨110⟩	60	800	1	1	0.011	0.006	90	170
⟨100⟩	65	700	10	90	0.053	0.040	9	13
⟨111⟩	490	7300	44	500	0.027	0.021	17	45

TABLE 6.3 (viz. Ref. 6.106)

Characteristic parameters for assisted focusing in tungsten.

$E_{F111} = 600$ eV	$E_{F100} = 200$ eV	$E_{F110} = 2700$ eV
$n_{F111} = 150$	$n_{F100} = 20$	$n_{F110} = 30$

We should also note that Nelson[106] has evaluated the above constants for assisted focusing in the ⟨100⟩, ⟨110⟩ and ⟨111⟩ rows in b.c.c. tungsten and molybdenum with the results shown in Table 6.3.

Finally, the important constant which describes the focusing effect is the focusing parameter $\lambda = \theta_2/\theta_1$. From Figure 6.25c it is seen that

$$2r\psi = \left(\frac{D_{100}}{2} - 2r\right)\left(2\theta_1 - \theta\right) \qquad 6.99.1$$

where R (=2r) is the hard sphere radius, and D_{100} the ⟨100⟩ axis atom spacing and $\theta_2 \cong \theta_1 + \psi$ Thus

$$\frac{\psi}{\theta_1} = \frac{\theta_2 - \theta_1}{\theta_1} = \frac{\theta_2}{\theta_1} - 1 = \lambda - 1 = \left(\frac{D_{100}}{2R} - 1\right)\left(2 - \frac{D_{100}}{2f_{100}}\right) \qquad 6.99.2$$

The value of λ deduced from this identity is plotted as curve T in Figure 6.26 where it is immediately apparent that the impulse approximation considerably underestimates λ. This is partly a result of the fact that θ is underestimated by considering the interaction over a short range only. Nevertheless, the method has the advantage of simplicity and leads to results which give, at least, the order of importance of assisted focusing in different lattice directions. We suggested earlier that neglect of the movement of the struck atoms in the neighbouring rows may lead to miscalculation of the focusing parameters by as much as 30%. Weijsenfeld[107] has recently recalculated the focusing parameter as a function of energy for ⟨100⟩ copper accounting for the momentum lost to the struck atoms but using an impulse type of approximation for the calculation. It was found that the agreement with Gibson et al's[23] machine data was considerably better than the simple theory and the calculations also revealed that for non-zero starting angles λ was less than for a head on sequence, suggesting that focusing might operate over a wider energy range than the head on criteria might allow. (c.f. with the similar result for ⟨110⟩ rows evaluated by Lehmann[100], (Equation 6.59)).

6.3.4.4. *The influence of thermal vibrations*

Because the lattice atoms vibrate about their equilibrium positions (even at 0°K) then it must be expected that these will scatter energy out of the focused sequences and thus curtail the focuson ranges. Nelson et al[108] have considered the influence of thermal vibration on the propagation of ⟨110⟩ sequences in gold, employing a Born-Mayer potential with constants $A = 8 \times 10^5$ eV, a = D/15. In this case the energy loss per collision due to the interaction with each ring of four neighbouring atoms is obtained, as for the copper case evaluated earlier, for no atomic vibration,

$$\Delta E_0 = 2E_F\left\{\exp\left(-\frac{D}{2a}\left(\frac{2c}{D} - 1\right)\right) - \exp(-D/2a)\right\} \qquad 6.100$$

where

$$c/D = \left\{3/4 + (a/D)^2\left(\log_e \frac{E_F}{E}\right)^2\right\}^{1/2}$$

and E_F, the focusing energy is 800 eV.

When the atoms vibrate perpendicularly to the focuson propagation direction, three possible sources of energy loss are apparent, i.e.

(1) The lateral component of thermal motion of the atoms will increase the angular deviation ϕ of these in the order of $\phi \cong \left(\frac{kT}{E}\right)^{1/2}$. For E ≃ 100 eV and kT = 0.1 eV, at the melting point ϕ is less than 3×10^{-2} radians.

(2) Lattice vibrations will cause the separation of neighbouring atoms to vary and thus change the energy loss at each passage through a lens. In the extreme case where two opposing atoms move away (and towards) the focuson row by the maximum distances δ, then Equation 6.100 is modified to

$$\Delta E \cong E_F(1 + \cosh \delta/a)\exp\left\{-\frac{D}{2a}\left(\frac{2c}{D} - 1\right)\right\} \qquad 6.101$$

The energy loss is increased above that of a static lattice by the factor 1 + cosh δ/a and if this is assumed to be distributed totally in the transverse direction, then the angular change ϕ, is of order 10^{-1} radians for a representative value of δ = D/10.

(3) The lateral displacement of atoms in the focused sequence will cause the collision angle to increase in the order of $\frac{\delta}{R}$ where δ is the relative lateral displacements of two consecutive atoms. Again for δ = D/10 at the melting point and in the focusing region where $R \simeq \frac{D}{2}$, ϕ is of order 0.2. This final effect is therefore the most serious although the second is of some consequence. We therefore consider the third effect only in detail. The sequence is depicted in Figure 6.27 where diagram (a) illustrates

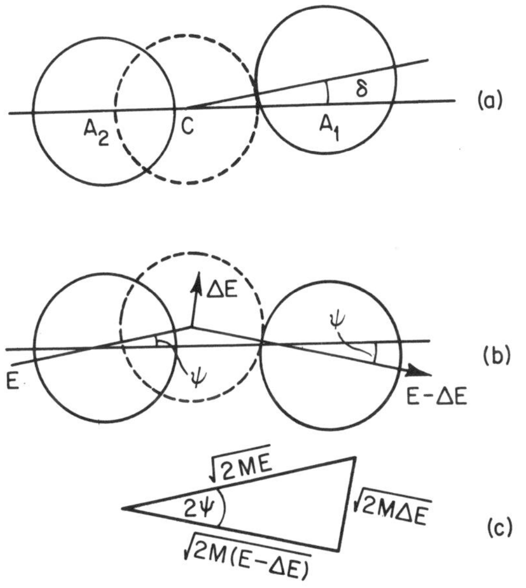

Fig. 6.27 (a) The scattering of energy from a focused sequence because of the thermal atomic vibrations. (b) The energy loss ΔE by scattering. (c) The triangle of momentum. (viz. Ref. 6.108)

the effect of additional deflection suffered by the first displaced atom because of the relative displacements δ of the primary and struck atoms, and (b) shows the energy loss suffered because of the displacement δ, and the triangle of momentum for an energy loss ΔE. If we consider motion in the Oyx plane only (x axis as the focusing row), θ_{l+1} the angles at which the lth and (l + 1)th atoms move with respect to the x axis and y_l, y_{l+1} the instantaneous displacements of these atoms relative to this axis, then it is a simple matter to relate θ_l and θ_{l+1} using the hard sphere approximation.

The angle ϕ_l through which the focused momentum is scattered at the collision is thus given by

$$\phi_l = \frac{y_l - y_{l+1}}{R} \qquad 6.102.1$$

and thus with a focusing parameter λ

$$\theta_l = \frac{1}{\lambda}\theta_{l+1} + \phi_l \qquad 6.102.2$$

If we write $\lambda = -\frac{1}{f}$ the previous equation indicates that the collision angle oscillates from side to side about the x axis during propagation of the sequence. Further, assuming that the focusing parameter remains constant as the focused energy degrades, the relation between the nth and $(n-1)^{th}$ angles is simply

$$\theta_{n-1} = (-f)\theta_n + \phi_{n-1} \qquad 6.103.1$$

and the $(n-1)^{th}$ and $(n-2)^{th}$

$$\theta_{n-2} = (-f)^2\theta_n + (-f)\theta_{n-1} + \phi_{n-2} \qquad 6.103.2$$

and finally

$$\theta_0 = (-f)^n\,\theta_n + \sum^{n-1} (-f)^l\phi_l \qquad 6.103.3$$

where θ_n is the angle at the start of the sequence and θ_0 the final angle. The first term on the right hand side of Equation 6.103.3 represents the focusing effects (c.f. Equation 6.51) and the second term, the scattering effect.

After many collisions, (n is large), and in the focusing range where $f < 1$, the final angle θ_0 may be obtained, with sufficient accuracy, by neglecting $(-f)^n\theta_n$ with the result

$$\theta_0 = \{(y_0 - y_1) - f(y_1 - y_2) + f^2(y_2 - y_3) - \ldots.\} \times \frac{1}{R} \qquad 6.104.1$$

where

$$\phi_l = \frac{y_l - y_{l+1}}{R}$$

The terms in this expression may be regrouped and the resulting expression squared to give

$$R^2\theta_0^2 = y_0^2 + (1 + f^2)\sum_1^\infty f^{2l-2}\,y_l^2 - 2(1+f)[y_0y_1 + (-f)y_0y_2 + (-f)^2y_0y_3 + \ldots\ldots] - 2(1+f)^2\left\{\sum_1^\infty f^{2l-1}\cdot y_ly_{l+1} - \sum_1^\infty f^{2l}\cdot y_ly_{l+2} + \sum_1^\infty f^{2l+1}\cdot y_ly_{l+3} + \ldots\ldots\right\} \qquad 6.104.2$$

One may average over many sequences, where the y_l's range over all possible values and evaluate the series term by term.

The average values $\overline{y_0^2}$ may then be assumed equal to y_l^2

$$\overline{y_ly_{l+n}} = \overline{y_0y_n} \text{ and } \overline{y_ly_{l+n}} = \overline{y_l^2}\cdot\beta_n \qquad 6.105$$

where β_n is the correlation coefficient between the y_l and y_{l+n} displacements. One then obtains the average value

$$\overline{\theta_0^2} = \frac{2\overline{y_l^2}}{R^2}\left\{1 + (1+f)\sum_1^\infty (-f)^n\beta_n/f\right\}(1-f)^{-1} \qquad 6.106$$

$\overline{y_l^2}$ and β_n may be derived from lattice calculations [109,110] with the results

$$\overline{y_l^2} = \frac{3\hbar^2}{Mk\Theta_0}\left[\frac{T^2}{\Theta_0}\int_0^{T/\Theta_0}\frac{x\,dx}{\exp x - 1} + \frac{1}{4}\right] \qquad 6.107.1$$

where T is the target temperature and Θ_0 the Debye temperature and

$$\beta_n = 2(1 - \cos n\eta\pi)/(n\pi\eta)^2 \text{ for } T \ll \Theta_0 \qquad 6.107.2$$

i.e. at very low temperature and

$$\beta_n = \frac{1}{2\pi\eta} \text{ for } T \gg \Theta_0 \qquad 6.107.3$$

i.e. at high temperatures where

$$\eta = \left(\frac{6\sqrt{2}}{\pi}\right)^{1/3}$$

$\overline{\theta_0^2}$ is the final angle in one plane Oxy only, and clearly one will expect an identical relation for the Oxz plane, thus the final focused angle, for atoms starting at an angle to either plane, will be given by $\overline{\psi_0^2} = 2\overline{\theta_0^2}$.

At low temperatures, one finally deduces

$$\overline{\psi_0^2} = \frac{8\overline{y_l^2}}{D^2L(1+L)}\left\{1 - \frac{2}{(1+L)}\left\{\left(0.139 - 0.047\cdot\frac{1+L}{1+L}\right)\right\}\right\} \qquad 6.108.1$$

where $L = \frac{2a}{D}\log_e E_F/E$ which indicates that even at $T = 0°K$, since $\overline{y_l^2}$ is non vanishing, there will be considerable scattering.

At higher temperatures

$$\overline{\psi_0^2} = \frac{8\overline{y_l^2}}{D^2L(1+L)}\left\{1 - \frac{1}{\eta(1-L)}\log_e\frac{2}{1+L}\right\} \qquad 6.108.2$$

Because, the lattice atoms vibrate, there will be an energy loss additional to that of the static lattice. For an angle ψ_l of the lth atom, and $\psi_{l+1} (\approx\psi_l)$ of the $l + 1^{th}$ atom, the angle between their respective directions of motion is approximately $2\psi_l$. Since energy ΔE_1 is lost perpendicular to the line of centres of the collision partners, then the triangle of momentum (figure 6.27) gives the momentum loss $2\psi(2mE)^{1/2}$ for an energy E, and thus $\Delta E = 4\psi^2E$.

Thus the average energy loss due to lattice vibration is given by

$$\Delta E_1 = 4\overline{\psi}^2_0 E$$

and so the total loss due to vibrations and due to interaction with neighbouring rows is given by

$$\Delta E = \Delta E_0 + \Delta E_1 \qquad 6.110$$

where ΔE_0 is obtained from Equation 6.100 and ΔE_1 from Equation 6.109 with $\overline{\psi}^2_0$ from Equation 6.108.2.

Consequently one may derive the total number of collisions, i.e. the range nD of a sequence starting with $\psi = 0$ i.e. an axial sequence.

Since ΔE is proportional to E, then to increase the number of collisions by dn, an extra energy $\Delta E \,.\, dn$ is required i.e. $dE = \Delta E \,.\, dn$ and

$$n(E) = \int_0^E \frac{1}{\Delta(E)}\, dE \qquad 6.111$$

Substituting the value of ΔE from Equation 6.110 this integral may be performed, with the results shown in figure 6.28 which indicates the decrease in the focuson range with increasing temperature, as a function of the primary starting energy. Clearly, increasing the temperature from 0°K to the melting temperature degrades the length of the sequence by 3 or 4, but even at 0°K, the zero point vibrations considerably diminishes the range below that expected for a static lattice (the dotted curve in fig. 6.28). In addition

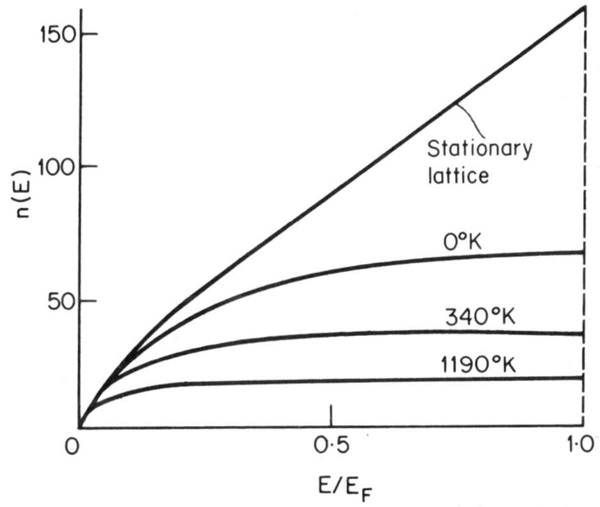

Fig. 6.28 The number of collisions n(E) made by a focused collision sequence in slowing down from an energy E to rest at various crystal temperatures. E_F is the focusing energy.

to this mechanism of focuson range degradation due to thermal vibrations in the focused sequence, Sanders and Fluit[111] have considered a further source of loss, namely energy loss to neighbouring rows, enhanced by the average closer proximity of the focused sequence atoms to these rows. These authors show that over the temperature range 315°K to 900°K for a copper lattice, the energy loss factor σ_T' is given by

$$\sigma_T' = \Sigma_0 \exp(3 \times 10^{-4}\, T) \qquad 6.112$$

where σ_0 is the energy loss factor deduced by Leibfried[98] as in Equation 6.60.1. Consequently the variation of the energy loss with the starting energy of a focused sequence turns out to possess the form shown in Figure 6.29 in which the energy loss factor

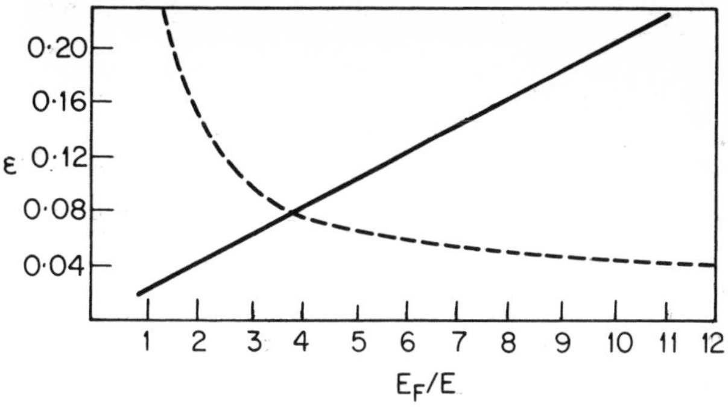

Fig. 6.29 The relative energy loss ϵ due to thermal scattering effects at 315°K as a function of the energy E. (E_F is the focusing energy).
Full curve: due to interaction with neighbouring rows
Dotted curve: due to scattering along row
} along ⟨110⟩ Cu
(Viz. Ref. 6.111)

$\sigma_T (= \Delta E)$ as deduced by Nelson and Thompson[105] is also shown for comparison at a temperature of 315°K. The starting energy variation of this energy loss factor σ_T' is similar at all temperatures and addition of σ_T and σ_T allows deduction of the focuson range as a function of sequence starting energy at various temperatures, as shown in Figure 6.30. Upon averaging over the probability of a focussed sequence starting with all energies E, (W(E)) it is then found that the average focuson range in the ⟨110⟩ direction in copper is reduced to only 5 atom spacings at 315°K and 2 atom spacings at 900°K. Quite clearly these reduced ranges will have considerable bearing upon the temperature variation of radiation damage and sputtering phenomena. We may note finally that, in addition to thermal defocussing effects, Kurkin and Odintsov[112] have shown that vacancies present in focuson rows also tend to reduce the range, because of the lack of focusing as the sequence crosses their sites. For example a density of 1 vacancy per ten row atoms in the ⟨100⟩ direction in gold reduces the range by about 50% but the actual values are a function of temperature (the atomic vibration) as well as the vacancy density. Since ion bombardment inevitably introduces vacancies into a target this effect may be of importance and is worthy of further consideration.

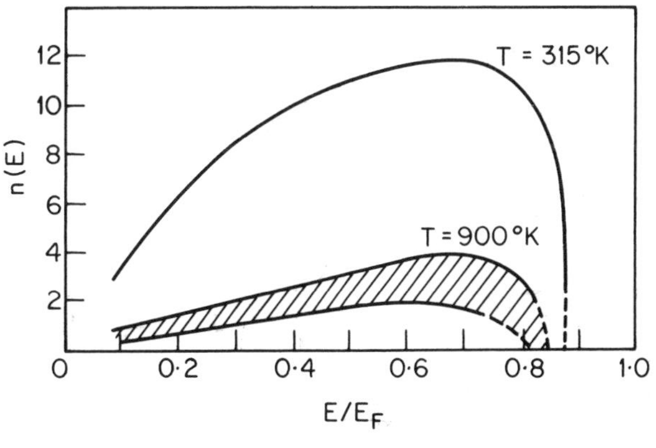

Fig. 6.30 The number of collisions n(E) made by a focused collision sequence in slowing down from an energy E to rest, taking into account energy lost by thermal scattering in the propagation low and neighbouring row interaction. Curves at 315°K and, in the shaded region bounded by the curves, at 900°K. (viz. Ref. 6.111)

We may therefore summarize the results of these calculations as follows. A displaced atom in a close packed row in crystals (e.g. ⟨110⟩ in Cu and Au) transfers energy to successive atoms in such a way that the energy is eventually transmitted with only a small energy loss along the row axis, provided that the initial energy of the sequence is of the order of 50 eV. No replacement events occur in this energy region, but for higher energies, the collision sequence becomes defocused and replacement events occur. In the energy region between 50 eV and 300 eV initially defocused, crowdion, sequences may subsequently become focused. For the less closely packed rows (⟨100⟩) focused sequences can also propagate because of interaction with neighbouring atomic chains and the focusing energy may be increased up to several hundred eV. Replacement events invariably occur in these rows however.

The range of focused sequences is the order of 100 atom spacings for an ideally static lattice, but because of the finite atomic vibrations, even at 0°K, the focuson ranges are reduced considerably below this. Crowdion ranges are of course much smaller than this again.

Finally, the use of the hard sphere approximation to describe the focuson propagation gives a quite adequate representation of these events. Since focuson propagation is essentially a rather low energy event, involving only relatively few displacements, it must be anticipated that these effects will modify the results for the number of displaced atoms of Equations 6.25.5 only slightly. On the other hand, crowdion like collisions may enhance the number of displacements, and since there is a definite correlation between the two types of event, it is necessary to discuss both in any evaluation of the damage production due to collision sequences. It is to this problem which we turn our attention in the following section.

6.3.5 Effect on radiation damage densities of correlated sequences

6.3.5.1 The results of the previous sections indicate that focuson and crowdion sequences may have some effect upon the rate of production of damage. The regularity of the lattice will, for example, condition the probability of displacement of a struck atom, and will also influence the manner in which energy and mass are transported away from the collision. Since we have already seen that the ejection probability distribution influences the magnitude of the damage, any correlation between lattice regularity and ejection probability will result in changes in the damage production density also.

Thus the probability of collision of a displaced atom with any one of the 12 nearest neighbours is seen from Equation 6.56.2 to be given by $W_s = 3\theta_s^2$. For $\alpha = 2$ i.e. the limiting case for focused collisions, $\theta_s = 1/2$ and $W_s = 3/4$. Thus the probability of a displaced atom escaping from the cage of 12 atoms, W_d, is given by $W_d = 1 - W_s = 1/4$. If the displaced atom loses an energy ΔE_0 during the displacement event, then from Equation 6.48.2 the maximum collision angle θ_0 corresponding to this energy loss is given by $\frac{\Delta E_0}{E_0} = 1 - \alpha^2\theta_0^2$ and the displacement probability

$$W_d = 1 - 3\theta_0^2 = 1 - \frac{3}{\alpha^2}\left(1 - \frac{\Delta E_0}{E_0}\right) \qquad 6.113.1$$

A reasonable assumption for ΔE_0 is $E_0/2$ with the results that

$$W_d = 1 - \frac{3}{2\alpha^2} = 5/8 \text{ for } \alpha = 2$$
$$= 1/2 \text{ for } \alpha = \sqrt{3} \qquad 6.113.2$$

Since the region near $\alpha = 2$ is that of maximum interest, then W_d is close to $1/2$. The energy at which this condition obtains exactly is deduced from the condition that $\alpha = \sqrt{3}$. For copper, with a Born-Mayer interatomic potential, with constants A = 22.5 keV and a = D/13 it is readily deduced that E_d lies between 24 and 25 eV, similar to the value suggested in the earlier discussion of a random target. It is clear, however, that W_d can vary between 0 and 1 for α values between ∞ and $\sqrt{3/2}$ which indicates that the displacement probability varies between 0 and 1 over a finite energy range, i.e. a distributed displacement probability. Since $W_d \simeq 1 - \frac{3}{2\alpha^2}$ in the energy region near the focusing energy then

$$W_d = 1 - 3R^2/D^2 \qquad 6.113.3$$

and since R varies only logarithmically with energy for the Born-Mayer potential, this displacement probability varies only slowly with energy. The linear increase of W_d proposed by Sampson, Hurwitz and Clancey[71], therefore appears to be reasonable, whilst assumption of an energy E_d above which displacement always occurs, appears equally possible.

One can suggest definition of an energy E'_d above which the displacement probability is unity and for the Born-Mayer potential, it is readily deduced that W_d is only above 0.9 for $E > 1{,}000$ eV. However, this definition of W_d assumes that displacement occurs only if the struck atom emerges in a spatial region between atoms of the surrounding lattice, whereas, we have seen that the atom is displaced also in an almost head on crowdion collision, i.e. $E > E_F$. The value of E'_d may therefore be taken as approximately

$$E'_d \simeq E_F; \text{ i.e. } E'_d \simeq E_F = 2.75\, E_d \qquad 6.114$$

In order to investigate the numbers of displacements occurring because of focuson and crowdion events, we need to know the numbers of atoms which receive energies around the focusing energy E_F. Consider an incident atom of energy E which eventually degrades through collision and produces $S(E, E_0)dE_0$ atoms in the energy range E_0 to $E_0 + \delta E_0$ where E_0 is less than the displacement energy E_d. Using the hard sphere approximation, then at the first collision, there is a probability $\frac{\delta E_0}{E}$ that the primary degrades into the energy region E_0 to $E_0 + \delta E_0$ and a probability that it enters an energy region E' to $E' + \delta E'$ (where $E' > E'_d$) of $(1/E)\, dE'$. The struck atom has similar probabilities of entering the same energy regions.

Thus the total number of atoms given energy in the region E_0 to $E_0 + \delta E_0$ is given by the integral equation

$$S(E, E_0)dE_0 = \left\{\frac{2}{E}\int_{E_d}^{E} S(E', E_0)dE' + \frac{2}{E}\right\} dE_0 \qquad 6.115.1$$

Since $S(E, E_0)$ must vanish for $E < E_0$, then the solution of this Equation can be shown to be

$$S(E, E_0) = \frac{2E}{(E'_d)^2} \text{ for } E < E'_d \qquad 6.115.2$$

The total number of atoms given energy less than E'_d is thus

$$\nu_\beta = \int_0^{E_d'} S(E, E_0)dE_0 = \frac{2E}{E_d'} \qquad 6.115.3$$

and the total energy contained in these events

$$E_\beta = \int_0^{E_d'} E_0 S(E, E_0)dE_0 = E$$

This final relation must evidently hold, since all struck atoms will eventually degrade into the region $E < E_d'$ with a total energy dissipation of E. Now let us consider crowdion and focuson events separately, knowing the number of atoms available for generating these events.

6.3.5.2 Crowdion Collisions

According to Equation 6.58.1 the probability of a crowdion event with range greater than n^*D is $W_c(n^*, E_0)$ for a starting atom energy E_0, thus the total number of crowdion events ν_c with ranges greater than n^*D for an initial primary energy E, is given by

$$\nu_c(E, n^*) = \int W_c(n^*, E_0)S(E, E_0)dE_0 \qquad 6.116.1$$

The probability W_c is only different from zero for a small range of values of η around $\eta = 0$, for large crowdion ranges, i.e. the energy range of interest is around E_F. We may therefore replace E_0 by E_F, introduce η as a new variable and integrate between limits $\eta = \pm \infty$. Thus

$$\nu_c = S \cdot \left(\frac{dE_0}{d\eta}\right)_{\eta=0} . \, 2 \int_0^\infty \frac{3\eta}{\exp(2\pi\eta n^*) - 1} \cdot d\eta$$

6.116.2

since S is independent of E_0 and η. Since $R(\eta) = \frac{D}{2} - \frac{D\eta}{4}$ then $E_0 = A \exp\{-(D/2a) - (D\eta/4a)\}$ and thus

$$\left|\frac{dE_0}{d\eta}\right|_{\eta=0} = E_F \cdot \frac{D}{4a} \simeq 3.25\, E_F \qquad 6.117$$

for the Born-Mayer potential in a copper lattice. Hence

$$\nu_c(E, n^*) \simeq \frac{16E \cdot E_F}{(E_d')^2} \cdot \frac{1}{(n^*)^2} \qquad 6.116.3$$

This result may be compared with that for a random lattice where

$$\nu(E) = \frac{E}{2E_d'}$$

and since $E_F \simeq 2.75\, E_d$ then

$$\nu_c = \nu \cdot \frac{10}{(n^*)^2} \qquad 6.116.4$$

Thus, even if n^* is taken as small as 10, ν_c is only 10% of the total number of displacement events, whilst for larger crowdion ranges the extra number of displaced atoms is smaller still.

On the other hand, although the number of extra displacements is small, the number of replacements is rather large. Since

$$\nu_c = \frac{10\nu}{(n^*)^2}$$

the number of crowdion events with range between n^*D and $(n^* + dn^*)D$ will be given by

$$Z_c(n^*)dn^* = 10\nu \frac{2}{(n^*)^3} dn^* \qquad 6.118.1$$

If there is an upper limit n^*_m to the crowdion range due to interaction with neighbouring rows or other causes (dislocations, etc.) then one obtains

$$Z_c(n^*) = 10\nu\left\{\frac{2}{(n^*)^3} + \frac{\delta(n^* - n^*_m)}{(n^*_m)^3}\right\} \text{ for } n^* < n^*_m$$

6.118.2

and the number of replacement collisions is

$$\mu_R \simeq \int_1^\infty Z_c(n^*)n^*dn^* = 10\,\nu\left(2 - \frac{1}{n^*_m}\right) \qquad 6.119$$

since each atom in the crowdion sequence is a replacement event.

Thus μ_R is, even for quite small n^*_m of order 20ν which should be compared with $\mu_R \sim 5\nu$ in the random lattice model. Thus the actual disordering of the crystal may be considerably larger than that observed from measurements of the number of displacement events. This effect will be of particular importance in targets composed of several species (e.g. an alloy such as Cu_3Au). In this particular case, since the Copper atom mass is much less than the Gold atom mass, with very inefficient energy transfer between adjacent Cu and Au atoms, then the range along a row containing both gold and copper atoms is about 4 atom spacings. Since, of the twelve close packed rows, only 4 will be composed of both atomic species, the number of gold-copper replacements events will be of order $\frac{10\nu}{3}\left(2 - \frac{1}{4}\right)$ i.e. $\sim 6\nu$. For a pile neutron in copper this leads to a value of μ_R of about 1,000, which is in reasonable agreement with experimental data of Blewitt, Coltman, Holmes and Noggle[113].

6.3.5.3 Focuson sequences

The probability of focused sequences is, from Equation 6.56.2, $W_F = -3\eta$ and thus the number of focusing events generated by displaced atoms in the energy range E_0 to $E_0 + \delta E_0$ is given by

$$Z_F(E_0) = S(E, E_0)\,(-3\eta) \qquad 6.120.1$$

Again, for small η, $E_0(\eta) = E_F \exp\left(\frac{D\eta}{4a}\right)$ from Equation 6.117 and thus the range of the focused sequences, given by $n^* = \frac{1}{\epsilon(\eta)} = n^*(o) \exp\left(\frac{D\eta}{4a}\right)$ is

$$n^*(\eta) = n^*(o) \frac{E_0(\eta)}{E_F} \qquad 6.121$$

where $n^*(o)$ is the focuson range for $\eta = 0$. Thus the number of focuson sequences with ranges between n^* and $n^* + dn^*$ atom spacings is

$$Z_F(E, n^*) = Z_F(E, E_0) \frac{dE_0}{dn^*} \qquad 6.120.2$$

i.e.

$$Z_F(E, n^*) = S(E, E_0)\,(-3\eta) \frac{E_F}{n^*(o)} \qquad 6.120.3$$

Since

$$-\frac{D\eta}{4a} = -3.25\eta = \log_e E_F/E_D = \log_e n^*(o)/n^*$$

then

$$Z_F(E, n^*) \cong S(E, E_0)\,.\,\frac{E_F}{n^*(o) \log_e \frac{n^*(o)}{n^*}} \qquad 6.120.4$$

Thus the number of focusons with range larger than n^* but less than $n^*(o)$ is given by

$$\nu_F(E, n^*) = \int_{n^*}^{n^*(o)} Z_F(E, n^*)dn^* \qquad 6.122.1$$

i.e.

$$\nu_F(E, n^*) = \frac{2EE_F}{(E_d')^2}\left\{1 - \frac{n^*}{n^*(o)}\left(1 + \log_e \frac{n^*(o)}{n^*}\right)\right\}$$

6.122.2

using the value of $S(E_1, E_0)$ given by Equation 6.115.2. Since $E_F \simeq E_d' = 2.75\, E_d$

Then

$$\nu_F = 1.5\nu\left[1 - \frac{n^*}{n^*(o)}\left(1 + \log_e \frac{n^*(o)}{n^*}\right)\right] \qquad 6.122.3$$

Since $n^*(o)$ is about 100, one obtains, for $n^* = 50$, $\nu_F(E, 50) \simeq \nu\,.\,0.22$ i.e. the number of focuson sequences with ranges half those of the maximum is of the order of 20%. This is about fifty times larger than crowdions of similar ranges, but if these are true focusons they will not produce a Frenkel pair unless they meet a defect. As we have seen, however, many focused sequences result in replacement if the energy is greater than E_r, and these replicons result in essentially a distantly spaced vacancy-interstitial pair. Since $E_r < E_d'$ the figure of 20% for focused. sequences production may be taken as approximately the number of pairs produced by focused events. This is essentially the situation when the primary energy E is considerably greater than E_d' so that most displacements are produced by non-focused sequences ($=E/2E_d$) and the fraction 20% is that proportion produced by ions whose energy eventually degrades below E_d'. When the incident ion energy itself is only in the region of E_d', then almost all ions may initiate focused sequences, and it is probable that these sequences will reduce the total damage production. Sigmund and Vajda[114] have evaluated the influence of focused collision sequences at relatively low primary energies in a rather different way from that described above. It is assumed that all focused collision sequences result in the production of replacements and at the ends of the sequence one defect pair due to a primary atom of energy E, as opposed to the $E/2E_d$ predicted by the Kinchin-Pease theory, then the Kinchin-Pease displacement model is modified to give an integral equation of the form

$$\nu(E) = p(E) + (1 - p(E))2\int_0^E g(E, T)\nu(T)dT$$

6.125.1

where p(E) is the probability of a primary generating a collision sequence. These authors suggest a form for $p(E) = 1 - \frac{E}{E_F{}^*}$ 6.125.2

where $E_F{}^*$ is the highest focusing energy of a target and that $p(E) = 0$ for $E > E_F{}^*$ and p(E) is given by the above relation for $E_d < E < E_F{}^*$.

Using the hard sphere approximation for g(E, T), Sigmund and Vajda have shown that the solution to 6.125.1 is

$$\nu(E) = \tfrac{1}{2}\left\{1 + \exp\left[\frac{2(E - 2E_d)}{E_F^*}\right]\right\};\ 2E_d < E < E_F^*$$

6.125.3

$$\nu(E) = \frac{E}{2E_F^*}\left\{1 + \exp\left[\frac{2(E_F^* - 2E_d)}{E_F^*}\right]\right\};\ E > E_F^*$$

6.125.4

Using Nelson and Thompsons[105] value of $E_f{}^* \simeq 300$ eV for ⟨111⟩ copper and $E_d = 30$ eV one obtains

$$\nu(E) = \frac{13}{1.7}\,.\,\frac{E}{2E_d} \text{ for } E > E_f{}^* \qquad 6.125.5$$

i.e. collision sequences reduce the apparent defect production by almost 50%. This result is clearly different from those derived by Leibfried[98] and is due to (1) assumption of one defect pair produced by every focused collision sequence and (2) assumption of the probability $p(E) = 1 - E/E_F{}^*$, which is essentially an averaged form over all collision sequence directions. Whatever the form eventually adopted for p(E), and for the relative importance of focuson, replicon and crowdion sequences we would still expect diminution in $\nu(E)$ due to the influence of correlated sequences, and according to the previous calculations this diminution may be quite large.

The energy involved in focusing collisions with range greater than n^*D is given by

$$E_F(E, n^*) = \int_{n^*}^{n^*(o)} E_F\,.\,\frac{n^*}{n^*(o)} Z_F(E, n^*)dn^* \qquad 6.123$$

In the focuson range

$$n^* \simeq \frac{n^*(o)}{3}, \text{ i.e. } E_d \leqslant E_0 \leqslant E_F \text{ and } E_F(E, n^*) = 0.2E$$

6.124

i.e. 20% of the energy is used up in large range focussing collisions.

We therefore conclude that neither crowdion nor focuson propagation changes the total number of displacements materially. However, since focusons are long range events, energy initially deposited at a given position in the lattice may be transported over large distances before it produces a displacement at, for example, the position where a close packed row meets a lattice irregularity. Thus a primary atom of high initial energy, creates a large number of defects close to its point of entry in the target, until the energies of the primary and its progeny degrade to the focusing region and further less dense damage results over a considerable spatial region. For primary energies of the order of 10 KeV to 100 KeV, the spatial extent of the initial heavily damaged area is similar and greater than focuson ranges (depending exactly, of course, upon the primary and target atom masses). For lower energies, the extent, but not the magnitude of the defect production, depends more upon focuson sequences. We should note, however, that use of a real potential in place of the hard sphere approximation and lattice vibrations will materially reduce the extent of the focusons treated here, whilst assisted focusing sequences will tend to offset this by increasing the number of such events, even at higher energies. Of course, the actual extent of the damage will be conditioned by the fact that the focusons will interact with defects and dislocations already present within the target material and depend upon the defect distribution.

Leibfried[115] has investigated this interaction as follows. The range of a focuson of energy E_0 is given by $L = \frac{D}{\epsilon(E)}$ or since $\epsilon(E_0) = \epsilon(E_F) \cdot E_F/E_0$, $L = L_m \cdot E/E_F$ where L_m is the range for head on collisions. Again since there are twelve close packed directions in the copper lattice, the number of focusons with starting energies in the range $E_0 \rightarrow E_0 + \delta E_0$ is given by (c.f. Equation 6.120).

$$Z(E, E_0) = \frac{2E \cdot 12a}{E_F^2 \cdot D} \log_e E_F/E_0 \qquad 6.126.1$$

Since $a = D/13$ the number of focusons with ranges between L and $L + \delta L$ corresponding to energies E_0 to $E_0 + \delta E_0$ is

$$Z(E, L) \simeq \frac{2E}{E_F L_m} \log_e \frac{L_m}{L} \qquad 6.126.2$$

Hence the number of focusons with ranges greater than L is

$$n(E, L) = \int_L^{L_m} Z(E, L')Dl' = \frac{2E}{E_F}\left\{1 - \frac{L}{L_m}\left(1 + \log_e \frac{L_m}{L}\right)\right\} \qquad 6.127$$

One should exclude low energy collisions below a cut off energy E_F' corresponding to the threshold for Frenkel pair production where a focused sequence meets a dislocation. Consequently n is constant below this energy.

Because the radiation effects are distributed it is immaterial what arrangement of dislocations is chosen. To simplify calculations it may be assumed that the dislocation lines are arranged parallel to each other in a rectangular lattice, with a separation between lines of λ and a splitting separation (length of dislocation line) equal to a.

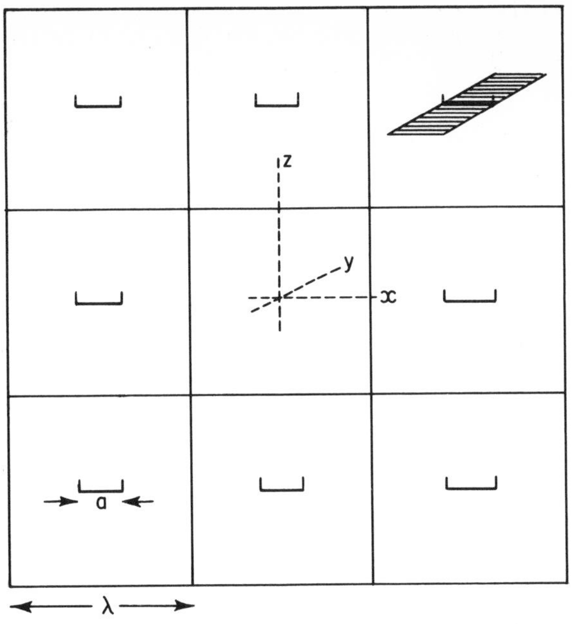

Fig. 6.31 Dislocations arranged in a lattice with lattice distance λ, and dislocation splitting separation a. The dislocations are parallel to the y axis and the shaded region illustrates the stacking fault area. (viz. Ref. 6.115)

This arrangement is displayed in Figure 6.31 where the stacking fault area extends to $\pm\infty$ in the y directions about the dislocation lines.

To find the average number of defects produced by the interaction of focusons with dislocation planes it is necessary only to find the average over one periodic area ($\lambda \times \lambda$) of the lattice since the dislocation arrangement is regular, and to confine one's attention only to the xOz plane since the dislocation planes are parallel.

If $f(x, z)dxdz$ is the number of defects produced by interaction of focusons generated in the spatial region $\delta x \delta z$ about the point (x, z) with the dislocation plane at the origin. Then the average number of defects produced through interaction with all dislocation planes is given by

$$\nu_D = \frac{1}{\lambda^2} \iint_{-\infty}^{\infty} f(x, z)dxdz \qquad 6.128.1$$

since the density of dislocation planes is $1/\lambda^2$. In a first approximation one may also consider that the focuson directions are distributed isotropically, and thus the number of focusons which cross an area $\delta x' \delta y'$ of the dislocation plane at the origin, starting at the position (x, y) distance r from the origin is given by $\frac{\delta\Omega}{4\pi} n(r, E)$ where $\delta\Omega$ is the solid angle subtended by the area $\delta x' \delta y'$ at the point (x, y) and thus $\delta\Omega = \frac{|z|}{r^3} \delta x' \delta y'$. Consequently the total number of defects produced in this dislocation plane is given by

$$\nu_D = \frac{1}{4\pi\lambda^2} \int_{-a/2}^{a/2} dx' \iiint_{-\infty}^{\infty} dxdy'dz' \frac{|z|}{r^3} n(r, E)$$

$$= \frac{a}{4\pi\lambda^2} \iiint_0^{\infty} |z|/r^3 . n(r, E)dxdydz \qquad 6.128.2$$

Transformation to polar co-ordinates readily gives the result

$$\nu_D = \frac{a}{2\lambda^2} \int_0^\infty n(r, E)dr \qquad 6.128.3$$

Substitution of Equation 6.127 for L leads finally to

$$\nu_D = \frac{2E}{E_F} \cdot a\frac{L_m}{8\lambda^2} \qquad 6.128.4$$

or, if a threshold energy for the production of a defect where a focuson interacts with a dislocation, $E_F' < E_F$ is assumed.

$$\nu_D = \frac{2E}{E_F}\, a\frac{L_m}{8\lambda^2}\{1 - \eta_1^2 + 2\eta_1^2 \log_e \eta_1\} \qquad 6.128.5$$

where

$$\eta_1 = E_F'/E_F$$

The energy required to produce a normal Frenkel pair, E_d, is about 24 eV, and one may assume, as a first approximation, that this is the energy required to create a permanent displacement at the dislocation plane. Thus $\eta_1 = 1/3$ and

$$\nu_D \simeq \frac{2E}{E_F}\, a\, \frac{L_m}{10\lambda^2} \qquad 6.128.6$$

This relation indicates that the number of defects produced by interaction of focusons with dislocations is proportional to the dislocation density. This is only true, however, provided that the dislocation density is so small that dislocations do not screen each other and prevent the maximum possible interaction with focusons. At high dislocation densities, even the focusons of shortest range produce a defect and so the maximum number of defects is simply equal to the total number of focusons (n(L = O, E)). Without a cut off energy E_F', $\nu_D = n(o) = \frac{2E}{E_F}$ but with cut off $n(o) \simeq \frac{2E}{3E_F}$ i.e. $aL_m/10\lambda^2$ cannot exceed a value of about $1/3$. Thus the behaviour of ν_D with dislocation density $\frac{1}{\lambda^2}$ is depicted as in Figure 6.32. Since focuson sequences are essentially low energy events, the total number of Frenkel pairs produced by a primary

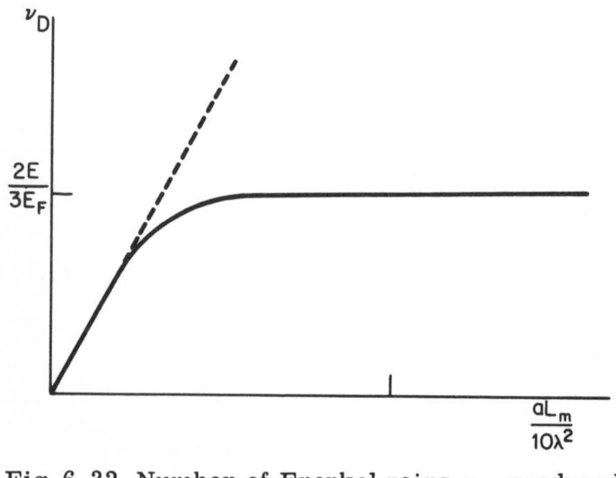

Fig. 6.32 Number of Frenkel pairs ν_D, produced by interaction of focused sequences with dislocations, at a primary energy E, as a function of the dislocation density $1/\lambda^2$. (viz. Ref. 6.115)

ion of energy E, will be given closely by the number produced in a quasi random lattice $\nu = E/2E_d$ as the primary energy degrades to the order of E_F, plus the number produced by focuson interaction with dislocations at energies below E_F, i.e. ν_D.

Thus the total number of Frenkel pairs produced by a primary of energy E is given by

$$\nu_t(E) = \nu(E) + \nu_D(E) = \nu(E)\left\{1 + \frac{4E_D}{E_F} \cdot \frac{aL_m}{10\lambda^2}\right\} \qquad 6.129.1$$

Using values of $E_F = 65$ eV, $E_D = 24$ eV

$$\nu_t \simeq \nu\left\{1 + 1.5\,\frac{aL_m}{10\lambda^2}\right\} \qquad 6.129.2$$

Seeger[116] has given values for the splitting separation a in copper for screw and edge dislocations, viz. $a \doteq 4.5$ D for screw dislocations, and a = 12D for edge dislocations. For the lower separation, the enhancement of defect production due to dislocation is proportional to dislocation density up to densities of about $\frac{10}{3aL_m}$ where the enhancement is about 50%.

It is thus clear that the introduction of dislocations to a crystal, by for example mechanical deformation (cold work) increases the number of defects produced during subsequent ion irradiation. The magnitude of this effect may be somewhat different from that predicted by the preceding simple theory, since (a) the displacement threshold E_d is not sharp, and as we have seen a distribution of E_d tends to reduce ν but tends to increase ν_D (b) the focuson ranges are shorter than predicted by hard sphere calculations when a realistic potential is used, but this may be offset by the increased number of focusing events due to assisted sequences and crowdion-focuson exchanges, and (c) annealing of defects by thermal and spontaneous migration during and after bombardment, which reduce the observed number of defects. This final influence will be considered shortly.

We may mention finally that Coltman, Blewitt, Klabunde and Redman[117,118] have observed a 30% increase in resistivity in heavily cold worked Copper during neutron bombardment in a reactor. Assuming that the resistivity increases linearly with the defect density this figure is in order of magnitude agreement with the above theory. Nevertheless we must emphasize that this analysis only gives order of magnitude estimates of the damage.

Leibfried[115] has also shown that the above treatment can be used to give an estimate of the increased pinning of dislocations by irradiation and the production of defects in the dislocations, which is again in order of magnitude agreement with experimental measurements on neutron irradiated copper. This latter effect is outside the scope of our present considerations however since in ion bombardment only the surface layers are materially damaged.

We therefore conclude that the inclusion of correlated sequences such as crowdions and the interaction of focusons with dislocations leads to an increase in the predicted number of defects produced, although the defect density still increases linearly with primary energy. However, as we suggested earlier, theoretical evaluations of damage production rates even in the random lattice approximation overestimate these, compared to measured data by factors as large as one or two orders of magnitude, whilst the observed damage rates decrease less rapidly than linearly with primary ion energy.

Correlated sequences therefore only tend to aggravate this discrepancy, and we must seek some other effect of lattice symmetry which is likely to reduce damage production.

6.3.5.4 Channelling events

In Chapter 5 we saw that an energetic ion moving along the axis between close packed lattice rows can travel large distances through the lattice transferring only small energies to atoms in the channel wall. Consequently a target atom which is ejected into a channel must also have a certain probability of channelling, and, since subsequent collisions are mainly subthreshold, no further displaced atoms result from this initial atom. In view of the results obtained by Lehmann and Leibfried[119], Nelson and Thompson[120] Oen and Robinson[121] and Beeler and Besco[122] it is not a bad assumption to set the probability P of a displaced atom becoming channelled, constant, independent of the energy of the displaced atom and its earlier history.

This primary ion of energy E, has a probability P of becoming channelled at its first collision and a probability (1 − P) of remaining unchannelled. Similarly the struck atom has a probability P of channelling and (1 − P) of remaining non channelled.

If, after the first collision the primary retains an energy in the range E_1 to $E_1 + \delta E_1$ and the struck atom acquires an energy in the range E_2 to $E_2 + \delta E_2$, then the number of displaced atoms produced by the primary $\nu(E)$ is given by

$$\nu(E) = P + (1 - P)\left\{\int_{E_d}^{E} g(E, E_1)\nu(E_1)dE_1 + \int_0^{E-Ed} g(E, E_2)\nu(E_2)dE_2\right\} \qquad 6.130.1$$

Where $g(E, E_1)$ is the probability that the primary of energy E enters the region E_1 to $E_1 + \delta E_1$ and where the displacement is certain for $E > 2Ed$ and the struck atom leaves with all energies between 0 and $E - E_d$. This is clearly the second Kinchin-Pease model for P = o, and for the hard sphere approximation $g(E, E_1) = 1/E$.

With a finite channelling probability P, and the hard sphere approximation Oen and Robinson[123] have shown that the solution to Equation 6.130.1 is

$$\nu(E) = \frac{1 - P}{1 - 2P}(E/2E_d)^{1-2P} - \frac{P}{1 - 2P} \qquad 6.130.2$$

which is identical to Equation 6.25 for P = o.

It is immediately apparent that Equation 6.130.2 indicates a less than linear dependence of $\nu(E)$ upon E, which is in agreement with experimental data on neutron irradiated Copper[118]. The reduction in $\nu(E)$ because of channelling is shown in Figure 6.33 for values of P between 0 and 1. Oen and Robinson[123] used a value of 0.07 (7% of displaced atoms are channelled) in order to obtain quantitative agreement with the experimental measurements by Coltman et al[118], but according to their own earlier estimates of P, and those by Davies et al[124], Sizmann and

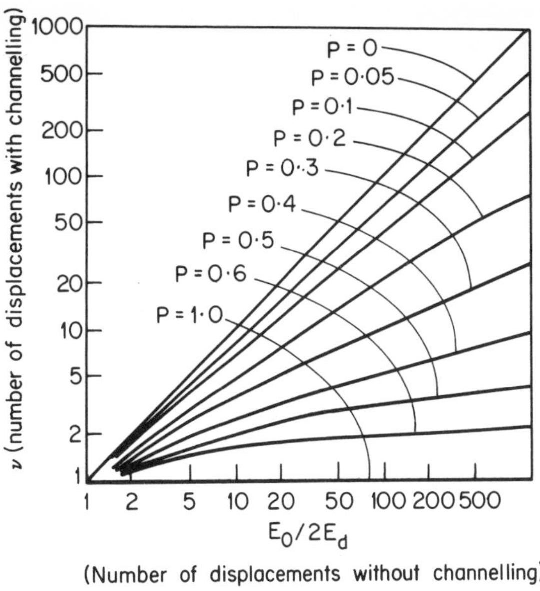

Fig. 6.33 Graph of equn. 6.130.2. illustrating the reduction in the total number of displaced atoms as the channelling probability is increased **from** 0 to 1. E_0 is the primary energy and E_d is the displacement threshold energy. (viz. Ref. 6.123).

Lutz[125] and Beeler[126] and Besco this is probably too large and a closer estimate would be P = 0.01.

Sigmund[127] has considered the solution of Equation 6.130.1 using a more realistic form for the scattering probability, namely

$$g(E, E') = \frac{\exp\{(-E/2 + E')/E_c\}}{2E \sinh E/2E_c}$$

originally suggested by Lehmann[73], and which is a scattering law with preferential forward scattering, with E_c as an adjustable scaling energy. This expression for $g(E, E_1)$ may be inserted in Equation 6.130.1 and assuming $P \ll 1$ the solution becomes

$$\nu(E) \simeq 1 + \frac{1 - \exp\left[-\frac{E - 2E_d}{2E_c}\right] . P}{2P \sinh E_d/E_c} \quad \text{for } E_c > 2E_d \qquad 6.131.1$$

For

$$P = o, \nu(E) = 1 + \frac{E - 2E_d}{2E_c \sinh E_d/Ec} \qquad 6.131.2$$

which for $E_c \gg E_d$ approaches the hard sphere relation $\nu(E) = E/2E_d$. This led Lehmann[73] as pointed out earlier, to conclude that the form of the scattering law does not effect $\nu(E)$ materially. However, when $P \neq o$, there is a considerable reduction in $\nu(E)$, as indicated by the curves in Figure 6.34 for the above form of the scattering law.

The actual reduction in damage due to channelling is seen to depend upon the quotient P/E_c. Comparison of these curves with the experimental data for neutron bombarded copper obtained by Coltman et al[118] at different neutron energies suggested that for E_c = 130 eV, P = 0.01. This value of E_c appears to be a reasonable choice (i.e. $E_c \approx 5E_d$, according to the

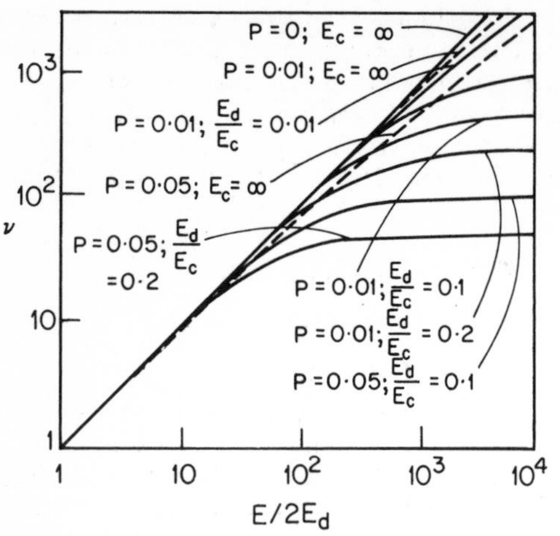

Fig. 6. 34 Solid curves; average number of defects in a cascade with a primary energy E assuming the scattering law given by equn. 6. 26. 1. for various values of the channelling probability P and the parameter E_c. Dashed curves correspond to hard sphere scattering as in Fig. 6. 33. (viz. Ref. 6. 127)

earlier analysis) and so the $P = 0.01$ value also appears to be acceptable. However, it should be emphasized that the P value results only from the choice of $g(E, E_1)$. Indeed Robinson[128] has suggested that, for the Born-Mayer potential, matched to an inverse power differential scattering cross section as illustrated in Chapter 2 to allow ready solution of the Kinchin-Pease equation by a Laplace transform method, the damage density may be considerably reduced below the Kinchin-Pease level, even with zero channelling. When a universally acceptable choice for the interatomic potential and so for the scattering law, becomes available, it will be more opportune to reassess the accurate value for P.

One way in which the theoretical model for damage reduction due to channelling can be likened more closely to the real physical situation is to employ, as suggested by Oen[129], separate and different channelling probabilities P_1 and P_2 for the primary and struck atoms respectively. Physically this is sensible since a struck atom must generally leave its position at such an angle as to escape from the surrounding atomic lattice and this angle would generally be larger than for the primaries for which immediate channelling is possible.

Under these circumstances one obtains equations identical to Equation 6. 130. 1 for the number of displaced atoms eventually produced by primaries and by struck atoms, each having separate channelling probabilities. The final result for the total number of displaced atoms is simply

$$\nu(E) = \frac{1 - P_1}{1 - P_1 - P_2} (E/2E_d)^{1-P_1-P_2} - \frac{P_2}{1 - P_1 - P_2} \qquad 6.132$$

for hard sphere collisions.

This equation is seen to reduce to equation 6. 130. 2 for $P_1 = P_2$. The possible values which may be assigned to P_1 and P_2 however, will allow this expression to be fitted more accurately to experimental data and the magnitudes of P_1 and P_2 should be definable.

It is clearly possible to repeat this calculation for any type of scattering law ($g(E, T)$) and Oen[129] has shown that for polynomial type laws $g(E, T) = \frac{1}{E} f\left(\frac{T}{E}\right)$ which do not differ too radically from hard sphere scattering, the resulting displacement numbers do not differ appreciably from the predictions of the above equation.

We should note a further consequence of channelling which is important at energies rather higher than under general consideration here. This is the reduction in damage due to ionization effects at energies greater than E_i, the ionization threshold. Since the channelling probability remains constant and unity for energies greater than about 10 KeV, more of the displacement cascades are due to nonchannelled atoms at primary energies greater than that value. Since the number of displaced atoms in the energy region greater than E_i, is $E_i/2E_d$ (i.e. a saturation limit), then there is an overall reduction in $\nu(E)$ becaūse of channelling events. Again, however, the exact calculations depend rather critically upon the scattering law.

We conclude therefore than channelled events can materially reduce the anticipated defect production, particularly at high ion energies, just as required to make analytical predictions agree with experimental measurements. However, exact analysis must await the availability of realistic interatomic potentials.

6. 3. 6. 1 Spike Phenomena

Up to this point we have generally made the explicit assumption that all collisions are isolated two body events between the primary displaced atoms and stationary target atoms. However we have already shown that as the primary energy degrades to the order of several hundred electron volts the distance between successive collisions decreases to the order of the interatomic distance. At this stage therefore the primary starts to act collectively with several lattice atoms relatively simultaneously and the displacement events are no longer widely separated. Consequently the primary expends its energy over a rather small atomic volume, creating violent localised damage, in which the displaced atoms move away from the (extended) centre of the region, and because their energies are low come to rest at small distances from this centre. A denuded vacancy rich region is thus created at the extended centre with a region containing an excess of interstitial atoms around the periphery of this volume. Furthermore, even with quite energetic primaries, sufficiently large energy transfers may be given to lattice atoms in a relatively distant collision, and, since the path of the primary is more or less undisturbed in this interaction it will make a succession of such encounters with adjacent lattice atoms. Thus it may be possible that a succession of displacement events will occur with only small separation between their generation and once again a spike will form. In the former type of event, only a few atoms will be displaced because the primary energy is low and so the spike will be of only small dimensions. In the latter event however, displacements will occur over a rather large portion of the primary ranges and an extended spike must be anticipated. Brinkman[25,26,130] has termed this type of event as a displacement spike and made a rather careful analysis of the conditions necessary for their formation, which we shall outline shortly. The model of a displacement spike, as conceived by Brinkman[26],

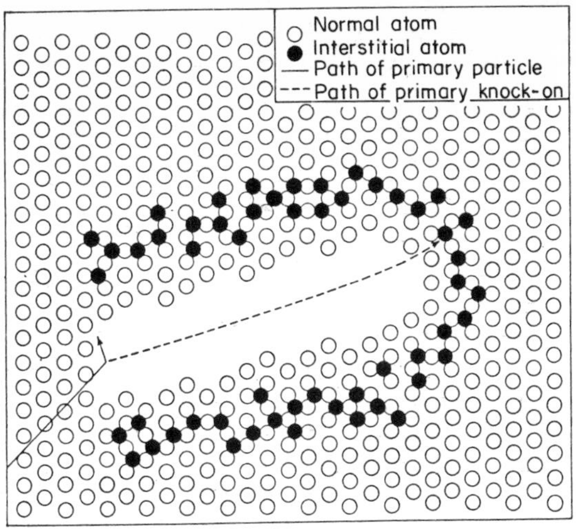

Fig. 6.35 Schematic representation of interstitial atoms around a multiple vacancy during production of a displacement spike. viz. Ref. 6.26.

is shown pictorially in Figure 6.35 just after the formation of the spike. Since this region of the lattice is grossly disordered, with resulting strains, it may be anticipated that many of the defects produced in the spike will subsequently migrate and take up a more energetically favourable configuration. However, it may be anticipated that a certain degree of disorder will still persist, and it is therefore necessary to consider such events in some detail, since the overall picture of damage will necessarily include their presence. We should note that this type of collective interaction is totally different from the isolated collisions leading to cascade events and should therefore be treated as an alternative to these.

We should also consider a second type of collective interaction event known as the thermal spike, treated in considerable detail by Seitz and Koehler[3]. When the primary atom energy has degraded to about 25 eV it becomes trapped, unable to generate further displacements, but in order to equilibrate with and achieve the mean energy of the lattice (kT) it must dissipate most of this excess 25 eV energy. Since the atom is trapped by the surrounding cage of lattice atoms it can only lose this excess energy in sub-threshold interactions with these atoms and their weakly bound electrons. The trapped atom vibrates at a high frequency (10^{13} - 10^{14} oscillations/sec) and so the transfer of energy to lattice atoms is rapid and these in turn commence to execute higher amplitude vibrations. This is equivalent to raising the lattice temperature, by, as we shall see, thousands of degrees K. Hence the terminology 'thermal spike'.

Indeed the temperature may be raised to, and above, the melting temperature, although the heated region resembles more closely a superheated solid rather than a liquid. This rather sudden increase in heat content of a small lattice volume is subsequently conducted away from the heated region by lattice vibrations and, to a much smaller degree by conduction electrons. During these thermal spikes, however, it may be anticipated that thermally activated events such as defect migration and annealing, disordering of alloys and plastic deformation can proceed at a greatly increased rate, and so defect production will be considerably affected in these regions. We will return to a more detailed discussion of such spikes and correlated effects shortly.

Finally, bombardment of solids by fission fragments, electrons and energetic photons, lead to other spike events such as fission, electron and gamma ray spikes, in which the basic mechanism of production are similar, but details differ from those spikes already outlined. We discuss first the displacement spike.

6.3.6.2 The displacement spike

The mean free path between collisions, is given in the hard sphere approximation by $\lambda_s = \frac{1}{n\pi r_o^2}$ where r_o is twice the hard sphere radius. r_o, in turn depends upon the primary energy through the relation $E_{Rel} = V(r_o)$ and thus upon the form of the interatomic potential. One choice for the onset of displacement spikes is where the distance between consecutive collisions becomes of the order of the interatomic spacing of the lattice or the mean atomic radius r_s, where r_s is obtained, approximately from $\frac{4\pi r_s^3}{3} = \frac{1}{n}$. Thus, as before $\lambda_s = \frac{4}{3}\pi\frac{r_s^3}{r_o^2}$ where $\lambda_s \approx r_s$. Clearly, therefore,

$$r_o^2 \simeq \tfrac{4}{3} r_s^2 \qquad 6.133$$

which, because r_o depends rather sensitively upon the choice of the interatomic potential V(r), leads to a rather critical choice of the onset energy for displacement spikes. Further r_s is a rather oversimplified choice of interatomic distance r_e, which in the f.c.c. lattice is given by $r_e^3 = \frac{\sqrt{2}}{n}$. Thus, in metals such as copper, gold and silver, Brinkman[25,26] has suggested, even in the case of b.c.c. metals such as Uranium[130]

$$r_o^2 \simeq \frac{1}{\sqrt{2\pi}} r_e^2 \qquad 6.134$$

Using an interatomic potential of the form $V(r) = E_a\left(\frac{1}{4} + \frac{a}{r}\right) \exp(-r/a)$ for copper where $E_a = 75 \times 10^3$ eV and $a \approx D/13$, Leibfried[62] has shown that the energy at which λ_s becomes of the order r_e is about 60 eV. Brinkman[25] in an earlier evaluation, using a Born-Mayer potential $V(r) = A \exp(-r/a)$ showed that E was similar order of magnitude to that deduced by Leibfried[62]. Of course since the primary energy is low, only relatively few displaced atoms will form and the damaged region will be spatially small.

This, however, is not the full picture of displacement spikes since the above analysis predicts only the energy at which the distance between collisions, whether displacement collisions or not, becomes comparable with the lattice spacing. A more stringent requirement for displacement spike generation is that the distance between displacement collisions should be of the order of the lattice spacing. Displacement events occur when the transferred energy is of the order of 25 eV and while these energies are readily transferrable in almost head on collisions from low energy primaries, there is a considerable chance of this occurrence during more distant collisions with higher energy primaries. In this latter case, since the primary will lose only a small fraction of its energy in a displacement collision the interaction can be treated by the momentum approximation.

Consequently, for equal mass primary and struck atoms, the energy transfer in a distant collision, is given, according to Equation 2.61b by $T = \frac{I^2}{2M}$ where

$$I = -\int_p^\infty \frac{\partial v}{\partial r}\sqrt{\frac{M}{2E}}\frac{p}{(r^2 - p^2)^{1/2}} \cdot dr$$

This integral has been evaluated earlier for the inverse distance potential (equation 2.61b) and for the Born-Mayer exponential and Bohr potentials (equations 5.116, 117).

Brinkman[130] has given rather careful consideration to the choice of an interatomic potential for copper, using elasticity data, and concludes that a representative potential for copper for large atomic separations is

$$V(r) = 1.9 \times 10^{-6}\, Z^{\,11/2}\,\frac{e^2}{2a_0}$$

$$\frac{\exp\left[-Z^{1/3} \,.\, r/1.5a_0\right]}{1 - \exp\left[-0.95 \,.\, 10^{-6} \,.\, Z^{7/2} \,.\, r/a_0\right]} \qquad 6.135$$

With this potential, the energy transfer is evaluated to be

$$T = \frac{p^2}{E} \,.\, A^2Z^4e^4\{B \,.\, F(A, B, p) + (A - B)F(A, A + B, p)\}^2 \qquad 6.136.1$$

where

$$F(A, B, p) = \int_p^\infty \frac{\exp(-Br)}{(r^2 - p^2)^{1/2}\{1 - \exp(-Ar)\}^2} = \sum_{\nu=0}^{\infty} (\nu + 1)K_0\{(B + \nu A)p\} \qquad 6.136.2$$

and K_0 is the Bessel function of the third kind, p is the impact parameter and the constants A and B are immediately obvious from comparison of the integrand of F(A, B, p) and the interatomic potential.

One requires values of the impact parameter for which T is of the order of the displacement energy $E_d = 25$ eV, and, having obtained this value from solution of Equation 2.24 this may be set equal to an effective hard sphere radius R_1, i.e. for values of $p < R_1$, displacement events will occur by an impulsive energy transfer and thus the cross section for these events will be of order πR_1^2. Finally the mean free path for displacement collisions

$$\lambda_D = \frac{1}{n\pi R_1^2} \qquad 6.137$$

may be deduced using this value of $R_1 = p$, since the primary suffers only slight deflection and has an almost identical impact parameter in its next atomic encounter. Brinkman[130] has evaluated λ_D as a function of energy, with the results shown in Table 6.4 compared with corresponding values of the collision free paths λ_S at the appropriate energies. It is immediately clear that λ_D is considerably less than λ_S at all energies, and even for E = 58 keV, displaced atoms are produced every two lattice spacings. Consequently the energy range over which displacement spikes may be produced is very large. However, in the case where displacement spikes are generated by distant collisions from energetic primaries, these primaries are relatively undeflected during the interactions, and so the spike is generated over a rather extended axial range with a sort of cylindrical symmetry. This is the situation depicted in Figure 6.35. For the lower energy primaries however, the primary loses its energy in a quite restricted spatial region, and so the spike has a spherical structure. The maximum energy required for the generation of the former type of spike depends quite critically upon the potential used, and thus upon the material in which the spike is produced. Using the potential of Equation 6.135 with appropriate constants, Brinkman[130] has evaluated the energy onset for spikes where $\lambda_D \sim r_0$ in Cu, Ag, Au and U, with the results shown in Table 6.5. In the case of Uranium it is seen that the highest energy for this type of spike is of the order of 10^5 eV whilst spikes will also form at considerably lower energies. Consequently it may be anticipated that fission fragment bombardment of this material will result in spike formation and indeed Brinkman[130] has interpreted experimental data of Noggle and Stiegler[131], Beierlein and Mastel[132] and several other investigators[46,48] as supporting this mechanism.

TABLE 6.4 (viz. Ref. 6.130).

Collision and Displacement free paths in Copper as a function of the primary copper atom energy.

E (eV)	λ_S (Å)	λ_D (Å)
55	1.98	1.67
1100	5.4	2.62
8400	16.4	3.8
58000	233	5.9

We should note that the above calculation of λ_D assumes an effective hard sphere radius equal to the impact parameter i.e. that all collisions at this primary energy occur with this impact parameter. Comparison of the values of λ_D and λ_S $\left(\text{proportional respectively to } \frac{1}{R_1^2} \text{ and } \frac{1}{r_0}\right)$ in Table 6.4 however, indicate that such an assumption should be quite good since $R_1 \gg r_0$ and the majority of the collisions will be remote, glancing collisions, where the momentum approximation is adequate. We must conclude, therefore, that intermingled with the normal isolated Frenkel pair production due to close atomic encounters, a fair proportion of violently disordered regions may be formed, at the highest primary energies, but when the primaries and their progeny eventually approach the displacement energy a considerable density of spikes will be formed.

We should also recall here the remarks made in Chapter 2 regarding the range of applicability of the momentum approximation in Copper. It was shown there that, for the maximum possible impact parameter p = D/2 (D = lattice spacing) the impulse approximation becomes of limited accuracy for primary energies in the range E < 600 eV or E < 100 keV depending upon the interatomic potential chosen. Below this range it is more correct to employ a model such as the hard sphere approximation. It is thus seen that our earlier calculations in this chapter of defect production rates, using the hard sphere approximation are probably most accurate up to primary energies in the region between say 500 eV → 20 keV. Above this range displacement spikes may be increasingly important, whilst below about 50-100 eV, rather less dense spikes will also occur.

In this description of displacement spikes we have so far assumed that both the low and the high energy events lead to essentially similar configurations of the displaced atoms. However in the model proposed by Brinkman[25,26] it is only the high energy event which is considered to be a true displacement spike, as the following reasoning shows. In the low energy event, the struck atoms acquire only a relatively small amount of energy and this is dissipated without excessive agitation of the lattice atoms surrounding the displaced atoms, i.e. the 'temperature' rise of the lattice is rather small. Consequently, following the displacement event the interstitials remain 'frozen' in their new positions with only a small void volume at the spike centre. However, in the high energy event, considerable energy is imparted to the lattice over a quite small spatial volume, i.e. many interstitials move out from the spike centre simultaneously, giving rise to rather excessive lattice disturbance (or heating). As pointed out earlier, for thermal spikes, the disturbed zone is probably not in the liquid state since the time scale involved in the 'heating' period is so small as to prevent excessive atomic migration and cause the disorder typical of the liquid phase. Nevertheless the agitated atoms will be in a state where thermally activated processes such as diffusion can be expected to proceed at a rapid rate. Moreover, the initial spike, which consists of a central vacancy rich zone surrounded by a relatively normal zone and which in turn is surrounded by the displaced interstitials is expected to be subjected to considerable mechanical stresses due to the excess interstitial concentration which tend to drive the normal lattice atoms into the central zone. This migration should be relatively easy for high deposited energies, since the effective temperature is sufficiently large to permit the atomic migration. Furthermore since the initial displacement event is a somewhat correlated event and the secondary migrations are less so, the final, equilibrium configuration of the disturbed region will differ considerably from that preceding the event. This may be condensed by saying that the displacement spike creates a damaged region which subsequently anneals to a structure differing from the original lattice. Immediately transparent consequences of such a model are the changes to be anticipated in alloyed targets due to disordering, and annealing out of Frenkel defects already present in the lattice prior to the spike formation.

Brinkman[25] has estimated the lower energy required to generate the above, true displacement spikes, by considering the times required for the lattice atoms to migrate to the central vacancy region under the imposed elastic stresses and for the 'lattice' temperature to fall below values necessary for the rapid diffusion to take place. If the former is the larger then the vacancy/interstitial cluster is maintained, whereas if the latter time is the larger, a displacement spike, with attendant re-ordering, obtains.

In order to estimate both times it is necessary to assume that over the short time scales involved, the normal laws of macroscopic diffusion are obeyed. However, since the times are so short and coupling between atoms and conduction electrons is rather weak, the thermal conductivity assigned to the problem is that due to the interaction between the lattice atoms as a whole i.e. vibrational waves.

If a quantity of energy Q eV is deposited at a given point in the crystal, which is an approximation to the real state of affairs in a displacement spike where energy is deposited over a small but finite spatial region, then the lattice rapidly heats up to a temperature T_a. The excess energy is then transported away from the central point, and in the process surrounding atoms also heat up, i.e. a temperature wave spreads from the centre. Assuming the normal laws of thermal diffusion[133] the temperature T, at a distance r from the spike centre at a time t after formation is given by

$$T = \frac{Q \, . \, C^{1/2}}{8(\pi K t)^{3/2}} \exp \; -\left(\frac{Cr^2}{4Kt}\right) \qquad 6.138.1$$

where C is the specific heat of the solid and K the thermal lattice conductivity.

This indicates that the temperature is constant (to within a factor of e^{-1}) up to a radius $r = \sqrt{\frac{4Kt}{C}}$ at a given time t. Thus the central region cools down to the melting temperature T_m which may be assumed to be of the order of 3,000°K for metals such as Uranium, in a time

$$t = 0.4Q^{2/3} \times 10^{-13} \text{ secs} \qquad 6.139$$

If, during this period, the narrow region of normal material can be forced back into the zone centre by the action of the peripheral pressures of the interstitials, then a displacement spike will have been said to occur. To obtain an order of magnitude for the time required for the relaxation it may be assumed that the atoms act under the influence of a pressure wave, and therefore travel with velocities of the order of the velocity of sound. Since the energy of the initially displaced atoms is small they will only be expected to travel distances of the order of 10-20Å away from the spike centre during the displacement event, and these are therefore the distances over which the lattice atoms subsequently travel to re-order the spike. The time taken for the re-ordering is therefore $t' \simeq \frac{10^{-7}}{10^5} \simeq 10^{-12}$ secs. For $t > t'$, the energy Q required is found from Equation 6.139 to be of the order of 350 eV and above. However, only a part of the energy dissipated by the primary atom goes into effectively increasing the lattice temperature, a further amount E′ is stored in the initially created Frenkel pairs which produce the spike. The average number of pairs produced is $E' = E_0/2E_d$ for a primary of energy E_0 and each stores an energy of the order of 5 eV.

Consequently the energy required for stable spike formation is given by $E_1 \simeq Q + \frac{E_0}{2E_d} \, . \, 5$ which assuming Ed = 25 eV leads to $E_1 \simeq 400$ eV. This energy E_1, is relatively independent of the target material because of only small variations in C, K and E_d for various materials. This is in marked contrast to the upper limit for spike formation which is quite sensitive to target structure because of changes in interatomic potential and spacing through the periodic table. Indeed as Table 6.6 deduced by Brinkman[25] indicates, there is a marked periodicity in E_2. The values of E_2 in this table should not be taken too seriously since Brinkman employed too hard a potential in its derivation. Indeed this table is included only to show the wide variation in E_2 which may be anticipated. The results of Table 6.5 are considerably more representative.

TABLE 6.5 (viz. Ref. 6.130)

The energy at which the displacement free path just equals the interatomic spacing for Cu, Ag, Au and U.

Metals	Energy (eV)
Cu	4000 (1000 for Huntington potential)
Ag	4500
Au	80000
U	79000

It is therefore seen, as suggested earlier that fission fragments in Ur should produce displacement spikes, but they should also be observable in other materials under ion bombardment. However in Copper for example the energy region between the minimum and maximum required for spike formation is rather small (400 eV-4000 eV) and so only a relatively few may form due to a high energy ion. It may be observed, however, that since the upper energy E_2 is very sensitive to the interatomic potential it is impossible to accurately evaluate the energy region where spikes should occur. We should also reassert at this stage that the cascade theory of defect production and the displacement spike concept are mutually exclusive in the energy region between E_1 and E_2 since the former requires no collective interaction between displaced atoms. In the energy regions between E_d and E_1 and above E_2, only displacement cascades should result whilst between E_1 and E_2 only spikes will form according to the Brinkman model.

To date there is no unequivocal evidence to indicate which concept is the more accurate in the energy range $E_1 \rightarrow E_2$ since direct observation of re-ordered zones is difficult. As we shall see in the next chapter

TABLE 6.6 (viz. Ref. 6.25)

Calculated values of E_2.

Z	Element	r_0(A)	E_2 (eV)	Z	Element	r_0(A)	E_2 (eV)
11	Na	3.708	180	56	Ba	4.34	860
12	Mg	3.190	550	57	Ta	3.73	4200
13	Al	2.856	1200	58	Ce	3.64	5900
19	K	4.618	140	59	Pr	3.633	6000
20	Ca	3.93	420	60	Nd	3.62	6500
21	Sc	3.205	2500	63	Eu	3.960	1500
22	Ti	2.91	5000	64	Gd	3.554	8300
23	V	2.627	9600	65	Tb	3.508	10000
24	Cr	2.493	15000	66	Dy	3.499	10000
26	Fe	2.476	20000	67	Ho	3.480	11000
27	Co	2.501	20000	68	Er	3.459	12000
28	Ni	2.486	23000	69	Tm	3.446	13000
29	Cu	2.551	23000	70	Yb	3.866	3700
30	Zn	2.659	19000	71	Tu	3.439	13000
37	Rb	4.87	150	72	Hf	3.14	33000
38	Sr	4.30	610	73	Ta	2.854	73000
39	Y	3.59	3000	74	W	2.734	110000
40	Zr	3.16	9000	75	Re	2.734	105000
41	Cb	2.853	25000	76	Os	2.670	150000
42	Mo	2.720	36000	77	Ir	2.709	120000
44	Ru	2.644	51000	78	Pt	2.769	110000
45	Rh	2.684	47000	79	Au	2.878	80000
46	Pd	2.745	43000	81	Te	3.401	16000
47	Ag	2.882	31000	82	Pb	3.493	14000
48	Cd	2.972	21000	90	Th	3.59	9000

however, some indirect evidence from sputtering measurements[134,135] indicates the reality of such spikes. On the other hand it is well established experimentally that vacancy-interstitial pairs are formed during ion bombardment, as are clusters of these, resulting primarily from the low energy events described here. Of course, even the displacement spike concept acknowledges that Frenkel pairs must be formed over some part of the primary energy spectrum and so the observation of these is expected.

In order to assess what observable properties may be influenced by spike phenomena Brinkman[26] has assumed that the volume of material re-ordered in a displacement spike is proportional to the primary energy E. This appears to be a well founded assumption since if the energy E is equally divided between all atoms in the melted zone of the spike, and one assumes an upper limit to the energy of each atom at and above the melting temperature to be about 1 eV, then the number of atoms in the spike is approximately E. If n_0 is the atomic density and V is the spike volume then $E = n_0 V$. For an initial ion of energy E_0 there will be a spectrum of primary knock on energies E, and so a spectrum of spike sizes will be observed for knock on energies between E_1 and E_2. If δn is the number of spikes in the volume range δV then

$$\frac{dn}{dV} = \frac{E}{V} \cdot \frac{dn}{dt} \qquad 6.140$$

since $E/V = \frac{dE}{dV} = n_0$.

The number of atoms contained in a spike created by a knock-on copper atom of 20 keV energy in Copper, is thus of order 2×10^4, and if the melted zone is assumed spherical the diameter of this will be about 75 Å. The smallest spikes will thus be about 20 Å in diameter. One should consider the primary energy in three regions. (a) $E < E_1$, then no displacement spikes will occur and only Frenkel pairs will be produced. (b) $E_1 < E < E_2$, then one displacement spike will occur for each primary, the size of each spike increasing with initial energy up to a maximum size at energy E_2. (c) $E > E_2$, then Frenkel pairs will be produced by the primary until, through collision its energy decreases below E_2, where a displacement spike will be produced. Since the primary knock ons may also acquire energy above E_2 then the number of displacement spikes produced will be greater than one per primary. Since in this model of the displacement spike, when the displaced atom of a Frenkel pair acquires energy less than E_2 it can no longer produce further pairs, but only displacement spikes the problem of finding the number of atoms generated in an energy range E' to $E' + \delta E'$ (where $E' < E_2$) is equivalent to that of finding the number of primaries in this energy range, in conventional cascade theory, but with the displacement threshold $E_d. = E_2$. The defining equation for the number of displaced atoms in the energy range $E', E' + \delta E'$ is thus

$$S(E, E') = 2 \int_{E_2}^{E} S(E_1, E') \frac{dE_1}{E^1} + 2 \qquad 6.141.1$$

using the hard sphere approximation for equal mass initial and target atoms. The solution of this, as we have seen, in Equation 6.115.2 is

$$S(E, E') = \frac{2E}{E_2^2} = \frac{dN}{dE'} \qquad 6.141.2$$

Thus the number of displacement spikes per unit energy range between E_1 and E_2 is independent of the energy, but increases with increasing primary energy E and decreasing limiting energy E_2. These results should be expected since increasing primary energy will increase the total number of Frenkel pairs and thus the effective number of primary knock-ons capable of generating spikes whereas decreasing E_2 will allow formation of more Frenkel pairs at energies above E_2 which can subsequently produce spikes. We may note that these results are only a first approximation since we have assumed that all knock-ons atoms acquiring less than E_2 generate spikes. In fact for primary knock-on atoms with energy less than E_1 no spikes will form but Frenkel pairs will be produced. Since the fraction of such atoms compared to the total number should be small (of the order E_1/E_2) then these will not be too important in determining the number of spikes formed. We conclude therefore that for high primary energies ($E > E_2$) a number of Frenkel pairs should be produced, then a uniform distribution of spikes of decreasing size, and finally some multiple vacancy-interstitial clusters. The uniform distribution of spike sizes between V_1 (due to primaries of energy E_1) and V_2 (primaries of energy E_2) is, of course only a consequence of our assumption of a hard sphere interaction. For any other potential, the actual distribution of spikes sizes will depend upon the form of the scattering law. Thus the coulomb potential which favours small energy transfers will lead to a preponderance of smaller volume spikes.

We see also that the number of Frenkel pairs produced in the higher energy region will be of the order of $\frac{E - E_2}{2E_d}$ since primary knock-ons with energy less than E_2 do not form Frenkel pairs. This value is considerably less than the cascade theory predicts if E and E_2 are similar. Consequently the number of Frenkel pairs produced will be reduced, although the displacement spikes themselves will be expected to produce at least a few Frenkel pairs. From the Equation 6.141.2 it is seen that the total number of displaced atoms generated by displacement spikes will be

$$\int_{E_1}^{E_2} E' \frac{dn}{dE'} dE' = \int_{E_1}^{E_2} E' \frac{2E}{E_2^2} dE' \qquad 6.142.1$$

i.e.

$$\frac{2E}{E_2^2}(E_2^2 - E_1^2) \qquad 6.142.2$$

using the result of Equation 6.141.2 and the fact that about 1 eV per atom will be expended in the spike.

Since $E_2 \gg E_1$, the final result is that just 2E atoms will take place in the displacement spikes. Thus, in order for the number of permanent displacements produced by displacement spikes to be less than those produced in a cascade theory, less than a fraction $\frac{1}{4E_d}$ of displaced atoms generated in the spikes must remain unannealed, i.e. 1%. Since it is difficult to say with certainty anything about the absolute magnitude of the retained displacements it is not certain that the above figure of 1% can be expected, i.e. whether spikes will lead to as many displacements as cascade theory. Nevertheless one should expect a certain number of these to be produced. However, since the displacement spikes cause local heating, then some, at least of the closer spaced pairs will recombine during bombardment. Brinkman[130,136] has suggested an alternative method of the diminution of Frenkel pair production due to spike formation. Since it is supposed that only the small energy transfer collisions result in spike formation whilst the large angle collisions cause Frenkel pair production in a cascade type process, then the integral equations for defect production may be divided into two parts.

Thus, the Kinchin-Pease model, for $\nu(E)$.

$$\nu(E) = \int_0^E \frac{d\sigma(T)}{\sigma} \nu(T) + \int_0^E \frac{d\sigma(E-T)}{\sigma} \nu(E-T) \qquad 6.143.1$$

is divided into two energy regions. One from 0 to E_d where the collisions are glancing and lead to spike-production, and one from E_d to E where the collisions are hard sphere type. Expansion of $\nu(E-T)$ up to terms linear in T, then leads to a modified integral equation.

$$\sigma_D \cdot \nu(E) = \int_{E_d}^{E} d\sigma(T) \cdot \nu(T) - \nu'(E)\, S_0(E) \qquad 6.143.2$$

where

$$\sigma_D = \int_{Ed}^{E} d\sigma(T);\; S_0(E) = \int_0^{Ed} T d\sigma(T)$$

and

$$\nu'(E) = \frac{d\nu(E)}{dE} \qquad 6.143.3$$

$S_0(E)$ describes the small angle energy losses and is proportional to the stopping power which may be determined from range—energy data. (i.e. $\frac{\partial R}{\partial E}$) particularly for high energy particles where almost the whole energy loss occurs in glancing type collisions. Brinkman[136] has solved equation 6.143.2 numerically, using experimental data for $S_0(E)$ for fission fragments in Ur and a hard sphere approximation for $d\sigma(T)$ and shown that this leads to about a 20% reduction in $\nu(E)$ below the Kinchin-Pease model. At lower energies, no calculations of the influence of spikes on the magnitude of $\nu(E)$ are available, but one may anticipate that as the energy is diminished, and spikes assume less importance, the normal cascade calculations of $\nu(E)$ should be quite adequate, particularly when the effects of lattice symmetry are considered. For low primary fluxes, where the displacement spikes do not overlap, the rate of production of Frenkel pairs dN/dt per unit volume will be given by

$$\frac{dN}{dt} = \alpha \frac{dn(E)}{dt} - \beta N \frac{dn(E)}{dt} \qquad 6.144.1$$

where $\frac{dn(E)}{dt}$ is the flux of primaries of energy E, α describes the number of pairs produced per primary ion, and β the rate of pair recombination due to spike production, or due to some other form of radiation induced recombination.

Integration of equation 6.144.1 gives the Frenkel pair density after a total ion bombardment n

$$N = \frac{\alpha}{\beta}(1 - \exp(-\beta n)) \qquad 6.144.2$$

and the saturation value $Ns = \alpha/\beta$. If it is assumed that a property of the solid, such as resistivity change increases linearly with pair density, then it is obvious that the resistivity change should increase exponentially with ion dose to a saturation change proportional to α/β. Such a behaviour has been observed in deuteron bombarded copper by Cooper, Koehler and Marx,[137,138] although this alone does not establish equivocally the concept of displacement spikes since the constant defined by β (radiation annealing) may arise through an altogether different mechanism, e.g. simple bombardment induced collision of interstitials and vacancies. If this latter situation was the case however both α and β would be expected to vary by the same factor if the nature or energy of incident particles were changed, whereas if the production process and recombination processes were due to pair production and spike production respectively, α and β would be expected to vary differently as the ion species or energy was varied. Since $N_s = \alpha/\beta$ the observed property change should vary with changes in the primary bombardment if spikes were the cause of radiation annealing. So far, however, only a very few experiments have been performed to establish this, but Brinkman[130] considers that Quere and Nakache's[139] data for resistivity changes in proton and deuteron bombarded Thorium and Uranium support the concept of displacement spikes. It is further clear that since displacement spikes increase the target temperature locally, a certain amount of re-ordering should occur. Thus an alloy such as Cu_3Au should show regions of local re-ordering although again the magnitude is difficult to assess. Moreover cascade theory would also predict a certain amount of re-ordering, but again absolute magnitudes are unpredictable. Because of the local temperature increase due to spike production it may be anticipated that diffusion processes should be enhanced during ion bombardment.

Consequently accelerated phase changes in alloys may be anticipated in alloyed targets and again Brinkman interpretes the rate of Molybdenum dispersion in a Ur-Mo alloy studied by Bleiberg[140] and Konobeevsky [141] as substantiating the displacement spike mechanism. It is also probable that spike events were observed by Denney[142,143] in a CuFe alloy after 9MeV proton bombardment where a change in an added ferromagnetic precipitate, associated with spike heating was noted. Gonser, Okkerse[144,145] and Fujita[146] suggested that volume changes in 12 MeV deuteron irradiated gallium antimonide were due to the local heating produced by spikes.

Moreover low energy diffraction studies of this material after bombardment revealed the presence of numerous regions of changed electron density of approximately 30 Å diameter, and the density of these regions was equivalent to the number of knock-ons produced by the deuteron bombardment. Finally Parsons and Balluffi[46] have recently presented evidence of re-ordering in Xe^+ ion and neutron irradiated Ge as exhibited in transmission electron microscopy and have ascribed these to displacement spike production. It should be noted that in this section, focusing, crowdion and channelling events have been neglected, whereas these will certainly occur even when generated from displacement spike regions. Indeed Seeger [37,147] suggests that a type of displacement spike may be formed with the vacancy rich core, but in which the interstitials are created remote from this core via focusing, crowdion and channelling events. Thus the conditions for collapse of the vacancy void and re-ordering are absent and the resulting structure is one of depleted zones (voids) and interstitial rich regions.

We must finally conclude therefore, that neither simple cascade theory, nor spike processes have been firmly established as the only mechanism producing defects and it is possible that both occur simultaneously.

6.3.6.3 Thermal Spikes

In the foregoing analysis we have considered that during a displacement spike, which occur for primary energies in excess of several hundred eV, the effective heating effect of the spike results in the re-ordering of the damaged volume. However heating effects will still occur even for lower primary energies, although complete re-ordering may not ensue during the period of the spike.

Such spikes may be expected to occur at energies in the region of the displacement energy where the primary can produce at most one extra displaced atom, and this of low energy, so that the spike formation volume is small. When the displaced atoms degrade their energies below 25 eV no further displacements will occur and this energy must be dissipated by lattice vibration and heating. This type of energy dissipation forms what is known as a thermal spike, and is very similar to the low energy displacement spike already discussed. Indeed it is unnecessary to differentiate between the thermal spike and the lowest energy displacement spikes as shown in a comprehensive analysis of thermal spikes by Seitz and Koehler[3].

In the following we will summarize the results obtained by these authors, assuming, for convenience, that the primary generating the spike has a typical energy of 50 eV. We may adopt the same approach as in the previous section to determine the temperature rise at and close to the spike centre and the subsequent decay of this with time. Thus the temperature at a distance r from the spike centre at a time t is given by

$$T = \frac{Q}{8(\pi K t)^{3/2}} \cdot C^{1/2} d^{1/2} \exp\left[\frac{-Cdr^2}{4Kt}\right] \qquad 6.138.2$$

where D is the thermal diffusivity equal to $\frac{K}{Cd}$ in which K is the thermal conductivity, C, the specific heat and d the mass density. This shows that the temperature rise is approximately constant up to a distance $r = (4Dt)^{1/2}$. Thus as time increases the high temperature zone increases in diameter, i.e. a temperature wave diffuses from the zone centre, and after its passage the lattice again cools. Thus the maximum radius r_m of the zone up to which the lattice reaches the melting temperature T_m is given approximately by $r_m^2 = 4D_m$ where t_m is the time taken for the zone to cool to T_m. Assuming that the melting temperature is 1000°K (typical of metals such as gold, copper and silver etc.) (c.f. the value of 3000°K assumed by Brinkman[130] for heavy metals such as U), and that each atom within the melted region acquires the same mean energy, 3kT (≅ 0.3eV), then the number of atoms contained in the melted zone for Q = 50 eV is given by $\frac{4}{3}\pi \cdot r_m^3 n_0 = \frac{50}{3kT_m} \cong 170$ where n_0 is the atomic density of the solid. The volume occupied per lattice atom is of the order $\frac{4}{3}\pi \times r_s^3 = \frac{1}{n_0}$ for an effective atomic radius r_s, and so r_m is of order $6r_s$ i.e. about 170 atoms are concerned in the spike. Further the time involved, t_m, is of order $40 \cdot t_0$ where t_0 is defined from $t_0 = \frac{Cdr_s^2}{K}$ i.e. the vibration period of a lattice atom ($\cong 10^{-13}$ secs). We should note that the 170 atoms contained in the spike are not displaced in the displacement spike but merely agitated. Nevertheless, since those atoms have been raised to the melting temperature, one may expect some defect production and annealing. The time for which the thermal spike under discussion persists, $\approx 40\ t_0$, is between 10^{-12} and 10^{-11} secs, but for smaller primary energies, the number of atoms involved and the time scale is considerably shorter. During the duration of the spike the heated atoms have the possibility of migration, as may be seen from the following considerations. In a typical first order reaction process, where the energy required for stimulation of the reaction is E_r, then the frequency with which the particles engage in the reaction is given by

$$\gamma = \gamma_0 \exp(E_r/kT) \qquad 6.145.1$$

where γ_0 is the frequency coefficient of order 10^{-13} sec^{-1}. Thus the number of times each atom in the spike zone may be expected to take part in any reaction, such as the formation of a Frenkel pair, during the spike duration is given by

$$n_j = \int_{t_0}^{\infty} \nu_0 \exp\left(\frac{-Er}{kT(t)}\right) dt \approx \nu_0 \int_0^{\infty} \exp\left(\frac{-Er}{kT(t)}\right) dt; \quad t > t_0 \qquad 6.146.1$$

where T(t) is the time dependence of the spike temperature, which may be assumed to be of the form

$$T(t) = \{Q/8(\pi Dt)^{3/2}\} \frac{1}{Cd}$$

in the spike centre. This integral may be rewritten

$$n_j = \tfrac{2}{3}\ \nu_0\ \alpha^{2/3} \int_0^{\infty} e^{-x} x^{-1/3} dx = \tfrac{2}{3}\ \nu_0\ \alpha^{2/3} \times \Gamma(\tfrac{2}{3}) \qquad 6.146.2$$

where

$$x = t^{3/2}/\alpha, \Gamma(\tfrac{2}{3}) = 1.35 \text{ and } \alpha = \frac{Q}{E_r} \cdot \frac{k}{Cd(4\pi D)^{3/2}}$$

Now Cd is of the order $3kn_0$ (i.e. the Dulong-Petit Law) and so

$$n_j = \frac{\tfrac{2}{3}\ \nu_0\ \Gamma(\tfrac{2}{3})\ r_s^2}{(324\,\pi)^{1/3}\ D} \cdot \{Q/E_r\}^{2/3} \qquad 6.146.3$$

or approximately

$$n_j \simeq 0.093\rho\ \{Q/E_r\}^{2/3} \qquad 6.146.4$$

where

$$\rho = \frac{\nu_0 r_s^2}{D}$$

measures the ratio of the atomic vibration frequency and the frequency with which the translational energy of the atoms is transferred, and is clearly of order unity. Thus for Q = 50 eV and a rate process with

$E_r = 1$ eV, $n_j = 1.25$ i.e. each atom engages in a reaction only about once during the duration of each spike, and this is still approximately true for $E_r = 3$ eV which is roughly the energy required for generation of a Frenkel pair.

Most of the integral contributing to n_j is associated with the time interval $t = o$ to $t = \alpha^{2/3}$ since for $t > \alpha^{2/3}$ the contribution to the integral is 10% or less.

Consequently the probability that an atom takes part in a reaction is small outside the sphere of radius

$$r = \frac{4}{(324\pi)^{1/2}}\left(\frac{Q}{E_r}\right)^{1/3} r_s$$

upon substitution of values of D in terms of r_s and use of equation $r^2 = 4Dt$ for r in terms of $t(= \alpha^{2/3})$.

For $Q = 50$ eV and $E_\nu = 3$ eV, the radius is about $3.3r_s$ i.e. about 30 atoms may participate in a reaction. These values are necessarily overestimates however, since the temperature pulse does not arrive at a given radius until a finite delay time after the initial spike formation. If this delay time is taken into account then it is found that n_j is very much smaller, and equal to about 1.7. On the other hand this treatment assumes that the reaction can only occur in one independent way e.g. an atom can only interact with one adjacent atom, whereas there are probably several independent interaction modes. If this number is as large as 10 then the number of activated atoms is calculated to be 7.

For a primary atom of energy 300eV, one may expect about six such spikes, with the production of 10 and 42 participating atoms respectively depending upon the number of possible interaction modes. In the case of an alloy such as Cu_3Au, theoretical estimates suggests that the former value for Cu and Au atoms which interchange positions, is the correct choice whereas experimental measurements by Brinkman Dixon and Meechan[148] of 9 MeV proton bombardment of Cu_3Au, indicate a value of 120. This disagreement indicates that the present calculation is unreliable for a real symmetrical lattice in which focusing effects can substantially alter the nature of the energy loss after the primary energy has degraded below 25eV. Indeed the earlier calculations of section 6.3.5.3 due to Leibfried[98] indicate that the focusing mechanism can adequately account for the increased disordering in an initially ordered alloy. However the calculations may be quite good for a random target array although it is difficult to measure effects in such materials experimentally.

Although, in a random solid, some of the agitated atoms will produce Frenkel pairs, only a few will be expected to persist at the high temperatures generated by the spike. Those which do persist will be due to displacements resulting from high energy primaries where the separation between the displaced interstitial and its associated vacancy is large. Thus, most permanent Frenkel pairs and vacancy-interstitial clusters will result from primaries with energies above 50eV. As pointed out by Seitz and Koehler[3] however, it is rather difficult to assess the magnitude of the number of Frenkel pairs under the influence of thermal production and annihilation due to migration and recombination. This question of diffusive migration will be taken up again in the following section.

We conclude therefore that whilst it is possible, and indeed probable, that both displacement and thermal spikes are formed during bombardment, it is rather difficult to make any quantitative assessment of their importance. As we shall see later and, in fact, as already suggested, experimental evidence for their presence is rather limited, but, this is due largely to the fact that the initial experiments to test for their validity have not been performed, rather than that the experiments have yielded negative results. Certainly one would expect some form of spike formation, but the effects of lattice symmetry not considered in the present discussion must be borne in mind in future assessments of the magnitudes of displacement events expected in these spikes, just as in simple cascade theory.

6.3.7 Annealing of Defects

We saw at the beginning of this Chapter that once a Frenkel pair has been formed the members of the pair may become spatially separated and require a finite energy for their migration, recombination and annihilation. It is not necessary that the members of the original pair should recombine in order to reduce the defect population since an interstitial from one pair may meet and recombine with a vacancy of another pair, or either species may migrate to and become trapped at various sinks, such as dislocations, defect clusters and surfaces in the target. Whatever the mechanism of defect annihilation or annealing each individual migration process will be typified by an activation energy required for movement of each species. i.e. each species is located in a potential energy well of depth equal to the activation energy for migration Q_j. At a given temperature T the frequency ν with which the species attains the energy Q_j is given by the Frenkel[149] equation $\nu = \nu_0 \exp(-Q_j/kT)$. Where ν_0 is the vibration frequency of the species, generally observed to be in the region $10^{13} - 10^{14}$ sec. If it assumed that each time an active species receives the energy Q_j, it migrates and is lost by mutual annihilation (as in vacancy-interstitial recombination) or that it migrates to a sink for such species, then the rate of destruction of these species is given by

$$\frac{dn_j}{dt} = \nu \cdot S_i \cdot n_j \qquad 6.147.1$$

where n_j is the species density and S_i the probability of migration to a sink. This may be rewritten

$$\frac{dn_j}{dt} = S_i\, n_j/\tau_j \qquad 6.147.2$$

where

$$\tau_j = (1/\nu_0)\exp(Q_j/kT) \qquad 6.145.2$$

If the sink density is inexhaustible, such as would be the case where interstitials or vacancies nucleate at dislocations, then Equation 6.147 is a typical first order rate of reaction equation and is readily soluble at a constant temperature since S_i is unity. If, on the other hand, annihilation is due to the recombination of vacancies and interstitials moving in 3 dimensions produced by bombardment, then S_j will be exhaustible and will be directly proportional to the number of unrecombined pairs i.e. $S_i = n_j$. Consequently Equation 6.147 will become second order, with, again, a straightforward solution. It may be anticipated that other types of reaction may occur and so a general rate equation

$$\frac{dn_j}{dt} = K_j (n_j)^x/\pi_j \qquad 6.148.1$$

may be formulated. This, however is an oversimplification since it is assumed that once the active species gains the energy Q_j it can migrate immediately to a sink. In general a migrating atom will not migrate smoothly to a sink but in a series of jumps from one potential well to another. The probability of migration of a given species will therefore depend upon its ability to jump unimpeded from well to well, i.e. upon the probability of occupancy of such sites. Consequently the migration of the entity to a sink will depend upon the population density of species i.e. the migration rate is concentration dependent. This immediately renders the problem one of a diffusive nature with the defining equation

$$D_j \Delta^2 n_j = \frac{\partial n_j}{\partial t} \qquad 6.149$$

where D_j is the diffusion coefficient at a temperature T, and, if the migration is due to an activated process, is given by

$$D_j = D_0 \exp(-Q_j/kT) \qquad 6.150$$

This equation is only true for one migrating species with the same or different values of D_j. If one species alone is involved, equation 6.149 is soluble knowing the initial species and sink concentrations.

We shold note, however, that Equation 6.149 is the normal diffusion equation of stochastic processes which is generally applied where the mean free path of migrating atoms is considerably larger than the interatomic spacing. This condition is no longer valid under many circumstances of defect migration where a defect migrates one lattice spacing at a time. Under these circumstances it is probably more correct to treat the problem by the calculus of finite differences, i.e. to consider the defect population of adjacent lattice planes only as conditioning the migration probability of a given entity. We will consider this approach in greater detail later and in Chapter 8 but note for the present, that it leads to essentially the same results as the infinitesimal calculus equation 6.149 under many circumstances. Indeed for the present we will neglect the fact that migration will be concentration dependent and make the simplifying assumptions that Equations 6.147.1, 6.148.1 are valid for first and x order reactions respectively. We will subsequently explore the consequences of this simplification.

It is readily deduced that the solution of Equation 6.147.1 at constant temperature is

$$n_{jt} = n_{jo} \exp(-t/\tau_j) \qquad 6.151$$

where τ_j is a constant.

If the temperature is varied as a function of time $T = f(t)$, then the solution is given formally by

$$n_j = n_{jo} \exp(-\int_0^t \nu_0 \exp(-Q_j/kf(t)).\,dt.) \qquad 6.152$$

In order to explore the effects of temperature upon the rate at which the defects anneal, consider first, Equations 6.145.2 and 6.151 with an assumed value of $Q_j = 1ev$.

It is readily seen that, with $\nu_0 = 10^{-13}$ sec^{-1}, τ_j is of order 10^{+5} secs, at room temperature, but is reduced to 1 sec at about 150°C, and at liquid nitrogen temperature (—196°C) is increased to 10^{59} secs. On the other hand if Q_j is considered to be 0.1eV, τ_j is observed to be only 10^{-6} secs at —196°C and much smaller at higher temperatures. Since experimental observations of property changes which depend upon defect concentrations will normally occupy times of the order of seconds up to weeks, it is evident that observable changes will occur at room temperature and above for processes with an activation energy of 1eV or so since the defect population will decrease by a factor of e^{-1} in a time τ_j. It is further clear that all defects of 0.1 ev activation energy will have annealed before observations commence, even at liquid Nitrogen temperature, and experiments designed to investigate such low energy events must be performed at even lower temperatures.

Equation 6.151 reveals one method by which activation energies may be measured, namely the Isochronal method. If the defect density were measured as a function of time at a constant temperature T_1 the slope of the log density/time curve would give $\nu_0 \exp(-Q_j/kT_1)$. Alternatively the time t_1 required to reduce n_j to a given logarithmic fraction of its initial value would give $t_1 \nu_0 \exp(-Q_j/kT_1)$. However ν_0 must be treated as an unknown parameter, and so deduction of the time t_2 to reach the same fractional change in n_j, at a slightly different temperature T_2 would give $t_2 \nu_0 \exp(-Qj/kT_2)$ and thus

$$t_1 \exp(-Q_j/kT_1) = t_2 \exp(-Q_j/kT_2) \qquad 6.153$$

and thence follows the evaluation of Q_j. The temperatures T_1 and T_2 must only be slightly separated, since as we have seen τ_j changes by many orders of magnitude for relatively small changes in T. Clearly the best procedure would be to determine the time t to reach the same fractional defect annihilation at a series of temperatures T, and from a logt./1/T graph determine Q_j accurately.

A second method involves determining the rate of annealing at a temperature T_1, $\left\{\frac{dn_j}{dt}\right\}_{T_1}$ and then suddenly changing the temperature to T_2 and reobserving the annihilation rate $\left\{\frac{dn_j}{dt}\right\}_{T_2}$. If the temperature change is rapid, then it may be assumed that n_j is the same at the end of the T_1 interval as at the start of the T_2 interval. Equation 6.151 then shows that

$$\left\{\frac{dn_j}{dt}\right\}_{T_1} \Big/ \left\{\frac{dn_j}{dt}\right\}_{T_2} = \exp\left\{-\frac{Q_j}{k}\left(\frac{1}{T_1} - \frac{1}{T_2}\right)\right\} \qquad 6.154$$

hence evaluation of Q_j. this method, the isothermal approach, is particularly useful if T_2 is less than T_1 such as may be the case when a specimen is rapidly quenched from a higher to a lower temperature. In this case, since the relaxation time τ_j increases rapidly with decrease in T, the condition than n_j remains constant at the step temperature change is well satisfied. If the temperature change is insufficiently rapid to maintain n_j constant, then the isochronal method should be adopted, measuring either the slope of the log annihilation rate/time curve or the time to reach a given fractional density change at both temperatures. It should be stressed again, however, that the choice of temperature is dictated by the energies of migration which it is required to measure. If the order of the reaction is not unity, then analysis of data is a little less straightforward since one requires not only the activation energy for migration but the order of the reaction.

For a general reaction order x the defining equation

$$\frac{dn_j}{dt} = K_j\ (n_j)^x \exp(-Qj/kT) \qquad 6.155.1$$

has three unknown, K_j, x and Q_j about which information is desirable. It is then deduced that

$$\frac{d^2n_j}{dt^2} = xn_j\left(\frac{dn_j}{dt}\right)^2 = x\left(\frac{dn_j}{dt}\right)^2 \cdot\left\{-\frac{dn_j}{dt}\Big/ Kj \exp (-Q_j/kT)\right\}^{1/x}$$

and thus the slope of the $\frac{d^2n_j}{dt^2}$ as a function of $n_j\left(\frac{dn_j}{dt}\right)^2$ graph yields the reaction order x, by measurement at a constant temperature T_1, and confirmation of this may be obtained from the slope of a simple $\log\left(-\frac{dn_j}{dt}\right)/\log n_j$ plot which again yields x. Unfortunately these methods require knowledge of n_j as function of time and thus, the initial value n_{jo}. These values may be difficult to assess accurately and so a more reliable, although tedious method of evaluation lies in evaluation of the

$$\log\left\{\frac{d^2n_j}{dt^2}\Big/\left(\frac{dn_j}{dt}\right)^2\right\}, \log\frac{dn_j}{dt} \text{ plot}$$

which yields $1/x$ as the slope, and

$$\log x + 1/x \log_e K_j\ (\exp(-Q_j/kT)$$

as the intercept, and requires knowledge only of the rate of annihilation and its derivative. However, neither K_j nor Q_j can be evaluated separately by this isothermal method as is indeed true of the first order kinetics considered earlier, and complete evalution of these requires experiments at different temperatures. Thus if the temperature is changed suddenly from T_1 to T_2, and n_j is assumed constant, the ratio of rates of annealing at the two temperatures, gives Q_j i.e.

$$\left.\frac{dn_j}{dt}\right|_{T_1} \Big/ \left.\frac{dn_j}{dt}\right|_{T_2} = \exp\left(\frac{-Q_j}{K}\left(\frac{1}{T_1} - \frac{1}{T_2}\right)\right) \qquad 6.154$$

Thus, with x and Q_j evaluated, the deduction of K_j is straight forward. The isochronal method is also applicable by measurement of the times required to attain a given fractional annihilation at two temperatures, which again gives Q_j explicity. Again however this suffers from the disadvantage of requiring knowledge of n_{jo} exactly and so a more precise, but inconvenient, method is to plot the intercept of the

$$\log\left\{\frac{d^2n_j}{dt^2}\Big/\left(\frac{dn_j}{dt}\right)^2\right\}\Big/ \log\frac{dn_j}{dt}$$

plot against logarithmic temperature for a range of the latter and thence deduce Q_j. Clearly the method is cumbersome and rather inaccurate because of errors made in obtaining derivatives of the annihilation rate.

A more convenient method is an intermediate between the isochronal and step temperature isothermal techniques in which the target temperature is varied as a known function of time, and which is applicable to any order reaction kinetics. Consider, initially, for the sake of simplicity, first order kinetics, defined by Equation 6.147 in which the temperature T is caused to vary as an arbitrary function of time T = f(t) and of which the general solution is

$$n_{jt} = -n_{jo}\ \nu_0 \exp \int_0^t (-Q_j/kf(t)).\,dt \qquad 6.156$$

or

$$\frac{dn_j}{dt} = -n_{jo}\ \nu_0 \exp(-Q_j/kf(t)) \exp \int_0^t \nu_0 \exp(-Q_j/kf(t))dt$$

$$= \frac{n_{jo}}{\tau_j(T)} \exp\left(-\int_0^t \frac{1}{\tau_j(T)}\, dt\right) \qquad 6.157$$

Since $\tau_j(T)$ decreases exponentially with increasing temperature, it will be readily appreciated that $\frac{dn_j}{dt}$ initially increases rapidly with increasing temperature, reaches a maximum and declines equally rapidly. The temperature range over which the bulk of the change in $\frac{dn_j}{dt}$ occurs will be quite small.

This may be appreciated analytically by differentiating equation 6.147 to deduce the condition for maximum annihilation rate $\frac{dn_j}{dt}$ which is shown to be

$$\frac{Q_j}{kT^2}\frac{dT}{dt} = \nu_0 \exp(-Q_j/kT) \qquad 6.158.1$$

Two temperature-time schedules are important, (a) the linear rise with time; T = a + bt and (b) The reciprocal rise with time $\frac{1}{T} = c + dt$

(a) leads to the temperature T_a at maximum rate, as

$$\frac{bQ_j}{kT_a^2} = \nu_0 \exp(-Qj/kTa) \qquad 6.158.2$$

(b) leads to the temperature T_b at maximum rate

$$T_b = -Q_j/k\ \{\log_e(-dQ_j/k\nu_0)\}^{-1} \qquad 6.158.3$$

T_a and T_b may be deduced graphically (and analytically in case b) for various values of Q_j and the heating rates b and d, and the resulting relations evaluated by Redhead[150] and Carter[151], are shown in Figures 6.36 a and b. It is immediately apparent that T_m is linearly dependent upon the activation energy Q_j with the constant of proportionality depending upon the heating rate. Consequently, measurement of the temperature at which the maximum annealing rate occurs, and reference to one of Figures 6.36 a and b, for linear and reciprocal temperature functions respectively enables evaluation of the activation energy. Since τ_j changes rapidly with increasing temperature the temperature range over which $\frac{dn_j}{dt}$ changes measurably is small, as may be deduced by solution of Equation 6.157 for a specific temperature rise function. For the linear temperature rise a typical rate/temperature curve is depicted in Figure 6.37 and

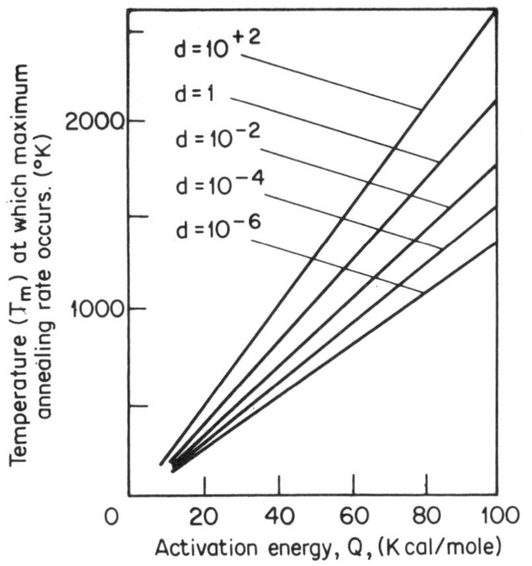

Fig. 6.36a The temperature at which the maximum annealing rate occurs during annealing with a temperature schedule $\frac{1}{T} = c + dt$, for various values of *d*. (viz. Ref. 6.150)

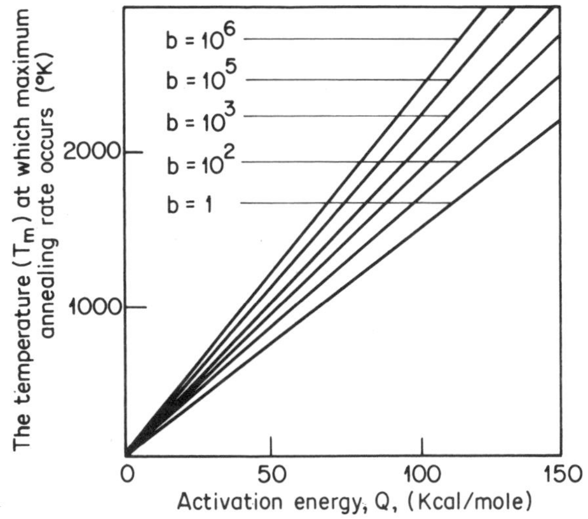

Fig. 6.36b The temperatures at which the maximum annealing rate occurs during annealing with a temperature schedule T = a + bt., for various values of *b*. (viz. Ref. 6.151)

N. B. 24 Kcal/mole ≅ leV

the sharply peaked nature of this curve about T_a is immediately obvious. Integration of this curve with respect to time reveals how the defect density also decreases rapidly with increasing temperature, as shown in Figure 6.37. An estimate of the width of the peak in Figure 6.37 may be obtained analytically by deducing the temperature difference between the points where the annihilation rate is e^{-1} of the maximum rate. Carter[151] has shown that this temperature difference is given by

$$\Delta T \simeq \frac{RT_m^2}{104Q_j} \qquad 6.159$$

for both the linear and reciprocal temperature rise functions where R is the universal gas constant. Figure 6.37, indicates that $T_m \approx 1.5 \times 10^{-2}\, Q_j$ for a considerable range of values of heating rate, and so

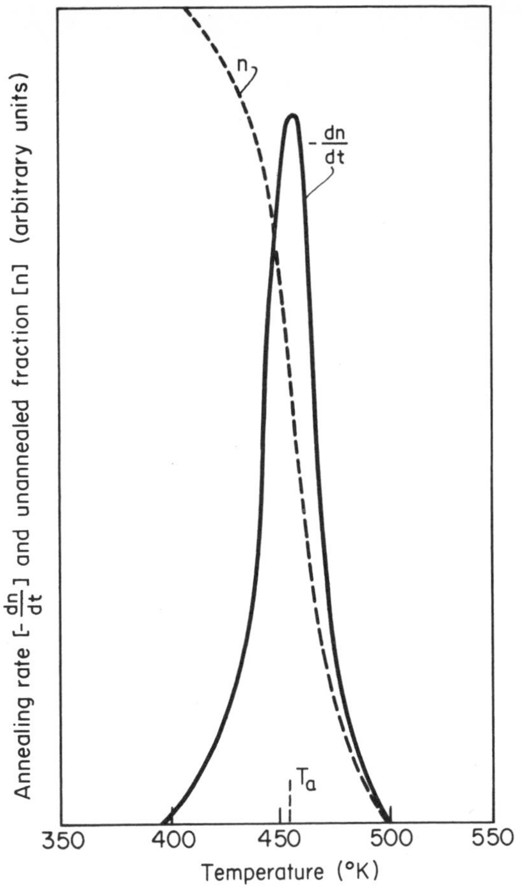

Fig. 6.37 Annealing Rate and Unannealed fraction as a function of temperature during annealing at a rate of 1°K /sec (linear temperature-time schedule T = a + bt) for an activation energy Q = 30 Kcal/mole. (viz. Ref. 6.151)

$\Delta T \approx 15\, Q_j$°K. For $Q_j = 1.0$eV, $\Delta T \simeq 15$°K whilst T_m is about 450°K, but for $Q_j = 0.1$eV, $\Delta T \approx 1.5$°K whilst T_m is about 45°K. Consequently the temperature rise must be controlled and measured quite accurately to determine Q_j exactly. Further the temperature range must be carefully selected and a logical choice would be $T_m - 2\Delta T$ to $T_m + 2\Delta T$. Inspection of Equations 6.158.2 and 3 shows that the temperature at which maximum annealing rate occurs is independent of the initial species density. This independence is characteristic of first order kinetics only and so experimental confirmation of this independence leads to immediate specification of a first order reaction.

If, however, a higher order reaction is involved, the temperature at maximum rate depends upon the reaction order and Carter[152] has deduced the defining Equations for the temperature at maximum rate for linear and reciprocal rates as

$$\exp(Q_j/kT_m) = K_j \nu_0 k T_m^2\, n_{j0}^{x-1}/bQ_j \qquad 6.160.1$$

for the linear sweep

$$\exp(Q_j/kT_m) = -K_j \nu_0 k n_{j0}^{x-1}/dQ_j \qquad 6.160.2$$

for the reciprocal sweep. Without knowledge of the reaction order or the initial defect population therefore, it is not possible to deduce Q_j by this method. However the maximum annealing rate can be shown to be

$$\left|\frac{dn_j}{dt}\right|_m = \frac{d}{k} \cdot Q_j n_{jo} \, (1/x)^{x/x-1} \qquad 6.161.1$$

for the reciprocal temperature sweep

$$\left|\frac{dn_j}{dt}\right|_m = -bQ_j n_{jo} \, (1/x)^{x/x-1}/KT_m^2 \qquad 6.161.2$$

for the linear temperature sweep. Consequently if any of the unknowns, Q_j, x, K_j, n_{0j} is measureable from a constant temperature experiment, two other measurements T_m and $\left|\frac{dn_j}{dt}\right|_m$ in a temperature sweep determination enable evaluation of the other unknowns. Clearly, a preliminary temperature sweep experiment with different initial values of n_{jo} gives immediate indication of whether the reaction is first order or not. If not, further measurements are necessary and n_{jo} itself may be determined from the total integrated area below a rate temperature curve.

Thus far we have assumed that only one defect species is migratory with an activation energy Q_j. However, it is usually observed that several different annihilation processes occur, with different energies of activation. If we assume that each migration is independent, i.e. no interaction or competition between migrating species, then, for first order reations each process is described by an equation such as Equation 6.157 with appropriate values of n_{jo} and Q_j. If only two activation energies are involved, and these are widely separated then at a temperature at which the defects with the lower activation energy anneal rapidly, almost complete annihilation of these will be affected, whilst those defects of higher energy will only deplete by a minor amount. Thus a study of the initial annihilation rate will give the lower activation energy whilst the annihilation rate after much longer times leads to the larger activation energy. Since, however, the relaxation time τ_j increases exponentially with activation energy the time scale required to determine both activation energies is impracticably large. An alternative method is to evaluate the lower energy Q_j at a temperature T_j at which the relaxation time constant τ_j is such as to allow meaningful observation of $\frac{dn_j}{dt}$ unequivocally, then raise the temperature rapidly to T_k at which Q_k is determinable. For widely spaced discrete activation energies this method is applicable to the determination of a multiplicity of these. However, if the separation between discrete activation energies is small, or if a continuum of activation energies exists, then the total annihilation rate of defects of energies Q_j and Q_k will be given by $\frac{dn_j}{dt} + \frac{dn_k}{dt}$ at any temperature, where $\frac{dn_j}{dt}$ and $\frac{dn_k}{dt}$ are of similar magnitude. The behaviour of annihilation rate with time will therefore be complex and analysis of the observations must be made rather carefully in order to determine the activation energies. One method of determining the separate activation energies is to heat the target and determine the temperature at which maxima occur in the annihilation rate, and which correspond to the appropriate activation energies via the relation deduced in Equation 6.158. As the temperature is increased each type of defect will produce a peak in annealing rate as shown in Figure 6.37a with each peak shifted slightly along the temperature axis as depicted in Figure 6.38.

Only the total annealing rate is observable in practice and so one determines the superposition of the two

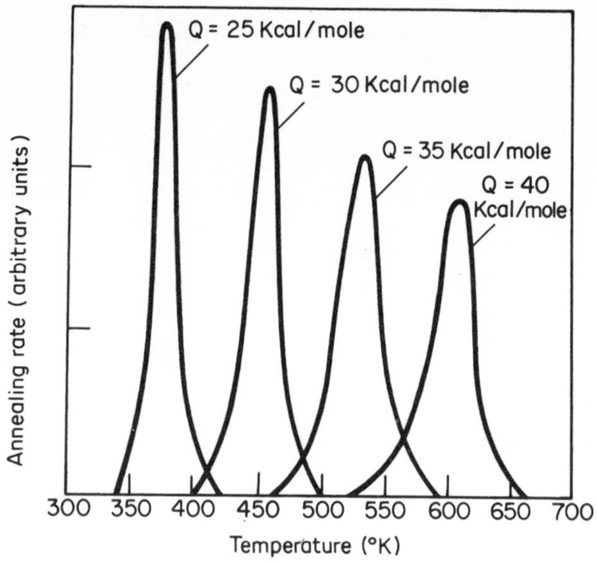

Fig. 6.38 Annealing Rate as a function of temperature employing a rate of 1°K/sec (linear temperature-time schedule T = a + bt) for different activation energies Q. (viz. Ref. 6.151).

peaks. If the temperature separation between the peaks is small, then it is clearly difficult to determine the maxima with any precision, and thus evaluation of the activation energies is also imprecise. It is readily shown from Equation 6.158 that the temperature separation between the peaks, for energies of activation Q_j and $Q_j + \Delta Q_j$ decreases with increasing rate of temperature rise and increasing Q_j. Thus in the limit of a step function temperature rise all defects annihilate simultaneously and evaluation of the separate activation energies is impossible. Thus in order to determine the activation energies for values closely spaced of these the heating rate must be specified rather carefully, i.e. the resolution of the technique depends upon the heating rate, and also upon the energies themselves. A reasonable criterion to adopt for resolution of peaks of the same height is that the valley in the centre of the superimposed peaks should be not greater than 74% of each peak maximum. This corresponds closely to the Rayleigh[153] criterion for optical resolution of two spectral lines where a 20% valley is required, and means that the temperature T_{je} at which the annihilation rate of the first species falls to e^{-1} of the maximum is less than the temperature T_{ke} at which the annihilation rate of the second species has risen to e^{-1} of the maximum. Carter[151] has shown that this criterion allows definition of a resolution $Q_j/\Delta Q_j$ given by

$$\frac{Q_j}{\Delta Q_j} = -\frac{1}{3}\left\{\log_e\left(-\frac{bQ_j}{k\nu_0}\right) - 0.2\right\} \qquad 6.162$$

for the reciprocal temperature sweep and a similar result for the linear temperature sweep. If b is of order 100°K/sec, then Equation 6.162 indicates that activation energies of 2.0 and 2.4 eV are just resolved, or that the resolution at 2.0 eV is 16.

The temperature range required for this is about 800-1200°K. To achieve a similar resolution in the energy range about 0.1 eV, it is evident that the temperature range is around 45°K and the temperature rise rate must be only of the order of a few °K/sec. The situation is more complicated when either the activation energy spectrum is continuous rather than discrete or when the order of reaction is greater than unity. If the former is the case Vand[154], Primak[155] and Carter[151] have shown that the most successful method of determining the initial population is to assume that the actual spectrum may be split up into narrowly spaced discrete energies and, for each energy a theoretical annihilation rate-temperature function is determined assuming an arbitrary initial population for each energy. The total annealing rate is then obtained by summation of the individual rates at a set of different temperatures and each total rate therefore contains linear functions of each initial population (c.f. Equation 6.157 for one discrete energy). Comparison of the theoretical and measured values of the total annihilation rate therefore yields a set of simultaneous linear equations containing the individual initial populations. Solution of these equations then yields the initial population density/activation energy spectrum. Care must be taken, however, to select the theoretical activation energies, so that any fine structure in the observed annihilation rate/temperature curve is accounted for. The maximum and minimum energies which must be considered are readily determined by the maximum and minimum temperatures which must be employed to commence and achieve complete annihilation in the time scale of the experiment, since τ_j's, the relaxation times, are necessarily of the order of the experimental times at the lower and upper temperatures, when annihilation commences and ceases. There is one rather simple case of an activation energy spectrum which does not require the use of arithmetic techniques to evaluate the spectrum, namely a uniform initial population of defects of all activation energies between Q_1 and Q_2. At a temperature T, the annealing rate of defects in the energy range Q_j to $Q_j + \delta Q_j$ is given by

$$\frac{dn_j}{dt} = -\frac{1}{\tau_j}\frac{N}{(Q_2-Q_1)}\exp\left\{-\int_0^t \nu_0 \exp(-Q_j/kT)dt\right\}.\delta Q_j \qquad 6.163.1$$

Where N is the total number of defects with activation energies between Q_1 and Q_2. The total defect annealing rate is thus obtained by integration over Q_j, with the result[156]

$$\frac{dn}{dt} = \frac{kT}{t}\{\exp(-t/\tau_1) - \exp(-t/\tau_2)\} \qquad 6.163.2$$

where

$$\tau_1 = \tau_0 \exp(Q_1/kT); \tau_2 = \tau_0 \exp(Q_2/kT) \qquad 6.163.3$$

are the relaxation times for the lowest and highest migration energies respectively.

This Equation shows that for times intermediate between $\tau_1 \ll t \ll \tau_2$ the annealing rate is proportional to the inverse power of time, but at short and long times the time behaviour is modified by the exponential factors. The lowest energy defects which are observed depends upon the lowest relaxation times observable which in turn depends upon the temperature used through the above relations for τ. If, at constant temperature, the annealing rate remains reciprocally time dependant for long periods the upper energy limit is difficult to determine. However, the temperature may be raised to a higher value after determination of the lower portion of the spectrum, and thus the complete spectrum determined in a piecemeal fashion. It is notable that, even for a non uniform initial population spectrum the rate of annealing depends upon t^{-n}, over considerable periods of time, where n is less than unity for increased population of higher migration energy defects, but n is greater than unity for overpopulation of lower energy defects. If it is suspected therefore, that a uniform population spectrum exists, an initial experiment at a constant temperature to investigate the time dependance of annealing rate can give useful information.

If the reaction is of multiple order it is difficult to determine the activation energies, even when discrete energies only are present, since the temperatures at peak rates are population dependent (viz Equation 6.161). This fact however, does immediately indicate whether multiple order processes are present if a population dependance is observed experimentally. However if the activation energies are widely separated, and initial populations of each species may be determined by integration of each rate peak, then the results may be used in conjunction with Equations analogous to 6.160 to determine the activation energies.

If there is only a small difference in the activation energies then the question of adequate resolution is again important, and it is interesting to note that whilst the resolution decreases with increasing temperature rise rate and activation energy (as for first order kinetics) this parameter increases with increasing initial population.

It is therefore advisable to commence with high initial populations if multiple order kinetics are anticipated, whereas this is unnecessary for first order kinetics. For all orders of reactions however, equations 6.161 illustrate that the annihilation rate always increases with increasing initial defect population, so that the measurement sensitivity increases.

It is clear, therefore, that in designing experiments to determine activation energies from thermal behaviour of annihilation rates, considerable care must be exercised in order to determine the required information accurately, even in the simplified model where it is assumed that all migrating species are independent and that essentially one jump diffusion is an adequate approximation.

If the former of these assumptions is untenable i.e. species A may interact with or convert to species B etc. then the situation is very complex and will not be discussed further here. If the latter assumption is invalid then one must be concerned not with the one jump diffusion Equation 6.147 but with the diffusion Equation 6.149 or its finite difference form.

If the macroscopic diffusion equation is used, $D_j\nabla^2 n_j = \frac{\partial n_j}{\partial t}$ then the diffusion coefficient

$$D_j = \gamma a^2 \nu_j \qquad 6.164$$

Where a is the mean jump distance of defects, γ a numerical constant describing the possible number of ways a defect can jump at each migration $\gamma = 1/24$ for interstitial movement in b.c.c. crystals and $\gamma = 1$ for vacancy diffusion in both b.c.c. and f.c.c. crystals) and $\nu_j = \nu_0 \exp(-Q_j/kT)$. If we first consider the case of inexhaustible sinks with one species migrating at constant temperature then one may write a set of functions

$$\nabla^2 \phi_i(r) + \lambda_i \phi_i(r) = 0 \qquad 6.165.1$$

at all points in the lattice apart from within or on the surfaces of sinks, and $\phi_i(r) = 0$ on the boundaries of sinks.

The λ_i are constants and evaluation of the Eigen functions $\phi_i(r)$ leads to solution of the diffusion equation

$$n_j(r,t) = \sum_{i=o}^{\infty} a_i\phi_i(r)\exp(-\lambda_i Dt) \qquad 6.165.2$$

with

$$a_i = \int_{\text{all space excluding sinks.}} \phi_i(r)n_j(r,o)dv \qquad 6.165.3$$

Thus the defect density at a given point (r) and the total defect density over all the lattice decays with time as a summation of damped exponential functions. The addition of these damped exponentials does not lead to a simple dependance of $\frac{dn_j}{dt}$ (r, t) with time, except for long times where the higher order exponentials have virtually disappeared and

$$n_j(r,t) = a_0\phi_0(r)\exp(-\lambda_0 D_j t) \qquad 6.165.4$$

i.e. the form of the first order, one jump reaction theory with $K_j = \lambda_0 D_j$. The time required to reach this form depends upon the initial concentration distribution (being faster for a uniform defect distribution) and the diffusion coefficient (the larger D_j the smaller the time to reach the asymptotic state). Another fact that may complicate the migration is the possibility that at some sinks the defects may not be trapped but reflected, and solution of the diffusion equation must incorporate this possibility. Many text books on diffusion and nuclear reactor theory[157] give satisfactory treatment of this effect and the reader is referred to these and to the text by Dienes and Vineyard[4] on Radiation Damage for a more detailed account. An important result of this latter treatment is that the final decay constant for a system containing sinks which are clusters of vacancies of radius r_0 and density N_0, is $4\pi r_0 N_0 D_j$ whilst for dislocation traps of infinite length, the decay constant is

$$2\pi N_0 D_j/\log_e\sqrt{N_0/\pi r_0^2}$$

Finally, where defects annihilate via recombination of interstitial and vacancy pairs, the kinetics will again be complex, approximating only to second order kinetics after long periods of time. In this case, the close spaced pairs will annihilate first with the more remote pairs recombining later. Thus, even if only one activation energy for migration is involved, the observed annealing rate/time dependence will be complex, and careful consideration must be given to the data in order to determine migration energies. Further, determination of the reaction order is also fraught with difficulties since the solution of the diffusion equation shows that this may lead to observation of an artificial reaction order, whereas the process may in fact be first order.

This difficulty is accentuated when the target temperature is varied in an attempt to determine the reaction order and activation energy. As we have already seen, if one jump diffusion theory is applicable, the temperature range over which rapid annihilation is observed, is very restricted. If multigroup diffusion theory is applied, one must seek solutions to Equation 6.149 with the condition that D_j is a function of time through the relations. $D_j = D_0\exp\left(-\frac{Q_j}{kT}\right)$ and $T = f(t)$.

Since only a very minor concentration of defects is considered, and further since migration distances are only of the order of the lattice spacing, then one should properly use the finite difference form of 6.149 given by Fletcher and Brown[158] and Kelly[159, 160], viz

$$n_j(x, t + \Delta t) = \left(1 - \frac{\Delta t}{\tau_j}\beta\right)n_j(x,t) + \frac{\Delta t}{\tau_j}\beta/2$$

$$\{n_j(x-\lambda, t) + n_j(x+\lambda, t)\} \qquad 6.166.1$$

where $n_j(x, t)$ is the number of defects in a lattice plane at x, at a time t, λ the lattice spacing, and β the probability that a defect will jump into a new plane upon migration.

For a low defect concentration gradient this reduces to the normal diffusion equation, but for an unrestricted gradient, the solution has been shown to be[160], for a constant target temperature.

$$n_j(r\lambda, t) = n_{jo}\exp(-kt)\{I_{p-r}(kt) - I_{p+r}(kt)\} \qquad 6.166.2$$

$$r = 0, 1, 2, 3 \text{ etc.}$$

where $n_j(r\lambda, t)$ is the defect concentration at the plane $x = r\lambda$ lattice planes removed from a plane sink and with an initial plane source of defects n_{jo} at $x = p\lambda$, and $I_n(z)$ is the modified Bessel function of the first kind.

i.e.

$$I_n(z) = \sum_{u=o}^{\infty} \frac{(z/2)^{n+2u}}{\lfloor u \, \lfloor u+u}$$

and

$$k = \frac{2D_j}{\lambda^2} = \frac{2D_0}{\lambda^2}\exp\left(-\frac{Q_j}{kT}\right)$$

The fraction of defects un-annealed at a constant temperature in a time t, is thus given by

$$\frac{n_{jo}-n_{jt}}{n_{jo}} = 1 - \exp(-kt)\{I_0(kt) + I_p(kt) + 2[I_1(kt) +$$

$$I_2(kt) + \ldots\ldots I_{p-1}(kt)]\} \qquad 6.167.1$$

For an initial defect concentration at one lattice distance from the plane sink, the solution is

$$\frac{n_{jo}-n_{jt}}{n_{jo}} = 1 - \exp(-kt)\{I_0(kt) + I_1(kt)\} \qquad 6.167.2$$

For large t, this solution is identical to the earlier Equation 6.151 and also to the solution of the differential Equation 6.149. Deviations are only important for small t, but clearly show that the unannealed fraction descreases less rapidly with time than according to the simple solution. For larger separations of the initial plane source of defects and the sink of defects (i.e. $p > 1$) the rate of annealing, is, at any time reduced even further than the simple one jump theory predicts and one may expect that in the case of a distributed initial defect concentration and distributed sinks, the annealing rate-time curve would be quite complex.

If the temperature is varied during annealing, then Equation 6.166.1 may be solved by insertion of the variation of k with time. This is generally a rather complex problem and another way of examining the effect of temperature upon the annealing kinetics is to evaluate the fraction of annealed defects at a specific time at different constant annealing temperatures. Thus Kelly[159] has deduced the annealed fraction after 20 mins. for $Q_j = 2.5$ eV at a series of temperatures T, with the results shown in Figure 6.39 for an initial source-sink separation of one lattice spacing. It is evident that the annealed fraction is between 0.1

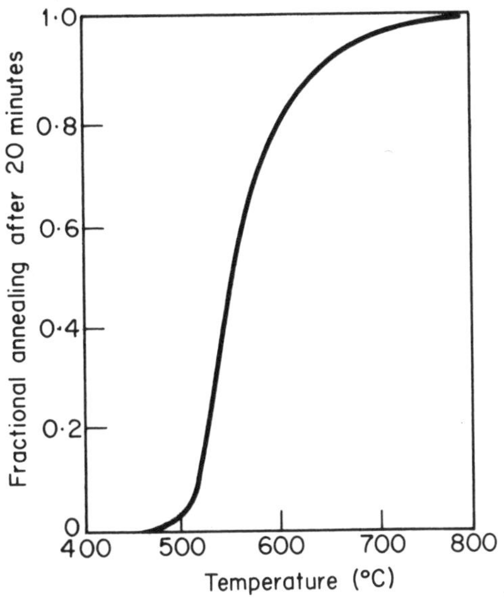

Fig. 6.39 Fractional annealing of defects after heating for 20 mins. at the temperature indicated. (viz. Ref. 6.159) for an activation energy $Q = 60$ Kcal/mole (≈ 2.5 eV).

and 0.9 over a temperature range of some 150°C and this will be the order of temperature range over which annealing will be observed in a continuous temperature variation type of experiment. This range of 150°C should be compared with the value of about 30°C evaluated from simple one jump theory. The situation becomes further aggravated when the distance between the initial source and sink is increased and Table 6.7 shows the calculated temperature range to achieve between 0.1 and 0.9 fractional annealing for $Q_j \simeq 1.5$ eV and source-sink spacings of 1, 10 and 100 lattice distances. Evidently the annealing temperature range is much larger than predicted by one jump theory, and one must expect even more distorted annealing data for distributed sources and sinks. i.e. neither the order of the reaction nor the activation energy is simply deducible.

TABLE 6.7 (Ref. 6.159).

Temperatures at which 10% and 90% of defects anneal after 20 mins. for various defect-sink spacings, and an activation energy of ~1.5 eV.

Defect-Sink Spacing (atomic planes)	T (10%)	T (90%)
1	245°C	335°C
10	325°C	435°C
100	420°C	575°C

Finally, if there is a distribution of activation energies, the annealing kinetics become even more complex, although it is interesting to note, for an initial uniform depth distribution of defects, with a uniformly populated spectrum of activation energies, migrating to a planar sink, the rate of annealing is reciprocally time dependent[161], as with the simple one jump theory. However, the temperature range over which the annealing occurs is again much larger than predicted by the simple theory. For a more complex positional and activation energy distribution, no simple annealing kinetics may be anticipated. We thus conclude that except in the simplest cases, it is a complex problem to assign precise values to the migration energy and the order of reaction involved. It is therefore difficult, in most cases, to determine with any precision the nature of the migrating species and the energy which must be expended to promote the migration. However, when the different competing reactions can be unequivocally identified much useful information may be obtained concerning the stability of various defect configurations. Indeed it is important to note that the recovery of close spaced Frenkel pairs should obey first order kinetics since the annihilating partners are correlated whereas long distance migration and recombination should obey second order kinetics. On the other hand defect migration to dislocations and surfaces should also obey first order kinetics. The question of defect stability is most important since we have seen that defects are stable for the order of time τ_j compared to the experimental times(seconds) at a temperature T only for energies Q_i given by $Q_i/kT \sim 30$. Thus defects formed by irradiation at room temperature must have energies of migration greater than about .75 eV in order that they may remain unrecombined and contribute to the observed damage. Defects formed with lower migration energies will rapidly annihilate and one must undertake many experiments at much lower temperatures in order to preserve all defects. It is therefore not surprising that the theoretical calculations of damage production presented earlier in this Chapter, which ignored all annealing effects, overestimate the damage density. This contribution must therefore be added to the effects of focusing and channelling already discussed.

Up to this point we have considered that recombination processes must be subject to some thermal activating mechanism to secure annihilation. The computer calculations by Gibson et al[23], which we shall describe shortly, however, show that even at equivalent 0°K, some defect pairs may be mechanically unstable due to the lattice strains set up in their production and may recombine rapidly without thermal activation. The computer results suggest for example, that an interstitial lying within about four atomic spacings from its associated vacancy may recombine spontaneously (within $\simeq 10^{-12}$ secs.) Clearly such a process can lead to underestimates of the total damage, whilst other effects where like defects cluster if their separation is small can lead to other differences from the anticipated damage pattern. These possibilities have resulted in a great deal of current activity to determine the effects of self anneal and agglomeration, notably by Leibfried and his collaborators[162, 163] and by Sizmann[164, 165]. In concurrence with the computer predictions these workers have assumed that spontaneous annihilation or agglomeration can occur if the defect pair is contained within a volume of about 100 atoms (say v_a) and postulate that the recombination time constant t_r is independent of pair separation within this volume v_a. The mathematics associated with the calculation of the stable numbers of defects is straightforward but laborious and involves the simultaneous solution of a set of coupled equations describing the time dependence of various configuration of interstitial-vacancy pairs, triplets etc. and their relaxation into lower order configurations. We shall merely quote the results for the case where defect production has ceased (bombardment ended) and the unstable pairs relax. It is evident, that for a random, uncorrelated spatial distribution of defects there will be an exponential type of annihilation until all unstable pairs have been removed. The calculations reveal that the final single specie density after the completion of recombination is given by

$$n_\infty = \frac{n_0}{1 + n_0 v_a} \qquad 6.180$$

where n_0 was the pair density before recombination. For large initial pair concentrations $n_0 v_a \gg 1$ and $n_\infty \rightarrow \frac{1}{v_a}$ thus $n_0 \gg n$ and a large annealing takes place. Thus the final pair density may be considerably less than predicted by simple theory. On the other hand agglomeration of like defects tends to increase slightly the value of n_∞.

The spontaneous annihilation effect will of course be important during the build up of damage during bombardment and after long bombardment doses one might expect a saturation density given by the above value $n_\infty = 1/v_a$. Simple theory would predict a continuous build-up but Schilling[166,167] has recently found that the electrical resistivity change of copper and silver reach saturation values independent of the bombarding species during irradiation at 4°K with neutrons, protons, and particles and fission fragments. This independence of the bombarding particle rules out recombination due to thermal spike annealing and suggests that the main saturating mechanism is due to spontaneous anneal of close pairs (These conclusions may be compared with those made by Brinkman[13] from the results of Quere and Nakache[139]).

Quite clearly this work is of considerable importance in determining damage rates at low temperatures and further experimental and theoretical work may be anticipated.

In this section specification of the nature of the migrating defects has been avoided, wherever possible to maintain generality of analysis. In succeeding sections we will review the experimental observations of defect annealing and show how the present analysis is used to interprete these results in terms of specific defect migration processes. Before making this comparison however we should note that our theoretical analysis of defect production type and rate, although lengthy has been unable to predict unequivocally the defect state of a real target after ion bombardment. We shall also see later that the available experimental evidence is meagre, and cannot, for example determine the relative importance of cascade and spike events. Because of this difficulty in assessing the true nature of damage either theoretically or experimentally, Vineyard and his colleagues chose an intermediate method of investigating the problem, using a computer to study the state of a model of a lattice following a low energy collision event.

The computer was also used to investigate the stability of defects in such a lattice and therefore provides information, not only upon the amount of damage to be anticipated but upon the nature of the individual components of the damage. We therefore devote the following section to a review of computational methods of determining radiation damage effects.

6.4 COMPUTER TECHNIQUES

6.4.1 Three groups of investigators have used computer techniques to evaluate radiation damage processes. The first of these calculations was made by Yoshida[168] employing a Monte Carlo technique to study damage in a simulated lattice of Germanium assuming, essentially the Snyder-Neufeld displacement model. Yoshida[168] determined the number of Frenkel pairs produced by a primary knock on of 10^4 eV and deduced a value of 231, compared with 200 predicted by the simple theoretical value.

Such a determination, whilst showing that computer techniques can duplicate theoretical calculations providing that common assumptions are made in each treatment, do not show whether these assumptions are tenable. In order to minimise the possibility of inadequate assumptions, Vineyard and his collaborators initiated computer studies of displacement events in models of several materials, assuming only the form of the interatomic potential, and deducing whether displacement occurred, or not, from the final resting positions of all atoms in the lattice when equilibrium had been attained. Similar studies have also been made by Beeler and Besco[35] with particular emphasis upon the effects of channelling events.

We consider, initially, the calculations of Gibson et al[23], who have evaluated damage effects due to primary knock on atoms of energies up to several hundred eV started in lattice models of Copper, Cu, Au alloy and iron. Most of the studies were performed with simulated copper lattice models which were rectangular parallelopipeds consisting of arrays of $5 \times 4 \times 4$ atoms, $2 \times 6 \times 7$ atoms, and $2 \times 9 \times 10$ atoms situated at the normal lattice spacings for f.c.c. copper. The forces between atoms were assumed to be represented by a Born-Mayer type of repulsive interaction with constants determined to agree with elasticity data. In order to preserve the cohesive forces which bind the lattice, constant forces were imposed normal to planar faces on atoms in these surfaces and parallel to unit cube diagonals on atoms in the crystallite edges. In addition, since any energy initially imparted to an atom in the crystallite must be dissipated by collective interactions of all the atoms in the surrounding real crystal as well, it was necessary to add spring and viscous forces to these static forces, in order to represent the interaction with the surrounding lattice. These forces were superimposed as normal and tangential forces to the surface atoms and the magnitudes of these were again determined from elasticity considerations of an isotropic medium. It was observed that the absolute magnitudes of these forces were not important in determining damage processes if the initial displacement occurred well within the crystallite boundaries but if the initial displacement occurred close to the surfaces the calculations were somewhat imprecise.

Basically, each atom was assumed to interact with each neighbouring atom via a Born-Mayer potential and one atom of the set was endowed with an initial arbitrary energy and direction of motion. The computer was then programmed to solve the equations of motion of each atom of the set until such a time that the atoms were considered to have equilibrated in their new, displaced, configuration.

The motion of each atom could be displayed oscillographically to show a complete history of each atom, or stored on magnetic tape for subsequent analysis. In order to maintain machine time within reasonable limits, crystallite axes were confined to those indicated previously, whilst lattice vibrations were assumed to be absent (i.e. the results were representative of a lattice at 0°K and with zero pressure).

Dynamic radiation damage sequences were explored by initiating displaced atoms with energies greater than about 25 eV, whilst static results, determining the equilibrium configuration of various types of defects were assessed by commencing the programme with the atoms in an assumed disordered structure and observing the subsequent relaxation of the atoms to the final equilibrium state.

Since exact solution of the large number of coupled differential equations describing the motion of all the atoms is time consuming, even on a high speed computer, an approximate analysis was made employing a finite differences scheme.

Thus if the x co-ordinate of the ith atom at time t is x_i (t) and the velocity is v_i (t) (where i = 1, 2, 3. . . . . N and N is three times the number of atoms in the crystals), then the classical equations of motion are written

$$m\dot{v}_i(t) = F_i\{x_i(t)\ldots\ldots x_N(t); v_i(t)\} \qquad 6.181$$

and $\dot{x}_i(t) = v_i(t)$ where F_i is the force on the ith atom at time t due to interatomic forces and constant and dissipative surface forces.

In the finite differences scheme, the differential forms of Equation 6.18.1 become

$$v_i\left(t + \frac{\Delta t}{2}\right) = v_i\left(t - \frac{\Delta t}{2}\right) + \frac{\Delta t}{m} . F_i\left\{x_i(t)\ldots\ldots x_N(t); v_i\left(t - \frac{\Delta t}{2}\right)\right\}$$

$$x_i\left(t + \frac{\Delta t}{2}\right) = x_i(t) + \Delta t . v_i\left(t + \frac{\Delta t}{2}\right) \qquad 6.182.2$$

The computer is then started with given values of $x_i(t)$ at an arbitrary time t and corresponding values of $v_i\left(t - \frac{\Delta t}{2}\right)$ which will be zero except for the one displaced atom. The machine then employs Equations 6.182.2 with known values of F_i to compute the new velocities $v_i\left(t + \frac{\Delta t}{2}\right)$ and co-ordinates $x_i(t + \Delta t)$ after an interval Δt. The process is then iterated to generate co-ordinates and velocities at later times $t + 2\Delta t, t + 3\Delta t$. . . . . . etc. The values of Δt are chosen to correspond to about one period of vibration of the coupled lattice atoms so that relaxation effects are readily apparent. However, when atoms are seen to be settling down to an equilibrium configuration, the values of Δt are increased to economise machine time.

Using this computational technique, static experiments were performed to study defect configuration stabilities, and dynamic experiment were simulated to deduce damage rates. The potential generally used was a Born-Mayer form expressed as

$$V(r) = A \exp(-\rho/D.(r\text{-}D)) \qquad 6.183$$

Where D is the nearest neighbour distance in copper = 2.551 Å, A = 0.051 eV and $\rho = 13$, although other values of A and ρ were also used to observe the effect of changing the strength of the potential. It was generally found that defect stability calculations were not greatly affected by changes in the potential, whereas the effective displacement thresholds in the dynamic computations were critically dependent upon this potential. Since, the potential outlined above gave best agreement with expected threshold energies (~ 25 eV), this was employed in the majority of the calculations.

In order to appreciate the results of the calculations it is necessary to describe briefly the co-ordinate system used. The origin was always chosen as the corner atom of a set with the x, y, z directions located along the parallelopiped edges. The spacing between atoms along a co-ordinate axis was arbitrarily chosen as 2 units and thus the starting positions of atoms anywhere in each of the three crystallites have co-ordinates as shown in table 6.8. Only initial displacements were considered for x values of 2 in each crystallites to ensure that surface effects were minimised.

TABLE 6.8 (viz. Ref. 6.23).

Characteristics of Fundamental Sets used in Computer Calculations.

Set	Range of Initial Atomic Positions	Number of Atoms
A	$0 \leq x \leq 10, 0 \leq y \leq 8, 0 \leq z \leq 8$	446
B	$0 \leq x \leq 4, 0 \leq y \leq 12, 0 \leq z \leq 14$	488
C	$0 \leq x \leq 4, 0 \leq y \leq 18, 0 \leq z \leq 20$	998

We now consider the results of these computations, commencing with the static lattice determinations.

6.4.(2) Defect stability configurations[23]

In these calculations, the computation is initiated by assuming the presence of a defect or set of defects, in a reasonable configuration as determined from simple theoretical considerations. The relaxation of the lattice is then followed until the equilibrium condition has been established.

In this way it was rapidly established that the vacancy in copper was perfectly normal and that any lattice atom could be removed from a normal position whilst the surrounding lattice relaxed to a stable configuration. The nearest neighbours relaxed towards the vacancy by an amount depending upon the actual interatomic potential but always of the order of a few percent of the nearest neighbour distance. The next nearest neighbours relaxed slightly away from the vacancy, but only about 1/20th of the nearest neighbour relaxations. This immediately suggests that the strain field at a point remote from a vacancy cannot be described by the strain field due to a point singularity in an isotropic elastic continuum, as suggested by the calculations of Eshelby[36]. A cubic elastic continuum model is required and the outward relaxation of next nearest neighbour atoms suggested by the computer results, are a manifestation of the anisotropic character of the medium.

The stability of various clusters of vacancies was also studied[169] and it was observed that divacancies, trivacancies, and several forms of tetravacancy, pentavacancy, and clusters of seven bound vacancies were possible. The binding energy of the divacancy against separation into isolated single vacancies was measured to be 0.06 eV, and that of the trivacancy to be 0.45 eV, which was somewhat lower than the value deduced theoretically by Damask, Dienes and Weizer[22], but possessed the same configuration suggested by these authors, which was shown earlier in Figure 6.3a. Configurations of tetravacancy and pentavacancy clusters, with their corresponding binding energies against dissociation are shown in Figures 6.40a and 6.40b although it should be pointed out that the actual magnitudes of these energies depends upon the assumed interatomic potential. Vineyard[169, 170, 171] has pointed out that even larger stable vacancy clusters may be anticipated, particularly in heavily damaged targets, and work on energies of binding and migration energies of binding and migration energies of the above and other clusters is reported to be continuing.

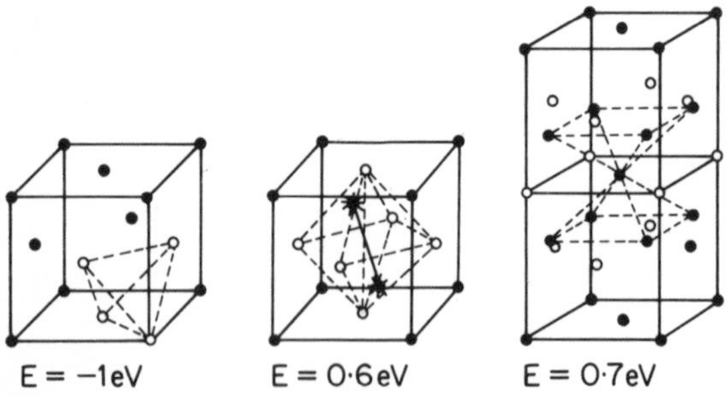

Fig. 6.40a Schematic representation of three tetravacancies calculated to be stable (or metastable) in Cu. Vacant lattice sites are shown by open circles, grossly relaxed atoms are shown by large dots. Binding energies are also shown. (viz. Ref. 6.171)

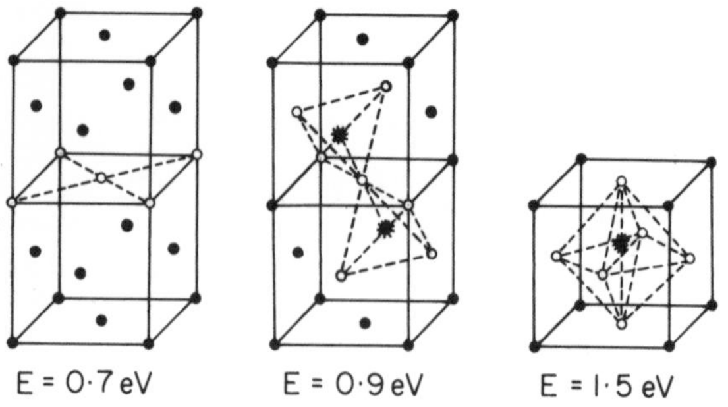

Fig. 6.40b Schematic representation of three pentavacancies calculated to be stable in Cu. (viz. Ref. 6.171)

The stable configuration of the interstitial in Copper[23] was also studied very carefully and found not to reside, as simple arguments may suggest, at the unit cube centre, but in the split interstitial configuration described earlier. In this configuration two interstitials share a lattice site symmetrically with their axis along a cubic ⟨100⟩ axis of the crystal, as shown in Figure 6.4a. Three orientations of this pair are therefore possible. It was also observed that two pairs of split interstitials were also stable with respect to dissociation into isolated pairs, and the four possible configurations are illustrated in Figure 6.41. The binding energies of these pair combinations are also indicated and it is evident that of the four only three were stable.

It is quite feasible that more complex interstitial configurations may be formed, although no calculations on these have yet been reported.

The single split interstitial configuration was also observed in b.c.c. Iron[172, 173] although, in this material, the dumbell axis is along the ⟨110⟩ direction.

In view of the possible existence of the static crowdion, as proposed by Paneth[44] and others[45], Gibson et al[23], investigated the stability of such a configuration by observing the relaxation of the lattice after insertion of an extra atom in various positions in a ⟨110⟩ row. In all cases the configuration was found to relax to the split interstitial mode by a simple rotation of a pair. However the relaxation was rather slow, suggesting that the crowdion configuration was only just unstable with the potential employed and that stability may have been achieved with a slightly different potential.

Another important result of the static calculations was observation of the relative stability of Frenkel pairs of varying separation. Figure 6.42 shows that the situation in a {100} plane where a split interstitial was formed at the lower left hand corner by creating vacancies at various positions in the plane. These positions marked by U denote vacancies which are unstable positions and are located in a region bounded by the dotted line, within which all vacancies are unstable, and it is clear that a considerable spacing is required between interstitial and vacancy to prevent rapid recombination. This is confirmed by observing the positions of stable vacancies, denoted by S in Figure 6.42 which are seen to be more remote from the interstitial. It is also evident that there is some correlation between vacancy-interstitial stability and lattice direction. Thus, pairs in the ⟨100⟩ directions tend to be more stable than those in close packed ⟨110⟩ rows.

This may be anticipated, since, as we have already seen, atomic motion is relatively easy in close packed rows (viz. focusing), whereas motion is more difficult along directions such as ⟨100⟩ since neighbouring rows are closer and exert greater influence on the row atoms (viz. assisted focusing). Calculations also showed that the energy required to produce a stable Frenkel pair was 2.67 eV, which, although lower than previously calculated and experimentally determined values, was felt to be reasonable. This type of cooperative influence just mentioned, is in fact, more evident in the result of dynamic calculations, to which we now turn our attention.

6.4.3 Dynamic Calculations

Primary knock on atoms in copper were initiated with a wide variety of starting positions, energies and directions, and in view of these rather comprehensive computations it is impossible to describe all runs in detail. Many computations yielded results, similar in general interpretation, but differing in detail, and so, in the following we will summarize as many common features as possible, and note any important details. In order to appreciate exactly what type of results the computer predicts, Figure 6.43 shows the trajectories (indicated by the full lines) and the final resting positions of atoms in adjacent planes following an initial displacement of atom A in the y-z plane with an energy of 40 eV at an angle of 15° with y axis. The large open circles indicate the initial positions of the atoms at time zero, and the radius of these circles indicates the hard sphere radius of each atom at a primary energy of 40 eV. Replacement collisions occur at B and C, a vacancy is left at A and a split interstitial forms at B. Focused collision sequences

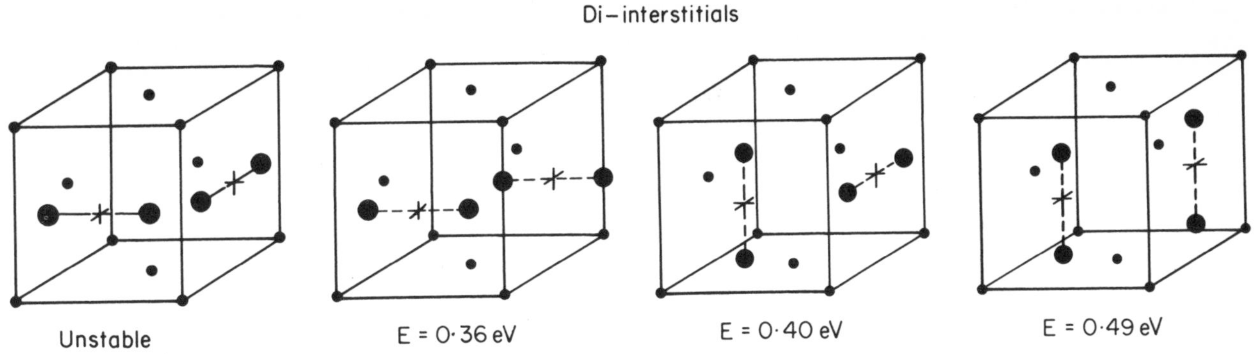

Fig. 6.41 Di-interstials in Cu. Energies of binding are shown. (viz. Ref. 6.170)

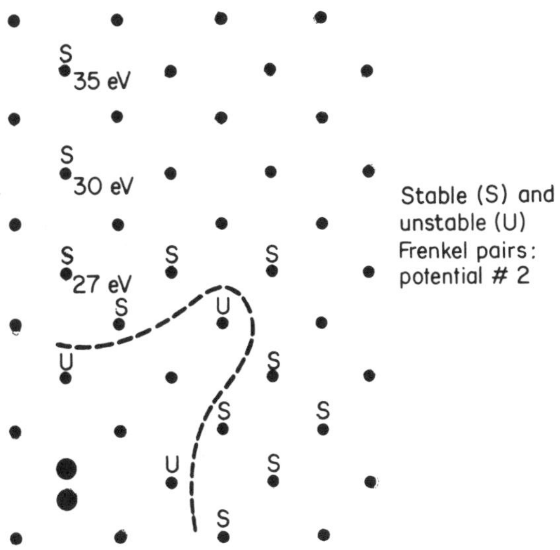

Fig. 6.42 Stability of Frenkel pairs in (100) plane of copper. The dashed line separates stable from unstable sites for a vacancy. Approximate threshold energies for dynamic production of three particular pairs are indicated. (viz. Ref. 6.23)

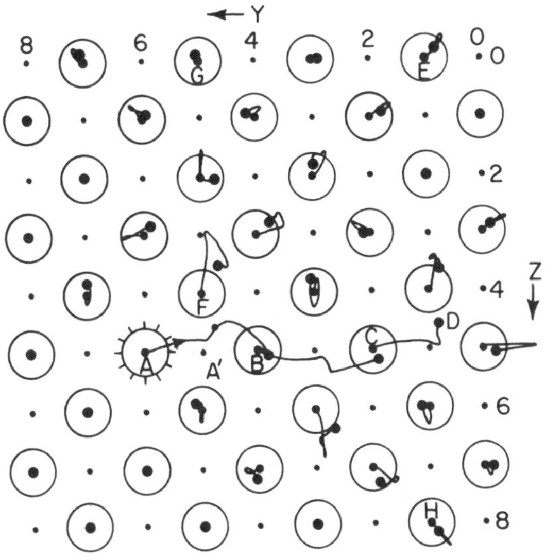

Fig. 6.43 Atomic orbits produced by a shot in (100) plane in Cu at 40 eV. Knock-on initiated at A and was directed 15° above y-axis. Large circles give initial positions of atoms in planes; small dots are atoms in plane below. A vacancy is created at A, a split interstitial at D. (viz. Ref. 6.23)

are seen to propagate along the close packed ⟨110⟩ directions AE, and BH, and assisted focused sequences propagate along AD and FG (⟨100⟩ directions.)

It is also seen that the replacements only occur in the latter directions, as predicted by Thompson and Nelson's[105] analysis, whilst only energy is transported along close packed rows. The large separation between the vacancy at A, and interstitial, at D, is also notable. When the initial starting angle was increased, similar focusing and replacement and displacement events were observed, although the numbers and extent of these varied.

A further type of displacement event occured when the primary energy was reduced to the order of the theoretical displacement energy (~25 eV). One Frenkel pair was found to form with the vacancy at 2, 2, 6 and the split interstitial around 2, 5, 7, but this pair was unstable and the interstitial eventually relaxed via a ring interchange process involving atoms on sites at 2, 5, 7; 2, 4, 8; 2, 3, 7, and 2, 2, 6, to the original configuration.

Runs conducted with knock on atoms with energies near and below 25 eV showed that permanent displacements would result for initial energies of about 25 eV, relatively independent of the starting direction. However more replacement events occurred, when primaries were directed along and near ⟨100⟩ rows than in the vicinity of ⟨110⟩ rows, whilst in the latter case the final interstitial appeared at a very large separation from the initial vacancy because of efficient focusing (e.g. the range of a 100 eV focuson was of the order of 150 lattice spacings).

Increasing the primary knock on energy up to the 400 eV maximum allowable with the assumed model revealed essentially similar effects as those described above, although naturally, an increased number of each type of event occurred. Focusing and assisted focusing sequences were evident in ⟨110⟩, ⟨100⟩ and ⟨111⟩ directions and replacement events occurred when the primary energies and directions were appropriate to those discussed in section 6.3.4. It is interesting to note that even in the ⟨110⟩ direction with direct or nearly direct head on collisions, replacement events can occur for sufficiently large primary energies, since the collision occurs (in a hard sphere approximation) closer to the equilibrium position of the struck atom than half the interatomic spacing in the ⟨110⟩ direction. (c.f. Results of section 6.3.4.1). The upper energy limit for focusing in the ⟨110⟩ direction was determined to be about 30 eV and in the ⟨100⟩ direction, about 40 eV. This latter value is lower than that deduced by Thompson and Nelson[105] for assisted focusing in ⟨100⟩ directions i.e. 74 eV, the error, it is believed lying in the inadequacy of the impulse approximation of these latter authors. However the agreement of this value with the results of the more exact calculations by Dederichs and Leibfried[104] is gratifyingly good, this method predicting an energy between 35 eV-45 eV depending upon whether a hard sphere or real Born-Mayer interaction potential was assumed.

By observing the angular change between collisions along focused rows, as a function of the energy of the moving atom, Vineyard and his co-workers were able to deduce the dependence of the focusing parameter $\lambda = \frac{\theta_i + 1}{\theta_i}$ as a function of this energy. The results of these calculations have already been presented in Figures 6.21 and 6.26 where it was shown that for the ⟨110⟩ directions, a modified hard sphere approximation gives an adequate representation of the focusing and neighbouring row influence is negligible, whilst in ⟨100⟩ and ⟨111⟩ directions, the modified hard sphere approximation is also adequate but due regard must be paid to the constraints imposed by nearest neighbour rows. The focusing parameter, although depending upon energy was found to be virtually independent of the starting angle of the primary displaced atom in a chain, as is anticipated by comparison of Equation 6.59. For energies greater than the value where λ exceeds unity (30 eV in the ⟨110⟩ direction) the collision sequence was found to be initially defocused, but, as the energy degraded along the chain, this dynamic crowdion motion reversed to a focuson, again as anticipated from the theoretical results of Equations 6.64. In such cases numerous replacement events were evident. Indeed in most events, at all energies and starting angles, the total number of replacement events was large compared to the number of displaced atoms. As in the static calculations, Frenkel pairs, although formed by the damage event, reverted back to an undamaged state if the separation of the vacancy and interstitials was not sufficiently large. When interstitials formed they invariably resided in the 'split' configuration.

The energy loss of successive atoms i and i + 1, in collision chains was evaluated and found to be given by

$$\Delta E_i = \{2/3 + E \sin^2 (\theta_i + \theta_{i+1})\} \text{ eV} \qquad 6.184$$

in ⟨110⟩ chains for a starting energy E. In the dynamic crowdion regime ($\theta_{i+1} > \theta_i$) and $E \gtrsim 30$ eV the angle initially increases rapidly with a resulting large energy attrition, so that the chain soon becomes focused. It is impossible however, from the machine data available, to confirm the condition of Equation 6.64 necessary to ensure the relaxation of an initial crowdion chain to a focuson.

In the unequivocally focusing region ($E < 30$ eV), the energy loss per collision is close to 2/3 eV, which should be compared with the value of about 1/3 eV derived in Equation 6.60.2 for hard sphere collisions. The energy loss of focusons in the ⟨100⟩ directions was much higher, of the order of 7-8 eV and thus focused sequences would be considerably shorter in these directions. Since energy losses are low in all chains however, it was found, as anticipated, that the chains transported energy, and in some cases atoms in the form of replacements, over large distances. Thus the final atom in the chain could become an interstitial providing its energy and direction of motion were correct, with a large separation from the vacancy thus producing a stable Frenkel pair. This pair formation was not efficient in ⟨110⟩ directions since the energy attenuation was lowest. The minimum energy required to produce a permanent displacement (Frenkel pair) was thus observed to be 25 eV in the ⟨100⟩ direction, between 25 eV and 30 eV in the ⟨110⟩ direction and about 85 eV in the ⟨111⟩ direction. Atoms started in arbitrary directions thus possessed a certain probability of producing at least one stable Frenkel pair and it was deduced that the probability of producing just one stable displacement rose smoothly from zero at about 24 eV to unity at about 85 eV, (i.e. the displacement probability distribution used by Sampson et al.[71] Even when no displacements occurred, however, replacements proliferated, even in the ⟨110⟩ direction, where calculation showed that replacements probably occur if the energy of the moving atom exceeds about 20 eV. (This should be compared with Leibfried's[98] value of 17 eV). It was shown that if the energy of an atom in the ⟨110⟩ chain falls below about 3.5 eV an interstitial is formed and the chain terminates. The number of replacements in a crowdion type chain was thus calculated, using the expression for the energy loss in a chain of Equation 6.184 and the calculated curve in Figure 6.21 of $\lambda = \frac{\theta_i + 1}{\theta_i}$ as a function of energy, above 30 eV for primary chain atoms initiated with various directions and energies and in which the chain energy eventually degraded to below 3.5 eV. The results of this calculation are shown in Figure 6.44 as a series of contours of constant number of replacements for various initial energies and angles. Since the number of replacements also conforms to the length of a chain, this Figure also gives the chain length as a function of starting angle and energy. Clearly low energy, small angle primaries produce longer chains, and more replacements than high energy large angle events, as anticipated by the Leibfried calculations presented earlier.

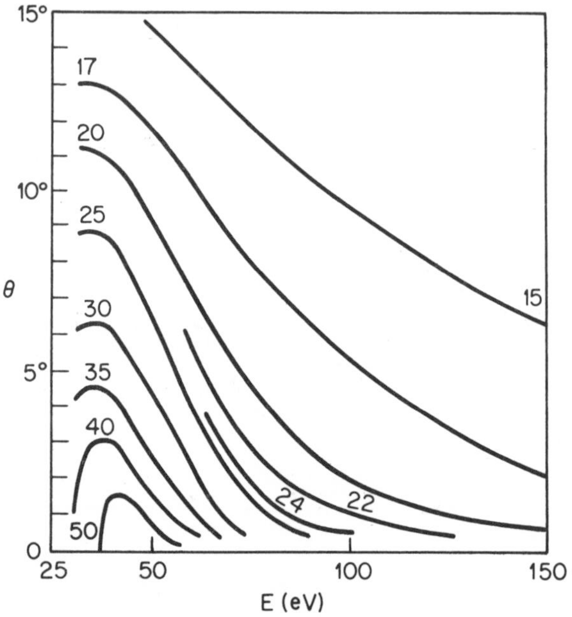

Fig. 6.44 Calculated lengths (number of atoms in sequence) of ⟨110⟩ collision chains started at various angles and energies. Lines are contours of constant chain length. (viz. Ref. 6.23)

Finally, in events initiated with rather large energies, evidence of clusters of vacancies, separated by large distances through focusing chains, from their associated interstitials was obtained, and in addition several interstitial clusters appeared to form, resembling to some extent the Brinkman[25] displacement spike, although no remixing of the damaged zone appeared to occur. This may not be anticipated however since the primary knock on energies were evidently lower than those evaluated by Brinkman.[25]

More recently Vineyard[172] and Erginsoy and Erginsoy et al[17,173] have reported further results obtained in a simulated Cu_3Au alloy and in α iron. In the former case focusing events were again observed to propagate along ⟨110⟩ directions but with reduced efficiency because of the mass mismatch. Considerable disordering was evident, however, just because of the gold-copper replacement events in the close packed rows.

In α iron, a Born-Mayer potential, with constants chosen to agree with the Abrahamson[174,175] potential for iron, a Morse type potential (difference of two exponential potentials) derived by Girifalco and Weizer[176] to duplicate the elastic constants of iron and a third composite potential which approximated the Born-Mayer at large separations and a Bohr potential at small separations were employed. The last of these potentials gave results for the displacements threshold energy which appeared to be more sensibly in agreement with experimental data and was therefore felt to be a better approximation and was investigated most thoroughly.

Because of the more open structure of b.c.c. iron and the relatively closer spacing between an atom and its second nearest neighbour, compared to that to the nearest neighbour, than in an f.c.c. lattice, it was necessary to retain the atomic interaction forces due to second nearest neighbours.

Focusing sequences were observed to operate along direction such as ⟨100⟩ and, much more efficiently, along the close packed cube diagonal ⟨111⟩ directions. In the former direction replacement events were formed quite readily, and as with copper the numbers of such events far exceeded the number of displacements. The threshold for displacement in the region of ⟨100⟩ direction was determined to be about 17 eV, in agreement with experiments by Lucasson and Walker[177,178] using electron bombardment of α iron. Erginsoy et al, [17, 172] also deduced that the displacement energy threshold around the ⟨111⟩ directions was about 38 eV whilst in ⟨110⟩ directions the threshold was 34 eV. These latter thresholds however were not experienced exactly along the crystal directions but at a small angle to these directions since replacement collisions were easier with some degree of defocusing in the collision chains. The displacement thresholds were also determined for primary atoms started between crystal rows and Figure 6.45 shows the angular dependence for angles between the three important ⟨100⟩, ⟨111⟩ and ⟨110⟩ directions, and the displacement probability was also determined as a function of primary energy for all directions. It was then possible to deduce an integrated displacement probability as a function of energy by averaging the displacement probabilities in all directions and the result of this calculation is shown in Figure 6.46. It is immediately clear that this probability function has a staircase function form as suggested by Lucasson and Walker with a minimum threshold of 17 eV (due to ⟨100⟩ displacements and a displacement probability of only 0.76 at 60 eV (the highest energy used in the computations).

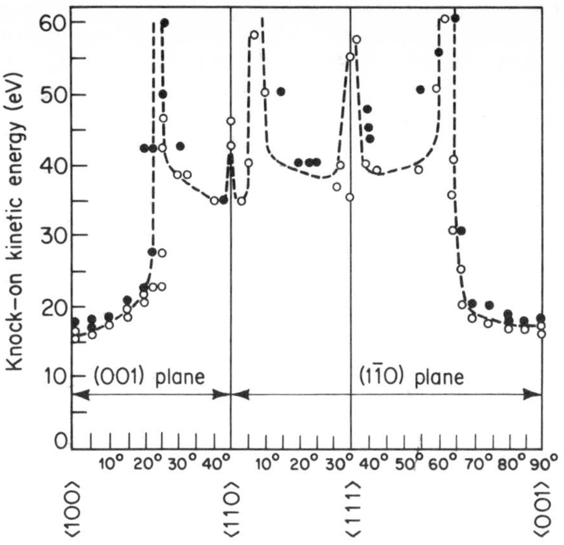

Fig. 6.45 Directional dependence of the displacement threshold energy in α Iron. The direction of earliest displacement is ⟨100⟩ giving $E_d \sim$ 17eV; thresholds in ⟨110⟩ and ⟨111⟩ are ~34 eV and ~38 eV respectively. (viz. Ref. 6. 17)

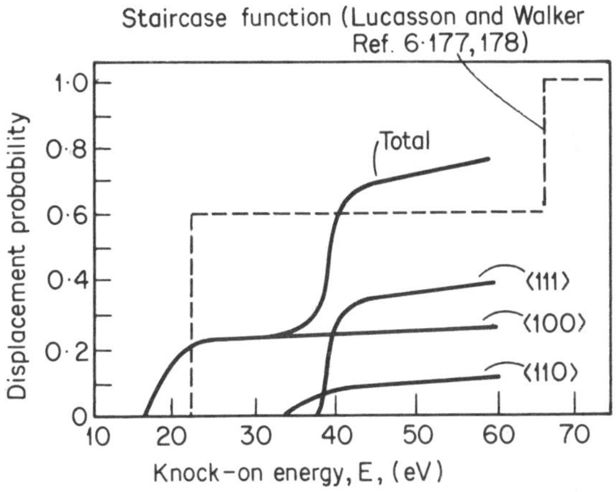

Fig. 6.46 The integrated displacement probability for a knock on of energy, E, randomly directed in α-Iron. The contributions of the three low index rows are indicated separately together with the total and the staircase function suggested by Lucason & Walker. (viz. Ref. 6. 17)

Replacement collisions were investigated in some detail and it was observed that in these important directions the initially displaced atom did not go into the interstitial configuration with the struck atom but caused a replacement sequence along the collision chains with the interstitial formed some distance from the point of generation. The higher the primary starting energy the further was the split interstitial removed from the generation point at which a vacancy (and at higher energies and certain starting directions a divacancy) was formed. Replacement was found to be most difficult in ⟨111⟩ directions (which coincides with the highest energy of 38 eV for replacements given above) since considerable energy had to be expended in passing through neighbouring arrays of atoms and more importantly in causing the displaced atom to pass beyond the mid point against the repulsive potential of the next atom in the close packed ⟨111⟩ row. The former energy loss mechanism was less in this direction than the ⟨100⟩ and ⟨110⟩ directions however, and this resulted in the efficient transfer of momentum in the former direction i.e. focuson propagation was most operative in the ⟨111⟩ row. The focusing parameter λ was determined as a function of energy in the ⟨111⟩ and ⟨100⟩ rows and the result for the former direction is depicted in Figure 6.47 which shows the focusing energy for this direction to be ~28 eV. The hard sphere estimate for this energy is 50 eV, which as in copper, overestimates the true energy. In the ⟨100⟩ rows focusing was only observed to operate below an energy of about 18 eV and neighbouring row interaction was observed to be rather important. Indeed an assumed isolated row was found to exhibit no focusing unless the starting energy was less than an estimated 5-7 eV which conflicts with values deduced by Nelson[106] using the impulse approximation for assisted focusing. Erginsoy, Vineyard and Shimizu subsequently[173] extended these computations to primary knock on energies of 1500 eV using the composite potential for iron. For ion energies greater than 100 eV at least one Frenkel pair was created by the primary, single vacancy production proliferated for knock ons directed near the ⟨100⟩, ⟨111⟩ and ⟨110⟩ axes whilst divacancies and double vacancies with larger separations were created at starting angles between these directions. A determination of the total number of Frenkel pairs produced by the primaries showed a closely linear behaviour i.e. $\nu(E) = \frac{E}{110\ \mathrm{eV}}$ suggesting that an effective threshold of $E_d \approx 55$ eV is a suitable value for iron. (This is not unreasonable when the complex form of p(E), starting at 17 eV and reaching unity at about 100 eV, is recalled). About four times as many replacements as displacement events were observed, which compares favourably with the original Kinchin-Pease estimate, and many replaced atoms themselves travelled considerable distances, forming further defects.

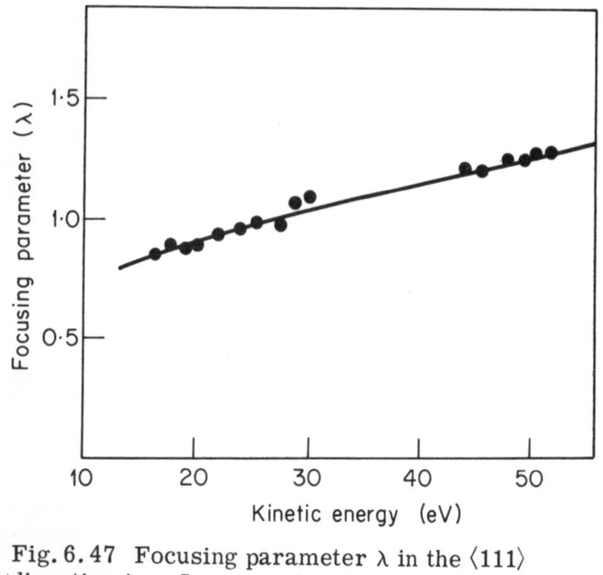

Fig. 6.47 Focusing parameter λ in the ⟨111⟩ direction in α Iron as a function of initial energy. (viz. Ref. 6.17)

These authors also found that even at primary energies of 1500 eV, no displaced atoms travelled distances which could be interpreted as channelling. This suggests that at low energies, and for the potential employed, channelling is ineffective in reducing ν(E). However, as we shall see presently, Beeler and Besco[179, 180] do observe a reduction in ν(E) due to channelling, using a different potential, and the importance of this parameter is therefore evident.

We thus conclude, that as in f.c.c. copper, the effects of lattice structure are very important in determining the magnitude and spatial distribution of defect production. The results are encouragingly close to the experimental data (Lucasson and Walker's[177,178] electron bombardment investigations) and suggests that further experimental work on the directional dependence of damage will be most revealing.

Because of the possibility of thermal spike formation during irradiation further results deduced by Vineyard[171] for a copper lattice are also of interest. Following a low energy displacement event the effective temperature of atoms in the array was computed by setting the kinetic energy of each atom at a given time averaged over two Debye periods centred on that time, to kT_{eff}.* Thus a displacement sequence as shown in Figure 6.43 may be reinterpreted in terms of temperature contours at a given time. This reinterpretation of a 100 eV primary knock on event is shown in Figure 6.48 immediately after making the

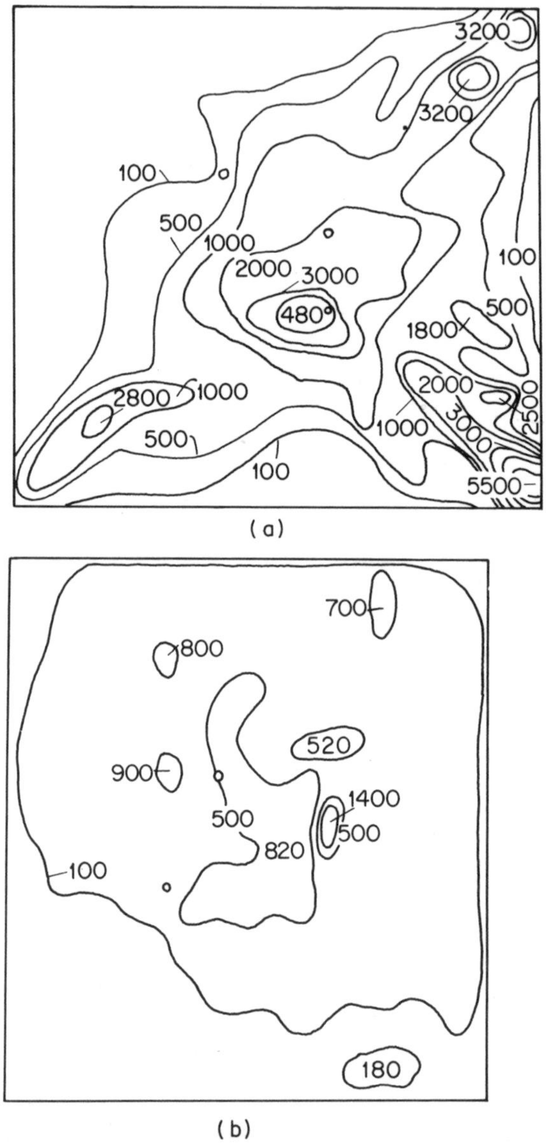

Fig. 6.48 Typical Isothermals in a thermal space in the following a 100 eV knock on event. a) 3.27×10^{-13} secs after initiation b) 9.9×10^{-13} secs after initiation. Note the directional dependence of effective temperature. (viz. Ref. 6.171)

* kT_{eff} is used instead of $3/2\ kT_{eff}$ since the excitation of each atom was confined to one plane only.

shot. The largest effective temperatures evidently exist along the close packed focusing directions and are much in excess of the boiling temperature. As time increases the temperatures certainly decrease, but anisotropically according as to which direction energy is transported from the initial hot spot. Indeed, the initial cooling is so rapid as to require a thermal diffusivity, at least an order of magnitude larger than isotropic diffusivity estimates. At much later times there appears to be a resemblance to isotropic cooling with a thermal diffusivity close to calculated values.

The overall picture however did not appear to inspire confidence in using classical methods to investigate thermal spikes. Vineyard[171] does suggest, on the other hand, that, in more open materials, or alloys, in which focusing may not be so important, thermal spike analysis on classical grounds may be justifiable. This possibility must be held in abeyance until further work has been performed.

In all these above computations, the initial displaced atom was started within the simulated lattice, rather than at the boundaries. Thus, whilst the calculations confirm the existence of expected phenomena such as focusing, they do not actually duplicate the conditions following an external irradiation although the results of such events would be expected to be very similar in character, if not in detail, to those just described. Moreover, because of limitations on the assumed model, the primary knock on energy was necessarily small ($<$400 eV).

In an attempt to duplicate the conditions of external irradiation, Beeler and Besco have performed a series of computations on the damage in BeO,[35,179,180] Aluminium[180] and tungsten[180,181,182] following Beryllium, Oxygen, Iodine or Krypton ion bombardment and for copper and iron atoms moving in their own respective lattices, with the results which we now discuss. The main features of the calculational procedure have already been described in the previous chapter and it is necessary only to summarize these briefly. Binary collisions only were treated so that co-operative effects due to the influence of all except colliding atoms were ignored, (i.e. focusing events were not observed). Because of this simplification it was possible to use a semi infinite ensemble of atoms, but of course no motion of an atom was observed until it suffered a collision. The interaction potential between colliding atoms was chosen to be the Bohr potential with a screening length appropriate to the target material assumed obtained by extrapolation of the values obtained from ion range data in copper, silver and gold, by Van Lint et al.[68] Displacement of a struck atom was allowed if it received an energy in excess of a threshold again appropriate to the target material, but generally of the order of 25 eV, whilst the energy retained by the struck atom was the difference between the energy transfer and the displacement energy. The model was thus essentially that suggested by Seitz and Koehler[3] and used in the machine calculations by Yoshida.[168] One novel feature of the computations, was the fact that at a collision both partners were tested for kinetic energy and the trajectory, and the damage caused, by the faster atom determined first. The slower moving atom was then followed and allowed to interact with the crystal damage engendered by the faster atom. Computations were performed at an effective zero temperature so that all defects which were formed were also retained. The configuration was then studied and any defects which had been shown by Gibson et al[23] to be unstable, were allowed to anneal, and the final damage pattern obtained.

Initial calculations[35] were made with a square planar lattice model of BeO in which the Beryllium and Oxygen occupied alternate positions. This was subjected to a simulated bombardment by Krypton or Iodine ions with energies up to 50 keV and direction of incidence variable between perpendicular and parallel incidence. Particularly interesting results were obtained when the primary incidence was normal or at 45° to the normal to the surface. In these cases the range of the primary was found to be abnormally large and the damage production abnormally low, both attributable, it was believed, to channelling phenomena between rows of atoms.

We shall return to a fuller discussion of these events shortly and concentrate, for the present, on results obtained with other incident angles which tend to be more representative of random lattice simulation.

In figures 6.49 a and b the path of a 5 keV Iodine atom incident at 30° to the normal on the BeO square planar lattice, and the initial damage created by this primary are depicted. Beryllium and oxygen atoms are denoted by 'X' and 'O' respectively and vacant sites originally occupied by such atoms are depicted by the same symbols surrounded by squares. From these figures four features are significant (1) The final iodine absorption point is surrounded by relatively undamaged material (2) Primary atoms of low energy which would be stopped close to the surface would be surrounded by severely damaged material, particularly at high primary dose rates where damage due to individual primaries commence to overlap. (3) Defects tended to appear in clusters, particularly vacancies. (4) Replacement collisions of one atomic species by the other induced considerable disordering of the lattice.

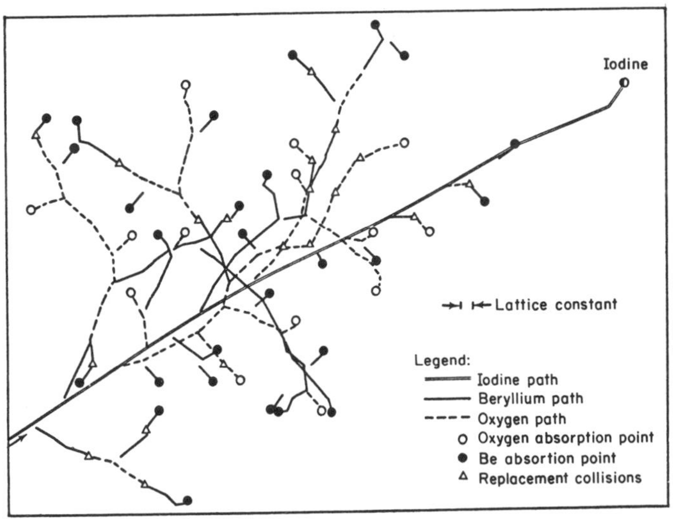

Fig. 6.49a Collision Cascade trajectories in planar BeO caused by 5-keV I^{127} bombardment. (viz. Ref. 6.35)

Allowing those defects which were unstable to anneal under the re-ordering energy of the crystal resulted in the annihilation of several of the defects as depicted in Figure 6.49 c. Vacancy clusters still remained and several static crowdions were evident although it was probable that these would also anneal out. It is also interesting to note that in a binary crystal the

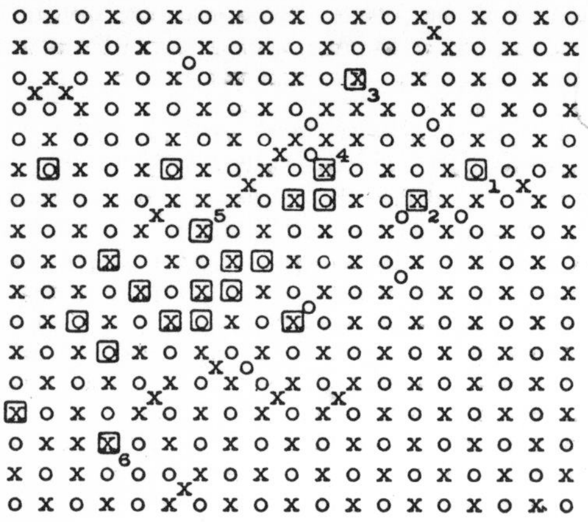

Fig. 6.49b Damage pattern in planar BeO immediately after bombardment by a 5-keV I^{127} atom at zero absolute temperature. This pattern contains unstable configurations. X denotes Beryllium atoms, O denotes Oxygen atoms, □denotes vacancies.

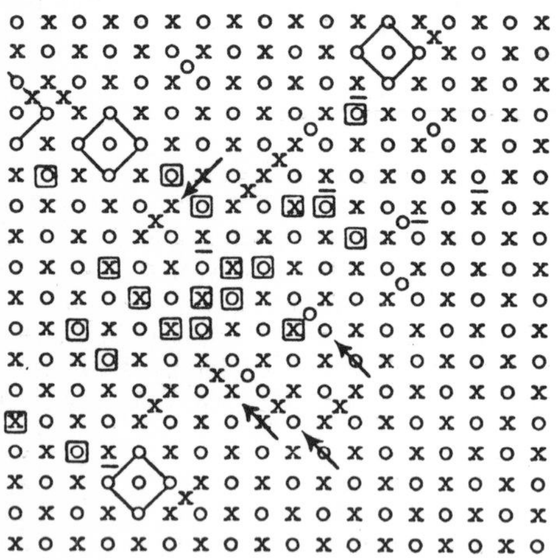

Fig. 6.49c Damage pattern in planar BeO for 5-keV I^{127} bombardment after relaxation for unstable configurations.

vacancy concentration of one species can actually increase during annealing as a result of the annihilation of vacancies of the other type by disordered atoms of this latter species. Since many of the vacancies resided in clusters, Table 6.9 is valuable in that it indicates the percentage of vacancies trapped in clusters of various sizes.

TABLE 6.9 (viz. Ref. 6.35).

Defect population in planar BeO immediately after irradiation by a 5-keV iodine atom at T = 0

	Vacancies	Interstitials
Beryllium	13	12
Oxygen	10	9
Total	23	21

When the primary ion energy was increased the number of defects increased also, with a tendency to form larger vacancy and interstitial clusters and more replacement events. Interstitials also tended to form around the peripheries of vacancy clusters. At high energies the initial trajectory of the primary ion upon entering the lattice was less influenced by collisions (high mean free path) and the surface region was relatively undamaged. As the primary energy degraded and produced more progeny a dense damage entanglement resulted, until the primary energy dropped so low as to produce little damage around its resting position. This picture of damage density conforms, at least qualitatively, with the predictions made earlier by the theoretical work of Leibfried[89-91] and Korchovei et al.[92] Very similar results were obtained when the primary ion species was changed to Krypton.[179] Since the vacancy clusters surrounded by interstitials, resemble the displacement spike suggested by Brinkman,[26] one run with a 15 keV copper atom incident in a copper lattice is of interest. The resulting damage configuration is shown in Figure 6.50 with two large vacancy clusters surrounded by denser zones packed with interstitials. Whether this structure would subsequently collapse with a high degree of re-ordering is a matter for speculation since the machine computations could not follow this annealing stage.

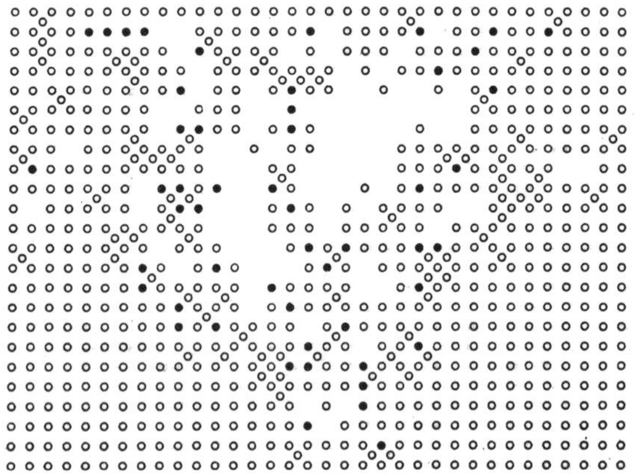

Fig. 6.50 Displacement spike in planar copper caused by a 15-keV copper atom. Blank spaces indicate vacancies and filled circles denote atoms affected by replacement collision. (viz. Ref. 6.35)

When the investigations were extended[180,181] to study damage in a simulated real BeO wurtzite structure the results were modified only in degree. Thus vacancy clusters were only observed to form for primary energies greater than 10 keV and penta-vacancies were the largest size stable clusters noted. Channelled trajectories were again observed to proliferate along the axes discussed in Chapter 5 but in this case the primary atoms tended to skip from one channel to another, causing negligible damage while in the channel but normal damage between channels. Indeed, averaging over many runs showed that the number of defects initially formed, before annealing, and accounting for replacement events, was within 1% of the predictions of the Seitz-Harrison model. It was also notable that 90% of the Be and O atoms acquired knock on energies below 400 eV. These knock on atoms could also be channelled according to their angle of entry into the channel 0°-10° for 0 and 0°-25° for Be) and Figure 6.51 a and b

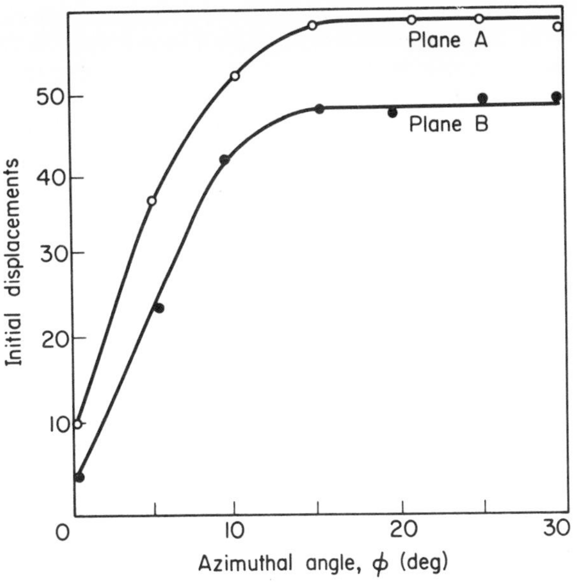

Fig. 6.51 Initial number of displacements produced by 6 keV, O knock on started at various angles to the channel direction in BeO. (viz. Ref. 6.180)

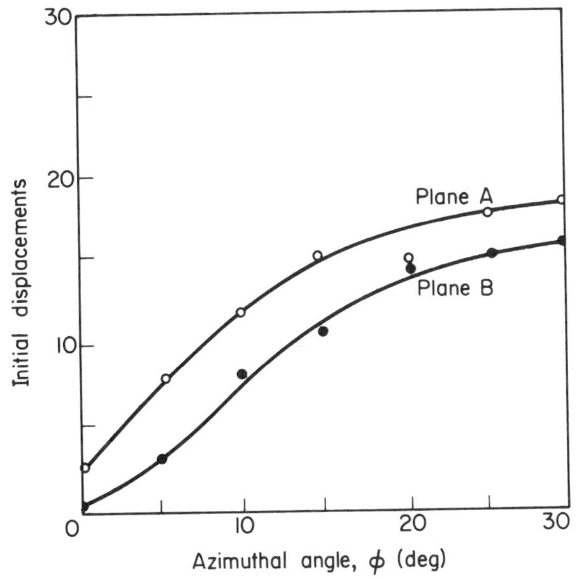

Fig. 6.51 Initial number of displacements produced by 2 keV, Be knock on started at various angles to the channel direction in BeO. (viz. Ref. 6.180)

shows the amount of damage produced by 6 keV oxygen atoms and 2 keV Beryllium atoms (the maximum energies for which essentially hard sphere collisions occur with a Bohr potential) as a function of the starting angle to a channel axis. Clearly the existence of channelled trajectories can seriously diminish the overall damage. It was notable also that not only pure channelled trajectories would decrease the damage production, but that the quasi channelled atoms which tended to skip between channels also gave reduced damage during their channel excursions. On the other hand vacancies in a channel wall or interstitials in a channel core terminated channelled events so that an increase in the overall damage would result in reduced importance of these events. Channelling events also tended to cause asymmetrical damage in that a knocked on atom which became channelled eventually trapped at very large separations from its associated vacancy. Analysis of the results in BeO suggested that a reduction of between 17% and 40% below the damage in a random lattice might occur because of channelling events.

Further extension of the computations to study Copper primaries moving in Copper lattices,[182] Iron primaries in Iron[182] and Krypton ions in Aluminium and Tungsten[180] revealed the same general characteristics regarding the inhibition of damage by channelling events.

For example 2 keV Fe primaries started at various angles to the ⟨100⟩ axis in b.c.c. iron showed very strong tendency towards channelling and produced no displacements in the channel wall until the starting angle was at 10° to the ⟨100⟩ axis. As the starting angle was increased (15°-30°) many more displacements occurred with magnitudes reminiscent of a random lattice, but at still larger angles ($\gtrsim 35°$) primaries become deflected into ⟨110⟩ channels which were again stable and produced little damage. Quantitative estimates of damage degradation in iron due to channelled events were also made by observing the number of atoms displaced by primary Fe atoms with energies between 0.1 and 30 keV started in random directions (excluding known channelling directions) from a point midway between two lattice positions. Defining the number of atoms displaced by one primary of energy E, by $\nu(E)$ and setting

$$\nu(E) = 1 \times k(E)\, E/Ed \qquad 6.185$$

where k(E) is an energy dependent function and E_d the displacement energy taken as 16 eV, then from the computational evaluation of $\nu(E)$ as a function of E (averaged over all starting directions) a plot of k(E) as a function of energy was obtained, using either the Bohr or the Erginsoy et al[172] type potentials for iron. These graphs are shown in Figure 6.52 together with values of k(E) determined from theoretical evaluations by Snyder and Neufeld[85] and Kinchin and Pease[82] assuming no channelling, and Oen and Robinson[123] and Sigmund[127] allowing for channelling. It was found that the computer results give a constant value of k(E) = 0.375 for 0.5 keV for the Bohr potential, in agreement with the Snyder-Neufeld random model (the numerical value differed because a different displacement energy was subtracted) but for energies above this, k(E) falls with increasing energy.

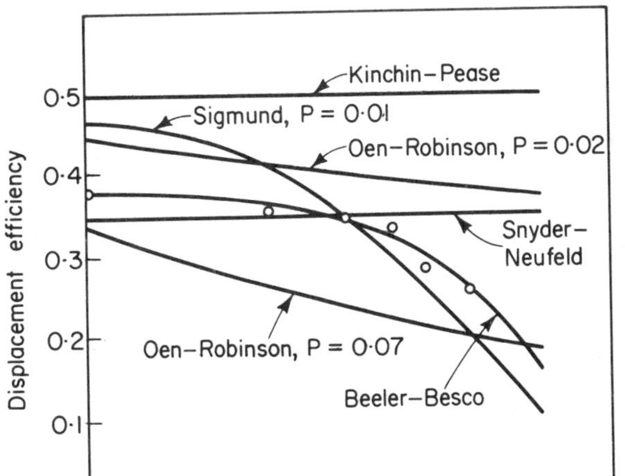

Fig. 6.52 Comparison of displacement efficiency K(E) deduced by Beeler & Besco for Iron primaries in α Iron, allowing for channelling. (viz. Ref. 6.182)

For the Erginsoy potential, the value of k(E) was always considerably reduced. This was interpreted as showing the existence of channelling of the knocked on iron atoms and was readily confirmed by studying the trajectories of knock ons which were channelled or quasi channelled in ⟨110⟩ and ⟨142⟩ directions.

Comparison of the machine calculations in Fig. 6.52 with the theoretical predictions of Oen and Robinson,[123] who employed a hard sphere scattering law, and Sigmund,[127] who used a forward peaked scattering, show that agreement is better with the latter predictions, even for a low value of the probability of a displaced atom becoming channelled, i.e. p(E) = 0.01. Beeler and Besco[182] suggest that a low value of p(E) is more realistic than the original value (0.07) adopted by Robinson and Oen and believe that their computations support the Sigmund theory. We should remember Robinson's[128] cautionary remarks, however, that the damage reduction may be partially a result of using the non hard sphere scattering law and that channelling may be only a relatively minor correction. The critical test, of course, is the degree of agreement attainable with experiment.

We should also note at this point that Gay and Harrison[183] have recently performed computer studies on lattice models of Copper using similar techniques to those of Gibson et al,[23] but with the particular purpose of determing the influence of the surrounding lattice upon the collision process between an incident ion and the lattice atom with which it came into most intimate contact. Thus the problem was essentially one of determining whether a two body collision process between the incident and struck particles was a good approximation to the motion of the two particles or whether the surrounding lattice atoms exert considerable influence upon the initial motion of these.

The general results of this study were that for incident primary (copper for simplicity) ion energies greater than ~5 keV, the interaction between the primary ion and the nearest struck atom was very closely specified by a two body even for all collision parameters up to half the lattice spacing. For lower energies (in the hundreds of electron volt range) the co-operative influence of the surrounding lattice became more important, particularly for large impact parameters. This co-operative influence was a function of the particular crystal face irradiated, the primary energy and the point of impact, and became of greatest importance where the incident ion effectively collided with several atoms simultaneously (large impact parameters) and very low ion energies. Since this dependence upon crystal structure was evident, Gay and Harrison[183] felt it was invidious to ascribe an 'effective' mass to a lattice because of collective interactions, as invoked by Henschke[184] in sputtering theory and Arifov[185] and Gurevich[186] in collision theory. Such a process may be more acceptable for essentially randomised lattices however. Moreover the variation and influence of collective interactions with ion energy and impact point led the authors to express doubt as to the validity of averaging processes (as used in radiation damage calculations) particularly at low ion energies, and that it may be necessary to consider each ion separately to determine the final averages. Again it appears that the distinction between two body-cascade type theory and co-operative spike like phenomena is rather vague, and further careful consideration must be given to these matters. Erginsoy, Vineyard and Shimizu[173] have also observed that two body interactions are often invalid in their computer evaluations in iron. Harrison, Leeds and Gay[187] subsequently extended the above work by following the motion of atoms moving near channel axes. As an atom passed into the vicinity of a crystallite edge two further lattice planes were added to the basic model to allow further interactions. In this way, and using the Gibson II potential[23] 5 keV atoms starting from lattice sites into the (110) plane were examined. From 120 primaries started at various angles to this plane from an initial lattice site on a ⟨101⟩ row only one eventually became channelled, and this was not into the intuitively now probable ⟨110⟩ channel but after a series of collisions, into a ⟨101⟩ channel. However a considerable number of atoms (up to 20%) were deflected into rather long trajectories between {111} or {001} planes where they performed a 'skimming' type motion with relatively frequent hard collisions with atoms in these planes (about 1 collision per 5-8 lattice units) which lead to displacement zones at this frequency.

According to this model therefore true channelling of displaced atoms is very rare and is unlikely to lead to the damage reductions predicted by Robinson and Oen,[123] Sigmund[127] and Beeler.[180] However the more frequent 'skimming' events may lead to essentially similar reductions. Clearly further work in this energy region with the N-body interaction model is desirable.

In addition, as we have seen, throughout this section, many effects will combine to change the amount of damage predicted, such as the low energy focusing events observed by Gibson et al,[23] and cluster formation and defect annealing as observed in all computations. What is desirable, although evidently expensive of time, labour and finance, is a marriage between the computations of Beeler and Besco who studied the higher incident energy range, and those of Vineyard's group who concentrated attention upon lower energies, since, during, irradiation, both types of event will surely occur consecutively. Nevertheless the machine calculations are valuable in that the plethora of different events which may occur have been well established and generally show a good degree of agreement with theoretical predictions in their ranges of applicability. It is certainly established that a theory allowing for all effects is desirable.

6.5 EXPERIMENTAL OBSERVATIONS OF DAMAGE

6.5.1 As we have just suggested, the final test of the adequacy of the theoretical deductions in Sections 6.3 and 6.4 is comparison with experimental results. We will see shortly, however, that experimental measurements of radiation damage induced by energetic ions are scarce, and those which do exist are more qualitative than quantitative. The reason for this lack of experimental observation has been undoubtedly a result of the difficulties in measuring damage production and its effects after ion irradiation, and it is only recently that sufficiently sensitive techniques have become available. Basically the difficulty lies in the fact that damage caused by low energy ion bombardment is confined to a region close to the target surface, and, in a bulk sample, the resulting macroscopic changes, in electrical, mechanical, optical properties etc., are vanishingly small. On the other hand, a considerably amount of progress has been made in the experimental study of damage production following electron, neutron, proton and deuteron and fission fragment irradiation of targets, since these particles, because of their longer ranges, cause more homogeneous damage. Although these primary particles are different from the ions under consideration here, the progeny they produce in the irradiated target, in the way of primary and higher order displaced atoms, will be identical. Consequently, although the magnitudes of the effects produced by such particles will differ from those resulting from ion irradiation, many of the detailed processes will be identical. Initially, therefore, we will give a brief survey of the important results which have been obtained via irradiation with these other particles, paying particular attention to those results which have a bearing upon our earlier theoretical calculations.

Let us consider initially the technique of high energy electron irradiation from the following three points of view (1) Measurement of the threshold energy for atomic displacement E_d. (2) Deduction of the nature of the defects produced and (3) The magnitude of the damage.

Since the energy transfer from an energetic electron to a much heavier target atom is very small[188,189] then it may be anticipated that only electrons in the energy range 0.5-1.0 MeV and above would impart sufficient energy (20-30 eV) to a target atom such as copper to ensure displacement. Moreover, since the energy transfer is low the nature of the damage should be particularly simple and consist only of Frenkel pairs. Following the initial suggestion by Mills[190, 191] of the applicability of electron irradiation to the study of displacement thresholds, numerous attempts have since been made to deduce such values in various materials. It is well known that the presence of excess vacancies and interstitials in materials considerably influence macroscopic properties and so investigation of numerous effects including changes in electrical resistivity, internal friction, and optical reflectivity, following electron irradiation have been made. Of these various methods, the change in electrical resistivity has been most widely used to observe defect production in electron irradiation and excellent review articles by Walker,[142] and Sosin,[191] should be consulted for a full description of this work. It was readily established that in order to obtain correct estimates of thresholds and damage rates it was necessary to conduct irradiation at very low temperatures (<20°K) in order that all damage produced should be retained and not anneal out. We shall return to the question of why the damage does anneal at such low temperatures shortly, and accept that this can be diminished by low temperature irradiation. Since there will be a certain equilibrium number of vacancies in a metal because of thermal activation at any temperature, which scatter electrons, there will always be a finite residual or Frenkel resistivity ρ_F per unit defect concentration. Following electron irradiation with a flux $\delta\phi$ an additional resistivity increment $\delta\rho$ will ensue, and it is clear that $\delta\rho = \rho_F \cdot \delta\phi \cdot \sigma_D$ where σ_D is the total displacement cross section given by

$$\sigma_D = \int_0^{T_m} P(T, T_0)\, d\sigma(T, T_m)$$

in which T is the transferred energy. T_0 the minimum displacement energy, T_m the maximum energy transferred by the electrons of energy E_0, and $P(T, T_0)$ is the ejection probability of a target atom at a transferred energy $E > E_0$.

Several authors have shown that if the differential resistivity increment with respect to flux, $d\rho/d\phi$ is evaluated as a function of the electron energy, which is of course easily related to the maximum energy transferred to target atoms, then, the energy at which $d\rho/d\phi$ becomes zero gives the minimum displacement energy of the target atoms. As the electron energy is slowly increased $d\rho/d\phi$ reveals the nature of the energy dependence of the displacement probability function $P(T, T_0)$. At higher electron energies, it can be shown (viz the earlier considerations of Lehmann[73] and Sampson et al's[71] results) that the damage production is almost completely independent of the form of the probability distribution function and is characteristic of a mean threshold energy.

At still higher electron energies, the displaced atoms receive sufficient energy to displace further atoms and the results reveal the characteristics of displacement cascades. Because the electron energy is degraded in passing through the target it is generally difficult to assess accurately the minimum displacement threshold energy by determining at what electron energy $d\rho/d\phi$ becomes zero. Consequently this minimum threshold energy is not known to an accuracy of better than about 1 or 2 eV. Sosin[191,193,194] suggests that 19 eV is the minimum value for this energy in Copper.

Furthermore it is often difficult to fit the variation of $d\rho/d\phi$ in the low electron energy region to an explicit form for the displacement probability function, assumed step or ramp functions often giving quite similar results. Indeed, in order to obtain the shape of the displacement function it is necessary to fit the experimental data to data obtained assuming a particular function at higher energies, which in turn requires knowledge or assumption of the Frenkel resistivity ρ_F. Walker and his collaborators[192,177,178,195,196] found that their experimental data in Copper were best described by a step function displacement probability at a mean threshold energy of 22eV, but this required assumption of a rather low value of the Frenkel resistivity $\rho_F = 1.3\mu\Omega$cm/at % compared with estimates derived from stored energy data of $>2.0\mu\Omega$cm/at %. On the other hand, Sosin[193] evaluated the displacement probability function on theoretical grounds, assuming that ⟨110⟩ displacements were most important at low electron energies (which was in accord with Gibson et al's[23] calculations) by deducing the energy required by a displaced atom to leave the surrounding cage of atoms in much the same way as the Leibfried[98] calculation. It was found that the displacement function was surprisingly insensitive to the constants of the interaction potential used (a Born-Mayer type) and that a minimum displacement threshold energy of 19eV gave best agreement with experiment for a choice of Frenkel resistivity of $2.5\mu\Omega$cm/at %. Sosin[193] has given an explicit relation for $P(T, T_0)$ which is complex and will not be reproduced here. It does have the general feature of rising from zero at $E_d = 19$eV to unity at some higher energy and its success is best appreciated by comparison of the theoretical and experimental displacement cross sections as shown in Figure 6.53. The theoretical data is normalised to the experimental data at 1.0 MeV (in the region where the shape of the probability curve is no longer important) by the above assumption that $\rho_F = 2.5\mu\Omega$cm/at %. Since this value of ρ_F is close to accepted values it is tempting to believe that 19 eV is the real threshold minimum for Copper. Subsequent investigations with oriented single crystal copper by Sosin and Garr[197] however, suggested that E_d was about 19 eV for both the ⟨100⟩ and ⟨110⟩ directions and thus Sosin's[193] earlier calculations may have been oversimplified. On the other

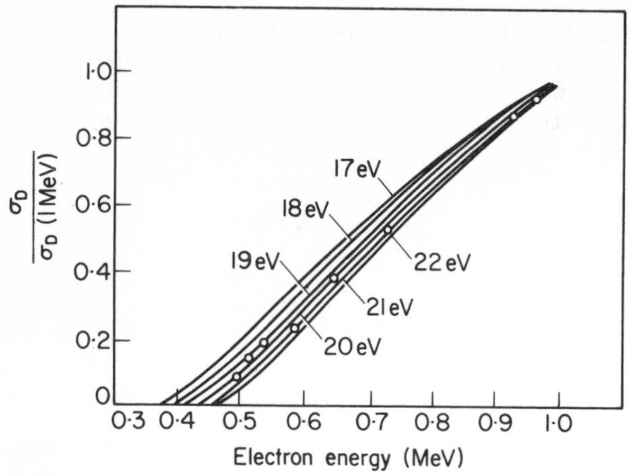

Fig. 6.53 Normalised differential resistivity/flux curves,

$$\sigma_0 = \frac{1}{pF}\frac{dp}{d\phi}$$

as a function of electron energy. Curves normalised at 1 MeV and plotted for different threshold displacement energies. Open circles are data points. (viz. Ref. 6.193)

hand Wollenberger and Wurm[198] have indicated, following Gibson et al's[23] computations and theoretical studies by Duesing and Leibfried,[101] that the form of $P(T, T_0)$ is more complex than suggested by Sosin,[193] with a minimum for E_d of about 9 eV at 5° to the ⟨110⟩ axis, but that E_d along ⟨110⟩ was indeed about 19 eV. Further work with single crystals is clearly needed. Later work[194] showed that a minimum threshold energy value of 24 eV gave the best fit for data obtained by Lucasson and Walker[177,178,199] for silver whereas these authors had previously believed a step function probability with a mean threshold energy at 28 eV to be most adequate These latter investigators[177,178] also believed that step function probabilities were adequate for copper, gold, nickel, iron, molybdenum and titanium with mean threshold energies of 22 eV, 33-36 eV, 24 eV, 37 eV and 29 eV respectively. However it was recognised that calculations with a step function, a linear function, or a staircase (double step) function with the same mean threshold gave more or less indistinguishable results, so that in copper the 22 eV value for the mean and Sosin's calculation for the minimum, are not at variance, nor are the respective data in silver. Indeed the results suggest that, in copper P rises from zero at 19 eV to unity at about 25 eV, but as seen above the true minimum for Ed may be at ~9 eV. In Aluminium however, data could not be realistically fitted to any simple and sensible threshold, and step function, due it was believed to the increased importance of cascade processes in this low mass metal at the energies used. In fact several calculations were made to determine the effects of cascade processes assuming the various cascade mechanisms described earlier in this Chapter. It was found that the inclusion of such effects gave considerably better agreement with experiment in Al. Particularly if the Seitz-Koehler model, without replacement, and with a threshold energy of 32 eV were assumed. Results on single crystals showing any orientation dependence are eagerly anticipated.

We may also note that Lucasson and Walker[199] have suggested that there should be a correlation between the displacement thresholds of various metals. They propose that the displacement energy will be related to the interatomic potential of an atom placed midway between normal lattice points, i.e. to Z^2/D where Z is the atomic number and D the equilibrium spacing. This will be direction dependent again, and would suggest that any series of metals such as Rh, Ag and Pd with similar values of Z^2/D would exhibit similar thresholds. Further experimental work will help to clarify these matters.

More recently Bauer and Sosin[200,201] have observed electron induced damage in copper and gold down to transferred energies as low as 11 eV and 18 eV respectively. However considerable damage only occurred above 16-19 eV and 33-36 eV respectively and these were taken to be the values typical of the pure samples. The lower values were interpreted as showing the influence of impurities (e.g. Be) in the samples which could be displaced more easily from substitutional positions to interstitial positions by focused sequences and resulted in vacancy production in the host lattice. Actual experiments[201] on Be doped samples tended to confirm this suggestion, but Wollenberger and Wurm[198] have preferred to interpret Sosin and Bauer's[200,201] low threshold data in terms of a minimum E_d, lower than 19 eV, occurring at a small angle to the ⟨110⟩ axis. These authors also suggested that the effective threshold energy in gold was actually 35 eV and that this must be associated with displacements in the ⟨100⟩ direction since Nelson and Thompson's[105] measurements of the focusing energies in gold from sputtering experiments give a displacement energy in the ⟨110⟩ direction of ~200 eV. This rather large difference in displacement energies for the two directions was believed to be responsible for the fact that the differential resistance/electron energy curves could not be fitted by a simple step function displacement probability of unity at 35 eV whereas this procedure is more successful with Cu where the displacement energies in the ⟨100⟩ and ⟨110⟩ directions are probably much closer than in gold. i.e. the effect of a rather large directional dependence of E_d is to render the simple step function probability quite inaccurate.

In elemental and compound semiconductors the situation is less resolved since the theoretical calculations of Kohn[75] suggested a directional dependence of E_d in Ge and Si whereas measurements by Brown and Augustyniak[77], Loferski and Rapperport[78] and Flicker, Loferski and Scott-Monck[79] have failed to reveal such a dependence, although the magnitudes of $E_d < 10$ eV were confirmed. Von Bauerlin[76] evaluated thresholds in group 111-V semiconducting compounds to lie below 10 eV with double values of E_d corresponding to displacement of each atomic species whereas Grimshaw and Banbury[202] have reported a single value of E_d ~17-18 eV in GaAs using Hall effect measurements. Clearly further work is desirable in these materials.

Electron irradiation near the threshold energy should produce only very simple defects, i.e. Frenkel pairs, although there may be a range of separations of these pairs. Consequently, annealing of an electron irradiated sample and observation of a parameter such as resistivity, which depends upon defect density, should enable deduction of the migration kinetics of these pairs. Resistivity changes during annealing after irradiation at between 4°K and 10°K have been observed by several investigators, and summaries have been given by Walker[192], Sosin[191] and Simmons et al.[203,204]. This observational method has been the one most widely used to study the effects of electron irradiation although post irradiation observation of annealing of the internal friction of copper has been reported by Lomer and Niblett[205]. Irradiations of copper by deuterons at various temperatures had shown earlier that much of the damage produced would anneal out and be unobservable unless the target temperature was maintained in the region of 10°K. Consequently most of the electron irradiation experiments have been conducted at, or below 10°K, and, after irradiation, the sample slowly warmed whilst the resistivity changes were followed. A typical differential resistivity/temperature annealing spectrum for copper is shown in Figure 6.54 taken from data observed by Corbett et al[206,207,208,195] in the range 10-80°K. Five peaks are evident below 60°K and are labelled substages IA, B, C, D and E. Peaks A, B, C and D are typical of a single order reaction, but D and E are a little broader than expected, and the peak E is conditioned by the extent of the irradiation and previous treatment of the sample and the impurity content. An interesting feature is that as the electron energy is decreased the relative amount of damage associated with peak A decreases whilst that associated with peaks B and C increases. The energies of activation for the five peaks are respectively 0.05 eV, 0.085 eV, 0.095 eV, 0.12 eV and 0.12 eV of which the final value is dose dependent. 85% of the damage produced at 10°K is recovered by annealing to 60°K. The remaining damage is recoverable by further warming to temperatures even in excess of room

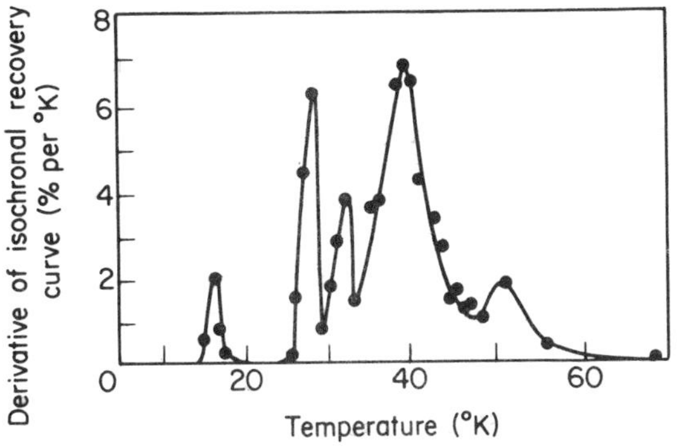

Fig. 6.54 Recovery of electron induced damage in Cu as a function of temperature during annealing. The percentage recovery during isochronal measurements at increasing temperatures was observed and this curve shows the temperature derivative of the observations, and illustrates the substages in stage I recovery. (viz. Ref. 6.206)

temperature and is characterised by stages II, III, IV, and V which anneal at about 60°K-240°K, 240°K-340°K, 340°K-500°K and >450°K respectively. Annealing of damage is very similar in silver, occurring at slightly lower energies than in copper, whereas gold exhibits an almost continuous annealing spectrum with a multiplicity of poorly defined peaks accounting for only about 25% of the total observed damage. Bauer and Sosin[209] have shown that all the annealing in gold from 15°K to 240°K is typical of a first order annihilation process since there was no dependence of the peak annealing temperature upon the initial total damage (c.f. Equation 6.158). This suggests that the annealing in gold is due to recombination of correlated close spaced Frenkel pairs since long range migration and recombination would lead to second order kinetics. Aluminium[194,210,211] exhibits two peaks at 35°K and 45°K which account for 75% of the total damage induced at 20°K whilst nickel reveals three peaks between 40°K and 105°K, containing 80% of the damage. Copper,[194,211,212] doped with various percentages of Ag, Cd and Be also exhibited the peak structure of pure copper but, in addition, showed structure in stage II. Fe, Mo and Ti[178] exhibit the same general features as do the above metals.

The interpretation of the peaks in copper[208,213,214] is a question of some considerable debate at present since their evaluation impinges directly upon the nature of stable post irradiation defects. We shall summarize the various mechanisms which have been reported, drawing upon evidence from other techniques such as quenching experiments to support our arguments.

Two general features appear to have been unequivocally established in that since only simple Frenkel pairs should be produced, the annealing in stage I, at least, is due to mutual annihilation of vacancies and interstitials. This argument finds quantitative support in measurements of the X-ray lattice parameter and linear macroscopic expansion during annealing of deuteron bombarded copper,[215,216,217] (which also gives similar stage I substructure in the annealing spectrum) which showed that vacancies and interstitials disappeared in equal number during annealing. i.e. mutual vacancy-interstitial annihilation. This fact, together with the values of migration energy for the vacancy and interstitial given in Section 6.2.1 reveal, immediately that it is the more mobile interstitial which must migrate. The arguments centre around the nature of this migration and thus of the interstitial itself.

Since the order of kinetics in substages A, B and C of stage I annealing is unity it is natural to associate these with recovery of close Frenkel pairs of vacancies and interstitials, each substage corresponding to a different separation of the pairs. Walker[192,207] suggests that the interstitials involved here are all in the dumbell (split) configuration. Substages ID and IE, however, exhibit higher order kinetics, and are dose, prior irradiation and impurity dependent, and these features led Walker to postulate that recovery in these substages is a result of annihilation of distant interstitial vacancy pairs in correlated and uncorrelated processes respectively. (In a correlated process the interstitial diffuses to and recombines with its own associated original vacancy whereas in an uncorrelated process recombination is random.) During stage IE annealing some interstitials may associate and form clusters and it is the final annihilation of such clusters which leads to the higher annealing stages. Walker[192] supports this argument by showing that irradiation at 80°K, prior to a 20°K irradiation, enhances stage IE and III annealing due to increased cluster formation. In addition the annealing of impure and cold worked targets also indicate greatly enhanced stage III annealing, which Walker suggests are due to the trapping of interstitials in clusters around foreign atoms, interstitial platelets and dislocations at low temperatures during bombardment with subsequent annealing in stage III. (These traps were described by Walker as nucleation and unsaturable traps respectively.) Using this trapping model Walker was able to show that the defect concentration increased as anticipated theoretically, during bombardment at 80°K in pure samples (only unsaturable traps such as dislocations present) in impure samples, (impurity nucleation traps) and in impure, cold worked samples (all traps present in large numbers). In order to explain the enhancement of stage IE and in a radiation doped sample however, it is necessary to assume a rather high interstitial clustering efficiency as compared with the direct interstitial-vacancy annihilation efficiency.

In stage III annealing, which has been shown by Meechan and Brinkman[214,218] to obey second order kinetics, the trapping model requires cluster (which are supposed in pure samples to be di-interstitials) annihilation by either cluster migration or dissociation, or by vacancy migration. The former appears to be vitiated by the order of the kinetics and the fact that in impure samples (where clusters are presumably trapped by impurities) stage II is still observed. This leaves the possibility of vacancy migration as the cause of stage III annealing since this type of migration should be observed under all circumstances (radiation doped, impure samples etc.). However the migration energy involved, 0.62 eV, is considerably lower than the value measured for copper by quenching and cold work experiment, viz 1.08 ± 0.03 eV by Seeger[37] and 0.88 eV by Simmons and Baluffi.[219] On the other hand the experiments of the former authors revealed an annealing peak associated with an energy of 0.64 ± 0.04 eV, which could possibly be interpreted as vacancy migration and in addition the Huntington-Seitz[10] theoretical calculation for the monovacancy migration energy gives rather wide limits of 1 ± 0.5 eV. Partly because of this difficulty in ascribing an unequivocal migration energy for the vacancy in copper, Meechan et al[214] and later Seeger [37] evolved an alternative proposal to account for the whole annealing spectrum. In this model the vacancy is assumed to be the migrating entity in stage IV with an activation energy of about 1 eV whilst stage III is associated with the partly correlated annihilation of distant dumbell interstitials and vacancies. This requires assumption of the dumbell migration energy of 0.62 eV whereas calculations[10,23] tend to place this energy in the region of 0.1 eV. Stage I annealing is then associated with the recombination of two different types of interstitial and vacancy close pairs, namely the dumbell configuration and the static crowdion. The crowdion configuration cannot be dismissed completely on the grounds of Gibson's et al's[23] calculations since the stability of this depended upon the potential assumed, and a different, more representative potential may have resulted in crowdion stability. Since dynamic crowdions are undoubtedly present during irradiation, if static crowdions are stable these will undoubtedly be formed quite densely, and, according to Seeger,[37] may lead to a higher energy annealing stage such as I D. because of their generally rather large separation from their associated vacancy. The close spaced crowdion vacancy pairs may anneal out in stage I A, whilst stages I B, I C and some of I E are associated with annealing of dumbell vacancy pairs of varying close separation. One fact that supports this suggestion is that as the electron irradiation energy is decreased, stages I A, I D and I E are suppressed relative to I B and I C. Production of dumbell interstitials in ⟨100⟩ rows is probably easier than that of ⟨110⟩ crowdion interstitials (viz. the results of Gibson et al[23]), so that degrading the electron energy diminishes the contribution of the latter. Meechan et al[214] also suggested that adoption of the crowdion also allows explanation of the fact that in cold worked Cu, stage I is suppressed and stage II enhanced, due it is believed to conversion of crowdions to dumbell interstitials on collision with dislocations.

This model is also open to criticism, however, both because of the rather large migration energy which it is necessary to associate with the dumbell, and because the radiation doping effect necessitates the introduction of the concept of trapping and clustering. Indeed, as we shall see shortly, interstitial clustering is evident in electron transmission microscopic examination of irradiated films and appears to be well established. It may be that a full explanation of the annealing behaviour will neccessitate simultaneous operation of both types of interstitial and of trapping but final resolution must await further experimental data. We should note, however, that the annealing of gold, studied by Ward and Kauffmann,[220,221] Bauer and Sosin[201] can be explained readily on the Seeger[37] mechanism with all stage I recovery due to close pair dumbell-vacancy combination and final recovery of dumbells in stage 2 at an activation energy of 0.71 eV and vacancies in stage IV. In this case there is no necessity to postulate crowdion formation, and indeed this is unlikely since stability considerations show that they should not persist and, in addition, their formation energy should be quite high. Very little stage ID and E recovery is found in gold (which is largely associated with crowdions according to Seeger[37]) although considerable stage II annealing is observed. In addition we may anticipate some of the results of electron microscopic investigation of ion bombarded gold obtained by Venables and Balluffi,[222,223] which will be described in greater detail shortly. These investigators have shown unequivocally that the migrating species in gold in stage III is some form of the interstitial with an energy of migration of 0.75 ± 0.06 eV, although the exact configuration of the interstitial was left unresolved.

Neutron and Deuteron bombardment should also produce similar effects in metals to those already described with electron irradiation, and Simmons et al[203] have summarised the results of such investigations. Generally speaking the annealing peaks show some correspondence with those observed in electron irradiated materials, but these are often superimposed upon a continuous annealing spectrum. Because of the higher primary knock on energies of the heavier particles it is reasonable to assume that multiple vacancy and interstitial clusters are formed in wide variety and that these contribute to the continuum. In addition, the larger transferred energies may be expected to produce a considerable number of thermal spikes, and the operation of these will materially affect subsequent annealing data. Indeed the rate of disordering of Cu_3Au bombarded by 9 MeV protons by Brinkman et al[148] is best explained on the basis of considerable thermal and displacement spike reordering, whilst fission fragment damage and its effect upon radiation induced annealing in Ur is also explained by Brinkman[130] on the displacement spike model. An interesting report of neutron induced damage in gold has been recently given by Swanson and Piercy[224]. As suggested earlier this material shows a remarkably small stage I recover of resistivity and Swanson and Piercy[224] showed that quenching the gold from 640°C before irradiation at 1.8°K resulted in a considerable increase in the earlier substages of stage I recovery but only a minor increase in the later substage recovery. Since the quench was expected to freeze in a considerable vacancy density it was considered that these trapped focusons and crowdions so that a larger density of close Frenkel pairs were produced which annealed out in the early substages of I. Further, since the enhanced vacancy concentration exerted little effect upon later stage I recovery, it was concluded that interstitial clustering was unimportant and thence that the anomalously low stage 1 recovery of gold was due to immobility of the stable form of the interstitial below 50°K. These results therefore tend to support Seegers[37] concept of defect production in gold.

Further experiments[225] on neutron irradiated Au and Al samples of various purities showed that the enhanced recovery in vacancy rich Au was also present in Al (but only above 30°K in the latter material) and that the addition of foreign impurity atoms slightly suppressed the stage I annealing. The damage rates in these materials was only slightly increased (15% at most in Au) by the addition of foreign impurities, or quenched in vacancies, but mechanical deformation which produced dislocations resulted in large enhancements of the damage rate in both materials. These latter damage enhancement results were interpreted (according to the model of Leibfried[115] on the interaction of collision chains with dislocations) as showing that in Au considerable defect production enhancement resulted from the stopping of focused sequences at dislocations. In Al it was believed that the enchancement effect was due to the termination of channelled sequences at dislocations (c.f. Beeler and Besco's[182] computer results for Fe) which increased the random trajectory motion of the Al atoms and so increased $\nu(E)$, since focusing is less important in this material. The increased recovery in the later part of stage 1 in vacancy doped Al, suggested that in this material, unlike Au, randomly migrating interstitials or crowdions could annihilate with vacancies at these temperatures.

Comparisons[203] of the observed amount of damage, at energies well above the displacement threshold, where cascade events should assume importance for both electron and heavy particle induced defect production, with theoretical estimates using the Kinchin-Pease or other simple models, have so far proved unsatisfactory. In 1.4 MeV electron bombarded copper the observed damage was 46% of the calculated damage, whilst in 9 MeV deuteron and 0.43 MeV mean energy pile neutron bombarded copper the observed damage was only 16% and 5% of the expected values respectively. Measurements were made upon electrical resistivity changes and all damage which does not thermally anneal would have been expected to be retained in these samples since irradiation was performed at 4°K. The electron induced damage value could be improved by assumption of a lower but rather unrealistic value for the Frenkel resistivity, but such a process leads to little improvement in the neutron and deuteron data. Since the electron bombardment leads to essentially low energy recoils, some anticipated damage may be lost via focusing events, whilst on the other hand, the larger recoil energies obtained in the neutron and deuteron bombardment cases may lead to channelling events. According to our earlier theoretical analysis, only a very small channelling probability is required to reduce expected damage rates considerably and this effect may well account for some of the low observed defect concentrations. One cannot preclude thermal spike operation in these latter cases either, and these would also reduce observed damage, whilst the effects of athermal (strain induced) annealing discussed by Dettmann et al[167] will also reduce the theoretically anticipated values. It must be concluded that the electron induced damage rate is in reasonable accord with simple cascade theory, although focusing events and athermal annealing processes are probable, but that the refinements of channelling and thermal spike and athermal annealing are required to explain the results of heavy fast particle bombardment.

As we have already stated there are no experimental results available for damage rates in low energy ion bombarded materials in which we are currently interested. However, we would expect the damage to exhibit qualitatively similar characteristics to fast heavy particle bombardment, and if such a compatability was observed, one could infer that the calculations for low energy ions should give a reasonable description of events. Fortunately two techniques have been developed recently which have allowed a rather direct observation and comparison of the nature of some of the defects produced during fast, or slow particle irradiation. viz, the electron transmission microscope and the field ion microscope. We shall discuss the operation of these in turn and indicate the useful comparisons of damage induced by different particle irradiation. We will then conclude with a survey of other indirect observations of damage induced by low energy ions and attempt to correlate these with direct observational techniques.

6.5.2 Electron Microscopy

Crystals whose thickness does not exceed a few 1000 Å are transparent to electrons of energy in the 100 KeV region as produced in the electron microscope. Since the transmitted electrons suffer diffraction effects in their passage through the crystal, any inhomogenities in the crystal, such as dislocations, stacking faults, atomic aggregations etc will be revealed as changes in contrast in the transmitted beam. Hirsch[226] has used the transmission techniques extensively to study the nature of dislocations in crystals subjected to various treatment (quenching, irradiation, etc.) and has given a comprehensive review of the techniques, applications and theory of operation of the device. Since the sample area exposed to electrons can be made small, by efficient focusing, and the transmitted beam can be expanded to produce a large image, for example on a fluorescent screen or photographic plate, very high magnifications may be achieved. Since, also, the effective electron wavelength is of the order of Angstroms, very high resolution of lattice defects is possible. Thus most contemporary microscopes can achieve resolutions between 10 and 20 Å, whilst careful operation often allows resolution in the region of 3-4 Å, i.e. upon the individual atomic scale. Several theories of image contrast have been advanced but we shall not discuss these here, the interested reader is referred to the above review by Hirsch[226] and to the papers by Ashby and Brown.[227,228] We will accept that the technique does in fact produce the results described by the various investigators and merely comment upon the interpretation of these results. Nor shall we dwell upon the technical details of microscopy except to note that crystals, sufficiently thin for transmission experiments, are readily prepared by electrochemical thinning techniques and that during observation it is often possible to operate the specimen at a variety of temperatures by mounting on a heated or cooled (by contact with refrigerants) stage within the microscope. Heating may be accomplished by the electron beam itself by using high beam densities. It should be noted that defect formation within the specimen has been attributed to the operation of the microscope itself, wherein heavy negative ions formed in the microscope are accelerated to and damage the specimen. We shall return to further discussion of this artifact subsequently but note that precautions must always be taken to prevent its operation. To date only a relatively few experiments have been conducted upon the damage produced by low energy ions, but a very considerable amount of information has been obtained following neutron, α particle and fission fragment bombardment of various metals and after quenching from high temperatures. Since these particles will produce primary knock-ons in a similar manner to low energy ions, although of different energy and magnitude, one would expect analogous effects in both types of measurement. We will therefore survey the pertinent data from these other measurements.

At high temperatures (of the order of half the melting temperature Tm) vacancies in metals become mobile and may aggregate. Subsequent quenching to lower temperatures will freeze in these aggregates in structures determined by the nature of the metal. Thus Hirsch[226] had discussed electron micrographs obtained by various authors after quenching different metals and shows that in Al., a large number of prismatic dislocation loops ($10^{15}/cm^2$) of diameter about 200 Å containing a total vacancy concentration of about 10^{-4} are formed by the collapse of discs of vacancies on (111) planes. In gold, the vacancies form tetrahedra of stacking fault. Observations have also been made on vacancy aggregates in Cu, Ni and Al and Cu alloys.

Silcox and Hirsch[23] and Makin, Whapham and Minter [54a] also observed small dislocation loops following neutron irradiation of copper and the former authors suggested that, as in quenched metals, these were vacancy aggregates formed during collapse of displacement spikes. However, Makin et al[54b] showed that the loops also formed during irradiation at −50°C and their size increased with increasing neutron dose. Since vacancies should be immobile at −50°C it could not be expected that the loops should grow by vacancy capture and these authors therefore concluded that the majority of the large loops were formed through interstitial aggregation. This point of view was supported by the work of Barnes[29,229,230,231] who showed that both the large loops (of radius $\gtrsim$ 200 Å) and small, unresolvable black dots (termed somewhat facetiously as 'measles' or 'black death'!) of radius 20 Å were formed during 38 MeV particle bombardment of Copper at 250°C.[28] It is known[29,229] that helium will aggregate as bubbles when stopped in a metal by capturing vacancies, and the interesting feature is that whereas the large loops and black dots were formed throughout the copper, both in the parasurface region where no helium bubbles were located and in the regions where helium bubbles nucleated, the subsequent annealing by heating up to 800°C of the two regions was markedly different. Thus in the region containing no helium the larger dislocation loops disappeared at about 350°C but in the region containing helium bubbles the loops began to grow in size and at 450°C formed a dislocation tangle. This was interpreted as indicating that the large loops were composed of interstitial atoms, which, in the helium free region, captured vacancies which must have been produced in equal numbers during irradiation. It was believed that these vacancies probably resided in the small unresolvable dots, during annealing, but in the bubble rich region the interstitial loops gave off vacancies during annealing which were captured by the helium bubbles. We shall discuss the bubbles in greater detail in Chapter 8 but note for the present that it is well established that these are very efficient vacancy sinks. It was also notable that there were regions completely denuded of large loops near grain boundaries (~8×10^{-5} cm wide) but that the smaller black dots persisted right up to such boundaries. This could be expected if the large loops were of interstitial character, since these could capture vacancies from the grain boundaries (which are very efficient vacancy sources) and annihilate them. Since it was believed that the small dots were composed of small vacancy clusters possibly in the form of vacancy tetrahedra these would persist up to the boundaries. Upon heating to 450°C bubbles were observed to form on grain boundaries, and were believed to be formed from the small vacancy clusters which captured helium atoms and subsequently grew by the acquisition of further vacancies from the large loops. The approximate equality of the number of bubbles and black dots originally present substantiated this belief. Estimates of the total numbers of interstitials in the large loops and vacancies in the small dots revealed approximate equality. General similarity of damage production was observed in α particle irradiation of Ag, Al, & Fe[231], but in the latter two cases no observable loop or dot production was perceived in the helium free regions of the sample. This was interpreted as revealing defect annihilation at the bombardment temperature.

Subsequent experiments[55,232] on α particle and fission fragment bombardment of Al at lower temperatures, (~ 80°C) however, showed that, dislocation loops were formed throughout the target. In the case of α particle bombardment observations of the contrast of the loops showed unequivocally that the earlier proposal that the large loops were interstitial in nature and that the small dots were vacancy clusters was correct.

In the case of fission fragment bombardment[55] (which was induced by irradiating Uranium foils in contact with the Al by neutrons) loops were observed throughout the target and were found to grow during bombardment. The loops were interpreted as constituting both interstitial and vacancy clusters, with the large interstitial loops lying near to ⟨110⟩ planes. As the irradiation dose increased the sizes of the loops increased and some evidence of aligned loops, as opposed to completely randomly distributed loops was obtained.

Heating the Al to only 100°C revealed definite evidence of loop migration and these factors led Westmacott et al[55] to suggest a mechanism for loop size increase. Since both interstitial and vacancy clusters grew simultaneously it was considered that growth could not have resulted from loop capture of single vacancies and interstitials since this would have required that vacancy loops would repel interstitials and vice versa. It was therefore believed that the smaller loops migrated by conservative climb to similar loops and the loop size increased through agglomeration. The larger loops however suffered slip and loops of different types agglomerated and partially annihilated. This latter process was shown to be in agreement with theoretical deductions of Kroupa and Price[233,234] and Johnson[235] and was substantiated by the observations of loops of one type having inclusions of loops of the other type. These observations readily explain the absence of loops in the earlier work on α particle irradiated Al at higher temperatures, where presumably loop migration is sufficiently rapid to cause immediate annihilation.

The agglomeration of similar small loops by conservative climb is confirmed by the observations that such clusters have a tendency to form in rows and it should be noted that similar rows of loops have been observed in Gold[50], chromium[236] and platinum[237,238]. Other work by Ruedl et al[239] on fission fragment and α particle irradiated Platinum has also given a rather convincing demonstration of the importance of focusing sequences. It was observed that small dislocation loops formed preferentially at coherent twin boundaries although the irradiation temperature was insufficient to permit loop migration to possible sinks at these boundaries (although in fact Barnes[29] has shown that coherent twin boundaries are not sinks for point defects) whilst no region close to the boundaries was denuded of loops. Therefore this phenomenon could only result through preferential formation at the twin boundary, and Ruedl et al[239] suggested that focused collision sequences arriving at a coherent twin boundary were suddenly brought into a non focusing direction (e.g. a ⟨110⟩ row becomes a ⟨114⟩ row at the boundary) and defects were formed which, if in sufficient numbers, clustered to form loops.

The work on neutron bombarded copper was subsequently extended by Makin, Whapham and Minter[54b] and Makin & Manthorpe[32] in which the distribution in loop sizes was studied as a function of irradiation dose and annealing treatment. The fraction of loops of a given size were found to remain constant, irrespective of neutron dose during irradiation, and this led Makin et al to propose that the loops of all sizes were instantaneously nucleated during bombardment and grew through capture of individual vacancies or interstitials, formed close to the embryo clusters. No growth through slip or climb was considered important, nor was it believed correct that the suggestion, by Barnes, that only interstitials were able to migrate was tenable, since loops of all sizes, which were both vacancy and interstitial in nature, were formed at the same rate.

Theoretical work by Varley[240] tended to confirm this model but more recently Hesketh[241,242] has proposed that the loops are generated instantaneously within a displacement spike and do not require diffusion of vacancies or interstitials from surrounding regions, to give the observed loop size distribution. Which is the correct picture cannot, at present be decided. It does appear however that the mechanisms of loop growth in Al and Cu at room temperature may be different, loops in the former growing by loop migration but not in the latter case. On the other hand the mechanisms of loop formation may be similar.

Makin and Manthorpe's[32] observations of loop annealing during heating showed that loops of diameter > 50°A disappeared initially at a much faster rate than the small loops < 50 Å (i.e. the measles), but that the loop sizes did not increase. This suggested that small, unobservable clusters of vacancies initially dissociated and annihilated some of the larger interstitial loops, whilst the larger vacancy loops > 20 Å and < 50 Å finally dissociated and annihilated the largest loops. Again the difference of behaviour between Al and Cu is evident and it is clear that the nature of damage production is markedly dependent upon the structure of the target and upon the nature of the primary particle. Further evidence of this dependence has been observed in irradiation of copper containing fractional additives of silver, which showed greatly increased cluster formation, nucleating presumably at the foreign atom inclusions. Again investigation of neutron irradiated Al gives rise to conflicting results. Makin[243] (unpublished) and Silcox[244] found no evidence of loops in Al irradiated with only relatively small doses, whilst Beirlein and Mastel[245] observed considerable loop production after irradiation with 10^{20} neutrons cm^2 and Smallman and Westmacott[246] observed a rather low loop rate production during neutron irradiation at −195°C.

In this brief survey we have attempted only to describe phenomena which have most immediate bearing upon the observations of low energy ion bombardment induced damage. Many other electron microscopic studies have been performed and related to property changes in irradiated material (e.g. beryllium, uranium etc.) such as radiation hardening, swelling etc. and reviews of this type of investigation have been given by Barnes[247-251]. In addition fission fragment tracks have been studied in such materials as platinum and uranium oxide by Bierlein and Mastel[132] and Whapham and Makin[252], in mica by Barnes and Silk[253] and Bonfiglio et al[254], in graphite by Izui and Fujita[255] and in molybdenum disulphide by Bowden and Chadderton[256]. Definite evidence for displacement spike production has been obtained, and the production of vacancy and interstitial clusters formed during neutron and α particle irradiation have been attributed to this mechanism. Whether or not these clusters are formed by the depleted zone process discussed by Seeger[37] in which the vacancy cluster is formed through the collapse of the displacement spike and the interstitial clusters through the generation of crowdion and replacement type focusing collisions is debatable.

Beevers and Nelson[257] studied the dislocation loops formed in Al irradiated at about 60°C with 85 keV ions of H, He, Ne, A, Kr and Xe and found evidence of such formation in all cases. The thickness of the targets was arranged such that the lighter ions passed completely through whilst A^+, Kr^+, and Xe^+ were stopped within the foils and presumably nucleated into bubbles. For a given dose of any ion the observed damage increased considerably with increasing ion mass as depicted by the micrographs shown in Figures 6.55 a and b for He^+ and Xe^+ ion bombardment respectively. After annealing at 400°C the loops formed during H^+, He^+ and Ne^+ bombardment disappeared whilst those formed during bombardment with the heavier ions increased in size to form a tangle via interaction with the gas bubbles which had precipitated. Increasing the total dose of any ion species at a given bombardment rate showed that a certain dose was necessary (e.g. 10^{16} H^+ ions/cm^2) before loops were visible in the microscope (loop diameter ~40 Å) and thereafter the loops grew until a dislocation tangle formed, but the number of loops decreased although the number of defects in all the loops increased. In other experiments where the total dose was maintained constant (4.8×10^{16} H^+ ions/cm^2) whilst the bombardment rate was varied over 3 order of magnitude (6.4×10^{11} ions/cm^2/sec to 6.4×10^{14} ions/cm^2/sec) showed that increasing the dose rate initially increased the total damage (up to a bombardment rate of 6.4×10^{13} ions/cm^2/sec) but at 3×10^{14} ions/cm^2/sec no damage was formed and at the highest rate the target melted.

These results suggested that some critical dose was necessary before loops were formed in Al, as opposed to Cu where neutron irradiation gives a constantly increasing production of defects, but at high doses the loops migrate by slip and climb and coalesce. The increased probability of loop formation at large bombardment rates resulted from a higher rate of defect production and their agglomeration, whereas at very high dose rates heating of the targets causes annealing out of the loops. It therefore appears that a higher rate of defect production is required in Al than in Cu in order to cause loop formation.

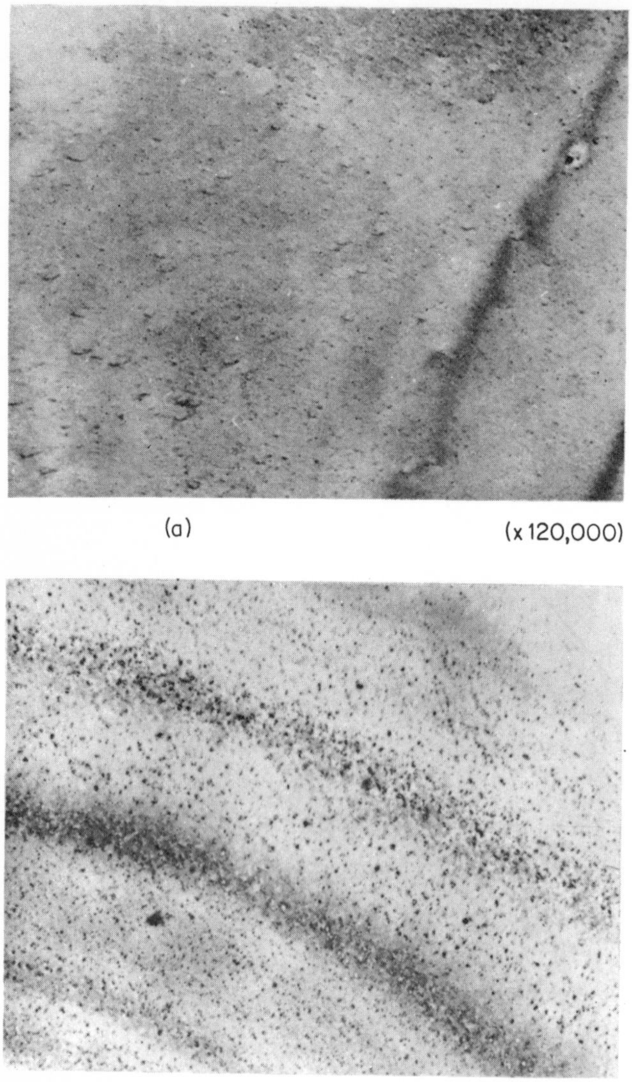

(a) (x 120,000)

(b) (x 32,000)

Fig. 6.55 Damage induced in Al by ion bombardment as observed by electron microscopy (viz. Ref. 6.257) **a)** 1.2 × 10^{16} He^+ ions cm^2 b) 5 × 10^{14} Xe^+ ions/cm ions/cm^2

The total number of defects preserved in the clusters were compared with the number expected from the simple Kinchin-Pease theory and showed that between 10^{-3} and 10^{-4} of the expected number were retained, suggesting that most of the defects must have annealed out to surfaces, grain boundaries and by mutual annihilation. In view of the radiation temperature being 60°C, and the results of electron irradiation which indicates that many point defects anneal out at temperatures below 0°C, this low retained damage is not unexpected.

It is further clear, however, that the rate of loop formation is very critically dependent upon the nature of the irradiating particle, the dose rate, the total dose and the target material since different competing processes of loop formation and annihilation will depend upon these parameters. It would also be anticipated that the bombarding particle energy and the target temperature would exert some considerable influence upon the damage production rate and one awaits such measurements eagerly. The conflicting reports on neutron irradiated Al outlined earlier, may possibly find explanation in this dependence on total dose and irradiation temperature.

Beevers and Mazey[258] studied loops formed in Molybdenum irradiated with 6 × 10^{18}/cm^2, 85 keV H^+ ions at 80°C and 38 MeV α particles at 400°C and as in the case of Al observed enhanced loop and dot preservation in the presence of He bubbles. With H^+ bombardment no evidence of bubble formation was observed, since the protons presumably passed through the 2000 Å thick targets, and the density of the loops was large although the loop diameter (~30 Å) was smaller than in He^+ bombardment. The increased loop density was attributed to the facts that the H^+ ion bombardment rate was larger and the temperature lower than with He^+ ion bombardment, whilst the smaller loop diameter was attributed to lower energy transfers from the H^+ ions. Annealing at 200°C produced no discernible loop changes, but at 900°C recrystallisation occured.

Pashley and Presland[259, 260] and others[261] have discussed one of the less attractive artifacts of electron microscope operation. The former authors have shown that apparently untreated (i.e. unirradiated) samples of gold and other metals often develop a small dot like structure during exposure to the electron beam only. By careful experiment and elimination of all extraneous effects it was shown that the dots were caused by bombardment of the targets by negative ions produced in the electron source of the microscope which passed through the focusing system and struck the target with energies of the order of 100 keV. These ions were certainly 0^- (as was later established by Surplice [261])and were evolved from the heated filament. The spot sizes were in the range 30-100 Å diameter and were observed in Ag, Cu, Pd, Pt, Rh and gold. In the case of gold these loops were formed at all temperatures up to 300°C and in this temperature region took on the features of tetrahedra of stacking fault. At elevated temperatures some of the loops grew suggesting acquisition of point defects but no evidence of loop migration by slip or climb was observed.

Although these observations are qualitatively similar to those reported by Beevers and Nelson[257] in heavy ion bombarded Al no attempt has been yet made to accurately define their exact nature. In view of the fact that the magnitude and energy of the incident ions is not unequivocally known, it is probably unnecessary to probe much further into the exact nature of the damage obtained in such experiments, more meaningful results are obtainable from samples irradiated under well defined conditions such as those described by Beevers and Mazey and others to be discussed shortly.

It is convenient to irradiate the targets in situ in the microscope however, since changes of temperature which occur during external irradiation and transfer to the microscope are obviated. In this respect the observations of Pashley and Presland[259, 260] are important and suggest further experiments under controlled conditions within the microscope. In fact Howe, Gilbert and Piercy[262] have used this negative ion irradiation artifact to bombard copper at 10°K with 100 keV 0^- ions in the microscope. Only small dislocation loops were observed (~10 Å) together with the smaller black dots beyond the microscope resolution. Subsequent annealing of the copper to room temperature evinced no change in the size or character of the loops, suggesting that these were of the same nature as those observed in neutron irradiated copper at room temperature and that they were formed instantaneously in a displacement spike and not through generation, migration and nucleation of isolated interstitials or vacancies (which would be frozen in). Further their lack of size expansion up to room temperature indicated that they did not trap further defects during annealing, suggesting, in agreement with Makin and Manthorpes[32] observations that they were in fact vacancy aggregates. Howe and McGurn[263] subsequently extended these observations by studying the effects on the damage produced between < 30°K and room temperature in Au oriented with the surface parallel to [100] by 100 keV 0^- bombardment through deliberate introduction of vacancy tetrahedra into the gold target before bombardment. Quenching of gold foils from 950°C to 0°C resulted in the formation of the characteristic vacancy tetrahedra originally described by Silcox and Hirsch[30] and the behaviour of these was studied during subsequent 0^- ion irradiation at temperatures as low as ~20°K, upon warming up to room temperature these vacancy clusters were observed to slowly diminish in size and finally vanish whilst radiation induced defect clusters appeared in the form of small spots. When the bombardments were conducted at room temperature the stage at which the tetrahedra finally disappeared occurred when the density of radiation induced spots was about 25 times the original vacancy tetrahedra concentration, whereas complete disappearance occurred at a bombardment temperature < 30°K for a value of this ratio of about 7. Upon warming a target bombarded at < 30°K, containing both vacancy tetrahedra and damage clusters, to 295°K, no change in the appearance of either tetrahedra or clusters occurred. Since it is generally accepted that only close Frenkel pairs annihilate below 30°K, these authors interpreted their results as indicating that the disappearance of the vacancy tetrahedra below this temperature could not be explained on the basis of the long range migration of free interstitials. We will anticipate here results of a similar nature obtained by Venables and Balluffi[222, 223] with Argon bombarded gold which will be described shortly, and which suggested that the cause of the vacancy tetrahedra disappearance at low temperature was the collision of focusons with the vacancy clusters and ejection of interstitials into the clusters, or, local micro heating through thermal spike generation which caused relatively long range interstitial transport. Since no change in the radiation produced spots nor the remaining vacancy clusters occurred upon warming to 295°K in Venables and Balluffi's[222] experiments it was concluded that these former must also be vacancy aggregates produced in the depleted zone type of event suggested by Seeger[37]. It is surprising however, if this is the case, that the radiation induced clusters are themselves not eliminated by further bombardment although this may be a result of a different configuration of these clusters. We will defer further discussion of these results until the work of Venables and Balluffi has been discussed.

Carroll and Birnbaum[264] have irradiated LiF with 100 keV 0^- ions in the microscope at about 200°C and observed regions of reorientation parallel to ⟨100⟩ directions, after short bombardments but that these regions were progressively removed after continued bombardment. This latter effect was believed to be due to annealing by the electron beam. Examination of the disoriented surface using diffraction pattern measurements suggested that these regions were composed of precipitated platelets of Lithium formed by clustering of cation and anion vacancies and precipitation of Li onto the voids. It was also believed that the Li crystallised in the unusual f.c.c. structure due to pressure from the surrounding Li F lattice.

A further very informative sequence of ion bombardment experiments performed outside the microscope, but under carefully controlled conditions has been described by Brandon and his colleagues. In this work[50] thin foils of Au, Cu and Ni, Pt, Cu_3 Au and gold-silver alloys, were bombarded at normal incidence by monoenergetic 100 eV A^+ ions in a special chamber and then transferred to the electron microscope for observation. Bombardments were executed at target temperatures from −30°C to +30°C but were subsequently operated in the microscope at about 17°C. Since no annealing was observed in the microscope after a low temperature bombardment it was believed that damage induced at the lower temperatures was preserved even at the higher microscope temperature. The early investigations showed that the ion bombardment resulted in the formation of small dislocation loops, sometimes faulted, and later work[50, 51, 265] confirmed and extended the observations. It was found that both glissile and sessile loops were formed in gold, the former only existing along ⟨110⟩ directions if these were parallel to the free surface and the latter along ⟨111⟩ directions if these were parallel to the surface. These results were interpreted as indicating that unless the loops formed in these directions they could slip out of the surface under the action of image forces. Examples of both glissile and sessile loops in gold are shown in Figures 6.56 a and

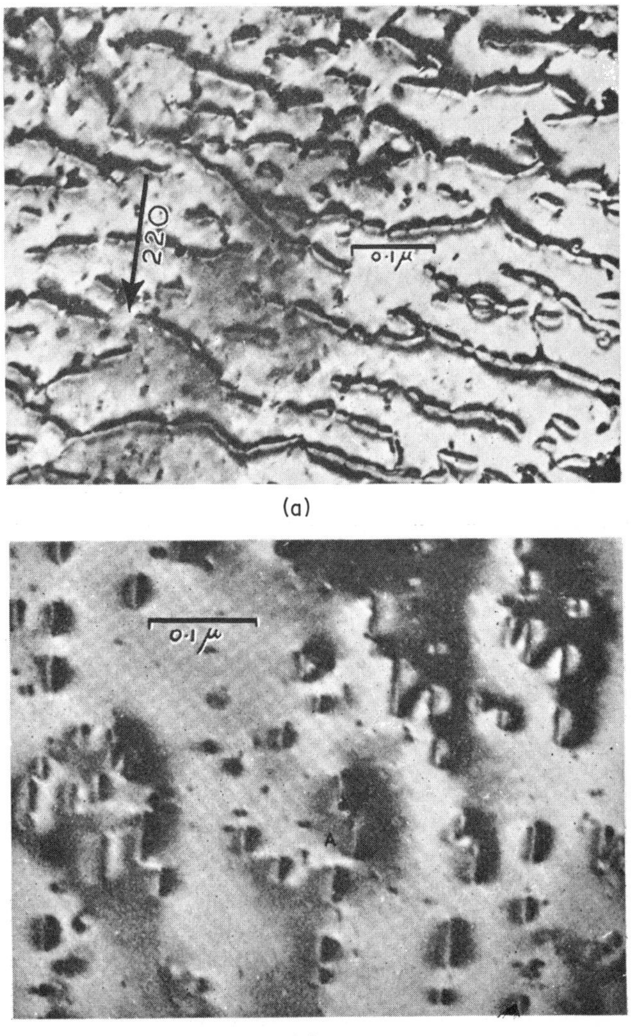

Fig. 6.56 a) Glissile sub surface dislocations in a Au foil (Direction of 220 direction giving reflection is arrowed).
b) Sessile sub surface dislocations in a Au foil. ⟨111⟩ streaking is evident. (viz. Ref. 6.51)

b and similar behaviour was observed with nickel but with a preponderance of sessile loops, whilst in copper only glissile loops were observed. Observations of the loop contrast showed that they were formed from interstitial clusters and were located within a region of about 100 Å from the free bombarded surface. At low temperatures ($< -30°C$) the density of loops was high and the size of the loops extended right down to the resolution limit of the microscope (~10 Å), but at 0°C only a relatively few, large loops formed and the thinner periphery of the foil was found to be denuded of loops, suggesting that the defects responsible for the loops could migrate rapidly to free surfaces at 0°C. Near the periphery, where the target thickness was small (~500 Å) it was believed that the defects could migrate to both surfaces so that loop formation was vitiated, whereas in the thicker target regions the defects were in the foil for larger times and could therefore nucleate and form loops. Similar behaviour was again evident in copper and nickel.

In addition to dislocation loops, dislocation dipoles were also formed, together with numerous strings of aligned small loops which could generate the larger dipoles. The presence of loops also appeared to be rather critically dependent upon grain orientation, since some grains in a bombarded foil contained large numbers of loops whilst others did not. Suggested reasons for this were variations in the probability of defect production with crystal direction, as would be experienced with grains of differing orientations, and variations in the stability of loops beneath grains of different surface orientations. In the grain where a high defect density was preserved the ratio of the number of defects observed to the numbers expected from the Kinchin-Pease model was of order 10^{-3} suggesting that most of the defects formed annihilated by recombination, or in view of the denuded region evidence at 0°C, migrated to free surfaces. It is notable that this fractional retention is very similar to the values obtained by Beevers and Nelson[257] in irradiated Al, where the same loss mechanisms were believed to operate. Again most useful information would be obtained by irradiation at liquid helium temperatures.

Since the incident Argon ions could not be expected to penetrate more than about two atomic layers the damage at 100 Å must have been caused by the creation of defects at this depth or at other depths from which they diffused and migrated to nucleate. Further, since the loops were proved to contain interstitial atoms they must have formed through the agglomeration and condensation of these atoms. Focuson and crowdion propagation would lead to interstitial formation deep within the crystal and moreover would be in just the correct directions to form the stable glissile and sessile loops. Since marked denudation of thin foil areas and reduced loop formation occurred at about 0°C it was clear that the interstitials could migrate rapidly at these temperatures and condense at the free surfaces without loop formation and possibly annihilate with vacancies which must have been produced simultaneously. The temperature range corresponds to stage III in electrical resistivity annealing and the obvious inference is that stage III in gold is therefore associated with single interstitial migration corresponding to Seeger's[37] interpretation. An alternative explanation could be that the interstitials which migrated were associated with an impurity atom or were in di-interstitial form (remembering that Vineyard[170] obtained an energy of di-interstitial migration (actually the binding energy) in Cu of 0.36-0.49 eV). However Seeger[147] criticised the latter point of view on the grounds that stage III is an impurity independent phenomenon, thus mitigating against interstitial-impurity complexes, whilst it is doubtful that a sufficient di-interstitial concentration could be generated during low energy ion or electron bombardment, particularly above the stage III annealing temperatures since the single interstitials would re-combine much more rapidly with vacancies (with which they are associated) than with other interstitials. If indeed di-interstitials produced by single interstitial agglomeration in stage I after electron bombardment were responsible for stage II annealing then bombardment at temperatures between stages I and III would lead to a smaller subsequent stage III annealing than after bombardment at temperatures below stage I where all interstitials would be frozen in. Such a behaviour is not observed experimentally, and again tends to confirm Seeger's picture of annealing in noble metals.

Baker[237] has also observed dislocation loops in 100 eV A^+ ion irradiated Platinum at -15°C. In this case the loops were found to line up in long strings and often consisted of parallel loop pairs. An unusual feature of these observations was that no annealing occurred at moderate temperatures and only heating to 1200°C caused the loops to climb to the foil surface where the pairs separated and reformed along ⟨112⟩ directions. This annealing behaviour again suggested as in the case of irradiated Al that the mutual annihilation of vacancies and interstitials was unimportant and that loop growth would be due to climb (and possibly slip) processes.

Mihama[266] has also obtained evidence of loop, spot and dislocation tangle formation in 5-10 keV A^+ ion bombardment MoS_2 and graphite. Castaing and Jouffrey[267, 268] bombarded gold with 4 keV Argon ions within the microscope itself and although the target temperature was in the region of 20°C, again observed dislocation loops of the order of 50 Å diameter. Similarly Brebec et al[269] observed loops, screw dislocations, tetrahedra of stacking fault, and bubbles of trapped gas in silver irradiated with several hundred electron volt Helium, Neon, Argon or Krypton ions. In none of the cases however was the effect of dose, gas trapping or temperature, during or after bombardment, studied, nor was the nature of the loops determined. Nevertheless it is interesting to note that these results suggest that at almost all ion energies, similar phenomena of bubble nucleation and both interstitial and vacancy loop formation occurs. However, investigations by Ogilvie, Sanders and Thomson[270] of ion bombarded gold did pay particular attention to the effects of ion flux, type and energy and target temperature on the type of damage produced. In this work polycrystalline gold with a preferred (111) orientation in the surface plane or single crystal gold with (100) surface orientations were bombarded with monoenergetic He, Ne, A and Xe ions in the energy range of 10 eV to 500 eV. Beam heating caused the target temperature to rise (to an unknown temperature, but $< 200°C$ but in some experiments liquid nitrogen cooling maintained the targets at $\lesssim 0°C$. The bombardment induced damage was subsequently examined by transmission electron microscopy and was invariably found to consist of a combination in greater or lesser degree of spots (< 50Å diameter), dislocation loops (> 50 Å diameter) and short and long dislocation lines (100 Å - 2000 Å) which were loops which intersected the surface. The relative numbers of each type of damage was dependent

TABLE 6.10 (viz. Ref. 6.270).

Ion energies (eV) for first appearance of the forms of {111} crystals of gold.

Ion	Spots	Loops	Short Lines	Long Lines
He	40	40	40	40
Ne	60	110	111-150	150-250
Ar	40	59	60	70-80
Xe	21	21	21	30

upon the ion type and energy and quite similar results could be obtained with ions of different species provided that their energy was correctly adjusted. For each ion an energy could be specified, within an eV or so, at which visible damage of the different types just appeared. Table 6.10 indicates the damage threshold energies for the four ions for the case of the (111) orientated gold. From this table it is clear that with Neon or Argon ion bombardment, spots form at the lowest energies, and increase up to a maximum of $5 \times 10^{10}/cm^2$ with increasing ion energy. Closed loops appear next, and finally dislocation lines of various lengths. In the case of He and Xe bombardment, however, spots, loops and lines form simultaneously from the damage threshold upwards. In the case of the (100) orientated single crystals, the damage produced by Ne and Ar bombardment is considerably less dense than in the (111) orientation case and consisted largely of the small spot structure. He and Xe bombardment gave much the same type of defect structure with both surface orientations however. Decreasing the ion flux increased the damage obtained with 90 eV and 150 eV $Neon^+$, particularly enhancing the line dislocation formation, but the damage due to 60 eV A^+ ions was very little changed by an order of magnitude reduction (5×10^{15}-5×10^{14} ions/cm^2/sec) in the ion flux.

Cooling the target to 0°C during bombardment showed no noticeable changes in the amount or type of damage, but post bombardment annealing showed that the small spots and loops generally disappeared between 200°C and 300°C, but that the dislocation lines often reorientated and could disappear anywhere in the temperature range 160°C-700°C. The specific behaviour for each ion is presented in Table 6.11. These results indicate that little or no damage annealing occurs during bombardment and the general consistency of annealing temperatures for each ion indicates that the nature of the damage produced is essentially identical for each ion. The odd results for the 25 eV Xe^+ ions were inexplicable.

By studying the intersection of loops with stacking faults it was shown that damage due to He and Xe ions extended to about 500 Å, but damage due to Ne and A ions was probably confined to a depth of about 150 Å beneath the surface, in agreement with Brandon's findings[51, 52]. Also in agreement with this author was the observation that generally speaking, below a (100) surface, only loops with these Burgers vectors parallel to this plane were formed; loops with other orientations presumably slipped and climbed out of the surface under the action of the resolved image forces.

These authors also interpreted their results in the same general way as did Brandon et al[51, 52], suggesting that focuson and replacement sequences generated an excess of interstitials below the surface, which migrated and nucleated to form the observed damage. Once nucleated these various types of loops accepted subsequent interstitials both by capture of migrating interstitials and stopping collision sequences. Since the large loops at least were of interstitial character, the annealing out of these above 300°C could be associated with vacancy migration and capture. This temperature range is in agreement with stage IV annealing of resistivity in electron irradiated gold which is generally associated with vacancy migration. The loops expand both towards and away from the surface but this latter process terminates since the number of interstitials produced falls off with increasing depth. The disappearance of the smaller loops at lower temperatures suggests that these are of different nature and may be vacancy aggregates. In cases where sputtering was also important this was also a determining parameter for the nature and extent of the damage since the receding surface could continuously destroy dislocation loops. (< 30 eV A^+ or < 60 eV Ne^+ ions for example caused sputtering but no damage (whilst He^+ ions of a similar energy resulted in both) resulting in loops residing closer to the surface. Thus 70-110 eV Ne^+ with a high sputtering efficiency tends to create only small loops, whilst low energy He, with little sputtering allows larger loops to form.

Values of the energy which gold atoms must acquire for the production of damage were obtained from the damage threshold energy for each ion and the maxi-

TABLE 6.11 (viz. Ref. 6.270).

Annealing characteristics for ion induced damage in gold.

Bombarding ions		Spots and loops disappeared	Lines
He^+	92 eV	220-250°C	disappear 420-500°C
	180 eV	250-280°C	rearrange 600-650°C disappear 650-700°C
Ne^+	150 eV	220-250°C	—
Ar^+	57.5 eV	220-250°C	—
	77 eV	220-250°C	rearrange 250-280°C
Xe^+	22, 30 eV	250-280°C	disappear 250-280°C
	25 eV	160-190°C	disappear 160-190°C

mum energy transfer coefficients. These turned out to be 2.9 ± 0.2 eV for He, 21.6 ± 1.3 for Ne, 25 ± 8 for Ar and 19.7 ± 1 eV for Xe which, except for He, are remarkably consistent and are in fair agreement with the value for the displacement threshold energy of 25 eV for Cu, given by Gibson et al[23], but, on the other hand, are lower than other estimates for Au based on electron irradiation experiments[201]. It was believed that the low value for Helium could be due to the influence of gas trapping upon damage events and indeed this possibility exists with all the bombarding ions. It is therefore quite clear that the nature of the damage is quite sensitively dependent upon both sputtering and gas occlusion, and therefore upon ion type and energy, dose rate and total dose, and target material. Different results would be anticipated with different materials, and it may be dangerous to consider any particular ion-target combination as typical.

Jouffrey[49, 271, 272] observed almost identical effects in 4 keV A^+ ion bombarded gold, to those described by Ogilvie et al[270]. The small black dots, dislocation loops and large and small lines or dipoles were obtained after bombardment of (001) oriented gold surfaces at room temperature, but the former two types disappeared upon annealing at 165°C and did not appear at all during bombardment at this temperature. The latter two types generally lay along (111) planes and upon annealing up to temperatures of 450°C they were observed to combine and eventually disappear. Small dots and loops only were observed after a short bombardment ($< 10^{15}$ ions/sq. cm) at room temperature, but a fourfold increase in the dose revealed the larger defect configurations.

In addition to these defects, small polyhedral faults of dimensions of about 10 Å - 20 Å were observed after doses of 2-7 × 10^{15} ions/sq. cm. at bombardment temperatures greater than 200°C. These were considered to be gas bubbles which were also found to condense upon the larger dislocation dipoles.

Jouffrey[49] interpreted his results as indicating that the dots and small loops were formed from the agglomeration of vacancies rather than interstitials, as proposed by Brandon[51, 52] and by Ogilvie et al[270]. The reasoning was that interstitials would migrate to sinks far too rapidly at the bombardment temperature to allow nucleation. However, the direct observation of the contrast of large loops by Brandon et al[51, 52] which showed unequivocally that these were interstitial in nature leads one to place more faith in this interpretation of the large loops. In addition, Jouffrey's[49] observation that gas bubbles nucleated on the larger loops also suggests that these were of interstitial nature, since gas bubbles would be expected to be dissolved into vacancy loops and not display any contrast after contacting the loops.

Further evidence of the nature of the defects produced in A^+ ion bombarded gold has been furnished by Venables and Balluffi[222, 223]. Using in situ bombardment by 200 eV ions in the electron microscope at temperatures between −130°C and +30°C, these authors obtained very definitive results and conclusions regarding the nature of irradiation damage.

Two types of target were used. The first was well annealed and found to be relatively defect free, but the second was quenched rapidly after annealing at high temperature and contained the vacancy tetrahedra reported by Silcox and Hirsch[30]. The presence of these vacancy aggregates was found to be a powerful tool in deducing the nature of the ion induced damage.

The results can be summarised as follows.

(a) In vacancy free samples, irradiated between −130°C and −10°C, damage consisting of the dot, loop and line structures observed by previous workers, was observed throughout the targets even in very thin (~100 Å) regions of the targets. These aggregates were shown to be interstitial clusters.

(b) In these targets, irradiated between +10°C and +30°C, a definite region close to the bombarded surface was denuded of all damage. The thickness of this region increasing from 150 Å at 12°C to 400 Å at 27°C.

(c) In foils containing a uniform distribution of vacancy tetrahedra, bombardment above 10°C led to annihilation of these tetrahedra to a depth of 1000 Å after a flux of 2 × 10^{16} ions/cm^2.

(d) In such foils, after bombardment below −10°C, most tetrahedra remained in the foil but a region partly denuded of tetrahedra of ~200 Å from the surface was formed.

(e) If foils irradiated as in (d) were subsequently warmed to +10°C, the vacancy denuded region increased to about 600 Å.

(f) Annealing all foils containing damage led to a disappearance of the smaller dots between 200°C and 300°C and a rearrangement and final annihilation of the loops and lines at 350°C. The vacancy tetrahedra were in no way affected by this treatment.

These results strongly suggested that single interstitials produced by focused collision sequences within the target were able to migrate freely with some rapidity above −10°C, with a migration energy 0.7 eV. The arguments supporting this conclusion are:-

(1) Since vacancy tetrahedra were not annihilated below −10°C it means that the defects responsible for annihilating these must move 1000 Å (the target thickness) at this temperature. The defect most likely to cause annihilation of the tetrahedra would be the single interstitial since it was quite clear that the mobility of the larger interstitial clusters was temperature independent in this range.

(2) The annihilation of tetrahedra <u>during</u> bombardment above 10°C suggests that the interstitials migrate freely above this temperature.

(3) The annihilation of many more tetrahedra <u>after</u> bombardment below −10°C and subsequent warming, suggests the sudden change from immobility to mobility at about this temperature.

Since the single interstitials would be immobile below −10°C it would appear surprising that interstitial clusters form at this temperature, but Venables and Balluffi believe that some mobility may be induced into a fraction of the interstitials by thermal spike heating from crowdion collisions. It may also appear odd that any vacancy cluster annihilation should occur below −10°C where all interstitials should be frozen in, but again Venables and Balluffi ascribe this to direct collision of focusons with the vacancy aggregates. Indeed the depth to which the tetrahedra are removed at −10°C suggests a mean focuson length of 100 Å, which we have seen earlier in this chapter to be quite acceptable.

Since in vacancy free targets a damage denuded region, the thickness of which increased with temperature above 10°C, was observed, it was concluded that this revealed that a certain critical cluster size was necessary before it would be stable. At temperatures above 10°C it was believed that the single interstitials migrated to the surface far too rapidly to nucleate such clusters, and the depth of this denuded region would therefore increase with temperature. Observation of the smallest cluster sizes resolvable and a careful analysis of the dependence of the width of the denuded zone upon temperature, enabled calculation of the minimum cluster size for stability, the interstitial migration energy and the binding energies of clusters. It was found that the minimum size stable clusters contained from 4 to 8 interstitials with a binding energy of about 0.1 eV per interstitial, and that the single interstitial migration energy lies in the range 0.75 ± 0.06 eV which is seen to agree with the estimate from the vacancy elimination data.

It is therefore quite clear that the defect responsible for the observations by Venables and Balluffi is the single interstitial which is seen to migrate freely at a temperature corresponding to Stage III annealing. Seeger's[147] suggestion therefore seems to be confirmed in gold at least and Brandon and Bowden's[52] observations of vacancy annihilation at around 0°C in Copper suggest a similar mechanism in this material.

A further important fact is that the vacancy clusters do not change whilst the interstitial clusters anneal out at 350°C. This shows that the interstital clusters do not emit interstitials to the vacancy tetrahedra nor receive vacancies from them. They must therefore be annihilated by vacancies from the free surfaces in stage IV annealing as previously suggested.

Finally, the results described above were independent of target purity, tending to vitiate the impurity trapping model suggested by Walker[192]. There are some apparent points of disagreement between this work and that of McGurn and Howe[263], which we should discuss briefly. Firstly the 100 keV 0^- bombardment did not produce any large dislocation loops or lines, whilst annealing of samples from <−30°K to +20°C in this case produced no change in the vacancy tetrahedra remaining after bombardment. In these investigations the target thickness was of the order 500 Å which is similar to the 0^- range and this may provide a clue to the differences of behaviour. Because of the non annihilation of vacancy clusters above 0°C it would appear that there are no free interstitials produced by the 0^- bombardment, which can annihilate the vacancies. In view of the high primary energy it would be anticipated that most interstitials would form towards the back (unbombarded) target surface and upon annealing would preferentially escape to this foil surface rather than annihilating clusters. The absence of large loops may also be evidence of this possibility since the local interstitial densities could be too low to permit aggregation on a large scale. The small ion induced spots could conceivably be vacancy aggregates therefore, as suggested by Howe and McGurn[263], but there is no unequivocal evidence of this since, as shown by Venables and Balluffi[223], no change in the nature of definitely interstitial clusters occurs up to 200°C whereas the former authors interpreted this result as showing that the clusters were necessarily of vacancy character. On the other hand, the non annihilation of these clusters could suggest their interstitial nature.

Clearly, further work at different ion energies, target temperatures and thickness is needed to elucidate these processes.

We should also mention a rather important experiment by Parsons and Balluffi[46] who irradiated amorphous Germanium (prepared by evaporation) with fast neutrons or mono-energetic Xe^+ ions in the energy range 20 keV to 140 keV and examined the effects of this irradiation in an electron transmission microscope.

It was observed that numerous small regions of the Ge appeared to recrystallise during bombardment and this was interpreted as revealing displacement spike formation since the amorphous Ge was known to readily recrystallise by short range atomic migrations.

The size distribution of the recrystallised volumes was determined for each ion energy, and each histogram showed a most probable size which increased with increasing ion energy from 40 to 100 keV. A typical recrystallisation pattern and a size histogram are shown in Figs 6.57 a and b for 70 keV Xe^+. The total

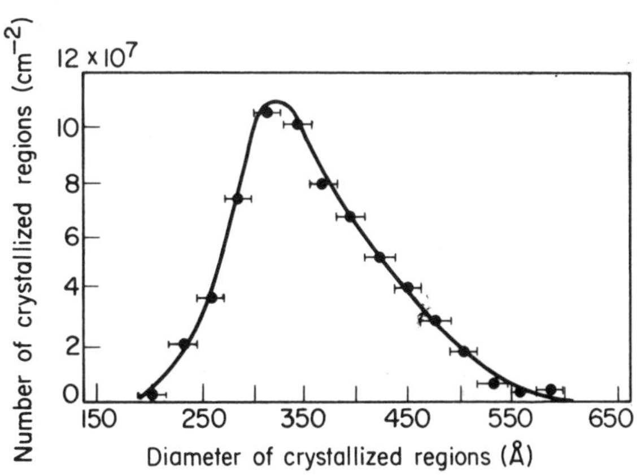

Fig. 6.57a Size distribution of crystallized regions observed in Ge irradiated with 70 keV Xe^+ ions. Horizontal lines indicate the width of histogram increments. Film thickness = 700 ± 100 Å. (viz. Ref. 6.46)

Fig. 6.57b Crystallised Regions produced in an amorphous Ge matrix by 70 keV Xe^+ ions. (viz. Ref. 6.46)

number of recrystallized volumes was also observed to increase linearly with ion dose, but the size distribution appeared to be dose independent. Below 20 keV no recrystallisation was observed whilst above 100 keV the most probable size decreased and above 140 keV, again no recrystallisation was noted. These latter results were also interpreted as confirming displacement spike formation since for Xe^+ energies greater than about 140 keV the major source of energy loss is in electron excitational, non displacement collisions and therefore few spikes would be expected to form. Further since the target thickness was only 700 ± 100 Å, Xe^+ ions of energy 100 keV would be expected to penetrate the target completely and this, coupled with inelastic processes would tend to reduce the spike size. The most probable spike (recrystallised volume) diameters were, in fact, found to agree almost exactly with calculations of Xe ranges in Ge using the Lindhard-Scharff treatment, and the size histograms such as in Figure 6.57b bear a marked resemblance to the range distribution discussed in the previous chapter. This evidence seems to clearly support the displacement spike hypothesis, and the low energy cut off (~20 keV) suggests a critical spike size to be necessary before the recrystallisation phenomenon can operate, in agreement with Brinkman's ideas of spike formation. At high energies the rate of displacement production in impulsive collisions must be sufficiently large as to promote spike formation. Fast neutron irradiation led to similar results and conclusions but it was difficult to predict accurately the expected spike size since the neutron energy spectrum was unknown.

Parsons[47] subsequently used a similar technique to study the effect of 100 keV O^- ion bombardment of crystalline germanium in the electron microscope. In this case it was found that the bombardment caused the reverse effect of disordering of zones in the Ge to the amorphous state and a count of the number of zones produced showed that about 1 in every 5 ions produced a disordered zone. The number of zones/ion remained constant up to an ion dose of about 1.4×10^{15} ions/cm^2 where a saturation occurred and complete disordering occurred to a depth of 590 Å.

At low doses the diameter of the zones decreased with increasing target temperature from a mean of 89 Å at 30°K to 68 Å at room temperature but the zones formed below 30°K did not increase in size on heating to room temperature. These amorphous zones were found to be of lower density than the surrounding crystal and it was found that as a bombarded specimen was annealed up to 665°C, the zones near crystal boundaries disappeared first and then in thicker regions of the crystal but dislocation loops formed in the thicker crystal and these finally annealed. A sample bombarded at 320°C, however, showed no signs of disordered zone production.

Parsons[47] interpreted these results as showing the formation of thermal spikes which disordered the zones but that about 10% of the atoms in the spikes were shot out into channels so that the zones were of reduced density. It was also suggested that recrystallisation of the zones could occur above 300°C, but that this freed vacancies which migrated to the surfaces or dislocation loops; which themselves finally anneal above 655°C.

A simple calculation of spike diameter based on the assumption of an upper spike temperature equal to the melting temperature gave 130 Å, not unlike the measured values whilst the more rapid quench of a spike at lower bombardment temperatures presumably gave rise to the larger spike sizes. The saturation state of totally amorphous structure can also be ascribed to spike overlap.

Recent, unpublished, studies of the irradiation of p type Silicon with 20-80 keV Ne, B and P ions by Mazey and Nelson and Matthews, Nelson and Sheldon, have revealed similar effects. At ion doses greater than 10^{13}/cm^2, regions of dark contrast greater than 1000 Å diameter were observed by electron microscopy and the density of these increased with increasing dose until a completely amorphous surface layer ensued. A very important observation was that the rate of formation of the amorphous regions was critically dependent upon the crystal orientation with respect to the ions. Thus along channelling directions, there was a marked reduction in the rate of amorphous zone production, a direct confirmation of the importance of channelling phenomena in ion induced damage production. The annealing behaviour was also studied and it was observed that heating to 400°C partially recrystallised the amorphous region whilst further annealing to 700°C caused dislocation loops and dipoles to form beyond the damaged region. As we shall see later this type of measurement is of considerable importance in ion implantation studies.

It is quite clear from these studies that electron transmission microscopy is a powerful tool for investigating the characteristic features of the damage produced in crystals by energetic ions. Its resolution is now approaching the single atomic scale and one may anticipate that in the forseeable future it will be possible to investigate individual point defects. Further experiments with different ions of variable energy and different target materials will undoubtedly enhance our understanding of damage processes and one may envisage an ion bombardment experiment conducted in the microscope at liquid helium temperature and the defect production observed directly. Subsequent annealing and observation of the defect migration with simultaneous measurements of electrical resistivity should give further direct evidence of the nature of the migrating species.

Whilst such an experiment is only speculative, there exists already, a further method of direct observation of point defects, with even greater resolution than the transmission electron microscope, and which is operable at liquid helium temperatures.

This method is that of Field ion microscopy to which we now turn our attention and which has been used for a few rather qualitative observations of ion induced damage.

6.5.3 Field Ion Microscopy

Müller[273] first reported the invention of the field ion microscope in 1951 and indicated how it could be used to resolve the structure of materials on the atomic scale. Little interest was shown in the device, however, until 1956 when Müller[274] demonstrated a considerably improved and sophisticated version, and since that time the applications of the technique have multiplied considerably. Reviews of the theory and practical applications of the microscope have since been published by Müller,[275] Gomer[276] and Brandon[277]. A typical field ion micrscope apparatus is shown in Figure 6.58 and the basic mechanism of operation is as follows. The specimen is a fine wire of refractory metal or alloy electropolished at the free end to a tip of a few hundred Angstroms radius, and maintained at a high positive potential. Helium (or Neon or Argon) gas at a pressure in the order of 10 torr, flows around the tip and is ionised by the high field at the tip. This high field results from the large tip voltage and small tip diameter, and ionisation of the gas results from tunnelling of an electron from a Helium atom into an unoccupied level in the

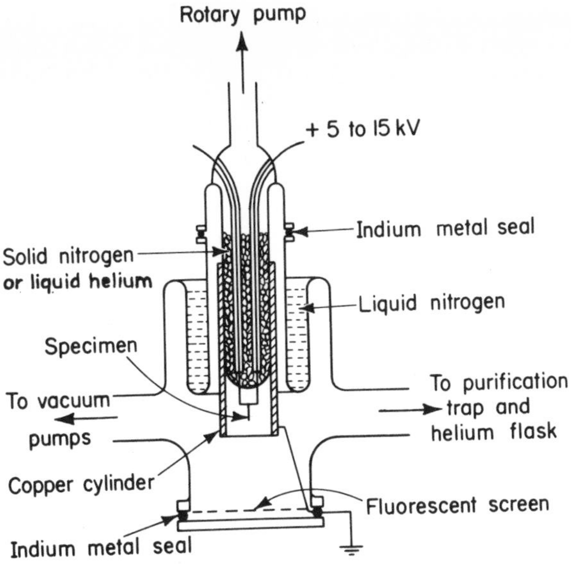

Fig. 6. 58 Typical Field Ion Microscope. (viz. Ref. 6. 277)

conduction band of the metal. The ionised Helium atoms are then repelled from the tip and strike a fluorescent screen placed several centimetres from the tip where an image of the tip is formed. The efficiency of ionization of the Helium atoms depends upon the surface structure of the tip, and is largest for protuberances on the tip. Thus the number of ions originating from a given point on the tip depends upon the atomic arrangement at that point and the magnification is roughly the ratio of the tip-screen distance to the tip radius and is typically 10^6. Field strengths of the order of 3V/Å are required to promote field ion formation and are quite strongly temperature dependent. At somewhat larger ($\sim 20\%$) fields a second phenomenon, which at low temperatures is only weakly temperature dependent, occurs, known as field evaporation. Here the atoms evaporate from the tip preferentially from protuberances and tend to smooth the tip surface. For successful Field ion microscopy, field evaporation must be suppressed, for example by operation at low temperatures, but the latter effect can be put to good use to remove surface layers at a known rate to produce atomically smooth surfaces. One restriction on very low temperature operation is that the operating gas should not condense upon the tip, thus invalidating the use of Ne or Ar at liquid Helium temperatures, although He itself may be used. Whilst neither phenomenon has been fully explained quantitatively (viz Brandon 1963[277]) the qualitative details are sufficiently well developed to allow us to accept the interpretations of observations by various authors without question. The technique is still only in its infancy and continuous progress is being made to understand the theory and extend the application, sensitivity and resolution of this device. Already, however, several reports have been made concerning the use of the field ion microscope in observing ion induced damage in refractory metals, notably by Müller and his colleagues and by Brandon et al.

In 1959, Müller[278] showed that α particle bombardment of the tungsten tip caused gross damage and rearrangement of the surface atom configurations. Subsequent experiments by Müller[279,280] and Sinha and Müller[53,281,282] with collimated beams of 20 keV He^+ or Hg^+ ions or atoms incident on tungsten at 21°K confirmed the earlier observations.

Typical pictures[53] of a 350 Å radius tip bombarded by 20 keV He^+ atoms (formed by charge exchange from ions in the microscope chamber) before and after bombardment are shown in Figures 6. 59 a, b and c, with the surface planes seen in the microscope, the direction of ion incidence and the defects formed, marked in. Single vacancies are revealed by removal of a previous bright spot, whilst interstitials were interpreted by the appearance of an extra bright spot between already existing bright spots. In Figure 6. 59 b a damage area, 65 Å in diameter, containing 7 interstitials or displaced surface atoms and 12 vacancies is seen together with other isolated interstitials, displaced atoms and vacancies. Continued irradiation, as in Figure 6. 59c adds more such defects to the surface, and all bombardments led to essentially similar patterns of isolated vacancies, interstitials and clusters. By observing the total defect population on the bombarded side of the tip and on the remote side, it was concluded that the ratio of near side to remote side damage was about 1. 8 and was roughly independent of the incident direction of the ion beam with respect to the various crystal faces of the tip. However the total surface damage was largest when the ions were incident along ⟨111⟩ directions, which, being close packed, would allow efficient focuson and crowdion propagation.

Comparison of the total surface defect density with the Kinchin-Pease formula showed that about half the anticipated density actually appeared as surface defects. This is the first real indication that the simple equation has any validity and is of course all the more reliable since the experiments were conducted at 21°K where most defects should be immobile. This high percentage also suggests that most of the energy of the primary knock-ons must be transported by focusing sequences away from their points of generation. By increasing the tip radii up to 1000 Å, and still observing remote side defects, although in reduced number, it was proved that the sum of the collision sequence ranges and the incident He atom ranges was greater than this value. No attempts were made to study the defects within the tip by deliberate field evaporation since it was observed that during microscopic observations some of the bright spots associated with interstitials disappeared, due it was believed to enhanced field evaporation because of their surface configuration. The mobility of these interstitials at 21°K was observed by noting that upon terminating bombardment bright spots continued to appear at the tip surface. After this ceased however, and upon annealing to 80°K very few further interstitials appeared but some of those originally formed, disappeared. Between 85°K and 95°K large numbers of interstitials again appeared, but the number of these could be markedly reduced by bombarding the tip for considerable periods and inducing heavy damage within the tip which presumably trapped the interstitials. Further annealing had no effect upon the surface structure.

The 21°K annealing although enhanced by the field stress again supports the conclusion that IA annealing is due to close Frenkel pair recombination whilst the appearance of large numbers of interstitials at 90°K suggests that in tungsten at least stage IE is also due to interstitial migration.

Generally similar results to those described above were obtained with 20 keV Hg^+ ion or atom and α

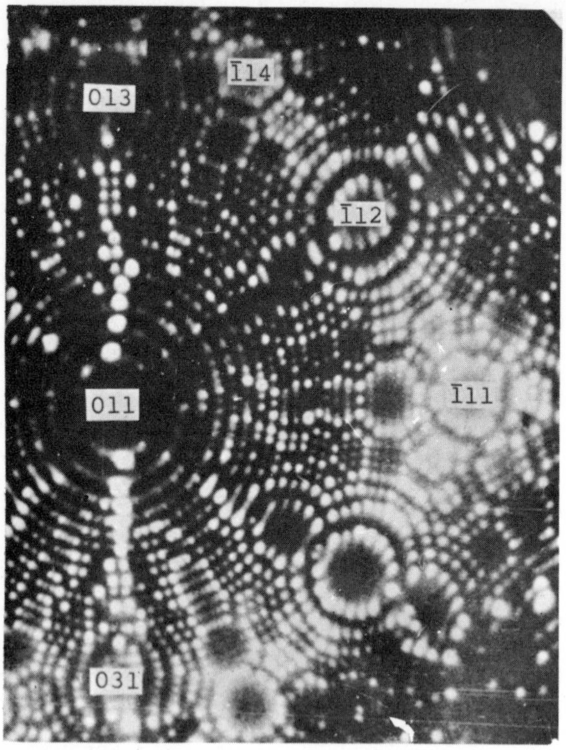

(a)

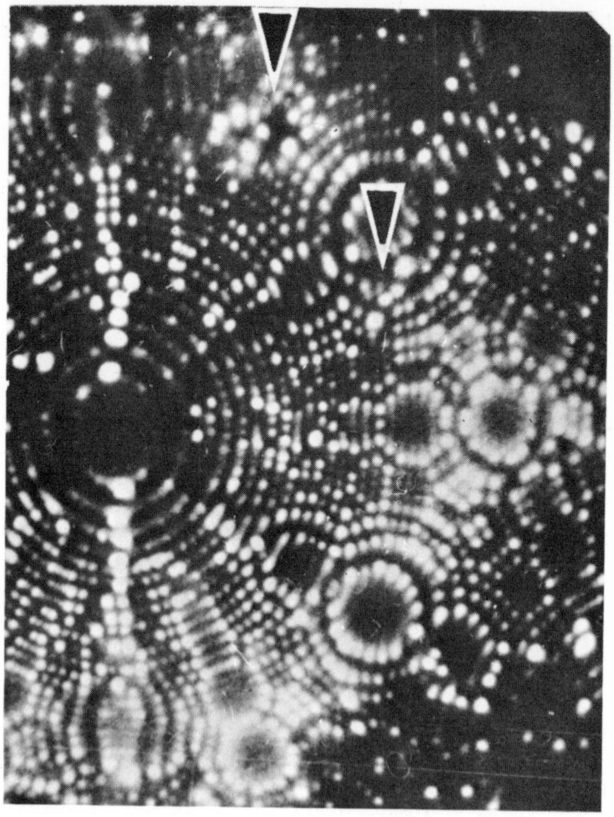

(b)

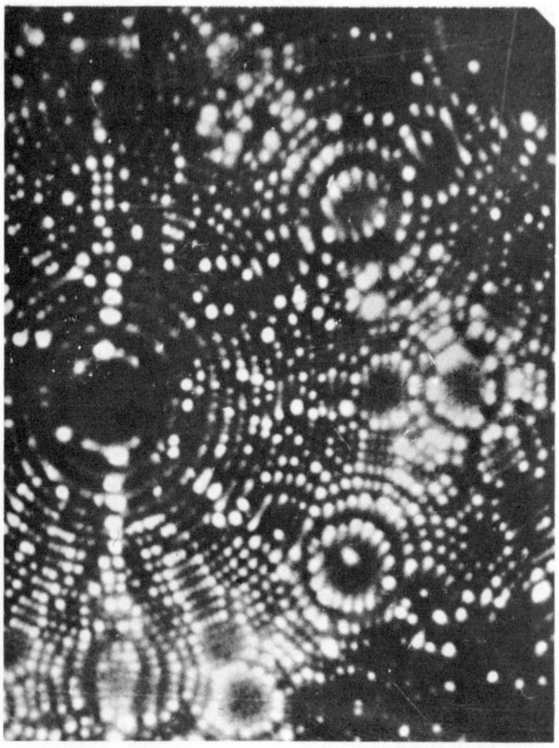

(c)

Fig. 6.59 a) Section of a 350 Å tungsten tip.
b) Damage spike of 65 Å diameter with a central pit on the $(\bar{1}13)$ plane, containing 7 interstitials, 9 displaced surface atoms in lattice sites and 12 surface vacancies. There is also a smaller spike below the $(\bar{1}12)$ plane and 14 further interstitials or displaced atoms plus 12 surface vacancies in the figure.
c) Further bombardment adds 31 interstitials or displaced atoms and removes 30 surface atoms. (viz. Ref. 6.53)

particle bombardment of the tungsten. The heavier mercury atoms caused considerably more damage however and the sizes of the clusters formed were generally larger, as would be expected since the mean free path of the mercury atoms would be much smaller and their energy would be dissipated in concentrated spatial volumes.

Brandon and Wald[283,284,285,286] observed analogous effects after α particle irradiation of molybdenum and tungsten and in the case of the latter metal showed, by field evaporation, that the surface density of vacancies was considerably higher than the bulk density, resulting again, it was presumed, from ejection of these surface atoms which were the terminating atoms in close packed rows (i.e. sputtering). The surface positions where vacancies appeared in greatest density was commensurate with focusing collisions along $\langle 111 \rangle$ and $\langle 100 \rangle$ directions with ranges greater than 200 Å. More recently Ralph[287] has re-examined the Brandon and Wald results and from a study of the points of production of surface defects suggest that the volume from which the defects originate is of the order of 1000 Å below the surface. This distance was believed to be too large to be due to focused sequences and it was concluded that most surface defects resulted from channelled atoms. Damage was also studied in the field ion microscope by Brandon et al[285,286] by bombarding the tungsten tip with monoenergetic Argon atoms (again produced by charge exchange) of energy between 100 and 300 eV. Again vacancies appeared at the side of the tip remote from the argon beam, but only if the argon energy was above 130 eV, which corresponded to a maximum energy transfer to tungsten atoms of 75 eV necessary to cause displacement. Strayer et al[288] have recently used a field ion microscope to study sputtering of W with Xe^+ ions of energies between 100 eV and 1200 eV. After cleaning the tip by field desorption, the tip was bombarded at 77°K with a relatively low ion dose (up to 1200 ions on one side of the tip) the field ion pattern was re-examined with He as the image gas. For low ion energies ($\leqslant$500 eV) very little sputtering occurred on the bombarded side of the tip, as evidenced by only few vacancies produced in the $\{110\}$ and $\{100\}$ major planes, but more atoms were displaced on the far side of the tip, illustrating the focusing mechanism. At higher energies (1200 eV) much more vacancy production occured on the bombarded side of the tip and field desorption showed that this extended about 6 atom layers into the tungsten. At the lower energies the damage was largely confined to the first atomic layer and it was believed that the Xe^+ ions were also stopped in this layer.

Field electron emission patterns were also studied after Cs^+ bombardment of the tip and this was shown to lead to roughening of the surface. For ion energies up to 300 eV the surface roughening increased steadily (with an apparent threshold of about 20-30 eV).

It is clear that these investigations have only scratched the surface of a potentially wide field of application, but already the possibilities of development are becoming evident. Careful investigation of the damage production as a function of the incident particle direction should give valuable information upon atomic displacement probabilities whilst it should be possible also to determine the range and energy requirements of different focused and channelled collision sequences. Investigation of the depth distribution of damage by controlled field evaporation could give information on the details of individual collision sequences and possibly on ion ranges, if trapped species can be identified as can, apparently, interstitials. Annealing studies and simultaneous observations of the defect configurations should also assist in understanding more fully the nature of these.

In addition to these direct observations of damage on the single atomic and atomic cluster scale, a considerable amount of work has been performed upon the direct observation of damage on a somewhat larger scale. This has been accomplished by studying post bombardment damage induced at the target surface at a lower resolution in the electron microscope. Observations of the surface topography by electron reflection or by changes in the transmission electron diffraction pattern reveal any re-orientations of the surface crystal structure and these methods have been used extensively by Trillat and his collaborators and by other investigators. We will briefly consider both these methods and refer the reader for a more comprehensive review to articles by Trillat.[289]

6.5.4 Electron Diffraction Studies

6.5.4.1 When a sufficiently thin single crystal is exposed to a beam of electrons and the transmitted electrons observed at low resolution one obtains the characteristic spot patterns of the material, which are indicative of the crystal plane separations as shown for silver in Figure 6.60a. This technique is a well established method of determining the atomic structure of crystals and since its introduction by Bragg & Laue its application has become widespread and any elementary Atomic Physics text gives adequate descriptions of the method. Trillat[290,291] observed, in 1956, however, that if single crystals of gold were bombarded with 12 keV Argon ions and subsequently observed in the electron diffraction camera, the characteristic spots were linked by bright rings, the intensity of which increased with increasing ion dose. This sequence is depicted in Figures 6.60 b and c and was interpreted by Trillat[289–293] as indicating that the single crystal surface had been disoriented so that many of the crystallites were reoriented in directions other than that of the original macrocrystal. Subsequent extension of these observations was made by Ogilvie[294] and Ogilvie and Thomson[295], who found again that the spot connecting rings formed during bombardment of silver by He^+, A^+ or Xe^+ ions but that their brightness and extent was quite critically dependent upon the ion energy, the temperature of the silver crystal and the crystal orientation of the bombarded surface. In addition to the connecting rings, which were often incomplete, the spots themselves were found to become broadened and were often superimposed with small crosses. The sequence of photographs in Figure 6.61 a, b and c, shows the effect of variation of the Argon ion energy from 130eV to 4 keV in the spot pattern determined from silver with a surface orientation of (110) perpendicular to the ion beam, whilst Figures 6.62. a, b, c and d reveal the effect of increasing the temperature of the silver crystal to 400°C during 130 eV Argon ion bombardment of a (111) surface.

The specific effects were dependent upon the crystal surface orientation but it was generally found that the disorientation (shown by the arc and cross formation) increased with increasing ion energy, ion dose rate and total ion dose, but decreased with increasing target temperature. Annealing after ion bombardment showed that the disorientation was rapidly removed upon heating above 250°C but that the rate of removal was insufficiently fast to explain the dimin-

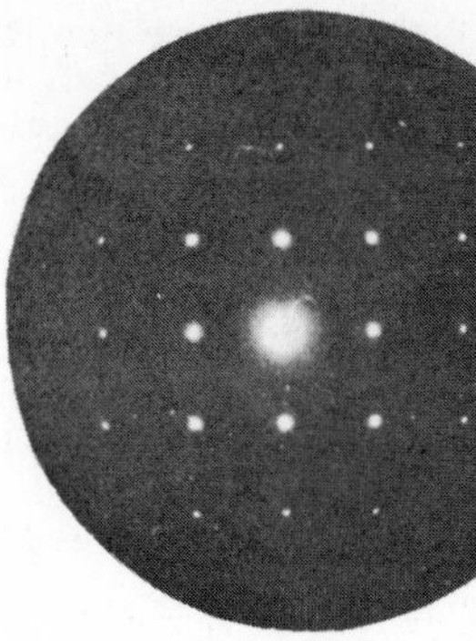

(a)

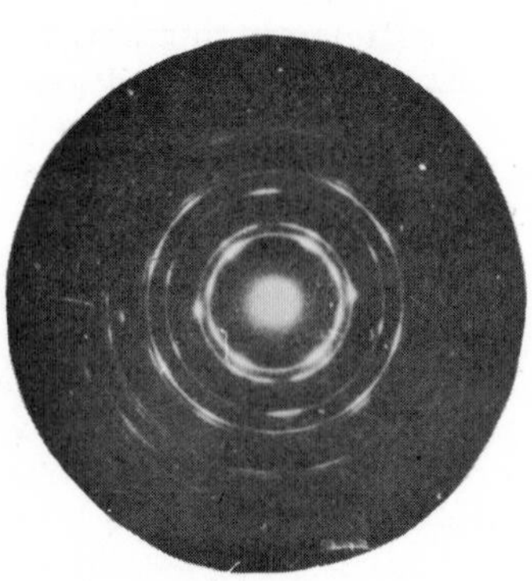

(b)

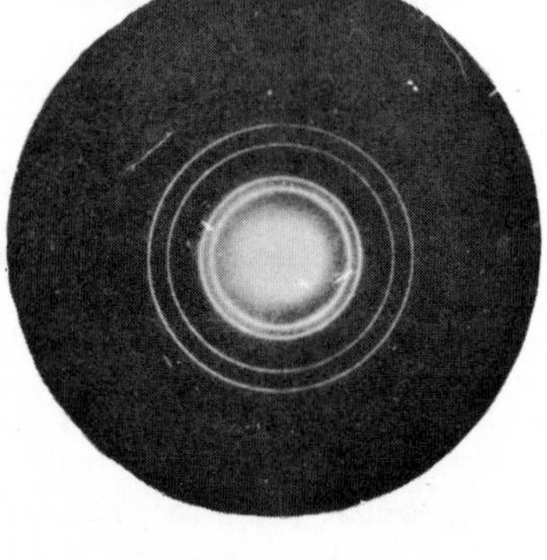

(c)

Fig. 6. 60 Electron diffraction reflection micrographs of single crystal Ag.
a) Unbombarded.
b) After one minute bombardment by 12 keV A^+ ions.
c) After three minutes bombardment by 12 keV A^+ ions. (viz. Ref. 6. 289)

(a)

(b)

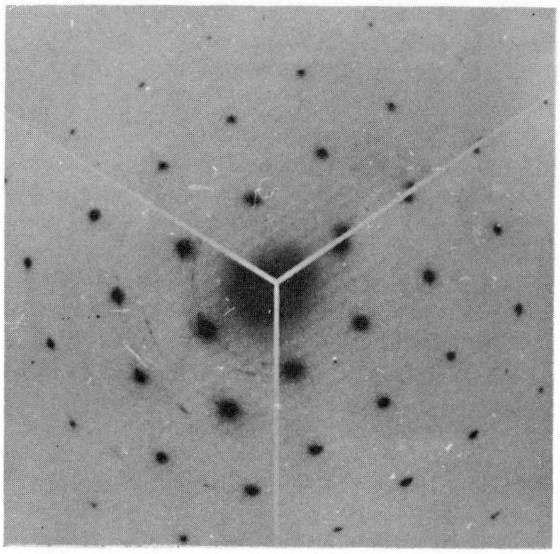

(c)

Fig. 6. 61 Transmission electron-diffraction patterns from a silver crystal with surfaces parallel to ⟨110⟩ bombarded at
a) 130 eV
b) 500 eV
c) 4 keV
(viz. Ref. 6. 294)

(a)

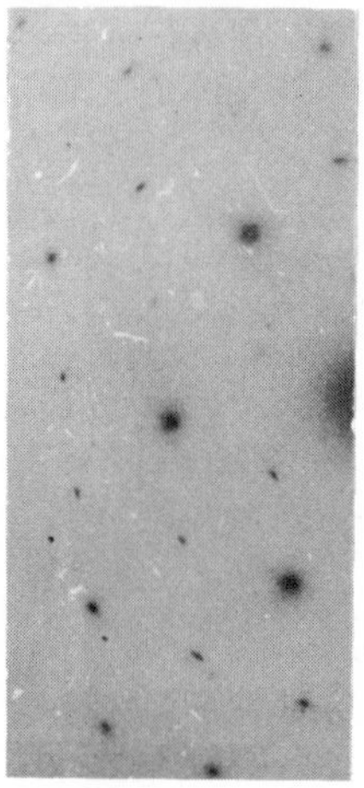

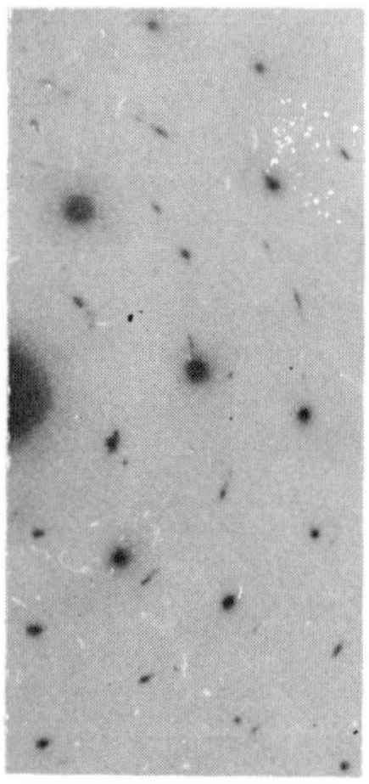

(b)

(c)

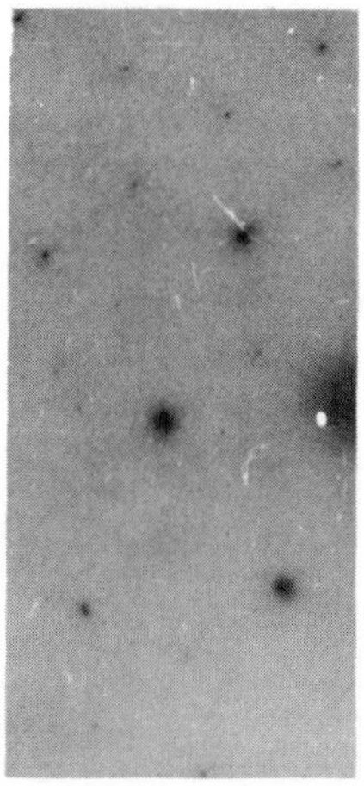

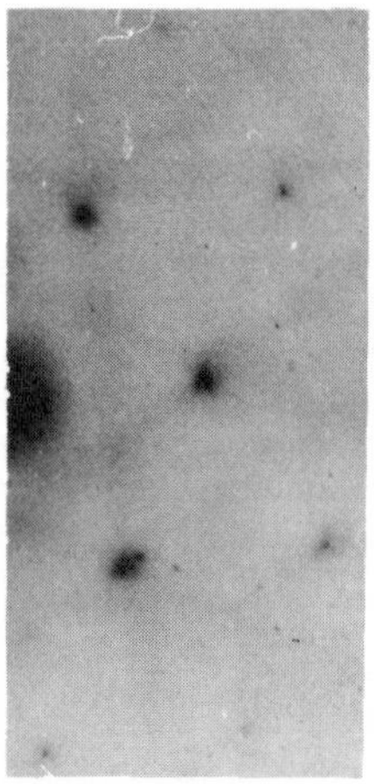

(d)

Fig. 6. 62 Transmission electron diffraction patterns from a silver crystal with surfaces parallel to (111) bombarded with 10^{19} A^+ ions at 130 eV.
a) Temperature during bombardment 150°C
b) Temperature during bombardment 250°C
c) Temperature during bombardment 350°C
d) Temperature during bombardment 400°C
(viz. Ref. 6. 295)

ished disorientation at the higher temperatures which operated during bombardment. It was therefore suggested that in addition to producing the disorientation the ion bombardment also provided a mechanism, other than simple target heating, by which the disorientation could disappear, i.e. a dynamic equilibrium was attained at any temperature between disorientation production by the ions and disorientation annealing by an ion induced mechanism (e.g. defect production and simple thermal processes. The disorientated crystallites were found to form in greatest number in the bombarded area and to a lesser extent around the periphery of this area, with linear dimensions of order 100Å and related to the unbombarded crystal plane by different angular rotations about ⟨112⟩ directions in this plane. The crosses on the spots were believed to be due to the presence of stacking faults in the (110) planes of the crystallites.

It was suggested that the crystallites were formed by the growth of dislocations from the crystal interior to the surface, which upon intersecting the surface produced tilted crystallites. The growth of the dislocations was believed to occur due to the acquisition of interstitials produced by the bombarding ions and a remarkable observation of disorientation for a bombarding energy of only 12 eV can surely only be interpreted on the grounds of focusing, and crowdion sequences which eject interstitials upon meeting a dislocation as suggested by Leibfried.[115] In the work of Ogilvie and Thomson[295] there is a suggestion that ions directed perpendicular to a (110) surface, i.e. along close packed ⟨110⟩ rows resulted in maximum disorientation, which concurs with the picture of the interaction of focusons and dislocations. In view of Brandon et al's[50,51] observation that dislocation loops are generated below the surface of gold targets by low energy ions it is probable that this was also an important cause of crystallite tilting in the above work, particularly at the higher bombardment energies.

Other studies of the disorientation effect have been made by Gianola[296], who used reflection electron techniques to show that 30 keV Helium ions severely disorientated silicon crystals to a depth of about 6000 Å. The depth of disorientation was determined by using a tapered crystal and studying the change in rectifying properties of a junction made with a metal contact to the crystal surface at various points. Trillat et al have also described similar disorientation effects in gold, silver and platinum single crystals.

The opposite effect to the above, namely the conversion of random crystallites to a single crystal structure, has also been reported by Trillat and his collaborators[297] and by Fert[298]. In this work NaCl crystals which had been superficially damaged by mechanical polishing showed electron diffraction pictures typical of a disorientated surface, but subsequent bombardment by several keV Argon ions restored the monocrystalline structure of the NaCl. Similar results were also obtained when polycrystalline gold films; vacuum deposited on NaCl were Argon ion bombarded and converted to monocrystalline form. In these cases the operating mechanism was probably the relative removal of polycrystalline facets by surface sputtering which is known to be highly orientation dependent (viz Chapter 7) and which eventually reduces the surface to planity. This method of producing clean, planar crystal has also been applied quite extensively to remove contaminants such as oxides, hydrocarbon layers and mechanical strain effects from crystal surfaces and we shall discuss these applications further in Chapter 9.

In addition to the above effects which are clearly radiation damage processes and are produced by inert gas ion bombardment, some observations of the effects of active gas ion bombardment has also been reported, which show that chemical effects may be important. For example films of nickel[289,299], zinc, iron pyrite (FeS_2)[300,301] beryllium and uranium,[302,303] subjected to oxygen or air ion bombardment (of energy 4 keV) show rapid conversion of the surface layers to oxides of the above metals, as detected by their electron diffraction patterns. Similarly nitrogen ion results in formation of superficial nickel nitride films.

Chemical-damage effects are also observed during inert gas ion bombardment of some crystals. Silver-bromide films show[304,305] a surface disorientation of the Ag-Br crystallites and finally complete conversion under argon, nitrogen or oxide ion bombardment, to pure silver. In this case the ions are believed to rupture the silver-bromine bonds and the bromine evaporates off leaving a silver rich surface. The disorientation suggests that dislocation formation proceeds parallel to the bond rupture mechanism. Similar enrichment of silver at the surface has been reported by Moore et al[306] following Argon ion bombardment of silver sulphide crystals whilst Gillam[307] has shown that a Cu_3 Au alloy is surface enriched with Au during low energy (15-4000eV) He^+, A^+ or Xe^+ ion bombardment. The enrichment effect was discernible at ion energies as low as 21 eV for Ar^+ ions and 16 eV for Xe^+ ions and the ratio of Au: Cu in the enriched layer decreased from almost that typical of pure gold at low voltages to more nearly the stoichiometric value at higher energies, for similar ion doses. Since the enrichment occurred gradually, copper atoms must have been removed initially at a rate more than three times that of the gold atoms, but when the final steady state was reached the ratio of the removal rates must equal the ratio of the Cu; Au fractions in the altered surface layer. This suggested that the copper and gold atoms necessary to maintain the equilibrium surface conditions originated from the relatively unchanged bulk, probably by focusing and crowdion collisions. Indeed the observed depth of the damage was always considerably larger than could be reasonably anticipated on the basis of the incident ion range and was presumably caused by interstitial production via collision sequences. The low ion energies required to initiate damage tend to confirm this picture.

Similar enrichment of nickel occurred during irradiation of a copper-nickel alloy and enrichment of silver in silver-palladium alloys with high palladium concentrations. No enrichment occurred in Ag-Au α brass or Ag_3Mg alloys however, and Castaing[308] reports no enrichment effect in a 4% Cu-Al alloy. It therefore appears that in addition to collision sequences the mobility of the interstitials may also be an important parameter in determining the enrichment characteristics. In addition to such decomposition effects, ion bombardment has been shown to markedly change the chemical reactivity of crystal surfaces. Thus Haymann[309] showed that Argon ion bombarded Uranium resisted oxidation in an oxygen atmosphere to a much greater extent than did a clean unbombarded surface. Aluminium bombarded by Helium exhibits[306] the same sort of passivation to oxygen. On the other hand Sosnovsky[310] reports an increased activity to oxygen chemisorption of Silver after Argon ion bombardment. This latter author suggests that the disorientation effect may produce extra chemisorption sites on the silver surface which result in its increased activity. Hondros and Bernard[311] have also observed passivation of copper to oxidation by Argon ion bombardment and their investigations also showed that post bombardment annealing restored the original activity of the copper. Why, in the cases of highly active aluminium, uranium and copper, inert gas ion bombardment results in increased passivity and in the case of the less active silver, an increase in activity is as yet unexplained. In all cases it will be true that surface disorientation will occur and this may result in the exposure of less favourable atomic configurations for chemisorption on Al, U and Cu but more favourable sites on silver. Occluded inert gases may also be important in determining passivity —by impeding oxygen migration into the crystal surface.

It is evident that the electron diffraction technique is most useful for obtaining information of changes surface structure due to both true radiation damage processes and physico-chemical effects. Although it is not possible to observe individual defects the macroscopic manifestations of these are readily discernible, and in conjunction with high resolution electron microscopy should be most valuable in determining both the microscopic and macroscopic effects of radiation damage.

6.5.4.2 Reflection Electron Microscopy

When the reflection electron pattern of a crystal is studied at low resolution, one obtains an image of the surface much as in an optical microscope, but at higher resolution and magnification of course. This image shows macroscopic defects such as scratches and polishing marks and an example of such a mechanically polished surface of gold is shown in Figure 6.63a in this case using optical microscopy. After ion bombardment[289] however the appearance of the surface shows marked changes as typical photographs in Figures 6.63b and c reveal. In addition to the regular ridged structure of these figures, which were produced by normally incident ions, regular and irregular shaped pits/or a contour ripple structure similar to ripples in sand may be formed. Examples of these effects are illustrated in Figures 6.64a for NaCl and 6.64b for Au bombarded with Argon ions,[312] the latter at an angle of incidence of 20°. Indeed the ion angle of incidence and energy are observed to be of major importance in determining the character of the surface alteration, whilst the nature of the target is also of great importance. Thus, as the angle of incidence approaches more closely the grazing condition the more are the ripples lined up parallel to each other and to the ion beam.[313-317]

Such behaviour has been reported on Argon bombarded (18 keV ions) Gold and Aluminium by Haymann [312-317] and Duker and Schlette[318], for Argon bom-

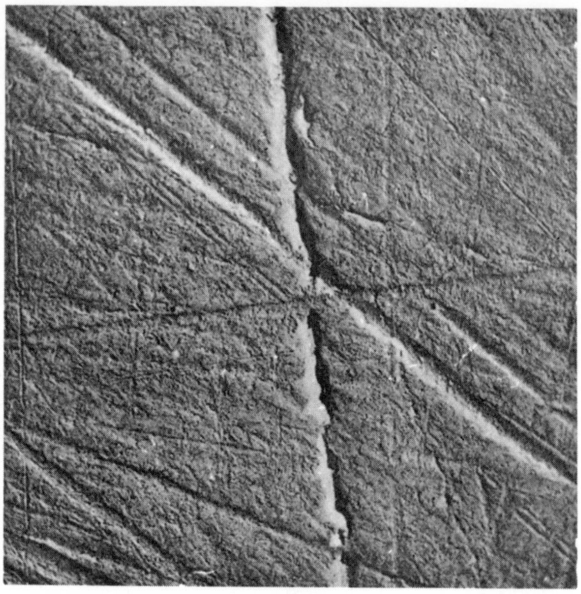

(a)

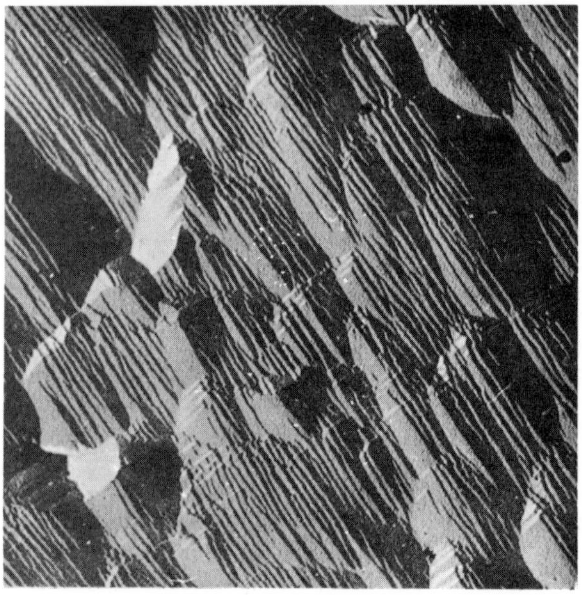

(b)

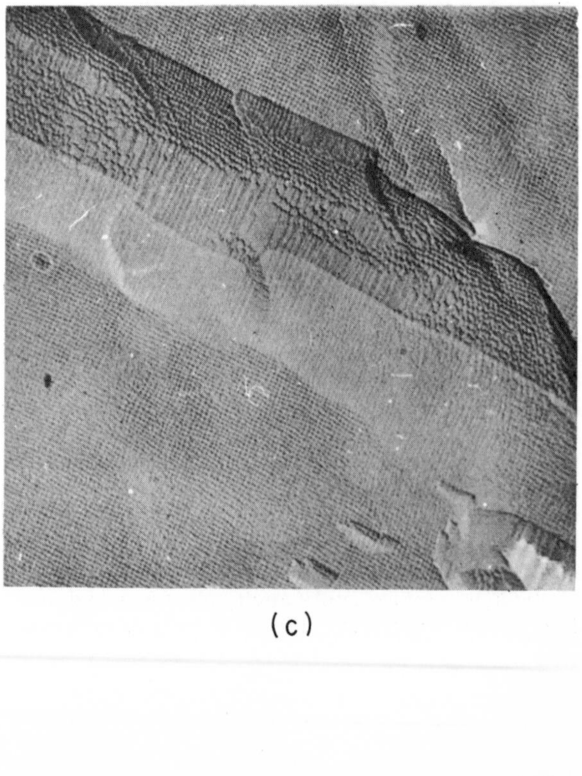

(c)

Fig. 6.63 Optical reflection micrographs of polycrystalline gold. (x 7,600).

a) Unbombarded Gold
b) After 1 hour of A^+ ion bombardment.
c) After 5 hours of A^+ ion bombardment.
(viz. Ref. 6.289)

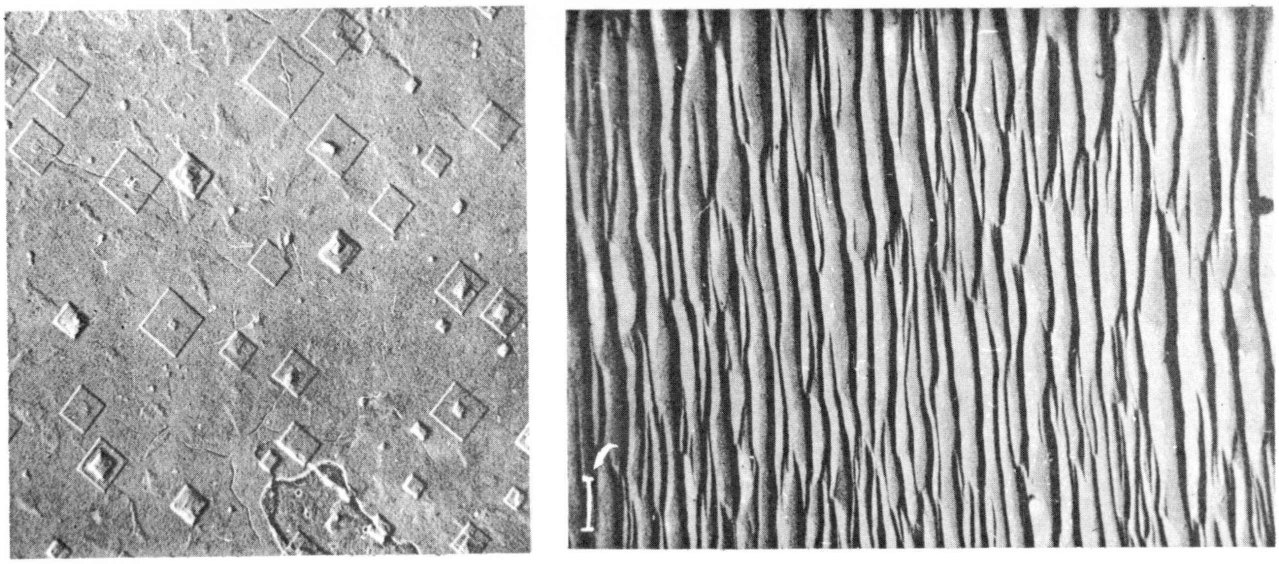

(a) (b)

Fig. 6. 64 a) Recrstallisation of NaCl by A^+ ion bombardment (× 7, 200).
b) furrows produced on polycrystalline gold A^+ ions bombardment at an angle of 20° to the surface.
(viz. Ref. 6. 289)

barded silver by Haymann and Waldberger,[316] by Cunningham et al[319] for single crystal Al, Zn, and Aluminium oxide and polycrystalline Au and Al, by Magnuson et al[320] for polycrystalline Cu, Au, Al, W, Ta, Mo and Ni bombarded by 500 eV Hg ions, by Wehner[321] for Si and Ge crystals and by Farnsworth and his collaborators[322, 323] for Ge and Si crystals and also by Honig[324] and Wolsky[325] for these latter materials.

Many of these studies reveal the importance of the angle of incidence upon the post bombardment etching configuration and also show how preferential sputtering from close packed lattice planes can lead to ready interpretation of the nature of the etch pits. In addition the effect of recondensation of atoms preferentially sputtered from these planes, can also be important in determining the formation of hillocks of material in addition to the expected pits.

Similar effects were observed by Hondros and Bernard [311] in Argon ion bombarded copper, and a quite comprehensive study of Argon bombarded glass has been reported by Navez and his collaborators.[326, 327, 328] In this latter case, when the ions were normally incident, the surface of the glass became covered with almost hemispherical pits of about 400 Å diameter, suggesting that thermal spikes occurred where the low energy ions were stopped and caused rapid evaporation of the glass. For ion incident angles between 30° and 60° the ridge structure was evident and was perpendicular to the ion direction but for an angle of incidence of 10° the ridges became parallel to the ion beam.

In metals there is a marked dependence of the etch pattern upon the crystal orientation of the surface and it is believed[319] that the selective etching is due to differential sputtering from the different crystal planes which intersect the surface.

Probably the disorientation effect accompanies preferential etching pattern and relies upon the formation and extension of dislocations below the surface. The selective sputtering is readily understood when the importance of focuson sequences in determining defect formation (and sputtering is the formation of surface defects) is recalled since the favourable collision sequences will intersect close packed planes and result in their more rapid erosion. The angular dependence of the etch pattern is also understable on the basis of the interaction of the incident ions with close packed planes of atoms since these should suffer the greatest flux density of ions and experience the greatest disorder. As the angle of incidence of the bombarding ions is removed progressively from the normal the ions will acquire a greater resolved energy parallel to the crystal surface and a smaller energy perpendicular to the surface. The thermal or displacement spikes created by the ions will then change progressively from ellipsoids of revolution with major axes perpendicular to the surface, through approximate hemispheres with radii roughly equal perpendicular to the surface and in mutually perpendicular directions in the surface plane, to ellipsoids with major axes in the direction of the ion at grazing incidence. In the first case, normal incidence, one would expect, as observed in amorphous glass, furrows in the direction of ion incidence, since maximum ejection would occur along the incident direction as observed in both glass and metallic, crystals, whilst at intermediate angles one would anticipate a furrow structure dictated, to some extent, by the grain structure of the surface and by the fact that the incident ions would tend to pile up atoms perpendicular to their plane of incidence by preferential forward ejection (c.f. the action of waves on sand). Alternatively one can say that the ellipsoidal displacement spike with major axis parallel to the direction of ion incidence will intersect the surface plane over a particular area. The more normal the ion beam the smaller will be the length of the axis of the ellipse of

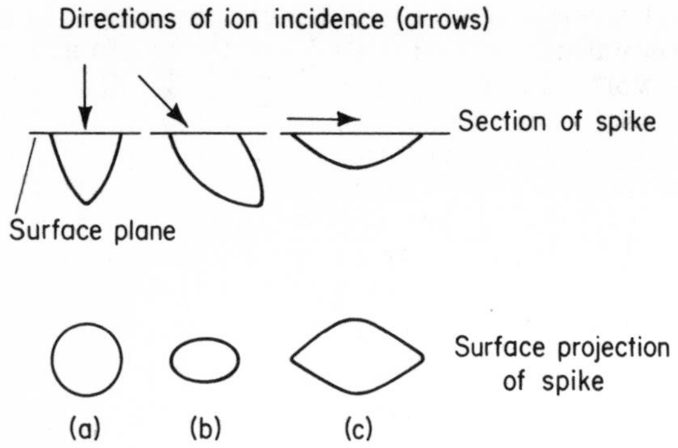

Fig. 6. 65 Schematic representation of spike formation below surface as direction of incidence of ion beam is varied from normal to the surface (a) to grazing incidence (c). The lower figures indicate the intersection of the spikes with the surface plane.

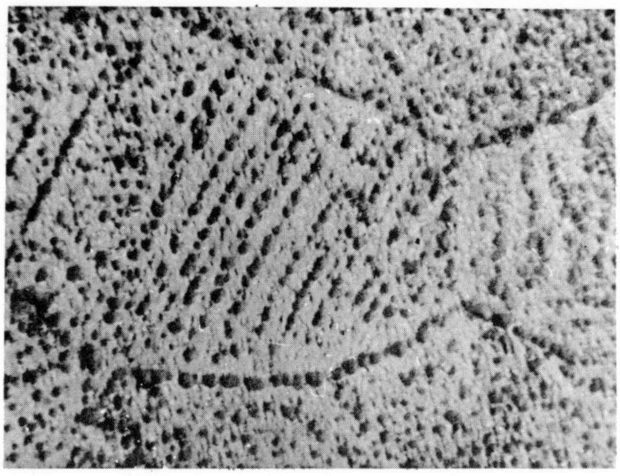

Fig. 6. 66 Decoration of a Uranium surface by 15 ke V A^+ ions bombardment. (note grain boundaries). (viz. Ref. 6. 289)

intersection of the displacement ellipsoid and the surface parallel to the ion direction compared to the length perpendicular to the ion direction and thus at large incident angles the furrows tend to line up perpendicular to the ion beam. Reference to Figure 6.65 should help to clarify this idea. It is notable that the studies of Navez et al [326,327,328] on glass show that for the intermediate angles the distance between adjacent furrows produced by 4 keV Argon ions and perpendicular to the incident plane, increases with decreasing incident angle. These results reveal the increasingly preferential forward propulsion of target atoms parallel to the target surface with decreasing angle of incidence. Even with crystalline materials it is seen that these effects become predominant. Haymann[312,316] has suggested that the regular step like structure produced in crystalline materials at large incident angles is due to simultaneous nucleation of close spaced dislocations which interact and give rise to step like features at the surface. Measurement of the angular dependence and ion flux dependence of the step sizes tend to confirm this picture. We should also note that these preferential etch patterns have also been observed by optical microscopy when the patterns have been sufficiently well developed to give detail and contrast with this apparatus. Fluit and Datz[329] have made a rather careful study of the etch patterns following 20 keV Argon ion bombardment at various incident angles of [100] oriented copper single crystals observing the angular change in optical reflectivity. These authors found preferential exposure of [110] planes because of focusing action along the ⟨110⟩ rows and, in addition, facets which were typical of the extent of the displacement spikes produced by the ions and their intersection with the surface. On the other hand, when ions were directed along open crystal directions channelling phenomena occurred and the displacement spike production was minimised perpendicular to the direction of ion incidence resulting in reduced facet production due to this effect. Kaminsky[330] has also suggested that etch pits may be formed by the bursting of gas bubbles of previously occluded atoms, when the surface recedes to these due to sputtering. Quite clearly these surface etching phenomena are of considerable value in observing damage processes and further, careful investigation with ions of various types and energies and targets of different surface orientation should give interesting information on the importance of correlated collision sequences.

One interesting feature revealed by this preferential etching technique is that such macroscopic features as grain boundaries and dislocations and glide planes become well defined by enhanced disturbance in their vicinity. Such a decoration[289] of a grain boundary is illustrated in Figure 6.66 for a Uranium surface bombarded by 5 keV Argon ions at 30° incidence. Numerous other similar examples have been reported of this technique and it is presumably a result of the fact that many boundaries act as sinks for point defects formed during bombardment (viz Barnes[29]) and the preferential collection at such boundaries and possible diffusion to the surface along the boundaries results in enhanced contrast at their points of emergence with the surface. Yurasova and collaborators [331] have used this ionic decoration technique extensively for the development of dislocation structures which intersect the surface and specific examples have been quoted by Wehner[321] and Mackel and Swalin[332] for Ge single crystals, by Cunningham et al[319] for Al, Zn, Au and Aluminium oxide and by Trillat[289] for Ur, Trillat and Mihama[300] for Au, Mihama for pyrite[333] (FeS_2) Haymann[312,334] for Ag, Sella and Trillat[335] for mica and graphite. These studies show that the ionic decoration technique is a powerful method for displaying various types of dislocation and indeed the method often reveals dislocation structures which are not exposed by other decoration techniques such as chemical or thermal methods of attack. Whilst providing useful information about the dislocation structure of a crystal, however, and indicating that such dislocations act as sinks for damage produced during bombardment, the method has not, as yet, been used to determine the nature and magnitude of the damage. It may be that careful studies of the decoration of dislocations at various temperatures will provide a means for determining migration energies of the different defect types produced during bombardment.

6.5.4.3 Low Energy Electron Diffraction

In addition to the techniques of high energy electron transmission and reflection microscopy discussed above, a further technique, originally developed some thirty-five years ago and successfully applied to surface structure and adsorption studies, [336] has been recently used for surface radiation damage investigation. This technique, low energy electron diffraction, (LEED) is basically the same as the higher energy electron reflection method already discussed, but employs low energy ($\lesssim$ 100eV) electrons, which, since the electron penetration depth is low, essentially probes the surface structure. The reflected electron beams can be observed directly, as a spot pattern through use of a fluorescent screen, or as an amplitude variation with electron collectors. For a clean, ordered surface one observes a characteristic reflected electron spot pattern, but the presence of surface disorder reduces the intensity of the various order reflected beams i.e. at angles where $n\lambda = d \sin \theta$. Thus several investigators[337,-343] have reported in a qualitative way the disappearance of the spot pattern following ion bombardment induced damage to several single crystal surfaces, but recently Jacobson and Wehner[344,345] and Farnsworth[346,347] and his co-workers have initiated more quantitative studies of the effect. Jacobson and Wehner examined the intensity degradation of the various order spots from 36 eV reflected electrons from a (111) Ge surface after exposure of the surface to A^+ ion bombardment at energies from 15 eV to 1 keV and at doses up to 10^{17} ions/cm^2. Although all spots diminished in intensity following bombardment, particular attention was paid to the degradation of the first order $n = 1$, (10) spot, following bombardment. It was observed that at all energies the intensity degraded considerably (to zero for energies greater than about 50 eV) and that as the ion energy increased, the dose necessary for a given degradation decreased. Thus 10^{16}, 100 eV A^+ ions completely removed the (10) spot whilst only 10^{14}, 1 keV ions achieved the same effect. Furthermore the dose dependence of the intensity degradation was exponential at any energy, suggesting that each ion could disorder a certain surface area, which increased with ion energy. For example 50 eV ions were believed to disorder about 1 surface atoms whilst 1 keV ions disorder about 50 atoms but at this stage it is not yet possible to compare the damage density with $\frac{E}{2E_d}$. In addition a threshold for disordering of about 20 eV was observed which is close to known damage thresholds in Ge. It was further observed that thermal annealing at temperatures up to 400°C could completely restore the ordered surface, and that several stages in the annealing could be discerned. At the higher bombardment energies, the annealing took place almost entirely above 250°C but at lower energies, annealing commenced even at the bombardment temperature. This suggests that the lower energy ions produce more isolated damage which anneals initially via short range vacancy migration, but that the higher energy ions produce a more completely amorphous structure which extends deeper into the target and requires longer range vacancy movement. In addition to the damage annealing it was observed that occluded ions were also released near the reordering temperature.

A final interesting observation was that a surface bombarded to extinction by 1 keV ions could be partly reordered by a lower energy (50 eV) subsequent bombardment, suggesting that these ions could promote some form of thermal spike reordering.

Boggio and Farnsworth[346] also used the technique to show that (100) tantalum surfaces developed (130) and (320) facets following A^+ ion bombardment with energies varied between 200 eV and 2 keV and doses exceeding 6×10^{14} ions/cm^2, provided that the crystals were annealed to 650°C after bombardment. Subsequent annealing of the crystals to 700°C caused the (130) facets to disappear and the surface to reform to a (110) structure but with an atom spacing 5 times larger than in the untreated specimens. In addition the work function of the annealed (130) faceted surface was reduced by about 0.17eV below that of the (110) faceted surface, whilst a non annealed (130) surface was lower in work function by a further 0.61 eV. This work indicates again the changed structure of surfaces following low energy ion bombardment, and as suggested by Boggio and Farnsworth may exert considerable influence on focuson sequences intersecting the surface.

Further work by Haque and Farnsworth[347] with Tungsten surfaces also showed degradation of the surfaces following ion bombardment but no apparent (310) facet development. An interesting observation was made however that increasing the A^+ ion energy in 50 eV steps from 100 eV continuously degraded the LEED pattern, until at 500 eV some restoration occurred up to 550 keV but then the degradation recurred until at 1000 eV complete obliteration ensued. As in Jacobson & Wehner's work it appears that some competition between ordering and disordering must operate. As in the case of tantalum, ion bombardment led to a small decrease (~0.06 eV) in the (110) surface work function.

We should also note that Park[348] has recently considered the effects of bombardment induced damage on LEED patterns. In addition to the diminution in intensity of the diffracted electron beams following 500eV Argon ion bombardment of the (100) face of a nickel single crystal, Park observed considerable broadening of the diffracted beams. This was interpreted as indicating the presence of occluded Argon within the surface plane rather than of disordered domains since the beam intensity diminution was insufficient to account for the defect density which would be required to explain the beam widening. Park indicates that in fact such beam broadening and intensity degradation observations may be used down to very low ion doses and thus the technique may become accurate for displacement threshold measurements at low damage levels.

In addition to these more or less direct observations of defect production a number of experiments have been performed to determine the effect of damage upon the macroscopic properties of materials as we shall now discuss.

6.5.5 Property changes due to damage production and other observational methods

In elemental targets the effects of damage induced by inert gas ions should be simple, since only the creation of vacancies, interstitials and their aggregates and the occlusion of bombarding gas should be instrumental in changing the macroscopic properties. In compounds or under active gas ion bombardment, the effects should be more complex since chemical action may accompany, or even swamp the displacement processes. Indeed, as we have already seen in the previous section oxygen or nitrogen ion bombardment of several materials can be directly observed to result in oxide and nitride production. Other studies of these chemical effects have also been performed using different observation techniques. For example Moore et al[306] have studied the decomposition of KNO_3 under bombardment of H^+, D^+, D_2^+ and He^+ ions of energy variable between 50 eV and 10 keV. These authors observed that the nitrate converted, under ion bombardment to potassium nitrite and oxygen, and the total nitrite yield per unit ion flux was found to increase slightly with the rate of ion bombardment, and at any dose rate to initially increase linearly with total dose but finally to saturate. The yield was also observed to increase with increasing ion energy, generally at a faster rate than linearly. It was believed that at low energies, H^+ ions generated a chemical reaction $H + NO_3 \rightarrow NO_2 + OH$. For He, D^+, D_2^+, D_3^+ bombardment the results were not inconsistent with ionic induced rupture of N — O bonds from which the Oxygen atom was removed leaving the nitrite molecule. Similar, but smaller, yields of nitrites were also obtained with nitrates of the alkali metals.

As we saw in Chapter 5 Hines[349] and Hines and Arndt[350] have studied the damage produced by 7.5 to 59 keV, H_2^+, D_2^+, He^+, Ne^+, A^+, Kr^+, and Xe^+, and 33.5 keV A^+ ion bombardment of glass, quartz and vitreous silica, by observing the changes in optical reflectivity of the surfaces after bombardment.

These changes in reflectivity were then related to the effective penetration depths of the ions or of the knock ons. It was observed that equal changes in reflectivity occurred when equal amounts of energy were deposited per unit volume by any of the incident ions, provided that the ion energy was below that at which ionization losses predominated. This suggested that the cause of reflectivity changes was the displacement of Si and O atoms and a calculation based on the Seitz-Koehler estimate of defect production and the ion range revealed that about 30% of the atoms in the bombarded layer in quartz would have been displaced, at least temporarily, to account for 50% of the total reflectivity change. In vitreous silica however, the total number of displacements required to give 50% reflectivity change was much smaller (~ 7%), which suggested that in this material, ordering was more important than disordering processes which occurred in quartz. These results should be compared with the earlier studies by Koch[351] and Hines[349] of the changes in the reflectivity of glass after 60 keV Kr^+ and 30 keV A^+ ion bombardment, where much higher ion fluxes were required to give saturation changes. Hines and Arndt[350] suggest that in this case the presence of other atoms such as Na and the preferential sputtering of these, was of importance. A conclusion supported by Holland[352] who noted the preferential removal of sodium from a soda glass during 3 keV A^+ ion bombardment. Hines and Arndt also showed that thermal spike formation was of little importance at the energies employed but that at lower energies these may have become dominant.

Arndt and Hines[353] subsequently used this reflectance change technique to observe radiation enhanced diffusion of Zn in a 10% Zn — 90% Cu alloy during 30 keV Ne^+ ion bombardment. In this work the denudation of the alloy surface of Zn simply by heating at various temperatures was correlated with reflectance changes. The surfaces were then bombarded during heating and the different rate of reflectivity changes measured. In this way the activation energy for diffusion was found to be reduced from 30 kcal/mole for the unbombarded to 9.3 kcal/mole during bombardment, and the diffusion coefficient was dependent upon the square root of the bombarding flux. These results suggested that the bombardment produced interstitial-vacancy pairs and that the zinc migrated via a vacancy process, and further that the steady state concentration of vacancies during bombardment was limited by pair annihilation and by migration to surfaces and dislocations. Hines[354] also bombarded diamond surfaces with 20 keV C^+ ions and observed similar changes in reflectivity (and optical transmission) as obtained with silica surfaces. These changes were ascribed to point defect production and post bombardment annealing studies revealed that the optical properties (& presumably the defects) annealed in distinct stages with activation energies of about 1.0 eV, 1.6 eV and 2.7 eV. The annealing was complete after this final peak occurring at 760°C.

McDonald and Haneman[355] have studied another property change of a surface following ion bombardment to study the depth of the damage, in this case the change in the sputtering coefficient of Ge. It was observed that if polycrystalline Ge was bombarded with 400 eV — 1 keV A^+ ions, then the sputtering coefficient of this damaged material during subsequent 100 eV A^+ ion bombardment was higher, by as much as 25%, than the sputtering coefficient of an undamaged surface. The Ge was evaporated on to an aluminium substrate on a quartz piezoelectric crystal which had a resonant oscillatory frequency dependent upon the thickness of the Ge layer (see Chapter 7 for further details of this technique) and, during sputtering the Ge layer thickness decreased and the change in resonant frequency was correlated with the sputtering coefficient. If before sputtering with 200 eV A^+ ions, the surface was bombarded with the higher energy ions, the subsequent sputtering coefficient was observed to rise above that for an undamaged target and then, as the damaged layer was sputtered away, to fall to that typical of the undamaged material. The stage at which the sputtering coefficient returned to that of the undamaged target then gave an indication of the depth of the damage layer from the measurement of the sputtering coefficient and the sputtering ion dose. In this way it was concluded that the depth of ion damage increased from 8 atom layers for 400 eV ions to 20-25 atom layers for 1 keV ions.

These values are about a factor of two higher than expected from simple mean range calculations from the Lindhard-Scharff formula, but since the former are maximum effective ranges this is not surprising. This technique is certainly worthy of further development since it appears in principle, to be applicable to all target materials. At the same time the importance of the effect in sputtering studies should be realised since these results indicate that a damaged, presumably more amorphous, target exhibits a higher sputtering coefficient than a crystalline target. This in itself may be an indication of the importance that the lattice symmetry exerts on sputtering events. In addition to these experiments, other work,[356-366] already described in Chapter 4 has shown that inert gas ion bombardment of tungsten or copper results in the emission of ions (and presumably neutral atoms also) of Na and K, which are impurities in the host metals, and also various oxides of the latter metal. This latter emission was not due to oxygen impurities in the bombarding ions since the emission eventually ceased after several cylces of bombardment and heating to 650°C. Similar results have been obtained by Bills and Evett[367] for Argon ion bombarded glass, and by Woodyard & Burleigh Cooper[368] for Argon ion bombarded Ta, by Smith et al[369] for Cu and by Liebl and Herzog[370] for a variety of target materials. The effect is presumably some form of differential sputtering process but may well include some chemical reaction or physical migration of impurities to the surface catalysed by the bombarding ions. We may note that Anderson[371] has observed that surface erosion by 1 keV H^+ ions can lead to changes in optical emittance and absorption of copper,

Aluminium and Titanium alloys, and that these effects, although not yet explained physically, can be of importance in space and satellite vehicle environments.

This technique of ion bombardment induced removal of impurities from a surface has been utilised by numerous workers to produce monatomically clean surfaces and a fuller description will be given in Chapter 9. However, comparison of various properties of ion bombarded surfaces, such as the slow electron diffraction pattern, the work function etc, with cleaved single crystal surfaces show an identity only if the bombarded surface is properly annealed after bombardment i.e. in addition to removing surface impurities the ions produce a damaged surface which it is necessary to repair before the single crystal structure is reproduced.

Most workers using this method of ion bombardment cleaning and subsequent annealing have paid little attention to the processes occurring during bombardment, being satisfied that the method does indeed produce a final clean undamaged surface. By 1960 only a few investigations[372-376] of ion induced property changes had been reported, but more recently activity in this field has increased, because of a desire to elucidate the basic physical processes and because of the technological applications that this method has revealed. Since, except for very thin target materials, the ion induced damage is confined to a relatively small proportion of the target depth, it is necessary to study a property change which is generally small compared to the bulk value or which is a typically surface property. Examples of this latter are passivation to gaseous adsorption and changes in reflectivity of an optically transparent medium. Another property which could appear to be vulnerable to bombardment induced changes would be the electrical characteristics. In the case of conductors, since the electron mean free path is long, the normal conductivity of a metallic film, thin enough to exhibit a sufficiently large relative change in conductivity, after irradiation, would be largely dictated by surface topography. It is therefore necessary to be cautious in interpreting any bombardment induced effects since electron scattering in the damaged layer may be swamped by changes in surface topography. Thus it is difficult to define the precise reasons for changes in the resistivity of Ti films (1000 Å thick) after argon ion bombardment as measured by Ivanovskii and Radzhabov[377] who observed gradually increasing changes in resistivity as the A^+ ion energy was increased from 0.8 keV to 2 keV, and a saturation of the resistivity change of about 2% at doses of 10^{16} sq. cm. However, in a metal, the configuration of surface atoms will dictate the energy states occupied by electrons, and these in turn will condition such properties of the conductor as work function, photoelectric threshold, contact potential etc. Thus far only two systematic studies of such a property change, that of the work function of Niobium, following A^+ ion bombardment, has been reported by Dillon and Oman,[378] and of single crystal tungsten following A, and Xe bombardment at 4 keV by Vernickel[379], although other authors[372-377] have also noted such effects during ionic cleaning processes. The former authors found that the work function of Niobium single crystals with (111) faces exposed to a 500 eV ion beam increased to a maximum then decreased steadily from that typical of a clean crystal, during bombardment at room temperature, to a quasi equilibrium value after an estimated removal of about 100 surface layers by ion erosion. Upon turning off the ion beam and then re-bombarding for a short period there was a recovery of the work function towards the maximum value but continuing bombardment for long periods returned the work function to the quasi equilibrium lower value. It was suggested that the mechanism responsible for these results was that of dislocation formation beneath the surface which reached a dynamic equilibrium value between ion induced production and annealing and thermal annealing at the bombardment temperature. These in turn caused surface crystal reorientations with the attendant changes in work function. It was also shown that the bombarded surfaces were passivated to oxygen absorption. On the other hand,[379] bombardment of the tungsten tip in a field emission microscope with 4 keV A^+, and Xe^+ ions and measurement of the work function of this showed only a 0.1 eV diminution and no effective alteration of the subsequent sorption properties of O_2, although gross alterations of the tungsten atomic pattern were evident.

It will be interesting to see if these studies can be extended to other materials and whether correlations can be found between displacement thresholds and the onset of work function changes and of the effects of target temperature and these latter variations.

In the case of semiconductors and insulators, which have much lower intrinsic conductivities, one may expect gross changes in the electrical properties following ion bombardment, since displacement events can produce donor and acceptor levels in the electron energy bands through the introduction of interstitials and vacancies. Moreover the bombarding ion itself may introduce such levels if it is of a specific type which normally is known to dope the host material, i.e. a chemical effect. McCaldin[380] has recently given a comprehensive review of the physical and chemical effects of ion bombardment induced changes in the electrical properties of semiconductors and in the following we shall adopt a similar approach by basically dividing the discussion into that due to physical processes and due to chemical processes.

It has been long known that irradiation of semiconductor surfaces can lead to desirable changes of the electrical properties of such materials over quite well defined depths into the target material. Thus Shockley[381] and his collaborators at the Bell Telephones Laboratories took out patents on various semiconducting devices fabricated by selective exposure to energetic ion beams as early as 1954 whilst Lark-Horovitz[382,383] had already patented devices formed by α particle injection in 1952. Most of this work, however, was aimed at device preparation, rather than physical process investigation although Shockley was well aware of the damage processes and interstitial-vacancy formation and of the effects of impurity doping attendant upon ion bombardment.

Further investigations were carried out at the Bell Telephone Laboratories by Ohl and his coworkers, [384-387] again with the general purpose of device construction, and it was shown that the rectifying properties of a point contact junction formed to an ion bombarded silicon sample were considerably better than those formed with an umbombarded intrinsic sample. Thus bombardment by H^+, He^+, N^+ and A^+ ions of energy up to 30 keV were found to increase the reverse breakdown voltage considerably, this parameter increasing continuously with increasing ion energy and to saturation values with ion doses up to about 3 × 10^{15} ions/sq cm and target temperatures of about 400°C. Some dependence upon ion type was evidenced but the most marked change occurred in heavily Boron doped p type silicon which, before bombardment, formed a non rectifying junction, but after bombardment exhibited very good rectification.

These results suggested that the ion bombardment shifted the Fermi level to the centre of the forbidden energy band gap, presumably by creation of equal numbers of vacancy acceptor centres and interstitial donor centres. The injected ions in this case could hardly be expected to contribute any doping effect themselves. Simultaneous changes in the photoelectric properties of bombarded silicon were also observed and Heinz et al[389] have suggested how these irradiation effects may be used to advantage in a low energy ion detector.

Subsequent work by Cussins[388] and by Lawrance, Gibson and Granville[389] showed that ionic bombardment of Germanium point contact rectifiers had the opposite effect by destroying the rectification properties in this case. Bombardment of both n type and p type Ge with twelve species of ions of atomic numbers from 1 (Hydrogen) to 51 (Antimony) and energy from 5 keV to 90 keV, revealed that in all cases a surface layer, whose thickness increased with ion energy, exhibiting p type characteristics was formed. This result had also been obtained by Brattain and Pearson[390] with α particle irradiated Ge. The ion dose required for the maximum change was only 4×10^{13} ions/sq cm whilst post bombardment heating to 500°C restored the original conductivity. Since no marked differences were observed between the effects of different ions it was concluded that chemical doping effects were unimportant and that only defects were responsible for the conductivity changes. However, since initially p type (10^{14} donors/cc) and n type (10^{19} donor/cc) Ge were converted to p type Ge with 2×10^{17} ionised acceptors/cc it was concluded that the bombardment introduced a variety of acceptor sites, some of which exhausted the donor levels, and a minority of which remained ionised at room temperature. Because of the relatively small acceptor concentration when saturation of the p type conductivity was reached, and since at this stage acceptor annihilation by bombardment must have equalled their production rate (suggesting a high annihilation efficiency), Cussins was led to the conclusion that rather than forming interstitial-vacancy pairs, the ions must have generated spikes containing the necessary vacancies and vacancy aggregates which acted as acceptors. This tends to agree with the electron microscope investigations of Xe^+ bombarded Ge by Parsons and Balluffi.[46] The difference in behaviour of silicon was interpreted in terms of the respective widths of the band gaps and that in Si most added energy levels would be near the centre of the gap, rendering the material intrinsic, whilst in Ge the energy levels would be close to the valence band edge and would be largely ionised, rendering the material p type. It may also be that in Ge interstitials and interstitial loops are unstable at room temperatures whilst they remain frozen in Silicon and a notable difference in the two materials is the fact that in Si, damage effects are evident for ion energies above 200 eV whilst for Ge such effects only occur, according to Cussins[388], above about 20 keV.

Bredov et al[391] also studied the reverse bias characteristics of tungsten point contacts to n type Si and Ge following both N_2^+ and 0^+ bombardment with energies of 5 keV and 10 keV. for both N_2^+ and 0^+ ion bombarded Ge the only effects were small decreases in conductivity which was attributed to formation of extra scattering centres by damage production. Similar results were obtained following N_2^+ bombardment of Si, but 0^+ bombarded silicon was transformed to strongly p type, presumably through the trapping of oxygen acting as acceptor centres. The difference in behaviour of 0^+ bombarded Ge and Si was ascribed to the different energy levels introduced by oxygen doping in the two materials. In the former the energy levels were presumably close to the valence band, but in the latter case, near the band centre.

Bredov et al[391] also calculated the ratio of trapped impurity atoms to the number of defects expected to be produced by these ions as a function of depth within the target. The latter calculation was effected using the Kinchin Pease model and the stopping cross sections for both calculations were obtained using a computer analysis based on a Born-Mayer type of interaction potential. However, extreme accuracy cannot be expected from such calculations since annealing effects, which we have seen to be most important, were ignored. On the other hand, such calculations may be a convenient starting point for more sophisticated treatments, whilst they certainly illustrate the conditions necessary for chemical doping on the one hand and damage doping on the other. For the latter type of process to dominate a high damage production and retention rate, which imply high ion energies and low target temperatures is required, and non-chemically dopant ions. The former process will be dominant with chemical dopants and where the target temperature is high enough to permit rapid damage annealing, and if necessary dopant diffusion and interstitial-substitutional reactions. Thus the independence of bombarding species in the case of Ge as noted by Cussins[388] and by Bredov[391] is explained by the dominance of damage production because of the relatively low target temperatures.

In addition Thornton and Hanley[392] showed that both He^+ and 0^+ ion bombarded silicon point contact rectifiers experienced an improvement in their reverse breakdown voltage, the latter ion producing the most marked effect. This again suggested that in addition to purely damage effects, oxygen ions also promoted chemical doping processes but the exact mechanism is difficult to formulate for a dopant atom such as oxygen. Damage effects due to bombardment in silicon by several ions of energy between 50 keV and 1 MeV which rendered the material effectively intrinsic have also been reported by Ferber[393], but no apparent change occurred for inert gas and N_2 ions. Pavlov et al[394] have shown however that atomic nitrogen ions introduced at 57 keV into Si can render the intrinsic material n-type provided that annealing to 700°C after bombardment is carried out. This annealing was necessary, it was believed, to remove the radiation damage, which masked the doping effects and led to Ferber's negative results for nitrogen implantation. In fact bombardment by A^+ ions showed no n-type doping after annealing and suggests that Nitrogen atoms can be made electrically active donors in Si. A similar result was obtained with N^+ ion bombarded p type Ge, but only if high doses ($\gtrsim$ 1000 $\mu C/cm^2$ compared with Si which showed a constant doping for ion doses from 50 - 5000 $\mu C/cm^2$) were used and annealing was effected at 450°C. Synorov, Bulgakov & Stepanov[395] have also investigated the effect of rather lower energy (1-3 keV) ion bombardment of Ge and observed that irradiation increased the conductivity of a 10Ω cm sample but that after bombardment, conductivity subsequently relaxed towards the prebombardment condition. Irradiation of the n-type region of a Ge p-n junction resulted in an increase of reverse current in the junction, but again, after bombardment the reverse current characteristics relaxed back towards the prebombardment condition. The interpretation of these results was partly in terms of defect production but it was believed that the major effect was due to ion induced removal of surface oxide layers and their subsequent reformation on the vacuum system (at a pressure of 10^{-4} torr).

Reid[396] has obtained qualitatively similar results after immersing p-n Si junctions in a glow discharge at about 500 V and again ascribed the results to oxide removal and reformation.

Zorin et al[397] have recently observed the changes in the electronic properties of n-type Ge after bombardment at 100°C with 40 keV N_2^+ or A^+ ions to total doses ranging from 10^{11} ions/sq cm to 10^{17} ions/sq. cm. The thermo-electric e.m.f., resistivity and reverse bias current (to a tungsten probe) were measured as functions of the total ion dose and were found to vary in a concurrent manner. The results suggested that after an initial conversion of the surface bombarded layer (to a depth of about 1000 Å) to p-type Ge due to bombardment with about 10^{13} ions/sq. cm., there was a gradual, but incomplete, return to n-type Ge. Zorin et al[397] interpreted these results as revealing the initial production of point defects which render the conductivity p-type (i.e. vacancies produce acceptor sites and hole conductivity), but gradually the displacement spikes produced by the ions overlap and change the structure of Ge to an amorphous nature which exhibits n-type characteristics. This suggestion concurs with that of Cussins[388] and with the production of spikes in Ge as observed by Parsons & Balluffi. Pavlov et al[398] used these changes in conductivity of n-type Ge after A^+ and N_2^+ ion bombardment to determine radiation damage (and ion penetration depth) profiles qualitatively. After the ion bombardment (at energies between 46 keV and 82 keV) the conductivity was probed as surface layers were successively removed by chemical etching. The measured conductivity is of course that of the remaining damaged region and the underlying crystal, but differentiation of this conductivity/depth removed profile gives the variation of the conductivity at a specific depth with depth. Although, as we have seen in Chapter 5, this etching technique cannot be relied upon to give accurate ion ranges, the depth at which conductivity changes were maximum were in reasonable agreement with the approximate Nielsen Range/Energy equation. It is more interesting to note however that both types of ion bombardment resulted in small conductivity changes near the surfaces, which then increased with depth to a maximum and then fell again to the bulk value. It is probable that this type of variation reflects the damage/depth profile, and it is notable that the position of maximum conductivity change moved deeper into the target with increasing ion energy and dose. The former effect is expected from simple damage theory whilst the latter effect may simply be a result of changes in the etching rate of the damage Ge which were wrongly interpreted as showing changes in profile, and indeed electron microscope examination of targets exposed to large ion doses ($> 10^{15}$ ions/cm^2) revealed that the surfaces became amorphous whereas at lower doses ($\sim 10^{14}$ ions/cm^2) the crystalline structure was retained. With improved etching techniques however this method should prove to be a useful tool for investigation of damage densities in semi-conductors.

In further work, Pavlov et al[399] investigated the effects of implanting 25-150 keV $Boron^+$ ions in (111) oriented n-type silicon. The changes in the conductivity of the doped surface layer (which generally became p-type) were observed using a four point probe technique, and, a 'utilization' efficiency f given by the ratio $f = \frac{n_p + Nd}{Ni}$ where n_p, the mean carrier concentration was determined from the mean conductivity of the p-layer, Nd was the donor density in virgin silicon and Ni the ion dose. Clearly for maximum efficiency f should tend to unity when all injected ions are electrically active.

It was found, however, that f could only be approximated to unity if the Si was annealed at about 600°C after bombardment with 1μ Coulomb/cm^2, whilst annealing at 1000°C or more was necessary for doses of the order of 1000μ Coulomb/cm^2. In addition to the apparent necessity of moving the implanted B to active positions by the annealing, part of the annealing was also necessary to remove radiation damage. Indeed if the Si was not annealed after bombardment at 90°C, f fell with ion dose up to values of this of about 2 μ Coulomb/cm^2 before rising to normal pre-annealing values suggesting that damage effects were initially most effective, and that there was always competition between doping and damage. Similar results were obtained over the entire ion energy range.

Wentorf and Darrow[400] have observed that diamond surfaces may exhibit p or n type conductivity after ion bombardment induced in a 1500 V glow discharge depending upon whether the ion species were hydrogen or nitrogen and argon respectively. The latter conversion was presumably a result of damage production (as was confirmed by electron diffraction patterns which showed gross surface reorientation) whilst the injection of H^+ ions presumably provided acceptor centres. He and O_2 ion bombardment produced only slight conductivity changes however, and all conductivity changes could be removed by annealing at 1500°C (This should be compared with Hines[349] observation that annealing was complete at 750°C). Changes in the conductivity and Hall coefficient of Ge after Argon bombardment have been reported by Kobayashi et al,[401] whilst Hagstrum[402] has noted changes in the secondary electron energy distribution from Ge after Argon ion bombardment, Forman[403] has noted changes in Field effect mobility and Madden and Farnsworth[404] observed changes in electron surface recombination velocity, again in Ge, as a result of Argon ion bombardment.

Artamonov et al[405] have also observed damage effects during bombardment of PbS surfaces by 100-400 eV, H^+, O_2^+, N_2^+ and A^+ ions where the surface conductivity was observed to become increasingly p type during the early stages of bombardment (up to 1.5×10^{14} ions/sq. cm.) but then reverted to n type and the conductivity decreased. Finally there was a stabilisation at a constant value after a dose of about 10^{15} ions/sq. cm. Cessation of bombardment allowed a recovery of the conductivity, and if the bombardment dose was only small (just greater than 1.5×10^{14} ions/sq. cm.) the conductivity reverted to p type. In addition large ion doses caused total disappearance of the photoconductive properties of the PbS. Part, at least of these effects must be ascribed to removal of surface oxide films by sputtering since the p type conductivity and photoconductivity could be restored, after bombardment, by annealing in air, whilst samples previously heated in air at 550°C had to be subjected to considerably higher ion doses in order to reduce the conductivity to the stabilised n type condition. Nevertheless it is probable that defect production, with simultaneous bombardment induced and thermal annealing, as evidenced by the saturation conductivity and recovery, also played a decisive role in determining the conductivity changes. It will be interesting to see if further work on this topic can give information on displacement thresholds and damage processes.

As we have just seen bombardment with active ions such as oxygen can lead to chemical doping effects in addition to purely damage induced processes. The effects of oxygen doping are particularly difficult to understand however and consequently results obtained with more conventional dopants are amenable to more straightforward analysis. In such cases, as will be seen shortly, parameters such as target temperature assume critical importance since these will condition the diffusion of injected atoms and the possibility of their dissolution in the host lattice. Generally speaking dopant ions will fall into two categories. Those which would undergo a substitutional reaction with the host lattice atoms under normal conditions of introduction (e.g. diffusion doping) and would therefore be expected to do so under ion bombardment conditions, and those which would normally reside in interstitial positions. During ion bombardment however, with the attendant production of many more vacancies than present under thermal equilibrium conditions, the dopant atoms may move from their interstitial positions to take up substitutional configurations. Vacancy clusters may act as sinks for the dopant atoms, as we saw earlier was the case for inert gas atoms in metals, and thus the dopant atoms may cluster and precipitate rather than remain dispersed. In such circumstances target temperature is anticipated to be of considerable importance.

In the case of normal substitutional dopants, the technique of ion injection was first applied by Moyer[406] and Shockley [407] to insert IIIrd and Vth period elements into Si and so form various commercial semiconducting devices. Rourke et al[408] subsequently showed that such elements could be injected into Si to achieve doping concentrations as high as 10^{18}/c.c. because of the low ion penetration depths, whilst King and Solomon[409] have reported similar doping at very high ion energies (>1 MeV) with Boron ions.

Alvager and Hansen[410] doped Si with 10 keV phosphorus ions to form a p-n junction suitable for solid state radiation detectors but reported that a 600°C anneal, necessary to remove damage centres and render the junction similar to those produced by normal diffusion processes, in fact led to a thicker junction than desired because of the phosphorus diffusion at this temperature. Subsequently, Strack[411] bombarded Si with about 1 keV H^+ with admixtures of B^+ and P^+ ions to produce p or n type surfaces respectively. The bombardment induced vacancies allowed a much more rapid diffusion via a substitutional-vacancy process of the B or P into the Si that obtained under normal diffusion conditions at the same temperature (~600°C) and very high concentrations were deduced near the Si surface (10^{20}/cc). An electrolytic sectioning technique showed that this concentration was maintained to about 5000 Å beneath the surface but thereafter fell off rapidly with increasing distance at a target temperature of 820°C. Values of the vacancy-impurity atom diffusion length were determined to be 3000 Å for P and 5000 Å for B at 820°C.

Amadei et al[412] subsequently extended these measurements to bombardments of Si at temperatures below 700°C and using both B^+ and P^+ ions of 500 eV energy observed a conversion of n to p type material. It was readily shown, by concentration profile and annealing experiments, that the conversion was effected by the introduction of damage, probably in the form of vacancies which diffused from the surface to depths as large as 2μ. Annealing at 700-800°C was sufficient to remove these damaged layers, but it should be noted that if P^+ bombardment was carried out above 700°C, there was no conversion to p type, only an added donor concentration as anticipated. Manchester, Sibley and Alton[413] and King et al[414] have also doped Si crystals with B and P ions of energies in the hundred of keV region to produce p-n junctions, radiation detectors and solar cells. In both cases, measurement of electrical conductivity and electron diffraction studies suggested that annealing in the region of 300°C to 600°C was necessary to remove damage and rather higher temperatures were required to cause the dopants to occupy the substitutional positions. The latter authors[414] also have doped intrinsic diamond with P via high energy bombardment.

Corresponding to the case of substitutional dopants, several experiments have been performed with ions which would under normal circumstances, reside interstitially in the host lattice. Lander[415] showed, in 1957, that H^+ ions injected into ZnO behaved as donor centres, and that very large hydrogen super-saturations could be attained to depths in the crystal much larger than expected from range predictions, indicating the diffusion of Hydrogen. Bredov and Nuromskii [415] extended Bredov's[391] earlier studies by observing the effect of injection of 5 and 10 keV Li^+ ions into p type Si (10^{15} acceptors/cc) upon the rectification characteristics of a tungsten point contact to the Silicon. The results showed that a surface layer was converted to n type Si after an ion dose of about 10^{15}/sq.cm. at either energy, by the addition of the donor Lithium atoms.

Recently Medved et al[417] bombarded (110) and (111) surface oriented single crystals of Si with 5 keV Cs^+ ions doses up to 2×10^{18}/sq. cm. and found an increased rectification efficiency after bombardment when evaporated silver electrodes were applied to the crystal. Improved photovoltaic behaviour was also observed after irradiation, and as in the case of the rectifying properties a maximum effect was obtained with ions incident on the (110) face. It is attractive to interpret this result as indicating a greater ion penetration perpendicular to the more transparent (110) surface, i.e. a channelling phenomenon. On the other hand, the Cs which was believed to give rise to donor levels and so render the Silicon n type, was measured by an etching technique to form a junction deeper within (111) oriented Si than in the (110) case. It was suggested that the Cs concentration at and near the surface was 10^{16}/cc. Similar, but more exhaustive experiments have been performed by McCaldin and his collaborators[418-423] in studying the injection of 3-10 keV Na^+ and Cs^+ ions into p type Si single crystals held at specified temperatures during bombardment. These workers diffused phosphorus into the silicon wafer on both sides of the boundary of the area of crystal struck by the ions and upon the side of the crystal opposite to the bombarded surface, thus producing n type layers and a field effect type of transistor structure. The bombarded area was found to convert to n type and measurements of the conductivity using the field effect suggested that, at the surface, a donor concentration of 10^{19}-10^{20}/cc could be attained. Smaller values were obtained if the acceptor concentration in the bulk sample was decreased. Capacitance and Avalanche breakdown measurements, however, suggested that this high concentration was only maintained near the surface to a depth of the same order of magnitude as the ion penetration range. More deeply in the Si the concentration of donors decreased rapidly and it was in this region that the junction between n and p types occurred.

This type of result was only obtained at target temperatures greater than 400°C, whilst at lower temperatures the donor concentration was markedly reduced, and at room temperature the bombarded area was rendered intrinsic. These observations led McCaldin[380] to suggest that much of the discrepancy between Cussins',[388] Medved et al's[417] and his own work should be attributed to differences in sample temperature. In Cussins' room temperature work the dominant process would be damage formation whilst in Medved et al's investigations at higher temperature there would be a combination of damage and impurity effects whilst finally, at high temperatures chemical doping would dominate. In addition McCaldin believed Medved et al's determination of the surface donor density of 10^{16}/cc from p-n junction characteristics to be erroneous since his own investigations showed that whereas this may be the case at the junction some distance below the surface, the surface density cannot be obtained by extrapolation. This in turn suggests that diffusion may be inhibited near the surface by damage processes, to allow the high donor concentrations. Doping of Si with 150 keV Cs^+, Nd^+, and Th^+ ions and GaAs, CdS and ZnS with Nd^+ ions has been successfully performed by Mayer et al.[424] Bombardment of Si at 500°C produced n type conversion, but no evidence of damage was obtained from surface X-ray and photo luminescence measurements. In CdS there appeared to be a substitutional reaction since the Nd^{+++} characteristic fluorescence lines were observed after bombardment at 600°C.

Anderson[425] extended this work on the location of ions injected into CdS crystals. Doses of about 10^{16}, 200 keV Nd^+ ions were injected into these crystals at temperatures of 300°C and 500°C and photoluminescence in the crystals at 77°K between 8800 Å and 9600 Å was then studied. After bombardment at the higher temperature photoluminescence lines were observed and identified as the $^4F_{3/2}$-$^4I_{9/2}$ transition of Nd^{3+} as one also observes after conventional diffusion doping of CdS with Nd. This suggested that the Nd_3^+ ions resided in sites normally occupied by Cd^{2+} ions and achieved these positions by displacing the latter ions during irradiation. After bombardment at 300°C only a broad luminescence structure appeared (suggesting considerable damage to the crystal) and an amorphous structure, but on annealing to 600°C the Nd^{3+} lines appeared, typical of a crystalline host CdS structure. Since many Cd interstitials will be produced by bombardment, then if the much smaller Nd concentration of atoms were located interstitially following bombardment, it is unlikely that these latter would compete favourably for Cd^{2+} sites during annealing. Again this suggests that the Nd^{3+} immediately becomes substitutional (via displacement) during bombardment rather than during annealing.

We may also note that Gibbons et al[426] have performed an informative experiment on the effect of radiation damage on implanted impurity atom profiles in Si single crystals. Two Si single crystals were bombarded along the ⟨111⟩ direction with 40 keV Potassium ions at about 100°C. The first was bombarded with a trace dose of $2 \times 10^{10}/cm^2$ P^{32} radiotracer ions and then with $5 \times 10^{14}/cm^2$ P^{31} ions whilst the second crystal was first bombarded with the large dose of P^{31} ions and then P^{32} radiotracer dose. After bombardment the crystals were annealed at 600°C and the impurity profile determined by sectioning and radiotracer counting. It was found that in the crystal subjected to trace bombardment first, that these ions were distributed with a large penetrating tail, due presumably to channelling, but in the other case the ion distribution conformed closely to the Lindhard et al theory for penetration in an amorphous target with no long tail. This result is similar to that discussed in Chapter 5, for the penetration of Xe in Si. Gibbons et al also found that after bombardment but no subsequent annealing, no apparent surface damage persisted, as revealed by electron diffraction analysis, suggesting that the ion bombardment did not cause gross re-orientation of the target to an amorphous state as occurs with Germanium but that ions blocked the channels. Clearly these effects are worthy of further examination and are of considerable technological importance. Gusev et al[427] have also doped p-type Si with 30 keV P^+ ions to form p-n junctions for solar cells. They found that such cells had an improved response in the infra-red, due, it was believed, to the fact that the bombarded crystals (annealed to 600°C after implantation) were more structurally perfect, and offered less recombination centres, than diffusion grown cells.

Abroyan[428] has studied the excess conductivity induced instantaneously in n type Ge by pulse bombardment with K^+ ions of energies between 100 eV and 10 keV at room temperature. Rectangular pulses of ions of duration 10-50μ sec and repetition frequency of 2-50 per second were injected into the target and it appears, although not stated by the author that the total ion dose was considerably less than that required to cause saturation of even one atomic layer of the target. The excess conductivity induced by the bombardment was determined by observing the current pulse through the target with a fixed impressed voltage. During the primary ion pulses, the excess current was found to increase to a maximum and then to decay back to the original value following an approximately exponential time dependence. No residual conductivity change was evidenced after cessation of bombardment. Because of these facts Abroyan concluded that the sole effect of ion bombardment was to generate electron-hole pairs by ion-electron collisions, which migrated to give the excess conductivity and subsequently recombined. The lack of permanent effects suggested that damage effects were unimportant, but it should be remembered that the ion densities and doses in this experiment were particularly low and damage effects may be masked by the pair generation process. A threshold ion energy between 300 and 400 eV was found before the excess conductivity could be observed, which was considerably lower than that expected from the Seitz theory of electron excitation losses given by Equation 2.83 of Chapter 2 which predicts 7 keV for an electron liberation energy of 3 eV.

Abroyan and Titov[429] subsequently extended these induced conductivity measurement in Ge to study the effect of crystalline structure. Phosphorus ions with energies up to 7 keV were injected into single crystal Ge targets at variable incidence angles and the ratio of the induced conductivity, Δi to the ion current i_+ was measured. If was found that the variation of $\frac{\Delta i}{i_+}$ with incidence angle was non-monotonic, and that, just as in sputtering, secondary electron emission etc., maxima and minima appeared. $\frac{\Delta i}{i_+}$ was found to exhibit maxima when ions were injected along low index directions (e.g. ⟨110⟩, ⟨111⟩ and ⟨112⟩ directions) and that these maxima and minima remained to ion energies as low as 2 keV. These directions for maxima in $\frac{\Delta i}{i_+}$ correspond to channel or transparent directions and Abroyan and Titov suggest that because of the minimised loss in elastic collisions in these channels, and because the valence electron concentration remains high in the Ge channels, electron excitation is enhanced.

This work is clearly of considerably importance and it will be interesting to see what results are obtained with other ions, dose rates and total doses, and different targets. A similar remark also applies to the other experiments described in this section since it is clear that electrical effects in semiconducting materials are a particularly sensitive measure of ion irradiation induced processes.

Irradiation effects have also been observed in electron bombardment of alkali halides and covalent crystals via the production of colour centres exhibiting changed optical properties. It is probable that similar effects will be produced in ion bombardment of crystals and we can again look forward to such observations.

We should, however, make a cautionary remark about the validity of the experiments described above. In much of the earlier work, investigations were generally carried out under rather poor vacuum conditions ($>10^{-6}$ torr) under which circumstances the target materials were undoubtedly covered with adsorbed gas layers. Since it is well known that the properties of semiconductors are considerably influenced by their surface conditions, at least some of the effects described may be attributed to the simple removal (and subsequent reformation) of these surface contaminants. Clearly definitive experiments with semiconducting surfaces, and for that matter any solid surfaces, should in future be conducted under ultra high vacuum conditions in order that the effects of radiation damage and chemical doping should not be obscured.

Summary

In this chapter we have studied the theoretical predictions of ion bombardment induced defect production in solids, and shown that simple theories based on a random arrangement of atoms and single collision processes lead to essentially similar results for the number of defects produced in a cascade process by an ion of energy E, virtually independent of the interatomic potential assumed and the existence of replacement processes i.e. $\nu(E) = \frac{\alpha E}{2E_d}$. It was then seen that the inclusion of effects associated with lattice regularity such as focusing, crowdion and channelling events, and of annealing processes, would markedly reduce the predicted damage densities. Furthermore, the conditions under which single atomic collisions would be invalid and the phenomena associated with collective collisions, were explored, and found to be of considerable importance. Computer studies showed the real possibility of such effects whilst consideration of experimental data proved the existence of these effects associated with lattice regularity and annealing. However it has not yet been possible to successfully compare any of the experimental damage studies directly with theoretical predictions since the former have not yet been performed at sufficiently low temperatures to preserve all the damage. On the other hand, quite strong evidence for the nature of the prominent defect in gold produced by ion bombardment has shown that the single interstitial is of major importance. The rapidly advancing studies using electron microscopy and field ion microscopy should remedy this situation in the near future and we end this chapter on a note of anticipation that both a satisfactory comprehensive theory and unequivocal experimental data will soon be available.

REFERENCES

1. Kistemaker, J. and Snoek, C. (1962) Le Bombardement Ionique. C.N.R.S. Bellevue. Paris (1962) p. 51
2. Snoek, C. Van der Weg, W. F. and Rol, P. K. (1964) Physica **30**, 341
3. Seitz, F. and Koehler, J. S. (1957) Progress in Solid State Physics **2**. (Academic Press Inc. New York (1957) p. 30
4. Dienes, G. J. and Vineyard, G. H. (1957) Radiation Effects in Solids. Interscience Publishers. New York (1957)
5. Billington, D. S. and Crawford, J. H. (1961) Radiation Damage in Solids. Princeton Univ. Press. Princeton (1961)
6. Chadderton, L. T. (1965) Radiation Damage in Crystals. Methuen and Co. Ltd. London (1965)
7. Proceedings of the International School of Physics. 'Enrico-Fermi' (1960) 18. Radiation Damage in Solids. Academic Press. Inc. New York (1962)
8. Van Bueren, H. G. (1960) Imperfections in Solids. North Holland Publishing Co. Amsterdam (1960)
9. Damask, A. C. and Dienes, G. J. (1963) Point Defects in Metals. Gordon and Breach Science Publishers Inc. New York (1963)
10. Huntington, H. B. and Seitz, F. (1942) Phys. Rev. **61**, 315
11. Zener, C. (1950) Acta. Cryst. **3**, 346
12. Darken, L. S. (1948) Trans. A.I.M.E. **175**, 184
13. Kuper, A., Letaw, H., Slifkin, L., Sonder, E. and Tomiyuka, C.T. (1955) Phys. Rev. **98**, 1570
14. Johnson, R. A. and Brown, E. (1962) Phys. Rev. **127**, 446
15. Johnson, R. A. (1964) Phys. Rev. **134A**, 1329
16. Johnson R. A. and Damask, A. C. (1964) Acta. Met. **12**, 443
17. Erginsoy, C., Vineyard, G. H. and Englert, A. (1964) Phys. Rev. **133A**, 595
18. Buffington, F. S., Bakalar, I. D. and Cohen, M. (1952) J. Metals **4**, 859
19. Koehler, J. S. and Leibfried, G. (1963) Conference on Crystal Lattice Defects. Conf. J. Phys. Soc. Japan, **18**, Suppl. (III) (1963) 266
20. Bartlett, J. H. and Dienes, G. J. (1963) Phys. Rev. **89**, 848
21. Lomer, W. M. (1959) Progress in Metal Physics. Pergamon Press. London (1959), p. 255
22. Damask, A. S., Dienes, G. J. and Weizer, V. G. (1959) Phys. Rev. **113**, 781
23. Gibson, J. B., Goland, A. N. Milgram, M. and Vineyard, G. H. (1960) Phys. Rev. **120**, 1229
24. Seeger, A. (1958) Proc. 2nd International Conference on Peaceful Uses of Atomic Energy **6**, 250
25. Brinkman, J. A. (1954) J. Appl. Phys. **25**, 961
26. Brinkman, J. A. (1956) Amer. J. Phys. **24**, 246
27. Martin, A. B., Austerman, S. B., Eggleston, R. R., McGee, J. F. and Tarpinian, M. (1951) Phys. Rev. **81**, 664
28. Barnes, R. S. and Mazey, D. J. (1960) Phil. Mag. **5**, 1247
29. Barnes, R. S. (1960) Phil. Mag. **5**, 635
30. Silcox, J. and Hirsch, P. B. (1959) Phil. Mag. **4**, 72
31. Hudson, B., Westmacott, K. H. and Makin, M. J. (1962) Phil. Mag. **7**, 1061
32. Makin, M. J. and Manthorpe, S. A. (1963) Phil. Mag. **8**, 1725
33. Hirsch, P. B., Silcox, J., Smallman, E. R. and Westmacott, K. H. (1958) Phil. Mag. **3**, 897
34. Silcox, J. and Hirsch, P. B. (1959) Phil. Mag. **4**, 1356
35. Beeler, J. R. and Besco, D. G. (1962) Radiation Damage in Solids. Vol. 1. International Atomic Energy Agency. Vienna (1962) p. 43
36. Eshelby, J. D. (1954) J. Appl. Phys. **25**, 255
37. Seeger, A. (1962) Radiation Damage in Solids. International Atomic Energy Agency. Vienna (1962) Vol. 1. 101
38. Huntington, H. B. (1942) Phys. Rev. **61**, 325
39. Huntington, H. B. (1953) Phys. Rev. **91**, 1092
40. Tewordt, L. (1958) Phys. Rev. **109**, 61
41. Tewordt, L. and Benneman, K. H. (1960) Zeits. Naturforsch. **15a**, 772
42. Benneman, K. H. (1961) Phys. Rev. **124**, 669 and (1961) Zeits. f. Phys. **165**, 445
43. Meechan, C. J. and Brinkman, J. A. (1956) Phys. Rev. **103**, 1193
44. Paneth, H. (1950) Phys. Rev. **80**. 708
45. Seeger, A., Mann, E. and V. Jan R. (1962) J. Phys. Chem. Solids **23**, 639
46. Parsons, J. R. and Balluffi, R. W. (1964) J. Phys. Chem. Solids **25**, 263
47. Parsons, J. R. (1965) Phil. Mag. **12**, 1159
48. Piercy, G. R. (1962) J. Phys. Chem. Solids **23**, 463
49. Jouffrey, B. (1963) J. de Microscopie **2**, 45
50. Brandon, D. G. and Bowden, P. (1961) Phil. Mag. **6**, 707
51. Bowden, P. and Brandon, D. G. (1963) Phil. Mag. **8**, 935
52. Bowden, P. and Brandon, D. G. (1963) J. Nucl. Mat. **9**, 348
53. Sinha, M. K. and Muller, E. W. (1964) J. Appl. Phys. **35**, 1256

54a,b Makin, M. J., Whapham, A. D., Minter, F. J. (1961) Phil. Mag. **6**, 465 and 1962. **7**, 285

55. Westmacott, K. H., Roberts, A. C. and Barnes, R. S. (1962) Phil. Mag. **7**, 2035
56. Orowan, E. (1934) Zeits. f. Physik **89**, 634
57. Taylor, G. I. (1934) Proc. Roy. Soc. (London) **A 145**, 362
58. Polanyi, M. (1934) Zeits. f. Physik **89**, 660
59. Frank, F. C. and Read, W. T. (1950) Phys. Rev. **79**, 723
60. See also Gilman, J. J. and Johnston, W. G. (1962) Solid State Physics **13**, 147
61. Holmes, D. K. (1962) Radiation Damage in Solids. Proc. International School of Physics. Enrico-Fermi. Academic Press Inc. New York (1962) 182
62. Leibfried, G. (1962) Radiation Damage in Solids. Proc. International School of Physics. Enrico-Fermi. Academic Press Inc. New York (1962) p. 227
63. Gombas, P. (1956) Handbuch der Physik 36, Springer-Verlag; Berlin. p. 109
64. Bohr, N. (1948) Mat. Fys. Medd. Dan-Vid. Selsk. **18**, No. 8
65. Born, M. and Mayer, J. E. (1932) Zeits. f. Physik **75**, 1
66. Leibfried, G. and Oen, O. S. (1962) J. Appl. Phys. **33**, 2257
67. Lehmann, C. and Robinson, M. T. (1964) Phys. Rev. **134** A, 37
68. Van Lint, V. A. J. and Wyatt, M. E. Jr (1962) United States Airforce. A.R.L. Report No. A.R.L. 62-389
69. Lindhard, J., Scharff, M. and Schiott, H. E. (1961) Phys. Rev. **124**, 128
70. Lindhard, J., Scharff, M. and Schiott, H. E. (1962) Mat. Fys. Medd. Dan-Vid. Selsk. **33**. No. 14. 3
71. Sampson, J. B., Hurwitz, H. and Clancey, H. F. (1955) Phys. Rev. **99**, 1657

72. Fein, A. E. (1958) Phys. Rev. **109**, 1076

73. Lehmann, C. (1961) Nukleonik. **3**, 1

74. Seitz, F. (1949) Disc. Farad. Soc. **5**, 271

75. Kohn, W. (1954) Phys. Rev. **94**, 1049

76. Bauerlein, R. (1962) Radiation Damage in Solids. Proc. International School of Physics. Enrico-Fermi. Academic Press Inc. New York. (1962) p. 358

77. Brown, W. L. and Augustyniak, W. M. (1959) J. Appl. Phys. **30**, 1300

78. Loferski, J. J. and Rappaport, P. (1955) Phys. Rev. **98**, 1861; (1955) Phys. Rev. 100, 1261 and (1958). Phys. Rev. **111**, 432

79. Flicker, H., Loferski, J. J. and Scott-Monck, J. (1962) Phys. Rev. **128**, 2254

80. Wertheim, G. K. (1959) Phys. Rev. **115**, 568

81. Mackay, J. W. and Klontz, E. E. (1962) Radiation Damage in Solids. International Atomic Energy Agency, Vienna. (1962) Vol. **3** (p. 37)

82. Kinchin, G. H. and Pease, R. S. (1955) Rep. Prog. Phys. **18**, 1

83. Kinchin, G. H. and Pease, R. S. (1955) J. Nucl. Energy **1**, 200

84. Harrison, W. A. and Seitz, F. (1955) Phys. Rev. **98**, 1530

85. Snyder, W. S. and Neufeld, J. S. (1955) Phys. Rev. **97**, 1636

86. Snyder, W. S. and Neufeld, J. S. (1955) Phys. Rev. 99, 1326

87. Brown, E. and Goedecke, G. H. (1960) J. Appl. Phys. **31**, 932

88. Lindhard, J., Nielsen, V., Scharff, M. and Thomsen, P. V. (1963) Mat. Fys. Medd. Dan. Vid. Selsk. **33**, No. 10. **3**

89. Holmes, D. K. and Leibfried, G. (1960) J. Appl. Phys. **31**, 1046

90. Leibfried, G. (1962) J. Appl. Phys. **33**, 1963

91. Leibfried, G. (1963) Zeits. f. Physik **171**, 1

92. Korchovei, A., Gika, G. and Greku, D. (1962) Fiz. Tverd. Tel. **4**, 2777. English Translation in Soviet Physics-Solid State (1963) **4**, 2037

93. Oen, O. S., Holmes, D. K. and Robinson, M. T. (1963) J. Appl. Phys. **34**, 302

94. Harris, E. G. (1955) Phys. Rev. **98**, 1151

95. Baroody, E. M. (1957) Bull. Amer. Phys. Soc. Ser. II. 2. 355

96. Baroody, E. M. (1958) Phys. Rev. **112**, 1571

97. Silsbee, R. H. (1957) J. Appl. Phys. **28**, 1246

98. Liebfried, G. (1959) J. Appl. Phys. **30**, 1388

99. Lehmann, C. and Leibfried, G. (1961) Zeits. f. Physik **162**, 203

100. Lehmann, C. Private Communication at Harwell Conference on Cascade Processes in Radiation Damage (1964) Unpublished

101. Duesing, G. and Leibfried, G. (1965) Phys. Stat. Solidi. **9**, 463

102. Frère, R. (1962) Radiation Damage in Solids. International Atomic Energy Agency. Vol. 1. Vienna (1962) p. 87. and Frère, R. (1963) Phys. Stat. Sol. **3**. 1253, 1441 and 1453

103. Baroody, E. M. (1961) Phys. Rev. **124**, 745

104. Dederichs, P. H. and Leibfried, G. (1962) Zeits. f. Physik **170**, 320

105. Nelson, R. S. and Thompson, M. W. (1961) Proc. Roy. Soc. (London) **A259**, 458

106. Nelson, R. S. (1963) Phil. Mag. **8**, 693

107. Weijsenfeld, C. H. To be Published

108. Nelson, R. S., Thompson, M. W. and Montgomery, H. (1962) Phil. Mag. **7**, 1385

109. Debye, P. (1913) Ann. Phys. Lpz. **43**, 49

110. Waller, I. (1926) Ann. Phys. Lpz. **79**, 261, and (1927) Ann. Phys. Lpz. **83**, 154

111. Sanders, J. B. and Fluit, J. M. (1964) Physica **30**, 129

112. Kurkin, S. A. and Odintsov, K. K. (1965) Fiz. Tverd. Tela **7**, 1573. English Translation in Soviet Physics-Solid State (1965) **7**, 1269

113. Blewitt, T. H., Coltman, R. R., Holmes, D. K., Noggle, T. (1957) Creep and Recovery (Amer. Soc. for Metals. Cleveland Ohio. U.S.A.) p. 88

114. Sigmund, P. and Vajda, P. Private Comm. (Harwell Conference on Cascade Processes in Radiation Damage (1964) Unpublished.)

115. Leibfried, G. (1960) J. Appl. Phys. **31**, 117

116. Seeger, A. (1955) Handbuch der Physik. Springer-Verlag. Berlin (1955) Vol. **7**, pt. 1. p. 609

117. Coltman, R. R., Blewitt, T. H., Klabunde, C. E. and Redman, J. K. (1959) Bull. Am. Phys. Soc. Ser. II. 4, 135

118. Coltman, R. R., Klabunde, C. E., McDonald, D. L. and Redman, J. K. (1962) J. Appl. Phys. **33**, 3509

119. Lehmann, C. and Leibfried, G. (1963) J. Appl. Phys. **34**, 2821

120. Nelson, R. S. and Thompson, M. W. (1963) Phil. Mag. **8**, 1677

121. Oen, O. S. and Robinson, M. T. (1963) Phys. Rev. **132**, 2385

122. Beeler, J. R. and Besco, D. G. (1963) Proc. International Conf. on Crystal Lattice Defects: Conf. J. Phys. Soc. Japan **18**. Suppl. III. 1963, p. 159

123. Oen, O. S. and Robinson, M. T. (1963) Appl. Phys. Letters **2**, 83

124. Kornelsen, E. V., Brown, F., Davies, J. A. and Piercy, G. R. (1964) Phys. Rev. **136**, A849

125. Lutz, H. and Sizmann, R. (1963) Phys. Letters **5**, 113

126. Beeler, J. R. and Besco, D. G. (1964) Phys. Rev. **134** A, 530

127. Sigmund, P. (1963) Phys. Letters **6**, 151

128. Robinson, M. T. (1965) U.K.A.E.A. Report A.E.R.E.—R4908. (1965)

129. Oen, O. S. Private Comm. (Harwell Conference on Cascade Processes in Radiation Damage (1964) Unpubl.) and Oak Ridge National Lab. Report O.R.N.L. 3676. October 1964

130. Brinkman, J. A. (1962) Radiation Damage in Solids Proc. International School of Physics. Enrico-Fermi Academic Press. New York and London (1962) p. 830

131. Noggle, T. S. and Stiegler, J. O. (1960) J. Appl. Phys. **31**, 2199

132. Beirlein, T. K. and Mastel, B. (1960) J. Appl. Phys. **31**. 2315

133. Carslaw, H. S. and Jaeger, J. C. (1947) Conduction of Heat in Solids. Oxford University Press. Oxford (1947)

134. Thompson, M. W. (1962) Radiation Damage in Solids Vol. 1. International Atomic Energy Agency, Vienna (1962) p. 239

135. Nelson, R. S. and Thompson, M. W. (1962) Phil. Mag. 7, 2015

136. Brinkman, J. A. (1963) Proc. International Conf. on Crystal Lattice Defects 1963. Conf. J. Phys. Soc. Japan **18**, Suppl. III, 1962. p. 150

137. Cooper, H. G., Koehler, J. S. and Marx, J. W. (1955) Phys. Rev. **97**, 599

138. Magnuson, G. D., Palmer, W. and Koehler, J. S. (1958) Phys. Rev. **109**, 1990

139. Quere, Y. and Nakache, F. (1959) J. Nucl. Mat. **1**, 203

140. Bleiberg, M. L. (1959) J. Nucl. Mat. **1**, 182

141. Konobeevsky, S. T. (1956) J. Nucl. Energy **3**, 356

142. Denny, J. M. (1954) Phys. Rev. **94**, 1417

143. See also Sloope, B. W. and Tiller, C. O. (1962) J. Appl. Phys. **33**, 3458

144. Gonser, V. and Okkerse, B. (1957) Phys. Rev. **105**, 757

145. Gonser, U. and Okkerse, B. (1958) J. Phys. Chem. Solids **7**, 1, 55

146. Fujita, F. E. and Gonser, U. (1958) J. Phys. Soc. Japan **13**, 1068

147. Seeger, A. (1964) Phys. Letters **8**, 296

148. Brinkman, J. A., Dixon, C. E. and Meechan, C. J. (1954) Acta Met. **2**, 38

149. Frenkel, T. (1924) Zeits. f. Physik **26**, 117

150. Redhead, P. A. (1962) Vacuum. **12**, 203

151. Carter, G. (1962) Vacuum **12**, 245

152. Carter, G. (1963) Vacuum **13**, 89

153. Lord Rayleigh (1879) Phil. Mag. **8**, 261

154. Vand, V. (1943) Proc. Phys. Soc. (London) **55**, 222

155. Primak, W. (1955) Phys. Rev. **100**, 1677

156. Smeaton, G. P., Carter, G. and Leck, J. H. (1962) 9th National Symposium of the American Vac. Society. Pergamon Press. London. p. 491

157. Glasstone, S. and Edlund, M. C. (1953) The Elements of Nuclear Reactor Theory. Macmillan. London (1953)

158. Fletcher, R. C. and Brown, W. L. (1953) Phys. Rev. **92**, 585

159. Kelly, R. and Brown, F. (1965) Acta Met. **13**, 169

160. Kelly, R. (1964) Acta Met. **12**, 123

161. Dayton, B. B. (1961) Transactions of 8th National Symposium of the American Vacuum Society, Pergamon Press. London (1961) Vol. 1. p. 42.

162. Leibfried, G. and Holmes, D. K. (1963) Oak Ridge National Lab. Solid State Division Ann. Progr. Report. May 1963. ORNL-3480, p. 6

163. Dettman, K., Holmes, D. K. and Leibfried, G. Private Comm. (Harwell Conference on Cascade Processes in Radiation Damage (1964) Unpublished)

164. Sizmann, R. Private Comm. (Harwell Conference on Cascade Processes in Radiation Damage (1964) Unpublished)

165. and Lück, G. and Sizmann, R. (1964) Phys. Stat. Sol. **5**, 683

166. Schilling, W. Private Comm. (Harwell Conference on Cascade Processes in Radiation Damage (1964) Unpublished)

167. Burger, G., Meissners, H. and Schilling, W. (1964) Phys. Stat. Sol. **4**, 281

168. Yoshida, M. (1961) J. Phys. Soc. Japan **16**, 44

169. Vineyard, G. H. (1962) Proc. International School of Physics. Enrico-Fermi. Academic Press Inc. New York (1962) **18**, 291

170. Vineyard, G. H. (1963) Proc. International Conf. on Crystal Lattice Defects, 1962. Conf. J. Phys. Soc. Japan **18**, Suppl. 1963, 144

171. Vinyard, G. H. (1961) Disc. Farad. Soc. **31**, 7

172. Erginsoy, C. and Vineyard, G. H. (1963) Bull. Am. Phys. Soc. II, 8, 196

173. Erginsoy, C., Vineyard, G. H. and Shimizu, A. (1965) Phys. Rev. **139**, A118

174. Abrahamson, A. A., Hatcher, R. D. and Vineyard, G. H. (1961) Phys. Rev. **121**, 159

175. Abrahamson, A. A. (1963) Phys. Rev. **130**, 693

176. Girifalco, L. A. and Weizer, V. G. (1959) Phys. Rev. **114**, 687.

177. Lucasson, P. G. and Walker, R. M. (1961) Disc. Farad Soc. **31**, 57

178. Lucasson, P. G. and Walker, R. M. (1962) Phys. Rev. **127**, 485

179. Beeler, J. R. and Besco, D. G. (1963) Proc. Int. Conf. on Crystal Lattice Defects. Conf. J. Phys. Soc. Japan **18**, Suppl. **3**, 159

180. Beeler, J. R. and Besco, D. G. (1963) J. Appl. Phys. **34**, 2873

181. Beeler, J. R. and Besco, D. G. (1963) Bull Amer. Phys. Soc. **8**, 339. Paper L5

182. Beeler, J. R. and Besco, D. G. (1963) Bull Amer. Phys. Soc. **8**, 339. Paper L6

183. Gay, W. L. and Harrison, D. E. (1964) Phys. Rev. **135**, A1780

184. Henschke, E. (1961) Phys. Rev. **121**, 1286

185. Arifov, U. A. (1961) Interaction of atomic particles with the surface of metals. Tashkent. (1961) English Translation in AEC. tr 6089

186. Gurvich, L. G. (1962) Izv. Akad. Nauk. S.S.R. **26**, 1418. English Translation in Bull. Acad. Sci. U.S.S.R. (1962) **26**, 1443

187. Harrison, D. E., Leeds, R. W. and Gay, W. L. (1965) J. Appl. Phys. **36**, 3154

188. Mott, N. F. (1929) Proc. Roy. Soc. (London) **A124**, 426

189. McKinley, W. A. Jr. and Feshbach, H. (1948) Phys. Rev. **74**, 1759

190. Mills, M. Unpublished. (Quoted in Sosin A. (1962) Ref. 191)

191. Sosin, A. (1962) Radiation Damage in Solids. Vol. 1. International Atomic Energy Agency (1962) p. 223

192. Walker, R. M. (1962) Proc. International School of Physics. Enrico-Fermi. Academic Press. New York (1962) p. 594

193. Sosin, A. (1962) Phys. Rev. **126**, 1698

194. Sosin, A. (1962) Proc. Int. Conf. on Crystal Lattice Defects. Conf. J. Phys. Soc. Japan. Vol. 18, Suppl. 3 (1963) p. 277

195. Corbett, J. W., Denny, J. M., Fiske, M. D. and Walker, R. M. (1957) Phys. Rev. **108**, 954

196. Corbett, J. W., Denny, J. M., Fiske, M. D. and Walker, R, M, (1956) Phys. Rev. **104**, 851

197. Sosin, A. and Garr, K. (1965) Phys. Stat. Sol. **8**, 481

198. Wollenberger, H. and Wurm, J. (1965) Phys. Stat. Sol. **9**, 601

199. Lucasson, P. G. and Walker, R. M. (1962) Phys. Rev. **127**, 1130

200. Bauer, W. and Sosin, A. (1964) J. Appl. Phys. **35**, 703

201. Bauer, W. and Sosin, A. (1964) Phys. Rev. **135**, A521

202. Grimshaw, J. A. and Banbury, P. C. (1964) Proc. Phys. Soc. (London) **84**, 151

203. Simmons, R. A., Koehler, J. S. and Balluffi, R. W. (1962) Radiation Damage in Solids. Vol. 1. International Atomic Energy Agency (1962) p. 155

204. See also Nilan, T. G. and Granato, A. V. (1965) Phys. Rev. **137**, A1233 and A1250 for recent work

205. Lomer, J. N. and Niblett, D. H. (1962) Phil. Mag. **7**, 1211

206. Corbett, J. W., Smith, R. B. and Walker, R. M. (1959) Phys. Rev. **114**, 1452

207. Corbett, J. W., Smith, R. B. and Walker, R. M. (1959) Phys. Rev. **114**, 1460

208. Corbett, J. W. and Walker, R. M. (1959) Phys. Rev. **115**, 67

209. Bauer, W. and Sosin, A. (1964) Phys. Rev. **136**, A255 and A474

210. Sosin, A. and Rachal, L. H. (1963) Phys. Rev. **130**, 2238

211. Sosin, A. and Neeley, H. H. (1962) Phys. Rev. **127**, 1465

212. Martin, D. G. (1961) Phil. Mag. **6**, 839

For other work on electron bombardment of Cu see:

213. Eggen, D. T. and Laubenstein, M. J. (1953) Phys. Rev. **91**, 238

214. Meechan, C. J. and Brinkman, J. A. (1956) Phys. Rev. **103**, 1193

215. Simmons, R. O. and Balluffi, R. W. (1959) J. Appl. Phys. **30**, 1249

216. Simmons, R. O. and Balluffi, R. W. (1958) Phys. Rev. **109**, 1142

217. Vook, R. and Wert, C. (1958) Phys. Rev. **109**, 1529

218. Meechan, C. H., Sosin, A. and Brinkman, J. A. (1960) Phys. Rev. **120**, 411

219. Simmons, R. O. and Balluffi, R. W. (1962) Bull. Amer. Phys. Soc. **7**, 233

220. Ward, J. B. and Kauffmann, J. W. (1961) Phys. Rev. **123**, 90

see also 221. Minnix, R. B. and Shearin, P. E. (1963) Bull. Amer. Phys. Soc. **8**, 196

222. Venables, J. A. and Balluffi, R. W. (1964) Bull. Amer. Phys. Soc. **9**, 295

223. Venables, J. A. and Balluffi, R. W. (1965) Phil. Mag. **11**, 1021 and 1039

224. Swanson, M. L. and Piercy, G. R. (1963) Phys. Letters **7**, 97

225. Swanson, M. L. and Piercy, G. R. (1964) Can. J. Phys. **42**, 1605

226. Hirsch, P. B. (1962) Radiation Damage in Solids. Proc. Int. School of Physics. Enrico-Fermi. Academic Press. Inc. New York (1962) p. 39

227. Ashby, M. F. and Brown, M. (1963) Phil. Mag. **8**, 1083

228. Ashby, M. F. and Brown, M. (1963) Phil. Mag. **8**, 1649

229. Barnes, R. S., Redding, G. B. and Cottrell, A. H. (1958) Phil. Mag. **3**, 97

230. Barnes, R. S. (1960) Phil. Mag. **5**, 635

231. Barnes, R. S. (1961) Disc. Faraday Soc. **31**, 38

232. Mazey, D. J., Barnes, R. S. and Howies, A. (1962) Phil. Mag. **7**, 1861

233. Kroupa, F. and Price, P. B. (1961) Phil. Mag. **6**, 243

234. Kroupa, F., Silcox, J. and Whelan, M. J. (1961) Phil, Mag. **6**, 971

235. Johnson, C. A. (1960) Phil. Mag. **5**, 1255

236. Hudson, B., Westmacott, K. H. and Makin, M. J. (1962) Phil. Mag. **7**, 377

237. Baker, A. J. (1961) Disc. Faraday Soc. **31**, 72

238. Ruedl, E., Delavignette, P. and Amelinckx, S. (1961) J. Appl. Phys. **32**, 2492

239. Ruedl, E., Delavignette, P. and Amelinckx, S. (1962) J. Nuclear Mat. **6**, 46

240. Varley, J. H. O. (1962) Phil. Mag. **7**, 301

241. Hesketh, R. V. (1962) Phil. Mag. **7**, 519

242. Hesketh, R. V. (1963) Phil. Mag. **8**, 487

243. Makin, M. J. (Unpublished)

244. Silicox J. (1960) Conference on Electron Microscopy, Delft. Vol. 1p. 362

245. Beierlein, T. K. and Mastel, B. (1962) J. Appl. Phys. **32**, 2873

246. Smallman, R. E. and Westmacott, K. H. (1959) J. Appl. Phys. **30**, 603

247. Barnes, R. S. (1962) Radiation Damage in Solids. Proc. Int. School of Physics. Enrico-Fermi. Academic Press Inc. New York (1962) **18**, p. 860

248. Barnes, R. S. (1963) The Metallurgy of Beryllium. Chapman and Hall Ltd. London (1963) p. 372

249. Barnes, R. S. (1963) U.K.A.E.A. Report No. AERE-R4429

250. Ghosh, T. K., Beevers, C. J. and Barnes, R. S. (1960-1961) J. Inst. Metals. **89**, 125

251. Rich, J. B., Walters, G. P. and Barnes, R. S. (1961) J. Nuclear Mat. **4**, 287

252. Whapman, A. D. and Makin, M. J. (1962) Phil. Mag. **7**, 1441

253. Silk, E. H. C. and Barnes, R. S. (1959) Phil. Mag. **4**, 970

254. Bonfigioli, G., Ferro, A. and Mojori, A. (1961) J. Appl. Phys. **32**, 2499

255. Izui, C. and Fujita, F. E. (1961) J. Phys. Soc. Japan **16**, 1032

256. Bowden, F. P. and Chadderton, L. T. (1962) Proc. Roy. Soc. **A269**, 143

257. Beevers, C. J. and Nelson, R. S. (1962) Phil. Mag. **8**, 1189

258. Beevers, C. J. and Mazey, D. J. (1962) Phil. Mag. **7**, 1061

259. Pashley, D. W. (1959) Phil. Mag. **4**, 324

260. Pashley, D. W. and Presland, A. E. B. (1961) Phil. Mag. **6**, 1003

261. Surplice, N. A. (1961) Brit. J. Appl. Phys. **12**, 220

262. Howe, L. M., Gilbert, R. W. and Piercy, G. R. (1963) Appl. Phys. Letters **3**, 125

263. Howe, L. M. and McGurn, J. F. (1964) Appl. Phys. Letters. **4**, 99

264. Carroll, D. B. and Birnbaum, H. K. (1965) J. Appl. Phys. **36**, 2658

265. Brandon, D. G., Wald, M., Southon, M. J. and Ralph, B. (1963) Proc. International Conf. on Crystal Lattice Defects. Conf. J. Phys. Soc. Japan **18**. Supp. II, 1963. p. 324

266. Mihama, K. (1963) Proc. International Conf. on Crystal Lattice Defects. Conf. J. Phys. Soc. Japan **18**. Suppl. II, 1963. p. 352

267. Castaing, R. and Jouffrey, B. (1961) Comptes. Rendus **252**, 2696

268. Castaing, R. and Jouffrey, B. (1962) Le Bombardement Ionique. C.N.R.S. Bellevue Paris (1962) p. 63

269. Brebec, G., Levy, V., Leteutre, J. and Adda, Y. (1962) Le Bombardement Ionique C.N.R.S. Bellevue Paris (1962) p. 155

270. Ogilvie, G. J., Sanders, J. V. and Thomson, A. A. (1963) J. Phys. Chem. Solids **24**, 247

271. Castaing, R. and Jouffrey, B. (1962) J. de Microscopie **1**, 2014

272. Castaing, R. and Jouffrey, B. (1963) J. de Microscopie **2**, 6

273. Müller, E. W. (1951) Zeits. f. Physik **136**, 131

274. Müller, E. W. (1956) J. Appl. Phys. **27**, 474

275. Müller, E. W. (1960) Avances in Electronics and Electron Physics. Academic Press Inc. New York. (1960) **13**, 83

276. Gomer, R. (1961) Field Emission and Field Ionization. Oxford University Press. London (1961)

277. Brandon, D. G. (1963) Brit. J. Appl. Phys. **14**, 474

278. Müller, E. W. (1959) Zeits. f. Physik **156**, 399

279. Müller, E. W. (1960) Proc. IVth International Symposium on the Reactivity of Solids. Amsterdam (1960) Elsevier Publ. Co. Amsterdam

280. Müller, E. W. (1963) Proc. International Conf. on Crystal Lattice Defects (1962) Conf. J. Phys. Soc. Japan **18**. Suppl. II, **1**, 1963

281. Sinha, M. K. and Müller, E. W. (1960) 7th Field Emission Symposium. Mc. Minnville, Oregon.

282. Sinha, M. K. and Müller, E. W. (1961) 8th Field Emission Symposium. Williamstown. Massachussetts.

283. Brandon, D. G. and Wald, M. (1961) Phil. Mag. **6**, 1035

284. Brandon, D. G., Southon, M. J. and Wald, M. (1961) Conference on Properties of Reactor Materials and Effects of Radiation Damage. Butterworths Press. London (1961)

285. Brandon, D. G. and Bowden, P. B. (1961) Disc. Faraday Soc. **31**, 70

286. Brandon, D. G., Bowden, P. and Wald, M. Conference on Sorption at Evaporated Metal Surfaces Liverpool (1963) Unpublished

287. Ralph, B. Private Communication. Harwell Conference on Cascade Processes in Atomic Collisions. Harwell. U.K. (1964) (Unpublished)

288. Strayer, R. W., Cooper, E. C. and Swanson, L. W. (1965) Proc. 25th. M.I.T. Conference on Physical Electronics. Massachussetts Institute of Technology. U.S.A. (1965) p. 150

289. Trillat, J. J. (1962) Le Bombardement Ionique. C.N.R.S. Bellevue. Paris (1962) p. 13

290. Trillat, J. J. and Tertian, L. (1956) J. Chim. Phys. **53**, 570

291. Trillat, J. J., Terao, N., Tertian, L. and Gervais, H. (1956) J. Phys. Soc. Japan **11**, 406

292. Trillat, J. J., Terao, N., Tertian, L. and Gervais, H. (1955) Comptes. Rendus. **240**, 1557

293. Trillat, J. J., Tertian, L. and Terao, N. (1958) J de Res. C.N.R.S. Bellevue, Paris. p. 156

294. Ogilivie, G. J. (1959) J. Phys. Chem. Solids **10**, 222

295. Ogilvie, G. J. and Thomson, A. A. (1961) J. Phys. Chem. Solids **17**, 203

296. Gianola, V. F. (1957) J. Appl. Phys. **28**, 868

297. Trillat, J. J. and Mihama, K. (1960) Bull. Microscopie. Appl. **10**, 61

298. Fert, C. (1954) Comptes Rendus **238**, 333

299. Trillat, J. J. and Tertian, L. (1958) Cahiers de Phys. p. 161

300. Trillat, J. J. and Mihama, K. (1959) Comptes Rendus **248**, 2827

301. Mihama, K. (1960) Metaux No. 418

302. Trillat, J. J., Tertian, L. and Bonnet-Gros, M. (1960) Comptes Rendus **251**, 10

303. Trillat, J. J., Tertian, L. and Terao, N. (1956) Comptes Rendus **242**, 1294

304. Trillat, J. J., Tertian, L. and Terao, N. (1957) Comptes Rendus **243**, 666

305. Trillat, J. J., Lecomte, C. and Tertian, L. (1957) Comptes Rendus **244**, 596

306. Moore, W. J., Logan, S. R., Luther, L. C. and Brown, S. N. Le Bombardement Ionique C.N.R.S. Bellevue. Paris (1962) p. 35

307. Gillam, E. (1959) J. Phys. Chem. Solids **10**, 55

308. Castaing, R. (1955) Rev. Metall. **52**, 669

309. Haymann, P. (1959) Comptes Rendus **248**, 2472

310. Sosnovsky, H. M. C. (1959) J. Phys. Chem. Solids **10**, 304

311. Hondros, E. D. and Benard, J. (1962) Le Bombardement Ionique C.N.R.S. Bellevue. Paris (1962) p. 211

312. Haymann, P. (1962) Thesis. University of Paris

313. Haymann, P. (1960) Comptes Rendus **251**, 85

314. Haymann, P. (1960) J. Chim. Phys. **57**, 572

315. Haymann, P. and Lecomte, C. (1961) Comptes Rendus **252**, 1746

316. Haymann, P. and Waldburger, C. (1962) Le Bombardement Ionique. C.N.R.S. Bellevue. Paris (1962) p. 205

317. Haymann, P. (1961) Mem. Sci. Rev. Metall. **18**, 73

318. Düker, H. and Schlette, W. (1962) Le Bombardement Ionique. C.N.R.S. Bellevue. Paris (1962) p. 83

319. Cunningham, R. L., Haymann, P., Lecomte, C., Moore, W. J. and Trillat, J. J. (1960) J. Appl. Phys. **31**, 839

320. Magnuson, G. D., Meckel, B. B. and Harkins, P. A. (1961) J. Appl. Phys. **32**, 269

321. Wehner, G. K. (1958) J. Appl. Phys. **29**, 217

322. Farnsworth, H. E., Schlier, R. E., Georege, T. H. and Burger, R. M. (1958) J. Appl. Phys. **29**, 1150

323. Dillon, J. A. Jr. and Oman, R. M. (1960) J. Appl. Phys. **31**, 26

324. Honig, R. E. (1957) Bull. Amer. Phys. Soc. **2**, 34

325. Wolsky, S. P. (1959) J. Electrochem. Soc. **104**, 142c

326. Navez, H. Sella, C. and Chaperot, D. (1962) Comptes Rendus **254**, 240

327. Navez, M., Sella, C. and Chaperot, D. (1962) Le Bombardement Ionique. C.N.R.S. Bellevue. Paris. (1962) p. 233

328. Navez, M. and Sella, C. (1962) Vth International Congress for Electron Microscopy. Academic Press Inc. New York. (1962) Paper C. 5

329. Fluit, J. M. and Datz, D. S. (1964) Physica **30**, 345

330. Kaminsky, M. (1964) Institute of Petroleum/A.S.T.M. Mass Spectrometry Symposium. Paris 1964

331. Yurasova, B. E. (1957) Kristallographia **2**, 770

332. Maekel, B. B. and Swalin, R. A. (1959) J. Appl. Phys. **30**, 89

333. Mihama, K. (1958) IVth International Congress for Electron Microscopy. Springer-Verlag. Berlin (1960) p. 414

334. Haymann, P. and Mihama, K. (1960) Proc. European Conf. on Elec. Microscopy (1960) Vol. 1. 253

335. Sella, C., Sella, M. F. and Trillat, J. J. (1962) Vth International Congress for Electron Microscopy Academic Press Inc. New York (1962) Paper C. 3

336. Farnsworth, H. E. (1933) Phys. Rev. **44**, 417; (1936) Phys. Rev. **49**, 458

337. Farnsworth, H. E., Schlier, R. E., George, T. H. and Burger, R. M. (1955) J. Appl. Phys. **26**, 252

338. Park, R. L. and Farnsworth, H. E. (1964) Surface Science **2**, 527

339. Oman, R. M. and Dillon, J. A. (1964) Surface Science **2**, 227

340. MacRae, A. U. and Gobeli, G. W. (1964) J. Appl. Phys. **35**, 1629

341. Lander, J. J. and Morrisson, J. (1963) J. Appl. Phys. **34**, 1403

342. Schlier, R. E. and Farnsworth, H. E. (1959) J. Chem. Phys. **30**, 917

343. Scheibner, E. J., Germer, L. H. and Hartman, C. D. (1960) Rev. Sci. Instr. **31**, 112

344. Jacobson, R. L. and Wehner, G. K. (1965) Proc. 25th. M.I.T. Conference on Physical Electronics. Page 161

345. Jacobson, R. L. and Wehner, G. K. (1965) J. Appl. Phys. **36**, 2674

346. Boggio, J. E. and Farnsworth, H. E. (1964) Surface Science **1**, 399

347. Haque, C. E. and Farnsworth, H. E. (1965) Private Communication

348. Park, R. L. (1966) J. Appl. Phys. **37**, 295

349. Hines, R. L. (1957) J. Appl. Phys. **28**, 587

350. Hines, R. L. and Arndt, R. A. (1960) Phys. Rev. **119**, 623

351. Koch, J. (1949) Nature **164**, 19

352. Holland, L. (1964) The Properties of Glass Surfaces. Chapman and Hall. London. 1964 p. 318

353. Arndt, R. A. and Hines, R. L. (1961) J. Appl. Phys. **32**, 1913

354. Hines, R. L. (1965) Phys. Rev. **138**, A1747

355. McDonald, R. J. and Haneman, D. (1966) J. Appl. Phys. **37**, 1609

356. Bradley, R. C. (1960) Phys. Rev. **117**, 1204

357. Bradey, R. C. and Ruedl, E. (1961) Vth International Conf. on Ionization Phenomena in Gases. Munich (1961) North Holland Publishing Co. Amsterdam (1961)

358. Bradley, R. C. (1959) J. Appl. Phys. **30**. 1

359. Bills, D. G. (1957) Phys. Rev. **107**, 994

360. Riddoch, A. A. and Leck, J. H. (1958) Proc. Phys. Soc. **72**, 467

361. Honig, R. E. (1958) J. Appl. Phys. **29**, 549

362. Ruedl, E. and Bradley, R. C. (1962) J. Phys. Chem. Solids. **23**, 885

363. Bradley, R. C. and Ruedl, E. (1962) J. Appl. Phys. **33**, 880

364. Bradley, R. C., Arking, A. and Beers, D. S. (1960) J. Chem. Phys. **33**, 764

365. Stanton, H. E. (1960) J. Appl. Phys. **31**, 678

366. Veksler, V. I. (1960) Zh. Teor i Eksper. Fiz. **38**, 324. English Translation in Soviet Physics. J.E.T.P. (1960) **11**, 235

367. Bills, D. G. and Evett, A. A. (1959) J. Appl. Phys. **30**, 564.

368. Woodyard, J. R. and Burleigh Cooper, C. (1964) J. Appl. Phys. **35**, 1107

369. Smith, A. J., Cambey, L.A. and Marshall, D. J, (1963) J. Appl. Phys. **34**, 2489

370. Liebl, H. J. and Herzog, R. F. K. (1963) J. Appl. Phys. **34**, 2893

371. Anderson, D. L. (1963) Transactions of the 10th National Vac. Symp. of the American Vacuum Society. Macmillan Book Co. London (1963) p. 37

372. Farnsworth, H. E. and Madden, H.H. Jr. (1961) J. Appl. Phys. **32**, 1933

373. Dillon, J. A. Jr. and Farnsworth, H. E. (1957) J. Appl. Phys. **28**, 174

374. Lander, J. J., Gobeli, G. W. and Morrison, J. (1963) J. Appl. Phys. **34**, 2298

375. Allen, F. G. and Gobeli, G. W. (1964) J. Appl. Phys. **35**, 597

376. Weissler, G. L. and Wilson, T. N. (1953) J. Appl. Phys. **24**, 472

377. Ivanovskii, G. F. and Radzhabov, T. D. (1966) Fiz. Tverd. Tela. **8**, 1271

378. Dillon, J. A. Jr. and Oman, R. M. (1964) Transactions of the Tenth National Vacuum Symposium. Am. Vac. Soc. (1963) p. 471 also 1964. Surface Science **2**, 227

379. Vernickel, H. (1965) 3rd International Vacuum Congress. Stuttgart. Germany (1965) (To be Published)

380. McCaldin, J. O. (1964) Progress in Chemistry of the Solid State. Vol. II. Pergamon Press

381. Shockley, W. (1954) U.S. Patent 2, 666, 814. Jan 19, 1954

382. Lark-Horovitz, K. (1951) Semiconducting Materials. Butterworths Scientific Press Ltd. London (1951)

383. Lark-Horovitz, K. (1952) U. S. Patent 2, 588, 254. March 4, 1952

384. Ohl, R. S. (1956) U.S. Patent 2, 750, 541 June 12, 1956 308

385. Ohl, R. S. (1952) Bell System. Tech. J. **31**, 104

386. Kinsbury, E. F. and Ohl, R. S. (1952) Bell System Tech. J. **31**, 802

387. Heinz, O., Gyorgy, E. M. and Ohl, R. S. (1956) Rev. Sci. Instr. **27**, 43

388. Cussins, W. D. (1955) Proc. Phys. Soc. **B68**, 213

389. Lawrance, R., Gibson, A. F. and Granville, J. W. (1954) Proc. Phys. Soc. **B67**, 625

390. Brattain, W. H., Pearson, G. L. (1950) Phys. Rev. **80**, 846

391. Bredov, M. M., Lepilin V. A., Schestakov, I. B. and Shakh-Budagov, A. L. (1961) Fiz. Tverd. Tela. **3**, 267. English Translation in Soviet Physics-Solid State (1961) **3**, 195

392. Thornton, C. G. and Hanley, L. D. (1955) Proc. I.R.E. **43**, 186

393. Ferber, R. R. (1963) I.E.E.E. Trans. Nucl. Science N5-10. 15

394. Pavlov P. V., Zorin, E. I., Tetel'baum, D. I. and Popov, Yu. S. (1965) Dokl. Akad. Nauk. SSSR. **163**, 1128. English Translation in Soviet Physics-Doklady **10**, 786 (1966)

395. Synorov, V. F., Bulgakov, S. S. and Stepanov, V. V. (1965) Fiz. Tverd. Tela. **7**, 1375. English Translation in Sov. Phys. Solid State (1965) **7**, 1108

396. Reid, R (1965) Private Communication

397. Zorin, E. I., Tetel-Baum, D. I., Popov, Yu. S. and Granitsyna, Z. K. (1964) Fiz. Tverd. Tela. **6**, 2017. English Translation in Soviet Physics-Solid State (1965) **6**, 1592

398. Pavlov, P. V., Zorin, E. I., Tetel-Baum, D. I. and Popov, Yu. S. (1964) Fiz. Tverd. Tela. **6**, 3222. English Translation in Soviet Physics-Solid State (1965) **6**, 2577

399. Pavlov, P. V., Zorin, E. I., Tetel-Baum, D. I. and Popov, syna, E. K. (1965) Fiz. Tverd. Tela. **7**, 2940. English Translation in Soviet Physics-Solid State (1966) **7**, 2386

400. Wentorf, R. H. and Darrow, K. A. (1965) Phys. Rev. **137**, A1614

401. Kobayashi, A., Sugiyama, K., Arata, H. and Oda, Z. (1961) J. Phys. Soc. Japan **16**, 2481

402. Hagstrum, H. D. (1961) J. Appl. Phys. **32**, 1015

403. Forman, R. (1960) Phys. Rev. **117**, 698

404. Madden, H. H. and Farnsworth, H. E. (1958) Phys. Rev. **112**, 793

405. Artamonov, O. M., Ya. Berlaga, R., Vinogradov, M. G. (1963) Fiz. Tverd. Tela. **5**, 959. English Translation in Soviet Physics-Solid State (1963) **5**, 703

406. Moyer, J. W. (1958) U.S. Patent 2, 842, 466. July 8th (1958)

407. Shockley W. 1957. U.S. Patent 2, 787, 564. April 2nd (1957)

408. Rourke, F. M., Sheffield, J. C. and White, F. A. (1961) Rev. Sci. Instr. **32**, 455

409. King, W. J. and Solomon, S. J. (1962) Abstract No. 58. Electronics Division Abstracts. The Electrochemical Soc.

410. Alvager, T. and Hansen, N. J. (1962) Rev. Sci. Instr. **33**, 567

411. Strack, H. (1963) J. Appl. Phys. **34**, 2405

412. Amadei, L., Gereth R. and Queisser, H. J. (1965) J. Appl. Phys. **36**, 1537

413. Manchester, K. E., Sibley, C. B. and Alton, G. D. (1965) Conf. on Electromagnetic Isotope Separators, related Ion Accelerators and Applications to Physics. Aarhus. Denmark (1965)

414. King, W. J., Burrill, J. T., Harrison, S., Martin, F. and Kellett, C. (1965) Conf. on Electromagnetic Isotope Separators, related Ion Accelerators and Applications to Physics. Aarhus. Denmark (1965)

415. Lander, J. J. (1957) J. Phys. Chem. Solids **3**, 87

416. Bredov, M. M. and Nuromskii, A. B. (1962) Fiz. Tverd. Tela. **4, 562**. English Translation in Soviet Physics-Solid State (1962) **4**, 409

417. Medved, D. B., Rolik, G. P., Speiser, R. C. and Daley, H. (1963) Appl. Phys. Letters **3**, 213

418. McCaldin, J. O. and Widmer, A. E. (1963) Bull. Amer. Phys. Soc. **8**, 473

419. McCaldin, J. O. and Widmer, A. E. (1964) Proc. I.E.E.E. **52**, 301

420. McCaldin, J. O., Widmer, A. E. and Glass J. (1964) Bull. Amer. Phys. Soc. **9**, 289

421. McCaldin, J. O., and Widmer, A. E. (1964) J. Appl. Phys. **35**, 1985

422. Walder, M., McCaldin, J. O. Widner, A. E. and McQuaid, P. E. (1964) Bull. Amer. Phys. Soc. **9**, 147

423. Waldner, M. and McQuaid, P. E. (1964) Private Communication

424. Meyer, N. I., Gibbons, J. and Moll, J. (1965) Conf. on Electromagnetic Isotope Separators, related Ion Accelerators and Applications to Physics. Aarhus. Denmark (1965)

425. Anderson, W. W. (1965) Appl. Phys. Letters **7**, 198

426. Gibbons, J. F., El-Hoshy, A., Manchester, K. E. and Vogel, F. L. (1966) Appl. Phys. Letters **8**, 46

427. Guzev, V. M., Timov, V. V., Guseva, M. I. and Kurinnyi, V. I. (1965) Fiz. Tverd. Tela. **7**, 2077. English Translation in Soviet Physics-Solid State (1966) **7**, 1673

428. Abroyan, I. A. (1962) Fiz. Tverd. Tela. **4**, 2719. English Translation in Soviet Physics-Solid State (1963) **4**, 1994

429. Abroyan, I. A. and Titov, A. I. (1965) Fiz. Tverd. Tela. **7**, 2007. English Translation in Soviet Physics-Solid State (1966) **7**, 1619

430. Kenworthy, H. and Neely, H. H. (1956) NAA-SR Report No. 1580. Aug. 1st 1956

431. Burke, E. A., Jimenez, C. and Lowe, L. F. (1966) Phys. Rev. **141**, 629

432. Bauer, W. (1965) Bull. Amer. Phys. Soc. **10**, 711

433. Denney, J. M. (1953) Phys. Rev. **92**, 531

434. Dugdale, R. A. (1955) Conference on Defects in Crystalline Solids. Bristol. (England) Phys. Soc. London (1955)

435. Klontz, E. E. and Lark-Horovitz, K. (1951) Phys. Rev. **82**, 763

436. Klontz, E. E. and Lark-Horovitz, K. (1952) Phys. Rev. **86**, 643

437. Vavilov, V. S., Smirnov, L. S., Galkin, G. N., Spitsyn, A. V. and Patskevich, V. M. (1956) Zhur. Tekh. Fiz. S.S.R. **26**, 1865

438. Vavilov, V. S., Smirnov, L. S., Galkin, G. N., Spitsyn, A. V. and Patskevich, V. M. (1958) Zhur, Tekh. Fiz. S.S.R. **28**, 960

439. Kulp, B. A. (1962) Phys. Rev. **125**, 1865

440. Kulp, B. A. and Kelly, R. H. (1960) J. Appl. Phys. **31**, 1057

441. Kulp, B. A, and Dertweiler, R. M. (1963) Phys. Rev. **129**, 2422

442. Neely, H. H. (1965) Bull. Amer. Phys. Soc. **19**, 1179

443. Iseler, G. W., Dawson, H. I. Mehner, A. S. and Kauffman, J. W. (1966) Phys. Rev. **146**, 468

CHAPTER 7

Sputtering

7.1 INTRODUCTION

When a beam of energetic particles is projected at a target under suitable conditions, traces of damage quickly appear on the surface of the bombarded material. Some effect such as this is of course to be expected as the incoming particles must impart their energy to the solid in slowing down, but the processes involved in the damage sequence are far more complex than would be anticipated at first sight. The basic mechanism involves a reversal of the incident momentum carried by the ions so that target atoms are ejected from the surface over a wide range of angles. The process of atomic ejection during bombardment is called 'Sputtering' and a sputtering coefficient S is defined as the number of atoms liberated per incident particle.

Sputtering has recently become of importance in connection with space flight as it was feared that the damage to rockets and satellites would be severe. The problem does not appear to be as serious as at first anticipated but it is still valuable to estimate the damage which will occur to various metals and to choose, where possible, a material with a low sputtering coefficient to enclose the space capsule. Clearly the chain of events leading to the ejection of a surface atom should be similar to those encountered in radiation damage sequences in the bulk so that the study of sputtering may help to determine the mechanism of radiation damage which is important in the development of surfaces to contain controlled nuclear fusion reactions. Other present day problems requiring a knowledge of sputtering include: surface cleaning by ion bombardment, sputter-ion pumping in vacuum systems, damage to grids in gas discharge tubes and to collectors in mass spectrometers and failure of ion rocket motors due to the growth of sputtered films of metals across insulated sections.

Many reviews have been presented on the subject of sputtering. Fruth[1] has presented a paper on the subject in which he lists one hundred and thirteen references to early work carried out between the years 1852 and 1930 and Glockler and Lind[2] have given a comprehensive review of pre-1939 work, but these two contributions are now purely of historical interest and must be considered out of date. Massey and Burhop[3] have presented a critical survey of more recent work and also Guntherschulze[4] and Wehner[5] have given excellent reviews of the subject. Three more reviews were presented in 1956 by Francis[6], Holland[7], and Haymann[8] and a good review of work up to 1960 has been presented by Moore[9]. Further advances are described by Thompson[10], Behrisch[11] and Kaminsky[12]. In the ensuing chapter it is proposed to mention briefly some early work and then to consider the many interesting aspects of sputtering brought to light in the past decade.

7.2 Early Research

It is unfortunate that nearly eighty years of wasted effort went into sputtering investigations before it was realized that the pressure surrounding the target was a vital parameter and had to be low enough to allow the sputtered atoms to escape! Many anomalies in early experimental results can be accounted for by the simple fact that the mean free path of the sputtered particles was less than the distance from the target to some 'collector surface. In consequence many of the liberated atoms diffused back to the surface after collisions with gas atoms and were then either re-sputtered, or buried underneath subsequent returning particles. Bearing in mind the above limitation we will proceed with the review of early work: results obtained under pressure conditions exceeding 1-10 millitorr (where mean free paths are of comparable dimensions to the experimental apparatus) are presented solely for their historical interest.

Sputtering was first recorded in 1852 by Grove[13] who noticed the disintegration of cathodes in glow-discharge tubes. The pressures in these tubes were of the order 0.1 Torr so that reproducible results could not be expected and researchers such as Blechschmidt[14], who performed most exhaustive studies on yields of H_2^+ on ten metals, N_2^+ on thirteen metals and A^+ on fifteen metals using the Grove type of discharge apparatus, did not make a significant contribution to sputtering data.

The effect of the ambient pressure was first demonstrated conclusively by Penning and Moubis[15] though the view that the pressure was an important factor had no doubt been held for a few years prior to this publication. They plotted the results of Guntherschulze and Meyer[16,17] and showed that the sputtering yield was independent of the product of pressure and discharge gap 'pd' when the pressure was such that the mean free path was much less than d, that is, when the sputtered atoms could escape to the anode. Realizing the need to reduce back-diffusion Penning and Moubis coupled a magnetic field to their discharge tube which increased the electron path lengths and thereby enabled the discharge to be maintained at lower pressures. Their apparatus comprised a cylindrical, water-cooled cathode, two centimetres in diameter by twenty-five centimetres long, surrounded at the ends by two anode rings. The magnetic field was parallel to the cathode axis. With this apparatus they were able to produce ion current densities of about 20 mA/cm^2 at energies of 500 to 1500 volts in a background impurity gas pressure of 10^{-5} Torr. Sputtering coefficients could be determined within several minutes and the technique used was to expose mica discs as collectors and measure their weight increase. Values obtained for A^+, Ne^+, N_2^+ and H_2^+ ions striking a silver target at 500 eV were 2.3, 1.8, 1.4 and 0.6 respectively. This particular experiment satisfies most of the necessary conditions for a reproducible sputtering investigation at high energies, but it is not satisfactory for yields at energies of less than 500 eV where the sputtering action of the bombardment is insufficient to maintain a clean surface.

Returning to the work of Guntherschulze and Meyer [16,17] for the moment; it is clear that this is one of the few early experiments preceding the findings of Penning and Moubis which satisfied the conditions for a reproducible sputtering determination. The discharge tube used by these workers contained an oxide-coated cathode surrounded by an anode cylinder and could be run at pressures of the order 1 to 10 millitorr. The cathode was suspended from a spring balance thus allowing weight losses to be determined during an experimental run without having to open the system to atmosphere. Targets were constructed of copper in the form of discs of five centimetres diameter and supported at a distance of 2.5 cm. from the cathode. Guntherschulze and Meyer took the precautions of removing initial layers of target material before starting readings, monitored their discharge gas and performed a separate experiment to determine the secondary emission coefficient γ from the copper target so that true ion currents could be evaluated. It is highly commendable that the results of these two experimenters obtained under more difficult circumstances are very close to present day values; for example in 1961, Weijsenfeld and Hoogendoorn[18] obtained a yield of 2.8 atoms per ion for 1 keV argon ions striking a copper target which compares favourably with the value 3.2 obtained by Guntherschulze thirty years earlier.

Fetz[19] improved the discharge technique by replacing the thermionic cathode by a mercury pool. This allowed greater purity in operation and eliminated the necessity of processing the cathode prior to operation. With this system, which was the fore-runner of an extremely successful apparatus employed by Wehner[5], Fetz studied the sputtering of molybdenum wires as a function of the wire diameter. He discovered that the yields were largest for wires of smallest diameter and decreased towards the value for plane targets as the diameter increased. The explanation of this trend was that the angle of incidence of the ions played an important part in the sputtering sequence; sputtering being more easily produced on thin wires where the majority of collisions were oblique. The technique used by Fetz for measuring yields was similar to a method devised by the Research Staff of the General Electric Company[20] on a less accurate apparatus and involved a relation between the resistance change of the molybdenum and the amount of material sputtered. As a check on this method Fetz also determined the weight loss of the molybdenum wires.

In an attempt to conduct their experiment in an environment away from the discharge region, where angle of incidence effects on the sputtering yield could be determined, Seeliger and Sommermeyer[21] developed the first recorded ion beam sputtering experiment. Argon ions were produced in a discharge tube as before, but a hole of about 2 mm. diameter was drilled into the cathode and the ions were collimated through this onto silver, or liquid gallium, targets at energies of 5 to 10 keV. The results of this experiment were not conclusive, but indicated that the distribution of sputtered deposits followed a cosine law, irrespective of the angle of incidence.

Timoshenko[22] using a capillary arc ion source, was able to produce a fairly mono-energetic beam of argon ions and bombard silver targets at energies from 3 to 6 keV. Pressures in the vicinity of the target were of the order 5×10^{-5} Torr and ion currents were in the range 100 to 200 $\mu A/cm^2$. Sputtering yields were calculated from the weight losses of targets and, by extending the experiments over long periods, the errors introduced by sputtering away initial impurity surface layers became small enough to be neglected.

7.3 RECENT RESEARCH

Experiments carried out since 1950 have been undertaken on a variation of two types of apparatus: the mercury pool discharge system, in which the target is inserted in the manner of a Langmuir probe into the discharge region, and the ion beam method, which differs mainly in the type of ion source employed. (A full discussion of ion sources is given in Chapter 9). The respective merits of these two techniques just about balance out; the discharge method enables very high ion current densities to be produced (of the order 10 mA/cm^2.), the bombardment is essentially normal and, although the pressure around the target is of the order 10^{-4} to 10^{-3} mTorr, adsorbed surface layers are removed by the intense bombardment and do not cause spurious results. On the other hand; mass analysis of the incident beam is not possible so that all positively charged discharge species and neutrals will contribute to the erosion of the target surface. Further, the angular dependence of sputtering cannot be easily investigated and corrections for secondary electron emission must be applied to the results (an electron leaving the target being otherwise recorded as an ion arriving). However the ion beam method only produces current densities of the order 100 $\mu A/cm^2$. which are insufficient to maintain a clean surface unless the background pressure is lower than 10^{-6} Torr. Smith et al[23] have demonstrated the effect of contamination during sputtering of copper targets by 500 keV He^+ ions. With a beam intensity of only 100 $\mu A/cm^2$ and a background pressure of 2×10^{-6} Torr a blue colouration appeared on the targets after 15 minutes tending to change to black after longer bombardments. Values of the sputtering coefficient were observed to decrease as bombardment proceeded until a certain total number of ions had struck the surface. Beyond this point the yield changed by very small amounts as bombardment continued. Smith et al have made the interesting suggestion that this normally unwanted surface layer, which is predominantly carbon formed by cracking of oil films on the target surface, would make an ideal protective coat for space capsules if some self-replenishing method could be devised.

In spite of the low intensity beams the ion beam method can be adapted for clean surface studies since, by using suitable focusing techniques, differential pumping can be employed between the ion source and target region and the ions can be focused into the dividing aperture so that pressures in the target region may be maintained at values better than 10^{-6} Torr without losing much current. The beam can be analyzed magnetically, or electrostatically, and double-charged and neutral species thereby eliminated. A secondary electron suppressor grid can be placed in front of the target and the effects of varying the angle of incidence of the ion beam can be more easily investigated. Whichever method is chosen the following conditions must be taken into consideration to ensure that results are reproducible:

1. The gas pressure must be such that the mean free path of ions and sputtered atoms is large compared with the tube dimensions; generally this implies $p < 10^{-3}$ Torr.

2. The ion current density (j) must be high and the background pressure (p_b) low, so that formation of surface layers is prevented during the sputtering experiment. This condition is usually satisfied provided $j/p_b > 10^8$ where j is in $\mu A/cm^2$. and p_b is in Torr, but it should be noted that it is the ability of

the ion current to sputter the absorbed gases that is the important criterion rather than the actual intensity of the beam. For example, a much larger current density would be required to maintain a clean surface during hydrogen ion bombardment where the sputtering yield will be low compared with, say, argon in bombardment. Pleshivtsev[24] states that the clean surface condition will be attained if

$$6.25 \times 10^{18}\, j \,.\, S \gg 3.5 \times 10^{20}\, p \,.\, k$$

Where

j is now in A/cm^2, p in Torr,

S is the sputtering coefficient in atoms/ion

and

k is the sticking probability.

The number 3.5×10^{20} represents the number of molecules of N_2 and O_2 incident on one square centimetre of surface per second at a pressure of one Torr.

3. The ions must strike the target at a known angle.

4. The energy spread of the incident beam must be small and,

5. The ionizing conditions should be such as to minimize the production of multiply charged species. In the case of a discharge tube ion source this amounts to restricting the voltage drop to values between the first and second ionization potential of the species under investigation.

An apparatus of the 'discharge' type has been successfully developed by Wehner and his co-workers[5] and is illustrated in Fig. 7.1. The auxiliary discharge is struck by discharging a four microfarad condenser through the ignitor and this discharge becomes anchored to the molybdenum strip within the mercury pool. This auxiliary discharge immediately overcomes the graphite grid obstruction since electrons passing near the grid holes are accelerated with higher velocities than in the auxiliary discharge toward the main anode; consequently ionizing collisions are more efficient and a larger plasma density is produced in this anode region than would normally be present without the grid. Insertion of a repeller electrode to turn electrons back and also the use of a properly designed magnetic field causes further increase in ionization and therefore higher target currents. In general the repeller and grid electrodes acquire a negative voltage relative to the anode-space plasma by an amount which is nearly equal to the tube voltage drop so unwanted sputtering may occur at these electrodes. Care must be taken in selecting materials which have low sputtering yields for these components.

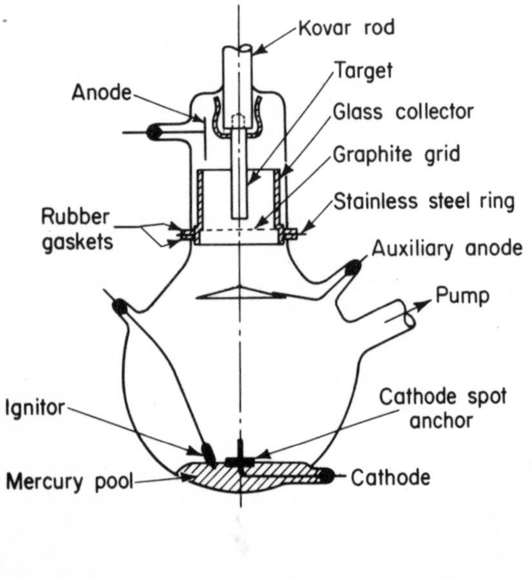

Fig. 7.1 Mercury pool discharge sputtering apparatus (viz. Ref. 7. 34)

With a main discharge current of 2.5 Amps. at 30 volts the ion current density can be made as high as 5 mA/cm^2. and this can be increased to 30 mA/cm^2. by using a magnetic field provided a non-uniform ion current density can be tolerated across the target. The mercury pressure in the tube reaches about 1 mTorr and the impurity background pressure is estimated to be 10^{-6} Torr. Targets must be maintained at temperatures above 300°C to prevent contamination by a mercury film.

By modifying the region above the grid and including a re-entrant cold trap the mercury in the discharge described above has been frozen out. Rare gases have been introduced which ionize in the anode discharge region so that sputtering yields between noble gas ions and various targets could be observed. The mercury background pressure has been reduced to about 10^{-5} Torr in this way and noble gas ion current densities of the order 100 mA/cm^2. have been obtained using a suitably designed magnetic field.

An alternative arrangement used by Wehner for studying sputtering by noble gas ions comprised a thyratron oxide-cathode and a cylindrical anode of titanium with targets immersed in the intervening space. Operating pressures in these tubes ranged from 1 mTorr for xenon to 40 mTorr for neon at discharge voltages between 25 and 65 volts, respectively. Impurity pressures were of the order 10^{-6} Torr and target currents of 3 to 15 mA/cm^2. could be maintained.

Ion beam methods have been employed by many investigators of sputtering phenomena including Keywell[25], Moore[26], Southern et al[27] and differ mainly in the type of ion source employed. Ion sources are discussed in Chapter 9 so their respective merits will not be enumerated here. Typical parameters in the experiments of Southern et al are; ion currents of 50 to 200 μA/cm^2. in the range 1 to 5 keV energy, for argon, and pressures of 2×10^{-7} Torr (due to residual gases) rising to about 7×10^{-6} Torr when argon is introduced for the experiment. These workers use an r-f source with which the energy spread can be maintained at about 50 eV.

Methods of detection of sputtered deposits will not be discussed fully at this stage as the particular aspect of sputtering to be studied determines the best technique. All methods are usually calibrated against direct weight-loss experiments and techniques usually employed include: use of radioactive tracers[28, 29, 30], spectrographic analysis[31], observing changes in the resonant frequency of a crystal on which the sputtered surface is plated[32], noting changes in target resistance[33], or, by observing changes in optical transmission as sputtered atoms cover a glass window[34].

7.4 GENERAL TRENDS IN SPUTTERING

7.4.1 Variation of yield with ion energy

It is now well established that the sputtering rate increases with ion energy in the manner indicated in Figs. 7.2 and 7.3. Referring to Fig. 7.2 it can be seen that no sputtering occurs until the energy of the ions reaches some threshold value E_T which is characteristic of the particular ion-target combination and, apparently, dependent on the previous history of the target surface[35]. Sputtering yields then increase initially in a quadratic manner, quickly reach a 'knee' and then increase approximately linearly with ion energy. As ion energies approach 1 to 5 keV (the exact point again depending on the ion-target combination) the curve approaches a maximum (see Fig. 7.3) and, at even higher energies, yields decrease again. This latter portion of the characteristic is often referred to as the 'back' of the sputtering curve and the decrease in sputtering yield is attributed to the fact that the ions are now penetrating further into the target lattice and dissipating their energy in collisions too deep to transmit a disturbance back to the surface.

7.4.2 Variations of yield with target material

The most exhaustive experiments to determine the variation of sputtering with the target material have been carried out by Wehner et al who first bombarded 26 metals with 0-400 eV mercury ions[34] and, later, performed a similar investigation with noble gas ions[36,37]; both the experiments being carried out in a discharge tube. The intense ion currents employed in these experiments (of the order 5 mA/cm^2.) caused target temperatures to rise to between 300 and 500°C and this factor, together with the correction to allow for secondary electron emission which is not always applied, should be remembered when results are compared with those of other experimenters. Wehner and his co-workers have discovered that the sputtering yield follows closely the state of the electron concentrations in the 'd' shells and also bears some resemblance to the reciprocals of the heats of sublimation of the target materials. Figs. 7.4 (a-f) show the results for 400 eV He^+, Ne^+, A^+, Kr^+, Xe^+, and Hg^+ ions as a function of atomic number Fig. 7.5 shows the number of electrons in the outermost 'd' shells and the reciprocal of the heat of sublimation as a function of atomic number for comparison. In fact neither pattern follows the sputtering yield exactly; for example on the 'd' shell basis the first group V element with a full complement of ten electrons in its 'd' shell is palladium, but it is the following element in the table, silver, which exhibits the maximum sputtering yield. Also chromium deviates from this general trend having a sputtering yield which would be expected to occur with an element three places higher in the atomic table on a 'd' shell basis. However, apart from these two minor deviations, the 'd' shell pattern gives a consistent picture of the sputtering trend over all target materials. The reason for this relationship is considered to be connected with the ranges of ions (discussed in detail in Chapter 5) which are generally larger in targets with more open electronic structure. Here the ions penetrate to such depths that the transmission of energy back to the surface where sputtering occurs becomes less efficient. In the hard sphere type of atoms with filled 'd' shells ranges are relatively small and the damage sequence is much more readily projected back towards the target surface. The same general picture for sputtering yields has also been observed at higher ion energies by Almén and Bruce[38,39] who used an analyzed beam obtained from an electro-magnetic isotope separator. Their results for 45 keV krypton bombardment are included in Fig. 7.6

Although the trend of yield as a function of target material appears to be well established from the above discussion the reader should be aware of the fact that results for a given material can vary widely depending on its history. Fig. 7.3 indicates the large differences in yields observed by various workers for argon striking copper surfaces. Southern et al[27] have illustrated such discrepancies for yields from copper obtained from three different sources and ascribe the variation to different preferred crystal orientations on the nominally 'polycrystalline' surfaces. It is shown later that yields are critically dependent on the orientation of the crystalline structure in monocrystalline studies so that all sputtering values for polycrystalline targets must be treated as approximations and will lie between the maximum and minimum monocrystalline values. A few points from the results of Magnuson et al[40] for single crystal copper are included for on Fig. 7.3 for comparison and it is seen that the polycrystalline results all lie between Magnuson et al's (110) and (111) results.

With regard to the phase of the target material, that is whether it is liquid or solid, very little data exists in the literature. Wehner et al[41] have carried out experiments on solid and liquid tin and found that at argon energies of 200 eV the yield from the liquid state surface was 25% higher than the corresponding yield from solid tin whilst, at 400 eV, the yield from the solid surface was higher by about 5%. Wehner et al concluded that the lower energy difference may be due to the better smoothness of the liquid surface allowing a larger percentage of grazing-angle ejected atoms to actually escape, but no explanation is offered for the 400 eV results.

7.4.3 Variation of yield with ion species

Almén and Bruce[42] have carried out a thorough investigation of the variation of sputtering yield with type of ion at energies of the order of 45 keV and have presented yield curves as a function of ion atomic number which again show a periodic nature (Fig. 7.7). Yields increase fairly steadily within each group of elements reaching a maximum for the inert gas species of the group. The yield then falls almost to zero and the pattern of yield versus atomic number repeats itself almost exactly in the subsequent group. Rol et al[43] have carried out a similar thorough study at lower energies (5-25 keV), again using an electromagnetic isotope separator as their ion source. Fig. 7.8 shows a plot of the sputtering yield as a function of ion atomic number taken from their results and the trend is seen to be similar to that shown by Almén and Bruce, although the rather sparse data does not illustrate the periodic nature of the process.

Relatively few experiments have been done to determine the effect of molecular ion bombardment on sputtering yield. The main contribution has been presented by Bader et al[44] who showed that copper and nickel targets were sputtered to the same extent by one normally incident N_2^+ ion as by two atomic N^+ ions of half the energy (see Fig. 7.9). This is expected if sputtering is governed by a process of momentum transfer as discussed later. However this simple relation between atomic and molecular yields does not hold for normal ion incidence on iron, molybde-

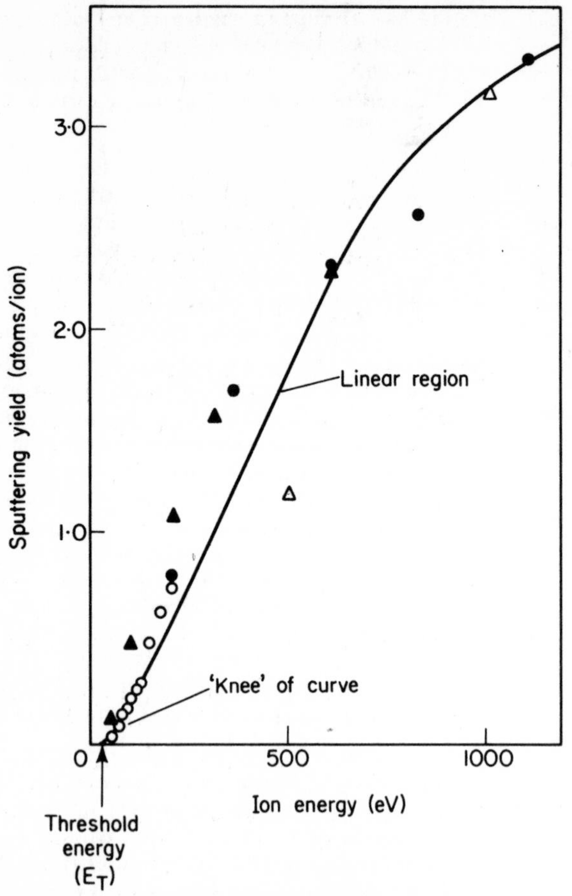

Fig. 7.2 Variation of sputtering yield with energy for argon ions bombarding copper (low energy region) ○ Henschke et al[191], ● Bader et al[44], ▲ Laegreid et al[36], △ Keywell[25]

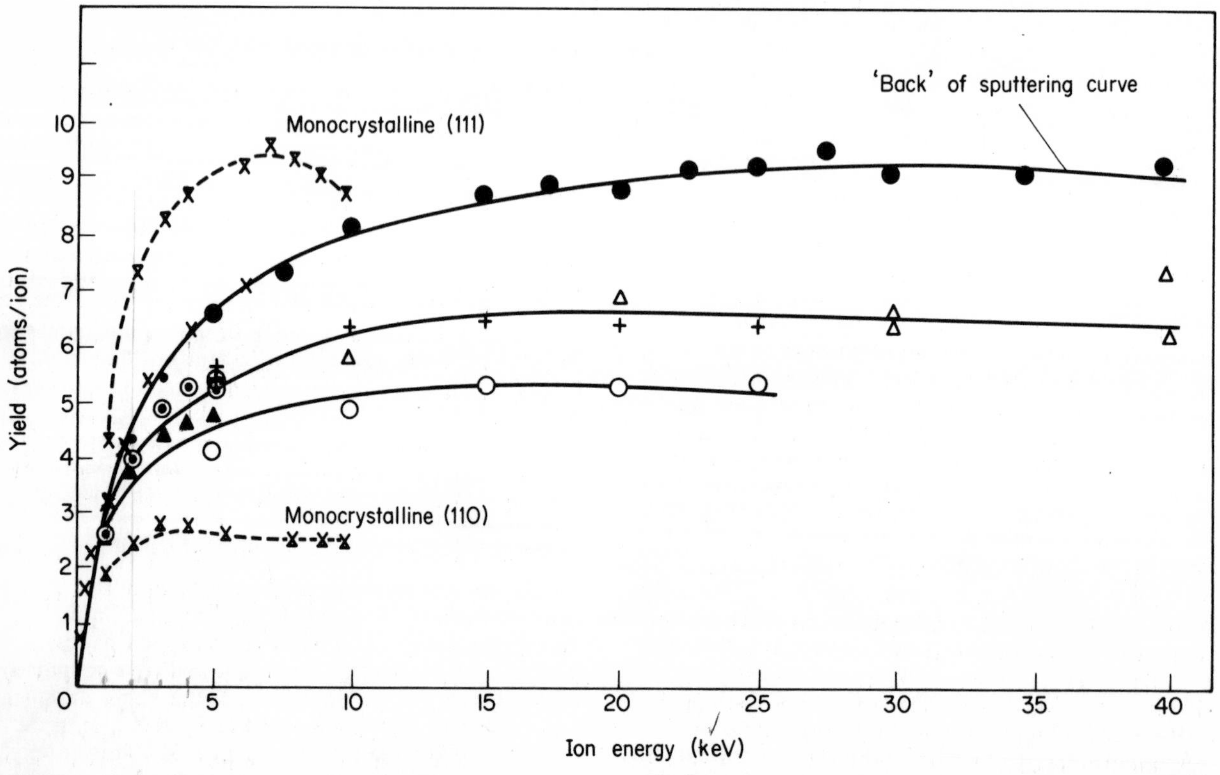

Fig. 7.3 Variation of sputtering yield with energy for argon ions bombarding copper (high energy region) + Rol et al[43]; ⊕ Keywell[25]; × Bader et al[44]; ● Yonts et al[181]; ○ Guseva[190]; • ◉ ▲ Southern et al[27] (three different samples of copper) ⊼ ⩞ Magnuson et al[40]; △ Almén et al[38]

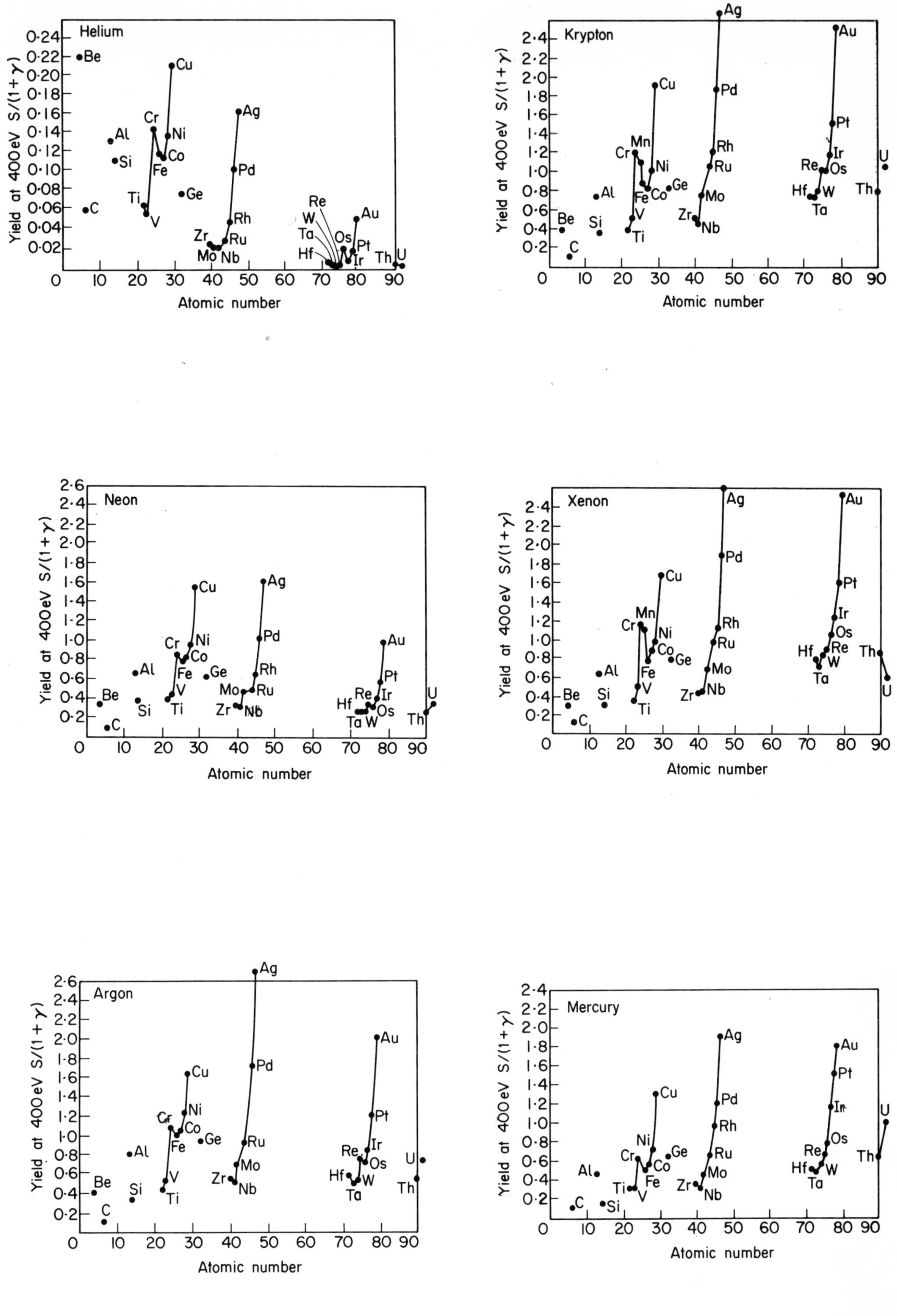

Fig. 7.4 Variation of sputtering yield with atomic number of the bombardment material for 400 eV noble gas and mercury ion bombardment (viz. Refs. 7.36 and 7.37)

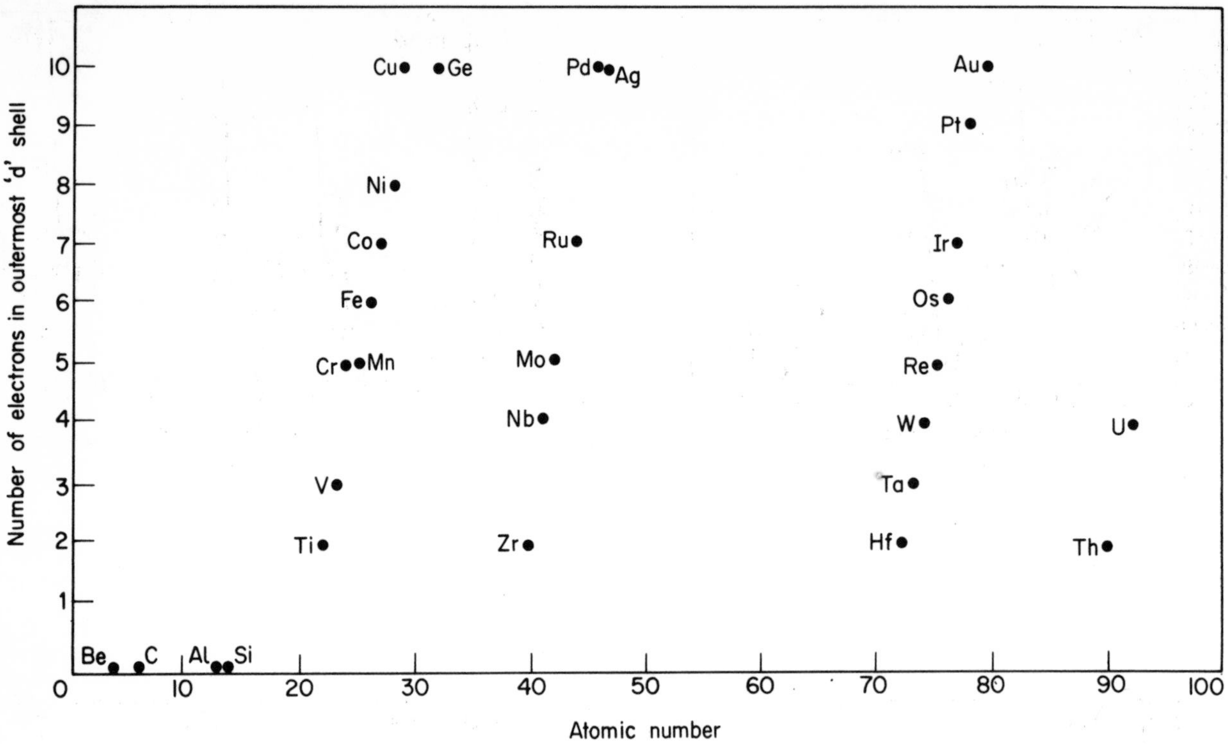

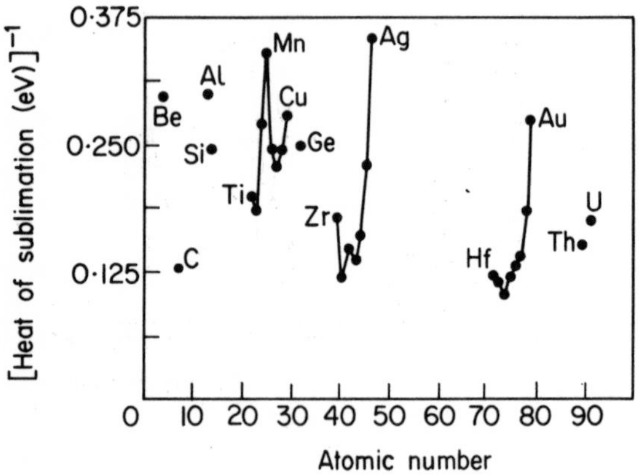

Fig. 7. 5(a) The number of electrons in the atomic 'd' shell as a function of the atomic number (b) The reciprocal of the heat of sublimation as a function of atomic number (viz. Ref. 7. 37)

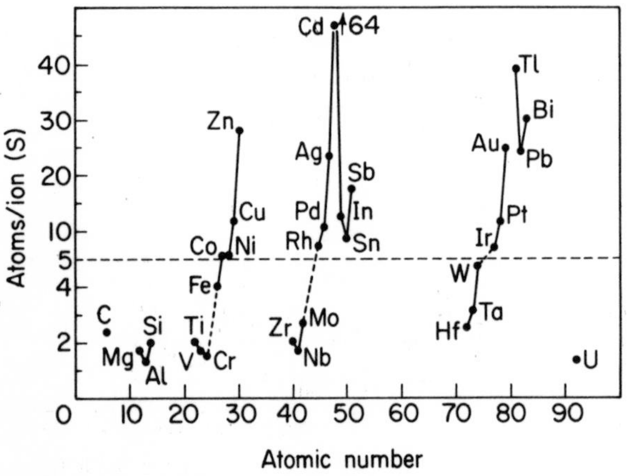

Fig. 7. 6 Variation of sputtering yield with atomic number of target for bombardment with 45 keV krypton ions (viz. Ref. 7. 39)

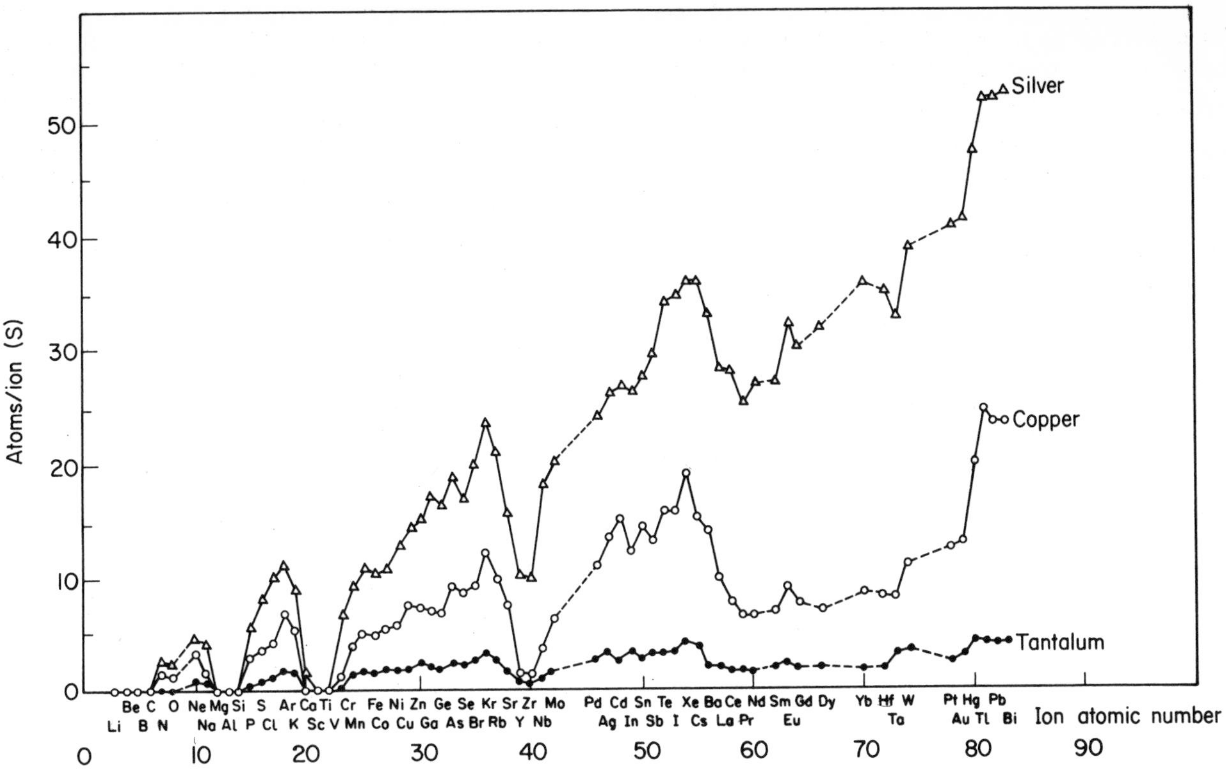

Fig. 7.7 Variation of sputtering yield with atomic number of the bombarding ion for 45 keV bombardment of copper, silver and tantalum targets. (viz. Ref. 7.42)

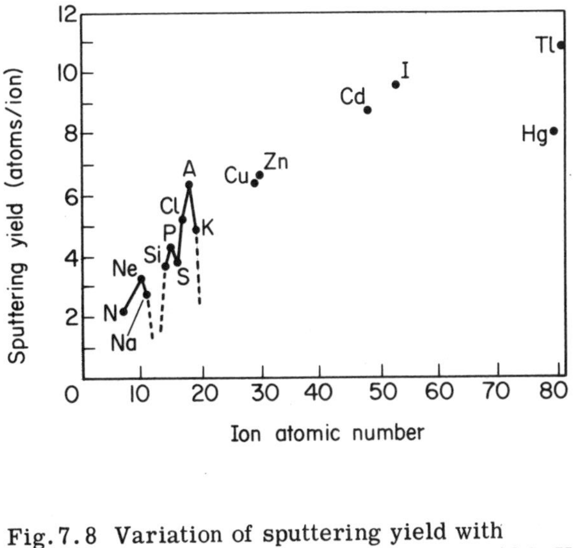

Fig. 7.8 Variation of sputtering yield with atomic number of the bombarding ion for 10 keV bombardment (viz. Ref. 7.43)

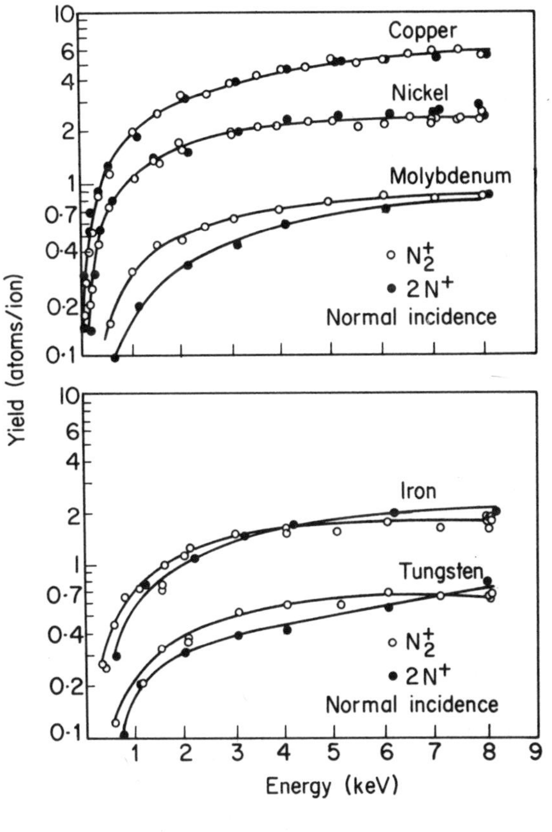

Fig. 7.9 Yield as a function of energy for bombardment by atomic and molecular nitrogen ions (viz. Ref. 7.44)

num, or tungsten, nor for 45° incidence on iron, molybdenum, nickel or copper and this cannot as yet be accounted for. Grønlund and Moore[45] found a similar situation for yields of atomic and molecular species of hydrogen isotopes, twice the atomic yield being less than the corresponding molecular yield except at higher energies (~12 keV) where these values approached each other.

7.4.4 Effect of ion charge on sputtering

A thorough investigation of the effect of ion charge on sputtering yields has not yet been carried out. Wolsky and Zdanuk[46] have obtained yields from silicon bombarded by single and double charged species at energies up to 800 eV and have found that yields for A^{++} at an energy E were four times those for A^+ at an energy 2E whereas they would be anticipated to be equal from pure momentum considerations. At ion energies of 10 keV however Weiss et al[47] found that yields for neutral species of H and He were larger than those for their singly ionized counterparts. Consequently no obvious trends in yields can be predicted, present data being merely sufficient to state that ion charge does appear to be an important parameter affecting sputtering.

7.5 BOMBARDMENT TIME

Ideally sputtering experiments should be carried out with one single ion fired at an undamaged clean target. In fact the bombarding ions penetrate into the target material where they disrupt the lattice and eventually, become trapped as discussed in Chapter 8. Consequently subsequent ions have to sputter a damaged surface and also must encounter the trapped ions so that sputtering yields can be very dependent on the number of ions which have struck the target previously. In certain experiments the target weight has even been found to increase with continued bombardment due to a build-up of sorbed ions having a sputtering yield themselves of less than unity. Almén and Bruce [39] found this effect for carbon ions striking silver, copper and tantalum targets; the target weights initially decreasing and then increasing again, reaching their original values when about 250 $\mu g/cm^2$ of C^+ ions had struck the target in the case of silver, and about 120 $\mu g/cm^2$ C^+ in the case of copper and tantalum. A similar situation was reported by McKeown et al[48] for 500 eV helium ion bombardment of aluminium targets where the target increased in mass by 12×10^{-9} gm due to sorption of helium during the first thirty minutes of the experiment. After this time the weight loss due to the sputtering mechanism predominated. For Ca^+ ions on silver Almén and Bruce found that the yield was large enough to make the initial weight loss continue though the effective yield was much lower than the initial sputter rate.

Apart from anomalous weight changes of targets it is anticipated that the presence of sorbed gas atoms will disrupt the atomic collision sequences which play an important part in the sputtering sequence and are discussed in detail in chapter 6. However, Nelson and Beevers[49] have investigated this problem experimentally by bombarding copper foils with argon ions at 60 keV, the targets being maintained at either 20°C, 350°C or 500°C. At the lowest temperature there was evidence of vacancy agglomeration and interstitial atoms whilst at 500°C there was clear evidence of bubble formation and a regular dislocation network. Similar results were obtained for He^+, A^+ and Xe^+ bombardments of silver, gold and aluminium targets. Consideration of the bubble density at the approximate depth of origin of the collision sequences responsible for sputtering showed that less than one percent of the foil area was affected. It thus appears from this work that the effect of sorbed bombarding atoms on the sputtering mechanism is negligible.

Fortunately the results of most practical interest are those obtained during extended bombardment so that the impossible task of obtaining a yield value allowing oneself a solitary ion and an undamaged target can be set aside. However, when theoretical considerations are undertaken it should be remembered that the calculated yields will not necessarily agree with those obtained in practice.

7.6 ANGULAR DEPENDENCE OF SPUTTERING

The first indication that sputtering was influenced by the incident angle of the bombarding ions was seen in an experiment of Fetz[19] who found that thin wires sputtered more rapidly than wires of larger diameter due to the larger percentage of oblique collisions. Wehner has also demonstrated the effect in a discharge tube[50] by immersing spherical targets in the plasma and observing their change of shape after prolonged bombardment. Typical examples obtained by Wehner for sputtering of iron, nickel and tantalum by mercury ions are illustrated in Fig. 7.10, the grey shadow indicating the original spherical shape. The parallel beam of mercury ions strike the leading edge normally and at varying angles along the spherical surface. If the sputtering process for the ion-metal combination is more efficient at a certain incident angle α a conical surface with half-angle α is produced and this surface then continues receding without further change in profile as the bombardment continues. Figs. 7.10 (a) and (b) show the surface states

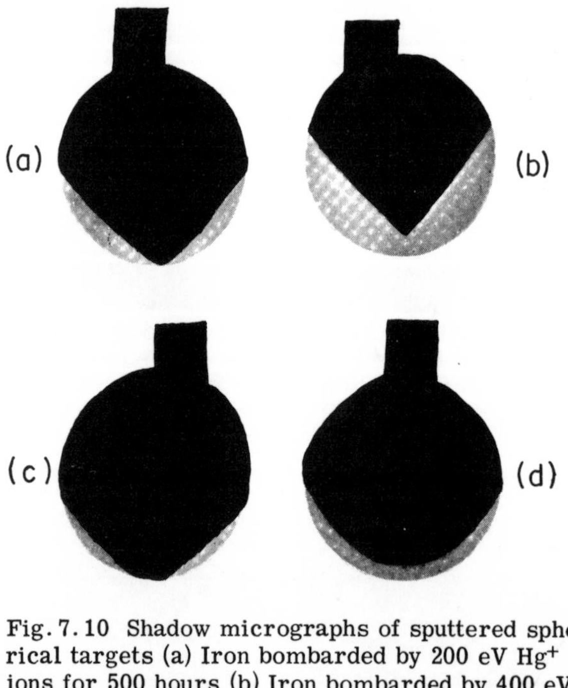

Fig. 7.10 Shadow micrographs of sputtered spherical targets (a) Iron bombarded by 200 eV Hg^+ ions for 500 hours (b) Iron bombarded by 400 eV Hg^+ ions for 168 hours (c) Tantalum bombarded by 200 eV Hg^+ ions for 500 hours (d) Nickel bombarded by 400 eV Hg^+ ions for 168 hours (viz. Ref. 7.50)

for Hg^+ ions on an iron target, where the angular dependence is fairly important. According to Wehner, for mercury bombardment, the yield is also strongly dependent on the incident angle for tantalum and molybdenum, of less importance for tungsten and nickel and almost negligible for gold, silver, copper and platinum. In experiments of short duration, where the incident angles presented to the beam did not have time to change appreciably, Wehner was able to evaluate the yield at each angle from the single shadow-micrograph. Results for 200 eV mercury bombardment of tungsten, nickel, molybdenum and platinum are presented in Fig. 7.11. Although the ion beam in

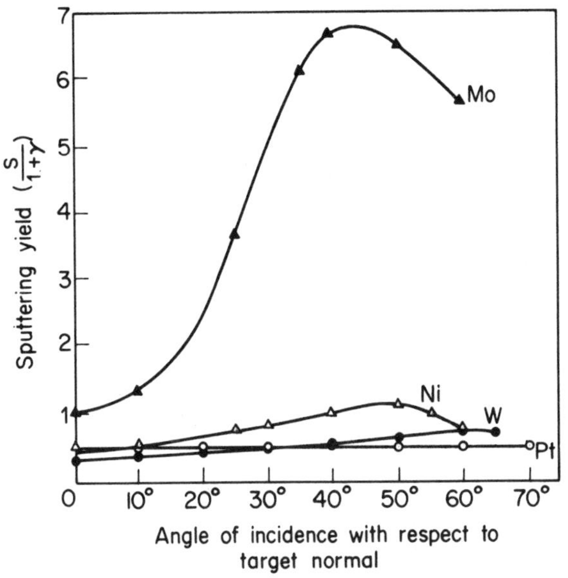

Fig. 7.11 Variation of sputtering yield with angle of incidence for 200 eV mercury ion bombardment of nickel, molybdenum, tungsten and platinum (viz. Ref. 7.50)

the above experiment was essentially uniform it is likely that the current density decreased toward the edges of the spheres; values of the yield for more oblique incidence may therefore be on the low side.

Rol et al[43] have investigated the dependence of the yield on the angle of incidence for Tl^+ — Cu and A^+ — Cu combinations at 20 keV and observe a similar trend to Wehner for angles with respect to normal of up to 50°. For N^+ — Cu at 5 keV Rol et al find that the ratio of the yield at normal incidence to that at 50° is 0.57, whilst Bader et al[51], again for N^+ — Cu at 5 keV, observe a ratio of 0.76 for normal to 45° yields. Again, for N_2^+, the former observe a ratio of 0.74, whilst Bader et al find 0.77. Only a rough agreement is to be expected, but the general trend is apparent: In Rol's work, where N^+, N_2^+, Si^+, A^+, and Tl^+ ions were used to sputter copper, the yield at 50° was greater than the normal value in all cases, likewise in Bader's work, which included studies of N^+ — Ni, N_2^+ — Ni, N^+ — Cu, N_2^+ — Cu, N^+ — Fe, N_2^+ — Fe, N^+ — Mo, N_2^+ — Mo and N^+ — W, N_2^+ — W, yields were again always larger at 45° incident angle than for normal bombardments. At higher energies (20-60 keV) Almén and Bruce[38] found that the yield was proportional to $\sec^{3/2}\theta$ (where θ is the angle of incidence with respect to the target normal) for krypton and neon ions bombarding several metal targets whilst, at even higher energies (60 and 110 keV), Ramer et al[52] have found the yield proportional to $\sec^2\theta$ for argon bombardment of copper and silver targets. It appears therefore that the angular dependence of yield changes with the energy regions under study. However, the fact that there is an angular dependence is not surprising when it is remembered that an incident ion has, in some way, to impart an impulsive force with a component in an outward direction from the surface to cause sputtering so that its task must become easier at angles of attack away from 90°. Another confirmation of this general rule is provided by Molchanov and Tel'kovskii[53] who have found that the relation;

$$S_\theta = \frac{S_0}{\cos\theta} \qquad 7.1$$

where S_0 is the yield at normal incidence, holds for 25 keV A^+ — Cu bombardment at angles near normal incidence. What is surprising however is the fact that a maximum yield is reached at incident angles of 40-80° after which yields decrease. Cheney and Pitkin[54] have studied the angular dependence of yields for xenon bombardment of copper, molybdenum and tungsten at energies up to 30 keV and have shown that the yield increases to a fairly sharp maximum at angles of incidence between 75° and 80°, the position of the maximum depending on the material and bombarding energy. The surface roughness was shown to be an important factor in determining the optimum sputtering angle; mechanically polished copper having a maximum yield at 80° whilst an electrolytically polished target of the same material had an optimum yield at 75°. Cheney et al suggested that the extra roughness of the mechanically polished surfaces gives the target a larger probability of absorbing the energy of the near grazing particle both as it approaches and as it leaves the surface.

7.7 THRESHOLD ENERGIES

The threshold energy of a given ion-solid combination may be defined as that ion energy below which no sputtering occurs (see Fig. 7.2). Clearly the determination of threshold values represents one of the most difficult tasks in surface studies as it is necessary to design an apparatus which measures zero sputtering! The problem is made worse by the apparent trend of yields which approach zero tangentially as the energy decreases. Obviously the observed threshold energy is going to depend primarily on the sensitivity of the apparatus to a sputter event. At best, one can measure a set of yields for energies approaching zero and extrapolate for the desired threshold value. However it is clear that, even then, threshold values are dubious and are critically dependent upon the previous history of the target material. Henschke[35] has gone so far as to define two threshold energies for any ion-solid combination: the 'full-plane' threshold, where energy is required to eject an atom from a completed crystal plane, and the 'minimum-bond' threshold, where energy is required to release an atom which is isolated and lies above a full plane of target atoms. Henschke further observes that the full-plane threshold would be registered in an experiment where sputtering is continued over a long period and the yield calculated from the build-up in sputtered deposits. If, on the other hand, the ions arrived at the surface with energies equivalent to the minimum-bond threshold, sputtering would again occur, but only for a short time until all the isolated atoms were released. Thus the more sensitive methods are expected to indicate minimum-bond thresholds whilst the older 'deposit' methods will give higher valued full-plane thresholds. Henschke has assumed that, if his hypothesis is true, the ratio of the two threshold energies discussed above should equal the ratio of the binding energies of an atom in a minimum-bond to one in a full-plane location, respectively, and has found reasonable agreement where results are available. The calculated ratios are of the order 1.85 and 2.14 for polycrystalline body-centred cubic and face-centred cubic targets, respectively, whilst the ratio of sputtering thresholds obtained from Wehner et al[31,55] are of the order 2.7. The discrepancy is explained by Henschke as due to an experimental shortcoming in obtaining the minimum-bond thresholds. He considers that the ion beam may contain doubly charged ions in sufficient number to make the measured threshold lower than the real value and also expresses a doubt as to whether all the ions strike normal to the surface; non normal sputtering being more efficient as discussed in the previous section.

Having warned the reader of the uncertainties associated with threshold energy studies we will now discuss some of the ingenious experimental techniques which have been devised to determine this quantity. It should be mentioned that these threshold energies are of special interest in connection with theories of radiation damage events and sputtering of satellites, the threshold energy regime representing relative speeds of order 10^6 cm./sec. which are equivalent to orbital satellite speeds at heights of about 200 km.

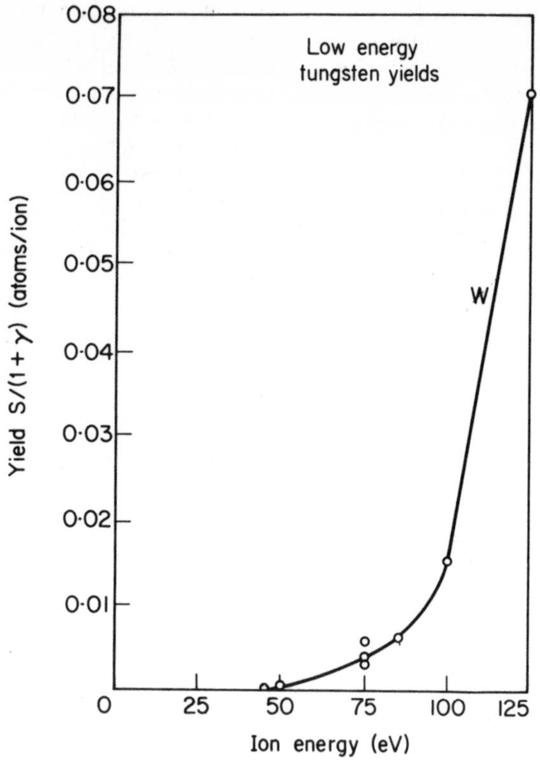

Fig. 7.12 Sputtering yield of tungsten at near-threshold energies for mercury bombardment (viz. Ref. 7.34)

Wehner[34] devised a method of extending the sensitivity of his sputtering apparatus which was dependent on the transmission of light through the sputtered deposit. Sputtered atoms were collimated onto a glass ribbon and light transmitted from a tungsten filament through the ribbon was monitored by a densichron light-intensity meter. The technique employed was to observe changes in densichron reading every five seconds and relate the maximum slope of the absorption-time curve so obtained to the yield. Yields obtained by this method were relative, but could be calibrated by comparing them with the direct weight-loss technique at higher energies. The principal disadvantages of the method were that it relied on all deposits striking the window sticking to the surface and also, for deposits such as tantalum and thorium which oxidized quickly to a more transparent film, errors could not be avoided. However, with this refinement, the discharge apparatus of Wehner could detect yields at much lower ion energies. In the case of tungsten bombarded by mercury ions a curve for yields at energies down to just below 50 eV was obtained and indicates the tangential approach to zero (Fig. 7.12).

A very sensitive microbalance method has been devised by Wolsky et al[46, 56-59]. This was capable of detecting weight changes of the order 0.13×10^{-9} Kgm. In the earlier work results were obtained for sputtering of silicon by argon ions and indicated a threshold value, by extrapolation, of 15-20 eV, the lowest yield actually recorded being taken at 35 eV. However, in later work, Wolsky et al[60, 61, 62] were able to improve the balance sensitivity so that weight changes of the order 5×10^{-11} Kgm could be detected Yields for A^+ ions striking (100) and (111) faces of monocrystalline copper and the (111) face of aluminium were obtained for energies down to 20 eV where sputtering was still measurable. The threshold energies for the above targets must therefore be lower than 20 eV but, owing to scatter in results, the actual values were not extrapolated. The scatter in results was of the order ±40% in some cases which, Wolsky et al suggest, represents a real variation in yield due to ion damage to the surfaces.

Scott[33] has refined the resistance-change method of Fetz[19] and adapted it to measure the low energy yields of a gold film under noble gas bombardment. In this experiment the discharge was produced between a central oxide cathode and a concentric anode cylinder and the gold film target, of dimensions 0.7 cm. wide by 2 cm. long, was located between these two electrodes. Resistances were measured with a Wheatstone bridge and were usually allowed to change by about 10-20 percent before switching off the ion beam. Results are slightly dubious because of the uncertainties in the ion species, ion energy and incident angle. An interesting outcome of this experiment was however that it indicated a linear dependence of the neon sputtering yield on the current density, an effect which cannot in this instance be explained by surface contamination. This effect may be due to chance variations in energy, angle of incidence or even ion species which accompany the necessary adjustments required to increase or decrease the target current. Scott suggests that the phenomenon indicates that there is a two stage ejection process: first, production of defects by the ions and second, liberation of atoms from the defect regions by subsequent ions. However he is not entirely satisfied with this argument and an alternative explanation may be that the target reaches a higher temperature with higher bombardment densities and therefore defects will be more likely to anneal out. This means that collision sequences (which are seen to play a very important role in the sputtering process in later sections) are able to propagate more efficiently, the overall effect being an increase in the yield, as observed.

One of the lowest threshold values presented in the literature to date was determined by using a radioactive tracer in the target material and making a radio count of the deposit. This experiment, carried out by Morgulis and Tischenko[29] produced a result of 8 eV for argon bombarding a nickel target with a one percent cobalt-60 tracer. In later work[30] these authors have carried out a more thorough study of threshold energies for A^+ and He^+ bombardment of Co, Zn, Zr, Ag, Sb, Ta, W, Ir and Tl, using the radioactive isotopes of each metal for determinations of the quantity of material sputtered. Fig. 7.13 shows

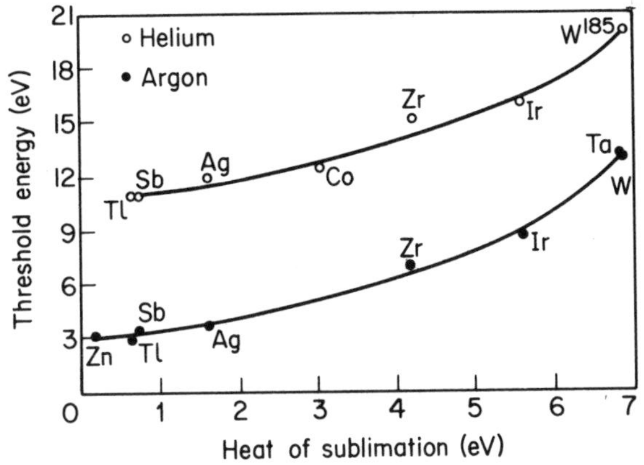

Fig. 7.13 Showing threshold energy as a function of the heat of sublimation of the target material for helium and argon ion bombardment (viz. Ref. 7.30)

the variation of the threshold energies (E_T) with the heat of sublimation (Q) of the target material and clearly indicates a smooth monotonically increasing function which is dependent upon the ion mass, but not, apparently, on the target mass. The authors demonstrate that neither the variation of the energy transfer factor $4M_1M_2/(M_1 + M_2)^2$ nor the effective accommodation coefficient $\alpha = Q/E_T$ with target mass have similar trends to the threshold energy variation and conclude that the neutralization energy (i.e. potential energy) of the ion may be an important factor in the ejection process.

Stuart and Wehner[31,31a] have devised an ingenious spectroscopic method of observing yields in their discharge apparatus. A monochromator and photomultiplier system is tuned to detect a strong emission line of the target material. When sputtering occurs the sputtered target atom is excited due to the intense discharge conditions and a plot of spectral line intensity against ion energy can be related to yield curves obtained by weight-loss methods at higher energies. The method is capable of observing yields down to 10^{-4} atoms/ion and indicates that the yields do not fall off as slowly with energy as has been previously anticipated. Results for noble gases obtained by Stuart et al[31,31a,63] by this method are illustrated in Fig. 7.14. Threshold values obtained when multiplied by the energy transfer factor (which, for an ion mass M_1 and target mass M_2, is defined by $T = 4M_1M_2/(M_1 + M_2)^2$) are noted by Stuart and

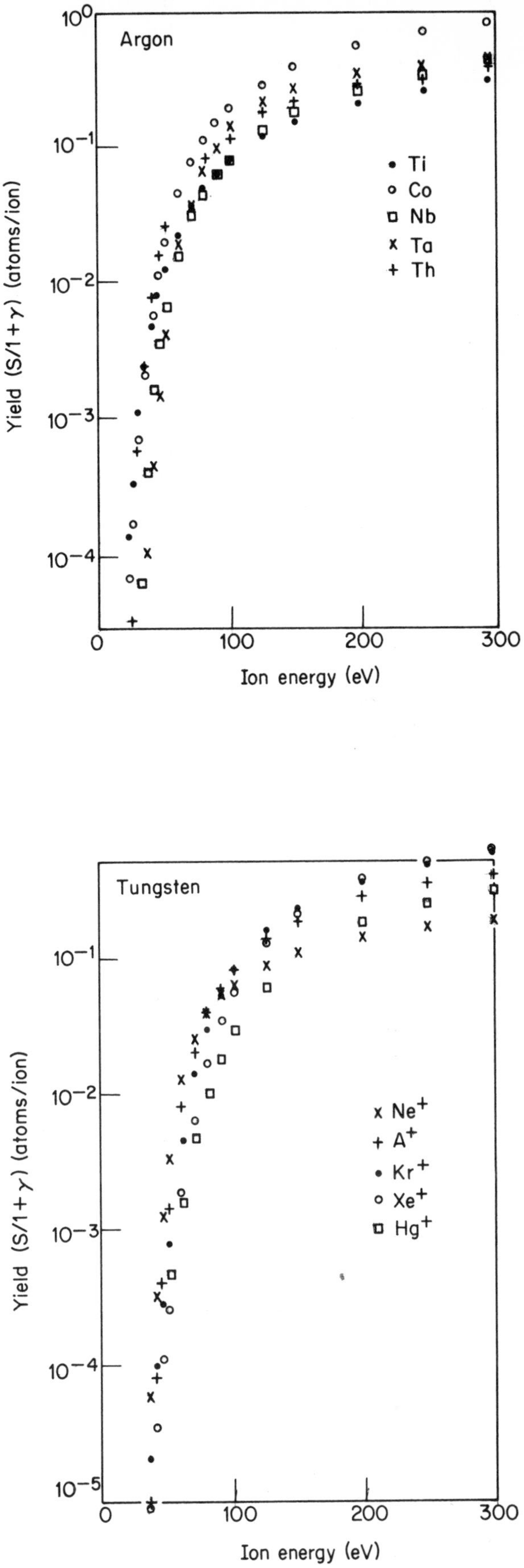

Fig. 7.14(a) Yield-energy curves for various metals at energies near threshold for argon ion bombardment (b) Yield-energy curves for tungsten bombarded by Ne^+, A^+, Kr^+, Xe^+, and Hg^+ ions at energies near threshold (viz. Ref. 7.31a)

Wehner to yield values near 25 eV, which is the energy generally associated with the displacement threshold for radiation damage.[64]

One shortcoming of the spectral line detection method arises in that the line intensity is a function of the velocity of the sputtered atom. At lower bombarding energies one would expect that liberated atoms would have lower velocities and therefore the yields would appear to be too high. Kreye[65] has demonstrated that the excitation probability does not itself depend on the atom velocity, but the time of residence of the atom in the observed region will of course still be velocity dependent so that results will vary with ejection velocity. Kreye has observed both the emission from sputtered gold atoms which have been excited in the discharge and the resonance absorption of 2676 Å radiation by neutral sputtered gold atoms. Both emission and absorption were seen to be related to the concentration of sputtered atoms above the target so that relative yields could be deduced by both techniques. Curves showing relative yield as a function of energy for absorption and emission were shown to be identical except for a constant scaling factor and, by extrapolation to zero yield, thresholds for A^+ bombardment of a (110) gold target were indicated to be 17 eV.

Results obtained by Medved and Poppa[66] indicate that yields for the thin films which they investigated are lower than yields obtained by Wehner et al on bulk metals. The method employed was to monitor the film thickness by electron attenuation and scattering techniques in an electron microscope. A sensitivity of 10^{-14} gm is claimed by the authors for this method and results for A^+, Kr^+, and Ne^+ bombardment of silver indicate threshold energies in the region of 20-30 eV.

A most interesting and successful piece of apparatus has been employed by McKeown[32] to measure sputtering of gold films at low energies. The technique employed is to construct an electronic oscillator incorporating a 10 Mc/s plated, optically polished, AT-cut, quartz crystal. The frequency of the oscillator is critically dependent on the resonating mass of the crystal, including its plating, so that a slight change in the mass of the latter can be detected electronically. McKeown used a Finkelstein type of ion source[67] which has a large energy spread and does not mass

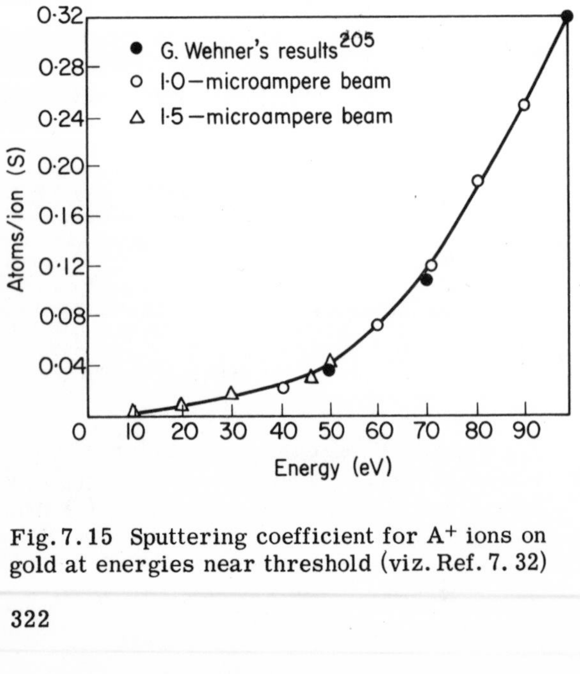

Fig. 7.15 Sputtering coefficient for A^+ ions on gold at energies near threshold (viz. Ref. 7.32)

analyze the incident beam. No correction has been made to results for secondary emission, but neutral beam effects have been subtracted and leave a yield curve of the form indicated in Fig. 7.15 for argon on gold.

7.8 SPUTTERING AT HIGHER ENERGIES

Once ion energies reach values well away from the thresholds yields begin to rise quite sharply and are less difficult to measure. The form of the yield-energy curve, which has already been discussed, is illustrated in Figs. 7.2 and 7.3 and, as most experimental techniques revolve around the basic discharge or ion beam method, little more need be done than to compile tables showing yields where available at 0.5 keV, 1.0 keV and 10 keV so that the reader merely interested in magnitudes of the phenomenon may readily extract the information required. As discussed earlier the yields can vary by a factor of as much as five depending on the preferred orientation of the particular polycrystalline target under consideration so that sputtering yields presented in these tables cannot be used for accurate calculations. Tables 7.1 to 7.3 present this data and contain readings for normal incidence which are not adjusted for secondary electron emission. Values quoted are therefore $S/(1 + \gamma)$ and will be slightly low. (γ is the secondary electron emission coefficient defined in chapter 3).

7.9 SPUTTERING OF ALLOYS

Little work has been done in this field; the most important contributions being presented by Gillam[68], Ogilvie and Thompson[69] and Wehner[70]. Gillam studied 0-5 keV noble gas bombardment of Cu_3Au and Ag-Pd combinations. Diffraction patterns were observed after bombardment and indicated that the composition of the first several atomic layers had been changed. Initially Cu_3Au became more gold-rich near its surface, but subsequent bombardment eroded three times as much copper as gold whilst the gold diffused into the bulk metal. It was discovered that the higher the ion energy, the lower the Au concentration in the altered surface layer; 68% Au at 30 eV and 45% Au at 3 keV for argon bombardment. Further it was found that the layer of altered composition was thicker for light ions (He^+; 40-80 Å) than for heavy ions (Xe^+; 30-40 Å). In his studies of Ag-Pd alloys of varying compositions Gillam found rather surprisingly that, for alloys containing small atomic percentages, of Pd, no altered surface layer was observable, whilst, for concentrations of Pd somewhere between 40 and 70 atomic percent, the sputtering mechanism changed and an altered layer deficient in Pd began to form. For alloys with 95% Pd the altered layer composition was drastically changed to 13% Pd.

Other investigations appear to have been conducted in rather high pressure discharges where yields may not have been reproducible. Asada and Quasebarth[71] observed an opposite situation to Gillam for an alloy of copper with a small percent of gold. Here the target was found to be richer in copper after bombardment by Hg^+ and H_2O^+ ions. Hanau[72] showed that yields for 99.99% pure aluminium were lower than those for a less pure sample which contained 4% Cu, 0.5% Mg and 0.5% Mn. He proposed that the extra yield would be due to greater sputtering of the impurity species, but on further investigation found that the sputtered deposits were not excessively rich in these deposits. Fisher and Weber[73] also concluded

TABLE 7.1

Sputtering yields at 500 eV ion energy

Target	H_2	He	Ne	N_2	K	A	Kr	Xe	Hg
Be 9.02		0.24	0.42			0.51	0.48	0.35	—
C 12.010		0.07	—			0.12	0.13	0.17	0.16
Al 26.97		0.16	0.73			1.05	0.96	0.82	0.57
Si 28.06		0.13	0.48			0.50	0.50	0.42	0.18
Ti 47.9		0.07	0.43†			0.51	0.48	0.43	0.38
V 50.95		0.06	0.48			0.65	0.62	0.63	0.39
Cr 52.01		0.17	0.99			1.18	1.39	1.55	—
Mn 54.93		—	—			—	1.39	1.43	—
Fe 55.84		0.15	0.88 0.63[18]			1.10 0.84[18]	1.07 0.77[18]	1.00 0.88[18]	0.66
Co 58.94		0.13	0.90			1.22	1.08	1.08	0.78
Ni 58.69		0.16	1.10 0.99[18]		1.1[201]	1.45 1.33[18]	1.30 1.06[18]	1.22 1.22[18]	0.89
Cu 63.57		0.24	1.80 2.1*[193] 1.35[18]			2.35 1.2[25] 2.0[18]	2.35 2.50*[193] 1.91[18]	2.05 1.91[18] 3.9*[193] 1.55[25]	1.70
Zn 65.38		—	—			—	—	—	—
Ga 69.72		—	—			—	—	—	1.47
Ge 72.6		0.08	0.68†			1.1†	1.12	1.04	0.76
Y 88.9		0.05	0.46			0.68	0.66	0.48	—
Zr 91.22		0.02	0.38			0.65	0.51	0.58	0.48
Nb 92.91		0.03	0.33			0.60	0.55	0.53	0.42
Mo 95.95		0.03	0.48 0.24[18]			0.80 0.64[18]	0.87 0.59[18]	0.87 0.72[18]	0.63
Rb 85.48		—	0.57			1.15	1.27	1.20	0.83
Rh 102.9		0.06	0.70			1.30	1.43	1.38	1.25
Pd 106.7		0.13	1.15			2.08	2.22	2.23	1.53
Ag 107.88	0.6[15]	0.20 1.0[25]	1.77 1.70[25] 1.80[15]	1.4[15]		3.12 2.4[25] 2.3[15] 3.06[203]	3.27 3.1[25]	3.32	2.54
Sm 150.43		0.05	0.69			0.80	1.09	1.28	—
Gd 156.9		0.03	0.48			0.83	1.12	1.20	—
Dy 162.46		0.03	0.55			0.88	1.15	1.29	—
Er 167.2		0.03	0.52			0.77	0.07	0.07	—
Hf 178.6		0.01	0.32			0.70	0.80	—	0.68
Ta 180.88		0.01	0.28			0.57	0.87	0.88	0.58
W 183.92		0.01	0.28			0.57	0.91	1.01	0.80
Re 186.31		0.01†	0.37			0.87	1.25	—	0.89
Os 190.2		0.01	0.37			0.87	1.27	1.33	0.95
Ir 193.1		0.01	0.43			1.01	1.35	1.56	1.51
Pt 195.23		0.03	0.63		0.3[201]	1.40	1.82	1.93	2.04
Au 197.2		0.07 0.10[200]	1.08 1.3[200]			2.40 2.5[200]	3.06	3.01 7.7[200]	2.42
Pb 207.21		— 1.1[25]	— —			— 2.7[25]	—	—	—
Th 232.12		0.00	0.28			0.62	0.96	1.05	0.82
U 238.07		—	0.45			0.85	1.30	0.81	1.28
PbTe (111)						1.4[203]			
GaAs (110)						0.9[203]			
GaP (111)						0.95[203]			
CdS (10$\bar{1}$0)						1.12[203]			
SiC (0001)						0.41[203]			
InSb (unknown orientation						0.55[203]			

† indicates an extrapolated value

* indicates the value for a (111) monocrystalline surface

values without reference numbers are from Wehner[192]

TABLE 7.2

Sputtering yields at 1 keV ion energy

	He	N	Ne		N_2	A				Kr			Xe	
Fe		0.55[44]	0.85[18]		0.78[44]	1.33[18]				1.42[18]			1.82[18]	
Ni		0.7[44]	1.22[18]		1.05[44]	2.21[18]	2.0[193]			1.76[18]	2.0[193]		2.26[18]	1.8[193]
Cu		1.5[44]	1.88[18]	2.75*[193]	1.95[194]	2.85[18]	3.2[25]	3.2[16]	4.5*[193]	3.42[18]	2.5[25]	4.65*[193]	3.6[18]	6.05*[193]
Mo		0.16[44]	0.49[18]		0.3[44]	1.13[18]				1.27[18]			1.60[18]	
Ag	1.8[25]		2.4[25]			3.8[25]				4.7[25]				
Sn						0.8[96]								
W		0.18[44]			0.2[44]									
Au	0.3†[200]		2.1†[200]			1.0[96]	4.9†[200]							
Pb	1.5[25]					3.0[25]								
UO_2			0.38[204]							0.66[204]			0.96[204]	

* indicates the value for a (111) monocrystalline surface

† indicates extrapolated value

TABLE 7.3

Sputtering yields at 10 keV ion energy

	H	H_2	H_3	D	D_2	D_3	He	N	Ne	Na	K	A	Cu	Kr	Ag	Xe	Cs	Hg
C																	1.97[138]	
Ti																	2.83[138]	2.7[195]
Fe												1.0[96]					4.21[138]	4.5[195]
Ni																	3.11[138]	7.2[195]
Cu				0.047[181]				2.1[43]	3.2[43]	2.7[43]	4.7[43]	{8.0[181] 6.25[43]}	6.4[43]					8.1[43]
"									3.1[39]			6.0[39]	5.5†[39]	8.0[39]		10.2[39]		12.0[195]
"												4.8[190]	9.2[190]	8.0[190]		9.3[190]		
Nb																	1.79[138]	
Mo																	1.14[138]	5.0[195]
Ag	0.03[45]	0.07[45]	0.11[45]	0.08[45]	0.17[45]	0.28[45]	0.40[45]					10.4[190]		14.8[190]	{16.4[190] 15.0†[39]}	15.9[190]		22.5[195]
Sn												2.1[96]						
Ta																	1.43[138]	3.2[195]
W																	1.60[138]	2.8[195]
Re																	1.07[138]	
Pt																	2.29[138]	9.9[195]
Au									3.7[39]			{8.8[39] 8.2[96]}		14.6[39]		20.3[39]		20.8[195]
NaCl												1.0[196]						
KCl												1.95[196]						
LiF												2.15[196]						
KBr												0.6[196]						
UO_2									0.9[204]					2.4[204]		3.5[204]		

† indicates an extrapolated value

that the sputtered material both from a stainless steel containing Fe, Ni, Cr and Nb and from 70-30 brass had a composition identical to the original target composition.

Wehner[70] studied yields of nickel base alloys, aluminium alloys and some steels under 0.1-0.5 keV Hg^+ bombardment and found, in general, that the yields were in accordance with yields of their component elements.

From the above data very little can be concluded. It is evident that in certain cases there is an initial 'settling-down' period for the target surface composition, but, after this, most evidence indicates steady-state conditions where the sputtered deposit is identical to the original alloy.

Further indication that the composition of a sputtered deposit is similar to that of the bombarded material is given by Wolsky et al[74] who collected sputtered films during bombardment of (111) faces of GaSb and found that they comprised very fine grained GaSb with slight enrichment in Ga. The enrichment in Ga is unexpected, but Wolsky et al propose that it may reflect an enrichment in the bombarded material which is known to exist when GaSb crystals are grown by conventional techniques. Further work by Haneman[75] showed that for bombardment of InSb the sputtered films retained the exact stoichiometric ratio of InSb and there was no preferential sputtering of either component.

7.10 SPUTTERING OF INSULATORS

Although glass is one of the main materials enclosing vacuum systems and valves, surprisingly little sputtering data is available for this substance. Akishin et al[76] have successfully devised an apparatus for experiments in which Kr^{84} ions bombarded mica, fused quartz and glass targets. Positive charge accumulating on the insulator surfaces was neutralised by an electron beam and the yields were obtained by a weight-loss technique accurate to 5×10^{-5} gm. For quartz, yields increased from 1 mol/ion at 5 keV to 2 mol/ion at 10 keV and then remained constant over the range of energies covered (up to 25 keV). Yields for mica were constant from 10 to 30 keV at a value of approximately 0.17 mol/ion whilst, for glass, the yield increased in the range 8-15 keV and then remained constant up to 25 keV. In the latter case the yield is quoted in atomic mass units per ion and varies from about 65 at 8 keV to 135 at saturation.

Anderson et al[77] have devised a high frequency method of sputtering dielectrics in their discharge tube and have been able to perform sputtering experiments on quartz, sapphire and diamond at energies of about 1 keV but no yield data have yet been published. However Jorgenson and Wehner[78] have devised another technique employing a Langmuir probe in a thermionically supported discharge. The current-voltage characteristic of the Langmuir probe was found to be extremely sensitive to deposits on the probe surface so that, by depositing a known amount of quartz by r.f. sputtering onto the surface and observing the time required for the I-V characteristic to return to its 'clean-probe' form for different bombarding energies, a set of yield vs energy data for the quartz was obtained in the region 20-100 eV. Yields as low as 10^{-5} molecules per ion were detectable by this method and a threshold energy of 16 eV is predicted by extrapolation of the curve. The yield at 100 eV was of the order 0.1 molecules/ion and the authors suggest that preliminary work on Pyrex 7740 indicated similar yields. It should be noted however that the rf sputtering did not transfer true quartz (SiO_2) to the Langmuir probe but $SiO_{1.6}$ so that yields will be slightly in error. However the technique is interesting and should be applicable to many more insulators.

A study of the composition of the sputtered components of silicon carbide has been presented by Honig.[79] He has found that, not only are neutral species of Si and C produced, but also there is some evidence for sputtering of SiC and SiC_2, though the former species is masked by the presence of the bombarding argon ion. There are, in addition, sputtered particles characteristic of adsorbed impurities as well as ionic components.

7.11 CONCERNING MATERIAL SPUTTERED

7.11.1 Ejection velocities of sputtered atoms

Determination of sputtered atom energies are of extreme importance as the results will assist a theoretical interpretation of the sputtering sequence. In 1939 Sporn[80] noted that magnesium cathodes in an oxygen discharge became covered with a thin luminous layer due to the ejection of excited magnesium atoms. From the known lifetimes of these excited states and the observed layer thickness he was able to estimate the average ejection energy of the atoms and obtained a value of about 7 eV.

Wehner[81] has allowed sputtered particles to travel against gravity onto a quartz pan which was supported on a spring balance. The impulsive forces on the pan due to the sputtered atoms coming to rest caused the pan to rise initially, but, due to the increased weight of the pan as more atoms stuck to it, it eventually returned to its original position. By observing the time required to return to this null position Wehner has been able to calculate average ejection velocities of atoms sputtered from nickel, tungsten and platinum polycrystalline, and gold (110) single-crystal, surfaces and found values of 6.5×10^5 cm/sec. (12.7 eV), 3.5×10^5 cm/sec. (12 eV), 4×10^5 cm/sec. (16 eV) and 3×10^5 cm/sec. (9 eV), respectively. Velocities of a sample of sputtered tungsten atoms ejected at 30° to the target normal were higher than the velocities of atoms ejected normally (5.5×10^5 cm/sec. (28 eV)).

In another set of experiments Wehner[82] has used a vane supported on a fine fibre and, from deflections of this vane, obtained values of the average ejection velocities of atoms of 22 metals as a function of the incident Hg^+ ion energy. Values for 100 eV Hg^+ bombardment of copper, silver and gold were, respectively 3×10^5 (3.0 eV), 3.1×10^5 (5.4 eV) and 2.4×10^5 (5.9 eV) cm/sec.

Stuart and Wehner[83] have adapted their spectroscopic technique, used in low energy yields, to determine velocities of sputtered atoms. The technique was to pulse the target to a fixed negative voltage for about 1 μsec; producing a group of sputtered atoms in the discharge tube. After a given delay time, which was varied from 0-300 μsec, photons emitted in an observation volume by the sputtered atoms 6 cm from the target were counted for a 1 μsec. interval and a velocity distribution computed from the results. The distribution for atoms ejected in the normal direction from copper under Hg^+ bombardment was of Maxwell-

Boltzmann form; having a maximum at 3.5×10^5 cm/sec. (4.0 eV) and decreasing tangentially to zero at about 12×10^5 cm/sec. (48 eV). Variations with energy of the incident beam showed that the peak in the distribution increased with higher ion energy, as shown in Figs. 7.16 (a) and (b). This apparatus was also used to study the variation of ejection velocity with angle of ejection and results showed that the most probable speeds of sputtered atoms in a non-normal direction were larger than for the normal direction under identical bombardment conditions up to angles of approximately 60°; this effect was even more pronounced on single crystal targets. In an extension of the above work to study noble gas bombardment Stuart and Wehner[84] have found that the ejection energies decreased for lighter ions as illustrated in Figs. 7.17 (a) and (b).

Smith et al[85] have ionized sputtered particles from copper during 2 keV A^+ bombardment and, from the shift of the mass 65 peak obtained when the incident beam is switched off, estimated that neutral species have energies of about 9 eV. In this experiment the bombardment was at 60° and detection at 30° to the target normal. This value is of the same order as obtained by Wehner,[83] but slightly higher. Other results of similar magnitude have been obtained by

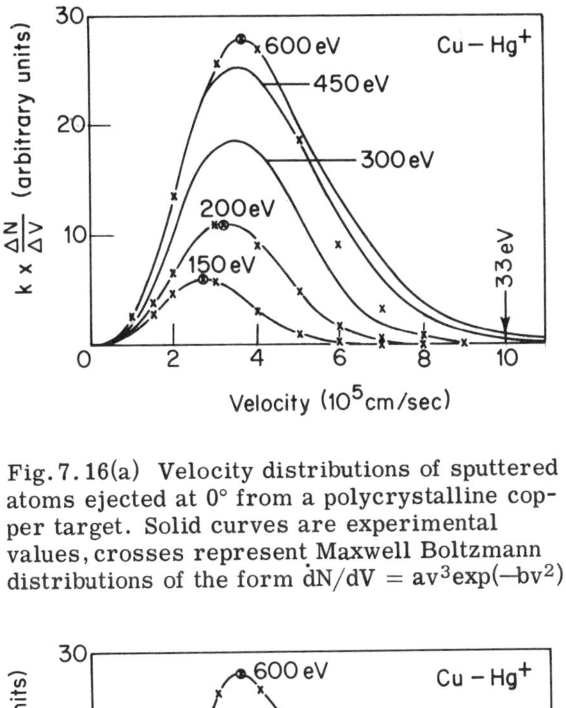

Fig. 7.16(a) Velocity distributions of sputtered atoms ejected at 0° from a polycrystalline copper target. Solid curves are experimental values, crosses represent Maxwell Boltzmann distributions of the form $dN/dV = av^3\exp(-bv^2)$

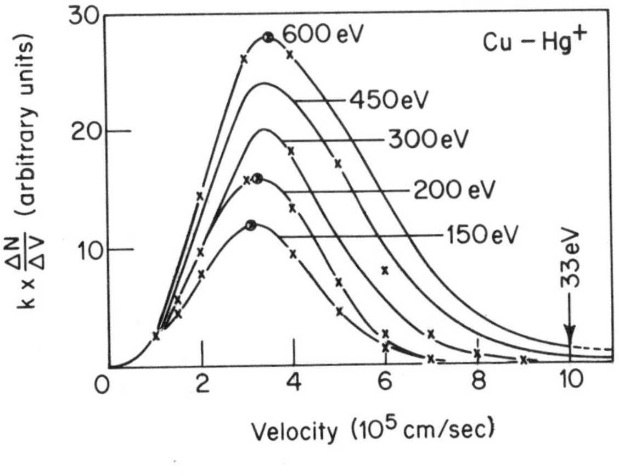

Fig. 7.16(b) Velocity distributions of sputtered atoms ejected from the (110) surface of a copper single crystal in the ⟨110⟩ direction parallel to the surface normal (viz. Ref. 7.83)

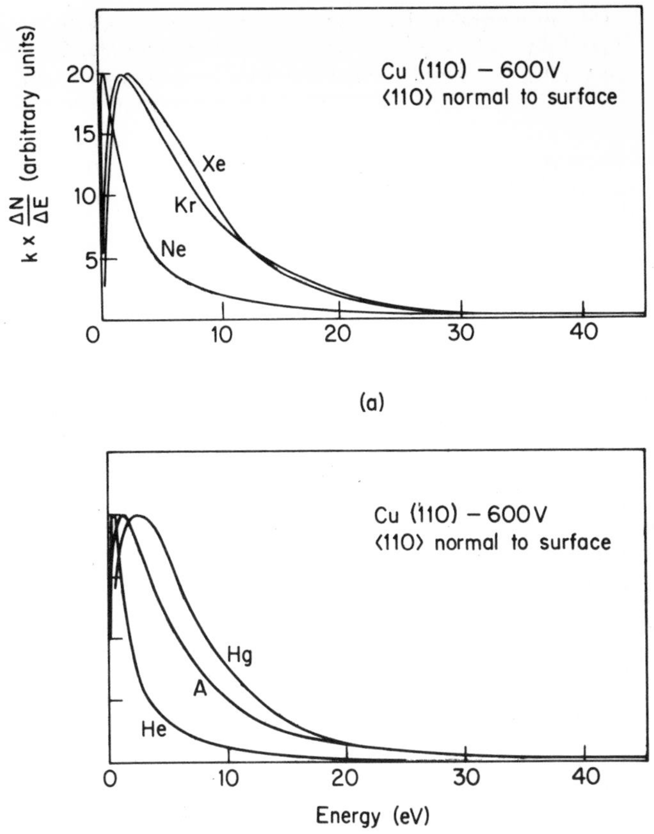

(b)

Fig. 7.17(a) Energy distributions of atoms ejected in the ⟨110⟩ direction from the (110) surface of copper under bombardment by normally incident 600 eV Ne^+, Kr^+ and Xe^+ ions. (b) Energy distributions of atoms ejected in the ⟨110⟩ direction from the (110) surface of copper under bombardment by normally incident 600 eV He^+, A^+ and Hg^+ ions (viz. Ref. 7.84)

Weijsenfeld[86] who obtained most probable energies of 10 eV for 400 eV Kr^+ bombardment of gold and even higher values of about 20 eV for the same combination at 1 keV energy. Weijsenfeld actually measured the heat transferred to an aluminium collector by the sputtered particles to obtain his results; a method less easy to calibrate and more liable to error than the Wehner technique. However, in later work, Weijsenfeld[87] has obtained lower average ejection velocities from single crystal and polycrystalline specimens of copper. Ejection energies for 1 keV Kr^+ bombardment were 3.4 eV (Cu (110)), 4.1 eV (polycrystalline Cu), and 4.7 eV (Cu (111)) and were seen to increase with incident ion energy. For 1 keV Hg^+ bombardment ejection energies were found to be all near the same value of 4.7 eV and fairly independent of ion energy whilst for 1 keV Kr^+ and Hg^+ bombardment of polycrystalline nickel ejection energies were, respectively, 4.5 eV and 10 eV and decreased rapidly as the ion energy was increased.

Kopitzki and Stier[88,89] found that the greater the mean energy of sputtered atoms the smaller the sputtering coefficient for the corresponding material. However Ben'yaminovich and Veksler[90] consider that the above results are not reliable as they include contributions due to reflected ions. Their own experiment, which involved a mercury discharge similar to that of Wehner from which the sputtered particles were extracted and analysed, showed that ejection energies were of the order 10-20 eV and increased only slightly with incident ion energy, in agreement with Wehner, but their results did not confirm the trend predicted by Kopitzki et al.

Thompson[91], in a cleverly designed experiment aimed at determining maximum energies required to initiate focused collision chains (which will be discussed later), has found a wide range of ejection energies obtaining during 40 keV A^+ bombardment of gold. The most probable value would appear to be 12 eV, which is again in line with Wehner's results since incident ion energies involved here are much higher.

However Thompson et al[92] have demonstrated that, during high energy bombardment of gold by argon and xenon ions, a fraction of ejected atoms had velocities of the order of those anticipated for thermal evaporation. They explained this effect as being due to the production of a thermal spike or region of atomic dimensions which becomes sufficiently heated during irradiation for a time long enough to cause thermal evaporation of atoms from the target surface. A full description of this process will be given later. The main point of interest here is that, although energies of sputtered atoms are, in general, much greater than those anticipated for thermal ejection certain circumstances, especially conditions of high energy bombardment, allow production of a proportion of atoms with thermal energies. A similar experiment by Beuscher et al[93] verifies the existence of this fraction of atoms with thermal energies which appear during 25 and 50 keV A^+ and Xe^+ bombardment of gold. These latter workers cannot however fit their results to the thermal spike equations derived by Thompson et al (see section 7. 1b).

7.11.2 Angular distribution of sputtered material

A study of directional characteristics of sputtered particles is of interest in the formation of sputtering theories, in determining recoil forces due to the ejection of the sputtered atoms and in design of apparatus for controlled production of thin films. Single crystal studies yield the most interesting results on ejection directions and a full discussion will therefore be presented under this heading.

For a general picture of the effect on polycrystalline targets we turn once again to Wehner et al[94] who collected deposits on suitably positioned glass strips and determined density distributions photometrically. Results of these investigations showed that ejection was 'under cosine', i.e. more material was ejected in non-normal directions than in the pure cosine case. These results were taken for Hg^+ bombardment of various metals at energies of 0. 1-1 keV. Ramer et al[52] and Rol et al[95], on the other hand, have found a 'gaussian' type of distribution for 15 keV bombardment of copper by various types of ion, but the latter have attributed this to a superimposition of many cosine distributions, each relating to atoms removed from a particular depth in the target. This interpretation has also been put forward by Patterson and Tomlin[96] who bombarded radio-active gold targets with 10 keV A^+ ions and generally found an under-cosine distribution. However their distribution approached cosine for thinner target materials where less atom layers could contribute, also, for bombardment by krypton ions which could not penetrate so far, the distribution again approached a cosine form. Grønlund and Moore[45] have found an almost exact cosine distribution for the silver atoms sputtered in 4 keV neon bombardment whilst Karmohapatro et al[97] have obtained over-cosine distributions for 3-7 keV noble-gas bombardment of radioactive silver (Ag^{110m}) targets and Chiplonkar et al[98] have found under-cosine distributions for 3-7 keV A^+ bombardment of silver. In the last mentioned work the ejected material was collected on a transparent plastic cylinder located with its circular end planes at right angles to the plane containing the ion beam. Deposits on a second cylinder orientated so that its circular mid-plane coincided with the plane of the incident beam indicated preferential ejection at directions near specular. In later work[99] similar results were found for gold targets and it was seen that the under-cosine distribution filled out with increasing ion energy eventually becoming almost exactly cosinusoidal at 5. 2 keV and then over-cosine at energies above this. Presumably, at higher energies, more atomic layers are involved, but according to Fluit et al[95] and Patterson et al[96] this should promote under-cosine ejection. The results are obviously in conflict and further work will have to be carried out to resolve the problem. It is interesting to observe what may be a rather fortuitous correlation on the work of Chiplonkar et al where the maximum in the yield-energy curve for the gold atoms was also found to occur at 5. 2 keV, the energy at which ejection was nearly cosine.

Cooper and Comas[100] have observed under-cosine distributions during bombardment of polycrystalline silver by 160-200 eV A^+ ions. This work was particularly interesting as Cooper et al were able to demonstrate that characteristic spot patterns (see section 7. 12) appeared for bombardment of Ag (100) and (110) monocrystalline targets, but that there was no evidence for these spot patterns when the same targets were sublimed at temperatures from 642 to 815°C and also, under these latter circumstances, the distribution of ejected material was almost exactly cosine. Thus we have strong evidence here that sputtering is not predominantly a thermal evaporation process, but relies on momentum transfer.

Malakhov et al[101] have studied ejection patterns for various angles of incidence and have shown that the principal ejection direction of lithium sputtered by 400 eV Argon ions is at 90° to the incident beam whilst a second principal direction develops at 40° (acute) to the incident beam for bombardment at angles above about 60°.

7.11.3 Structure of sputtered deposit

We mention briefly here the work of Campbell and Stirland[102] who have shown that, under certain conditions, it was possible to obtain epitaxial deposits of silver and gold on rock salt at room temperatures by sputtering. In the alternative method of evaporation of the silver or gold a minimum substrate temperature above ambient would have to be maintained to allow epitaxial growth so the sputtering technique is seen to have a considerable advantage in simplicity of operation. Wolsky et al[103] have found that sputtered germanium films deposited on single crystal sapphire substrates at temperatures of 200-600°C always form a polycrystalline structure whereas at higher temperatures large areas of the deposited film were monocrystalline. For calcium fluoride substrates the reverse was true, single crystal deposits being produced at temperatures of 250-350°C and films with polycrystalline areas for substrate temperatures in excess of 500°C.

7.12 SINGLE CRYSTAL STUDIES

The most interesting information on the sputtering mechanism results from investigations of the bombardment of monocrystals. In 1957 Silsbee[104] proposed that energy could be transported along a line of atoms and, with certain restrictions, may be focused into the line. The principle is discussed in Chapter 6 and it is shown that a series of collisions will focus into the atomic line provided $D < 2R_T$ and also $\cos\theta_0 \geqslant \frac{D}{2R_T}$ where R_T is the combined radii of the two colliding spheres, D the interatomic spacing in the atomic row under consideration and θ_0 the angle the primary recoil atom makes with this atom row. The above expressions lead one to expect more focusing in directions where D is least, i.e. in close-packed directions which are, for bcc crystals, the ⟨111⟩ direction and for fcc crystals, the ⟨110⟩ directions.

Whilst there is little doubt that such focusing sequences are responsible for ejection of atoms during bombardment by ions with energies greater than 10 keV theoretical studies of Harrison et al[104a] indicate that the crystal dependence of ejection can be explained by near-surface collisions only for ion energies below 10 keV. Harrison et al have selected an elementary area of crystal lattice and used a computer programme to evaluate the possible ejection directions using the classical laws of motion for the interactions. The theoretical ejection patterns for A^+ ions on (110), (100) and (111) faces of copper agree quite closely with the experimental patterns obtained by Southern et al[27] whilst the collisions giving rise to these ejection patterns are clearly shown by Harrison et al to result from glancing billiard-ball interactions at the surface and are not due to focused collision chains. Lehmann and Sigmund[104b] have further considered this problem and have shown that much of the data, previously assumed to indicate the presence of focusons, can be described by simple collisions with a symmetrical target array. From consideration of efficiency of energy transfer it is clear that ejection will occur most favourably in directions corresponding to collisions with least energy loss. For example, the most efficient process of ejection of a surface atom occurs when it is struck head-on by its nearest neighbour so that sputtered deposits should, on this argument, form dense spots in the close-packed directions. A simple calculation of this process indicated that the angular width of such a spot to half maximum density was ± 7° to the close-packed direction which is the same order of magnitude as obtained experimentally[117]. A similar argument shows that an atom in the second layer from the surface escapes with least energy loss along the axis of symmetry of a ring of surface atoms. Thus, although Wehner[105] and many other workers have ascribed their results to Silsbee-type focusing, the correlation has been fortuitous and many of the conclusions reached by these workers must be looked at again rather critically.

The first observations of sputtering in preferred directions were made by Wehner[105] and more recent experiments by many workers have confirmed the anisotropic nature of ejection from monocrystalline targets[27,106-120]. Fig. 7.18 shows typical ejection patterns obtained by Anderson and Wehner[111] for bombardment of the fcc crystals Cu (111), Ni (111) and Au (111) by Hg^+ ions. The principal spots correspond to ejection in the close-packed ⟨110⟩ directions. Thompson[112] has also shown that atoms were preferentially ejected from the back side of thin gold foils in these close-packed directions during bom-

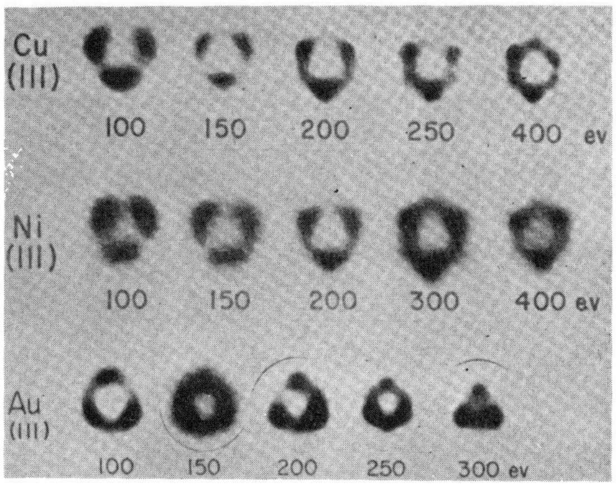

Fig. 7.18 Atom ejection patterns collected on flat disks for (111) surfaces of Cu, Ni and Au (viz. Ref. 7.111)

bardment by high energy protons (greater than 300 keV). Certain deviations to this rule of ejection in nearest and next-nearest neighbour directions show up in practice where ejection is seen to occur, either, in directions near to those expected above, or, in directions such as ⟨114⟩ or ⟨116⟩ which do not apparently constitute atomic rows in the crystal. The former deviations, observed by Nelson[113] and Anderson[109,114], are anticipated to be due to crystal damage at or near the surface, which could disrupt normal focuson events. The atom which would normally be sputtered from the end of a collision chain may be in the vicinity of a surface vacancy and therefore, in relaxation, move slightly out of its normal line. It would thereby suffer a more glancing blow during the sputter sequence which would cause ejection in a slightly different direction[109,113,114,115]. Ejection in ⟨116⟩ or ⟨114⟩ directions is again ascribed to surface damage, but here it is postulated that the formation of first order twins, or, multi-layer twins, respectively, are responsible (i.e. two atoms are arrayed equidistant from a site normally occupied by a solitary atom)[111,114,116].

Yurasova et al[117] have proposed that many of the unexpected ejection directions reported in the literature result from errors in determining spot pattern angles and from uncertainties introduced by obtaining patterns from a small surface for arbitrary bombardment and collection directions. They claim to have eliminated all these uncertainties by sputtering a spherical single crystal ball and obtaining ejection patterns on a spherical collector. Results obtained by Yurasova et al indicated ejection primarily in the nearest neighbour directions with weaker spots in the next nearest neighbour directions for both fcc and bcc structures. The distribution of ejected material across a spot for these structures is shown in Fig. 7.19a to be more 'peaked' than a cosine distribution and later work[118] has shown this to be true also for hexagonal zinc single crystals. Ejection from diamond-type lattice structures produces spots with density distributions almost exactly cosine as shown in Fig. 7.19b, but the predominant directions were found to be ⟨110⟩ whilst Anderson et al[111,114,119] have consistently found ⟨111⟩ ejection to predominate. Anderson et al[119] have shown however that a relationship between bombarding energy and the annealing temperature required to reproduce the characteristic spot pattern exists and it is possible that Yurasova et al's results represent ejection from a damaged surface.

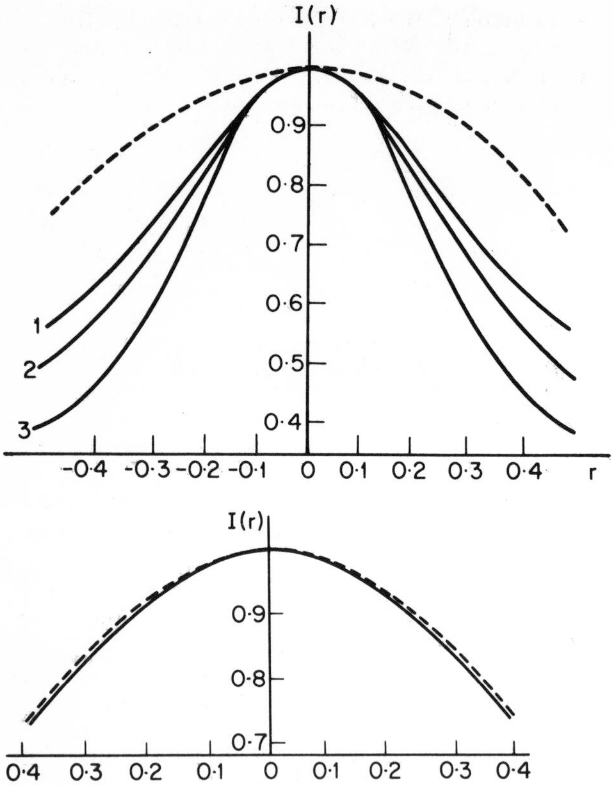

Fig. 7.19(a) Photometric density curves of separate spots produced by sputtering a single-crystal tungsten ball. Curve 1 : ⟨100⟩ spot at 200°C, Curve 2 : ⟨111⟩ spot at 1300°C, Curve 3 : ⟨111⟩ spot at 200°C. Dashed curve : cosine distribution. (b) Photometric density curves of ⟨110⟩ spot developed on a cylindrical collector during sputtering of InSb. Dashed curve represents a cosine distribution (viz. Ref. 7. 117)

An interesting experiment is described by Weijsenfeld[120] who bombarded copper and silver monocrystalline targets with 1 keV krypton ions and measured the ejection density as a function of angle and also the average energy of the sputtered atoms. The sputtered atom flux was determined from the resistance change of the 100 Å sputtered film whilst ejection energies were interpreted by a calorimetric technique. Results for the (110) surface of copper indicated characteristic spots at azimuthal angles of ± 31. 9° for a polar angle of 61°. The spots were thus shifted by 3. 3° towards the ⟨100⟩ direction in the surface plane compared with values expected and Weijsenfeld proposed that this was due to an asymmetric potential acting on the ejected atom as it emerged from the surface in an oblique ⟨110⟩ direction. The asymmetry arises due to unequal spacing of the atoms on the (110) plane and Weijsenfeld was able to calculate a shift of 2. 9° by assuming a Born-Mayer potential. This shift in angle was observed to be less for ejection from a (110) silver surface.

Ejection in the polar direction was also considered and seen to be affected by three factors:

(1) The relaxation of the surface plane of atoms (see Fig. 7. 20)

(2) A further asymmetric potential effect of atoms 'A' and 'B' in Fig. 7. 20 and

(3) The binding energy of the atom to the crystal lattice; this latter will reduce the normal component of the ejected atom velocity and therefore encourage it to be emitted more obliquely.

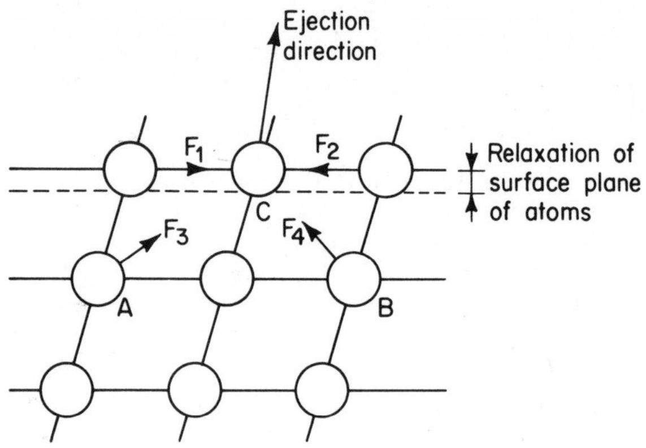

Fig. 7. 20 Illustrating deflection of an ejected atom from the atomic row direction due to surface relaxation and asymmetry of atomic forces

Factors (1) and (2) above cause bending towards the normal by 2° and 4. 5° respectively for copper (110) ejection whilst factor (3) was calculated to cause a bending away from the normal of 10. 7°.

The above arguments concur with those of Southern et al[27] who observed errors in spot locations by about 2 to 5 degrees towards the normal for A^+ bombarding (011) monocrystalline copper targets.

Nelson, Thompson et al[115] have carried out some very useful experiments, particularly designed to illustrate various focusing aspects and their work has contributed substantially to a better understanding of the phenomenon. In standard experiments determining the ejection directions of sputtered atoms from tungsten and molybdenum when bombarded by 50 keV A^+ ions Nelson[113] has found the usual trends; the ⟨111⟩ spots were each surrounded by three spots at an angle measured in the (110) plane of 10° to the ⟨111⟩ direction, these spots having one quarter the intensity of the real ⟨111⟩ deposits. Of next importance were ⟨100⟩ spots which also were surrounded by four spots at an angle measured in the (100) plane of 4° to the true ⟨100⟩ directions. These spots were of intensity of about one-tenth of the main ⟨100⟩ deposits. ⟨110⟩ deposits were the least intense of the group and were oval in shape with a maximum diameter lying along the intersection of (100) planes and the collector. Relative intensities of tungsten in one ⟨111⟩ spot and its three subsidiaries to that in a ⟨100⟩ spot and that in a ⟨110⟩ were, respectively,

12 : 6 : 1

Nelson[113] has suggested three ejection mechanisms responsible for the formation of the spots described above. Ejection in the ⟨111⟩ direction is attributed to the Silsbee[104] mechanism, the necessary conditions for which are that $4R \geqslant D^{111}$ where R is the hard-sphere radius and D^{111} the atomic spacing in a ⟨111⟩ row of atoms. R, of course, is a varying factor, a smaller effective collision radius being presented to a more energetic moving particle. It can thus be seen, that, as E increases, R will decrease and approach a limiting value $R^{111} = D^{111}/4$, below which focusing chains in the ⟨111⟩ direction cannot propagate, i.e. at high enough energies, above E_f^{111}, where the collision radius associated with E_f^{111} is given by $R = R^{111} = D^{111}/4$ no focusing is possible. (This is not quite true as was seen in the discussion of focusing events in Chapter 6,but it is a good first approximation. In practice an atom can undergo a few collisions of non-focusing nature as it enters the collision chain thereby reducing its energy to a value below the focusing limit).

An elegant experiment has demonstrated the above effect quite conclusively[91]. In fact fcc crystals of gold were used which have closest packing in ⟨110⟩ directions so, to be in accord with the above, we expect to find the Silsbee mechanism failing at higher energies in these directions. The basis of the experiment was to direct a beam of radioactive sputtered particles across a known flight distance onto a rotating drum. By carefully chopping the beam and synchronizing the rotor the energies of the ejected atoms were apparent from the spread-out distribution on the drum surface and a curve showing intensity against time of flight, as shown in Fig. 7. 21 was obtained. It was considered that the small peak was due to atoms ejected along channels in the crystal in ⟨110⟩ directions as discussed later. However, the main peak illustrates the energy-spread of the Silsbee-type focused atoms and it is clear that the high energy side would cut off quite sharply at a time corresponding to 35 μsec, giving an E_f^{110} value of 280 ± 50 eV for gold, which agrees reasonably well with theoretical predictions[121].

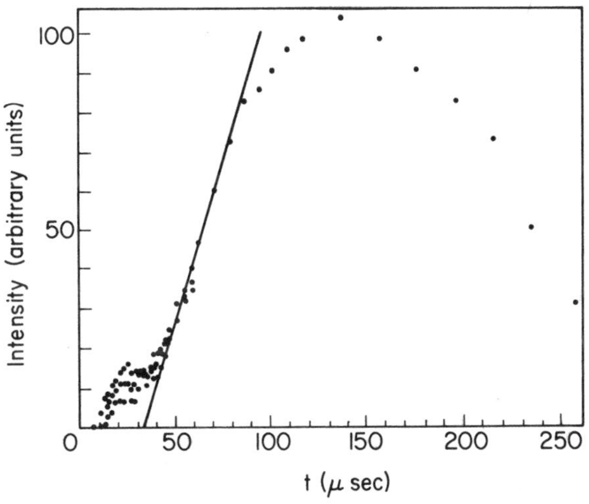

Fig. 7. 21 Time of flight spectrum of atoms ejected from gold in the ⟨110⟩ direction during sputtering by 40 keV A^+ ions (viz. Ref. 7. 91)

The second focusing mechanism proposed by Nelson to account for the ⟨100⟩ ejection observed in bcc crystals does not rely solely on a collision process, but introduces the concept of the focusing action on the moving atom by the surrounding atom rings i.e. assisted focusing. In the ⟨100⟩ direction the Silsbee limitation $R^{100} = D^{100}/4$ still applies and, as $D^{100} > D^{111}$, $E_f^{100} < E_f^{111}$ so that focusing cannot occur in these directions until the recoil atom energy is reduced even further. However, the probability of ⟨100⟩ focusing is improved by the action of rings of atoms having axes in ⟨100⟩ directions. The effect, which was discussed in Chapter 6, is demonstrated in Fig. 7. 22.

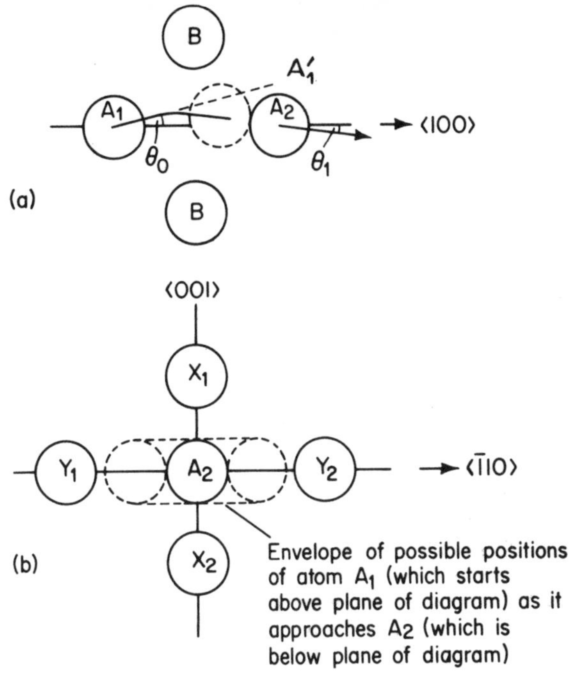

Fig. 7. 22 Illustrating assisted focusing by rings of atoms in fcc crystals. (a) Simple ring focusing in ⟨100⟩ direction. (b) Eccentric focusing in ⟨110⟩ direction

Atom A_1 would normally have proceeded along its initial direction A_1A_1', but the repulsive forces acting on it by the ring of atoms B deflect A_1 inwards, causing it to collide with A_2 at an angle much nearer the atomic line direction. Because of this effect focusing is possible at energies E_f^{*100} slightly larger than E_f^{100}. As we have also seen in Chapter 6 it is also possible for atoms initially moving with energies two or three times E_f^{100} to be focused back into line sufficiently whilst their energy decreases to E_f^{100}, after which Silsbee focusing continues. The nature of the interacting forces in a particular crystal array determines whether A_1 actually leaves its site permanently in transmitting energy to its neighbour, or, whether it merely oscillates about its original position with sufficient amplitude to transfer momentum to the next atom in the row.

The mechanism of focusing in the ⟨110⟩ directions is again different in that the atomic rings of atoms are so situated that they cause de-focusing in one plane and focusing in a plane at right-angles to this. The resultant effect is that the atom A_1 (Fig. 7. 23) oscillates from side to side in the plane containing Y_1, Y_2 A_2 and only permanently focuses in the plane $X_1X_2A_2$. In this type of collision sequence A_1 must move to A_2 and cannot transmit its momentum by vibration about a rest position. The oval-shaped spots obtained experimentally for ejection in ⟨100⟩ directions confirm the above mechanism; their major axes lying parallel to Y_1Y_2.

The above three mechanisms account for the main ejection sequences, but there are several less intense streaks which Nelson and Thompson consider are due to the focusing of recoil atoms between widely separated atomic planes, such as the (110) planes in

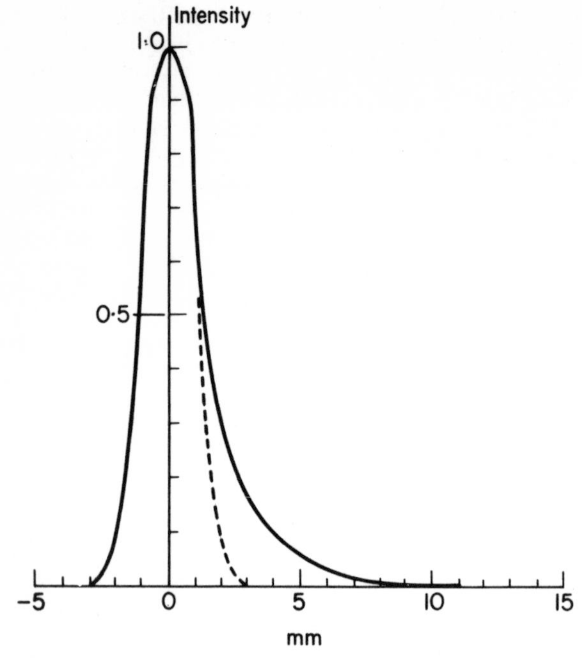

Fig. 7.23 Distribution of ejected atoms velocities obtained during 43 keV bombardment of gold. 1 mm is equivalent to a velocities of 2.254×10^6 cm/sec (viz. Ref. 7.92)

bcc crystals i.e. channelling phenomena. Results from an experiment with copper targets demonstrate this mechanism[108]. At lower energies (25 keV), deposits produced during bombardment of the copper by argon ions indicated that the ejection was predominantly along close-packed directions, i.e. ⟨110⟩, with slight deposits corresponding to ejection in ⟨111⟩ directions. At higher energies however (75 keV) the situation was reversed; ions now penetrated so far into the target that recoil chain collision processes were inefficient. The principal ejection was now along inter-planar spaces, which offered less resistance to the passage of the recoils.

Thompson et al[122] have considered a further mechanism of atom ejection of special importance at high energy bombardments and have been able to demonstrate this new phenomenon experimentally for 43 keV Xe^+ and A^+ bombardment of gold. They consider the postulate of Seitz and Koehler[123] that, in spreading the primary recoil energy by focused collisions over a small region of the crystal, the cascade will produce a local heating effect which may itself contribute to the sputtering process.

The experiment involves the determination of ejection energies of sputtered atoms. These were collimated and allowed to traverse a fixed distance onto a rapidly rotating drum, as discussed earlier. The targets were radioactive so that the smeared out distribution of sputtered atoms on the drum could be obtained by a radio count and it was apparent that, as well as the distribution of energies anticipated by the focused collision chain mechanism, there was a group of atoms of mean energy 0.15 eV for Xe^+ bombardment and 0.2 eV for A^+ bombardment. Fig. 7.23 demonstrates the presence of these atoms; a symmetrical sputtered deposit would normally be anticipated (dashed curve) but the existence of slower ejected atoms is apparent by the enlargement of the curve to the right of the peak. It is clear from the arguments presented by these authors that the low energy atoms are produced by heating of small areas of target of about 100 Å in diameter to temperatures of 1750°K for times of the order of 10^{-13} second. The region is thus considered as a 'spike' of local heating and the thermal ejection mechanism referred to as a thermal spike process.

Further confirmation of the existence of these thermal spikes is presented by Nelson[124] who has observed the variation of sputtering yield with temperature and found that it rises exponentially as the melting point of the particular target material is approached. He demonstrates that this rise can be attributed to the onset of thermal sputtering and is able to deduce, by fitting his theoretical curves to the experimental yields, that spike radii are again of the order 100 Å and total spike temperatures are about 1700°K. Thus, by two distinctly different techniques, the existence of thermal spikes has been verified and a consistent prediction of their characteristics obtained.

Fluit et al[125] have carried out an interesting experiment on copper monocrystals demonstrating conclusively the effects of the periodic nature of the atoms on the sputtering process. In actual fact their results

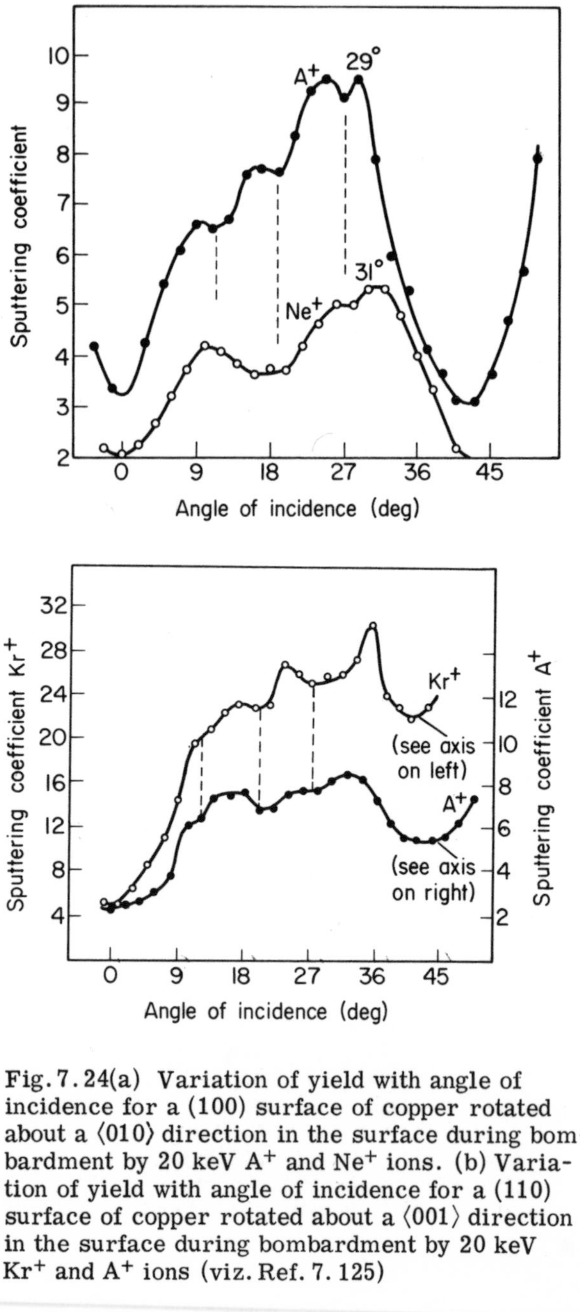

Fig. 7.24(a) Variation of yield with angle of incidence for a (100) surface of copper rotated about a ⟨010⟩ direction in the surface during bombardment by 20 keV A^+ and Ne^+ ions. (b) Variation of yield with angle of incidence for a (110) surface of copper rotated about a ⟨001⟩ direction in the surface during bombardment by 20 keV Kr^+ and A^+ ions (viz. Ref. 7.125)

simply demonstrate that, when the copper crystal is aligned so that incoming ions can see a clear path between the atomic planes or rows, then the penetration depths of these ions is so great that transmission of the damage sequence back to the surface is unlikely. Thus, minimum sputtering yields were obtained on a (100) surface of copper in directions corresponding to ⟨010⟩, ⟨015⟩, ⟨013⟩, ⟨012⟩ and ⟨011⟩ (see Fig. 7.24a), i.e., 0°, 14°, 18°, 27°, and 45° with respect to normal directions, respectively. On a (110) surface minima were found in ⟨011⟩, ⟨035⟩, ⟨012⟩, ⟨013⟩ and ⟨010⟩ directions (Fig. 7.24b), i.e., 0°, 14°, 18°, 27° and 45° with respect to the normal direction, respectively. A simple geometrical study of the crystal structures indicated that these particular directions were the most transparent to the ions and, in a later article, Fluit and Rol[126] were able to show that the inverse ratio of the transparencies in two directions 29° : 42° (= 4.3) was of the same order as the ratio of the magnitude of the sputtering ratios in these directions (9.5 : 2.5) for 20 keV A^+ bombarding a (100) copper surface rotated about a ⟨010⟩ direction in the surface. Further, by assuming that the projected target spheres just touched when viewed at 29° (maximum sputtering direction) and competely shadowed each other at 42° (minimum sputtering direction) the effective radius of the atoms could be evaluated by a simple geometrical calculation (see Fig. 7.25).

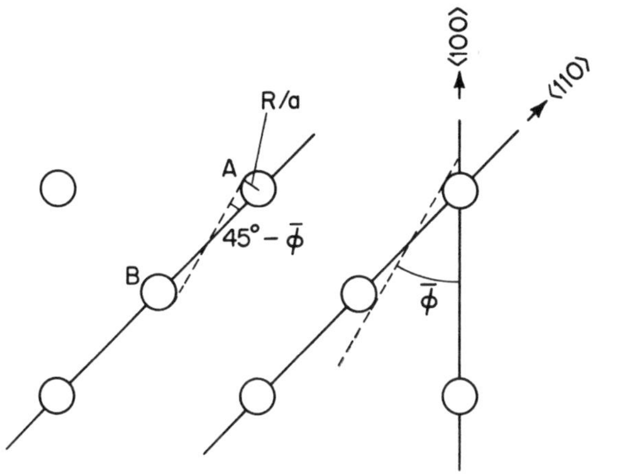

Fig. 7.25 Illustrating the method of interpreting the effective radius of target atoms by geometric calculation

Table 7.4 shows the effective radii obtained by this method in comparison with the hard sphere radii of Bohr. Agreement is only to a first order, but it was noted that the effective radii calculated were consistent in that calculations for other minima in the yield-angle of incidence characteristic, using these effective radii, predicted correct half width intervals.

TABLE 7.4 (Ref. 7.126)

Effective radii of copper atoms for 20 keV ion bombardment

Ion	Effective radius (Å)	Bohr radius (Å)
Ne	0.25	0.12
A	0.29	0.17
Kr	0.24	0.23

A similar pattern of sputtering yields as a function of the angle of incidence has been observed by Molchanov et al[127,128] for argon ions bombarding nickel and copper monocrystals. When the direction of the ion beams approached one of the principal crystallographic axes of the target the sputtering coefficient was seen to fall off abruptly. This decrease occurred at angles of 0°, ⟨100⟩ axis, 35°, ⟨112⟩ axis, and 55°, ⟨111⟩ axis, for rotation of a cubic crystal about the diagonal of a face and at 0°, ⟨100⟩ axis, and 45°, ⟨110⟩ axis, for rotation about an edge of the cube. One of the crystals was intentionally cut at an angle of 20° to the (110) plane and the experiment repeated. The resulting dips in the yield occurred again when the ion beam was in line with a crystal axis even though the angle of incidence at the surface was now 20° different.

Mashkova et al[129] have carried out a parallel study of sputtering yields and secondary electron emission yields as a function of incident angle for 30 keV A^+ ion bombardment of a (110) copper surface as it was rotated around the ⟨110⟩ and ⟨100⟩ axes. The values of both coefficients were observed to change with orientation angle in the manner described above although the sputtering yield pattern was slightly more rugged in shape than that for secondary electron emission.

Returning to the total yield-energy relation for the moment it is clear that, at higher energies (1-20 keV) on fcc targets bombarded by argon ions, yields follow the pattern[27, 40, 95, 130]:

$$S_{(111)} > S_{(100)} > S_{(110)}$$

whilst, at lower ion energies (0-100 eV)[62, 131]

$$S_{(100)} > S_{(111)}$$

Zdanuk et al[62] proposed that the change in order may be due to the reduced importance of crystallographic effects at the lower energies so that the binding energies of atoms on each crystal face become the dominant factor. If the binding energy of an atom on a (100) face of an fcc crystal is less than that on the (111) face the yields would in fact differ in the manner described above.

Denoux[130] has studied 10-50 keV H^+ bombardment of several faces of monocrystalline copper and has found that yields on a particular face vary linearly with $\log E_0/E_0$ (where E_0 is the incident ion energy) whilst yields on different faces are proportional to $\log \sigma/\sigma$ (where σ is the number of atoms on a given face per unit surface). Denoux was thus able to state a general rule for sputtering coefficients

$$S = k_1 \log E_0/E_0 + k_2 \log \sigma/\sigma \qquad 7.2$$

where, for H_1^+ bombarding copper at 50°C $k_1 = 14$ and $k_2 = 0.5$. At 400°C the parameter k_1 was found to increase to 17 whilst k_2 remained invariant.

7.14 EFFECT OF TARGET TEMPERATURE

Our brief resumé of single crystal effects has illustrated how important these studies are in determining the true picture of the sputtering process. Having ascertained that high energy sputtering involves collision cascades along rows of atoms it is a short step to the realization that these atomic rows do not comprise stationary atoms, but rows of atoms each vibrating about its mean position according to the temperature in the locality of the damage event. As it is well known that the vibrations increase with the temperature of the specimen, it is clear that transfer of momentum along favoured crystal directions will become less feasible, and hence the sputtering yield would be expected to decrease as the target temperature rises. On the other hand, during bombardment, regions of damage are created which reduce the efficiency of momentum transfer along collision chains. These damaged regions will begin to anneal out at higher temperatures thus causing an increase in yield with temperature. There are thus at least two temperature dependent phenomena each causing the yield to vary in an opposite sense.

In studies of the bombardment of gold with argon at 43 keV Nelson et al[132] have shown that the density distribution of the material forming the spots produced by ⟨110⟩ ejection spreads out as the temperature is increased and that this broadening can be explained by variations in thermal vibration of the target atoms. Yurasova et al[133] have also observed a broadening of spots as the temperature of copper targets was increased above 500°C whilst, for tungsten, the spots were seen to sharpen as the temperature was raised from 1000 to 1300°C so some other process, such as annealing out of defects, must have predominated here. In the above, bombardment was by 10 keV Kr^+ ions. Fluit[134], on the other hand, finds that sputtering of polycrystalline copper by 20 keV argon ions is independent of temperature in the range 75-320°K, whilst yields from a (111) copper crystal actually increase slightly with temperature and yields from a (110) crystal decrease at a lesser rate. However it should be pointed out that, at these low temperatures, yields may be affected by the presence of argon contamination on the surface. Fluit et al[135] have in fact shown that the neon content in copper after bombardment by this gas was higher at lower target temperatures and proposed that its presence may explain the interesting pattern of yield against temperature. In the region 20-60°K yields were seen to increase, this being attributed by Fluit et al to the onset of annealing processes so that collision chains could start to become effective again. In the region 60-100°K however the yields again decreased and it was proposed that this was due to the liberation of some adsorbed neon which allowed greater penetration of the ions and therefore transfer of energy back to the surface was made more difficult. At still higher temperatures (100-150°K) yields were seen to increase again. This was attributed to the annealing out of frozen Frenkel-pair defects which allowed the collision chains to become more effective and, consequently, yields to increase. Again, in the higher temperature, but lower ion energy, regime, Snouse and Bader[136] have found that yields from polycrystalline copper during 3 keV N_2^+ bombardment show a marked decrease as the temperature increases. Fig. 7. 26 shows the results obtained by these experimenters in the region 60-470°C. It should be noted that these experiments were carefully carried out with a view to ensuring that contamination on the target surfaces did not interfere with the results.

Using a 300 eV A^+ — Ni system Wehner[137] has observed an increase in sputtering yield with temperature up to 300°C (an effect probably due to the mercury background in the system contaminating the nickel target) and then a slow decrease with temperature, though he attributes the latter to changes in the sensitivity of his detector at these higher temperatures, the real result being therefore a constant value for the yield at temperatures above 300°C. Almén and Bruce[38] have also found downward trends in sputtering yields of platinum and nickel and they attribute this to more rapid annealing processes at higher temperature so that the damage event of a preceding ion is dispersed before further ions penetrate the region. In an experiment with silver targets however their yield does show an increase with target temperature, but this increase is possibly due to vaporization.

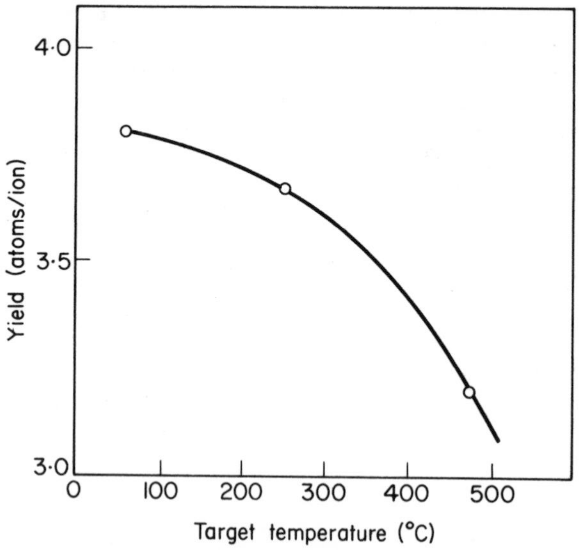

Fig. 7. 26 Variation of sputtering yield with target temperature for 3 keV N_2^+ ions on copper. Each point on the curve is the mean of several measurements (viz. Ref. 7. 136)

Lebedev et al[138] have observed changes in yield as a function of temperature over the range 700-1100°C and found in general that yields increased by about 50% in this region, the main increase occurring at about 900°C. The fact that the rate of increase in yield is greatest at a given temperature for all targets studied may indicate some change in surface contamination at this point rather than a real sputtering effect. The bombardment in this experiment was by 2-10 keV Cs^+ ions which were fired at Fe, Ni, Ti, Pt, Mo, C, Re, W and Ta targets.

Studies of various types of crystal structure by Carlston et al[139] have shown that the temperature dependence of the yield is characteristic of the type of crystal bombarded. On the two polycrystalline fcc samples studied (Cu and Al) they found that the yield was approximately independent of temperature in the tange 350-1000°K for 2, 5 and 10 keV A^+ bombardments whilst for the polycrystalline bcc metals Mo, W and Ta the yields increased linearly with temperature by 26, 28 and 39 percent, respectively. The picture is further complicated however by their results on monocrystalline targets, for example, the bcc Mo (100) surface indicated a yield independent of temperature whilst the Mo(110) surface showed an increase of 12% between 350 and 1000°K. Again, for the fcc Cu (110) surface S was independent of temperature but for Cu (111) yields decreased as the temperature increased by amounts depending on the ion bombarding energy (2 keV- 24%, 5 keV-12%, 10 keV-16%).

Thus it is not yet clear what overall effect target temperature has on sputtering except that a temperature increase will certainly cause defocusing of collision chains. Some further light on the process comes from an interesting experiment of Anderson et al[119], [119a] who bombarded germanium single crystal targets with Ne^+, A^+, Kr^+ and Xe^+ ions at 0-800 eV and looked for the characteristic ejection spots for bombardments carried out at various target temperatures. They found that for target temperatures below some critical value, T_a, no spots were produced whilst for the same bombardment conditions but a target temperature exceeding T_a spots are produced. T_a values for bombardment of the (110) surface of Ge by Ne^+, A^+, Kr^+ and Xe^+ were 500°K, 560°K, 570°K and 590°K, respectively whilst, for bombardment of (110) InSb, the values were 320°K, 350°K, 355°K and 360°K and for

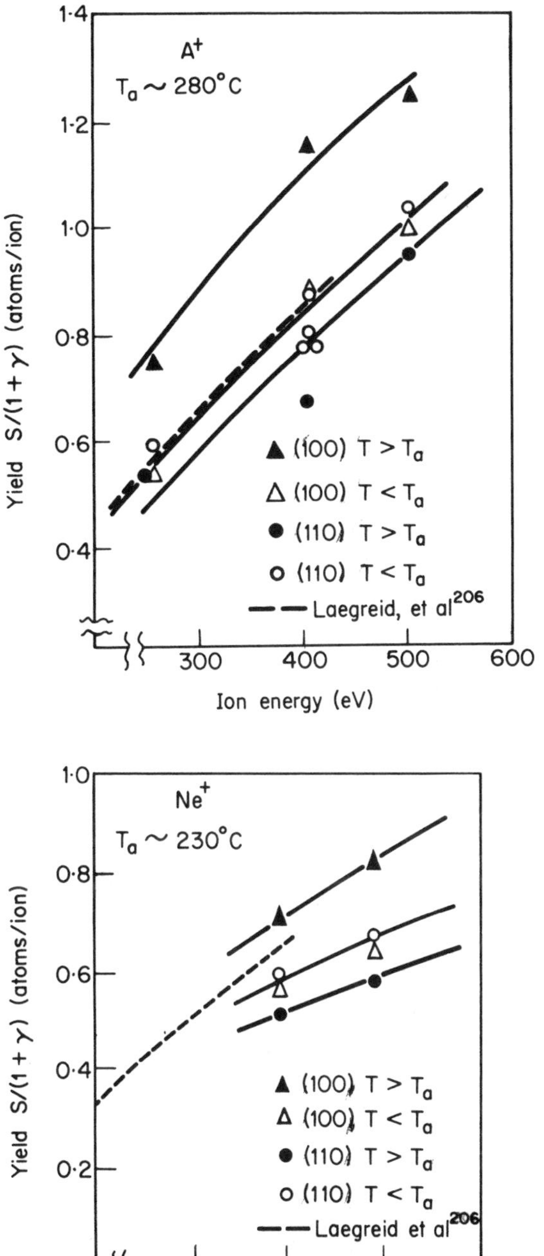

Fig. 7.27(a) Sputtering yield of Ge (100) and (110) faces as a function of A^+ ion energy. (b) Sputtering yield of Ge (100) and (110) faces as a function of Ne^+ ion energy (viz. Ref. 7.119b)

InAs (120) 333°K, 363°K, 363°K and 383°K. Anderson et al have concluded that at the lower temperatures the defects introduced by the bombardment were formed at a rate exceeding the annealing rate so that the targets were no longer monocrystalline at the near-surface layers. In later work[119b] Anderson has looked at the sputtering yields of Ge(100) and (110) surfaces at temperatures below and above the critical T_a value and has found that distinctly different yield-energy curves exist in the two cases. Figs. 7.27 a and b illustrate the results for A^+ and Ne^+ bombardment and it is intersting to observe that the curves for both (110) and (100) faces are almost identical at $T < T_a$. This is expected as the surface is damaged and should not exhibit any preferred crystalline characteristic. Anderson offers no conclusive statement as to why the (100) yield exceeds the (110) yield for $T > T_a$ but suggests that the atom positions are more favourable on the (100) surface for a momentum reversal process.

7.15 SURFACE STUDIES

Before discussing theoretical aspects of sputtering we shall briefly consider the experimental data on the effects of bombardment on surface structure. Spivak et al[140,141] have suggested that many anomalies between etch patterns produced on the surface can be ascribed to inhomogeneity of the ion beam or to distortion at surface irregularities. At cavities for example they have proposed that the equipotential distorts and secondary electrons focus to a point at the centre of the hollow region causing a negative sheath which pulls more ions into the cavity and promotes its growth. This growth only terminates when the cavity is of such a depth that the sputtered atoms find it difficult to escape. However, in spite of these occasional distorting effects much has been learnt about sputtering from a study of surface damage. Wehner[5] presented evidence that sputtering by mercury ions caused preferential etching of surfaces so that characteristic patterns of grooves and hillocks were developed on the surface of the bombarded material. He showed that, for 100 eV Hg^+ bombardment of monocrystalline germanium, characteristic etch patterns were produced; a (100) surface having pits with fourfold symmetry, a (111) surface pits with threefold symmetry and a (110) surface pits with two-fold symmetry. The pits, which have also been observed by Sirotenko and Spivak[142] during 1 keV Kr^+ bombardment of Ge, appeared at random positions and were more numerous for bombardment of targets at low temperatures[143]. Ogilvie et al[144] studied bombardment of polycrystalline specimens of silver at ion energies between 20 eV and 4 keV and found that He^+, A^+ and Xe^+ ions tended to produce smoother surfaces whilst Hg^+ and O^+ ions produced facets. Bombardments were essentially normal in these experiments and Ogilvie concluded that the facets may result from a chemical reaction rather than physical damage. Further investigations by Ogilvie [145] on single crystals of silver showed that the bombardment of (110) and (100) faces produced a disorientated surface layer, the disorientation being most marked for low energy ions. The experimental evidence indicated that crystallites of thickness near 100 Å at the target surface were tilted during the bombardment. The mechanism proposed was that the ions were able to penetrate in directions parallel to the close-packed directions (i.e. along channels) and were arrested near the first dislocation line. Hence a large concentration of point defects and interstitials were generated at these points and a net transfer of target material from these high density regions was initiated. It is this transfer of material on the one hand and the tendency of the surface atoms to be pulled down towards dislocations on the other that was assumed by Ogilvie to exert the necessary coupling force to tilt the crystallites.

Cunningham et al[146] have studied etching by 8 keV A^+ ions at glancing angles on various surfaces. Remarkable correlation between incident beam direction and some of the characteristics of the etch pattern were frequently observed. For example, for 60° bombardment of gold, arrow-shaped points were consistently produced with the arrows always pointing in the direction of the lateral component of the incident beam. The arrows were however of differing shape on various grains. If the bombardment was made more intense for a longer period of time a series of parallel grooves were produced which were parallel to the plane of the incident beam. No distinctive damage was produced by bombardment in a normal direction which adds weight to the theory that sputtering is basically a momentum transfer process. Similar grooves were observed after bombardment of Zn (0001) monocrystals whilst, for bombardment of (100) and (111) aluminium, terraces were seen to develop with deeper steps on the (111) face. As ejection from the closest packed (111) planes is anticipated as being more efficient due to Silsbee focusing[104] (Wehner[105] found that the ratio of yields from (111) and (110) silver targets was approximately 1.6 to 1 respectively), these deeper steps on the (111) face of aluminium were anticipated. There was also some evidence that hillocks were associated with grain boundaries (i.e. discontinuities where collision chains are annihilated so that atoms nearby are protected and left on the surface).

Work of Magnuson et al[147] bears out many of the points already discussed. Hillocks were again observed parallel to the incident beam direction (see Fig. 7.28), there was no observable damage pattern for normal incidence and the etch patterns were of better detail when sputtering was not prolonged.

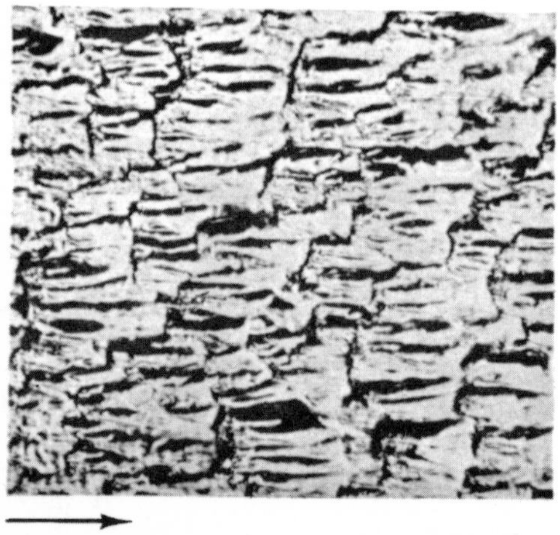

Fig. 7.28 Etch patterns formed on a polycrystalline copper target sputtered at 60° incidence by mercury ions. (Magnification 243 ×) (viz. Ref. 7.147)

One interesting aspect of this work was that, during bombardment of polycrystalline tantalum by mercury ions, sets of hillocks were formed in the beam direction. Rotation of the target through 90° about an axis normal to its plane resulted in obliteration of these original hillocks and formation of new ones parallel to the new beam direction. The main point of interest was that these new hillocks originated at the same points as their predecessors indicating that the line of dislocation giving rise to them extended perpendicularly below the surface. Atoms at this dislocation are again 'isolated' from collision chains to a great extent so that they tend to remain whilst surrounding atoms are sputtered away. Thus we see even in this very brief study of etching data that the evidence is strongly in favour of a momentum transfer mechanism and many of the patterns can be simply explained by reference to collision sequences and channelling phenomena. The etching phenomenon is not however restricted to bombardment of metallic specimens as is clear from the work of Navez et al[148] who have bombarded glass targets with 4 keV ions produced in a 10^{-1} Torr air discharge and have found that various etch patterns can be produced depending principally on the geometrical conditions of attack. Fig. 7.29 shows parallel grooves formed by 4 keV bombardment of glass at 80° incidence (i.e. near grazing).

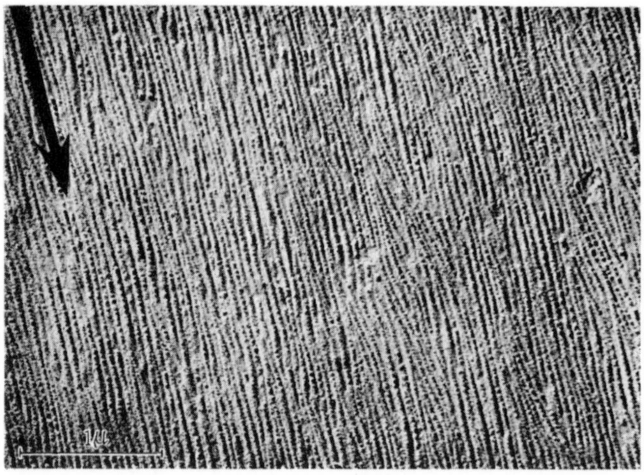

Fig. 7.29 Grooves formed on glass during bombardment at 80° incidence by 4 keV ions of air (viz. Ref. 7.148)

Fluit et al[149] have observed very different surface structures for normal and 45° incidence bombardment of Cu (100) by 20 keV A^+ ions. By observing the reflection of a finely focused light beam these workers have shown that, at angles of incidence where the penetration depth was small (i.e. greater than 45°), the surface was damaged by a competition of two favoured mechanisms; (1) the development of facets normal to the surface and (2) the developement of (110) surfaces (since five ⟨110⟩ close-packed, and therefore efficient ejection directions, terminate on these surfaces). At 43° incidence however irregularities having only a small angle of inclination (about 15°) to the surface were produced and it was concluded that, at this incident direction, the incoming ions were channelled into the crystal to large penetration depths, thereby minimizing surface damage.

7.16 SPUTTERING THEORIES

At the time of writing there are many empirical rules which describe the sputtering events of certain ion-target combinations in certain energy regimes, but none of these can be converted to a universal equation governing sputtering yields nor do the majority of them take into account the refined collision events which, from single crystal studies, obviously occur.

One of the earliest attempts at postulating a mechanism to describe the sputtering process was presented by J.J.Thomson[150] who proposed that radiation was released as the ion struck the target surface and that this in turn caused atomic ejection. Bush and Smith[151] envisaged a situation where the gas adsorbed by the material expanded and, thereby, caused a minor explosion producing sputtered atoms. However these early descriptions did not survive the test of time and were soon replaced by a mechanism known as the 'Hot-Spot Theory'. Von Hippel presented this theory in 1926.[152] It envisaged a situation where the energy dissipated by the ion in slowing down was sufficient to raise the temperature of a small hemispherical region of atomic dimensions so that target atoms were evaporated. The theory was developed further by Townes[153] to obtain an estimate of the absolute yield values and the calculation, applied to argon ions bombarding a barium target at low energy, was found to agree with an experimentally obtained results of Rockwood[154]. However the correlation was fortuitous as the experimental yield was later discovered to be too high. More recently Fluit et al[155] in an elegant experiment have demonstrated that the isotopic composition of sputtered lithium is far more deficient in Li^6 than would be anticipated for a mechanism involving evaporation where the ratio Li^6 to Li^7 would normally be in the region 1.05 to 1.08.

Again it is the single crystal investigations which have directed theoretical investigations into the correct channels. The preferred ejection directions observed[106-110] completely contradicted any suggestion of a thermal evaporation mechanism and, also, ejection velocities of the liberated atoms were found to be an order of magnitude too large.[80-83,85,86,91] Clearly the theory must be based on a momentum transfer process between the ion and target atoms to explain the anisotropic ejection found in single crystal studies.

The first attempt at such a theory was made by Lamar and Compton[156] who proposed that ions may penetrate the target material, be reflected from a lower atomic layer and recoil to strike a surface atom in an outward direction. Present day theories are based on this mechanism, but usually consider that many more internal collisons occur before an atom is finally ejected. A treatment on these lines has been developed by Keywell[25 157] who applied the analogy of the *cooling* of neutrons by the atoms of a moderator to the sputtering sequence. An incoming ion was presumed to penetrate the surface and strike a target atom. This atom was not itself sputtered, but, in its turn, collided with neighbouring atoms producing secondary displacements. The general overall effect on the atomic array was similar to a diffusion process or 'random walk' of mobile atoms, some of which reached the surface with sufficient energy to collide with and liberate surface atoms. The basic assumption made by Keywell was that each displaced atom would represent a sputtered atom if it could escape so that the problem resolved to a calculation of the number of displaced atoms produced and the escape probability. From neutron cooling theory[158] the energy retained by an ion of mass M_1 after n collisions with a moderator of mass M_2 is given by

$$E_n = E_o \exp(-n\xi) \qquad 7.3$$

where

$$\xi = 1 - \frac{(M_2 - M_1)^2}{2M_1 M_2} \ln\left(\frac{M_1 + M_2}{M_1 - M_2}\right) \qquad 7.4$$

The average fraction of energy transferred to the target atom is given by $\epsilon = 2M_1 M_2/(M_1 + M_2)^2$ so that the average energy of the (n + 1)th recoil atom will be given by

$$\overline{E_{n+1}} = \epsilon E_o \exp(-n\xi) \qquad 7.5$$

According to Seitz[159] the number of displaced atoms produced by a recoil atom of energy $\overline{E}$ in a metal having an atomic displacement energy E_d is given by

$$n_s = ½\left(\frac{\overline{E}}{E_d}\right) \qquad 7.6$$

However Keywell used the expression

$$n_s = \frac{\overline{E}}{E_d}^{1/2} \qquad 7.7$$

which yields approximately the same values of n_s for low energy ions. Thus the number of displaced atoms produced by the recoil at the nth collision of the primary will be:-

$$n_s = \left(\frac{\overline{E_n}}{E_d}\right)^{1/2} = \left(\frac{\epsilon E_o}{E_d}\right)^{1/2} \exp(-(n-1)\xi/2 \qquad 7.8$$

The total number of displaced atoms will therefore be given by

$$N = \sum_s n_s = \left(\frac{\epsilon E_o}{E_d}\right)^{1/2} \sum_{n=1}^{n_c} \exp(-(n-1)\xi/2 \qquad 7.9$$

where event n_c is defined as the last collision which produces a displaced atom i.e.

$$n_s = 1$$

Hence

$$n_c = 1 + \frac{1}{\xi}\ln\left(\frac{\epsilon E_o}{E_d}\right) \qquad 7.10$$

$$\simeq \frac{1}{\xi}\ln\left(\frac{\epsilon E_o}{Ed}\right) \qquad 7.10a$$

Keywell next introduced an expression relating the number of displaced atoms formed at a depth x to those escaping from the surface n_e

$$n_e = n_s \exp(-\beta x) \qquad 7.11$$

The depth x is related to the number of collisions the incoming atom has made by assuming it progresses by a random walk. Hence $x = k\sqrt{n}$ and the expression for the number of sputtered atoms becomes

$$n_a = \left(\frac{\epsilon E_o}{E_d}\right)^{1/2} \sum_{n=1}^{n_c} \exp(-\alpha\sqrt{n}).\exp(-n-1)\xi/2 \qquad 7.12$$

where

$$\alpha = k\beta \qquad 7.13$$

The above expression is further complicated by the fact that a fraction F_R of the ions will rebound thereby initiating a recoil chain with average energy $\overline{E_R}$ given by

$$\overline{E_R} = \epsilon E_O\left(1 + \tfrac{1}{2}\left(1 + \frac{M_1}{M_2}\right)\right) \qquad 7.14$$

Ejected atoms due to these rebounding ions are given by subsitituting n = 1 in equation 7.12

$$n_a{}^R = \left(\frac{\overline{E_R}}{E_d}\right)^{1/2} \exp(-\alpha) \qquad 7.15$$

In practice values of $n\,{}^R_a$ are such that the above is well approximated by

$$n\,{}^R_a = 1.32\left(\frac{\epsilon E_O}{E_d}\right)^{1/2} \exp(-\alpha) \qquad 7.16$$

so the expression for the number of sputtered atoms may be written

$$S = n_a = \left(\frac{\epsilon E_O}{E_d}\right)^{1/2} \sum_{n=1}^{n_c} (F_p + 1.32\,\delta_{n1} F_R)$$

$$\exp(-\alpha\sqrt{n}).\exp[-(n-1)\xi/2] \qquad 7.17$$

where F_p is the probability of an ion penetrating the target ($F_p = 1 - F_R$), $\delta_{nl} = 0\ (n \neq 1); = 1\ (n = 1)$ When no atoms are sputtered $E = E_T$ and the equation reduces to

$$E_T = \frac{E_d}{\epsilon} \qquad 7.18$$

ϵ may be evaluated, E_T, the threshold energy for sputtering, can be found experimentally and therefore E_d, may be calculated. This expression for the sputtering yield is shown by Keywell[25] to give a very satisfactory fit to experimental results and Rol et al[43] have shown that the theoretically predicted curve of Keywell in the 0-5 keV region smoothly joins their 5-25 keV experimental curve for A^+ bombardment of copper.

Goldman and Simon[160] assumed, for light ions, that the first collision with a metal atom was of the Rutherford type (see Chapter 2) and that subsequent collisions of displaced atoms were similar to collisions of hard spheres. They further assumed that the number of primary knock-on particles per incident particle was inversely proportional to the mean free path λ of the incident particle and also that the sputtering ratio was proportional to the average number of displaced particles $\overline{\nu}$, which is given by Seitz and Koehler[161] as

$$\overline{\nu} = \left[0.895 + 0.561 \ln\left(\frac{x+1}{4}\right)\right] \frac{x+1}{x} \qquad 7.19$$

where

$$x + 1 = \frac{4M_1M_2}{(M_1 + M_2)^2} \cdot \frac{E}{E_d} \qquad 7.20$$

Finally, assuming that the basic feature of sputtering was the displacement of an internal bound atom in the lattice with an energy (E_d) of approximately 25 eV, Goldman and Simon were able to derive the following expression for the sputtering yield:

$$S = 0.17 \cdot \frac{\overline{\nu}\, Z_1^2.Z_2^2.M_1}{E.E_dR^2M_2} \cdot \frac{1}{\cos\theta} \qquad 7.21$$

Z_1, Z_2 are the atomic numbers of the ion and target respectively, R the hard-sphere radius for the secondary collisions and the angle of incidence of the ion beam with respect to the target normal. The equation may be written in the more general form

$$S = A.\overline{\nu}.\frac{\sigma_d}{\sigma_s} \qquad 7.22$$

where σ_d is the cross-section for the displacement of a primary atom, σ_s the cross-section for the collision of the displaced atom with lattice atoms and A a coefficient characterising the emergence of displaced atoms from the metal. At high energies the expression of Goldman and Simon predicts a linear decrease in the S − log E curve. Fig. 7.30 presents data obtained by Kaminsky together with theoretical curves of Goldman and Simon and others for 0.1 to 2 MeV D^+ bombardment of Cu (100) and Ag (100) and the agreement is seen to be particularly good for the Goldman and Simon expression, (curve d of Fig. 7.30) though this must be to some extent fortuitous as their expression allows no correction for channelling and focusing events which must occur in the single crystal copper target.

Pease[162], has given a much simplified mean free path theory which follows closely the treatment given Kinchin and Pease[163] and Goldman and Simon[160] above for radiation damage events. He has assumed that ions make several collisions with target atoms before coming to rest and has derived an effective collision cross-section for low, medium and high bombarding energies, using hard-sphere, weakly screened Coulomb collisions and unscreened Coulomb collisions, respectively. Consideration of the probable number of primary 'knock-on' target atoms which can reach the surface with sufficient energy to liberate a surface atom leads to the following sputtering formula:

$$S = \frac{\overline{E}}{4E_d}\left[1 + \left(\frac{\ln \overline{E}/E_s}{\ln 2}\right)^{1/2}\right]\sigma_p.n^{2/3} \qquad 7.23$$

where, $\overline{E}$ = average energy transferred from an ion to a target atom, E_d = displacement energy, E_s = energy required to remove an atom from the target surface, n = number of atoms of target material per unit volume and σ_p = displacement cross-section in collision, calculated using one of the three interaction potentials listed above according to the energy regime considered. Values calculated from this expression by Grønlund and Moore[45] show that they are one half those measured experimentally, but curve b in Fig. 7.30 shows that the trend of the yield curve is correctly predicted. The agreement is very satisfactory when it is remembered that the expression for the yield contains no adjustable parameters and indicates that the picture provided by the collision theory may be essentially correct.

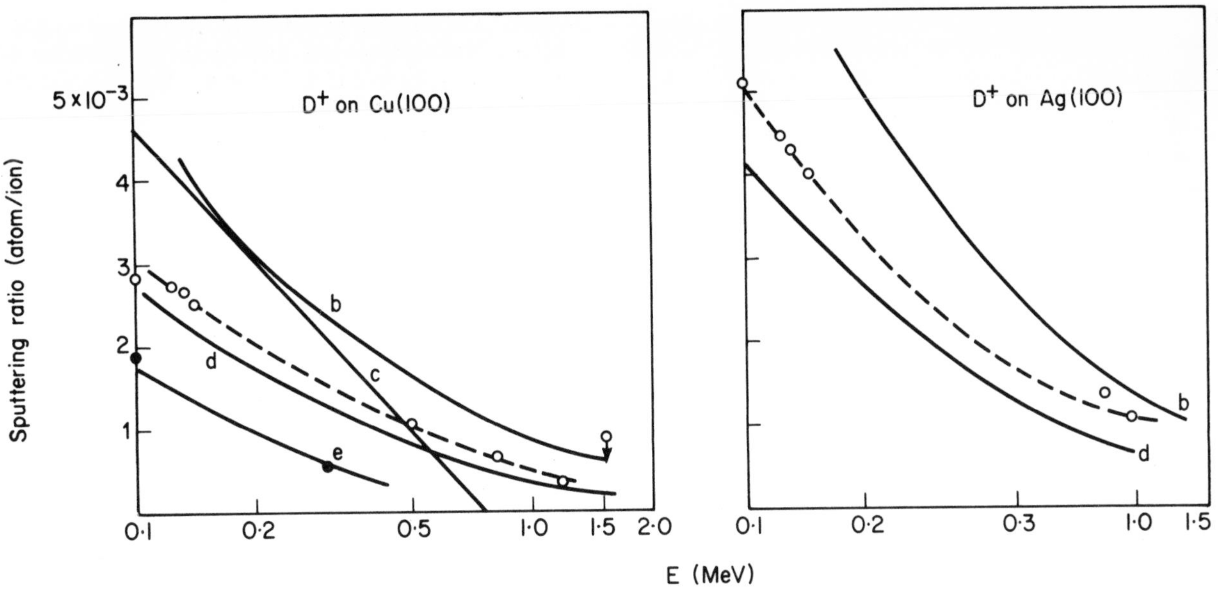

Fig. 7.30 Comparison of calculated sputtering ratios with experimental values for D^+ ions on Cu (100) and Ag (100) in the high energy (Rutherford Collision) region b Pease[162]; c Thompson[178]; d Goldman and Simon[160]; e Goldman Harrison and Coveyou[197]; ● Harrison[177]; ○ Experimental values of Kaminsky[198,199] (viz. Ref. 7.110).

Henschke[164] has presented a more complicated theoretical treatment on the lines of Pease and obtains a formula for S which is in good agreement with experimental results. He assumed that the ions and target atoms undergo purely mechanical and perfectly elastic collisons and that energy was lost during the collisions by the excitation of Debye waves (phonons) in the lattice. Formulae were derived for sputtering yields at normal and oblique ion incidence and, from the general expression, an equation for the threshold energy could be obtained. In a later paper[165] Henschke showed that his expression for the threshold energy was identical to the relationship quoted by Wehner[70]:

$$E_T = \frac{Q}{\Lambda} \cdot C \qquad 7.24$$

where Q is the heat of sublimation of the target material, $\Lambda = 4M_1M_2/(M_1 + M_2)^2$ and C is a constant of proportionality. Henschke's theory further showed that the sputtering rate was dependent on the filling of the 'd' shells in the target atoms; an effect demonstrated experimentally by Laegreid and Wehner[36].

A theory which gives a good fit to experimental sputtering yields at very low energies has been developed by Langberg[166] who showed that the interaction between atoms may be represented by a Morse potential and that the sputtering sequence may be considered as a series of binary collisions. By considering the most efficient sequence for ejection of an atom under normal ion bombarment and taking into account the number of bonds holding the sputtered particle to the surface N and also its nearest neighbours n Langberg determined a threshold value

$$E_N = \frac{10}{\Lambda} \cdot Q \cdot \left(1{\cdot}1\frac{N}{\Lambda} + 0{\cdot}2\right) \left[1 - \frac{1}{ad}\ln(1 + 0{\cdot}83\sqrt{N})\right]^{-2} \qquad 7.25$$

where

Λ, is the energy transfer factor $4M_1M_2/(M_1 + M_2)^2$,

Q is the heat of sublimation

d = equilibrium atomic spacing

and

$$a = \frac{1}{2}\sqrt{\left(\frac{nk}{Q}\right)}$$

where

$$k = \frac{M_2c^2}{d^2} \quad (c = \text{velocity of sound})$$

Langberg further showed that this theory is well approximated by Wehner's empirical threshold law (equation 7.24). For sputtering at energies just above threshold Langberg assumed that the probability of ejection was a function of the energy of the ion in excess of E_N. Assuming this probability was a constant, b, for energies between the minimum-bond threshold E_b and the full-plane threshold E_a the yield was derived by Langberg to be

$$S = \tfrac{1}{2}b(E - E_b)^2 \qquad 7.26$$

and, for energies in excess of E_a,

$$S = b(E - E_b)[E - \tfrac{1}{2}(E_a + E_b)] \qquad 7.27$$

The theory thus predicts the initial quadratic tail of the sputtering curve and Langberg was able to show that the predicted yields could be made to fit experimental values by varying the parameter 'b'.

Rol et al[167] deduced from experiments on monocrystalline targets of copper that the collisions of the ion which take place closest to the target surface are mainly responsible for sputtering, in other words the yield is dependent on the possible energy transferred in the first collision of the ion and the mean free path of the ion into the target material (λ). Thus they obtained:

$$S \propto \frac{1}{\lambda(E)} \cdot \frac{M_1 M_2}{(M_1 + M_2)^2} \cdot E \qquad 7.28$$

When oblique incidence is considered the distance from the surface to the probable collision depth changes to $\lambda(E) \cos\theta$ so that:

$$S = K \frac{1}{\lambda(E) \cos\theta} \cdot \frac{M_1 M_2}{(M_1 + M_2)^2} \cdot E \qquad 7.29$$

For the rigid sphere model the collision radius for a screened potential can be calculated as[123]:

$$R = C \frac{a_0}{Z_1^{2/3} + Z_2^{2/3}} \ln\left(\frac{Z_1 Z_2 e}{\epsilon_0 R E'}\right) \qquad 7.30$$

where, $E' = M_1 E/(M_1 + M_2)$, C is a constant, a_0 = radius of the hydrogen atom, e the electron charge and ϵ_0 the dielectric constant in vacuo. The mean free path is then given by

$$\lambda = (\pi R^2 n_0)^{-1} \qquad 7.31$$

where n_0 = number of lattice atoms per unit volume. By choosing K as 1.67×10^{-11} m/eV and C as 1 (Bohr value) the sputtering yields for bombardment of copper by several ion species could be predicted fairly accurately.

Almén and Bruce[39] have also put this formula to the test with great success and have found that, by suitable choice of the constant K, nearly all their experimental curves could be faithfully predicted. They have further sought an empirical rule to govern the constant K, and found, from correlation with their experimental results, that the rule:

$$K = a \exp(-E_B b \sqrt{M_1}/(M_1 + M_2)) \qquad 7.32$$

where E_B is the binding energy of the target atoms and a and b are further constants, was approximately true. By determining a and b from their curves they were able to derive the expression;

$$S \simeq 4.24 \cdot 10^{-10} n_0 R^2 E \cdot \frac{M_1 M_2}{(M_1 + M_2)^2} \cdot \exp\left(-10.4 \cdot \frac{\sqrt{M_1}}{M_1 + M_2} \cdot E_B\right) \qquad 7.33$$

where energies are in eV, R, the collision diameter which is related to the mean free path by equation 7.32, is in metres and n_0 in atoms per cubic metre. In general this equation gives results deviating by less than 20% from the measured values in the 10-60 keV region, but results for metals forming oxides are not reliable.

Southern et al[27] have used similar basic assumptions to Rol et al[167], but have presented a completely different theoretical treatment based mainly on effects at the first collision. Their basic assumptions were:

(i) the sputtering yield is determined with sufficient accuracy by the first collision of the incident ion with the atoms of the target, and,

(ii) the collision may be imagined to take place between hard spheres whose size determines the total microscopic cross-section for scattering of the incident ions by the target atoms. The energy transferred in the first collision is some transmission probability $\tau(E, \underline{u})$, where $\underline{u}$ specifies the incident ion direction, multiplied by the incoming ion energy E. $\tau(E, \underline{u})$ is defined by

$$\tau(E, \underline{u}) = \frac{2\overline{T}(E, \underline{u})}{T_m(E)} \qquad 7.34$$

where $\overline{T}(E, \underline{u})$ is the average energy transferred and $T_m(E)$ the maximum that could be transferred, thus $\tau(E, \underline{u}) \leq 1$. The probability of collision will be inversely proportional to the mean free path $\lambda(E, \underline{u})$ so that the yield, according to Southern et al, may be written as:

$$S(E, \underline{u}) = \alpha \frac{\tau(E, \underline{u}) \cdot E}{\lambda(E, \underline{u})} \qquad 7.35$$

They next considered an elementary section of lattice contained within the cube whose edges were formed by translations t_{hkl}, $t_{h'k'l'}$ and $t_{h''k''l''}$ in three crystal directions hkl, h'k'l and h"k"l"; these being mutually at right-angles in a cubic crystal. The translations were the maximum distances in the three directions before the crystal pattern repeated. Assuming that a fraction, p_{hkl}, of the incident ions collide within this elementary area and the average distance to the collision point is $\bar{x}_{hkl}$, then the remaining fraction $(1 - p_{hkl})$ of ions were presumed to have a fixed mean free path λ_0 which is independent of direction, but a function of energy. Therefore;

$$\lambda(E, u) = \lambda_{hkl}(E) = p_{hkl} \cdot \bar{x}_{hkl} + (1 - p_{hkl}) \cdot \lambda_0(E) \qquad 7.36$$

The energy transferred in a collision may be defined in terms of the impact parameter b (defined in Chapter 2). For hard-sphere collisions of radius R

$$\tau(E, \underline{u}) = 2\left(1 - \left\langle\frac{b^2}{R^2}\right\rangle_u\right) \qquad 7.37$$

where $\left\langle\frac{b^2}{R^2}\right\rangle_u$ is the average value. If the sphere 'shadows' do not overlap when projected onto the (hkl) plane $\frac{b^2}{R^2} = \frac{1}{2}$ and, therefore, $\tau(E, \underline{u}) = 1$ so, assuming that shadowing beyond the elementary section of the lattice is negligible,

$$\tau(E, \underline{u}) = \tau_{hkl}(E) = (1 - p_{hkl}) \times 1 + p_{hkl}\left(2 - 2\left\langle\frac{b^2}{R^2}\right\rangle_{hkl}\right)$$

$$= 1 + p_{hkl}\left[1 - 2\left\langle\frac{b^2}{R^2}\right\rangle_{hkl}\right] \qquad 7.38$$

Inserting these values into equation 7.35 Southern et al obtained:

$$S_{hkl}(E) = \frac{\alpha\left[1 + p_{hkl}\left(1 - 2\left\langle\frac{b^2}{R^2}\right\rangle_{hkl}\right)\right]E}{p_{hkl}\,\bar{x}_{hkl} + (1 - p_{hkl})\lambda_0} \qquad 7.39$$

A computer programme was then devised for evaluations of the terms p_{hkl}, $\bar{x}_{hkl}$, $\left\langle \frac{b^2}{R^2} \right\rangle_{hkl}$, following as many as ten thousand histories in crystals comprising one thousand atoms or less and the above equation was fitted to the experimental curve for monocrystalline copper targets bombarded by argon ions at normal incidence. Calculated and observed yields were found to be in good agreement, but the parameter required to fit the curves was found to decrease according to $E^{-1/2}$. In other words, the equation should not be of the form $S \propto E$, but $S \propto E^{1/2}$, indicating that it is the momentum which dictates the sputtering yield rather than the ion energy.

Smith[168] has improved the model of Southern et al by introducing a momentum conductance factor $p(\underline{u})$ which removes the dependence of yield upon the first collision depth and takes account of momentum focusing along close-packed directions. Equation 7.35 which gives the yield for the theory of Southern et al is therefore modified to

$$S(E, \underline{u}) = \alpha \frac{\tau(E, \underline{u})}{\lambda(E, \underline{u})} \cdot p(\underline{u}) \qquad 7.40$$

where $p(\underline{u})$ is defined as the distance to the first collision (i.e. $\lambda(E, \underline{u})$ times the sum of the inverse distances form the collision to the surface under consideration. Thus

$$p(\underline{u}) = \lambda(E, u)\Sigma i / |\underline{\nu_i}| \qquad 7.41$$

where $\underline{\nu_i}$ is the ith $\langle 011 \rangle$ vector from the collision point intercepting the surface specified by $\underline{u}$.

For purposes of comparison the momentum conductance factor was normalized with respect to some crystal surface, arbitrarily chosen as (001), thus

$$P_{(hkl)} = p_{(hkl)}/p_{(001)} \qquad 7.42$$

Fig. 7.31a illustrates the variation of $P_{(hkl)}$ as a function of the crystal orientation $\langle 0kl \rangle$ chosen by Southern et al and Fig. 7.31b shows the results (points) and theoretical curve for the yield before modification of the Southern et al theory. It is clear that the correction factor is greatest where the existing theory is most in error and Smith concludes that this indicates that the introduction of the additional factor $P_{(hkl)}$ will yield better quantitative agreement between theory and experiment.

Southern et al were not convinced that their theory was strict enough to decide whether the law is $S \propto E$ or $S \propto E^{1/2}$. Magnuson and Carlston[40], on the other hand, considered that the indications were sufficient to derive a more simple theory on similar lines to the above using momentum transfer as the main parameter. Again an elementary crystal area was studied and ions passing through this area were not considered useful in the sputtering sequence so were neglected. The yield was assumed to be proportional to the product of the absolute value of the momentum transferred to lattice atoms in the first collision of the bombarding ion and the probability that a collision would occur in the elementary crystal section. The collision probability was described by the 'opacity' which is the reciprocal of the 'transparency' term introduced by Fluit et al[125]. Thus the yield could be written;

$$S_{hkl} = K_{hkl} \cdot E^{1/2} \cdot Pc_{hkl} \qquad 7.43$$

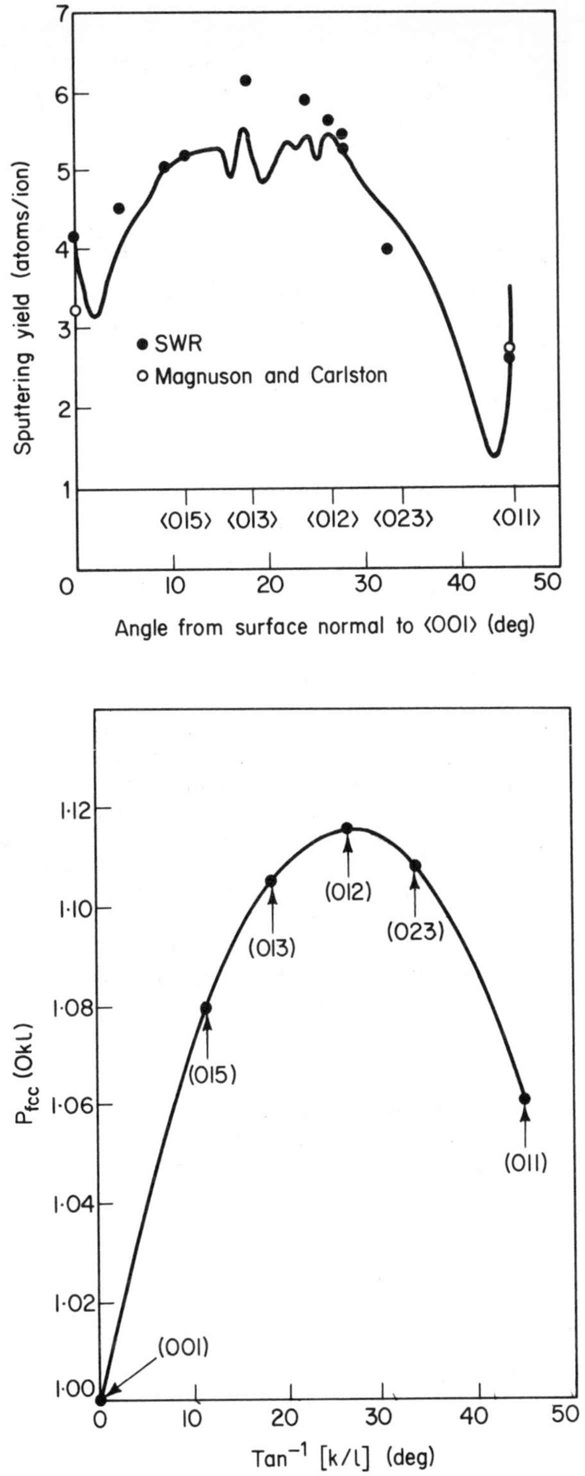

Fig. 7.31 (a) Sputtering yield of (Okl) Cu monocrystals under normally incident 5 keV A^+ ion bombardment plotted against the angle between the surface normal and $\langle 001 \rangle$. Solid curve is predicted by theory of Southern et al[27]. ● Experimental points of Magnuson et al[40]. (b) Momentum conductance factor P(hkl) for (Okl) fcc monocrystals plotted against the angle between the surface normal and $\langle 001 \rangle$ (viz. Ref. 7.168)

where K_{hkl} = proportionality constant dependent on the crystal plane bombarded, Pc_{hkl} = probability of collision between an ion and lattice atom for an ion incident normally on the (hkl) plane. All mass factors were absorbed into the constant K. Consideration of an elementary parallelopiped of the lattice allowed determination of the opacity of the material and

$$Pc_{hkl} = \frac{A_C}{A_T} \qquad 7.44$$

where, A_C = total projected area of lattice atoms and A_T = total area of (hkl) surface considered.

A Bohr screened coulomb potential was used to determine collision cross-sections, but it was found that a slight adjustment of this potential was required to fit theoretical predictions with experimental results. Thus, the following was used:

$$V(r) = \left(\frac{Z_1 Z_2 e^2}{r}\right) \exp\left(-\frac{r}{a_B}\right) \qquad 7.45$$

where

$$a_B = \frac{ka_0}{(Z_1^{2/3} + Z_2^{2/3})^{1/2}} \qquad 7.46$$

a_0 = Bohr radius, k = adjustable parameter and r = radial separation between atoms. Actual radii of hard spheres were taken as $R = c. R_{HC}$ (where R_{HC} is the hard-core approximate radius) to allow for the apparent shortcoming of the Bohr treatment. The parameters k and c were varied to fit the (111) experimental curve shape and the ordinate was fixed by suitable choice of K_{111}. The same k and c values were then used for other planes and K_{hkl} only was varied to normalize the theoretical curve to the experimental points. Typical k and c values are shown in Table 7.5, and theoretical predictions compared with results of Fluit et al[125] are shown in Table 7.6.

TABLE 7.5 (Ref. 7.40)

Parameters k and c (defined in text) to fit theoretical values of the sputtering yield to experimental data

	k	c
Cu	1.20 ± 0.20	2.35 ± 0.05
Ag	1.50 ± 0.20	2.45 ± 0.05

TABLE 7.6

Theoretical sputtering yields for 20 keV A⁺ ion bombardment of copper using the calculation of Magnuson et al[40] compared with experimental values obtained by Fluit et al[125]

Crystal Face :	(111)	(100)	(110)
Theory :	6.5	2.9	1.9
Experiment :	7.3	3.2	2.2

The agreement with experimental data is extremely good except in the more open planes ((100) and (110)), presumably because the theory does not consider the depth below the surface at which collisions causing sputtering occur, nor are chaining collisions considered. Both Southern et al[27] and Magnuson et al[40] considered that the reason for the Bohr collision cross-sections being too small was probably due in part to the presence of ions buried in the target material as neutral species and to the continual upheaval and damage to the surfaces during bombardment.

Another treatment which considers that relevant sputtering collisions occur in the first atomic layer of the surface has been presented by Bulgakov[169], though the expression derived by him does not take into account differences in collision radii in different crystal directions so the resulting equation must be applied to polycrystalline materials only. The following model was considered; referring to Fig. 7.32.

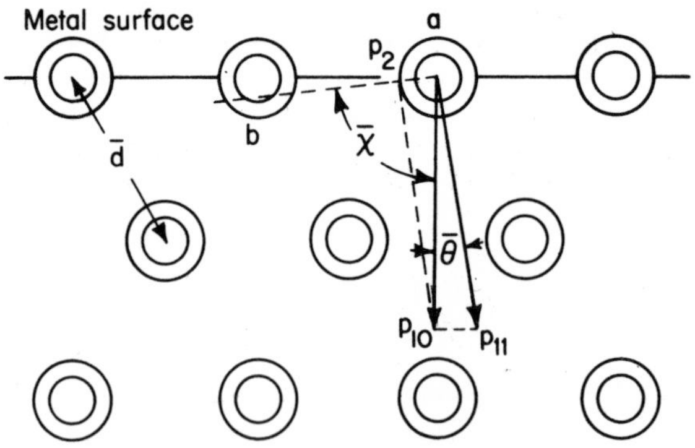

Fig. 7.32 Illustrating the displacement of a primary atom by an ion. p_{10} is the initial momentum and p_{11} the momentum of the ion after scattering. p_2 is the momentum of the displaced atom. The figure is drawn to the scale of a collision of a 30 keV deuteron with a copper atom. Outer circles correspond to collision radii for copper-copper collision whilst inner circles correspond to deuteron-copper collision (viz. Ref. 7.169)

(i) an incoming ion strikes atom 'a' and is deflected by angle θ and then lost in the body of the metal,

(ii) 'a' moves off at angle $\overline{\chi}$ and may collide with surface atom 'b', or, reflect itself from a strongly bound atom in the second layer and be sputtered, or, penetrate the second layer and be lost in the body of the metal,

(iii) it is assumed that primaries such as 'a' will contribute to sputtering if $E > E_H$ and the collision is within the first atomic layer, where E_H is the heat of sublimation,

(iv) it is further assumed that the mean energy of primaries is equal to several times E_H.

Thus the sputtering ratio could be represented by $\omega_1 \times \omega_2$, where ω_1 = probability of creation of a sufficiently energetic primary and ω_2 = probability of its collision with target atoms in the first layer. If σ_H is the cross-section for transfer of energy $E > E_H$.

$$\omega_1 = \sigma_H / q \qquad 7.47$$

where q is the mean area per atom of surface layer. ω_2 is given by the ratio of the path length of the primary before it crosses the second layer boundary to the length of its free-path in the metal;

$$\omega_2 = 1 - \exp(\overline{D}/\lambda\ \overline{\cos\chi}) \qquad 7.48$$

$\overline{D} = n^{-1/3}$ = mean interatomic spacing in metal,

$\lambda = (n\sigma_s)^{-1}, \sigma_s$ = cross-section for scattering of displaced atom on collision with its neighbour.

According to Bohr[170] and Seitz and Koehler[123] σ_H may may be evaluated from:

$$\sigma_H = \pi . \frac{M_1}{M_2} . \frac{Z_1^2 Z_2^2 e^4}{E_0 . E_H} \qquad 7.49$$

for sufficiently high values of E_0 ($\gg 2E_{Ry} \times Z_1 Z_2^{4/3}$, where E_{Ry} is the Rydberg energy; 13.5 eV) the incident ion energy. $\sigma_s = \pi R^2$ can be calculated from the model of strongly screened Coulomb collisions, where R is obtained from

$$\frac{\overline{E}}{2} = \frac{Z_2^2 e^2}{R} \exp\left(-\frac{R\sqrt{2}. Z_2^{1/3}}{a_0}\right) \qquad 7.50$$

a_0 is the Bohr radius and

$$\overline{E} = E_H \ln\left(\frac{4M_1}{M_2} . \frac{E_0}{E_H}\right) \qquad 7.51$$

Also, for $M_1 \ll M_2$

$$\overline{\sin^2 \tfrac{1}{2}\theta} = \frac{M_2}{4M_1} . \frac{\overline{E}}{E_0} \qquad 7.52$$

and, for small θ

$$\overline{\theta} = \left(\frac{M_2}{M_1} . \frac{\overline{E}}{E_0}\right)^{1/2} \qquad 7.53$$

Finally

$$\overline{\cos\chi} = \overline{\cos \tfrac{1}{2}(\pi - \theta)} = \tfrac{1}{2}\overline{\theta} = \tfrac{1}{2}\left(\frac{M_2}{M_1} . \frac{\overline{E}}{E_0}\right)^{1/2} \qquad 7.54$$

Thus, ω_1 and ω_2 were determined completely and the yield could be written;

$$S = 4\pi a_0^2 \left(\frac{\rho N_0}{M_2}\right)^{2/3} \frac{M_1}{M_2} . \frac{Z_1^2 Z_2^2}{E_H . E_0} . E_{Ry}^2 \Big[1 - \exp\left\{-\left(\frac{\rho N_0}{M_2}\right)^{2/3} \left(\frac{4M_1 E_0}{\overline{E} . M_2}\right)^{1/2} . \sigma_s\right\}\Big] \qquad 7.55$$

where N_0 is Avogadro's number.

Bulgakov found that the above expression gave low yields at high energy, but attributed this to the fact that the treatment overlooked the possibility that two or more atoms of 'primary' status may be initiated by one incoming ion.

Odintsov[171] has presented a theory which attempts to describe the effect on yield of the rotation of a single crystal. The theory is identical to that proposed for secondary electron emission in Chapter 3 so that it will not be reiterated here. The resulting expression shows that

$$S = \frac{1}{A_0 \cos^2\theta}\left\{\alpha_{1,2} \pi R^2 . \frac{E_{max}}{2} + \alpha_{3,4} S_3 \overline{E}_3 + \alpha_{5,6} S_5 . \overline{E}_5 + \ldots\right\} \qquad 7.56$$

where θ is the angle of incidence of the incident beam with respect to the surface normal.

The parameters $\alpha_{1,2}, \alpha_{3,4}, \ldots$ etc. represent the contribution of each pair of successively deeper planes in the material and were found by fitting the equation to an experimental curve. In fact the first three α values are approximately equal at 0.00165 eV^{-1} whilst, for $\alpha_{7,8}$ and lower planes, values are so small that their contribution can be neglected for large angles of incidence. These planes should however be considered for angles of incidence approaching normal.

The theory describes the results of the angular dependence of yield obtained by Rol et al[126, 172] for 20 keV Ne^+ and A^+ bombardment of copper and Molchanov et al[127, 129] for 27 keV A^+ bombardment of copper and nickel fairly well, but for the above theory to fit experimental results the hard sphere radius for collisions has to be assumed to be exceptionally large. Martynenko[173] has presented a more rigorous theory which calculates the contributions of each atomic layer to the sputtering process and further considers that the energy transferred to the target atoms is redirected to the surface by means of focusons. The theory which considers only ⟨110⟩ focusons in fcc crystals indicates that a marked screening effect is provided by the surface atoms on atoms in the second atomic layer, so much so that the shadow of an atom on the second plane has an effective radius 5-8 times the hard-sphere radius used in the atomic collision calculation. It is this shadowing effect that has made the apparent radii used by Odintsov[171] to appear so large. Martynenko takes this screening effect of upper layers of atoms into account and derives the mean energy transfer to an atom in any plane

$$\overline{\epsilon} = \overline{\epsilon}_0 \, F(r_i, \delta_i) \qquad 7.57$$

where $\overline{\epsilon}_0$ is the mean energy transferred to surface atoms and the function $F(r_i, \delta_i)$ determines the probability of collision between the ion and an atom in the ith layer and is calculated for various positions on the atomic planes below the surface. If δ_i is the projection of the distance between the screened and screening atom onto a plane perpendicular to the motion of the ions and r_i is the radius of the shadow produced by the screening atom in the ith layer

$$F(r_i, \delta_i) = \begin{cases} r_i p^2(\Lambda E); & \delta i < r_i - p(\Lambda E) \\ \tfrac{1}{2} + \dfrac{\delta_i - r_i}{4p(\Lambda E)}; & r_i - p(\Lambda E) < \delta_i < r_i + p(\Lambda E) \\ 1 - \dfrac{r_i p^2(\Lambda E)}{(r_i^2 - \delta_i^2)^2}; & r_i + p(\Lambda E) < \delta_i \end{cases} \qquad 7.58$$

where $p(\Lambda E) = 0.88R$, where R is the minimum distance to which an ion can approach an atom in a head-on collision and $\Lambda = 4 M_1 M_2/(M_1 + M_2)^2$. The value of R and r_i were determined by using an interaction potential of the form

$$V(r) = \frac{Z_1 Z_2 e^2}{r} . \chi . \frac{(\sqrt{Z_1} + \sqrt{Z_2})^{2/3} . r}{4.7 \times 10^{-9}} \qquad 7.59$$

where χ is the Thomas-Fermi screening function. Using this potential the mean energy transferred in the atomic layer is given by

$$\overline{\epsilon}_0 = \epsilon_0 . \frac{\ln(1 + E/E_1)}{E/E_1} \qquad 7.60$$

where

$$E_1 = 43.5\ Z_1 Z_2\ (\sqrt{Z_1} + \sqrt{Z_2})^{2/3}\ (\text{eV}) \qquad 7.61$$

and the radius of the shadow

$$r_i = 2.2\left(\frac{d_i . A}{(\mu + 1)E}\right)^{1/3} \qquad 7.62$$

where $\mu = M_2/M_1$ and d_i is the projection of the distance between the screened and screening atoms on the direction of motion of the ions. Having obtained the energy tranfer Martynenko applies a simplified version of Leibfried's[174] expression to obtain the number of focusons which give rise to atomic ejection. The number of focusons with energy between E and E + dE, X(E) is written

$$X(E) = \begin{cases} \dfrac{2a_0}{D} . \dfrac{\epsilon}{E_F{}^2} . \ln \dfrac{E_F}{E}\ \left(1 + \dfrac{1}{2} \ln \dfrac{E_F}{E}\right) & E > E_F \\ O & E > E_F \end{cases} \qquad 7.63$$

where E_F is the maximum energy at which focusing is possible and D is the interatomic spacing in the focusing direction. By integrating this expression over all the focuson energies which can lead to ejection of a surface atom Martynenko obtained the number of atoms liberated due to the collision momentum which is transferred to the ith layer,

$$n_i = \frac{2a\epsilon}{D. E_F}\left[2 - \frac{E_m}{E_F}\left(2 + 2 \ln \frac{E_F}{E_m} + \frac{1}{2} \ln^2 \frac{E_F}{E_m}\right)\right] \qquad 7.64$$

E_m is the lowest energy of focusons in the ith layer which can cause sputtering and is given by

$$E_m = E_b + E_F . aRi/L \cos \chi \qquad 7.65$$

where E_b is the binding energy of a surface atom. L is the maximum distance which can be covered by a focused collision chain, χ the angle between the surface normal and the focusing chain direction and aR is the shortest distance between atomic planes.

Equation 7.64 shows that n_i is proportional to the energy transferred in the layer ϵ and the expression could be re-written

$$n_i = \nu_i . \overline{\epsilon_i} \qquad 7.66$$

with ν_i the constant of proportionality. The sputtering yield is thus given by

$$S = \Sigma_i \frac{\alpha_i}{\cos \phi} . \overline{\epsilon_i} \qquad 7.67$$

where Σ denotes summation over all $\langle 110 \rangle$ directions, α_i is the sum of ν_i contributions in each possible focusing direction and ϕ is the angle of deflection of the incident beam at the ith plane. Using equation 7.57 the expression for the yield may also be written

$$S = \frac{\epsilon_0}{\cos\theta . \cos\psi} \Sigma_i\ \alpha_i\ F(r_i, \delta_i) \qquad 7.68$$

where θ is the angle of incidence of the ion beam with respect to the target normal and ψ the angle between the incident beam and the inner normal to the crystallographic plane considered. If n is the number of focusons emerging from the surface and n^0 number in all directions on an isotropic model

$$\Sigma n = \frac{1}{\cos\psi} \Sigma n^0 \qquad 7.69$$

Martynenko calculated the yield for 30 keV A^+ bombarding copper (100) and (110) surfaces and has obtained very good agreement with the experimental data of Molchanov et al[53 129] as indicated in figures 7.33a and b.

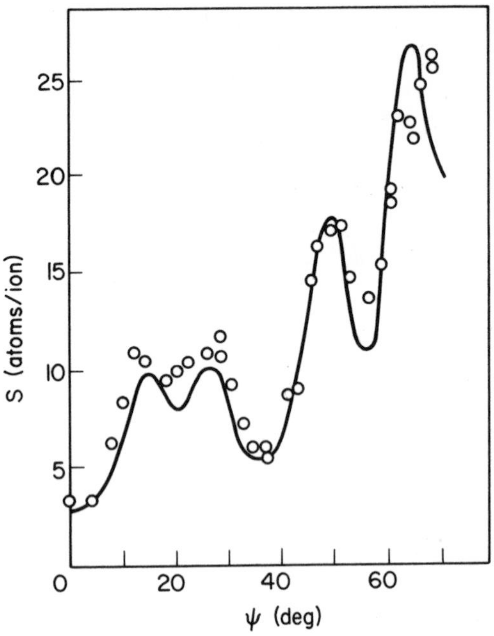

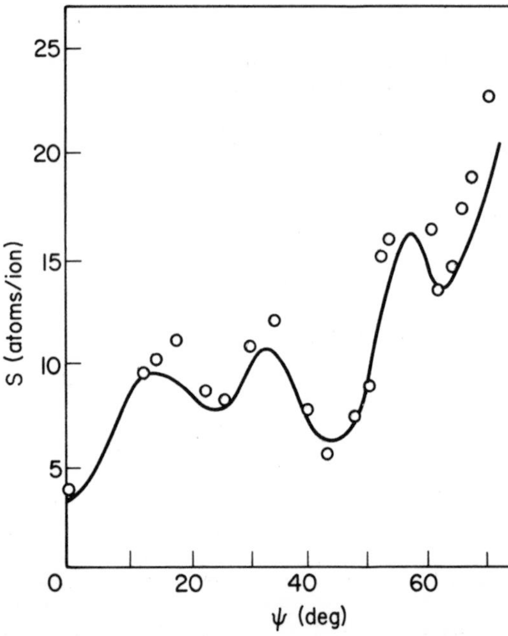

Fig. 7.33(a) Theoretical yield as a function of angle of incidence for 27 keV A^+ bombardment of the (100) surface of monocrystalline copper rotated about the $\langle 110 \rangle$ direction; circles represent experimental results of Molchanov et al[53]. (b) Theoretical yield as a function of angle of incidence for 30 keV A^+ bombardment of the (110) surface of monocrystalline copper rotated about the $\langle 100 \rangle$ direction. Circles represent experimental results of Mashkova et al[129] (viz. Ref. 7.173)

In a later paper Martynenko[173a] has obtained a generalization of the sputtering formula (equation 7.68) for large ion energies where the interaction potential becomes Coulombic. Assuming on average that there are four ⟨110⟩ directions which reach the surface he obtained a simplified expression for $\overline{\alpha_i}$ using equation 7.64

$$\overline{\alpha_i} = \frac{11.4a}{DE_F}\left(1 - \frac{E_b}{E_F} - \frac{\sqrt{2}.D}{L}.i\right)^3 \qquad 7.70$$

Thus, substituting in equation 7.68 and assuming that

$$\sum_i^{-i_m} \alpha_i = \sum_i^{-i_m} \overline{\alpha_i} \qquad 7.71$$

(where i_m is the number of the layer for which $\delta i_m - r i_m = 0$) and replacing $F(\delta_i, r_i)$ by equation 7.58 and $\cos^{-1}\theta$ by $\sqrt{2}$, Martynenko obtains an expression for the yield from polycrystalline targets

$$S = \frac{16a\epsilon_0}{D.E_F\cos\psi}\left(1 - \frac{E_b}{E_F}\right)^3 \frac{\ln(1 + E/E_1)}{E/E_1}\, i_m$$

$$\left[1 - \frac{3}{2}.\frac{i_m}{i_1} + \left(\frac{i_m}{i_1}\right)^2 - \frac{1}{4}\left(\frac{i_m}{i_1}\right)^3\right] \qquad 7.72$$

If the radius of the shadow of atoms is less than the maximum impact parameter p_0 equation 7.72 reduces to

$$S = \frac{16a\epsilon_0}{D.E_F\cos\psi}.\left(1 - \frac{E_b}{E_F}\right)^3 i_m\left(\frac{E_b{}^2\ (\mu + 1)}{A}\right) \qquad 7.73$$

The conditions for equation 7.73 to hold are satisfied for 5-10 keV sputtering by heavy ions and Martynenko has shown that this expression gives results in reasonable agreement with experimental values for 20-200 keV Ne^+, A^+, Kr^+ and Xe^+ bombardment of copper obtained by Yonts et al[181], Rol et al[95], Almén et al[38] and Perovic et al[202]. Further, the theory predicts $S \propto \ln E_0/E_0$ at higher energies in accordance with the theory of Goldman and Simon.

Many other theories have been developed, including a rigorous statistical approach by Harrison[175 176 177] and a treatment taking into account focusing in crystal directions by Thompson[178], but the former concludes with equations containing unknown parameters which are difficult to fit to actual cases. We conclude this theoretical survey with a brief account of the high energy sputtering theories of Thompson[178] and Lehmann[179] which are the only theories apart from Martynenko's treatment which take into account focused collision chains. Thompson's theory considers two high energy regions (1) $E_0 < L_A$ where

$$L_A = 2E_R\, Z_1Z_2\, (Z_1^{2/3} + Z_2^{2/3})^{1/2}\, (M_1 + M_2)/M_2 \qquad 7.74$$

Here collisions can be described by the Bohr screened-Coulomb potential and (2) $E_0 > L_B$ where

$$L_B = 4E_R^2 Z_1^2 Z_2^2\, (Z_1^{2/3} + Z_2^{2/3}) M_1/M_2 E_b \qquad 7.75$$

In this region collisions are described by an unscreened-Coulomb potential. In the above, E_R is the Rydberg energy and E_b the binding energy of target atoms.

The range of an incident ion is given by Nielsen[180] as

$$R_1 = \frac{2\pi^2\ em}{5h^2\ d}.\frac{(Z_1^{2/3} + Z_2^{2/3})^{1/2}.M_1 + M_2}{Z_1 + Z_2\qquad M_1}.E_0 \qquad 7.76$$

(see Chapter 5) where m = electron mass, h = Planck's constant, d = atomic density and e is the base of natural logarithms. Thompson's theory applies for cases where $R_1 \gg R_f{}^{110}$ where $R_f{}^{110}$ is the range of a focused collision chain in the close-packed ⟨110⟩ direction of a fcc lattice. This condition, together with the assumption that the distance travelled by the recoil atom before focusing is much smaller than $R_f{}^{110}$, restricts the theory to cases where $Z_1 < \frac{1}{5} Z_2$. As seen in Chapter 6, the number of focused collision sequences in a particular ⟨110⟩ direction with energies in the range E to E + dE produced by a recoil with energy E_2 is given by Liebfried[174] as

$$X_1(E_2, E)dE = \begin{cases} \frac{2a}{D}.\frac{1}{E_0}\ln\frac{E_F}{E} & E < E_2 \\ 0 & E > E_2 \end{cases}$$

For $E_2 < E_F$ 7.77a

$$X_2(E_2, E)dE = \begin{cases} \frac{2a}{D}.\frac{E_2}{E_F{}^2}\ln\frac{E_F}{E} & E < E_F \\ 0 & E > E_F \end{cases}$$

For $E > E_F$ 7.77b

so that the number of sequences travelling in a ⟨110⟩ direction with energy in excess of a value E due to the recoil E_2 is given by:

$$n_1\ (E_2, E) = \int_E^{E_2} X_1\ dE \qquad 7.78a$$

$$n_2\ (E_2, E) = \int_E^{E_f} X_2\ dE \qquad 7.87b$$

If the ⟨110⟩ direction makes an angle ϕ with the surface normal then the total number of sequences per incident ion due to a recoil atom with energy E_2 in the slab of material extending between r and r + dr from the surface (measured along the ⟨110⟩ direction) is given by:

$$S\ (E_2)dE_2.\,dr\ \cos\phi.\,n(E_2, E) \qquad 7.79$$

where, for $E_0 < L_A$,

$$S(E_2)dE_2 = \pi\alpha^2 d.\,L_A\, dE_2/e\Lambda E_0{}^2 \qquad 7.80$$

and is the number of recoils produced with energy E_2 per unit volume due to bombardment by one ion per unit area. In this equation $\alpha = a_0\ (Z_1^{2/3} + Z_2^{2/3})^{-1/2}$ a_0 = the Bohr radius and $\Lambda = 4\ M_1M_2/(M_1 + M_2)^2$. In the case $E_0 > L_B$

$$S(E_2)dE_2 = 4M_1 Z_1^2 Z_2^2 E_R^2 \pi a_0^2 d.\,dE_2/M_2 E_0 E_2^2 \qquad 7.81$$

for $E_b < E_2 < E_0$, otherwise it is zero.

The functions $n(E_2, E)$ may be transformed to functions of r. For an initial recoil energy E_f the range is R_f so that the energy loss per unit distance for sequences which terminate at the surface of the target is $(E_f - E_b)/R_f$ i.e. approximately, E_f/R_f. Thus the range of recoils having an energy greater than E is a value greater than r where

$$r = (E - E_b)/(E_f/R_f) \qquad 7.82$$

Therefore

$$E = E_b + E_f . r/R_f \qquad 7.83$$

and n (E_2, E) becomes $n(E_2, E_b + E_f . r/R_f)$ which will be written $n(E_2, r)$.

Hence the number of atoms ejected in direction ϕ by a recoil with energy E_2 to $E_2 + dE_2$ at depth r to r + dr is given by

$$dN_\phi = S(E_2)\ n(E_2, r)dr \cos \phi . dE_2 \qquad 7.84$$

Therefore

$$N_\phi = \int_E^{\Lambda E_0} \int_0^{R_f} S(E_2)\ n(E_2, r)dr \cos \phi\ dE_2 \qquad 7.85$$

The limits of the first integral cover all possible recoil energies E_2 and the limits of the second-all possible values of r small enough to transmit energy to the surface.

The total yield for a random array of f.c.c. crystals each having 12 ⟨110⟩ directions is given by $3N_\phi/\cos \phi$ so that, using equation 7.85, substituting the appropriate expression for $S(E_2)$, and neglecting E_b/E_f in comparison with unity

$$S \simeq \frac{3\pi\alpha^2 d.\Lambda L_A}{4e} \cdot \frac{a}{D} \cdot \frac{R_f^{110}}{E_f^{110}} \left[1 + \left(\frac{E_f^{100}}{E_0}\right)^2\right] \text{for } E_0 < L_A \qquad 7.86$$

or, for $E_0 > L_B$,

$$S \simeq \frac{6Z_1^2 Z_2^2 E_R^2 \pi a_0^2 d.M_1}{M_2} \cdot \frac{a}{D} \cdot \frac{R_f^{110}}{E_f^{110}} \cdot \frac{F(E_0, E_f^{100}, E_b)}{E_0} \qquad 7.87$$

where

$$F(E_0, E_f^{110}, E_b) = (\ln x)^2 - 2 \ln x + 3/2 + [1 - (4/x)] \ln(\Lambda E_0/E_f^{110}) \qquad 7.88$$

$$x = E_f/E_b \gg 1$$

F is a slowly varying function of E_0 so that in this region S varies approximately as E_0^{-1}. Values of the focusing energy E_f^{110} and range R_f^{110} can be calculated from the assumed repulsion potential. For a Born-Mayer potential

$$V = A \exp(-r/a) = 1/2 E \qquad 7.89$$

The rule for focusing, given earlier in this chapter, is

$$R^{110} \geqslant 1/4 D^{110}. \text{ Thus } 1/2 E_f^{110} = A \exp(-D^{110}/2a) \qquad 7.90$$

Attenuation of these sequences occurs mainly by interaction with neighbouring lines of atoms and the range R_f^{110} for a sequence starting with energy E_f^{110} is quoted by Thompson as

$$R_f^{110} = 1/2 D^{110}/[\exp(-3D^{110}/8a) - \exp(-D^{110}/2a)] \qquad 7.91$$

Curves calculated by Thompson (Fig. 7.34) are shown to follow the trend of results by Yonts et al[181] for D^+-Cu and the yield is seen to decrease with increasing energy after passing through a broad maximum which is the trend anticipated by experimental results. At low energies when $R_1 \simeq R_f^{110}$ the quantity $S(E_2)$ must be a function of depth so that the deeper the ions penetrate, the greater is the energy imparted to the sputtering process. Thus S is a function of range and, as the range is an approximately linear function of E_0, the theory predicts an initial linear yield-energy pattern.

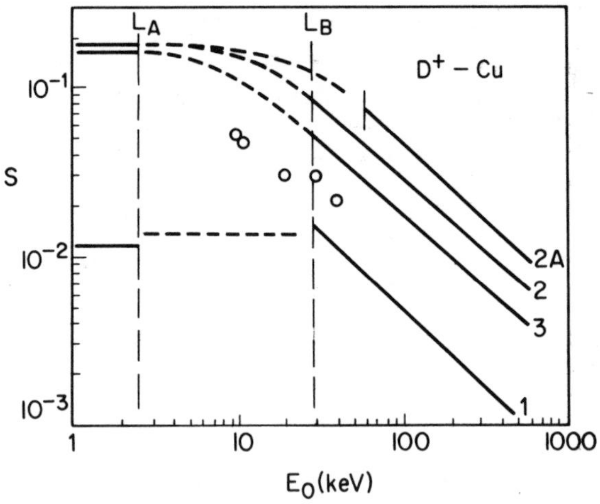

Fig. 7.34 Sputtering ratios of copper under D^+ bombardment; observations of Yonts et al[181] ○ are compared with predictions of equation 7.86 and 7.87 for three Born-Mayer potentials: (1) A = 9×10^5 eV D/a = 17, (2) A = 2.2×10^4 eV D/a = 13, (3) A = 2.9×10^3 eV D/a = 10.3. Case 2A shows the effect of changing E_b from 7 eV to 3.5 eV (viz. Ref. 7.178)

It was mentioned earlier in this chapter that Thompson and Nelson[122 124] have demonstrated that a proportion of sputtered atoms are ejected with thermal energies, in a manner consistent with the creation of microscopic hot regions, which have been named 'thermal spikes'. We include here a calculation of the thermal spike contribution to sputtering presented by Nelson and Thompson[122].

It is calculated that the production of such a thermal spike during a radiation damage event occurs in a time of the order 10^{-13} second. The main process of energy loss from the spike is by ion-ion collisions since electron-electron collisions reach equilibrium too quickly and ion-electron collisions too slowly to contribute to a thermal emission process. Assuming that the spike radius = r_0 and the temperature T_1 is constant over this radius. then, if E_2 is the recoil energy, $\overline{E}_0$, the mean energy given to each atom in the spike, is (as shown in Chapter 6)

$$\overline{E}_0 = \frac{E_2}{4/3 \pi r_0^3 d} = \frac{\text{total energy available}}{\text{number of atoms in spike}} \qquad 7.92$$

where d is the atomic density of the target.

If T_0 is the ambient lattice temperature, then

$$3/2 kT_1 = \overline{E}_0 + 3/2 kT_0 \qquad 7.93$$

Assume (again as in Chapter 6)

$$\text{For } r < r_0 \text{ and } t < \tau r_0^2 \qquad T = T_1 \qquad 7.94a$$

For $r > r_0$ or $t > \tau r_0^2$ or both, $T = T_0$ 7.94b

and r_0 = constant, independent of E_2.

($\tau = C\rho/4k$ where C = specific heat, ρ = mass density and k = conductivity. τr_0^2 = characteristic time of cooling). For A^+, Xe^+ on gold with $E_0 < 100$ keV a hard-sphere approximation of Bohr may be adopted. The collision cross-section is:

$$\sigma = \frac{2\pi a_0}{e} \cdot \frac{E_R}{E_0} \cdot \frac{Z_1 Z_2 (M_1 + M_2)}{E_0 (Z_1^{2/3} + Z_2^{2/3})^{1/2} M_2} \qquad 7.95$$

where e is the base of natural logarithms. As shown in Chapter 2, the fraction of recoils with energy E_2 to $E_2 + dE_2$ is given by $dE_2/(\Lambda E_0)$. Differentiating equation 7.92

$$d\bar{E}_0 = \frac{dE_2}{\frac{4}{3}\pi r_0^3 d} \qquad 7.96$$

and hence, the number of spikes with energy $\bar{E}_0$ to $\bar{E}_0 + d\bar{E}_0$ is given by

$$\frac{4}{3}\pi r_0^3\, d.\, d\bar{E}_0/(\Lambda E_0) \qquad 7.97$$

Nelson and Thompson considered that the spike was equivalent to a sphere of metal of radius r_0 heated to a temperature T_1. If the centre of this sphere were at a distance x from the surface of the metal where $x < r_0$ a heated slice of the sphere would be exposed of area $\pi(r_0^2 - x^2)$. Further, if the probability of spike formation at depth x were taken into account ($= \exp(-x/\lambda \cos\Omega)dx/(\lambda \cos\Omega)$) the contribution of heated areas from all possible spikes can be evaluated and an average heated area per incident ion evaluated thus

$$\bar{A} \doteq \frac{2}{3}\pi r_0^3\, \sigma\, d.\sec\Omega \qquad 7.98$$

If it is assumed that the distribution assumes a Maxwell-Boltzmann form then the number of atoms liberated per second per unit area with energies between E and E + dE can be derived

$$N(E)\, dE = \left(\frac{2}{\pi M_2}\right)^{1/2} \frac{2d}{(kT_1)^{3/2}} \exp\left\{-\frac{E_b}{kT_1}\left(1 + \frac{E}{E_b}\right)\right\} dE \qquad 7.99$$

The total number of atoms liberated due to the thermal spike was obtained by multiplying this expression by τr_0^2, the mean area $\bar{A}$ (equation 7.98), the fraction with energy $\bar{E}_0$ to $\bar{E}_0 + d\bar{E}_0$ (equation 7.96) and integrating over all possible values of $\bar{E}_0$. Hence

$$\frac{dS_T}{dE} \doteq \frac{16.\pi^{3/2}\,\sigma\,\tau\, d^3\, r_0^8\, (\hat{E}_0 + \frac{3}{2}kT_0)(E/E_b)\exp(-m)}{3^{3/2} M_2^{1/2}\Lambda E_0 (1 + E/E_b)} \times \sec\Omega \qquad 7.100$$

where

$$m = \tfrac{3}{2}(1 + E/E_b)E_b/(\hat{E}_0 + \tfrac{3}{2}kT_0) \gg 1$$

and $\hat{E}_0$ = maximum mean atom energy in a spike.

A maximum occurs in the above expression for $E = \frac{2}{3}\hat{E}_0 + kT_0$ and, by fitting the theoretical maxima to the experimental value for Xe^+ bombardment of gold ($E \doteq 0.15$ eV), the value of r_0 is found to equal 110 Å and T_1 to equal 1750°K. Integrating equation 7.100 an expression for the thermal sputtering ratio was obtained:

$$S_T = \frac{3^{5/2}\pi^{3/2}\sigma\,\tau\, d^3 r_0^8 E_b^5}{M_2^{1/2}\Lambda E_0\, \hat{E}_0 + kT_0)^{7/2}} \exp[-\tfrac{3}{2}E_b/(\hat{E}_0 + \tfrac{3}{2}kT_0)]\sec\Omega \qquad 7.101$$

If E_b is taken as 4.2 eV the thermal sputtering yield is 6, which is the value obtained experimentally by Thompson and Nelson.

The above theory gives a reasonable explanation of the low energy sputtered atoms and predicts a spike radius of about 100 Å and a temperature of 1750°K with a lifetime of 10^{-11} second. The existence of such 'spikes' is postulated by Parsons[182] as an explanation for the formation of small discrete crystallized regions during neutron or xenon ion bombardment of thin films of amorphous germanium. The density of crystallized regions was found by Parsons to increase linearly with neutron dose and, in the case of ion bombardment, the crystallized region size was seen to be closely equal to the calculated ion range for ion energies of between 40 and 90 keV.

We finally discuss briefly Lehmann's theory[179] which considers both the transparency of the lattice and the existence of defect cascades. An ion approaching the crystal was assumed by Lehmann, either, to undergo a collision within the first repeat distance of the lattice $d^{\langle hkl\rangle}$, or, to be lost as far as the sputtering process was concerned. The lattice was assumed to be an array of hard spheres of radius R(E) where R is the distance of closest approach for a head-on collision between the ion 1 and a lattice atom 2 and can be obtained from the interaction potential $V_{12}(r)$ by the relation

$$V_{12}(R) = E_0\{M_2/(M_1 + M_2)\} \qquad 7.102$$

where E_0 is the incident ion energy. Thus there is a probability $y^{(hkl)}(E_0)$ that the ion will make a collision at all, where $y^{(hkl)}(E_0)$ is the ratio of the closed to total area of the spheres projected onto the (hkl) plane (i.e. the opacity). If a collision does occur within the distance $d^{\langle hkl\rangle}$ the ion is deflected in a random direction and from then on reacts as if the lattice were randomly distributed. The lattice can be treated as a gas with density $n(n = D^{-3}\, 2^{1/2}$ for a fcc lattice where D is the nearest neighbour distance) and a mean free path for the recoiling ion may be derived:

$$L(\tau) = \{n\pi R^2(T)\}^{-1} \qquad 7.103$$

where T is the energy retained by the ion after the collision. At the end of the first free path l the recoiling ion transfers a fraction of its remaining energy T to the lattice which is used for formation of a defect cascade. The ion then traverses further free paths and makes more collisions, but Lehmann assumes that these later collisions do not contribute significantly to the sputtering process. Lehmann also assumes that the initial distance $d^{\langle hkl\rangle}$ is negligible in comparison with the mean free path L(T) (a reasonable approximation for low index directions and not too small energies) so that the first collision is, in effect, at the target surface. The defect cascade is the Silsbee focusing sequence discussed in section 7.12 and, providing the initial impact is within a certain angle to the close-packed row, the sequence propagates and focuses the momentum. If such a sequence intersects the surface of the crystal the final atom can be ejected. If $S_1(T)$ is the number of all surface atoms sputtered due to the recoiling ion via cascades and focusing collisions and $g(T; E)$ the distribution function of retained energy T then the partial sputtering yield due to the ion

$$S_1^{(hkl)}(E_0) = y^{(hkl)}(E_0) \int_{T=E_0(1-\Lambda)}^{T=E_0} S_1(T)g(T; E)dT \qquad 7.104$$

where $T = E_0(1-\Lambda)$ is the minimum retained energy and $\Lambda = 4M_1M_2/(M_1 + M_2)^2$. The first collision partner of the ion within the distance $d\langle hkl\rangle$ can also recoil a distance L(E-T) where it collides with a second atom and can initiate another cascade. Let $S_2(T')$ be the number of surface atoms sputtered by this sequence where $T' = E-T$ is the energy retained by the first collision partner. Then the partial sputtering yield, $S_2(E_0)$ due to this atom is

$$S_2^{(hkl)}(E_0) = y^{(hkl)}(E_0) \int_0^{\Lambda E_0} S_2(T') g(E-T'; E)dT' \qquad 7.105$$

Thus the total yield

$$S^{(hkl)}(E_0) = S_1 + S_2$$

$$= y^{(hkl)}(E_0) \int_{E_0(1-\Lambda)}^{E_0} \{S_1(T)g(T) + S_2(E-T)g(T)\} dT \qquad 7.106$$

Assuming equal mass ions and atoms and using the hard sphere relation

$$g(T; E) = E_0^{-1} \qquad 0 \leqslant T \leqslant E_0$$

$$0 \qquad \text{otherwise}$$

$$S^{(hkl)}(E_0) = y^{(hkl)}(E_0).2 \int_0^{E_0} S(T).E^{-1}\, dT \qquad 7.107$$

The factor 2 appears since $S_1(T)$ and $S_2(E-T)$ are indistinguishable in the equal mass case.

The problem resolves into the determination of the function S(T) in equation 7.107. According to Leibfried[174] the number ν of focusing collisions starting in one single close-packed direction and having ranges greater than nD where D is the nearest neighbour distance is given by

$$\nu = \tfrac{1}{16}(T/E_d) \{1 - (n/n_0) [1 - \ln (n/n_0)]\} \quad 0 \leqslant n/n_0 \leqslant 1$$

$$0 \qquad \text{otherwise} \qquad 7.108$$

where E_d (~25 eV) is the threshold energy for atomic displacement in the bulk, n_0D is the maximum range and T is the energy used for the formation of a cascade. If, as described earlier, we neglect the distance $d^{\langle hkl\rangle}$ then the first cascade originates from the end of a vector **l** at an angle ϕ to the surface normal. If a close-packed direction exists in the surface direction from this cascade at an angle ϵ_n to the surface normal then its length is α_n **l** $\cos\phi$ where $\alpha_n = \sec \epsilon_n$. The number of atoms sputtered can be written simply as the number of collision chains exceeding this length if the binding energy is neglected.

$$\nu(\alpha_n, T, l) = \tfrac{1}{16} (T/Ed) \{1 - Z)1 - \ln z)\}$$

for $0 \leqslant z = \alpha_n\, l \cos\phi\, n_0D \leqslant 1$;

$\cos\phi = (T/E)^{1/2}$

O, otherwise 7.109

It is now necessary to sum over the contributions from all close-packed directions n and integrate over the distribution function w(**l**; L(T)) of the free path **l**

$$S(T) = \int_0^{\infty} d\mathbf{l}\, \Sigma_n\, \nu(\alpha_n, T, \mathbf{l})\, w(\mathbf{l}; L(T)) \qquad 7.110$$

For a random gas of hard spheres the distribution function of is

$$w(\mathbf{l}; L(T)) = (1/L(T)) \exp\{-\mathbf{l}/L(T)\} \qquad 7.111$$

Putting $\mathbf{l}/d = \lambda$, $T/E = \tau$ the yield expression of equation 7.107 becomes

$$S^{(hkl)}(E_0) = y^{(hkl)}(E_0)\{E_0/8E_d\} \sum_n \int_0^1 \tau.\, d\tau$$

$$\int_0^{\lambda_{max}(=\lambda_{z=1})} [1-z(1-\ln z)]\{D/L(\tau)\} \exp(-\lambda D/L(\tau))d\lambda \qquad 7.112$$

where $o \leqslant z = \alpha_n\, \lambda\tau^{1/2}/n_0 \leqslant 1$

The second integral in equation 7.112 ($= I_n(\tau)$) can be evaluated by use of the relation

$$\int_0^{\infty} e^{-ax} \ln x dx = -(c + \ln a)a^{-1}$$

with **a** positive and c = 0.577, Euler's constant.

$$I_n(\tau) = 1 - [(c + \ln w_n)/w_n] + [E_i(-w_n)/w_n] \qquad 7.113$$

where $w_n(\tau) = (D/L(\tau))(n_0/\alpha_n\, \tau^{1/2})$

and, according to Jahnke et al[183], $-E_i(-x) = \int_x^{\infty} (e^{-t}/t)dt$. The E_i term in equation 7.113 may be neglected for $w_n > 1.5$.

Having obtained the expression for the total yield Lehmann has applied it to the case of copper ions on copper using a Born-Mayer type of potential.

$$V_{22}(r) = A \exp\{-r/a\} \qquad 7.114$$

with A = 22.5 keV and a = D/13 According to equation 7.102 the hard core radius becomes

$$R = a \ln (2A/E) \qquad 7.115$$

The maximum range of focusing collisions along the close packed ⟨110⟩ directions in a copper lattice is 100D ($n_0 = 100$) hence

$$w_n(\tau) = \frac{D}{L(\tau)} \cdot \frac{100}{\alpha_n\, \tau^{1/2}} = P_n \frac{\ln^2(\tfrac{1}{2}\tau E/A)}{\tau^{1/2}}$$

where $P_n = \pi.\, 2^{1/2}.\,(a/D)^2.\, 100/\alpha_n$

and the yield is given by

$$S^{(hkl)}(E_0) = y^{(hkl)}(E_0).\frac{E_0}{8Ed} \sum_n \int_0^1 d\tau.\, \tau$$

$$\left\{1 - \frac{c}{w_n} - \frac{\ln w_n}{w_n}\right\} \qquad 7.116$$

The integral may be evaluated by tabulated functions or a simple graphical method. The α values are:

(110) $\alpha_1 = \alpha_2 = \alpha_3 = \alpha_4 = 2\ \alpha_5 = 1\ \alpha_n = 0$ for $n \geq 6$

(100) $\alpha_1 = \alpha_2 = \alpha_3 = \alpha_4 = 2^{1/2}$ $\alpha_n = 0$ for $n \geq 5$

(111) $\alpha_1 = \alpha_2 \doteq \alpha_3 = (3/2)^{1/2}$ $\alpha_n = 0$ for $n \geq 4$

Fig 7.35 shows the sputtering yields of three low-index planes of copper as a function of energy and the trend of the curves is seen to be in good agreement with the data of Magnuson et al[40] for A^+-Cu. The yields at a given energy are predicted to be in the order $S^{(111)} > S^{(100)} > S^{(110)}$ and the energies at which maxima appear in the yield curves increase from (110) through (100) to (111), again in agreement with experimental data. Lehmann has pointed out that the main limitations of the present theory cause errors which tend to cancel out; the hard-sphere assumption neglects 'collisions' just outside the hard-sphere radius which may cause deflection of the ion into a sputtering sequence so that the hard-sphere approximation under-estimates the opacity of the lattice (which reduces the predicted yield) whilst this same approximation over-estimates the length of collision chains (which increases the predicted yield). The theory neglects ejection in ⟨100⟩ directions and does not account for the binding energy of surface atoms but the correlation with experimental data is extremely good. However, as discussed earlier in the chapter, Lehmann[104b] considers that, at the lower (< 10 keV) energies in particular collision chains are not really the dominant mechanism and that simple near surface collisions suffice to describe much of the single crystal data. Harrison's computer studies of the problem[104a] agree with this supposition and theories on these lines will no doubt be developed in the near future.

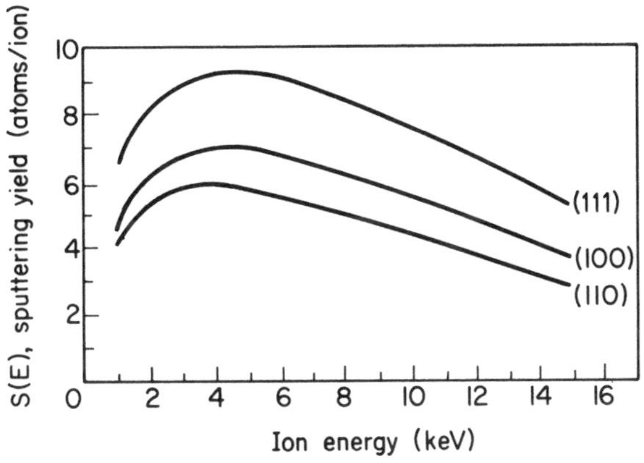

Fig. 7.35 Yield-energy relation for sputtering from (110), (100) and (111) surfaces for Cu^+ ions on Copper (viz. Ref. 7.179)

7.17 Sputtering in space

The main problem facing the designer of a space-craft is not so much the erosion of surfaces due to sputtering, but rather the protection of sensitive surfaces, such as solar cells, against damage when high speed protons or helium ions are captured. For example, it is now fairly well established that satellites in near-earth orbits do not suffer sputtering rates more than about 100 Å per day[185]. Consider a satellite orbiting at 220 km., its speed will be of the order 8×10^3 m/sec and it will sweep through an atmosphere comprising 4×10^9 N_2 molecules, 3×10^9 O atoms, 10^6 N atoms and about 10^2 O_2 molecules per cubic centimetre. Equivalent energies of impact are, respectively, 9.3, 5.3, 4.6 and 10.6 eV, which are all below, or very near, threshold energies for sputtering. The largest yield would be expected to come from the N_2 component where there are $8 \times 10^5 \times 4 \times 10^9 = 3.2 \times 10^{15}$ molecules striking each square centimetre of target per second. However yields must be of the order 10^{-4} atoms per ion at these low energies which means that the total number of atoms leaving the surface per second is approximately 3×10^{11}, and possibly a similar contribution from the O_2 components. Thus a monolayer is sputtered every 1000 seconds or so, i.e. about 3 Å per hour or 75 Å per day. In fact a satellite in the 220 km. orbit would be approaching the earth very quickly so the above calculations apply to satellites near the end of their life only. At higher altitudes the density of particles in space falls off rapidly so that, although energies are higher, there are less atoms to collide with and, also, these atoms are of lighter mass. In these orbits satellites have erosion rates nearer 100 Å per year. Jaffe and Rittenhouse[186] have set an upper limit of 0.1 Å per year for sputtering in the radiation belts and 100 Å per year due to sputtering by solar protons. Whipple and Fireman[187] have estimated that yields in interplanetary space due to cosmic ray spallation products in meteorites are such that maximum erosion rates would be 30 Å per year.

McKeown[185] has obtained sputtering yields from the flights of Discoverer 26 and 32 by attaching his crystal oscillator detection system (discussed earlier) to the spacecraft. Yields obtained for an elliptical orbit (perigee 230 km., apogee 810 km.) indicated that sputtering rates were less than 5×10^{-6} atoms per incident particle for a gold film; this is equivalent to an erosion rate of 0.2 Å per day. Stuart[188] is of the opinion that the majority of this observed yield is due to a weight loss from the detector by outgassing. In any event one must conclude from this experiment that, since the result is so low for such an efficient sputtering material as gold, then other materials should not suffer appreciably in space flight.

An interesting study of probable sputtering events on the moon's surface has been presented by Wehner[189]. Because of energetic proton and helium bombardment he estimates a probable erosion of 40 metres from the lunar surface in 10^9 years. A further interesting observation is that lighter atoms, when sputtered, are more likely to be energetic enough to escape from the moon's gravitational field. Thus the surface will be enriched in heavier atoms which have been sputtered and then fallen back to form a relatively porous but solid crust.

Conclusion

The reader must, by now, appreciate that sputtering studies are still in a very elementary stage. Thanks to the work of Wehner and Almén and Bruce substantial yield data have been compiled for many ion-target combinations at medium and high energies. There are still large gaps in yield values available at low energies and in the 5-20 keV region. Single crystal studies are proving most interesting and are able to verify the existence of collision sequences and various focusing mechanisms and have generally assisted theoretical interpretation of the phenomenon.

REFERENCES

1. Fruth, H. F. (1932) Physica **2**, 280
2. Glockler, G. and Lind, S. C. (1939) 'Electrochemistry of Gases and Other Dielectrics', 400. J. Wiley & Sons Inc.; New York
3. Massey, H. S. W. and Burhop, E. H. S. (1952) 'Electronic and Ionic Impact Phenomena.' Oxford University Press; New York
4. Guntherschulze, A. (1953) Vacuum **3**, 360
5. Wehner, G. K. (1955) Advances in Electronics and Electron Physics **7**, 239
6. Francis, G. (1956) Handbuch der Physik. **22**, 154 Springer-Verlag. Berlin
7. Holland, L. (1956) 'Vacuum Deposition of Thin Films', Chapter 14. Chapman and Hall; London
8. Haymann, P. (1956) J. Chem. Phys. **57**, 572
9. Moore, W. J. (1960) American Scientist **48**, 108
10. Thompson, M. W. (1962) Brit. J. Appl. Phys. **13**, 194
11. Behrisch, R. (1964) Ergeb. Exakt. Naturw. **35**, 295
12. Kaminsky, M. (1965) 'Atomic and Ionic Impact Phenomena' Springer-Verlag; Berlin
13. Grove, W. R. (1852) Trans. Roy. Soc. (London) 142, 87
14. Blechschmidt, E. (1926) Ann. Physik **81**, 999
15. Penning F. M. and Moubis J. H. A. (1940) Koninkl. Ned. Akad. Wetenschap. Proc. **43**, 41
16. Guntherschulze, A. and Meyer, K. (1931) Zeits. f. Physik **62**, 607
17. Meyer, K. and Guntherschulze, A. (1931) Zeits. f. Physik **71**, 279
18. Weijsenfeld, C. H. and Hoogendoorn, A. (1962) Proc. Fifth Conf. on Ionization Phenomena in Gases, Munich (1961) **1**, 124, North Holland Publishing Co.; Amsterdam
19. Fetz, H. (1942) Zeits, f. Phys. **119**, 590
20. Research Staff of the General Electric Company, London (1923) Phil. Mag. **45**, 98
21. Seeliger, R. and Sommermeyer, K. (1935) Zeits. f. Physik **93**, 692
22. Timoschenko, G. (1941) J. Appl. Phys. **12**, 69
23. Smith, H. P. Jr., DeMichele, D. W. and Khan, J. M. (1965) J. Appl. Phys. **36**, 1952
24. Pleshivtsev, N. V. (1964) Pribory i Tekhn. Eksper. **5**, 5. English translation in Soviet Phys—Instrum. and Experimental Techniques (1964) **5**, 929
25. Keywell, F. (1955) Phys. Rev. **97**, 1611
26. Moore, W. J. (1956) Annals New York Acad. Sci. **67**, 600
27. Southern, A. L., Willis, W. R. and Robinson, M. T. (1963) J. Appl. Phys. **34**, 153
28. Thompson, M. W. (1962) Phil. Mag. **7**, 2015
29. Morgulis, N. D. and Tischenko, V. D. (1956) Zh. Eksper. i Teor. Fiz. 30, 54 English translation in Soviet Phys JETP (1956) 3, 52
30. Morgulis, N. D. and Tischenko, V. D. (1956) Izv. Akad. Nauk SSSR Ser. Fiz. **20**, 1190. English translation in Bull. Acad. Sci. USSR Physics Series (1957) 20, 1082
31. Stuart, R. V. and Wehner, G. K. (1960) Phys. Rev. (Letters) **4**, 409

31a. Stuart, R. V. and Wehner, G. K. (1962) J. Appl. Phys. **33**, 2345

32. McKeown, D. (1961) Rev. Sci. Instr. **32**, 133
33. Scott, H. G, (1962) J. Appl. Phys. **33**, 2011
34. Wehner, G. K. (1957) Phys. Rev. **108**, 35
35. Henschke, E. B. (1962) J. Appl. Phys. **33**, 1773
36. Laegreid, N. and Wehner, G. K. (1961) J. Appl. Phys. **32**, 365
37. Rosenburg, D. and Wehner, G. K. (1962) J. Appl. Phys. **33**, 1842
38. Almén, O. and Bruce, G. (1961) Nucl. Instrum. and Methods **11**, 257 North Holland Publishing Co. Amsterdam (1961)
39. Almén, O. and Bruce, G. (1962) Trans. 8th National Vacuum Symp. Washington (1961) **1**, 245 Pergamon Press Inc.; New York
40. Magnuson, G. D. and Carlston, C. E. (1963) J. Appl. Phys. **34**, 3267
41. Wehner, G. K., Stuart, R. V. and Rosenburg, D. (1962) Nov. General Mills Annual Report No. 2356
42. Almén, O. and Bruce, G. (1960) 'Electromagnetic Separation of Radioactive Isotopes' Vienna, May p. 227. Springer-Verlag; Wien
43. Rol, P. K., Fluit, J. M. and Kistemaker, J. (1960) 'Electromagnetic Separation of Radioactive Isotopes' Vienna, May p. 207 Springer-Verlag; Wien
44. Bader, M., Witteborn, F. C. and Snouse, T. W. (1961) N. A. S. A. Report No. TR-R-105; Washington
45. Grønlund, F. and Moore, W. J. (1960) J. Chem. Phys. **32**, 1540
46. Wolsky, S. P. and Zdanuk, E. J. (1961) Phys. Rev. **121**, 374
47. Weiss, A., Heldt, A. and Moore, W. J. (1958) J. Chem. Phys. **29**, 7.
48. McKeown, D. and Cabezas, A. Y. (1962) July General Dynamics/Astronautics Annual Report
49. Nelson, R. S. and Beevers, C. J. (1964) Phil. Mag. **9**, 343
50. Wehner, G. K. (1959) J. Appl. Phys. **30**, 1762
51. Bader, M., Witteborn, F. C. and Snouse, T. W. (1960) June Proc. Atomic and Molecular Beams Conference, Denver; 167
52. Ramer, C. E., Narasimham, M. A., Reynolds, H. K. and Allred, J. C. (1964) J. Appl. Phys. **35**, 1673
53. Molchanov, V. A. and Tel'kovskii, V. G. (1962) Izv. Akad. Nauk SSSR Ser. Fiz. **26**, 1359. English translation in Bull. Acad Sci. USSR Phys. Ser. (1963) **26**, 1381
54. Cheney, K. B. and Ptikin, E. T. (1965) J. Appl. Phys. **36**, 3542
55. Wehner, G. K. (1954) Phys. Rev. **93**, 633
56. Wolsky, S. P. (1957) Phys. Rev **108**, 1131
57. Wolsky, S. P. and Zdanuk, E. J. (1961) J. Appl. Phys. **32**, 782
58. Wolsky, S. P. and Zdanuk, E. J. (1960) Proc. Vacuum Symposium, 6, Pergamon Press Ltd.; London
59. Wolsky, S. P. and Zdanuk, E. J. (1961) Vacuum Technology Transactions 282, Pergamon Press Inc.; New York
60. Wolsky, S. P. and Zdanuk, E. J. (1961) Vacuum Microbalance Techniques **1**, 35 Plenum Press; New York
61. Wolsky, S. P. and Zdanuk, E. J. (1962) Vacuum Microbalance Techniques **2**, 37 Plenum Press; New York
62. Zdanuk, E. J. and Wolsky, S. P. (1965) J. Appl. Phys. **36**, 1683
63. Stuart, R. V. (1962) Trans. 8th National Vacuum Symp. Washington (1961) **1**, 252 Pergamon Press Inc.; New York
64. Dienes, G. J. and Vineyard, G. H. (1957) 'Radiation Effects in Solids' Interscience, New York
65. Kreye, W. C. (1964) J. Appl. Phys. **35**, 3575

66. Medved, D. B. and Poppa, H. (1962) J. Appl. Phys. **33**, 1759

67. Finkelstein, A. T. (1940) Rev. Sci. Instr. **11**, 52

68. Gillam, E. (1959) J. Phys. Chem. Solids **11**, 55

69. Ogilvie, G. J. and Thomson, A. A. (1961) J. Phys. Chem. Solids **17**, 203

70. Wehner, G. K. (1958) Phys. Rev. **112**, 1120

71. Asada, T. and Quasebarth, K. (1929) Z. Phys. Chem. **A143**, 435

72. Hanau, R. (1949) Phys. Rev. **76**, 155

73. Fisher, T. F. and Weber, C. E. (1952) J. Appl. Phys. **23**, 181

74. Wolsky, S. P., Zdanuk, E. J. and Shooter, D. (1964) Surf. Sci. **1**, 110

75. Haneman, D. (1960) J. Phys. Chem. Solids **14**, 162

76. Akishin, A. I., Vasil'ev, S. S. and Isaev, L. N. (1962) Izv. Akad. Nauk. SSSR Ser. Fiz. **26**, 1356. English translation in Bull. Acad. Sci. (USSR) Physics Series (1963) **26**, 1379

77. Anderson G. S., Mayer, W. N. and Wehner, G. K. (1962) J. Appl. Phys. **33**, 2991

78. Jorgenson, G. V. and Wehner, G. K. (1965) J. Appl. Phys. **36**, 2672

79. Honig, R. E. (1961) Proc. Fifth Conf. on Ionization Phenomena in Gases, Munich (1961) **1**, 106. North Holland Publishing Co.; Amsterdam

80. Sporn, H. (1939) Z. Physik **112**, 279

81. Wehner, G. K. (1959) Phys. Rev. **114**, 1270

82. Wehner, G. K. (1960) J. Appl. Phys. **31**, 1392

83. Stuart, R. V. and Wehner, G. K. (1963) Trans 9th National Vacuum Symposium, Los Angeles (1962) 160 Macmillan; Pergamon; New York

84. Stuart, R. V. and Wehner, G. K. (1964) J. Appl. Phys. **35**, 1819

85. Smith, J. A., Cambey, L. A. and Marshall, D. J. (1963) J. Appl. Phys. **34**, 2489

86. Weijsenfeld, C. H. (1962) Physics Letters **2**, 295

87. Weijsenfeld, C. H. (1963) Proc. Sixth International Conf. on Ionization Phenomena in Gases. Paris S.E.R.M.A. (1963) **2**, 43

88. Kopitzki, K. and Stier, H. (1961) E. Z. Naturforsch. **16a**, 1257

89. Kopitzki, K. and Stier, H. (1962) E. Z. Naturforsch. **17a**, 346

90. Ben'yaminovich, M. B. and Veksler, V. I. (1963) Izv. Akad. Nauk UzSSR Ser. fiz-mat. nauk **3**, 29

91. Thompson, M. W. (1963) Physics Letters **6**, 24

92. Thompson, M. W. and Nelson, R. S. (1962) Phil. Mag. **7**, 2015

93. Buescher, H. and Kopitzki, K. (1965) Z. Physik **184**, 382

94. Wehner, G. K. and Rosenburg, D. (1960) J. Appl. Phys. **31**, 177

95. Rol. P. K., Fluit, J. M. and Kistemaker, J. (1960) Physica **26**, 1000

96. Patterson, H. and Tomlin, D. H. (1962) Proc. Roy. Soc. **A265**, 474

97. Karmohapatro, S. B. and Narasinham, A. V. (1963) Proc. Symposium on Collision Processes Dehradun. Reported in Proc. Natl. Acad. Sci. India Section A **33**, 629 (1963)

98. Chiplonkar, V. T. and Rane, S. R. (1965) Indian J. Pure and Appl. Phys **3**, 131

99. Chiplonkar, V. T. and Rane, S. R. (1965) Proc. Indian Acad. Sci. **A61**, 100

100. Cooper, C. B. and Comas, J. (1965) J. Appl. Phys. **36**, 2891

101. Malakhov, V., Stein, R. P. and Smith, H. P. Jr., (1963) Univ. California Report AS-63-7 Nov. 25

102. Campbell, D. S. and Stirland, D. J. (1964) Phil. Mag. **9**, 703

103. Wolsky, S. P. and Wallis, G. (1965) Trans. 12th National Vacuum Symposium Sept. 1965 (To be published)

104. Silsbee, R. H. (1957) J. Appl. Phys. **28**, 1246

104a. Harrison, D. E. Jr., Johnson, J. P. and Levy, N. S. (1966) Appl. Phys. Letters **8**, 33

104b. Lehmann, Chr. and Sigmund, P. (1966) Phys. Status Solidi **16**, 507

105. Wehner, G. K. (1956) Phys. Rev. **102**, 690

106. Koedam, M. and Hoogendoorn, A. (1960) Physica **20**, 351

107. Koedam, M. (1961) Philips Research Reports **16**, 101

108. Nelson, R. S. and Thompson, M. W. (1962) Physics Letters **2**, 124

109. Anderson, G. S. (1963) J. Appl. Phys. **34**, 659

110. Kaminsky, M. (1966) Advances in Mass Spectrometry **3**, Paper No. 4 Paris 1964 Institute of Petroleum, London

111. Anderson, G. S. and Wehner, G. K. (1960) J. Appl. Phys. **31**, 2305

112. Thompson, M. W. (1959) Phil. Mag. **4**, 139

113. Nelson, R. S. (1963) Phil. Mag. **8**, 693

114. Anderson, G. S. (1962) J. Appl. Phys. **33**, 2017

115. Nelson, R. S., Thompson, M. W., Farmery, B. W. and Hall, M. J. (1962) Atomic Energy Research Report No. R 4014

116. Cunningham, R. L., Gow, K. W., Ng-Yelim, J. (1963) J. Appl. Phys. **34**, 984

117. Yurasova, V. E. and Sirotenko, I. G. (1961) Zh. Eksper. i Teor. Fiz. 41, 1359. English translation in Soviet Physics—JETP (1962) 14, 968

118. Yurasova, V. E. and Murinson, E. A. (1962) Izv. Akad. Nauk SSSR Ser. Fiz. **26**, 1445. English translation in Bull. Acad. Sci. (USSR) Physics Series (1963) **26**, 1470

119. Anderson, G. S., Wehner, G. K. and Olin, H. J. (1963) J. Appl. Phys. **34**, 3492

119a. Anderson, G. S. and Wehner, G. K. (1964) Surface Sci. **2**, 367

119b. Anderson, G. S. (1966) J. Appl. Phys. **37**, 2838

120. Weijsenfeld, C. H. (1965) Proc. Seventh Conf. on Phenomena in Ionized Gases, Belgrade August 1965 (to be published)

121. Lehmann, Chr. and Leibfreid, G. (1961) Zeits. f. Physik **162**, 203

122. Thompson, M. W. and Nelson, R. S. (1962) Phil. Mag. **7**, 2015

123. Seitz, F. and Koehler, J. S. (1956) Solid State Physics Editors Seitz, F. and Turnbull, D. **2**, 323 Academic Press Inc.; New York (1956)

124. Nelson, R. S. (1965) Phil. Mag. **11**, 291

125. Fluit, J. M., Rol. P. K. and Kistemaker, J. (1963) J. Appl. Phys. **34**, 690

126. Fluit, J. M. and Rol, P. K. (1964) Physica **30**, 857

127. Molchanov, V. A., Tel'kovskii, V. G. and Chicherov, V. M. (1961) Dokl. Akad. Nauk SSSR **137**, 58 English translation in Soviet Physics—Doklady (1962) **6**, 222

128. Endzheets, G., Molchanov, V. A., Tel'kovskii, V. G. and Faruk, M. A. (1962) Zh, Tekh. Fiz. **32**, 1032 English translation in Soviet Phys—Techn.Phys. (1963) **7**, 752

129. Mashkova, E.S., Molchanov, V.A. and Odintsov, D.D. (1963) Fiz. Tver. Tela **5**, 3426 English translation in Soviet Phys.—Solid State (1964) **5**, 2516

130. Denoux, M. (1962) Le Bombardment Ionique, Colloques Internatl. du Centre National de la Recherche Scientifique. Bellevue, Paris, December (1962) **113**, 191

131. Ogilvie, G. J., Sanders, J. V. and Thomson, A. A. (1963) J. Phys. Chem. Solids **24**, 247

132. Nelson, R. S., Thompson, M. W., and Montgomery, H. (1962) Phil. Mag. **7**, 1385

133. Yurasova, V. E., Sirotenko, I. G. and Buhanov, V. M. (1962) Le Bombardment Ionique. Colloques Internatl. du Centre National de la Recherche Scientifique Bellevue, Paris, December (1962) **113**, 221

134. Fluit, J. M. (1962) Le Bombardment Ionique. Colloques Internatl. du Centre National de la Recherche Scientifique Bellevue, Paris, December (1962) **113**, 119

135. Fluit, J. M., Snoek, C. and Kistemaker, J. (1964) Physica **30**, 144

136. Snouse, T. W. and Bader, M. (1962), Trans. 8th National Vacuum Symp. Washington (1961) **1**, 271 Pergamon Press Inc. New York (1962)

137. Wehner, G. K. (1961) General Mills Annual Report No. 2243 Part IV November (1961)

138. Lebedev, S. Ya, Stavisskii, Yu. Ya. and Shut'ko, Yu. V. (1964) Zh. Tekh. Fiz. 34, 1101 English translation in Soviet Phys.—Techn. Phys. (1964) **9**, 854

139. Carlston, C. E., Magnuson, G. D., Comeaux, A. and Mahadevan, P. (1965) Phys. Rev. 138A, 759

140. Spivak, G. V., Yurasova, V. E., Prilezhaeva, I. N. and Pravdina, E. K. (1956) Izv. Akad. Nauk SSSR Ser. Fiz. **20**, 1189. English translation in Bull. Acad. Sci. (USSR) Physics Series. (1957) **20**, 1075

141. Krokhina, A. I. and Spivak, G. V. (1959) Izv. Akad. Nauk SSSR Ser. Fiz. **23**, 741. English translation in Bull. Acad. Sci. (USSR) Physics Series (1960) **23**, 701

142. Sirotenko, G. V. and Spivak, G. V. (1960) Izv. Akad. Nauk SSSR Ser. Fiz. **24**, 629. English translation in Bull. Acad. Sci. (USSR) Physics Series (1961) **24**, 687.

143. Wehner, G. K. (1958) J. Appl. Phys. **29**, 217

144. Ogilvie, G. J. and Ridge, M. J. (1959) J. Phys. Chem. Solids **10**, 217

145. Ogilvie, G. J. (1959) J. Phys. Chem. Solids **10**, 222

146. Cunningham, R. L., Haymann, P., Lecomte, C., Moore, W. J. and Trillat, J. J. (1960) J. Appl. Phys. **31**, 839

147. Magnuson, G. D., Meckel, B. B. and Harkins, P. A. (1961) J. Appl. Phys. **32**, 369

148. Navez, M., Sella, Cl. and Chaperot, D. (1962) Le Bombardment Ionique. Colloques Internatl. du Centre National de la Recherche Scientifique Bellevue, Paris, December (1962) **113**, 233

149. Fluit, J. M. and Datz, S. (1964) Physica **30**, 345

150. Thomson, J. J. (1921) 'Rays of Positive Electricity' Longmans Green, New York (1921)

151. Bush, V. and Smith, G. C. (1922) Trans. American Inst. Elec Engrs. **41**, 627

152. Hippel, A. Von. (1926) Ann. Physik **81**, 1043

153. Townes, C. H. (1944) Phys. Rev. **65**, 319

154. Rockwood, G. H. (1941) Trans. American Inst. Elec. Engrs. **60**, 901

155. Fluit, J. M., Friedman, L., Boerboom, A. J. M. and Kistemaker, J. (1961) J. Chem. Phys. **35**, 1143

156. Lamar, E. S. and Compton, K. T. (1934) Science **80**, 541

157. Keywell, F. (1952) Phys. Rev. Letters **87**, 160

158. Orear, J., Rosenfeld and Schluter (1950) Notes on 'Enrico Fermi School of Nuclear Physics' Univ. Chicago Press (1950)

159. Seitz, F. (1949) Discussion Faraday Soc. **5**, 271

160. Goldman, D. T. and Simon, A. (1958) Phys. Rev. **111**, 383

161. Seitz, F. and Koehler, J. S. (1956) See Ref. 123 p. 323

162. Pease, R. S. (1960) Rendiconti, S. I. F. **13**, 158

163. Kinchin, G. H. and Pease, R. S. (1955) Reports Prog. Phys. **18**, 1

164. Henschke, E. B. (1957) Phys. Rev. **106**, 737

165. Henschke, E. B. (1961) Phys. Rev. **121**, 1286

166. Langberg, E. (1956) Ph. D. Thesis 'Analysis of Low Energy Sputtering' Dept. Elec Engng. Princeton Univ. April (1956)

167. Rol, P. K., Fluit, J. M. and Kistemaker, J. (1960) Physica **26**, 1009

168. Smith, H. P. Jr. (1964) J. Appl. Phys. **35**, 2522

169. Bulgakov, Yu. V. (1963) Zh. Tekh. Fiz. 33, 500 English translation in Soviet Phys—Tech. Phys. (1963) 8, **369**

170. Bohr, N. (1948) 'The Penetration of Atomic Particles Through Matter' Kgl. Danske. Vidensk. Selsk, Matfysiske Medd **18**, 8

171. Odintsov, D. D. (1963) Fiz. Tver. Tela **5**, 1114. English translation in Soviet Physics—Solid State (1963) **5**, 813

172. Rol, P. K., Fluit, J. M., Viehbock, F. D. and deJong, M. (1960) Proc Fourth Conf. on Ionization Phenomena in Gases, 257. North Holland Publishing Co. Amsterdam

173. Martynenko, Yu. V. (1964) Fiz. Tver. Tela. **6**, 2003 English translation in Soviet Phys—Solid State (1965) **6**, 1581

173a. Martynenko, Yu. V. (1964) Fiz. Tver. Tela. **6**, 3529 English translation in Soviet Physics—Solid State (1965) **6**, 2827

174. Leibfreid, G. (1959) J. Appl. Phys. **30**, 1388

175. Harrison, D. E. Jr. (1956) Phys. Rev. 102, 1473

176. Harrison, D. E. Jr. (1957) Phys. Rev. 103, 1202

177. Harrison, D. E. Jr. (1960) J. Chem. Phys. 32, 1336

178. Thompson, M. W. (1962) Proc. Fifth Conf. on Ionization Phenomena in Gases Munich (1961) **1**, 85 North Holland Publishing Co.; Amsterdam

179. Lehmann, Chr. (1965) Nucl. Instr. and Methods **38**, 263

180. Nielsen, J. O. (1956) 'Electromagnetically Enriched Isotopes and Mass. Spectrometry' Butterworths; London

181. Yonts, O. C., Normand, C. E. and Harrison, D. E. Jr. (1960) J. Appl. Phys **31**, 447

182. Parsons, J. R. (1964) Thesis, Chicago Univ. Illinois

183. Jahnke, E., Emde, F. and Lösch, F. (1960) 'Tables of Higher Functions' McGraw-Hill; New York

184. Federal Works Agency Work Projects Administration New York (1940) 'Tables of Sine, Cosine and Exponential Integrals'

185. McKeown, D. (1963) Proc. Third International Symposium on Rarefied Gas Dynamics, Paris, June 1962 Ed. T. A. Laurmann Vol. 1 p. 315 Acad Press Inc.; New York

186. Jaffe, L. D. and Rittenhouse, J. B. (1962) American Rocket Soc. J. **32**, 320

187. Whipple, F. L. and Fireman, E. L. (1959) Nature **183**, 1315

188. Stuart, R. V. (1964) American Inst. Aeronautics and Astronautics J. **2**, 1678

189. Wehner, G. K. (1961) American Rocket Soc. J. **31**, 438

190. Guseva, M. I. (1959) Fiz. Tver. Tela. **1**, 1540 English translation in Soviet Physics—Solid State (1959) **1**, 1410

191. Henschke, E. B. and Derby, S. E. (1963) J. Appl. Phys. 34, 2458

192. Wehner, G. K. (1962) General Mills Report No. 2309 July, 1962

193. McKeown, D. and Cabezas, A. Y. (1962) Annual Report Space Sci. Lab. General Dynamics/Astronautics July 1962

194. Snouse, T. W. (1964) N. A. S. A. Tech. Note D-2235 April 1964

195. Wehner, G. K. and Rosenberg, D. (1961) J. Appl. Phys. 32, 887

196. Navinšek, B. (1965) J. Appl. Phys. 36, 1678

197. Goldman, D. T., Harrison, D. E. Jr. and Coveyou, R. R. (1959) ORNL Report No. 2729

198. Kaminsky, M. (1962) Phys. Rev. 126, 1267

199. Kaminsky, M. (1963) Bull. Am. Phys. Soc. 8, 338

200. McKeown, D., Cabezas, A. and Mackenzie, E. T. (1961) Annual Report on Low Energy Sputtering Studies 15 July 1960–14 July 1961

201. Chaikovskii, E. F. and Ptitsyn, G. V. (1964) Zh. tekh. fiz. USSR **34**, 2194 English translation in Soviet Physics—Tech. Phys. (1965) **9**, 1962

202. Perovic, B. and Cobic, B. (1962) Proc. Fifth Conf. on Ionization Phenomena in gases Munich (1961) **2**, 1165 North Holland Publishing Co., Amsterdam

203. Comas, J. and Cooper, C. B. (1966) J. Appl. Phys. **37**, 2820

204. Gautsch, O., Mustacchi, C. and Wahl, H. (1965) Euratom Report EUR 2515e

205. Wehner, G. K. (1959) Conference Report, The Rand Corporation conference on Aerodynamics of the Upper Atmosphere (unpublished).

206. Laegreid, N., Wehner, G. K. and Meckel, B. B. (1959) J. Appl. Phys. **30**, 374

CHAPTER 8

Ion Trapping and Gas Release Processes

8.1 In the previous three chapters we have studied the progress of an ion incident upon a solid target, assuming that it eventually comes to rest within the target when its energy degrades below some prescribed level. We have also discussed the damage to the lattice produced by the irradiation, both within the bulk of the target and at the surface where the macroscopic effect is one of erosion and recession of the surface. In this chapter we will discuss the nature of the ionic entrapment and the effects exerted by the bulk damage and the surface erosion upon the spatial distribution of the trapped atoms. In addition we will consider the effects of migration of the trapped gas due to thermally activated processes.

Before discussing the mechanisms involved in the entrapment of individual ions and the factors which condition the spatial distribution of these ions in detail, we will briefly summarise the processes which are likely to affect these parameters.

Let us consider, initially, the situation following the irradiation of a plane surface of a virgin target with a short pulse of monoenergetic ions and assume, for simplicity, that bulk damage and surface erosion is unimportant in determining the trapping processes. Some of these ions will be reflected on first impact with the surface, whilst the remainder will enter the target and follow trajectories determined by the conditions of incidence and the interatomic potential. Most of these will eventually come to rest within the lattice, but a certain fraction will emerge from exposed target surfaces, and some form of penetration distribution will result as described in Chapter 5.

On the macroscopic scale it will be possible to specify the fraction of the incident ions which will enter and be trapped within the target, and this parameter may be defined as a trapping efficiency.

Now consider the effects of the known sputtering and radiation damage upon the fate of subsequent bombarding ion pulses. Again, for simplicity, let us assume that the sputtering process is uniform, so that the bombarded surface recedes uniformly at a rate determined by the product of the ion bombardment rate and the sputtering coefficient, and that it is independent of bombarding gas occlusion or bulk damage within the target. The next ion pulse therefore impinges on a target similar to the first pulse, although the surface has slightly receded, so that the ions penetrate to the same depth distribution as the first pulse but from the new surface, with the same total trapping efficiency. The total distribution function of trapped atoms is thus the sum of the first distribution from the initial surface and the second distribution from the second, slightly displaced, surface. However, in eroding a small depth of target, the first pulse would also release gas trapped within this layer, so that simultaneously with the gas trapping a gas release process would occur. Consequently after even the first ion has struck the target the net rate of gas trapping will fall due to simultaneous release. Indeed it is readily visualised that after a long bombardment and quite appreciable gas trapping at the instantaneous surface, a situation of dynamic equilibrium or saturation will occur where the rates of gas trapping and release just balance and the observed trapping efficiency will be reduced to zero.

In addition to this gas release mechanism it is also probable that impinging ions can release trapped gas via a second type of sputtering process where the incident ions can transfer sufficient energy to the trapped atoms, either by direct collision or via an intermediate collision with a target atom, to ensure gas escape from the target. Furthermore, because of the damage induced within the target it is quite probable that the ion penetration and trapping mechanisms will change with increasing bombardment. Thus the stopping power of the target may be expected to change as various damage configurations are formed and also as gas becomes embedded in the target. Moreover an incoming ion striking a trapped gas atom could cause the latter to be ejected from its trapping site and progress further into the target. Evidence of these processes has already been given in Chapter 5. In addition, the mechanisms by which the gas atoms become trapped could also change as damage is introduced since new defect configurations may provide different or even enhanced trapping centres from those existing in the virgin material. Thus the possibilities of trapping at damage centres such as dislocation loops and clusters and at nucleated bubbles, must be borne in mind. Consequently the trapping efficiency and distribution functions may be expected to change in quite complex fashion with increasing irradiation.

So far we have assumed that the incident ion arrives at and is trapped at particular lattice positions following a trajectory determined completely by its energy and the interatomic forces. Upon becoming trapped it is frozen into the position unless struck by further ions or energetic target atoms. However this must be an idealised picture since thermally activated processes should also occur. For example, it might be expected that the binding energy of each trapped atom would depend upon the configuration of surrounding target atoms, particularly after damage production, or upon the cluster size if it resided in such positions. Some of these binding energies could be sufficiently low to allow escape of the atoms at the bombardment temperature during the duration of the experiment and leave them free to wander, via some form of diffusion process throughout the solid. Of these liberated atoms some may become retrapped and others evolve from the surface; in any case both the trapping distribution function and the gas release rate would differ from those anticipated on the basis of migration free trapping. The diffusion process itself would also be anticipated to be quite complex. Firstly the migrating atoms could conceivably move according to the normal type of diffusive action for that particular atom dissolved in the target, i.e. a vacancy or interstitialcy mechanism under the action of the vacancy and atomic concentration gradients. Because of the damage induced by the irradiation however the normal lattice pattern becomes distorted and it is probable that the migrating atoms could diffuse along paths created by the damage, with an activation energy differing from that typical of the unbombarded target. In many cases these paths could offer less resistance to the atomic migration and short circuit the normal routes. Gas atoms trapped in bubbles could also move with different velocities, depending upon their size and the driving force, (such as a pressure or temperature gradient), than single atoms, in much the same way as air bubbles rise in a liquid. These forms of gas diffusion have all been demonstrated experimentally, as we shall subsequently see, and are therefore not merely speculative at this stage. Finally one can envisage a bombardment induced type of diffusion wherein the energetic ions and their progeny cause vacancy production and/or thermal spikes and promote enhanced diffusion by any of the processes just outlined.

These diffusion processes may or may not occur during and after bombardment depending upon the activation energy for a particular diffusive process and the target temperature. Operation at different temperatures may activate processes frozen in at lower temperatures, and, through defect annealing, cause accompanying atomic migration. On the other hand low temperature operation may slow down some diffusive motion and change the observed trapping effects. Post bombardment heating of irradiated targets can thus be an important technique in determining trapping and migration energies, as we shall show later.

It is quite clear, therefore, that the processes governing gas trapping and release are certain to be complex, even with the assumptions made here regarding the random structure of targets and the simple nature of sputtering. Since most real targets exhibit regular crystalline structures the initial ion penetration function may quickly become distorted due to Channel blocking by trapped gas and displaced atoms. The surface will also become distorted via the preferential etch patterns described in Chapters 6 and 7 so that again the trapping and release processes will be bombardment dependent. We are therefore confronted with the task of determining the relative importance of the various competing processes, and to do this we should briefly describe some simple, but illustrative experiments which reveal the macroscopic effects observed during ion trapping.

8.2. BASIC EXPERIMENTAL DATA

Many of the early experimental observations of ion trapping were performed using poorly defined surface and ion bombardment conditions as obtained in gas discharge tubes of various geometries. This was only natural since in 1851, Plücker[1] observed the continual removal of gas from X ray tubes and suggested that this was a result of energetic positive ion formation through electron impact and the subsequent trapping of these ions in negatively charged regions of the tubes such as the cathode and the containing vessel. Subsequent investigation[2] proved the validity of this belief, but because of the technological importance of the gas disappearance in discharge tubes much of this investigation was confined to a study of ion trapping phenomena in such devices. Only recently has the necessity been realised of closely defining the ion bombardment parameters and target conditions in order to obtain unequivocal estimates of the important processes of ion trapping. Nevertheless this earlier investigation of gas 'clean up', as it became known, has proved of technological value and pointed out the precautions which must be taken to deduce meaningful data. Reviews of this earlier work may be found in the book by Dushman[3] and in articles by Alpert[4], Carter[5,6] and Strotzer[7]. These surveys show that the majority of the experimental work has been directed to investigation of ion trapping processes in ionization gauges, again because of the technological importance of such devices and because of their relative simplicity. Indeed the first of these motivations is of major importance, since the gauge is employed as a pressure transducer, and if by reason of its inherent ion trapping properties, which are equivalent to gas removal processes and hence to pumping properties, it changes the pressure reading, its utility is diminished.

Let us now consider the type of observation made with such a device. The ionization gauge under consideration itself is essentially a Triode arrangement with a heated filament acting as an electron source, a helically wound electron accelerating and collecting electrode and an ion collector, contained within a glass or metal envelope. The actual electrode configuration may vary with the type of gauge but need not concern us for the present. Electrons, accelerated from the cathode oscillate through the transparent electron accelerating electrode held at $\gtrsim +100$ V with respect to the cathode before eventual capture there. Some will collide with gas atoms present in the gauge and cause ionization. These ions will drift to and strike the ion collector electrode, held $\lesssim -10$ V with respect to the cathode and any other surfaces negative with respect to the electron collector. The total current of ions i_+ will be directly proportional to the current of electrons i_e, and the gas pressure p, i.e.

$$i_+ = ki_e p \qquad 8.1$$

The ion energy, however will not be closely defined since this will depend upon the potential at the spatial point of ion formation and the surface which these ions eventually strike.

Imagine now that such an ionization gauge is connected into an evacuated enclosure of total volume V litres at a pressure p torr and isolated from all sources of gas supply and sinks (such as pumps). The ions which strike the various tube surfaces may be trapped with an macroscopic efficiency η, so that the rate of ion, and thus gas atom, removal is $ki_e p\eta$

From Boyle's law the total gas content of the enclosure is proportional to pV, so that the gas removal leads to a reduction in this quantity at a rate

$$-C\frac{d}{dt}(pV) = -CV\,dp/dt \qquad 8.2.1.$$

Thus

$$-CV\,dp/dt = ki_e p\eta \qquad 8.2.2.$$

which has the solution

$$p = p_0 \exp(-S/V\,.\,t) \qquad 8.2.3.$$

Where S has absorbed the quantities C, k, i_e, and η. S is also given by V/p . dp/dt i.e. the rate of gas removal divided by the pressure at which the gas is removed, which in the terminology of conventional vacuum technique is the pumping speed of the device in litres/sec. This speed clearly increases with electron current (and it is more correct therefore to speak of speed/unit current) and with the trapping efficiency η. Equation 8.2.3 shows that the pressure is expected to fall exponentially to zero with time, and Figure 8.1 illustrates the results of an experiment conducted under the conditions described above, plotted semi logarithmically. Such an experiment has been conducted many times by numerous investigators and although the magnitudes differ from gas to gas and with the electrode configuration and potentials employed, this graph may be considered typical. Clearly the initial pressure diminution follows an exponential law, suggesting a constant initial trapping efficiency, but after some time, depending upon the gas and tube conditions, the rate of fall decreases and generally the pressure tends to a limiting value. Since, invariably, all other parameters are maintained constant, this can only suggest a fall in the apparent trapping efficiency. Further experiments suggest a reason for this decrease.

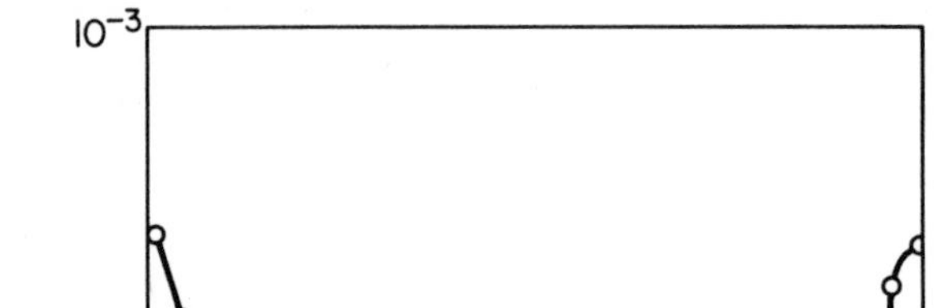

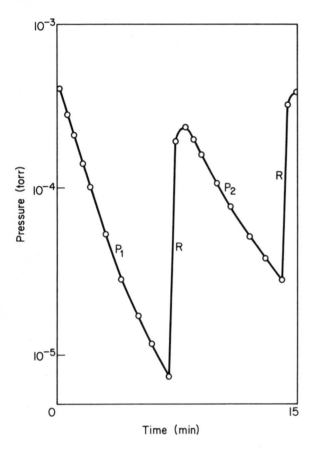

Fig. 8.1 A typical pump down in a Bayard-Alpert ionisation gauge operated in an isolated system containing Argon. P_1 and P_2 are pumping periods, R denotes readmission of gas (viz. Ref. 8.14)

If the electron ionising beam is turned off at any instant during pumping and thereafter operated intermittently, to instantaneously probe the pressure without further pumping, it is invariably observed that, after turn off, the pressure rises, generally to some constant value $p_f < p_0$ which depends upon the pumping history. This indicates a spontaneous recovery of gas from the trapping regions, and an alternative method of observation, wherein a second gauge, operated at low emission to minimise pumping, is used in parallel with the first to monitor the pressure, confirms the effect. Since this recovery behaviour is evidenced to some extent during all stages of pumping it is reasonable to suppose that it occurs simultaneously with the pumping. Moreover, since it is evidenced upon removing the ion bombardment, it does not require this agency to cause its activation. Consequently this effect must be regarded as some form of thermally activated release process operating simultaneously with and mitigating against the trapping effect. Generally speaking the rate at which this release process occurs initially increases with the quantity of gas trapped, so that as the pressure, and therefore the rate of ion trapping is reduced, the release process commences to compete strongly with the trapping mechanism, leading to an effective diminution of trapping efficiency. Confirmation of this may be obtained by introducing more gas to the system after recovery has apparently ceased, to increase the pressure to $\sim p_0$, and recommencing pumping. This is illustrated in the second pump down of Figure 8.1 where the initial speed (slope of the curve) is seen to be almost equal to that of the first pump down. This is expected since the rate of gas trapping would now greatly exceed the recovery rate. For the present we will not speculate on the physical processes which lead to this recovery, but remember that this phenomenon suggests operation of the thermally activated diffusion processes considered in the introduction. However if the processes of gas pump down, recovery and readmission are repeated many times successively, it is found that the diminution in pumping speed at the commencement of each pump down cannot be wholly accounted for by the recovery rate obtaining at that stage. This suggests that a further process must operate to reduce the apparent trapping efficiency. Indeed it is observed that after pumping large quantities of gas, the pumping action appears to stop altogether, whereas the subsequent recovery rate is small. Since the recovery process does not require the activating agency of bombardment, it is natural to assume that other release processes will occur which do require ion bombardment to induce their operation, which would not be observed during post bombardment recovery. The reality of this assumption may be demonstrated by the following simple experiment.

A differential pressure manometer, such as a mass spectrometer, which can determine partial pressures of component gases, as opposed to the ionization gauge which measures total pressures, is included in the evacuated system. After an initial pumping of one gas species, in the ionization gauge, a second gas species is admitted to the system, and immediately the mass spectrometer records an increase in the partial pressure of the initially trapped gas species. This reveals that the second type of ion bombarding species can activate the release of the first type of trapped gas. Since it is possible to observe this re-emission phenomenon for all initially trapped gas species and all releasing ion types, it is evident that any bombarding ion will be capable of causing release of any trapped atom type, in particular atoms of its own species trapped at an earlier stage of pumping. Generally speaking this release process again increases in importance with the quantity of gas trapped, and will therefore become increasingly competitive with the trapping processes. Again we will defer discussion of the physical processes involved in this 'bombardment' induced re-emission phenomenon, but recall that such a mechanism was envisaged in the gas sputtering and damage enhanced diffusion phenomenon outlined in the introduction.

From this evidence it is quite clear that ion trapping alone is insufficient to explain observed phenomena and that thermally and ion bombardment induced release processes must operate simultaneously. It is true to say, however, that when little or no gas has been trapped, any release process will be of minor importance. Consequently observations of the trapping efficiency of the ions initially incident upon targets should not be largely influenced by these processes, and true trapping efficiencies should be adduced. The most obvious way of obtaining such trapping efficiencies is to measure the number of ions trapped in a target as a function of the number of ions striking the target, and from the initial slope of such a graph, determine the real trapping efficiency. It should be pointed out that since this will be the trapping efficiency typical of a target with no trapped gas or bombardment, the results should be free from the influences of surface sputtering, bulk damage and gas occlusion. To what extent this is true depends upon the minimum detectable quantities of trapped gas, i.e. upon the sensitivity of the experiment, and upon the validity of extrapolation of data to the zero bombardment condition. It is to these considerations that we now turn our attention.

8.3. INITIAL TRAPPING EFFICIENCIES.

As already stated the majority of the investigations of gas trapping have been concerned with studying pumping processes in ionization gauges and other gas discharge devices. It is unfortunately true that in such tubes there are many complicating factors which tend to render experimental data less valuable from the fundamental physical point of view. These complications may be listed as follows:-

(1) Since, in an ionization tube there will be several exposed surfaces with potentials less positive than that of the electron collector, any ions formed can be impelled into a variety of such surfaces, generally of differing composition. For example, in an ionization gauge[8], ions can be driven into both the cathode and into the ion collector, and into support leads which communicate the electrodes with the external world. In addition many gauges employ glass envelopes, and these, under the influence of the electrons in the tube generally acquire a surface potential close to that of the cathode and may thus be efficient as sinks. Even with a metal envelope gauge it is impracticable to operate this at the high electron collector potential and so the metal envelope will also be an ion sink.

The numbers of ions which strike each particular surface will depend upon the potentials of these surfaces, their geometric configuration and area, and so bombardment conditions will vary from tube to tube. For example, in the conventional triode ion gauge, which consists of an axial heated wire cathode, a helical electron collector and a cylindrical ion collector coaxial with the other electrodes and of 2 to 5 times the diameter of the electron collector, it is the ion collector which will receive the majority of the ions since it shields the envelope from the discharge and is geometrically and electrically more efficient as an ion sink than the cathode. On the other hand the Bayard Alpert[9], inverted triode, ionization gauge consists of a wire filament displaced from the tube axis, with a helical electron collector and a wire ion collector located on the common, tube and electron collector, axis. In this case ions should strike both the ion collector and cathode in similar numbers, but because of the effective electrical transparency of the system many more will impinge upon the glass or metal envelope.

Macroscopic measurements of ion loss rates thus give an integrated value over all trapping surfaces and in order to obtain specific trapping efficiencies the contributions of the various sinks must be analysed.

(2) Again, because of the geometric and electrical configuration of electrodes it will be impossible to ascribe any single energy to the ions incident on a particular surface. Since ions may be formed by electron impact at any spatial position where the electron energy exceeds the ionization potential of the gas atoms, the energy with which such ions strike the surfaces will be given by the difference in potential between that of the particular surface and that at the spatial point of formation. A considerable energy spread will therefore result, and the ion energy distribution function will be difficult to predict since the ionization efficiency will also be a function of spatial potentials and the nature of the gas atoms. In the Penning[10] type of cold cathode ionization gauge, with magnetic confinement of the electrons, the electron trajectories are particularly complex and the energy of ions striking the cathodes is extremely difficult to predict. Moreover the distribution of ions over the cathode surfaces is quite unknown, as is the direction of incidence. Multiple ionization effects and dissociation by electron impact of molecular gases will also cause uncertainties in both the ion energy and ion type. Furthermore it is often difficult to specify accurately the potential of insulating surfaces, such as a glass envelope, since these will be exposed to simultaneous electron and ion bombardment, both of which agencies can cause secondary effects by electron ejection processes. Indeed, as we shall discuss in some detail later, it has been observed that the glass envelope of a Bayard-Alpert[9] gauge can operate at either of the two stable potentials, one close to cathode and the other close to the electron collector potential, depending upon the secondary electron emission conditions at the envelope. Such a possibility can not only affect the ion bombardment conditions at the envelope, but because of the distortion of the electric fields in the tube, can determine the ion bombardment of other electrodes.

(3) It is also difficult to specify, precisely, the ion bombardment rate of insulating parts of the tube, and of other regions such as the cathode, which receive ions and deliver electron currents also. In the case of insulators it is sometimes possible to replace these by conductors or to render them conducting and determine the ion current. However, most insulating surfaces will be exposed to both ion and electron bombardment which will cause the insulator to attain a stabilising potential where the net current is zero. Consequently, operation of a conducting surface at this potential will determine zero current and it will only be possible to measure the contributions of both current sources by operation at potentials where one or the other component is vanishing and to extrapolate to the stable potential condition. This inevitably leads to some error.

(4) In heated cathode tubes, the thermal radiation from the cathode will elevate different surfaces to different temperatures depending upon their opacity and thermal contact with the surroundings. Furthermore, certain molecular gases may dissociate at the heated filament and again lead to uncertainties of ion type.

(5) Molecular dissociation, provoked either by reaction with the hot cathode or via electron impact may form atoms or compounds with the cathode material which upon collision with tube surfaces are strongly

physically or chemically absorbed, whereas the parent molecule is non reactive. Such behaviour can lead to apparent trapping efficiencies which are much too large and are typical of atomic interactions rather than ionic entrapment. Examples of this type of behaviour occur with molecular hydrogen and oxygen, the characteristics of which have been long appreciated, and with molecular nitrogen which has been found, more recently, to exhibit similar reactions.

(6) Indeed, in discharge tubes where the electron energy is variable over a wide range the effects of electron impact may be quite complex. Thus in addition to ionizing collisions, excited states may be formed, even in inert gases, and at higher pressures, molecular complexes of such gases may form. In the case of molecular nitrogen it is now believed that excitation and dissociation processes must account for a considerable proportion of the observed pumping action and it has been proposed, on several occasions, that absorption of inert gas atoms even occurs via excited metastable states rather than via energetic ion trapping. This belief has never been substantiated however and all the currently available evidence points to ion trapping as the important pumping process in the inert gases.

(7) Most ionization tubes are of quite compact design so that impurities evolved from heated parts may often condense upon other, cooler, regions of the tube and render these surfaces impure. Indeed the view has been expressed that ion trapping in glass surfaces requires the presence of a thin surface film of evaporated metal or other contaminant from the cathode for its efficient operation. This view will be given further consideration shortly.

Further, the ion bombardment of exposed surfaces will lead to their erosion by sputtering and the possibility of deposition on other regions of the tube because of differential bombardment and/or sputtering coefficients. This effect should not influence initial trapping rates but could well be of determining importance in saturation processes. This rather depressing list of disadvantages might tend to suggest that a study of ionization tube 'clean up' phenomena would render measurements relatively useless from the stand point of a physical understanding of the basic processes of ion trapping. Fortunately however, it is often possible to arrange matters such that many of the disadvantages are removed or at least minimised. In addition there are several advantages of the method which are of real significance. Before discussing these we should briefly reconsider what details an ideal method of ion trapping measurement, should possess.

Clearly one would desire a clean, pure, single crystal target of known orientation and bombardment by a parallel beam of monoenergetic single species ions, at a known angle of incidence and striking a well defined target area. The surface of the target should remain free from contamination during the course of the bombardment, by operation, for example, at very low pressure. It would then be necessary to measure the proportion of the incident beam which was trapped in the target, at as low total ion doses as possible. As we shall see later the target and beam requirements, and operation in ultra high vacuum conditions are now becoming realised experimentally, whilst the possibility of determination of small trapped gas concentrations is being explored by several techniques. Even before the attainment of satisfactory beam and target conditions however, it was possible using the ionization tube clean up, or 'Sorption' phenomenon, to realize clean surface conditions and sensitive measurements of trapped gas concentrations, and if only for these reasons, consideration of tube pumping processes is worthwhile.

Although such measurements were indeed possible we should point out that until 1940, the precautions necessary to obtain useful results from ionization tube pumping were not considered important. Thus, as the reviews by Dushman[3] and others show, earlier work than that described by Schwarz[11] in 1940 is fraught with difficulties of interpretation. In particular much of the early work was conducted at relatively high gas pressures, e.g. in the glow discharge region, where the determination of ion energies is difficult and where sputtering processes do not proceed at their normal rate since the atomic mean free path is so short that considerable re-deposition of sputtered material occurs. In the following survey, therefore we will not consider this equivocal work, but refer the interested reader to the reviews already mentioned. It should be realized however, that although of doubtful fundamental significance, the pre 1940 investigations did reveal the complexity of the problem and led finally to a more satisfactory experimental approach. Returning to the question of the merits of tube pumping phenomena we see that since the early 1950's, the means have been at our disposal[12] for producing, and maintaining, very low residual pressures in vacuum systems ($<10^{-9}$ torr) so that many of the pumping experiments to be described shortly, which were performed after that period, were already satisfying the requirement of clean, contaminant free surfaces. To illustrate this we may recapitulate the often quoted formula derived from gas kinetic theory, that the time required for the formation of a monomolecular layer of perfectly adsorbing gas upon a clean surface, is given by $t \simeq 10^6 p$ where t is measured in seconds and p in torr. Thus at 10^{-9} torr, the time required for monolayer contamination is of the order of 1000 seconds. Since meaningful information can generally be obtained in pumping experiments in times one or two orders of magnitude less than this, the condition for surface cleanliness is satisfied. Considering, next, the question of experimental sensitivity, we see from equation 8.2.2 that the quantity of gas trapped $CV\delta p$, during operation of a gauge at a pressure p for a time δt is simply, $ki_e p\eta\delta t$. In ionization gauges, k is of the order of 100 milliamps of ions per milliamp electron current per torr pressure, distributed over various surfaces.

Thus the number of ions removed per second at a pressure p in a volume of 1 litre is of the order $6 \times 10^{18}\, p\eta$. The value of C is readily obtained from gas kinetic theory and is 3.24×10^{19} atoms/litre torr at 0°C. Consequently the pressure drop δp per second is given by $\delta p \simeq 0.2 p\eta$. It is possible by conventional methods of observation to see a pressure change of 1% per second, so that an ion trapping efficiency of 0.05 is readily observable. However by backing off the initial pressure signal and studying only the initial pressure changes, and by sensitive time recording apparatus it is possible to increase this sensitivity to .005% per second and thus trapping efficiencies as low as 2.5×10^{-4} are theoretically observable—although no such experimental data have so far been reported in this range.

It is also important to note that if the initial gas pressure is p, the number of ions which strike exposed surfaces per second is of the order 6×10^{18}p. Generally speaking the exposed surface area may be as high as 100 cm^2, and thus the rate of ion bombardment is $6 \times 10^{16}p$ ions/cm^2/sec. Pressures between 10^{-4} torr and 10^{-10} torr have been used to determine trapping efficiencies and it is seen that for a bombardment time of 1 second the number of bombarding ions can vary over the range 6×10^6 ions/cm^2 to 6×10^{12} ions/cm^2. Even the larger bombardment dose, which is the equivalent of about 1 ion per 100 surface atoms, should therefore result in only minor radiation damage for ion energies up to 1000 eV, and so the trapping efficiency will therefore be typical of the undamaged surface. This sensitivity is therefore a useful advantage of the gauge sorption method of determining ion trapping rates.

Let us now consider how the remaining disadvantages can be minimised or allowed for. Firstly the effects of dissociation at the cathode or in the electron beam may be eliminated by operation in inert gases only. Although electron bombardment can lead to excited atomic states, there is no unequivocal evidence that such processes are responsible for inert gas sorption and we will therefore ascribe all pumping effects in these gases to ion trapping. Contamination of pumping surfaces by cathode products has been suggested by Varnerin and Carmichael[13] to be necessary to promote rapid sorption of Helium in glass and indeed enhanced pumping does occur with this combination with relatively thick metallic layers deliberately deposited upon the glass. However work by Cobic et al[14] and Carter and Leck[15,16] with all the inert gas ions bombarding glass surfaces over long periods of time during which any contamination effects should have led to changes in the pumping properties, revealed no such changes. This suggested that surface cleanliness was unimportant, for the heavier gases, at least as long as contaminant layers were not too thick (as used in Varnerin and Carmichael's[13] work). On the other hand it is quite probable that other surface contamination is of importance when studying active gases such as oxygen or nitrogen as the investigations of Bills and Carleton[17] reveal, and possibly the inert gases He and Ne as measurements by Grant and Carter[18] suggest.

Considering next the question of the disposition of ion currents over exposed surfaces we should rember that this will be a function of the tube configuration and generalizations are difficult. One useful technique of determining the importance of various surfaces as trapping sinks is to heat these after bombardment when, invariably, a recovery of trapped gas is observed. The relative recovery of the various parts indicates which regions have the highest values of the product (ion bombardment rate x trapping efficiency). In this way Bloomer and Haine[19] have shown that in a conventional triode ion gauge, most ion trapping occurs in the cylindrical metal ion collector, and a small fraction in the part of the glass envelope unshielded by this collector. On the other hand, these authors and James and Carter[20] have shown that in a Bayard-Alpert ionization gauge, the ion trapping is largely confined to the glass envelope in a region opposite the electron collector and is uniformly distributed. Maddix and Allen[21,22,23] have observed that in an inert gas filled R. F. discharge tube with external electrodes gas trapping is again confined almost entirely to the envelope region between the electrodes.

In the case of the Bayard-Alpert gauge, which is of most significance to our discussion since most experiments have employed this device, Young[24] and Carter and Leck[25,26,27,28] have determined the magnitude of the ion current to the glass envelope by use of a conducting coating on, or a conducting cylinder near to, the envelope, at voltages where the electron current contribution is suppressed, and subsequent extrapolation back to the normal operating potential of the envelope gives the normal ion current. The envelope current was thus determined to be between 5 and 10 times as large as the current to the normal ion collector. Since, as we shall see later, the ion trapping efficiencies into metals are generally low (~0.1 at ion energies of a few hundred volts), whereas total trapping efficiencies are often considerably larger, the assumption that the trapping occurs mainly in the glass envelope is reasonably accurate. In electrodeless discharges tubes the ion current to the envelope, which is the only sink, may be calculated.

The trapping at the cathode is difficult to assess since it is impossible to measure the ion current to this electrode, but it should be almost negligible since operation at high temperature markedly decreases trapping efficiency as we shall see subsequently. Trapping at support electrodes should also be small because of their generally small surface area. The question of ion energy spread is probably the most serious disadvantage of the gauge sorption method of determining trapping efficiencies. Basically this spread may be between OeV and several hundred eV because of the spatial variation of potential and multiply charged ion production. Carter[27] has shown that it is possible, by making some assumptions as to the spatial variation of potential and the electron transmission efficiency through the electron collector, and using known cross sections for ion production by electron impact, to determine a mean ion energy for the simple case of ion collector bombardment in a conventional triode. It turns out that this mean energy is about half the electron collector voltage and increases roughly linearly with this parameter, but the calculation is only approximate and certainly cannot be applied to the Bayard-Alpert gauge structure. Moreover since the variation of trapping efficiency with ion energy is unknown, one does not obtain a value of mean trapping efficiency as a function of mean ion energy by this method.

Varnerin and Carmichael[29] have used a tetrode type structure with a metal envelope to render ion energies more precise and in this case the trapping efficiency/ion energy data is more reliable.

In addition to the difficulty in determining ion energy because of the spatial potential variation, a further complication arises in glass envelope tubes since the potential of this latter can vary. Carter,[25] Carter and Leck,[26,28] Cobic et al[30] and James and Carter[31] have observed that the glass envelope potential can stabilise at either of two potentials, one close to the cathode potential and the other close to the electron collector potential. Since the glass is an insulating surface and is bombarded by both electrons and ions it can only reach a stable operating potential such that the net current it receives is zero. Electrons, and to a much smaller extent ions, can also release secondary electrons from the glass, with an efficiency varying from zero to above unity, which must in turn be collected by some electrode. Thus there will be three or more contributions to the envelope current and stabilisation will only occur for zero total current. One way in which this may occur is that the envelope potential should be slightly less than the cathode potential, where the secondary electron emission is negligible and the ion current to the envelope is balanced by those electrons, emitted from the cathode with a Maxwellian energy distribution, which can surmount the potential barrier. Comsa and Musa[32,33,34] and James and Carter[31] have shown theoretically that this leads to an envelope potential which varies slightly with gas pressure but which is always ≃ −5 V with respect to the cathode and the latter authors have obtained experimental confirmation of this. In this case, the so called Mode B of gauge operation, singly charged ions incident upon the glass possess energies between O eV and the cathode-electron collector potential difference. (~150-200 eV). A second way in which stabilisation may occur is when the primary electron current to the envelope is balanced by the current of secondary emitted (and collected) electrons. The envelope potential at which this occurs is determined by the efficiency with which secondary electrons are collected by the electron collector and thus the envelope potential depends upon the electron collector potential and is generally somewhat negative with respect to this latter. Cobic et al[30] and James and Carter[31] have shown that the envelope potential increases as the electron collector potential increases above a value of the latter of about 200 V which is apparently necessary before this mode of stabilisation, mode A, is observed.

It has also been found[30,31] that the possibility of achieving stabilisation at this potential is conditioned by such parameters as electron emission current, gas pressure, thermal and sorption history, and most interestingly, by the manner of activation of gauge potentials. For example application of the electron collector potential before cathode activation generally leads to Mode A operation since the envelope becomes capacitively charged to a high positive potential before electrons flow, resulting in a preference for this operational mode.

This envelope potential has been studied carefully by the authors mentioned above by surrounding the gauge with a conducting cylinder, which forms an effective capacitor with the charged inner surface of the envelope, and using this as part of an earthed capacitance divider chain in conjunction with an electrometer amplifier to determine the potential.

In the Mode A operation, the ion current to the envelope will still exist since the envelope potential is negative with respect to the electron collector, but its magnitude is impossible to measure since the electron current is totally dominant. Measurements of trapping rates for the effective ion energy in this mode, and changes in the amount collected by the ion collector, suggest that the envelope current is diminished by a factor of 5 to 10.

It is clear therefore that in order to obtain at least an approximation to the ion energy in insulating envelope tubes the potential of these should be specified, but this difficulty is removed with conducting envelope tubes. However the ion energy spread still exists in such cases and this markedly reduces the utility of the results. Despite this drawback, however, the mean ion energy should be within a factor of about 2 or 3 of that determined by the electron collector potential, and the results should therefore give a reliable order of magnitude estimate. Finally the question of heating of tube parts by thermal radiation from the filament should be considered. In conventional triode gauges or in structures totally optically enclosed where the bombarded surface, is for example, an enveloping metal can, the ion collector may reach quite high temperatures, estimated for example by Varnerin and Carmichael[29] to be about 300°C. In a Bayard Alpert structure gauge, measurements of the outer glass envelope[31] temperature when surrounded by an enclosure, and of thermal evolution of trapped gas during post bombardment heating [15] suggest that the inner surface of the envelope may be raised to about 50°C by cathode irradiation. The temperature of the ion collector in this case is difficult to assess, but because of its lesser importance in pumping it may be ignored.

We thus conclude that in a Bayard-Alpert type gauge, measurements of total trapping efficiencies should reflect the ion trapping efficiency in the glass quite well, provided due regard is paid to the ion energy spread and the envelope potential.

In deliberately designed tube structures where ions strike predetermined surfaces, e.g. tetrode tubes and Penning type discharge tubes the nature of trapping surfaces is less equivocal, but in the latter case mean ion energies are very poorly defined.

It therefore appears, that, apart from the inadequate specification of ion energy, ionization tube pumping methods may be usefully employed to determine trapping efficiencies. Before enumerating the results of these studies we should give a brief further consideration to the techniques of measurement and the deduction of η from tube pumping measurements. In the isolated volume, or static pumpdown technique mentioned earlier the slope of the semilog pressure time graph is seen to give the produce $k\eta$, where k is the rate at which ions strike the pumping surfaces per unit pressure per unit electron current. In order to deduce η therefore, k must be determined separately. This may be effected by measuring the ion current to the effective sinks as a function of gas pressure and type, electron current and accelerating voltage, directly for conducting surfaces and by the method outlined above for insulating surfaces. It is invariably found that below gas pressure of $\sim 10^{-3}$ torr and emission currents below ~10 ma, the factor k is constant and for the collector surface of a Bayard-Alpert gauge has a value of 5 to 20 ma./torr pressure/ma. electron current and for the glass envelope 20 to 100 ma/torr/ma. The constant k is gas species dependent because of the variation of ionization cross section, but generally speaking lies within an order of magnitude of the above figures from He through to Xe. k also increases with electron acceleration energy to a maximum at 100 to 200V and then decreases slowly up to 1000 V, again because of the variation of ionization cross section with electron energy. Actual values can be obtained from a study by Cobic, Carter and Leck.[30] At higher gas pressures and electron currents than given by the above, changes in k occur because of the increasing importance of space charge phenomena. This has been confirmed in studies of gauge sensitivity by Schulz[35] and by observations of the constancy of the initial gauge pumping speed for Argon over a wide pressure range up to a maximum of about 10^{-3} torr by Cobic et al.[14] In addition several studies of the initial pumping speed (Cobic, Carter and Leck,[14] Jenkins and Trodden,[36] Florescu[37] and James et al[38]) indicate a linear increase of speed with electron current, again revealing the constancy of k.

In addition to the static pump down method of determining speed (=$k\eta$) several other methods have been used which we will now consider. Bills and Carleton[17] and Comsa and his collaborators[39,40,41] used a quasi-dynamic system to study the pumping of O_2 and N_2, and inert gases respectively by continuously bleeding gas into the static volume via a control valve at such a rate as to maintain the gas pressure constant. In this case the rate of gas admission balanced the loss due to pumping processes, and accurate measurement of the former rate L_t enabled deduction of the instantaneous gauge pumping speed S_t, since $L_t = S_t \cdot p$. Any diminution of pumping speed as gas was trapped was reflected as a change required in the admission rate L_t.

One advantage of this method is that it allows maintenance of the gas pressure p at a level much higher than the background pressure p_b of the vacuum system, so that degassing effects of background gases are minimised. In the static system technique, p decreases and pumping processes may be swamped by release of adsorbed surface contaminant gases when $p \simeq p_b$, so that true saturation and release of trapped gas processes are masked. In this method, the quantity of gas pumped by the gauge is given simply by

$$\int_0^t L_t dt \qquad 8.3$$

Another, truly dynamic method has been used by Carter and Leck[15,16,20,42,43] and their collaborators to determine pumping speeds in the inert gases. In these experiments gas is allowed to flow through the ionization tube continuously and is pumped by a diffusion pump of speed S_D, such that the gas pressure is maintained constant. Thus if L is the gas influx rate, and S the gauge pumping speed then

$$L = (S_D + S)p \qquad 8.4.1$$

and if $S_D \gg S$, as is generally the case,

$$p = \frac{L}{S_D} = \text{constant.} \qquad 8.4.2$$

This method again possesses the advantage of a high ratio of operating to background pressure so minimising contamination effects, but possesses the disadvantage of requiring further experiments for the determination of S. This is achieved by heating the ionization tube after gas trapping (in the glass envelope) and noting the increase of pressure on a second gauge or a mass spectrometer.

If after ion trapping the source of gas is removed and the gauge heated up to about 450°C, previously trapped gas is released at a rate R_t. If the trapping tube is isolated from the pumps by means of a valve the total rate of pressure rise is given by

$$V\,dp'/dt = R_t \text{ or } p' = \frac{1}{V}\int_0^t R_t\,dt \qquad 8.5.1$$

A graph of p′ against t shows a rapid rise with increasing temperature until p′ becomes constant when no further gas is evolved. The total quantity of gas evolved and therefore previously trapped is thus given by

$$\int R_t dt = V(p_f' - p_i') \qquad 8.5.2$$

where $p_f' - p_i'$ is the pressure increase. Comparison of the quantity released with that pumped in a static type pump down experiment where the actual quantity of gas pumped is measured shows that all trapped gas may generally be recovered by heating to 450°C. A useful feature of this method is that it allows determination of the rate of gas evolution as a function of recovery temperature, which as we shall see later has some particular significance in the interpretation of trapping processes.

If instead of isolating the gauge during thermal recovery, the diffusion pumps are allowed to pump the evolving gas, the gas flow equation becomes

$$V\frac{dp'}{dt} = R_t - S'p' \qquad 8.6.1$$

or

$$R_t = V\,dp'/dt + Sp' \qquad 8.6.2$$

The quantity of gas recovered up to any time t is thus given by

$$\int R_t dt = \int_{p_i'}^{p'} V\,dp'/dt \,.\, dt + \int_0^t Sp'dt \qquad 8.6.3$$

and the total quantity of gas recovered when the pressure transient is over and p′ reduces to the initial pre-release value p_i' is

$$Q_t = \int_0^t Sp'dt \qquad 8.6.4$$

Thus observation of the pressure transient as a function of time (and this is observed to rise to a maximum with increasing temperature and then fall to zero at about 450°C) and time integration of the transient allows deduction of the quantity of gas evolved.

Again, comparison with a static pump down reveals that generally speaking all trapped gas is recovered.

In order to determine trapping efficiencies with this method it is necessary to measure the amount of gas trapped $Q_t = \int k i_e p \eta dt$ as a function of the total ion bombardment received by the trapping surfaces. ($ki_e pt$), and the initial slope of this curve gives the initial trapping efficiency directly. One further advantage of this method is that it allows rapid achievement of saturation conditions since the rate of ion bombardment of trapping surfaces is maintained at a constant high value ($=ki_e p$) whereas in the static volume technique the rate of bombardment varies and decreases rapidly during each pump down.

Other methods which are intermediate between the static and dynamic method have also been used by Comsa and Musa,[32] Comsa and Iosifescu[39] and Cobic et al.[44] If in the above technique the pumping speed of the alternative pump and the flow rate are maintained constant at S_D and L respectively, the instantaneous gas pressure is given by

$$p_t = \frac{L}{S_D + S} \qquad 8.7.1$$

If initially only the alternative pump operates, a constant pressure p_1 is established where

$$p_1 = L/S_D \qquad 8.7.2$$

The trapping tube is then activated and commences pumping with a speed of S_i so that the pressure is reduced to a new value

$$p_2 = \frac{L}{S_D + S_i} \qquad 8.7.3$$

The speed S_i is then readily determined since

$$S_i = L(1/p_2 - 1/p_1) \qquad 8.7.4$$

If the pump speed S_i then falls because of re-emission effects the pressure rises and the instantaneous speed S_t is determined from $S_t = L(1/p_2 - 1/p_t)$. Some caution must be applied here since the actual flow equation upon activation of the trapping gauge is given by $V\frac{dp}{dt} = L - (S_i + S_D)p$ which has the solution

$$p = \left\{p_1 - \frac{L}{S_i + S_D}\right\} \exp\left(-\frac{S_i + S_D}{V} . t\right) + \frac{L}{S_i + S_D} \qquad 8.8.1$$

and so the pressure p falls exponentially to the value p_2 determined by the time constant $\frac{V}{S_i + S_D}$. If this time constant is large, so that an appreciable time may be required to establish the new equilibrium, and if in this time the speed falls, the final pressure p_2 may not be representative of the initial speed and thence trapping efficiency. The quantity of gas trapped during the pressure fall period given, by $\int Spdt$ is determined from equation 8.8.1 to be

$$\frac{SL}{S + S_D}\left\{t + \frac{VS}{S + S_D} \exp -\left(\frac{S + S_D}{V} . t\right)\right\} \qquad 8.8.2$$

or when p_2 is reached

$$\frac{S}{S + S_D} . Lt \qquad 8.8.3$$

As long as the time constant $\frac{V}{S + S_D}$ is short, this latter value may be used at all stages of pumping.

If it is arranged that $S \approx S_D$, then the pressure changes will be large and for a known S_D and L, S is readily deduced.

Having discussed the methods of determining trapping efficiencies we are in a position to investigate the results obtained from these studies. In the first instance we shall enumerate only the data for inert gases since these should be free from the influence of other dissociation and absorption phenomenon. Before doing this we should point out that our definition of trapping efficiency is somewhat arbitrary. As we shall see later a considerable quantity of trapped gas is always recovered over a period of time commencing from the instant of trapping. This implies that trapping and evolution are constantly competing processes and that if the trapping time of an atom is short compared to experimental observation times the measured trapping efficiency will be low. We therefore must define η as the efficiency of trapping of ions which remain trapped for the duration of the experimental measurements.

The available data for inert gas ion pumping is summarised in Table 8.1. The initial pumping speed is given (in l/sec/ma), where possible, since this parameter is valuable for technological purposes. Where surface bombardment rates have also been determined the ion trapping efficiency is evaluated and the effective ion energy quoted. The method of determination of pumping speed and the nature of the pumping tube and trapping surface (glass or metal) is also given whilst comments on the measurements by the various investigators supplement the data.

In addition to the variation of trapping efficiency with trapping surface (as evidenced by this Table 8.1), the former parameter varies with ion type and energy and the trapping surface temperature. In figure 8.2 the variation of ion trapping efficiency with effective ion energy (the electron accelerator voltage) is shown for He, Ne, A, Kr and Xe ions incident on the Pyrex envelope of a Bayard-Alpert gauge as observed by Cobic et al,[14] whilst Figure 8.3 depicts similar curves obtained at lower energy for Ne, A, Kr and Xe ions incident on the glass envelope of a simple diode

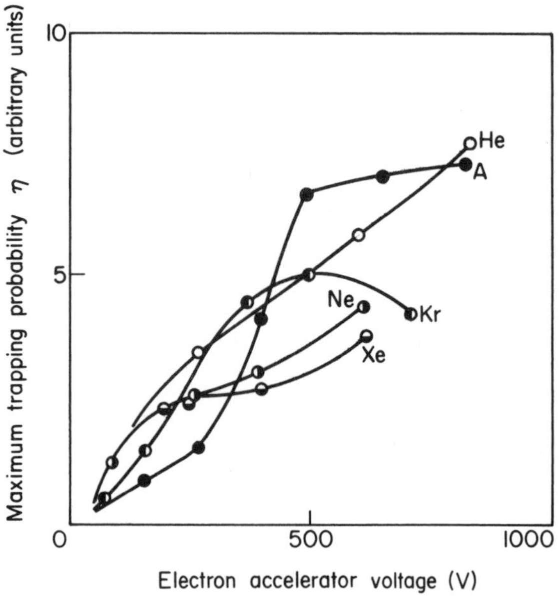

Fig. 8.2 The variation of the trapping probability (η) as a function of the Ion energy (proportional to electron collector voltage) for inert gas ions incident on Pyrex. (viz. Ref. 8.14) in a Bayard-Alpert gauge. Absolute values of η are not given

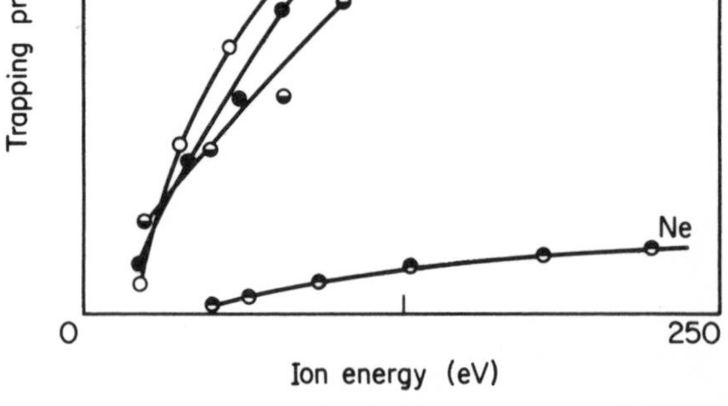

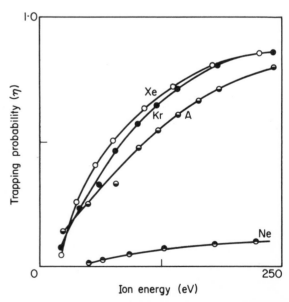

Fig. 8.3 The variation of the trapping efficiency (η) in absolute units as a function of ion energy for Ne^+, A^+, Kr^+ and Xe^+ ions incident on Pyrex in a simple diode tube (viz. Ref. 8.18)

TABLE 8.1.

Trapping efficiences for various inert gas ions on different targets.

Ion type	Ion energy	Target material	Target temperature	η	Pumping device	Pumping speed litres/sec/ma electron current	Investigators	Reference and Remarks
Helium	150 ev	Molybdenum	≅300°C	0.35	Tetrode	1.6×10^{-2}	Varnerin & Carmichael	8.29
	500 ev	Molybdenum	≅300°C	0.57	Tetrode		Varnerin & Carmichael	8.29
	1 Kev	Molybdenum	≅300°C	0.67	Tetrode		Varnerin & Carmichael	8.29
	1.5 Kev	Molybdenum	≅300°C	0.71	Tetrode		Varnerin & Carmichael	8.29
	2.5 Kev	Molybdenum	≅300°C	0.79	Tetrode		Varnerin & Carmichael	8.29
Helium	150 ev	Nickel	≅300°C	0.65	Tetrode	8.10^{-3}	Carmichael and Knoll	8.81 Ion current approximated
Helium	2 Kev and 4 Kev	Tungsten	≅20°C	0.19	Ion beam		Corkhill and Carter	8.74
Helium	150 ev	Molybdenum	60°C	1	Triode		Fox and Knoll	8.49 Value at 60°C not known exactly but values at −80°C and −196°C expressed relative to arbitrary value of 1.0 at 60°C. Ion current approximated.
			−80°C	2.3	Triode		Fox and Knoll	
			−196°C	3.6	Triode		Fox and Knoll	
Helium	250 ev	Pyrex glass	≅ 20°C	0.87	Triode	5×10^{-4}	Cobic, Carter and Leck	8.14
	≅200 ev	Pyrex glass	≅ 20°C	0.2	Bayard-Alpert gauge		Alpert	8.4
Helium	50 ev	Platinum	≅ 20°C	0.54	Special tube		Teloy	8.45
	100 ev	Platinum	≅ 20°C	0.60	Special tube		Teloy	8.45
	200 ev	Platinum	≅ 20°C	0.62	Special tube		Teloy	8.45

TABLE 8.1.

Trapping efficiencies for various inert gas ions on different targets.

Ion type	Ion energy	Target material	Target temperature	η	Pumping device	Pumping speed litres/sec/ma electron current	Investigators	Reference and Remarks
Neon	150 ev	Molybdenum	≅300°C	0.05	Tetrode	4.5×10^{-2}	Carmichael and Knoll	8.81 Ion current approximated.
Neon	150 ev	Nickel	≅300°C	0.73	Tetrode	2×10^{-3}	Carmichael and Knoll	8.81
Neon	50 ev	Tungsten	≅ 20°C	≅ 10^{-5}	Ion beam		Kornelsen	8.72
	100 ev	Tungsten	≅ 20°C	0.06	Ion beam		Kornelsen	8.72
	1 Kev	Tungsten	≅ 20°C	0.6	Ion beam		Kornelsen	8.72
Neon	250 ev	Pyrex glass	≅ 20°C	0.55	Triode	5×10^{-4}	Cobić, Carter and Leck	8.14
Neon	100 ev	Pyrex glass	≅ 20°C	0.05	Diode		Grant and Carter	8.18
	200 ev	Pyrex glass	≅ 20°C	0.08	Diode		Grant and Carter	8.18
Argon	150 ev	Molybdenum	≅300°C	0.05	Tetrode	1.5×10^{-2}	Carmichael and Knoll	8.81 Ion current approximated
Argon	0.7-4 Kev	Molybdenum	≅ 20°C	0.60	Ion beam		Colligon and Leck	8.70
Argon	50 ev	Molybdenum	≅ 20°C	0.01	Special tube		Teloy	8.45
	100 ev	Molybdenum	≅ 20°C	0.04	Special tube		Teloy	8.45
	200 ev	Molybdenum	≅ 20°C	0.10	Special tube		Teloy	8.45
	200 ev	Molybdenum	≅ 20°C	0.15	Special tube		Kay and Winters	8.46, 8.47
	300 ev	Molybdenum	≅ 20°C	0.28	Special tube		Kay and Winters	8.46, 8.47.
Argon	150 ev	Nickel	≅300°C	0.40	Tetrode	1×10^{-3}	Carmichael and Knoll	8.81 Ion current approximated

Argon	200 ev	Nickel	≅ 20°C	0.10	Special tube		Kay and Winters	8.46, 8.47.
	300 ev	Nickel	≅ 20°C	0.25	Special tube		Kay and Winters	8.46, 8.47.
Argon	150 ev	Titanium	≅ 20°C	0.25	Triode	3×10^{-2}	Jenkins and Trodden	8.36
	300 ev and above	Titanium	≅ 20°C	0.5	Triode	4×10^{-2}	Jenkins and Trodden	8.36 Ion current approximated.
Argon	500 ev	Aluminium	≅ 20°C	0.06	Ion beam		Brown and Davies	8.76
	1 Kev	Aluminium	≅ 20°C	0.5	Ion beam		Brown and Davies	8.76
	5 Kev and above	Aluminium	≅ 20°C	1.0	Ion beam		Brown and Davies	8.76
Argon	100 ev	Tungsten	≅ 20°C	7×10^{-4}	Ion beam		Kornelsen	8.72
	1 Kev and above	Tungsten	≅ 20°C	0.6	Ion beam		Kornelsen	8.72
	250 ev	Tungsten	≅ 20°C	0.01	Ion beam		Corkhill and Carter	8.74
	500 ev	Tungsten	≅ 20°C	0.04	Ion beam		Corkhill and Carter	8.74
	1 Kev	Tungsten	≅ 20°C	0.10	Ion beam		Corkhill and Carter	8.74
	2 Kev	Tungsten	≅ 20°C	0.16	Ion beam		Corkhill and Carter	8.74
	1 Kev	Tungsten	≅ 20°C	0.16	Ion beam		Brown and Davies	8.76
	5 Kev	Tungsten	≅ 20°C	≅0.21	Ion beam		Brown and Davies	8.76
	10 Kev	Tungsten	≅ 20°C	≅0.7	Ion beam		Brown and Davies	8.76
	0.7-4 Kev	Tungsten	≅ 20°C	0.25	Ion beam		Colligon and Leck	8.70
Argon	0.7-4 Kev	Platinum	≅ 20°C	> 0.7	Ion beam		Colligon and Leck	8.70
Argon	50 ev	Platinum	≅ 20°C	0.1	Special tube		Teloy	8.45
	100 ev	Platinum	≅ 20°C	0.52	Special tube		Teloy	8.45
	200 ev	Platinum	≅ 20°C	0.52	Special tube		Teloy	8.45
Argon	250 ev	Pyrex glass	≅ 20°C	0.31	Triode	6×10^{-3}	Cobic, Carter and Leck	8.14
Argon	100 ev	Pyrex glass	≅ 20°C	0.55	Diode		Grant and Carter	8.18
	200 ev	Pyrex glass	≅ 20°C	0.80	Diode		Grant and Carter	8.18
Argon	= 200 ev	TiO_2 and other metallic oxide powders	≅ 20°C	≅0.15	Recoils from α irradiation		Kelly	8.50

TABLE 8.1.

Trapping efficiencies for various inert gas ions on different targets.

Ion type	Ion energy	Target material	Target temperature	η	Pumping device	Pumping speed litres/sec/ma electron current	Investigators	Reference and Remarks
Krypton	150 ev	Molybdenum	≅300°C	0.09	Tetrode	4×10^{-3}	Carmichael and Knoll	8.81 Ion current approximated
	0.7-4 Kev	Molybdenum	20°C	0.15	Ion beam		Colligon and Leck	8.70
Krypton	150 ev	Nickel	≅300°C	≅ 1.0	Tetrode	2.5×10^{-4}	Carmichael and Knoll	8.81 Ion current approximated
Krypton	100 ev	Tungsten	≅ 20°C	3×10^{-6}	Ion beam		Kornelsen	8.72 Extrapolated from slightly higher energy
	1 Kev	Tungsten	≅ 20°C	0.5	Ion beam		Kornelsen	8.72
	5 Kev	Tungsten	≅ 20°C	0.7	Ion beam		Kornelsen	8.72
	1 Kev	Tungsten	≅ 20°C	0.1	Ion beam		Brown and Davies	8.76
	5 Kev	Tungsten	≅ 20°C	0.52	Ion beam		Brown and Davies	8.76
	10 Kev	Tungsten	≅ 20°C	0.88	Ion beam		Brown and Davies	8.76
	0.7-4 Kev	Tungsten	≅ 20°C	0.1	Ion beam		Colligon and Leck	8.70
Krypton	0.7-4 Kev	Platinum	≅ 20°C	0.1	Ion beam		Colligon and Leck	8.70
Krypton	250 ev	Pyrex glass	≅ 20°C	0.62	Triode	6×10^{-3}	Cobic, Carter and Leck	8.14
Krypton	100 ev	Pyrex glass	≅ 20°C	0.60	Diode		Grant and Carter	8.18
	200 ev	Pyrex glass	≅ 20°C	0.85	Diode		Grant and Carter	8.18
Krypton	≅200 ev	TiO_2 and other metallic oxide powders	≅ 20°C	0.03	Recoils from α irradiation		Kelly	8.50
Xenon	100 ev	Aluminium	≅ 20°C	0.05	Ion beam		Brown and Davies	8.76
	500 ev	Aluminium	≅ 20°C	0.30	Ion beam		Brown and Davies	8.76
	1 Kev	Aluminium	≅ 20°C	0.60	Ion beam		Brown and Davies	8.76
	5 Kev and above	Aluminium	≅ 20°C	1.0	Ion beam		Brown and Davies	8.76

Xenon	500 ev	Tungsten	≅ 20°C	≅ 10^{-2}	Ion beam		Kornelsen	8.72
	1 Kev	Tungsten	≅ 20°C	0.2	Ion beam		Kornelsen	8.72
	5 Kev	Tungsten	≅ 20°C	0.6	Ion beam		Kornelsen	8.72
	1 Kev	Tungsten	≅ 20°C	0.1	Ion beam		Brown and Davies	8.76
	5 Kev and above	Tungsten	≅ 20°C	1.0	Ion beam		Brown and Davies	8.76
Xenon	2 Kev	Tungsten	≅ 20°C	0.10	Ion beam		Corkhill and Carter	8.74
	4 Kev	Tungsten	≅ 20°C	0.23	Ion beam		Corkhill and Carter	8.74
Xenon	1 Kev	Beryllium	≅ 20°C	0.23	Ion beam		Brown and Davies	8.76
	5 Kev and above	Beryllium	≅ 20°C	≅1.0	Ion beam		Brown and Davies	8.76
Xenon	1 Kev	Nickel	≅ 20°C	0.20	Ion beam		Brown and Davies	8.76
	5 Kev and above	Nickel	≅ 20°C	≅1.0	Ion beam		Brown and Davies	8.76
Xenon	1 Kev	Zirconium	≅ 20°C	0.43	Ion beam		Brown and Davies	8.76
	5 Kev and above	Zirconium	≅ 20°C	≅1.0	Ion beam		Brown and Davies	8.76
Xenon	1 Kev	Tantalum	≅ 20°C	0.37	Ion beam		Brown and Davies	8.76
	5 Kev and above	Tantalum	≅ 20°C	≅1.0	Ion beam		Brown and Davies	8.76
Xenon	5 Kev	Silver	≅ 20°C	≅0.4	Ion beam		Brown and Davies	8.76
	10 Kev	Silver	≅ 20°C	≅0.5	Ion beam		Brown and Davies	8.76
Xenon	1 Kev	Gold	≅ 20°C	0.05	Ion beam		Brown and Davies	8.76
	5 Kev	Gold	≅ 20°C	≅0.65	Ion beam		Brown and Davies	8.76
	10 Kev	Gold	≅ 20°C	≅0.7	Ion beam		Brown and Davies	8.76
Xenon	250 ev	Pyrex glass	≅ 20°C	0.41	Triode	2×10^{-4}	Cobic, Carter and Leck	8.14
Xenon	100 ev	Pyrex glass	≅ 20°C	0.65	Diode		Grant and Carter	8.18
	200 ev	Pyrex glass	≅ 20°C	0.85	Diode		Grant and Carter	8.18
Xenon	≅200 ev	TiO_2 and other metallic oxide	≅ 20°C	≅0.15	Recoils from α irradiation		Kelly	8.50

structure. In this latter work by Grant and Carter[18] no evidence was found for appreciable He trapping and the Ne trapping efficiency was lower than that observed by Cobic et al.[14] This led Grant and Carter[18] to suggest that the earlier work may have been performed with a glass surface with a contaminant metal film, thus leading to the higher η values. Fig. 8.4 shows the variation of η with the energy (approximately monoenergetic ions were used) of He ions incident on a molybdenum surface,[29] operated at about 300°C in a special tetrode tube, whilst Figures 8.5a and b display similar results[45] for low energy A^+ ions trapped on Mo and Pt surfaces and He^+ ions in a Pt surface at room temperature, and Figure 8.6 shows alternative values[46,47] for η for A^+ ions of energy up to 300 eV on Ni and Mo surfaces. Table 8.1 reveals that different investigators have obtained differing results depending upon the geometrical configuration of their pumping tubes, but a general result is that ion trapping efficiencies of the inert gases are of order 10^{-1} at ion energies of about 100 eV and increase to the order of unity at 1 KeV ion energy, on glass surfaces. Cobic et al[14] find that the trapping efficiency for He is apparently higher than that of the other inert gases, at least at the lower energies, but Grant and Carter's[18] and Varnerin and Carmichael's[13,29] work suggests that metallic deposits are required upon glass surfaces to ensure this high efficiency.

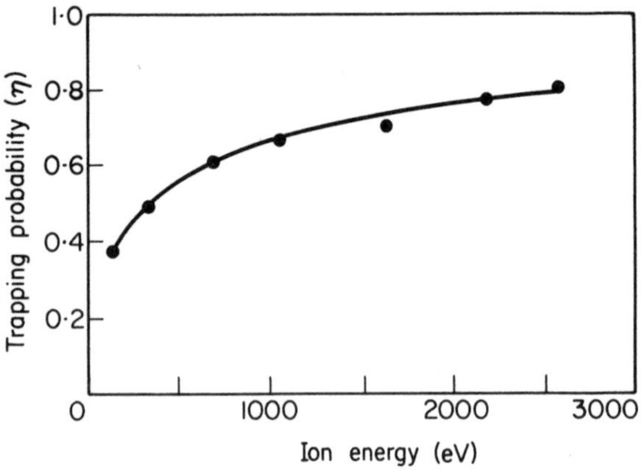

Fig. 8.4 The variation of the trapping probability (η) as a function of ion energy for He^+ ions incident on Molybdenum (viz. Ref. 8.29)

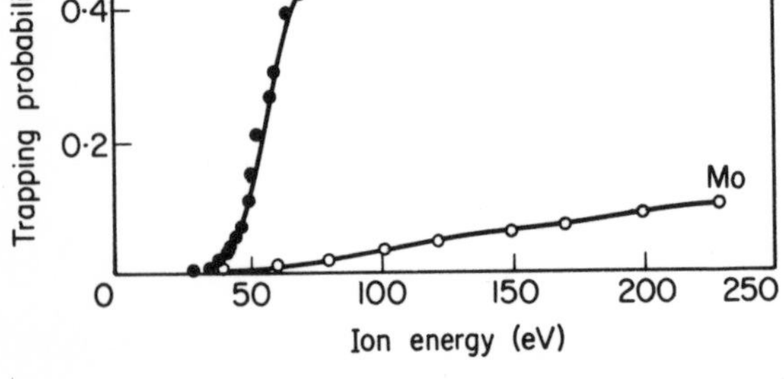

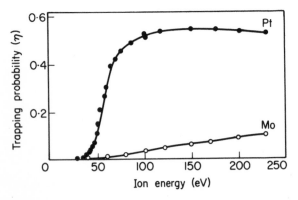

Fig. 8.5a The variation of the trapping probability (η) as a function of ion energy for A^+ ions incident on Pt and Mo surfaces (viz. Ref. 8.45)

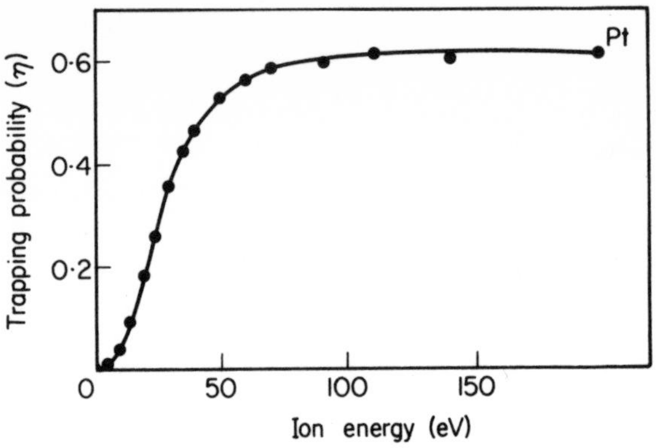

Fig. 8.5b The variation of the trapping probability (η) as a function of ion energy for He^+ ions incident on a Pt surface (viz. Ref. 8.45)

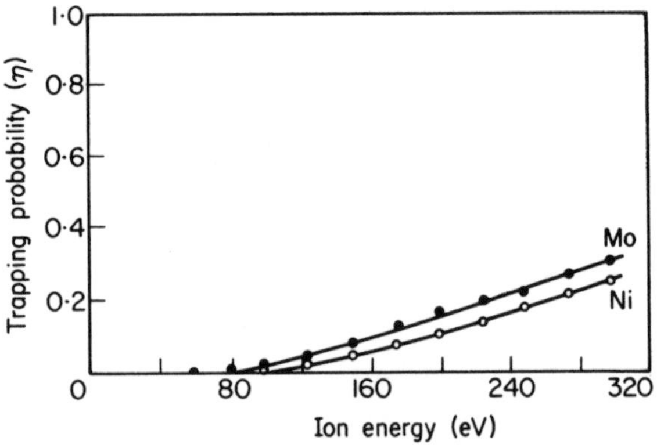

Fig. 8.6 The variation of the trapping probability (η) as a function of ion energy for A^+ ions incident on Ni and Mo surfaces (viz. Ref. 8.46)

Ion trapping efficiencies in unequivocally metal surfaces appear to be somewhat smaller than those at corresponding energies in glass surfaces although there is a considerable difference between different metals. This fact is seen to be true by comparison of the data of Figures 8.2-6 and Table 8.1 and we will see later that this conclusion has been substantiated by ion beam methods.

The variation of ion trapping efficiency with surface temperature has also been studied for inert gas ions[14] and ions of residual gases[48] incident on glass surfaces maintained at temperatures between −196°C and 300°C and for He^+ ions incident on Mo surfaces[49] at 77°K, 190°K and 330°K. Figure 8.7 shows that the trapping efficiency for all inert gas ions in glass decreases with increasing temperature and the temperature at which the efficiency apparently becomes zero apparently increases with increasing ion mass. A fourfold reduction in η on increasing the temperature from −196°C to 57°C is also evident for the positive ions in Mo surfaces and a reduction in trapping efficiency for residual gas ions in glass on increasing the temperature has also been observed.[48] This decrease of trapping efficiency is associated with the shorter trapping times at higher temperatures, a fact which we shall substantiate in later discussion.

We should also mention related work by Kelly[50,51] who observed that tubes filled with Argon, Krypton and Xenon and containing TiO_2, Al and numerous other powders, showed some attachment of the inert gas to the powders after fast neutron irradiation. The neutron bombardment resulted in (n, γ) events and gave rise to inert gas atom recoil energies of the

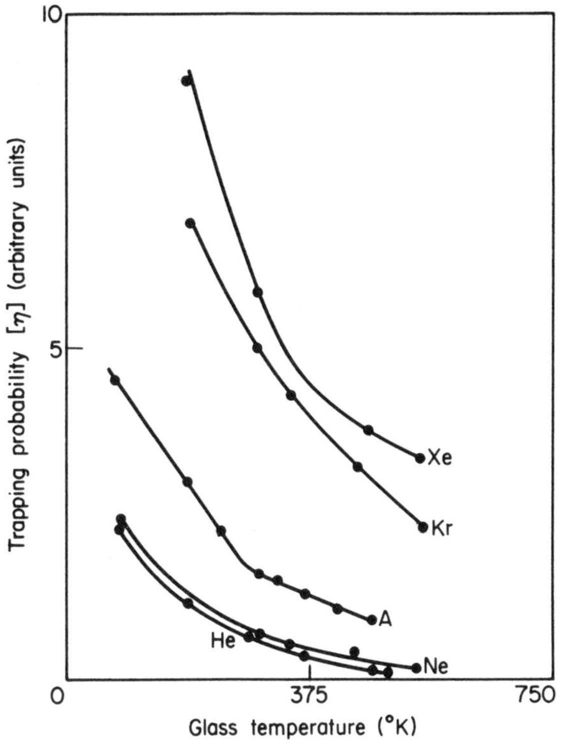

Fig. 8.7 The form of the variation of the ion trapping probabilities for ~ 250 eV inert gas ions on a Pyrex glass surface in a Bayard-Alpert gauge as a function of the temperature of the glass (viz. Ref. 8.14). η values are not absolute nor to scale. (viz. Fig. 8.2 for relative magnitudes at 250 eV and 300°K)

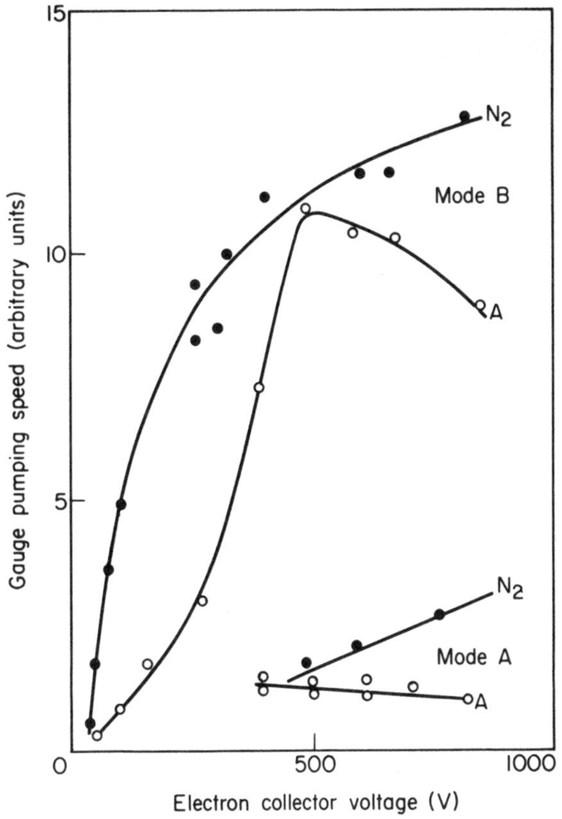

Fig. 8.8 The variation of the pumping speed of a Bayard-Alpert ionsation gauge for A and N_2 as a function of the electron collector voltage (proportional to the ion energy) for both enable modes of operation (viz. Ref. 8.30)

order of 100 eV, and measurement of the amount of gas attached allowed estimation of the trapping efficiency. Values of 0.1–0.2 were obtained for A on TiO_2 and lower values 0.02–0.04 and 0.01–0.025 for Kr and Xe on TiO_2 respectively. Similar orders of magnitude were obtained for all the powders investigated and these are clearly of essentially the same magnitudes to those discussed above.

In addition to these observations, Carter and Leck[26,28] and Cobic et al,[30] have studied the effects of glass envelope potential variations on the pumping speeds for the inert gases. Since it is not possible to determine envelope ion currents when the envelope stabilises at a potential close to the electron collector it is not possible to evaluate trapping efficiencies in this mode of operation. However, it has been found that in this operational condition, the ion pumping speed is markedly reduced, which must be an anticipated result since the energy of ions which can strike the envelope is certainly diminished. However increasing the electron collector potential results in an increased pumping speed even in this mode of operation, as shown in Figure 8.8 for N_2 and A ions and this is again explicable since the difference between the electron collector potential and the envelope potential is known to increase as the former potential is increased, thus leading to increase in the ion energy (and probably ion current).

Simultaneously with these changes in ion pumping speed induced by envelope potential changes, variations in the manometric sensitivity of Bayard-Alpert gauges due to these effects have also been reported.[28] Since this sensitivity indicates the number of ions striking the ion collector, it is evident that the envelope potential must exert such an influence on the electron trajectories as to result in a reduced ion production and collection efficiency. We should note finally that although ion trapping efficiencies have been determined over a quite wide energy range, no unequivocal measurements of threshold energies for trapping have yet been reported by these methods. This is partly due to the fact that the ion energy spread in such tubes is large, although Figures 8.2 and Table 8.1 suggest that a threshold may exist somewhere below 30 eV.

Whilst ion trapping efficiencies can be deduced with relative accuracy for inert gases, the situation is considerably more complex in the case of chemically active gases. It has long been established that, in the presence of hot surfaces (cathodes) hydrogen and oxygen undergo chemical reaction which increases their probability of sorption. Thus it is well known that oxygen will react with a pure tungsten filament to produce WO_2 and WO_3 which in turn evaporates to the envelopes and is rapidly adsorbed. In addition filaments containing carbon provoke formation of CO and CO_2 which may also be readily adsorbed at the envelope. These reactions have been studied by Langmuir,[52,53,54] Schlier,[55] Young,[56] LeGoff and Letort,[57] Jenkins and Trodden[36] and Becker et al[58] and many others[3,59-62] and the results of their investigations show quite clearly that the above sorption phenomena constitute pumping actions far more efficient than any that could be determined by ion trapping actions.

Thus Bills and Carleton[17] find O_2 pumping speeds in a Bayard-Alpert gauge to be ~10^{-1}l/sec/ma, at least two orders of magnitude higher than any ion trapping action would reveal.

Similarly the pumping of hydrogen must be largely ascribed to chemical effects, since it is well known that H_2 dissociates at a heated filament[3] and the resulting hydrogen atoms become strongly adsorbed at the glass envelope. In addition these H atoms may provoke reactions at the envelope causing production of CO, CO_2, H_2O, CH_4 etc., which in turn may react with the heated filament.[63,64] Once again pumping speeds are determined to be several orders of magnitude larger than value anticipated from simple ion trapping processes. These observations should not be interpreted as suggesting that ion trapping efficiencies could not, in any circumstances, be measured with the ionization tube pumping method since the reactions cited above generally occur at rapid rates for cathode temperatures $\gtrsim 1000°C$. It may be possible, through use of a low temperature cathode (such as Lanthanum Hexaboride) to deduce these efficiencies.

The case of nitrogen pumping is most interesting, and it is only relatively recently that adequate explanations of the anomalous behaviour of this gas have been available. If trapping efficiencies are determined from the ratio of the gauge pumping speed to the rate of ion bombardment of exposed surfaces then investigations have shown these to be of order unity and often higher than this value,[44] even after allowance for errors of ion bombardment rate determination. Since this molecule has a mass intermediate between Ne and A it is difficult to explain why it should possess an apparent ion trapping efficiency, not only 5 to 10 times greater than either of these atoms but greater even than unity. This latter fact suggests that one is not determining all the particles active in trapping when the bombarding ion current is measured, and leads one to suspect that other entities, in addition to N_2^+ ions contribute to the measured gas removal rates. On the other hand several investigators[37,44] have shown that pumping processes are absent when electron accelerating potentials are not applied and that the gauge pumping speed is a linear function of the ionizing electron current[37,44] and increases with the electron accelerating potential. The former fact shows that cathode dissociation effects are unimportant but the latter fact suggests that other molecular activation effects induced by electron impact must be important. Alpert[4] and other investigators have suggested that metastable molecules produced at lower energies than those required for ion formation may also be adsorbed by the glass. Some confirmation of this hypothesis has been obtained by Bills and Carleton,[17] Jaeckel and Teloy[65,45] and Donaldson, Winters and Horne[66,67] who observed ion pumping processes when the electron accelerating energy was sufficient to excite only metastable states and not ions. However it is unlikely that merely metastable molecules would possess any greater probability of sorption at a glass surface than a neutral molecule, and this led Carter et al[68] and Donaldson et al[67] to suggest that whilst the metastable molecules were the particles responsible for adsorption, the actual sorption process required the dissociation of the metastable molecules at the surface into atoms which became strongly absorbed on the glass.

Careful experiments by Donaldson et al[67] using monoenergetic electrons to form molecular N_2 ions in addition to metastables revealed that the ions were also adsorbed with high efficiency ($\eta > 1$) at kinetic energies as low as 30 eV. Again it was suggested that these molecular ions also dissociated at the surface where the atoms became strongly adsorbed.

It thus appears that the trapping mechanism of molecular nitrogen ions is totally different from that of the inert gases, and in any experimental tube where ionization, dissociation and excitation of metastables can occur the observed trapping efficiency will be completely meaningless. There is clearly an analogy with dissociation effects at the heated filament as in H_2 sorption and one may anticipate similar electron bombardment induced dissociation effects in other molecular gases. Where dissociation and chemisorption processes are possible, ion trapping measurements must be treated with extreme caution.

In addition to the above measurements of ion trapping efficiency using tube pumping methods several investigations of the variation of η with ion energy for inert gas ion beams incident on metal targets have been reported. Common to all these investigations was the fact that the ion currents and energy were well defined as were the cleanliness and surface area of the bombarded targets. Considerable differences in the detection sensitivity for trapped gases were, however, present. Thus Burtt, Colligon and Leck[64] and Colligon and Leck[70] bombarded Mo, Pt, and W targets with Ne, A and Kr ions of energy between 0.68 KeV and 3.45 KeV, derived from an R.F. electrodeless discharge source and observed the quantity of gas trapped as a function of the number of bombarding ions.

The method of observation of the amount of gas trapped was to heat the target to 2000°C after irradiation and measure the quantity of gas released using a mass spectrometer in the continuous flow system of observation described earlier.

There was no guarantee that all trapped gas was recovered by this method, but as we shall see shortly, independent measurements by Kornelsen[71,72] suggest that at least 90% of the trapped quantity should have been released. Unfortunately the minimum detectable quantity of trapped gas was of the order of 5×10^{13} atoms/cm^2 of the target and the minimum bombardment dose of the order of 5×10^{14} ions/cm^2 whereas saturation quantities were only 2 to 10 times the former value. Consequently it was impossible to measure trapping efficiencies from the initial slope of the trapped quantity/bombardment dose curve with any accuracy, and consequently these authors[69,70] claim values of $\eta \sim 0.1$ for Kr^+ ions on the three target materials at all energies between 0.7 and 3.5 KeV and values of $\eta \simeq 0.6, 0.25$ and 0.7 for A^+ ions on Mo, W and Pt respectively in this energy range. In view of the work on W reported by Kornelsen[71,72] which we discuss now, the above results must be regarded with a great deal of suspicion.

Kornelsen[71,72] bombarded polycrystalline tungsten targets in an ultra high vacuum system with monoenergetic Ne, A, Kr, and Xe ions with energies between 40 eV and 3 KeV at doses as low as 10^{11} ions/sq.cm. up to doses as high as 10^{17} ions/sq. cm.

Subsequent recovery of trapped gas into a closed volume was effected by flashing the target to 2400°K at a constant temperature rise rate of 60°K/sec. Plotting the quantity recovered against the bombarding dose gave graphs of constant initial slope up to a bombardment dose of 5×10^{13} ions/sq. cm and the slopes of the graphs gave the initial trapping efficiencies at various bombarding energies. It was checked that most of the gas trapped during bombardment was released in the heating cycle by bombarding a target with 30 keV radioactive Kr^{85} ions from an isotope separator and after thermal recovery, using the electrolytic stripping technique described in Chapter 5 (by McCargo et al[73]) to determine the percentage of gas unrecovered. This percentage turned out to be always less than 10% (at 10 keV, <2%) so that almost all gas must have been recovered by bombarding with only 3 keV ions. The variation of η with ion energy obtained by Kornelsen is shown in Figure 8.9 and reveals that at ion energies $\lesssim$ 100 eV the trapping efficiency is very low, $<10^{-1}$ for all ions, but rapidly increases until at 3 keV, η increases to about 0.6 for all ions. At energies below 1 keV, the trapping efficiency decreases in the order Ne, A, Kr, Xe and in this energy range, the η versus energy curves for the four ions remain roughly parallel and increase at the same rate. At the higher energies, $\gtrsim$ 2 keV, η tends to saturate and even decrease for Ne and A ions, due in part, it was believed to incomplete recovery of the trapped gas, but η for the heavier ions, Kr and Xe, continued to increase up to the highest energies studied. Corkhill and Carter[74] have also studied the trapping of inert gas ions incident of a polycrystalline W target at energies up to 4 keV and report consistently lower values for η than Kornelsen. Thus η increases from only 0.01 for 250 eV A^+ ions to 0.16 eV for these ions, 0.19 for 4 keV He^+ ions and 0.10 and 0.23 for 2 keV and 4 keV Xe^+ ions respectively. The reasons for the discrepancy between these and Kornelsen's data is not understood, but there is at least order of magnitude agreement.

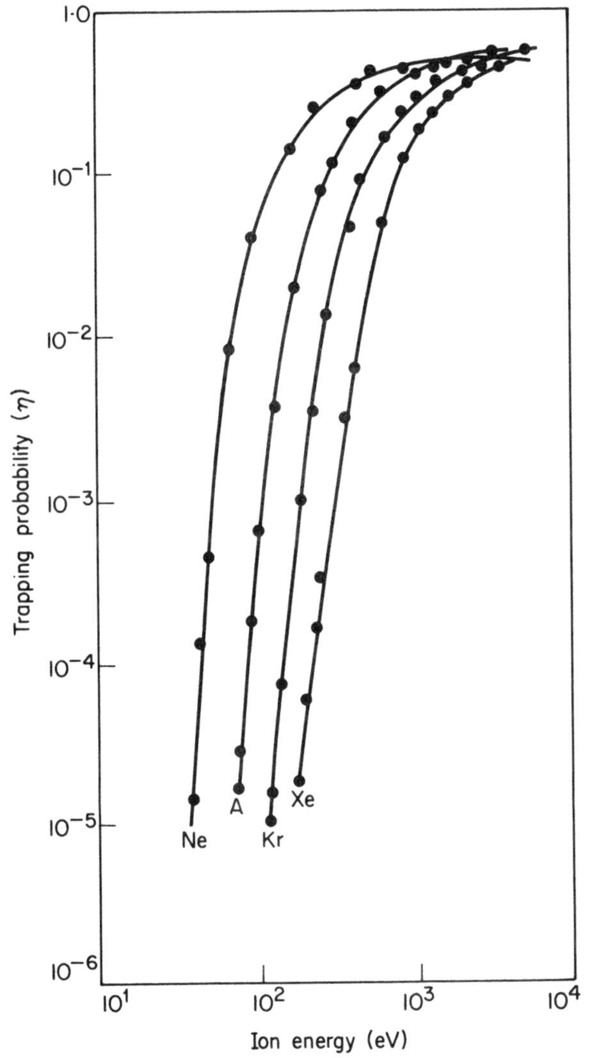

Fig. 8.9 The trapping probability (η) as a function of ion energy for Ne^+, A^+, Kr^+, Xe^+ ions incident on W (viz. Ref. 8.72)

Ivanovskii and Radzhabov[75] have also used an ion beam method to measure η for A^+ ions incident on Ti films over the energy range 600 eV to 2.5 keV. They find that η increases from 0.15 at 600 eV to 0.46 at 2.5 keV but that there are signs of saturation in η at this energy. One must be a little cautious in accepting these values as being totally accurate however since η was determined from the ratio of the quantity of A recovered after bombardment, by flashing the Ti to 1000°C, to the ion dose. There was some evidence that a certain quantity of A may have still remained in the target after flashing, and one would expect this quantity to increase with increasing ion energy, thus rendering η values too low.

Similar results have been obtained by Brown and Davies[76] over an extended energy range for Xe ions incident upon Al, Be, Ni, Zr, Ta, Au, Ag and W targets and A and Kr ions upon Al and W targets. Radioactive ions were derived from an isotope separator and the number of ions trapped following a given bombardment dose was determined from the total activity of the target. Since it was impossible to measure target currents with any precision it was not possible to determine trapping efficiencies from a bombardment dose/trapped quantity curve, nor in fact to give accurate specification to the actual value of η. On the other hand it was observed that for Xe ion energies > 5 keV on Aluminium the apparent (measured) value of η remained constant and independent of ion energy up to 150 keV. It was therefore decided to select η as unity for this combination at these high energies and to measure all other values of η relative to this. We should point out, however, that this assignment of $\eta = 1$ is not without foundation, since as we saw in Chapter 5, when Xe ions with energy > 20 keV penetrate an Al target the trapping distribution does not commence at the surface (e.g. 98% of 30 keV ions are trapped at distances > 30 Å from the surface) so that few incident ions should escape. Because of scatter in experimental points and the presence of neutral atoms in the ion beam, values of η obtained below 1 keV were uncertain. The energy variation of η for Xe and A in Aluminium, Xe in Be, Ni, Zr, Ta, Ag and for A, Kr and Xe in W is shown in Figures 5.82 a, b, c, d, e. The general features of these curves are that η is always fractional below 5 keV but increases to unity above this energy, except for A and Xe in Ag and Au and A, Kr and Xe in W. Comparison of the latter data below 5 keV with those of Kornelsen[71, 72] shows considerably smaller values of η, and this was interpreted as the result of contaminant layers on the surface in these measurements. For Xe on Ag and Au the trapping efficiency increased to unity only at about 150 keV and showed a decrease as the bombarding flux or dose were increased, presumably due to saturation and diffusion enhanced release processes.

Almen and Bruce[77, 78] have also measured η for inert gas beams incident upon a number of target materials, using radioactive tracer and nuclear transmutation methods for detection. The value of η at 45 keV energy for Kr and Xe ions was always close to unity for target atom masses < 25, as Table 8.2 shows for Kr. ions.

For heavier target atom masses, Table 8.2 illustrates, and Figure 8.10 substantiates, through a plot of η versus target atom mass, a curious result. Namely, the variation of η is periodic with target atom mass, showing minima and maxima. We will see later that these minima correspond with minima in the amount of gas which may be trapped and maxi-

TABLE 8.2. (Ref. 8.77).

Trapping Probability η for Kr ions of 45 keV. Experimental error in η is about 0.1.

Target	η	Target	η
Be	1.0	Mo	0.95
C	1.0	Rh	0.70
Mg	1.0	Pd	0.60
Al	1.0	Ag	0.35
Ti	1.0	Cd	0.20
V	1.0	In	0.70
Cr	1.0	Sn	0.50-0.70
Fe	0.95	Sb	0.80
Co	0.85	Ta	1.0
Ni	0.85	W	0.80
Cu	0.75	Pt	0.50
Zn	0.75	Au	0.35
Ge	0.80	Tl	0.30
Zr	1.0	Pb	0.30
Nb	1.0	Bi	0.50

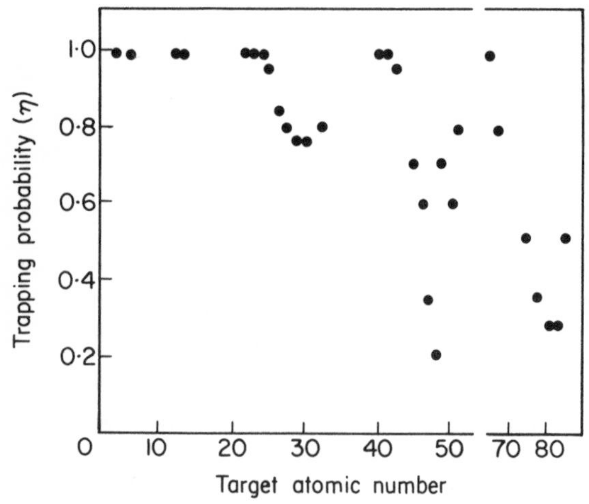

Fig. 8.10 The variation of the trapping probability (η) for 45 keV Kr^+ ions as a function of the target atomic number (viz. Ref. 8.77) Errors in η are of the order 0.1)

ma in the sputtering coefficients for each target material. This periodicity was interpreted as revealing that diffusion type release processes or target transparency (i.e. interatomic spacing) may be important in determining η when (M_{ion}) $\lesssim$ (M_{target}) in that such processes would be expected to vary with the type and magnitude of interatomic binding forces in the target, and thence condition η. Backscattering processes alone could not account for such a periodicity since η would then decrease steadily with increasing target atom mass.

Ne and A ions were found to have approximately the same values of η as Kr and Xe with both Ta and Mo targets (the only target materials studied with the former ions) but it would be most interesting to know η for the first named ion for other materials in which the periodicity is most marked, since Ne is a very much smaller atom than the other three and should possess considerably different diffusion properties.

The general trend of results between different investigations is clearly quite consistent, indicating small values of η at low energies, $\lesssim$ 1 keV, increasing to values of the order of unity at about 5 keV and we now attempt to interpret these observations.

The trapping mechanism will consist of three processes. (1) the penetration of the incident ion past the surface layer of atoms (2) migration through the lattice with a certain possibility of escape through the surface (3) eventual trapping within the lattice. Process (3) can involve trapping in interstitial or substitutional sites or in a new configuration of lattice atoms produced by damage effects. For the present we will defer further discussion of the latter two processes until we have presented experimental data with which we can compare the possible mechanisms. Considering the first requirement for trappign, penetration through the surface layer necessitates the bombarding ion passing within at most a distance of 0.5 lattice spacings from a surface atom. This is the most favourable position for penetration since the energy transfer to the lattice atoms will be a minimum at this position. Since the target atoms will not have time to relax during the collision the energy required for penetration should be close to that required to overcome the repulsive potential of the surface atoms at an ion-atom spacing of 0.5 x lattice spacing. Kornelsen[72] has determined the potential energy of Ne, A, Kr, and Xe atoms and Tungsten atoms at half the mean lattice spacing for a randomized target, using a modification of the potential deduced by Abrahamson[79] (viz Chapter 2). Thus if U_{11} (r) is the interatomic potential for tungsten and U_{22} (r) that for the inert gas atom, the potential employed was $U_{12} = \sqrt{U_{11}U_{12}}$, and values of this energy are compared with the experimentally observed Kinetic energies required for a trapping efficiency of 10^{-5} for Ne, A, Kr and Xe ions on W in Table 8.3. The agreement is remarkable although

TABLE 8.3. (Ref. 8.72)

Calculated and experimental threshold energies.

Ion	U_{12}(R) (eV)	$U_{exp}(\eta = 10^{-5})$ (eV)
Ne	41	39
A	69	72
Kr	121	118
Xe	165	170

somewhat fortuitous since an arbitrary value of 10^{-5} for η was assumed whilst the ions probably interact with several atoms simultaneously and the potentials used could be erroneous since they pertain correctly to free atoms. These calculations also showed that the interaction potential energy of the four inert gas atoms with tungsten increased at constant relative rates up to > 1 keV and so the parallelism of the curves in Figure 8.9 below this energy is in accord with expectation. It is notable also that Grant and Carter's[18] measurements for Ne^+, A^+, Kr^+ and Xe^+ ions on glass surfaces and Teloy's[45] observations with He^+ on Pt and A^+ on Pt and Mo surfaces suggest a minimum energy of 10-20 eV for the onset of trapping.

Since the energy dependence of η has not been obtained with great accuracy for other materials it is not considered worthwhile to extend Kornelsen's[72] calculations to other targets. Nevertheless it is to be noted that η increases with energy in all cases and for the particular case of glass which has an open structure (large average interatomic spacing) the trapping efficiencies are generally larger than in metals at corresponding energies. This will also be due to the weaker interatomic potential of the glass atoms. Similar behaviour is observed in the lower energy data of Brown and Davies[76] where η is larger for Xe in Al than in heavier target materials and in the measurements [80,81] at 180 eV of trapping efficiencies of He, Ne, A and Kr in Ni and Mo targets where η is seen to be consistently larger in the former metal. On the other hand the higher values of η for A^+ in Pt than in Mo as observed by Teloy[45] or in W as measured by Kornelsen[72] are difficult to explain on this basis since one would expect $\eta_W < \eta_{MO} < \eta_{Pt}$ whilst for A^+ in Ni and Mo as measured by Kay and Winters and Winters where $\eta_{MO} > \eta_{Ni}$ one may expect $\eta_{Ni} > \eta_{MO}$. In this case however, there is only a slight difference between η_{Ni} and η_{MO}. The difference between Pt and the other metals could be due to their differing structures, but one would like to see measurements of η for different metals made in the same type of experiment before attempting further discussion. Indeed an unusual feature of Teloy's[45] results is the apparent constancy of η for He^+ and A^+ in Pt and Mo for energies greater than only about 100 eV—a result quite different from all other work and indeed the author suggests that some ion trapping may occur in sputtered layers rather than the target.

In addition the values of η are generally larger the lighter is the bombarding ion and thence the lower is the interaction potential. However, as the results for glass and Ni reveal, η does not always increase sequentially from the lightest to the heaviest ion and the results for A, Kr and Xe in W confirm this. Since these latter measurements were generally performed at higher energies where $\eta > 0.1$ then some of the penetrating ions presumably entered the lattice closer to target atoms than half the lattice spacing and the values of η are those obtained by averaging over all surface positions. Consequently at these energies the trapping efficiency will also depend upon the probability that the incident ion retains forward momentum after the surface collision. This forward scattering will be most probable when the ion mass is comparable with or greater than the target atom mass. Thus at intermediate energies (>5 keV) η is greater for Xe in W than either Kr, A or Ne in this material, and this transition from most probable to average penetrability probably accounts for the energy variation of η for various ions in glass and for the fact that η does not decrease sequentially from He to Kr with Ni and Mo targets.

In addition one would expect, on this basis, that for light ions on heavy targets with considerable backscattering, the trapping efficiency would be relatively smaller at higher energies, as is indeed observed with Ne, A and Kr on W targets and Xe in Ag and Au at energies between 5 keV and 10 keV and with He on nickel targets.

It is therefore quite clear that, at the intermediate energies, the trapping efficiency depends not only upon the maximum ease of penetrability conditioned by interatomic potential considerations but upon the average ease of penetrability which is conditioned by the probability of forward scattering. (At these energies light ions may even be reflected back out of the target by sub-surface collisions.) Kornelsen has calculated[72] the trapping probabilities of Ne and A on W at about 1 keV by assuming isotropic scattering and that ions scattered at a laboratory angle $<\frac{\pi}{2}$ are reflected and not trapped, obtaining values of 0.55 and 0.61 respectively. These are again in remarkably good agreement with the corresponding experimental values of 0.54 and 0.60.

At still higher energies, >10-20 keV, all ions are sufficiently energetic to overcome the simple atomic potential barriers and forward scattering should predominate. Consequently trapping efficiencies should tend towards unity in all cases and the work of Brown and Davies[76] reveals this to be true. On the other hand the periodicity of η with target atom mass in cases where M ion < M target, as observed by Almen and Bruce[77] for high energy ions shows that the interatomic spacings and forces must also be important in conditioning gas retention even when entry is ensured. It would be most interesting to have further information about this periodic variation of η for other ions at various energies, whilst variations of target temperature should assist in determining the importance of diffusion processes.

The variation of η with temperature for inert gas ions in glass[14] (and, for the one ion/metal combination studied[49]) also requires explanation and to do this we should recall our cautionary remark on the nature of the observed trapping efficiency, viz. this parameter determines only those ions which are trapped on a time scale similar to or larger than the experimental time. We have already seen that a spontaneous release of gas occurs upon cessation of trapping, due, it is believed, to some form of activated diffusion process and indicating that some trapped ions have trapping time constants of similar order to the experimental times. Upon increasing the target temperature it would be expected that diffusion processes will occur at enhanced rates and that trapping time constants will be materially reduced. Those which are of the order of the experimental time at room temperature will be reduced below this time and some of those with higher trapping times will reduce to the order of the experimental time. Thus the measured trapping efficiency will not include contributions due to these shortened life-time trapped atoms and will therefore decrease with increasing temperature. This behaviour is shown in Figure 8.7 for all inert gas ions on glass, and as we shall see later the temperature at which η tends to zero corresponds to that at which all trapping time constants reduce to zero. In addition the increase in η below room temperature suggests that, at low energies, some trapped atoms have very low trapping times which can only be increased, thus increasing η, by freezing in these atoms. Although no data is available on the temperature variation of η at high energies, (where η at room temperature is unity and penetration depths are large,) it would be expected that η would fall with increasing temperature due to diffusion induced release, but reducing the temperature below room temperature would have no effect upon η since all ions are trapped anyway.

Finally we may note that although no directional dependence of η has been reported for monocrystalline targets, such a dependence may be anticipated similar to the known ion range, sputtering, electron emission and, as we shall see shortly, maximum trapped gas quantity variations. A study of this behaviour could well provide additional information on inter-atomic potentials as suggested by Kornelsen's[72] evaluation of η.

8.4. BOMBARDMENT—TRAPPING CURVES.

As we have already noted, after a certain quantity of gas has been trapped the apparent trapping efficiency begins to fall. The reasons for this diminution have been discussed briefly and include thermal and bombardment induced release processes. The former is expected to be dominant when only small quantities of gas are trapped and where the bombardment and trapping rates become materially reduced as in a static pumping experiment; whilst the latter should predominate when large quantities of gas are trapped and the bombardment rate is maintained constant as in a dynamic pumping or ion beam type of experiment. Both processes will always be present to some extent, and in addition the real trapping efficiency may become reduced by other effects such as saturation of available trapping centres or changes in the penetration profile and ion stopping cross sections.

A general equation describing the rate of atom trapping may be written:

$$\frac{dn}{dt} = I\eta_t f(n) - g(n)k(t) - l(I)S_{1t}k(n) \qquad 8.9$$

where n is the quantity of gas trapped at time t when the ion bombardment rate is I. The first term on the right hand side of this equation describes the rate of ion trapping with an instantaneous efficiency η_t and illustrates the possibility of a dependence upon the quantity of gas trapped through the function f(n). The second term describes the spontaneous thermal release dependent upon the quantity of gas trapped through g(n) and upon the temporal nature of the process through k(t). The final term describes the bombardment induced re-emission process and illustrates its dependence upon the bombardment rate, which may not be first order, through l(I), upon the instantaneous release efficiency per trapped atom through S_{1t} and upon the quantity of gas trapped through k(n).

In addition when trapping is terminated and thermal recovery is observed one has

$$\frac{-dn}{dt'} = m(n)r(t') \text{ at a later time } t'. \qquad 8.10$$

Further, if bombardment is recommenced with a second ion species, the rate of release of the first trapped species is

$$\frac{-dn}{dt'} = q(n)u(t') + v(J)S_{2t'}W(n) \qquad 8.11$$

Where J is the bombardment rate of the second ion species and $S_{2t'}$ is the release efficiency per trapped atom due to the second species. In this final equation it is assumed that thermal and bombardment induced processes may interact, i.e. bombardment induced release may condition thermal release and vice versa, and so the thermal release contribution g(n)u(t') is different from that obtained under bombardment free conditions, i.e. m(n)r(t').

Clearly the form of the trapped quantity/time or total bombardment (It) curves and of the release rate/time or total release bombardment (Jt) curves depends critically upon the forms and magnitudes of the various quantity and time dependent functions, and we shall briefly enumerate the various proposals which have been put forward for these functions and examine these later in the light of experimental data to be described shortly.

The trivial case where it is assumed that no thermal or induced re-emission occurs and all ions are trapped with equal efficiency, which is identical with the case assumed in equation 1) is certainly known to be invalid, viz. Fig. 8.1. Alpert[12], Von Meyern[82, 83] and Young[24] also suggested that the first two effects could be ignored but assumed that the number of available trapping centres was limited and that a bombarding ion would be trapped only upon striking such a vacant centre. This case is analogous to the Langmuir theory of monolayer physical adsorption, and the defining equation has the form $-\frac{dn}{dt} = I\left(1 - \frac{n}{n_o}\right)$ where n_o is the total number of trapping centres. In a static volume experiment the number of trapped atoms n is proportional to the pressure drop ($p_o - p$) and the bombarding ion flux to the instantaneous pressure p. Equation 8.11 thus becomes second order in the pressure, i.e.

$$-\frac{dp}{dt} = a + bp + cp^2, \qquad 8.12.2$$

and solution shows that p falls and n increases according to a complex exponential form. In a dynamic experiment where I is maintained constant the increase of n with t is a simple exponential form. Young[24] has fitted the static pump down results of nitrogen ion trapping in a Bayard-Alpert gauge to the solution of equation 8.12.2 and found good agreement provided that an appropriate choice of n_o is made. However, if the ion induced emission is of a simple form and directly proportional to the number of atoms trapped and the bombarding ion current, then the pumping equation must include the extra term $IS.n/n_o$. As far as the form of the pump down equation is concerned the introduction of the extra term has no effect except that the constant C is multiplied by (1 — S), so that the presence or absence of ion induced emission cannot be proved. Without other knowledge of S or n_o neither can be determined unequivocally although Bills and Carleton[17] claim to evaluate S and n_o from studies of the pumping speed/quantity pumped curves of O_2 and N_2 on glass and evaporated W surfaces using the quasidynamic system. In this case, and at constant pressure, $\frac{dn}{dt}$ is proportional to the pumping speed, and analysis, taking account of de-excitation and reflection processes of the trapped atoms shows that this speed should be hyperbolically dependent upon the quantity of gas trapped. Again determination of arbitrary constants is necessary. Since the results refer to O_2 and N_2 however they are of little significance to the present discussion but illustrate the difficulties in exact interpretation of results unless specific values of the relevant constants are available.

We should also note that according to equation 8.12.2 pumping speed/pumped quantity curves, obtained at constant pressure, should be linear, falling to zero speed at $n = n_0 (1 - S)$, whilst pumped quantity/time or bombardment dose curves should increase exponentially to a maximum at the above value of n. Experiments on the inert gases pumped into glass by Carter and Leck[16], Cobic, Carter and Leck[14], and Comsa and Iosifescu[39] fail to satisfy this prediction, as the speed/quantity curves of Figure 8.11 reveal.

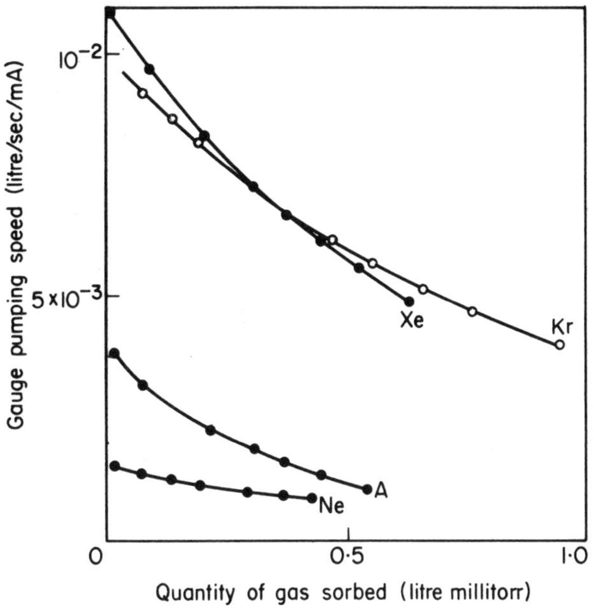

Fig. 8.11 The variation of the pumping speed of a Bayard-Alpert Gauge for Ne, A, Kr and Xe as a function of the quantity of gas sorbed in the Pyrex glass envelope (viz. Ref. 8.14)

Maddix et al[21, 23] have observed an increase in the quantity of trapped gas proportional to the half power of pumping time during bombardment at a constant ion flux or quartz surfaces in an R.F. discharge tube whilst Bartholomew and la Padula[84] have observed similar effects at the cathodes of glow discharge tubes. The former work indicated no tendency to saturation as have all other investigations, and this may have been a result of the very high ion flux (10^{19} ions/sec/cm^2) used which led to intensive damage production and enhanced diffusion processes or to high surface temperatures induced by the discharge. We should therefore regard these results as typical only of the particular discharge target conditions. On the other hand, the ion beam experiments of Burtt et al[69], Colligon and Leck[70], and Kornelsen[71, 72] fail to obey the exponential trapped quantity/bombarding dose relationship as curves in Figure 8.12 for A ions incident of W reveal. Indeed up to trapped quantities of the order of 10^{13} atoms/cm^2 no perceptible change in trapping efficiency occurs, but saturation is evident above a level of about 5×10^{14} atoms/cm^2.

In order to explain this type of result Carmichael et al[80, 81], Carter et al[85] and Almen and Bruce[77] have assumed that trapped atoms are released due to surface erosion because of target sputtering, and the release rate is then determined by the surface concentration of trapped gas. The mathematical expression of this release rate cannot be put into a simple form in terms of the quantity of gas trapped and we will defer further discussion of this release process until later when we have presented further details of the bombardment induced release process.

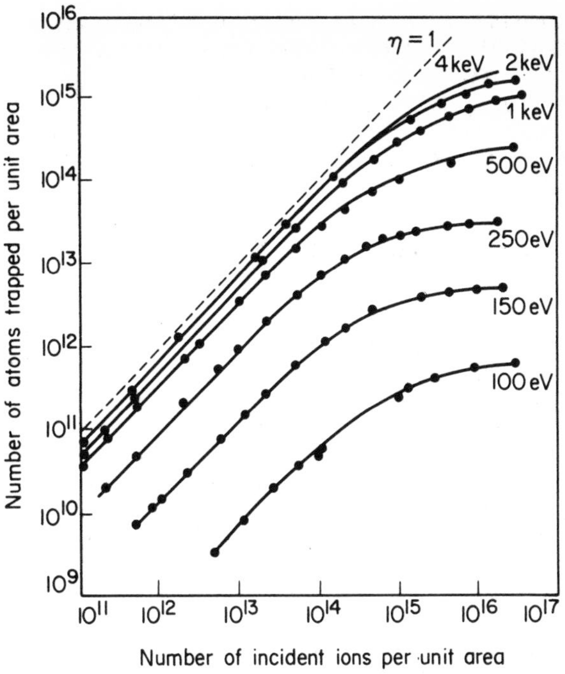

Fig. 8.12 The variation of the number of Argon atoms trapped as a function of the incident ion dose at ion energies from 100 eV to 4 keV (viz. Ref. 8.72) The line $\eta = 1$ corresponds to the case where all incident ions are trapped

Several forms have also been proposed for the thermal release mechanism. Varnerin and Carmichael[29, 86], Carmichael and Knoll[81] and Fox and Knoll[49], suggested that the release rate at a time t′ after trapping δn atoms was proportional to

$$\frac{\delta n}{t'} \qquad 8.13.1.$$

for times between 1 second and several hours. Blodgett and Vanderslice[87] suggested a similar form, viz.

$$\frac{\delta n}{(t')^{\cdot 1/2}} \qquad 8.13.2.$$

whilst Hobson[88, 89, 90] modified the form to

$$\frac{\delta n}{t' - t_c} \qquad 8.13.3.$$

with the provision that the release rate was zero up to a time t_c after trapping. On the other hand, Robinson and Berz[48] and Comsa[91, 92] proposed a release function of the form

$$\delta n \left\{ \exp - \frac{t'}{\tau_1} + \exp - \frac{t'}{\tau_2} \right\} \qquad 8.13.4.$$

whilst Baker and Giorgi[93, 94] proposed a function

$$\delta n(C(t')^{-1/2} + D). \qquad 8.13.5.$$

Finally, Smeaton, Carter and Leck[95, 96] suggested a generalised function

$$\frac{\delta n}{t'} \{\exp(-t'/\tau_1) - \exp(-t'/\tau_2)\} \qquad 8.13.6.$$

for small quantities of gas pumped. For short emission times this function reduces to

$$\frac{\delta n}{t'}\left\{\exp\left(-\frac{t'}{\tau_1}\right)-1\right\}, \qquad 8.13.7.$$

which is finite at time zero; for intermediate times the function is $\frac{\delta n}{t'}$, and for long times

$$\frac{\delta n}{t'}\left\{1-\exp\left(-\frac{t'}{\tau_2}\right)\right\} \qquad 8.13.8$$

This function possesses the advantage of finite rate at zero time whereas the other forms give infinite or extremely large values at this time, which is clearly untenable. It was further shown that for larger quantities of gas trapped the function at intermediate times was of the form $(\delta n)^x(t')^{-m}$ 8.13.9. where m was of order unity and x varies between 1 and 0 depending upon the quantity of gas trapped.

We should point out that the inverse power time functions and the exponential functions can all be fitted to experimental data provided that appropriate constants are employed. The physical reason for the inverse power time functions has been assigned to diffusion of trapped atoms with various concentration-depth profiles and a single activation energy for diffusion. The exponential functions have been ascribed to single jump diffusion processes but with at least two, and probably a spectrum, of diffusion energies. For the present we will not attempt a further critical examination of the validity of any of these equations, but note that whichever is used, a considerable complexity in the pumping equations is introduced. Thus if a quantity of gas δn is pumped at a time T in an interval dT, the rate of release due to this fraction at a later time t′ may be given in general terms by

$$(\delta n)^x k(t') \qquad 8.14.1.$$

Throughout the interval from O to t (=T + t′) however, gas will be continuously trapped, the rate at a given time depending upon the variation of bombarding conditions. Thus the overall release rate at t is given by

$$\int_0^t \left(\frac{dn}{dt}\right)^x k(t-T)dT \qquad 8.14.2$$

This will generally give rise to a considerable degree of complexity in any pumping equation, i.e. the equation becomes integro-differential, since both the variation of n with time and the functional dependence k(t′) must be known for correct solution. It is quite clear that judicious choice of x and k(t′) may often lead to an adequate fit to experimental data although they are formally incorrect. Cobic and Carter[97] have studied this problem where n decreases exponentially with time, when x = 1 and

$$k(t') = \exp(-t'/\tau) \qquad 8.14.3.$$

and shown that the resulting solution contains so many undetermined constants as to be virtually useless.

We thus conclude that without knowledge of the exact form of the thermal and bombardment recovery processes, any solution of the pumping equation must be imprecise, and that experiments which determine these forms are mandatory. In subsequent sections we will review this experimental work and physical interpretation.

We should note, however, that one feature will be common to all solutions of equation 8.9 which involve release processes, namely that a saturation quantity of gas n_s will be trapped, i.e. $dn/dt = o$ when trapping and release processes balance i.e.

$$I\eta_s f(n_s) = g(n_s)k(t) + l(I)S_1 h(n_s) \qquad 8.15$$

The saturation quantity of gas which can be trapped will therefore be dependent upon the ion trapping and bombardment induced release efficiencies and upon the nature and magnitude of the thermal release processes. As we have already suggested, thermal release processes are most important when the quantities of trapped gas are small and/or the bombardment and trapping rates are low whereas bombardment induced re-emission is most important when trapped quantities of gas or bombardment rates are large. Static pumping experiments therefore tend to give information only upon the former process. In addition, thermal release of impurity gases or atmospheric leaks may cause an apparent saturation in static experiments, unless a partial pressure analyser is used to monitor the test gas, and this detracts from the value of such experiments. On the other hand dynamic or ion beam experiments lead to a saturation which is conditioned by both release processes, but largely by the bombardment induced mechanism. In the following section therefore we examine only saturation levels observed in this latter type of experiment since these quantities represent the maximum quantity of gas trapped under any circumstances. However, we will then discuss the relative importance of the release processes and show that this identification of final saturation is valid.

8.5. THE MAXIMUM TRAPPED QUANTITIES OF GAS

Since the majority of pumping experiments have been performed with static systems or with active gases, where trapping and release processes are outside our interest at the moment, in dynamic systems, only a relatively small amount of information is available. Carter and Leck[15,16] have used a dynamic flow system to determine the saturation levels of inert gases on glass surfaces whilst Cobic, Carter and Leck[14] have approximated this method in a static system by continuous re-introduction of gas after pump down until saturation effects were evident through the lack of gauge pumping.

The variation of the saturation quantity n_s for 250 eV inert gas ions on Pyrex glass obtained by Cobic et al[14] as a function of the temperature of the glass is shown in Figure 8.13. The saturation quantity decreases, for all gases, with increasing temperature, from −78°C up to 350°C and approaches zero at similar temperatures to those at which the trapping efficiencies also approach zero (cf. Figure 8.7). This must be expected since as $\eta \to 0$ equation 8.9 indicates that $n_s \to 0$. Carter and Leck[15,16], Cobic et al[14] and James and Carter[42,98] have studied the variation of n_s with the ion energy (electron collector voltage) for the inert gas ions incident upon glass. In all cases the value of n_s increases with energy as shown by Figure 8.14 although the relationship is complex.

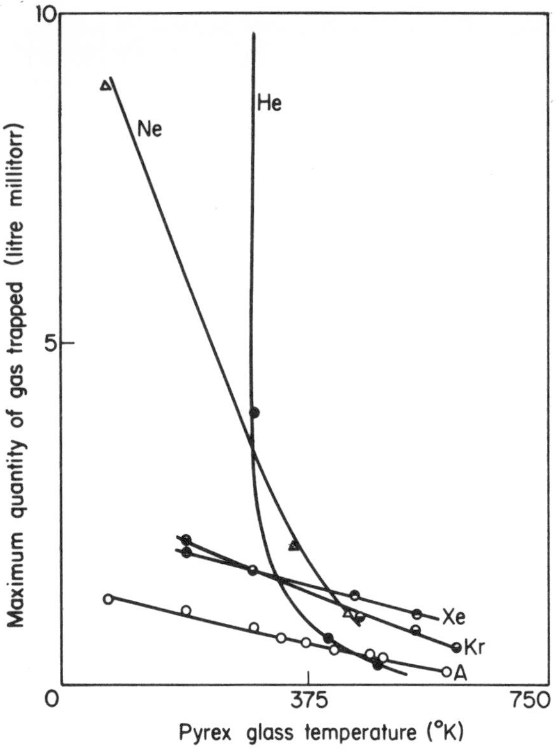

Fig. 8. 13 The variation of the maximum quantity of gas which can be trapped in the Pyrex Glass envelope of a Bayard-Alpert Gauge as a function of the temperature of the glass. Ion Energy 250 eV (viz. Ref. 8. 14)

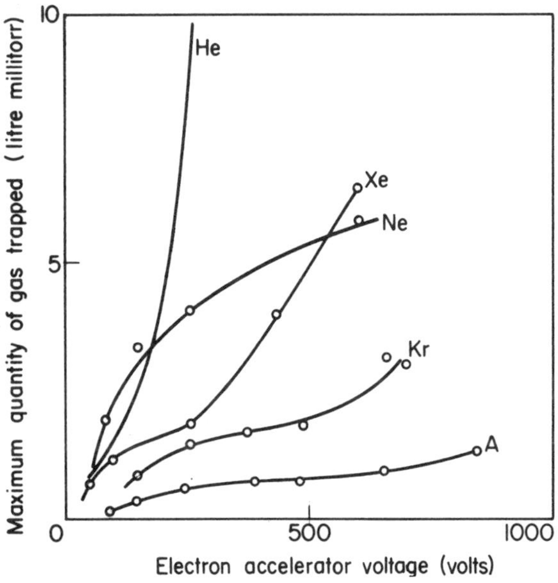

Fig. 8. 14 The maximum quantity of gas which can be trapped in the Pyrex Glass envelope of a Bayard-Alpert Gauge as a function of the electron collector voltage (proportional to the ion energy) for inert gas ions (viz. Ref. 8. 14)

Generally speaking, at all temperatures and ion energies the saturation quantity n_s corresponds to an inert gas content of the target between 0.1 and 1.0 equivalent mono-layer but the case of He at all ion energies and temperatures below about 50°C is anomolous since no saturation could be achieved even after prolonged pumping, whilst Ne appears to exhibit a greatly increased value of n_s at low temperatures. This behaviour may be associated with increased diffusivity of the smaller inert gas ions or the presence of surface metal films which inhibits gas release.

Carmichael and Trendelenburg[80] have measured the saturation trapping limits for 100 ± 50 eV He, Ne, A and Kr ions in nickel at room temperature and for the latter three ions obtain values corresponding to 0.37, 0.042 and 0.009 equivalent monolayers respectively. As in the case of glass no saturation limit for He ions was observed up to trapped quantities as large as 100 equivalent monolayers and this must presumably be ascribed to the very different solubility, diffusion and sputtering properties of this atom, since its increased range in the material is insufficient to account for differences as large as five orders of magnitude.

Brown and Leck[99] have observed values of n_s for inert gas ions trapped in the cathode surfaces of Penning gauges for ion energies in the region of 4 keV with cathode surfaces of nickel, molybdenum and aluminium. There appeared to be little variation with the surface material and n_s was of the order of 1 equivalent monolayer for inert gas ions from He to Kr.

De Angelis[100] measured n_s for approximately 1000 ev Kr ions in platinum, silicon and germanium targets and observed this parameter to increase in the order in which the elements are written above, from 7×10^{14} atoms/cm^2 for Pt to 2×10^{15} atoms/cm^2 for Si and Ge. These values correspond to just under and just over equivalent monolayer coverage respectively. The increase in n_s with bombarding energy, as seen by comparison of the previous two sets of data, again corresponds with the results for a glass surface.

On the other hand Maddix and Allen[21, 23] have observed that very large numbers (e.g. hundreds of equivalent monolayers) of inert gas ions (He, Ne and A) can be trapped in quartz during bombardment with low energy (12-20 eV) but high density (10^{20} ions/cm^2/sec) ions in an R.F. excited glow discharge. These authors found that after an initial rapid trapping action the trapping rate decreased and became proportional to the inverse square root of the trapping time. At low temperatures ($\lesssim$ 200°C) the initial fast process was dominant but as the temperature was increased, the inverse square root time process assumed greater importance, but at about 750°C, the trapping rate, although of $t^{-1/2}$ form diminished. Post bombardment desorption at temperatures above 200°C also showed a $t^{-1/2}$ recovery rate. These authors have interpreted their results in terms of in-diffusion of gas trapped near the surface under the concentration profile induced by the incident ion flux and measurements of the activation energy for trapped atom diffusion support this suggestion. Such an interpretation is probably valid however only where the target temperature is sufficiently high to promote rapid diffusion, and a similar mechanism has been invoked by Cobic et al[44] to explain the extremely large quantities of He which can be trapped in Pyrex glass. Experiments by Blodgett and Vanderslice[101] on the trapping of Ne, A and Kr in metal surfaces upon which fresh metal layers were continuously deposited by differential sputtering also showed that many hundreds of equivalent monolayers of gas could be trapped and there was no doubt that the major effect was one of ion trapping and simultaneous burial beneath the continuously growing metal surface. It is unlikely that this effect could have also occurred in the work of Maddix et al[21,23]. However Bartholomew and La Padula[102] also obtained anomalous results during trapping of Kr^+ ions in Penning discharge tube cathodes, observing that whilst only an approximately equivalent monolayer of gas was trapped at saturation, the apparent median penetration depth was $>10^4$A°. These authors suggest that this result indicated operation of a diffusion process due to the relatively high ion bombardment, and therefore surface damage rate, ($\gtrsim 10^{17}$ incident ions/cm^2/sec.). However the ion energy was less than 30 eV and it seems unlikely that the surface damage rate could promote diffusion to such depths. A more likely explanation of these results is that the cathodes were differentially sputtered, as is known to occur in Penning gauges and that the gas which was reported to have diffused to large depths was actually buried beneath sputtered layers. This certainly occurred in the work of Blodgett and Vanderslice[101]. However, it is possible that an enhanced diffusion due to vacancy production at the surface may occur and we should not, at this stage, deny this possibility.

Measurements of n_s as a function of ion energy have been made by Burtt et al[69], Colligon and Leck[70], Corkhill and Carter[74] and Kornelsen[71,72,103] using the ion beam method, from which all condensation phenomena have been eliminated, and these studies show unequivocal evidence of saturation. Colligon and Leck[70] observed that n_s increased roughly linearly with ion energy between 0.7 Kev. and 3.75 KeV. for Ne, A and Kr ions incident upon W, Mo and Pt targets as Figure 8.15 indicates. At

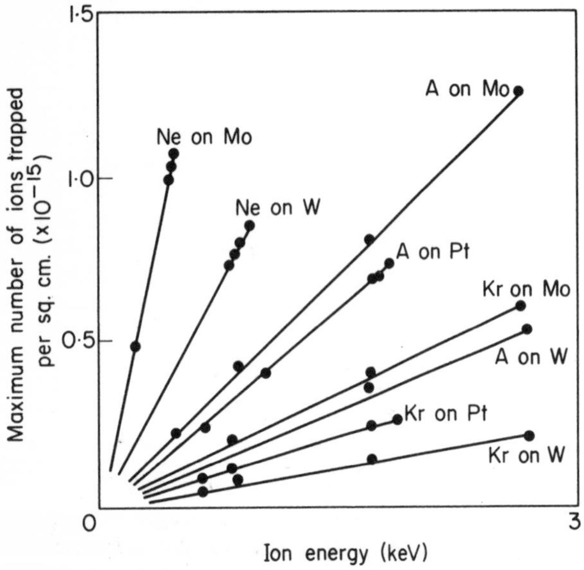

Fig. 8.15 The variation of the maximum number of Ne^+, A^+ and Kr^+ ions which can be trapped in Mo, Pt and W surfaces as a function of the ion energy (viz. Ref. 8.70)

the highest energies the saturation limits on tungsten were of the order of 27, 6 and 3 equivalent monolayers and linear extrapolation back to $\simeq$100 eV energies suggest n_s to be of the order 0.6, 0.15 and 0.07 equivalent monolayers respectively. Such extrapolation is probably unjustified, however, since observations by Kornelsen[72] on the variation of n_s for A ions with energies in the range 40 eV $\rightarrow$ 5 keV on tungsten show that n_s increases rapidly with energy between 100 eV and 500 eV and less rapidly above this energy. The approximate energy dependence of n_s for A on W taken from Kornelsen's[72] data is shown in Figure 8.16 and it is clear that at 100 ev, $n_s \simeq 6 \times 10^{-4}$ equivalent monolayers, and at 4 keV, $n_s \simeq 2$ equivalent monolayers. Both values are lower than that for 100 eV A^+ on Ni observed by Carmichael and Trendelenburg[80] and for A^+ on W at 3.75 keV deduced by Burtt et al[69,70], but we tend to place more faith in the Kornelsen data because of the improved sensitivity of the method. Corkhill and Carter's[74] measurements of n_s for A^+ and Xe^+ ions on tungsten however, are also slightly larger than Kornelsen's data[72], as illustrated in Table 8.1 but again order of magnitude agreement is obtained.

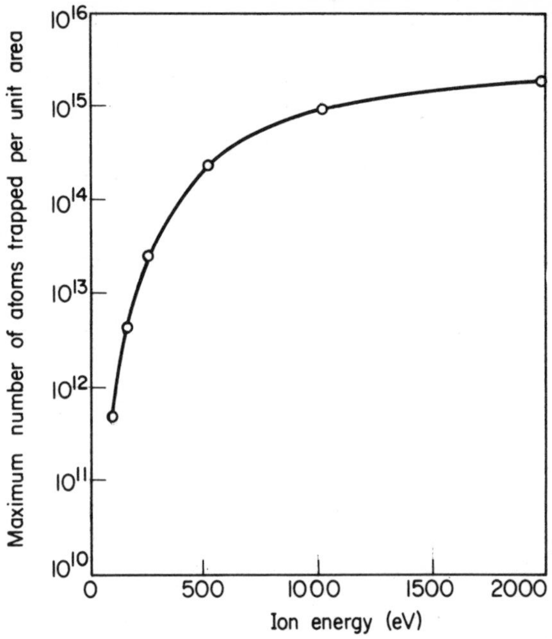

Fig. 8.16 The maximum number of A^+ ions which can be trapped in a W target as a function of the ion energy. (taken from Fig. 8.12 viz. Ref. 8.72)

At higher ion energies, saturation levels have been measured by Koch[104], Thulin[105], Brown and Davies[76], and Fluit et al[106], for a few target materials, but Almen and Bruce[77] have conducted more exhaustive investigations of the variations of n_s with bombarding ion and target material type, target temperature and ion flux and energy between 5 and 65 keV. The most complete measurements were made with inert gas ions using radioactive (for Kr and Xe) methods to measure the quantity of trapped gas or subsequent irradiation of the gas loaded targets (for Ne and A) with protons which gave rise to nuclear reactions with a γ ray production proportional to the occluded gas density. A typical trapped quantity/bombardment dose curve for 45 keV Kr^{85} ions incident on a Mo target is shown in Figure 8.17 and reveals similar characteristics to the measurements by Burtt et al[69,70] and Kornelsen[71,72]. The saturation shown in this curve was reproduced for many other ion/target combina-

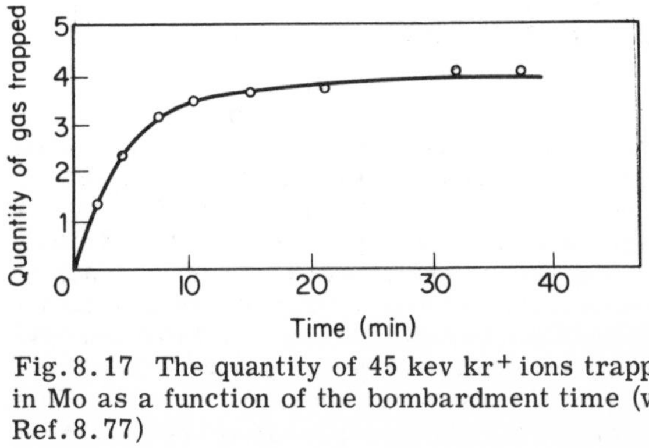

Fig. 8.17 The quantity of 45 kev kr^+ ions trapped in Mo as a function of the bombardment time (viz. Ref. 8.77)

tions and values for n_S for Ne, A, Kr and Xe incident at 45 keV upon a number of metallic targets is shown in Table 8.4, and n_S is also plotted in Figure 8.18, for Kr and Xe ions as a function of the target atomic number. This figure illustrates that there is a periodicity in the variation of n_S with target atomic number, revealing minima and maxima.

TABLE 8.4. (Ref. 8.77).

Saturation values of Ne, Ar, Kr and Xe at 45 keV ion energy in some metal foils.

Target material	Ne ($\mu g/cm^2$)	Ar ($\mu g/cm^2$)	Kr ($\mu g/cm^2$)	Xe ($\mu g/cm^2$)
Al			5.2	4.1
Ni	2.1	2.4	4.7	1.9
Cu	1.7	1.2		
Mo	4.7	3.8	2.0	2.0
Ag	0.8	0.8		
Ta	5.0	3.7	3.1	
W	4.5	2.5		
Pt	1.7	1.6	1.4	1.3
Au	1.0	0.7		
Ti			4.7	3.3
Co			2.3	1.5

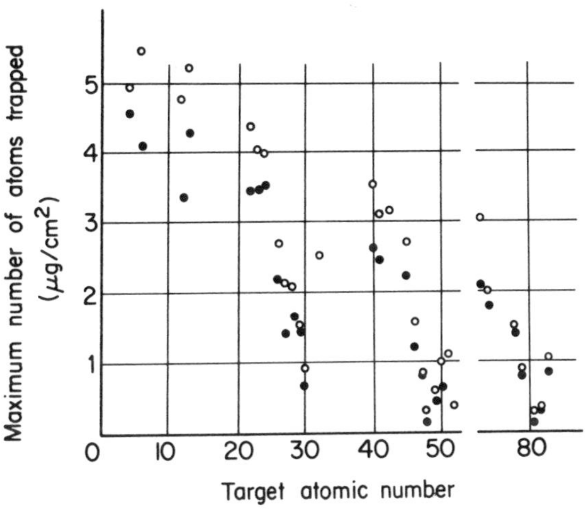

Fig. 8.18 The variation of the maximum number of 45 keV kr+ and 45 keV Xe+ ions which can be trapped in targets as a function of their atomic number (viz. Ref. 8.77)
O — denotes Kr+ ions
● — denotes Xe+ ions

It is of significance that the sputtering ratio measurements by these authors, referred to in the preceding chapter, show similar periodicity with target mass, with the special feature that maxima in the sputtering ratios coincide with minima in n_S and vice versa. In some cases the type of curve in Figure 8.17 was not obtained, and the quantity of trapped gas increased to a maximum and then diminished to a lower saturation level (e.g. for Kr^+ in Mg, Be, Zn and H_f) which was believed to be associated with initial removal of a surface oxide layer. The variation of n_S with the bombarding ion flux density was also investigated and the behaviour for different ion/target combinations was different. Thus 45 keV, A^+, Kr^+ and Xe^+ ions bombarding almost all the target materials given in Table 8.4 showed no variation of n_S with the bombarding flux density. However, decreasing the ion current for Kr^+ ions incident on Al or Sn targets showed marked increases in the saturation quantity of gas trapped. As we shall see later this suggests operation of a diffusive release process in these materials.

Further evidence of this was obtained by noting that n_S decreased by as much as 40% upon heating targets such as Ag, and Cu to 600°C during bombardment although the diminution was less for Mo and Ta; whilst post bombardment heating of a target to 600°C maintained at 20°C during bombardment, caused up to 85% release of trapped Kr or Xe. Just as the diminution of n_S was less marked for heated Mo and Ta, the post bombardment release of trapped gas through heating to 600°C was negligible for these materials and for Ni and Pt. A further interesting feature was that a small percentage of Kr recovered from copper even at room temperature whilst almost all trapped Neon was recovered within a few days at this temperature. The formation of a porous oxide surface was held to be responsible for this anomalous behaviour. The energy variation of n_S was also studied and typical results for Kr^+ and Xe^+ incident upon Al, Ta, Ni and Ag targets are shown in Figures 8.19 a and b. The

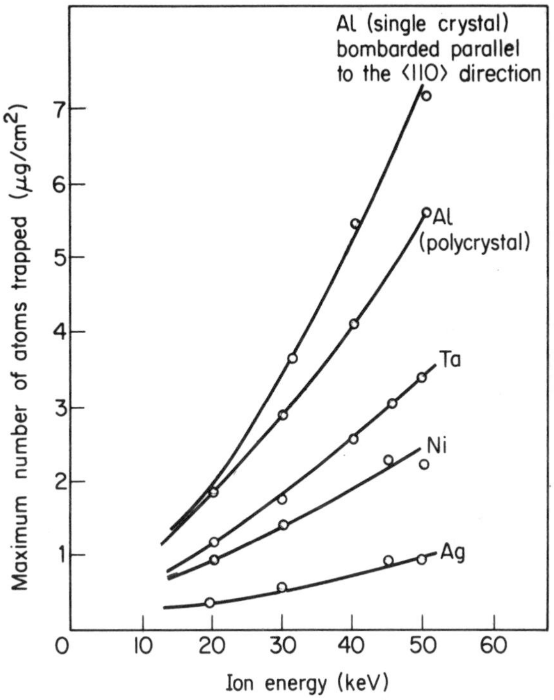

Fig. 8.19a The maximum number of Kr^+ ions which can be trapped in Al (single & Polycrystalline), Ta, Ni and Ag targets as a function of ion energy (viz. Ref. 8.77)

n_S/energy relationships are clearly almost linear in all cases, as found by Burtt et al[69,70] at lower energies. The value of n_S was also found to be dependent upon the direction of ion incidence (ϕ to the normal) as shown for 45 keV K_r^+ ions in Figure 8.20. The decrease of n_S with ϕ could be adequately described by a law of the form

$$n_S(\phi) = n_S(O) \cos^2 \phi \qquad 8.16$$

illustrating the shorter normal component of penetra-

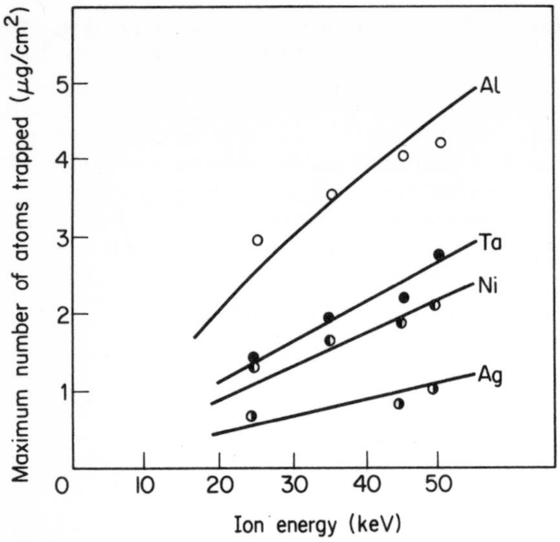

Fig. 8.19b The maximum number of Xe^+ ions which can be trapped in Al (polycrystal), Ta, Ni, Ag targets is a function of ion energy (viz. Ref. 8.77)

tion depth with ϕ and the increase of sputtering coefficient with ϕ, which both reduce the value of n_s (ϕ). This relation was most accurately obeyed when the ion mass M_1 was greater than the target atom mass M_2 since the scattering would be preferentially forward and the projected normal component of the ion range would more nearly approximate (R_{normal}) cos ϕ. Perhaps the most significant measurement was the variation of n_s with the orientation of the ion beam with respect to the [111] surface of a copper single crystal. This relation is shown in Figure 8.21 for

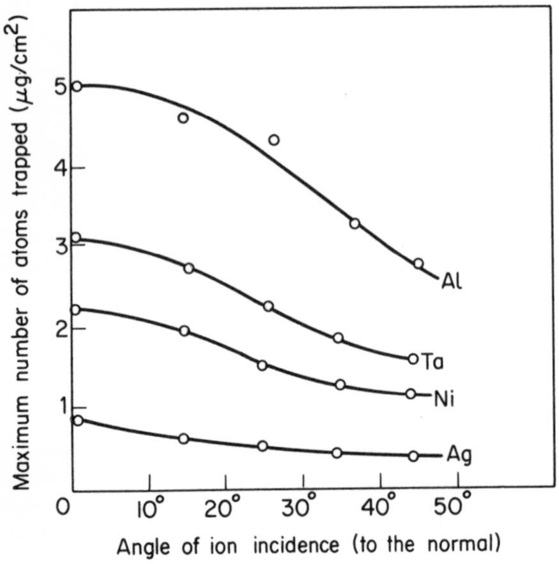

Fig. 8.20 The variation of the number of 45 keV Kr^+ ions which can be trapped in Al, Ta, Ni and Ag targets as a function of the angle of incidence of the ions to the targets

45 keV K_r^+ ions and it is immediately seen that maxima occur when the directions of incidence corresponded to ⟨110⟩, (35.3°); ⟨233⟩, (10.0°); ⟨111⟩, (0°); ⟨112⟩, (19.5°); ⟨114⟩, (35.3°) and ⟨100⟩, (54.7°). The standard curve for polycrystalline copper is included for comparison. As we saw in the previous chapter these directions correspond to directions of minima in the sputtering ratio orientation curves, and of course, to transparent, or channel directions. The

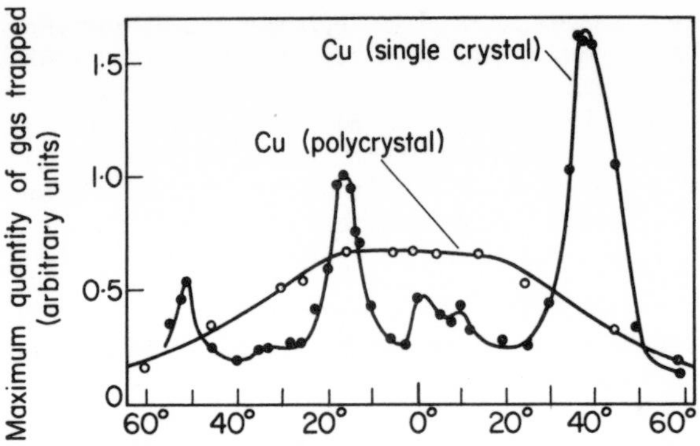

Fig. 8.21 The maximum number of atoms trapped in a Cu single crystal turned around a <110> axis in the (111) plane. The <111> direction is 3° from zero. The values of n_s are also shown for a Cu polycrystal (viz. Ref. 8.77)

increase in n_s along these directions must therefore be associated with deeper penetration along the channels, and perhaps by increased diffusion along these directions.

Somewhat similar results were observed with Al single crystals, as the n_s/energy curves of Fig. 8.19a for polycrystalline and single crystal Al show. Measurements of n_s were also made for 45 keV Y^+, Zr^+, Rb^+ and Yb^+, ions on Cu and Ta targets by observing the total dose after which the sputtering rate became constant following the initial changes due to loading of the target with gas. Values of n_s for the Ta target are 12 μg/cm²; 15 μg/cm²; 4.2 μg/cm² and 4.5 μg/cm², for the ions listed in the order above.

It is therefore quite clear that the process of saturation involves a complex combination of sputtering and thermally induced release mechanisms and as we shall see shortly, changes in ion penetration functions. In the following sections we will discuss the experimental observations of these separate processes and attempt to incorporate the results into simple theories of the saturation effects. Initially we consider the sputtering or bombardment induced re-emission process.

8.6 BOMBARDMENT INDUCED GAS EMISSION

As we saw in the previous chapter, ion bombardment causes erosion of solid targets via the sputtering process. It would therefore be anticipated that gas atoms trapped beneath the surface would be exposed during erosion and would escape into the gas phase. This mechanism of gas release due to target sputtering, would provide one process for saturation effects, since if the probability of trapping remained constant during bombardment at a flux density B, the rate of ion trapping would be balanced by the rate of gas removal due to erosion when

$$B\eta = BS_t\,\theta$$

where S_t is the target sputtering coefficient in atoms/ion and θ is the fractional gas content of the surface in gas atoms/target atom.

Since η and S_t are both fractional for energies less than 1 keV one might expect θ to be between 10 and 100 atomic percent at low energies but since S_t probably increases more rapidly than η above 1 keV the fraction may fall. Nevertheless this order of gas content is extremely high and one would question whether at such concentrations η and S_t will remain typical of a virgin target or whether gas occlusion will alter their values.

This possibility suggests another mechanism wherein trapped gas may be released by bombarding ions. Namely by transfer of sufficient kinetic energy from the ion to the trapped atom to ensure release of the latter from the constraints of the target atoms. Such a process may occur via direct interaction of the bombarding ion and the trapped atom or via intermediate lattice atom collisions. Whereas the former would be most efficient from an energy transfer standpoint ($T = E_{ion}$ for equal mass ions and trapped atoms, whilst the transfer via target atoms of mass M_2 would be a maximum of

$$T = \frac{4M_1M_2}{(M_1+M_2)^2} \cdot \frac{4M_2M_1}{(M_2+M_1)^2}$$

which for M_1/M_2 could be quite small), the direction of energy transfer would be directed into the target for direct ion atom collisions resulting in less efficient removal than if momentum is reversed via a succession of target atom collision so that the trapped atom is struck in an outward directed sense.

As we shall see later trapped gas atoms only require energies between 1 and 10 eV for their release from solid targets so that a 1 keV ion could conceivably release many trapped atoms. This gas sputtering mechanism could therefore lead to effective gas sputtering coefficients S_g, much larger than the target sputtering coefficients, with of course considerable reduction in the value of θ. An alternative, but similar release process can be envisaged where the vacancies produced by the bombarding ions allow more rapid migration of trapped gas than under normal ambient conditions.

Essentially these processes of gas removal would be equivalent to a cascade type of displacement process- and by analogy one could surmise a spike mechanism which would result in gas removal. As we saw in Chapter 6, quite low energy ions can result in thermal excitation of microvolumes of the target and, since the energy required for gas release is quite low, thermal activation of migration and release processes could occur in these spikes. Again one could anticipate large effective values of the gas sputtering coefficient and consequent small values of the saturation gas content.

With these possible mechanisms of gas release in mind we are now in a position to describe and discuss the experimental measurements of the bombardment induced gas release efficiency. Schwarz[107] observed in 1944, that Argon trapped in the glass envelopes and metal ion collectors of triode ionization gauges could be released by subsequent operation with nitrogen, and that the reverse process was also possible. No quantitative information can be obtained from Schwarz's[107] data and a similar comment applies to later studies by Brown and Leck[99] of the bombardment induced release of trapped inert gases from Penning gauge cathodes. More quantitative studies of emission from nickel have since been reported by Carmichael and his collaborators[80,108] and from glass by James and Carter.[42,43,98] In the former series of investigations[80,108] inert gas ions formed in a triode structure were driven into the cylindrical nickel ion collector. The ion energy was between 50 eV and 150 eV, the spread resulting from the geometric structure of the tube, but it is reasonable to expect that most ions possessed energies in the region of 100 eV. After entrapment of a certain number of atoms, a pulse of ions of a second gas species was allowed to strike the collector surface and the number of primary atoms released was determined mass spectrometrically. Repetition of the bombardment pulses caused further release of gas and, in this way, histograms of the number of ions released by successive pulses were constructed for various combinations of trapped and releasing ion species. Since the ion pulses were sufficiently small (equivalent to about 10^{15} ions/cm^2/sec) the histograms could be smoothed and represented as the number of atoms released per bombarding ion as a function of the total releasing ion dose and a typical graph of the results for A releasing trapped Kr is shown in Figure 8.22. Variation of the amount of primary gas trapped

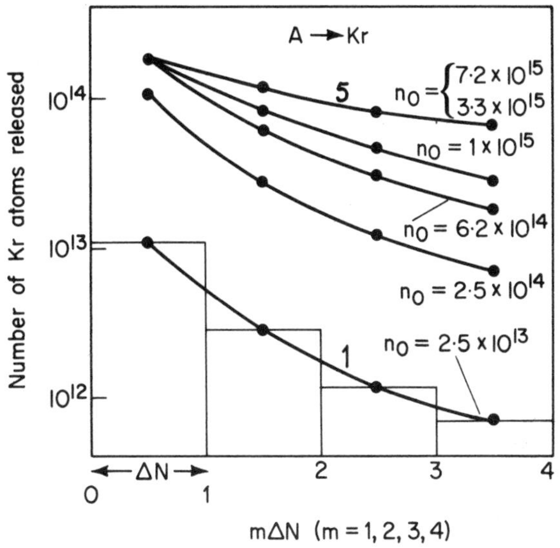

Fig. 8.22 The variation in the number of Kr atoms released by successive pulses of $\Delta N = 5.0 \times 10^{16}$ A^+ ions (mean energy $\simeq$ 100 eV) for different values of n_0, the number of Kr atoms trapped before A^+ ion bombardment (viz. Ref. 8.80). The gas release efficiency is the value of any ordinate divided by 5×10^{16} multiplied by $n_0/3 \times 10^{16}$

then allowed observation of the release efficiency (i.e. the rate of release of trapped atoms per bombarding ion) as a function of the releasing ion dose for different values of the initial quantity of gas trapped and several such curves are shown in Figure 8.22. The release efficiency falls with increasing secondary ion dose according to this figure and the most important condition occurs at the commencement of secondary ion bombardment where the release rate is maximum. This maximum release efficiency is plotted as a function of the quantity of primary gas initially trapped in Figure 8.23 for various combinations of trapped and releasing ion species. In this Figure, A→Kr for example, denotes Argon ions releasing previously trapped Kr atoms. Apart from the Kr-He case, all curves show an initial linear increase of release efficiency with the quantity of gas trapped then a saturation level where the release efficiency becomes independent of the amount trapped. The Kr-He case is special since the amount of trapped He itself showed no sign of saturation up to 100 equivalent monolayers. The release efficiency/ion dose curves for different initial trapped quantities exhibit

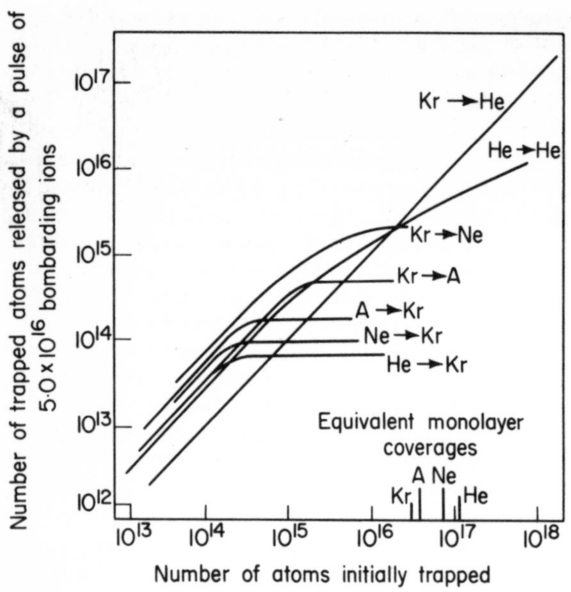

Fig. 8. 23 The number of trapped inert gas atoms released by a pulse of 5.0×10^{16} bombarding ions as a function of the number of atoms initially trapped. The gas release efficiency is thus deduced from any ordinate divided by 5×10^{16}, the result multiplied by the ratio of the appropriate abscissa value to the equivalent monolayer coverage value (also marked) (viz. Ref. 8. 80)

this initial linear increase and final saturation of release efficiency with trapped quantity. They also show that later in the re-emission cycles the release efficiency does not reach the saturation level until larger initial quantities of gas have been trapped.

One of the most important parameters in determining the mechanism of gas release is the magnitude of the effective gas sputtering coefficient. From the slopes of the initial linear portions of the curves in Figure 8. 23 one deduces the number of trapped atoms released per bombarding ion per trapped atom, or the probability of release of a trapped atom per bombarding ion. Target sputtering ratios are always characterised by the probability of release of a surface atom per bombarding ion with the tacit assumption that a complete surface layer of atoms is exposed to the ion. Thus in order to determine a comparable quantity for gas sputtering the probability of gas atom release per bombarding ion deduced as above should be normalised to a value at equivalent monolayer coverage of gas atoms. For most inert gas atoms, approximately 10^{15} atoms/cm^2 constitutes monolayer

TABLE 8. 5 (Ref. 8. 81).

Effective values of the gas sputtering ratios for 100 eV ions trapped in Ni.

Trapped atom	Bombarding Ion	S_g
He	He	0. 6
He	Kr	0. 2
Ne	Kr	0. 7
A	Kr	0. 3
Kr	He	0. 2
Kr	Ne	0. 4
Kr	A	0. 35

coverage, so that multiplication of the release probabilities by this quantity gives values of S_g. Table 8. 5 gives the appropriate values of S_g for the ion-atom combinations shown in Figure 8. 23 and it is evident that all values are less than unity but always greater than 0. 1. The He-Kr, Ne-Kr and A-Kr values of S_g are all close to 0. 2, as are the Kr-He and Kr-A values. S_g for the Kr-Ne combination is 0. 8 however.

If one inspects the values of S_t for 100 eV inert gas ions striking a Ni surface as reported by Wehner[109] it is evident that these are also of order 0. 2 for Ne^+, A^+ and Kr^+ ions but about an order of magnitude less for He^+ ions ($S_t \sim 0.03$). This means that for Ne^+ or A^+ ions releasing Kr atoms, about one Ni atom should be sputtered for each gas atom released, whilst for He^+ ions releasing Kr atoms about 7 Krypton atoms are released for each Ni atom sputtered. The values of one gas atom released per sputtered target atom is not unreasonable if it is assumed that gas release depends upon the erosion of the target. However the higher ratios of S_g/S_t of 7 and 4 cannot be understood on this basis since this implies that removal of one target atom releases considerably more trapped gas atoms. It is therefore suggested that these high values of S_g are indicative of some gas sputtering phenomenon, and, since they occur for quite widely differing bombarding ion masses (He and Kr) it is natural to believe that such processes may also operate in the cases of Ne and A. These measurements were subsequently extended by Carmichael and Waters[108] to investigate the effects of using almost equal mass trapped and releasing ions and employed He_3 and He_4 as the test particles. The important result of this work was that the S_g values for the He-He combination was about 5 times as large as that for the Kr-He combination (i.e. of order unity) but that the efficiency of removal of trapped He by bombarding He decreased with the quantity initially trapped. The He-He characteristic in Figure 8. 23 exhibits this behaviour. Increasing the releasing ion energy to 1100 eV for the He-He combination resulted in an increase in S_g of only 30%, whereas the same energy increase for Kr^+ releasing trapped He resulted in an increase of S_g by a factor of 3. 5. This latter result is of a similar order of magnitude to the increase in S_t for Kr sputtering N_i between 100 eV and 1100 eV, but the increase for the He-He combination is very much smaller than the corresponding increase in S_t. Further if the energy of the primary trapped He atoms was increased from 100 eV to 1100 eV and these were released by 100 eV Kr^+ or He^+ ions, S_g fell by a factor of about 3 for the first combination but only by 30% for the latter. Again it is difficult to explain these results on a simple basis of gas release attendant on target erosion since, if such were the case, one would expect the same relative reduction, for both bombarding ion species. A further interesting result was that as the quantity of initially trapped He was increased, the fraction of ions trapped in a subsequent He^+ ion release pulse also increased, i.e. the sticking efficiency apparently increased with increasing quantity. Of course we should recall that He showed no sign of trapping saturation up to 15 equivalent monolayers of gas and so trapping and release processes with this gas may involve quite different mechanisms than for the other gases. Nevertheless, it does appear that some of Carmichael et al's[80,108] results must be attributed to gas sputtering. Although these author's have preferred to interpret most of their observations on the basis of target sputtering. Further work on this topic is evidently desirable.

According to Equation 8.17 the saturation fractional gas content of a surface should be given by $\eta/S_t = \theta$. Kornelsen[72] has interpreted his measurements for the trapping of the inert gas ions in Tungsten, in terms of this relation and from measurement of θ and η concludes that the values of S_t for Ne, A, Kr and Xe ions with energies in the 70-400 eV region should be larger by factors of 65, 20, 20 and 14 respectively than the actual values measured for these combinations by Wehner.[109] This strongly suggests that in fact gas sputtering, with effective values of S_g much larger than S_t, must be the major source of atom release, but one must be cautious in this interpretation since η is assumed constant up to final saturation. This parameter may decrease as saturation is approached but since the fractional gas content of the surface is only 10% at saturation it is difficult to believe that sufficient increase in target stopping power could result, (in order to achieve the required approximately 100 fold reduction (in the case of Ne in Ni)) necessary for a target sputtering mechanism to be acceptable.

Furthermore, Kornelsen's[72] data suggest that S, deduced from the ratio θ/η should only increase by a factor of at most 2 upon increasing the ion energy from 100 eV to 1 keV. The sputtering coefficient for tungsten increases by an order of magnitude over this range, once more indicating the apparent inoperability of this mechanism.

We should also remark that the deductions of S from Carmichael and Trendelenburg's[80] and Kornelsen's[72] measurements assumes that all the trapped atoms reside in the surface layer and are therefore all equally susceptible to removal. It is more likely that the trapped atoms are distributed with depth in the target so that the numbers of trapped atoms in the surface layer are less than those used to evaluate S_g. Consequently the values of S_g may be even larger than quoted and this further confirms our belief in gas sputtering.

James and Carter[20,42,43,98] have studied the bombardment induced release of trapped inert gases from Pyrex glass surfaces using the glass envelope of a diode structure as the ion collector and produced quite unequivocal evidence of some form of gas sputtering process. The technique used was very similar to that employed by Carmichael et al[80] except that after entrapment of a known quantity of gas, the experimental surface was bombarded at a constant rate with an alternative ion species and the release rate of the primary trapped gas observed mass spectrometrically until release terminated. The primary and bombarding mean ion energies were generally in the region of 250 eV (with an energy spread of ± 250 eV because of tube geometry) but some experiments were conducted at both increased and diminished mean primary and bombarding ion energies.

By employing a static system and measuring the actual quantity of primary gas trapped it was established that all of this gas could be recovered by heating the tube to 450°C. It was then further established that bombardment induced release of gas was not 100% effective in that, following bombardment until no induced release was observed, heating the tube resulted in a further release of gas. The experimental observations therefore fell into two categories. First the initial rate of release of trapped gas A upon commencing bombardment with ions B was determined as a function of the amount of gas A trapped before bombardment, for all combinations of A and B selected from He, Ne, A, Kr, and Xe. Thus, for example both the He-Ne combination and the Ne-He combination were investigated. Secondly the percentage of trapped gas A which could be recovered by bombardment alone by B ions was measured as a function of the initial quantity of gas A trapped, again for all combinations of A and B.

Typical initial release rate/quantity of gas sorbed curves for trapped Argon released by He^+, Ne^+, Kr^+; or Xe^+ ions are shown in Figure 8.24a whilst Figure 8.24b illustrates the reverse sequence when trapped

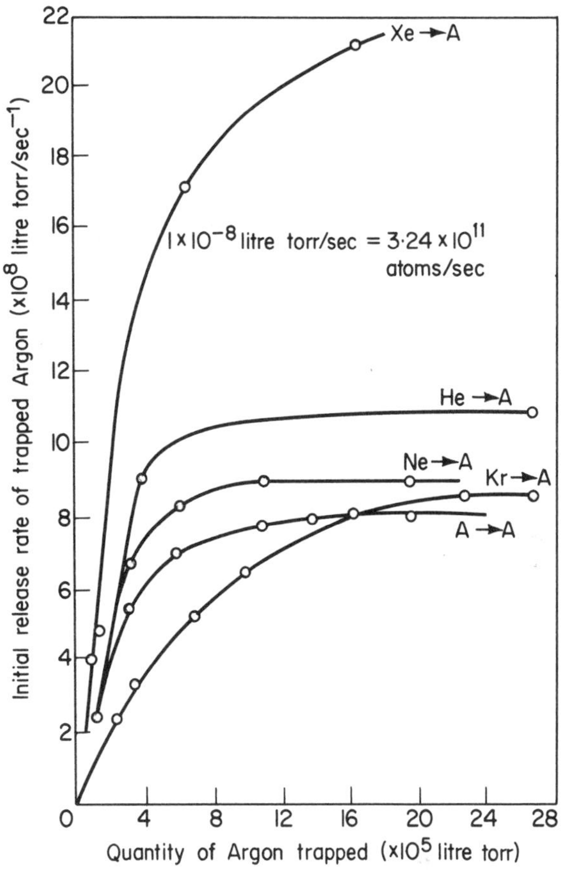

Fig. 8.24a The initial release rate of argon atoms trapped at 250 eV in a Pyrex glass by He^+, He^+, Ne^+, Kr^+ and Xe^+ 250 eV ions, as a function of the quantity of Argon initially trapped (viz. Ref. 8.43, 8.96). The A → A characteristic is interpolated

He, Ne, Kr or Xe atoms are released by A^+ ions. Figure 8.24c shows a complementary curve for the percentage of trapped gas released by bombardment alone. The final points on these curves illustrate the saturation quantities of primary gas which could be trapped and these are generally of the order of 0.1 equivalent monolayers. Quite analogous curves were obtained for all gas combinations and the general features are that the initial gas release rate increased to a maximum with increasing initial trapped quantity whereas the percentage of recoverable trapped gas decreased monotonically with increasing trapped quantity. If, at each quantity trapped point, on these curves, the release rate or recoverable percentage is replotted as a function of the bombarding ion or trapped atom mass, it is possible to interpolate the appropriate values for each ion effectively releasing atoms of the same type and eventually the full interpolated characteristics may be exhibited as in Figures 8.24 a, b, c. From one set of characteristics e.g. A^+ ions releasing He, Ne, Kr or Xe atoms the A^+ ion

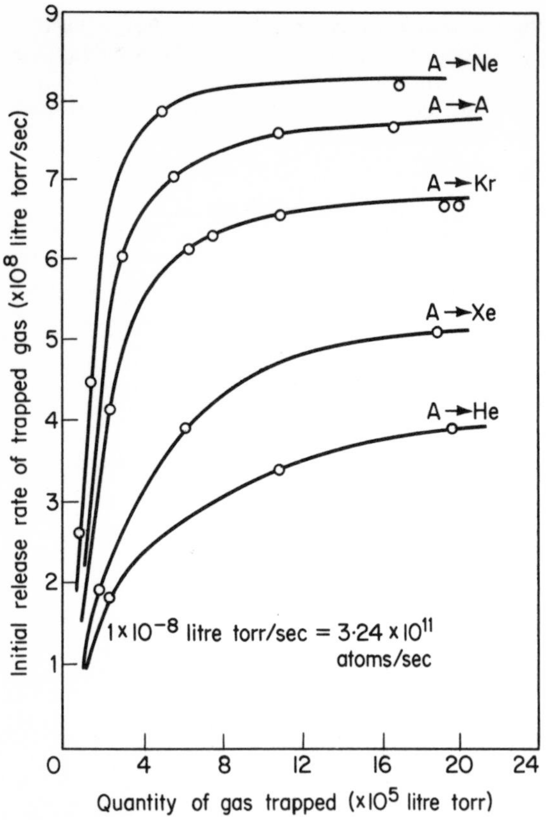

Fig. 8.24b The initial release rate of He, Ne, Kr and Xe atoms trapped at 250 eV in a Pyrex glass by 250 eV A^+ ions, as a function of the number of atoms initially trapped (viz. Refs. 8.43 and 8.96) The A → A characteristic is interpolated

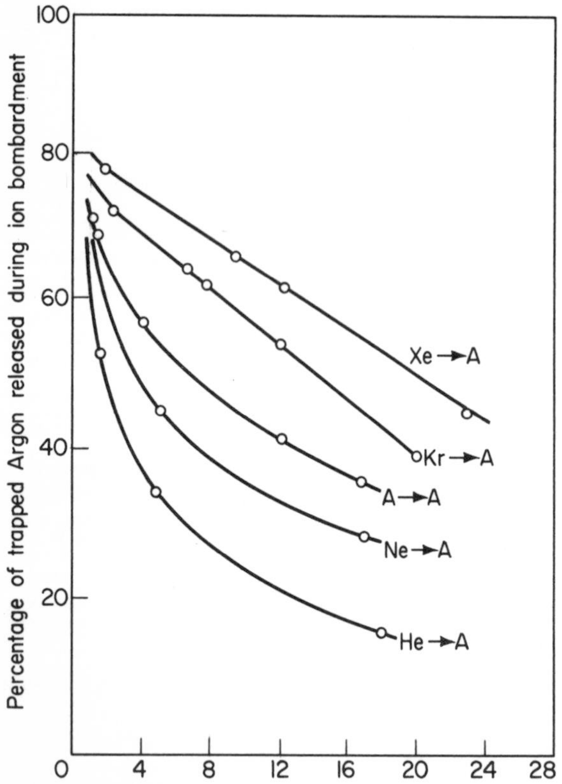

Fig. 8.24c The percentage of A atoms initially trapped at 250 eV in a Pyrex glass which can be released by bombardment with 250 eV, He^+, Ne^+ Kr^+ and Xe^+ ions as a function of the quantity of A initially trapped (viz. Refs. 8.43 and 8.96) The A → A characteristic is interpolated

releasing A atoms curve is obtained whilst from the other characteristics of He^+, Ne^+, Kr^+, or Xe^+ releasing A atoms, a second set of A^+ ions releasing A atoms is obtained. To show how good are the two

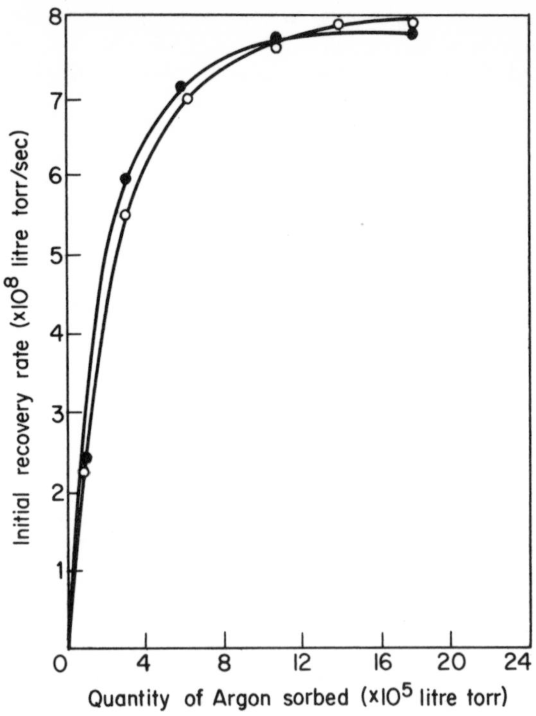

Fig. 8.25 Comparison of the interpolated A → A characteristics in Figs. 8.24a and 8.24b for A release by He, Ne, Kr and Xe and He, Ne, Kr and Xe released by A (viz. Refs. 8.43 and 8.96)

methods of assessing the self release characteristics, Figure 8.25 shows these self release characteristics, (initial release rate) obtained from both interpolations and plotted together for A. Similar agreement is found for Ne and Kr, whilst the slightly poorer agreement found with He and Xe is understandable since they require extrapolated rather than interpolated data points. As in Carmichael's[80, 108] studies the most informative parameter is the ion-atom release efficiency. By dividing the slope of the initial release rate/quantity adsorbed curves, at zero quantity trapped, as in Figures 8.24 a and b, by the known rate of releasing ion bombardment, one obtains the maximum release efficiency of trapped ions per bombarding ion per trapped atom (i.e. this work measured)

$$\left|\frac{d}{dn_t}\left(\frac{dn_t}{dt}\right)\times\frac{1}{B}\right|_{n_t = 0}$$

which is identical to the parameter determined from Carmichael's experiments

$$\left|\frac{d}{dn_t}\left(\frac{1}{B}\frac{dn_t}{dt}\right)\right|_{n_t = 0}$$

where n_t is the quantity of gas trapped and B the bombardment rate.) Multiplication by the effective monolayer coverage factor for each trapped atom ($\sim 10^{15}$ atoms/cm^2) then allows deduction of the effective gas sputtering coefficients for each atom by any other ion and from the interpolated curves the self sputtering coefficients. These values of S_g are enumerated in Table 8.6 a for all the combinations of the five

TABLE 8.6a. (Ref. 8.43 and 8.98).

Gas Release Efficiency (Sputtering Coefficient) For Each Inert Gas Sorbed Bombarded by the Other Gas Ions (at 250 eV).

	Bombarding Ion.				
Sorbed Gas	Helium	Neon	Argon	Krypton	Xenon
Helium	5.5	12.0	50.0	40.0	5.0
Neon	9.0	20.5	35.0	33.0	10.0
Argon	10.0	35.0	22.0	18.0	12.5
Krypton	7.5	38.0	12.0	11.5	6.0
Xenon	13.0	24.0	40.0	62.0	63.0

atoms used at ion energies of 250 eV. Other work in which argon was initially trapped at various ion energies between 100 eV and 1 keV and subsequently released by 250 eV Kr^+ ions showed that S_g increased

TABLE 8.6b. (Refs. 8.43 and 8.98).

Sputtering Coefficient for Argon Sorbed at 250 eV and Released by Bombarding Krypton at Various Energies.

Krypton Energy	Sputtering Coefficient.
100 eV	16.0
230 eV	18.0
450 eV	27.0
950 eV	40.0

by only a factor of 2.5 over this range (viz. Table 8.6b). Further if Argon, initially trapped at 250 eV, was released by Kr^+ ions with energies between 100 e and 1 keV the S_g value increased slightly for energies between 100 eV and 400 eV, but thereafter reached a saturation value. These studies also indicated that a threshold energy of 20-30 eV was required for release of trapped Argon by Krypton ions.

We should also emphasize that the initial release rate of a gas A was linearly dependent upon the bombardment rate of B ions, and, for small initial trapped quantities of gas, the rate of release decreased roughly exponentially with the total bombarding ion dose. In addition we mentioned earlier that trapped atoms could be released, without bombardment, via heating of the tube to 450°C, a continuous recovery occurring between room temperature (the tube operating temperature during trapping) and 450°C. If, however, bombardment induced release was effected, the subsequent thermal release was markedly reduced at the low temperature end of the range but to a much smaller extent at the upper end of the temperature range. This result is shown in Figure 8.26 which illustrates the rate of release of trapped Argon with increasing tube temperatures, with and without bombardment induced release.

James and Carter[42] and James, Carter and Leck[43,95] have interpreted these observations as furnishing conclusive proof that the bombardment induced release of low energy ions from a glass surface is essentially a gas sputtering process. Reference to Table 8.6 shows that the effective values of S_g are all greater than unity and even rise to 60 for the Xe-Xe combina-

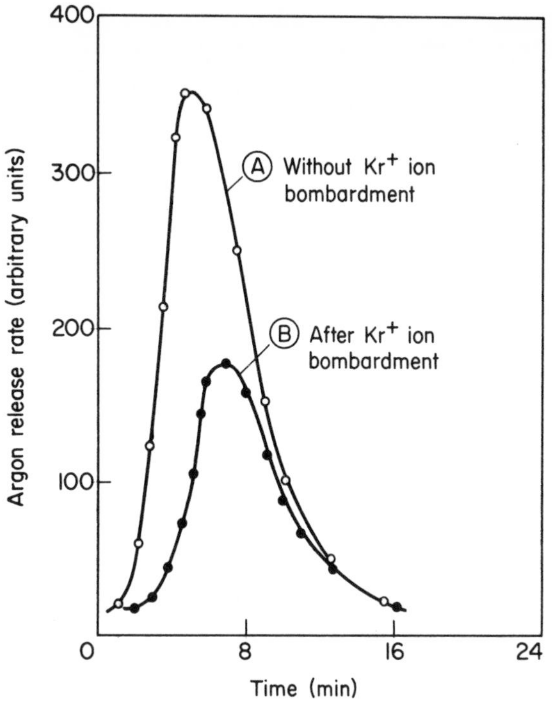

Fig. 8.26 The rate of release of argon atoms, trapped in Pyrex Glass at 250 eV, during heating at a rate of about 25°C/min from room temperature.
Curve A indicates desorption immediately following trapping
Curve B was obtained after bombarding the surface with 250 eV Kr^+ ions also before commencing desorption (viz. Ref. 8.20)

tion. Available values for S_t for glass[110] in this energy range, measurements at higher energy, and analogous results for metals, quartz and other insulators at low energies (viz. Chapter 7) suggest that S_t should be fractional in the energy range of the above experiments. The apparently larger values of S_g (by one to two orders of magnitude) must indicate a gas sputtering mechanism. In addition, if only target sputtering was operative, the values of S for a particular trapped atom should depend only upon the target sputtering coefficient of the bombarding ion and should therefore follow the same sequence for all bombarding ions independent of the trapped atom. Table 8.6a shows that this is not the case e.g. for trapped Ne, S_g increases in the sequence He < Ne < Xe < Kr < A, whereas for trapped Xe, the sequence is He < Ne < A < Kr < Xe. Further it is difficult to understand, on a target sputtering basis, why all trapped gas cannot be removed by ion bombardment alone, since such a mechanism would eventually result in a sufficient target erosion to expose and release all trapped gas. It could be argued that asymmetrical sputtering of the bombarded area results in preferential burial of trapped gas in less sputtered parts of the tube but such a process would mitigate against the fact that saturation of trapped gas was always observed in experiments. The increase in S_g with the energy of Kr^+ ions releasing trapped A atoms should also be considered as evidence against a target sputtering mechanism, since as in the earlier arguments concerning Carmichael and Trendelenburg's[80] results with Ni, the value of S_t would be expected to increase by an order of magnitude over this energy range.

The present conclusions must therefore favour the gas sputtering mechanism, certainly in the case of a glass target and very probably, in the case of some metal targets also. However, the observations do not decide unequivocally whether the gas sputtering process is one of a cascade displacement type or of a thermal spike type, but as the following considerations show the latter mechanism appears preferable.

If one assumes a cascade type energy transfer process, then a bombarding ion of energy E_0 can produce, in a target array of equal mass atoms, a number of displaced atoms and vacancies given approximately by $E_0/2Ed$. For a value of $E_0 = 250$ eV and $E_d =$ 25 eV (the generally accepted approximate value for dynamic displacements) the number of displaced atoms is 5. Whilst this value is acceptable for the results observed with metals and marginally acceptable for some of the results for glass, the extreme values for Kr and Xe in glass cannot be easily explained.

Furthermore, it is well known that such a simple theory cannot explain the measured fractional target sputtering coefficients and what is applicable to the target-ion collisions should be equally applicable to the ion–trapped atom collisions. One could suggest that E_d for the trapped gas is grossly different to that for the target atoms. The thermal energy for the movement of trapped atoms in glass lies, as we shall see later, between 1 eV and 2.5 eV whereas the binding energy of glass atoms is probably about 2.5 eV–3 eV (glass melts in the region of 600°C) and it is therefore unlikely that E_d values for the trapped atoms are very much different to the E_d values for the glass atoms.

The alternative mechanism of release via spike heating appears to be an equally valid alternative. A 250 eV ion, according to the results of Chapter 5 would be expected to possess a range in glass of the order of only a few Angstroms (say 5 Å for the sake of argument) and thus loses its energy in a volume of about 60 Å. This volume contains about 20 glass atoms and if the 250 eV is partitioned equally between these atoms, each will receive about 12 eV, far higher than either the energy required for gas release or for evaporation of the glass. If this were the case extremely high values for the sputtering of glass would be observed, which is certainly not true. However, of the 250 eV ion energy a considerable proportion will be expended upon displacement collisions and perhaps only the final 25 eV will be dissipated, in non displacement, thermal activation processes. Thus the energy given to the target and trapped atoms is of the order 1 eV, which is insufficient to promote target evaporation but sufficient to cause gas atom migration and release.

Such a mechanism can account for the observation that bombarding ions release that portion of the trapped gas which possesses the lower release energies and that all trapped gas may not be recoverable. On the other hand the energy imparted to any species of trapped atom should increase as the effective spike temperatures increase and thus in the same sequence for different bombarding ions but independent of the trapped atom. We should realise however that the penetration depth distributions of the trapped atoms will depend upon their mass and so the differing spike temperatures and volumes may encompass different proportions of each trapped species, leading to a dependence of S_g upon both the bombarding and the trapped atoms.

We can progress no further than these simple hypotheses at this stage since insufficient evidence is available for ion ranges, damage rates and spike temperatures in glasses or metals at such low ion energies. We should note however that in order to bring spike consideration into alignment with the observations, some degree of cascade production is necessitated, and it may be that the gas release process relies partly upon displacement events and non displacement spike production. It does appear evident that gas sputtering must be seriously considered at the low ion energies discussed here.

We should note finally that, according to simple theory[111] the fractional gas content of a surface should be of the order of η/S. Since η has been measured to be about 0.25 on average for the inert gases[14,15] on glass surfaces whilst the fractional surface coverage at saturation is estimated at about 0.1 equivalent monolayers[15,16] this suggests values of S in the region of 2. Although the maximum values of S_g (deduced at essentially zero coverage) are in the region of 20, Figure 8.24 shows that S_g decreases rapidly as saturation is reached (by a factor of about six for A releasing A) so that the effective values of S_g at saturation are not unreasonable in predicting 0.1 for θ. The studies for both glass and metal surfaces do reveal the important point that S_g is not a constant independent of the quantity of gas trapped, as suggested by several authors, but is only approximately so for relatively small gas contents (~1% atomic concentration for both glass and Ni surfaces) and then declines rapidly towards the saturation limit of the target.

Since, in the case of Ni it is marginally possible that target sputtering is responsible for gas release we should explore the effects of this phenomenon further and also try to explain why glass and nickel surfaces give such widely different values for S_g. This latter behaviour may be connected with the higher thermal diffusivity of nickel resulting in lower spike persistence times, which are insufficiently long to promote migration processes. It is also possible that activation energies for trapped atom migration and release in Ni are higher than in glass so that again, spikes are unable to promote rapid release.

We have largely concerned ourselves so far with the results of low energy bombardment induced release, and indeed at the present time there is experimental evidence only in this energy region. However one may speculate that at higher trapping and bombarding energies target sputtering effects may assume greater importance. As the primary ion energy is increased the ion range distribution shifts away from the target surface (viz. the results of Kr trapping in Al by Brown and Davies[76]) so that the trapped gas concentration will tend to be low near the surface. In addition the bombarding ions will produce spikes deeper in the target so that these may be unable to promote release of the subsurface trapped gas. Further the target sputtering coefficient itself may become quite large and dominate any gas sputtering processes.

If one assumes that only target sputtering is responsible for trapped gas release then, as shown by Carter, Colligon and Leck[85], it is a straightforward matter to evaluate the trapping and release characteristics. Let us assume that the probability of an ion penetrating to and becoming trapped at a distance x below the target surface is p(x), and that this is independent of the quantity of gas already trapped in the target, i.e. trapped gas does not change the stopping power of the target. Then, in the absence of sputtering, the quantity of gas trapped per unit area at any depth x below the target would increase linearly with time to a value $Bp(x)\cdot t$

at time t and with an ion bombardment rate B ions/sec unit area. However target sputtering will cause simultaneous erosion of the surface, at a rate of v/sec and this will mean that a plane originally at a depth x below the initial surface will only be a distance x-vt below the actual surface at a time t. Thus the trapping probability at this plane will vary continuously from p(x) to p(x-vt) and so the gas build up rate also varies continuously. In addition the recession of the surface past previously trapped gas results in the emission of this gas so that there is simultaneous ion trapping and gas release.

If we introduce a new parameter

$$\xi = x - vt \qquad 8.18.1$$

the distance of a plane from the instantaneous target surface at a time t and which was originally a distance x from the target surface, the rate of gas trapping in a distance element $\delta x (= \delta\xi)$ per unit area is $Bp(\xi)\delta\xi$ 8.18.2. We also assume that upon reaching the depth ξ the trapped ion is immobilised, i.e. no diffusion, until released by target recession.

If we further suppose that the maximum ion range is L, then we have

$$p(\xi)d\xi = 0;\ \xi > L$$

$$p(\xi)d\xi = p(\xi)d\xi;\ 0 < \xi < L \qquad 8.19$$

$$p(\xi)d\xi = 0;\ 0 > \xi$$

We also see that the total trapping efficiency is the total probability of trapping between 0 and L i.e.

$$\eta = \int_0^L p(\xi)d\xi \qquad 8.20$$

which is assumed to be independent of the quantity of gas trapped. Further the target erosion rate

$$v = BS_t/n. \qquad 8.21$$

where n is the target atom density. The quantity of gas trapped in the depth interval $\delta\xi$ in a time t is thus given by

$$dN_{\xi,t} = B\int_0^t p(\xi)d\xi dt \qquad 8.22.1$$

and thus the total quantity trapped up to the maximum penetration depth L, at a time t,

$$\delta N_t = B\int_0^L \int_0^t p(\xi)d\xi dt \qquad 8.22.2$$

This integral comprises two regions. The first where the distance of the plane at ξ from the initial surface is greater than L up to a time given by x-vt = L, i.e. $t = \frac{x-L}{v}$ at which no ions are trapped until this time, and a second where the plane at ξ is always less than L, but all gas in a layer of depth x = vt is removed by erosion. The total quantity of gas trapped is then, rewriting $p(\xi) = p(x-vt)$

$$N_t = B\left\{ \int_{vt}^{L}\int_0^t p(x-vt)dx.\,dt + \int_L^{L+vt}\int_{\frac{x-L}{v}}^{t} p(x-vt)dx\,dt \right\} \qquad 8.23.1$$

If we put

$$\sigma(x) = \int p(x)dx;\ \psi(x) = \int\sigma(x)dx \qquad 8.23.2$$

we obtain,

$$N_t = \frac{B}{v}\left[\psi(0) - \psi(vt) + \sigma(L)\,.\,vt\right] \qquad 8.23.3$$

When the surface recedes past the maximum ion range (at a time T = L/v) the first term in equation 8.23.1 is zero, so that the total number of ions trapped for t > T is given simply by

$$N_S = \int_{vt}^{L+vt}\int_{\frac{x-L}{v}}^{t} p(x-vt)\,dxdt =$$

$$\frac{B}{v}[\psi(O) - \psi(L) + \sigma(L)\,.\,L] \qquad 8.24.1$$

$$\text{In fact for } t = T,\ N_S = N_T \qquad 8.24.2$$

and according to Equation 8.24.1 remains constant and independent of time thereafter i.e. saturation is reached. Physically this occurs since, as the surface recedes, the rate of ion trapping at L takes on all values from B.p (L) through B.p (x) back to B. p (O) and thus the number trapped at L is simply $B\int_L^O p(x)dx$ when the surface recedes to L. This quantity is clearly B.η (the total rate of ion trapping) and so when the next pulse of ions erodes the surface it releases the same number of ions from the surface layer as are simultaneously trapped in the target, i.e. saturation obtains. Equation 8.24.1 can be reduced to a particularly simple form, by noting that the mean ion range

$$\bar{L} = \int_0^L \frac{xp(x)dx}{\int_0^L p(x)dx} = \left[x\sigma(x) - \int\sigma(x)dx\right]_0^L =$$

$$L\sigma(L) - \psi(O) + \psi(L) \qquad 8.25$$

i.e. $N_S = \eta\,.\,\frac{B}{v}\,.\,\bar{L}$ and since $v = B\,.\,S_t/n$

Thus

$$N_S = n\eta\bar{L}/S_t \qquad 8.26.1$$

and is independent of the bombardment rate. These trapped atoms are trapped over a distance L, so that the total number of target atoms in this depth N = n . L. Thus, the average gas concentration at saturation

$$\frac{N_S}{N} = \eta/S_t.\quad \bar{L}/L \qquad 8.26.2$$

If the range is single valued

$$\bar{L} = L \text{ and } N_S/N = \eta/S_t \text{ or } N_S = NL\eta/S_t \qquad 8.26.3$$

Further, after saturation, the number of ions trapped at any depth ξ below the instantaneous surface remains constant and is given simply by the number of ions trapped at this depth ξ during the time that the surface recedes from a distance L to a distance ξ away from the plane i.e.

$$\delta N_\xi = B\int_L^\xi p(\xi)d\xi dt = \frac{B}{v}[\sigma(L) - \sigma(\xi)]d\xi \quad 8.27$$

This is simply the backwards integral of the penetration probability function from L to ξ and so measurement of the number of atoms trapped as a function of depth below the surface after saturation, and differentiation gives the penetration probability function.

Before saturation the number of atoms trapped at the instantaneous surface is given by

$$B\int_0^t p(x - vt)dx \;.\; dt = \frac{B}{v}[\sigma(-vt) - \sigma(o)]dx \quad 8.28.1.$$

which is simply

$$B\int_0^x p(x)dx \quad 8.28.2$$

where the surface has receded a distance x in the time t. The rate of trapping in the whole target is given by time differentiation of Equation 8.23.3 i.e.

$$\frac{dN_t}{dt} = B[\sigma(L) - \sigma(vt)] \quad 8.29.1.$$

for t = o

$$\frac{dN_t}{d(Bt)} = \sigma(L) - \sigma(o) = \int_0^L p(x)dx = \eta \quad 8.29.2.$$

i.e. the initial rate of trapping per bombarding ion, is as anticipated, simply equal to the trapping efficiency. We also note that double differentiation of the presaturation curve of N_t/t gives p(vt), or since the target surface recedes at a uniform rate p(vt) = p(x) i.e. the penetration probability function.

It is therefore apparent that this penetration can be derived in four ways. First if the target is bombarded with a short pulse of ions, the ions are trapped according to the simple penetration probability function since there is minimal target erosion. If the target is subsequently sectioned, the p(x)/x function is derived simply.

One possible method of sectioning is to bombard with a second ion species and provided that gas removal is due to unequivocally target sputtering only, the depth dependence of p(x) is derived simply from a knowledge of the second ion bombardment rate B_2 and the target sputtering coefficient S_2 since the depth of target eroded in a given time t_2 is

$$B_2S_2t_2/n \quad 8.30.$$

After saturation, the same technique can be used to give the integral $\int_L^x p(x)dx$ and differentiation provides p(x). Since the erosion depth is proportional to S_2 both techniques should give equivalent results. Thirdly in the presaturation regime, double differentiation of the number trapped/bombardment dose curve also gives a function proportional to p(x) but also dependent upon the target sputtering coefficient of the primary ion. If S_t is known, results for p(x) will be identical to the other methods of derivation.

Finally, again in the presaturation regime, if the surface concentration of trapped atoms is measured as a function of dose by sectioning after determined doses, this function also gives $\int_0^x p(x)dx$ and is dependent upon the primary ion sputtering coefficient.

This simple theory has been applied with some success by Colligon et al[85] to explain the saturation effects of 2 keV A^+ and Kr^+ ions in tungsten[70], using one or the other species as the primary or eroding species. In this case penetration probability functions derived from the build up and saturation distribution were as close as allowed by errors in sputtering coefficients for the two ions. However, the depth resolution of this technique was rather poor and Colligon[111] expressed the opinion that initial gas release during erosion could well have been due to gas sputtering, whilst we have already seen that η values measured by these authors[70] are much lower than similar data deduced by Kornelsen.[72] In addition Burtt et al [69,70] also observed that, frequently, all trapped primary gas was not recovered by a second ion bombardment sufficient to erode the surface well beyond the expected primary range (even after consideration of channelling processes), suggesting that secondary ion bombardment could cause knock on of the previously trapped atoms.

As we have already noted, Kornelsen[72] was able to interpret his data for ion trapping in tungsten, only on the basis of a gas sputtering mechanism, and indeed, for incident ion energies less than about 500 eV, saturation conditions were achieved when less than one monolayer of target had been removed, suggesting that target erosion was not responsbile.

The interpretation of their 100 eV ions in Ni data by Carmichael et al[80] in terms of a target sputtering process must also be regarded sceptically, since during second gas erosion the quantity of target removed was considerably less than a monolayer. If, in fact, one attempts analysis of Carmichael's[80] data on the target sputtering basis one is faced with several conflicting results. If, for a low trapped quantity, Curve 1 of Fig. 8.22 reflects the penetration probability function, then curve 5 at saturation should be the backwards integral of this, which it clearly is not. In addition the maximum depth of trapped atom location (i.e. the maximum range L) should be the same for both curves 1 and 5. It is again clear that this is not so. Further, according to Figure 8.22 the number of atoms trapped in the surface layer increases linearly with the total number of atoms trapped. It is readily deduced from Equations 8.22.1 and 8.23.3 that the only form of p(x) which can satisfy this condition is log p(x) = Ax + const. which, on the basis of curve 1 of Fig. 8.22 is not true.

It is difficult to reconcile these conflicting results on a simple target sputtering picture and it seems quite as possible that, because of their low energy the primary ions are trapped in the surface layer itself so that the build up in this layer is directly proportional to (in fact equal to) the total number of atoms trapped. As in the case of glass, saturation of the release efficiency with increasing trapped quantity may result from individual spikes encompassing a limited number of trapped atoms.

For much higher ion energies one may anticipate that the target sputtering theory just developed may give improved agreement with experiment and we should note that Almen and Bruce[77] have in fact used the above derivations to interpret their data for the trapping of inert gas ions (5-65 keV) in numerous metals.

Unfortunately we can only make quantitative comparisons with the theory for the inert gas ion/Al system since adequate range data is only available for this material. In addition several of Almen and Bruce's[77] results indicate a saturation trapping dependent upon ion dose rate, which is in conflict with the simple theory and as we shall see later, implies a simultaneous diffusion of trapped gas. The ion/Al cases do not appear to exhibit this behaviour.

From the theory, saturation is anticipated when the Al surface has receded to a depth equal to the maximum ion range. According to the Almen and Bruce[77] data saturation of 45 keV Kr^+ ions occurs when about 150 Å of Al have been eroded, whereas Davies'[112-115] results suggest that the mean ion range is more than three times this value, whilst the maximum observable ion range is probably an order of magnitude larger than this. Further, double differentiation of the presaturation Almen and Bruce's[77] data suggests a mean ion range of about 20 Å. $\overline{L}$ and L are clearly different by orders of magnitude. If, in addition, we use Almen and Bruce's[77,78] values for N_s and S_t in equation 8.26.1 one deduces a value of L of about 90 Å, again much lower than measured values. Before discussing possible reasons for these discrepancies we should point out that the general trend of Almen and and Bruce's data is indicative of target sputtering. Thus the periodicity with target atom mass of the target sputtering ratio for a given bombarding ion is reflected by an inverse periodicity in the saturation quantity. Of course some discrepancies occur, due probably in part to the diffusion effects noted by these authors, and probably due to fluctuations in $\overline{L}$. In fact since the variation of $\overline{L}$ with target atom mass is unknown, this itself may account for the variations in N_s, without involving the variation of S_t. However it is unlikely that such extreme variations of $\overline{L}$ do occur and we conclude that these variations of N_s are due to fluctuations in the sputtering coefficient. It is of course quite possible that a gas sputtering coefficient could exhibit such periodicity, and without other evidence we must leave this question in abeyance.

Returning to the question of why ranges deduced from saturation experiments are considerably lower than those deduced from short pulse experiments (at least for Kr in Al and probably for other combinations) we should inspect our assumptions implicit in the simple theory. Apart from the possibility of diffusion effects, (which certainly occur in the Kr/Ag and Kr/Sn systems as evidenced by variation of N_s with the bombardment rate but probably not in the Kr/Al case), the other major assumption was that the trapping probability at any depth was independent of the gas content of the target. However, we should recall the measurements by Brown and Davis[76] described in Chapter 5, where it was shown that as an increasing quantity of A or Xe is trapped in Al, the penetration probability function becomes displaced to shallower depths, i.e. gas occlusion or radiation damage increases the effective target stopping power so that ion ranges are decreased. For 30 keV A and Xe the reduction in range is about a factor of 4 and a similar result may be anticipated for Kr. We should also recall that analogous range diminution occurs as a result of ion trapping in Si[115], and one may anticipate some such effect for all target materials. Since the ion ranges are reduced by trapping it is probable that a larger proportion of ions will escape from the target as the trapped quantity increases and evidence of this is afforded by the Brown and Davies[76] data which shows that at saturation a much larger fraction of ions have essentially zero range. This implies that the trapping efficiency η decreases as the trapped quantity increases which is contradictory to the initial assumptions.

These effects invalidate our simple theory but do indicate that saturation may occur at much earlier stages of trapping (before removal of a depth layer L) since L decreases with increasing trapped quantity, just as required to bring estimates of L from saturation experiments into closer agreement with measured values of L. Although the simple theory is inadequate, it should be possible, when fuller information is available about the dependence of p(x) upon the quantity trapped, to suitably modify the theory.

In this connection we should also remember that the measurements of Brown and Davies[76] for A and Xe in Al showed that ions trapped early in the bombardment cycle were displaced into the target by succeeding ions, suggesting a knock on process. Again, when fuller details of the variation of the knock on efficiency with trapped quantity are available, it should be possible to incorporate these into a more adequate theory. Our conclusions must be that at this time there is insufficient evidence to support a target sputtering mechanism for saturation effects in metals, and even if this is the case, due account must be taken of the increased stopping power of gas loaded targets and the possibility of knock on and diffusion phenomena. Clearly this sphere of activity is ripe for experimental exploration.

8.7 THERMALLY ACTIVATED RELEASE PROCESSES

8.7.1 As we have already noted there is considerable evidence to show that trapped gas atoms migrate during sorption due to some form of thermally activated diffusion process. These migration phenomena are observable as recovery of gas from the trapping surface after the cessation of bombardment or variations in the quantity of gas trapped with the individual parameters, ion bombardment rate and trapping time, not just their product, bombardment dose.

Thermally activated migration processes should show a strong temperature dependence both during and after bombardment and we will therefore divide the following into discussion of two topics.

(1) Processes occurring during or after bombardment at the bombardment temperature.

(2) Processes occurring after bombardment at temperatures different from that during bombardment.

Initially we will describe the experimental results obtained by both observational methods and then attempt to fit all the facts into a relatively simple model.

Attempts have been made in the past to describe the results obtained by one observational technique in terms of too simple concepts and without reference to other types of observation, and as we shall see these attempts lead to somewhat absurd conclusions.

8.7.2 Into this category falls the observed dependence of the saturation trapped quantities upon the bombardment rate for 45 keV Kr^+ ions in Ag and Sn, by Almen and Bruce.[77] For Kr^+ ions in Sn a fourfold reduction of ion bombardment rate (from 12.8μa/cm^2) increased N_s by about 40%, but the change for a similar current reduction for Kr in Ag was only a few percent. On the other hand Corkhill and Carter[74] have found no dependence of the trapped atom concentration upon the ion dose rate for He, A and Xe ions of energies from 250 eV to 4 keV on tungsten polycrystals. This, unfortunately, is the only unequivocal experimental evidence on this topic, although we should note that extensive studies with glass surfaces using the dynamic flow technique have shown the quantity of gas trapped to be a function of the total bombardment and not the individual parameters bombardment rate and time, at least for values of this time greater than about 10 minutes. As we shall see shortly, one might anticipate variations of the trapped quantity by 10% or so with bombardment times shorter than this.

In addition Almen and Bruce[77] have observed that the quantity of gas trapped at a given dose decreases with increasing target temperature for 45 keV inert gas ions in numerous metals, whilst Cobic, Carter and Leck[14] have observed reductions in both trapping efficiency and saturation quantity with increasing target temperature for 250 eV inert gas ions in glass. Furthermore Cobic et al[14] and Hobson[116] have observed increases in η and n_s for 250 eV inert gas ions in glass for target temperatures below the normal operating condition at 20°C.

The work of Maddix and Allen,[21,22,23] which shows a square root time dependence of the trapped atom density for He, Ne, A and Kr in quartz is also illustrative of a simultaneous diffusion during sorption, but as we have noted earlier this was probably a consequence of operating the bombarded surface at temperatures where such diffusion was probable.

8.7.3 Much more extensive data has been gathered on the release, or desorption, of trapped gas from targets after termination of bombardment at the same temperature as obtained during bombardment, but as we shall now see, a great deal of misinterpretation of this data is possible because of the imprecise specification of the bombardment conditions.

Considerable stimulus for this type of reemission study derived from observations of gas release from ionization gauges used as ion pumps in Ultra high vacuum systems.[4] Consequently the majority of the information on re-emission phenomena has been obtained with ionization gauges, where the majority of trapping has occurred in the containing glass envelopes. Studies with metal surfaces have tended to employ the same geometry, simply replacing the glass envelope by a metallic ion collector. Von Meyern[82,83] and Schwarz[11] observed the re-emission of trapped inert gases and nitrogen from glass surfaces but did not make quantitative measurements. Subsequently Robinson and Berz[48] determined the release rate of previously trapped residual gases in a low pressure vacuum system (10^{-7} torr) from glass surfaces, Baker and Giorgi[93,94] Cobic, Carter and Leck[14] and Cavaleru Comsa and Iosifescu[91,92] studied the re-emission of trapped Argon from glass, Blodgett and Vanderslice[87] also observed the release of trapped Argon from a variety of glasses, Hobson[88,89,90] studied re-emission of sorbed N_2 from glass whilst, more recently, Smeaton, Leck and Carter[95,96] investigated the desorption of trapped He, A and Xe from Pyrex glass surfaces.

All these investigators used the glass envelopes of Bayard-Alpert gauges or diodes as the trapping surfaces, and with the exception of the later work of Smeaton et al[96] and Cavaleru et al[91,92] used the static pump down technique to entrap the gas. Thus the system of measurement was to admit the gas under study to the isolated experimental tube and note the pressure reduction due to ion pumping as a function of time.

The gauge was then switched off and any release of gas observed by an increase in total pressure recorded on an auxiliary non pumping gauge, or partial pressure recorded on a mass analyser. Generally the rate of release of gas was observed, by the rate of rise of gas pressure, as a function of time until no further release was noticeable. Probably the most significant result of all these studies was the apparent lack of agreement between different investigations. The general method of presentation of results was to exhibit the logarithmic recovery rate as a function of time after the commencement of recovery. Robinson and Berz[48] found that this gave a recovery rate/time dependence of the form $-\frac{dn}{dt} = A \exp(-ab) +$ $B \exp(-bt)$ whereas Baker and Giorgi[93,94] reported an exponential recovery form $-\frac{dn}{dt} = C \exp(-ct)$. The values of the constants depending upon the quantity of gas previously trapped. On the other hand, Blodgett and Vanderslice[87] found that the recovery curve was adequately expressed by the relation $\log\left(-\frac{dn}{dt}\right) = -\frac{1}{2} \log t + D$ provided that 'saturation' was achieved during pump down. Saturation, in this context, meaning that the pressure had ceased to fall and that pumping and release processes equilibrated. Since the quantities of trapped gas involved were of the order of 10^{-3}-10^{-2} equivalent monolayers the saturation determined by bombardment induced release was never achieved. If the recovery characteristic was determined at some other stage of pump down its form could be expressed approximately by $\log\left(-\frac{dn}{dt}\right) = m \log t + D$ where $-\frac{1}{2} < m < -1$. Blodgett and Vanderslice[87] also noted that the recovery rate was approximately proportional to the quantity of gas initially trapped.

Hobson,[88,89,90] however, observed a recovery characteristic for nitrogen of the form $-\frac{dn}{dt} = K\frac{n_T}{t}$ for recovery times greater than about a second, where n_T was the quantity of gas trapped.

Cobic, Carter and Leck[14] found that the apparent reduction in pumping speed during a static pump down, where only small quantities of gas were trapped, was due entirely to the thermal re-emission obtaining at the end of that sequence. As we have already seen, however, when large quantities of gas are trapped it is the bombardment induced re-emission which causes the apparent reduction in trapping efficiency.

The observations by Smeaton, Carter and Leck,[95] using the static pump down technique, also showed that the recovery rate was proportional to the quantity of gas trapped, up to about 1/10th the saturation quantity and that the form of the recovery curve could be expressed approximately by $\log\left(-\frac{dn}{dt}\right) = m \log t + D$ for recovery times between 10 secs and 10^3 secs, but for shorter and longer times the slope of the characteristic (m) changed. Of greater significance, however, was that the form of the characteristic, (values of m and D,) depended upon the manner in which a given quantity was trapped before recovery commenced. Thus if the same quantity of gas was trapped by pumping for different times and varying the initial pumping pressure or ionising current, the release curves could be quite different. In addition the quantity of gas recoverable by release was also a function of the bombardment conditions of pressure and time and was found to vary between 1% and 30% depending upon these parameters. Such wide variations have also been reported by the other investigators and are therefore presumably attributable to the differing bombardment conditions. These facts led immediately to the conclusion that the recovery characteristic depended not only upon the total dose to the trapping surfaces but upon the individual parameters of dose rate and bombardment times which was not unreasonable if recovery was the result of a diffusion controlled mechanism.

All the static pump down experiments involve a time varying bombardment rate, so that although the same quantities of gas may be trapped in similar static experiments the bombardment rates and times may be quite different, leading to variations in the recovery characteristics. Consequently it is believed that the later work by Smeaton et al[96] and by Cavaleru, Comsa and Iosifescu,[91,92] using dynamic bombardment conditions leads to more meaningful results. In these experiments the gas pressure was maintained constant during trapping so that the surface bombardment rate was also kept constant. It was not possible to determine directly the total quantity of gas trapped in these experiments although it appears that this is not the important parameter determining recovery but the bombardment rate, time and dose. In Smeaton et al's[96] investigations the results for 250 eV He^+, A^+ and Xe^+ ions on Pyrex glass surfaces at 20°C were qualitatively similar and it is only necessary to summarise the results for A^+ ions. If trapping was performed for a fixed period of time (between 1 and 1000 minutes) but at increasing pressures (surface bombardment rates) the recovery rate at any time during recovery was also observed to increase, initially as a linear function of bombardment rate but finally a saturation limit obtained as shown in Figure 8.27. These logarithmic recovery rate/

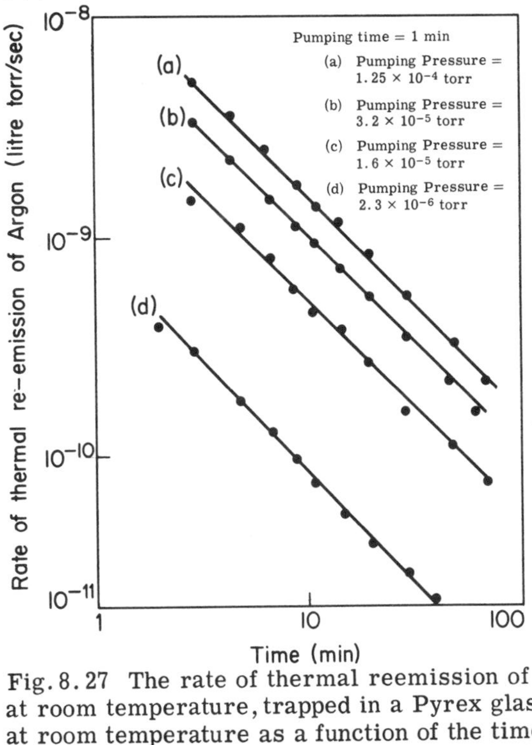

Fig. 8.27 The rate of thermal reemission of A, at room temperature, trapped in a Pyrex glass at room temperature as a function of the time after cessation of trapping for various initial A^+ ion bombardment rates of the glass (viz. Ref. 8.96 and Smeaton G. P. private communication)

time curves also exhibit the characteristic feature of linearity extending from short recovery times to long recovery times (>1 hour) i.e. the curves can be described by equations of the form $\log\left(-\frac{dn}{dt}\right) = m \log t + C$.

The index m was found to vary between about −0.3 and −1.0 according to the bombardment rate, the value of m increasing with increasing bombardment rate to a saturation value. In addition $|m|$ was observed to decrease with increasing bombardment time t_p at any given bombardment rate, again to a saturation value after large values of t_p, and this dependence of $|m|$ upon B and t_p is shown in Figure 8.28. The recovery rate also diminished for long trapping times at any bombardment rate. Figure 8.27 shows that for a pumping time of 10 minutes at a surface bombardment rate of about 3×10^{11} ions/cm^2/sec, the initial recovery rate was of the order of 3×10^9 atoms/cm^2/sec but this fell rapidly until after 100 minutes recovery the rate was reduced by two orders of magnitude.

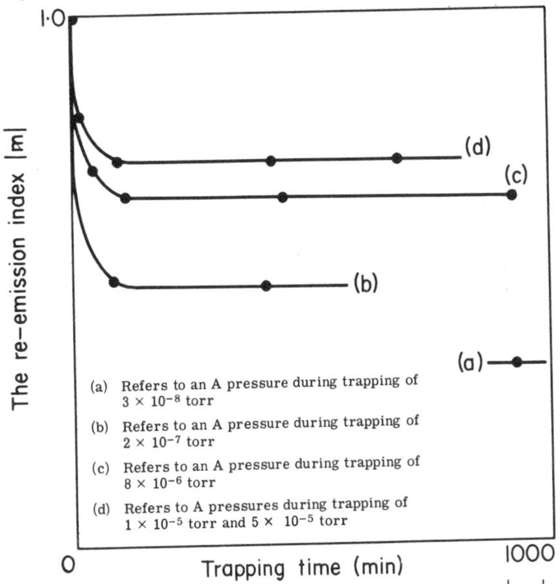

Fig. 8.28 The thermal re-emission index $|m|$, (slope of thermal re-emission rate/re-emission time curves as in Fig. 8.27) as a function of the time of bombardment of 250 eV A^+ ions on a Pyrex glass surface at room temperature for different, constant, argon pressures (and thus bombardment rates) during bombardment (viz. Ref. 8.96)

Similar experiments by Cavaleru et al[91,92] showed qualitatively similar results but these authors preferred to exhibit their recovery characteristics as a function of time semi logarithmically and interpreted the data as showing a recovery of the form $-\frac{dn}{dt} = A \exp(-at) + B \exp(-bt)$. However their data has been replotted logarithmically and shows similar characteristic form to the data of Smeaton et al,[96] with a re-emission index $\simeq -1.1$, obtained for a surface bombardment rate of 3×10^{10} ions/cm^2/sec for a period of 5 mins. Comparison of the index with the curves of Figure shows quite adequate agreement. One can also approximately compare the static pump down index of 0.5 obtained by Blodgett and Vanderslice[87] since this was only attained after trapping was carried to 'saturation' involving pumping for long periods (1000 minutes) at the final bombardment rate which was approximately constant (4×10^9 ions/cm^2/sec). This index is approximately the result anticipated from Figure 8.28 and we should also recall that Blodgett and Vanderslice[87] measured larger values of m for non saturation conditions where the bombardment rate was higher.

On the other hand, Maddix et al[21-23] have measured quite unequivocal −0.5 index recovery curves after trapping large quantities of different inert gases in quartz, and in view of these large trapped quantities and this time dependence we should ascribe their results to a normal diffusion process induced by the relatively high target temperatures.

Some measurements of recovery characteristics have also been reported for inert gas ions trapped in metal targets, namely He,[29] Ne, A, Kr[81] in Ni and Mo surfaces and again the majority of this work was carried out using a static pumping technique and therefore a time varying bombardment rate. However it appeared that in these materials the form of the recovery curve was unaffected by these variable conditions and that for release times between 1 and 1000 minutes the recovery rate/time curve was adequately expressed by $-\frac{dn}{dt} = K\frac{n_o}{t}$ for $1 \text{ min} < t < 1,000$ mins where n_o was the quantity of gas initially trapped and t the time following commencement of recovery. This dependence upon n_o and t was followed up to equivalent surface coverages of trapped gas of about 0.01 monolayers (~1/10th of the saturation value) but at n_o values approaching saturation the dependence of the recovery rate upon n_o also approached a saturation value, whilst the time dependence departed from a simple $m = -1$ relation. Figure 8.29 shows a typical recovery curve and Table 8.7 gives values for the constant K derived for He^+ ions of different energies trapped in Ni targets by Varnerin and Carmichael[29] and for 100 eV, He, Ne, A and Kr ions trapped in Ni and Mo targets by Carmichael and Knoll.[81] These values were obtained for target temperatures in the region of 300°C but similar data for Ni surface cooled in liquid nitrogen[86] showed complex dependence of the recovery rate upon n_o and t.

As with the data for glass these re-emission data were limited to recovery times greater than 1 minute after the commencement of recovery because of experimental difficulties associated with measurement of recovery before this time. However Fox and Knoll[49] improved this time resolution by increasing the sensitivity of the pressure monitoring device, so that recovery times down to about 1 second were observable. In addition these authors approached more nearly the desirable feature of constant bombardment rate, since although using a static system, the bombardment was pulsed for short periods so that the pressure drop and thus the change in bombardment rate was minimised. These investigators were then able to show that the recovery characteristic $-\frac{dn}{dt} = \frac{Kn_o}{t}$ for A^+ ions in Ni was also obeyed for t values as small as 1 second, provided that the trapping period t_p was small compared to the recovery interval measured, i.e. if trapping was performed for 1 second the $m = -1$ index was only observed for recovery times greater than about five seconds. For shorter recovery times the index appeared to approach 0. This means that a finite re-emission rate occurs at $t = 0$ whereas a t^{-1} dependence predicts an infinite release rate at $t = 0$. The values of K deduced from these short time studies were the same as those obtained for longer recovery times by Varnerin and Carmichael[29] and Carmichael and Knoll[81] and indicate that recovery is conditioned by the same

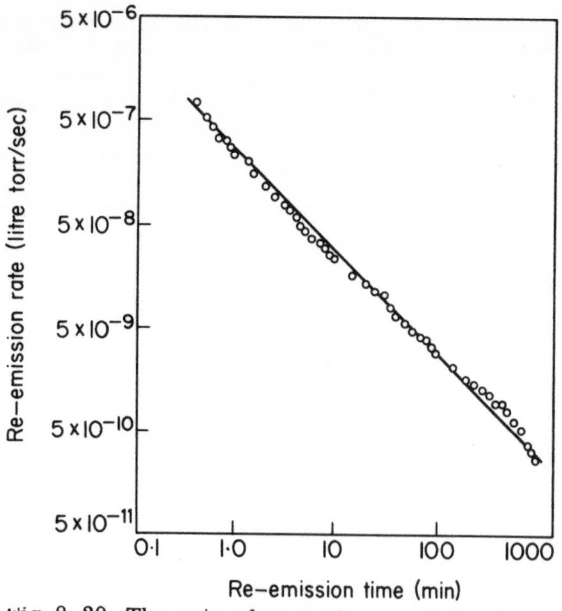

Fig. 8.29 The rate of re-emission of Kr atoms, trapped at 100 eV in a Ni surface, as a function of the time after cessation of trapping (viz. Ref, 8.81

TABLE 8.7. (Refs. 8.29 and 8.81).

Values of K for inert gas ions incident on Ni and Mo targets.

Ion	K × 100
Helium	4.4 ± 1.8.
Neon	5.2 ± 4.6
Argon	.57 ± .07
Krypton	.32 ± .16

Molybdenum Target. (100 eV ions).

Ion	K × 100
Helium	1.3 ± .05
Neon	4.0 ± .3
Argon	15 ± 5
Krypton	14 ± 1
Helium (1100 eV)	0.59
Helium (2100 eV)	0.43

process over the whole range of recovery times. In addition the quantity of trapped gas recovered was observed to increase with decreasing trapping time, and for very short bombardment pulses (< 1 sec) as much as 90% of the trapped gas was recovered. It thus appears legitimate to summarize the data for glass and metals by the statement; Rate of gas recovery $\propto \frac{n_o}{t^m}$ for values of n_o up to 1/10th saturation and for $1 < t < 10,000$ sec. The value of m depending upon the actual bombardment conditions.

8.7.4 Trapped gas can also be recovered at temperatures different from that obtaining during bombardment, in particular, increasing the target temperature leads to greatly accelerated re-emission of gas and restores the pre bombardment target conditions. Schwarz first reported this process qualitatively for A^+ ions trapped in glass and Dushman and Carter summarized other qualitative results. Subsequently Carter and Leck[15,16], James and Carter[20,42,43] and Grant and Carter[18] made quantitative measurements on the release rate of trapped inert gas ions from glass surfaces. In these, gas atoms were initially trapped in the glass envelopes of Bayard-Alpert gauges, and the release of this trapped gas was subsequently observed as the envelopes were heated at a constant rate (≃40°C/minute) to about 450°C. A typical recovery transient for 250 eV A^+ ions trapped in glass is shown in Figure 8.30 where the instantaneous release rate is exhibited as a function of the temperature of the glass. The characteristic features of this curve are (1) Release commences at, or just above, the temperature of the glass during bombardment. (2) The release rate reaches a maximum at about 200-250°C and (3) The release rate then falls to zero at temperatures between 350°C and 450°C. By using a static system it could be established that such a desorption cycle generally resulted in recovery of all the previously trapped gas except in the cases of He and Xe ions which apparently required temperatures in excess of 450°C to recover all trapped gas completely (perhaps 10-20% remaining above this temperature). Factors which influenced the precise shape of the recovery transient were[20, 42, 43]

(a) The nature of the trapped gas

(b) The energy of the bombarding ions

(c) The quantity of gas trapped.

Of these parameters, (c) exerted least influence and caused the transient to shift slightly to higher temperatures, i.e. proportionally more release at higher temperatures so that maximum release rate also occurred at higher temperatures. The dependence upon (a) was not fully investigated but the results suggested, and this was confirmed by Grant and Carter,[18] narrow and lower temperature peaks for helium and neon although a considerable tail persisted to high temperatures, a wider peak for Argon as shown in Figure 8.31 and a wider peak still for Xe with a broad high temperature tail. Increasing the ion energy was found to progressively broaden the peak as shown in Figure 8.32 for A^+ ions with energies between 100 eV and 1 keV, and for the higher energies and for Xe it is probable that all gas is not recovered by heating to 450°C only. There was no evidence to suggest that the peak shape and the temperature at maximum rate were significantly dependent upon the heating rate. A further observation was that if, during heating, the temperature was maintained constant at any stage, the gas release fell rapidly to zero. If the glass was then cooled to room temperature and heating re-commenced, no further gas release occurred until the temperature was about the same as that which the release rate had originally fallen to zero. Again, Carter,[27] and Hobson and Edmonds[116] have noted that if the glass is cooled below room temperature during bombardment then gas release occurs immediately upon warming up above the bombardment temperature and continues above room temperature as before.

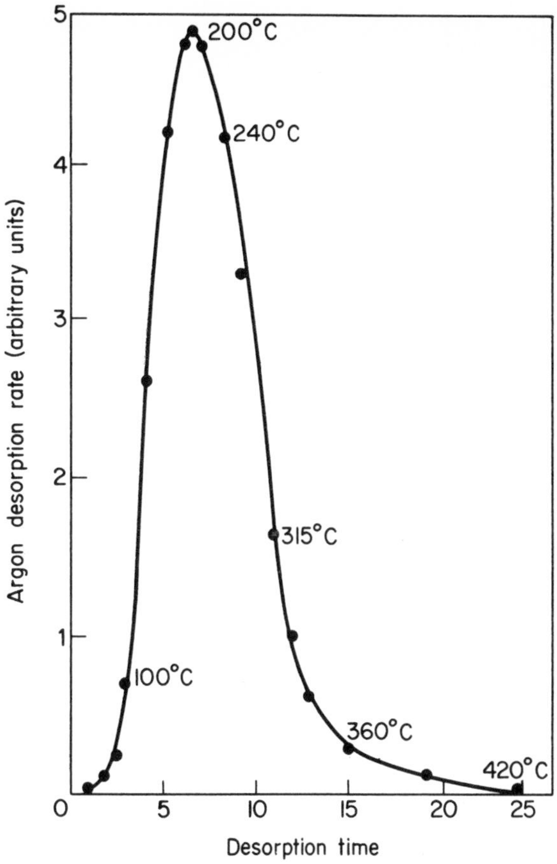

Fig. 8.30 Typical desorption transient for A^+ ions trapped at 250 eV in a Pyrex glass surface. The desorption rate is plotted as a function of time during heating and appropriate temperatures are indicated (viz. Refs. 8.15 and 8.16)

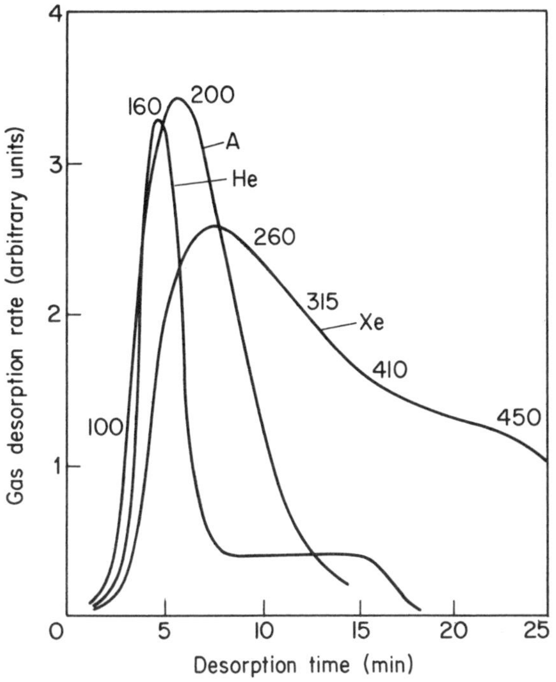

Fig. 8.31 Typical desorption transients for He^+, A^+ and Xe^+ ions trapped at 250 eV in a Pyrex glass surface. The desorption rate is plotted as a function of time during heating and appropriate temperatures are indicated (viz. Ref. 8.38)

A considerable amount of similar work has been reported for metal targets by Kornelsen,[71, 72] Colligon and Leck[70] and others. Kornelsen[72] bombarded polycrystalline W with inert gas ions from Ne to Xe with ion energies between 60 eV and 4 keV and subsequently released the trapped gas by heating at an approximately constant rate of 66°K/second to 2400°K. Typical release transients for Ne and Xe are shown in Figure 8.33a, b which reveal multiple peak structure for all ion energies. Again the relative amplitude of the peaks depended upon the three parameters mentioned for glass surfaces as can be seen from Figure 8.34a and from Figure 8.34b which shows the variation of the spectrum with number of

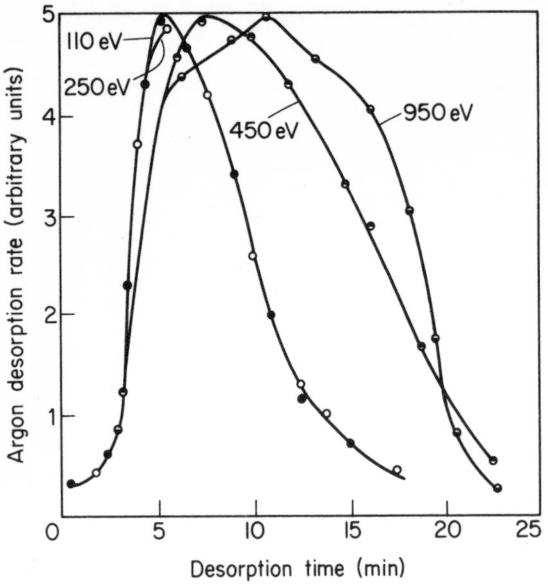

Fig. 8.32 Typical desorption transients for A^+ ions trapped at 110 ev, 250 ev, 450 ev and 950 ev in a Pyrex Glass Surface. The desorption rate is plotted as a function of time during heating. Temperature scales correspond to those in Figs. 8.30 and 8.31. (viz. Rev. 8.43)

ions trapped for 400 eV Ne and 500 eV Xe. One feature which is apparent from Figure 8.33, and is also valid for A^+ and Kr^+ ions, was that only the lower temperature peaks are well populated for low energies (of the order of the threshold sticking energy) labelled by Kornelsen[72] peaks a–d since there were four definable peaks). Whilst at higher energies two further peaks e and f appeared at higher temperatures and became preferentially populated.

One of the most interesting features of the results was that the temperatures at which the lower temperature peaks occurred were almost independent of the nature of both the bombarding ion species and ion energy suggesting that migration of target atoms was instrumental in effecting gas release, but that the temperatures for release of the e and f peaks increase slightly with increasing ion energy. Figure 8.34 shows that the relative population of the lower temperature (α) and higher temperature (β) groups of peaks increases in opposite ways for increasing doses of Ne or Kr ions. The increasing relative population of the β peaks for Ne was believed to be due to knock on effects causing trapped Ne to be impelled deeper into the target and the increasing relative population of the α peaks for Kr was believed to be caused by an increase in the stopping power of the Kr containing surface layers.

As with the investigations with glass, the positions of the peaks did not appear to vary with the rate of heating of the W.

Kornelsen[72] also performed a release experiment in conjunction with an electrolytic stripping technique and found that whereas the normal range profile existed before heating to 2400°K (c.f. the data of McCargo et al[73] in Figure 5.77a) and that 50% of trapped 10 keV Kr^+ ions resided within 20 lattice constants from the surface, after heating, the concentration profile changed remarkably so that only 0.1% of any remaining gas was within this surface layer but a much larger fraction than previously was located deeply in the target, Figure 8.35 showing this behaviour. This reveals that heating also causes diffusion of trapped gas into the target.

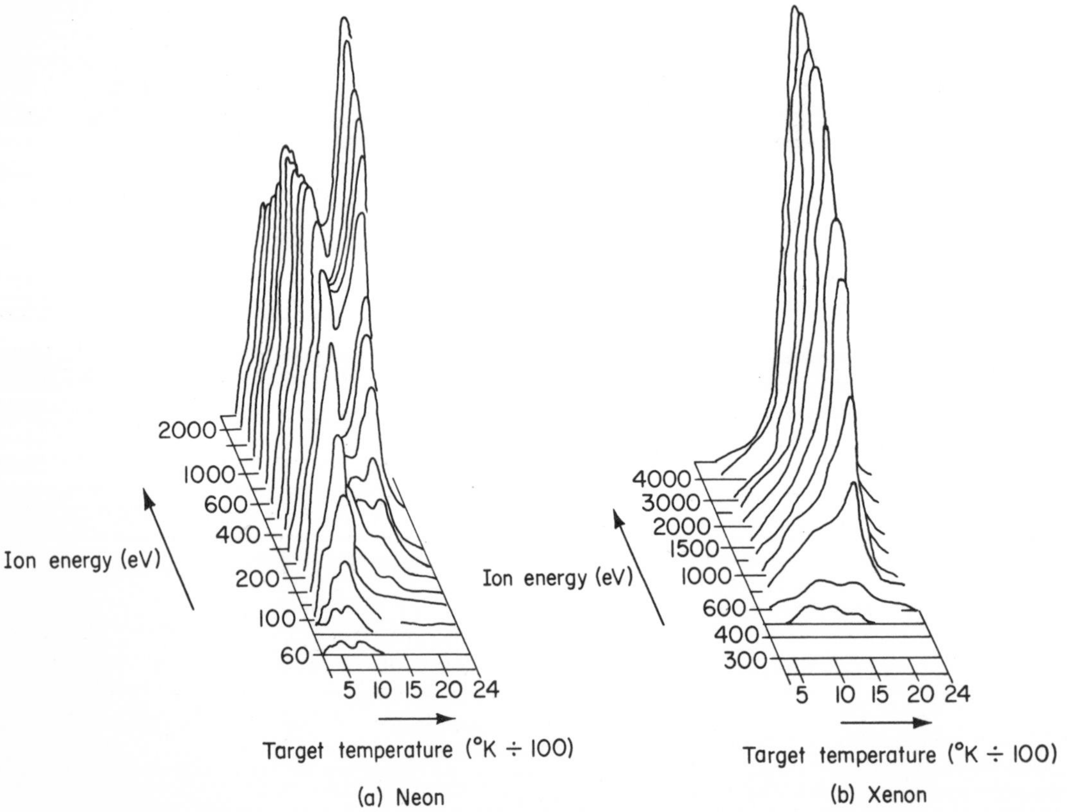

Fig. 8.33 Desorption spectra of Neon and Xenon from polycrystalline tungsten. Desorption rate is plotted as a function of temperature for various ion energies (viz. Ref. 8.72)

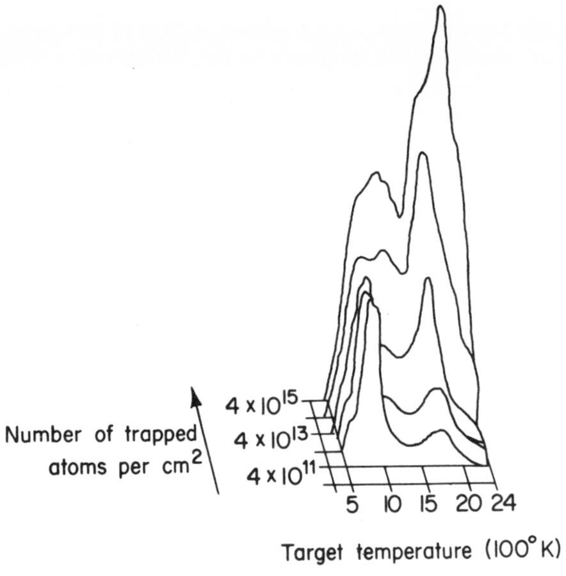

(a) 400 eV Ne^+ ions

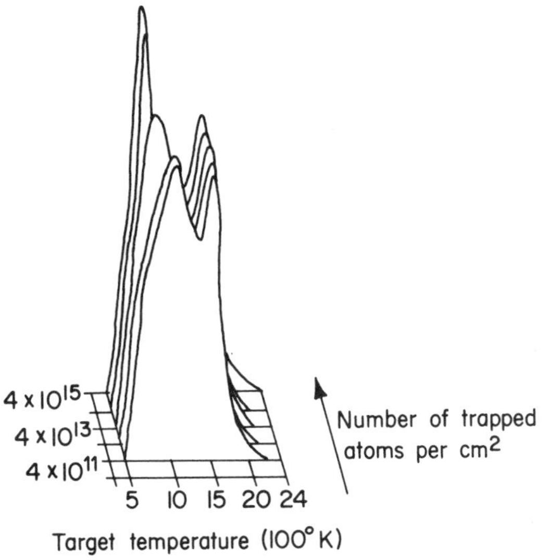

(b) 500 eV Kr^+ ions

Fig. 8. 34 Desorption spectra of 400 eV Ne^+ and 500 eV Kr^+ ions from polycrystalline tungsten for various numbers of atoms trapped per unit area. Desorption rate is plotted as a function of temperature (viz. Ref. 8. 72)

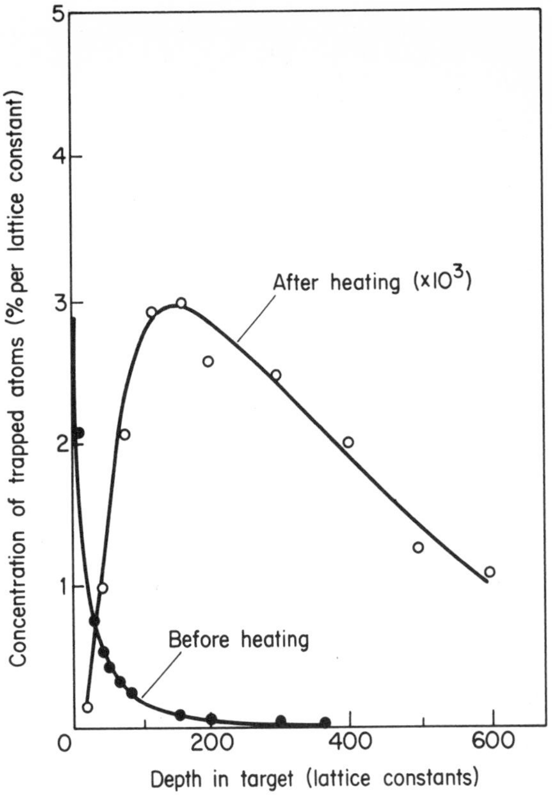

Fig. 8. 35 The concentration of 10 keV Kr^+ ions trapped in polycrystalline tungsten as a function of depth in the target, before and after heating the target to 2400°K (viz. Ref. 8. 72)

Kornelsen[199,200] has recently reported similar data using single crystal tungsten targets with the ions striking well defined surface planes. As in the case of the polycrystalline targets, peaks were again noted for all ion species from Ne to Xe but there appeared to be distinct temperature differences for the peaks of each ion whilst the surface plane bombarded exerted considerable influence. Thus bombardment of a (100) surface resulted in four or five peaks whilst bombardment of a (112) surface exhibited seven or eight peaks at different temperatures. This suggests that polycrystalline samples exhibit composite patterns of all exposed faces.

Erents and Carter[201] have also studied the thermal desorption of He^+ ions injected into polycrystalline tungsten at energies between 100 eV and 3 keV. The release energies for these ions were again similar to those for the heavier inert gases suggesting again that it is a property of the tungsten which effects gas release. An interesting feature of this work and of Kornelsen was that for very low ion energies (100 eV He^+ and Ne^+), where the maximum energy transfer to tungsten atoms is very small (<10 eV for He ions), the peak structure was still maintained. It would appear impossible to produce even the simplest damage (Frenkel pairs) in such cases and so some at least of this lower temperature gas release must be associated with migration in normal tungsten rather than in radiation damaged material.

Burtt et al[69] and Colligon and Leck[70] performed similar thermal release experiments for several inert gas ions on W, but observed the total fractional release of gas following 100°K increases in temperature up to 2000°K. Data obtained by this method can be summed to give the total gas release up to any temperature and the resulting histogram smoothed and differentiated to give release rate/temperature profiles. Unfortunately the size of the temperature steps results in lack of resolution of the peak structure, but, as in the work of Kornelsen[72], envelopes of groups of closely spaced peaks were found, as shown in Figure 8. 36 for A in W. Relative variations in the amplitude of these peaks was also observed for variations in the ion mass, from Ne to Xe and for ion energies of 700 eV to 4. 0 keV.

Measurements were also made with Mo and Pt targets and the peak structures again observed. In the case of Pt it appeared that considerable gas evolution occurred right up to the melting temperature so that there would be some unreliability in determining quantities of gas trapped by this method unless the target was fused.

If a target bombarded with one ion species was then bombarded with a second species and the thermal

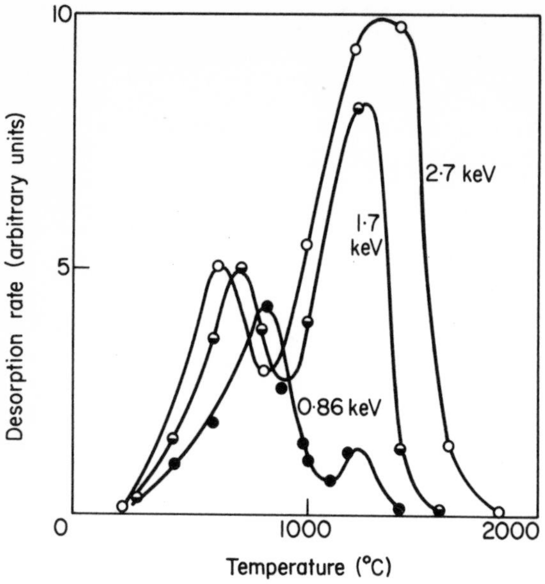

Fig. 8.36 The rate of desorption of Argon as a function of temperature after injection at 0.86 keV, 1.7 keV and 2.7 keV into polycrystalline tungsten (viz. Ref. 8.69)

release of the first species subsequently studied, it was observed that part of the release spectrum of that gas had been removed, generally in the region where the second ion species was normally found.

Tucker and Norton[117] observed the release of 40 keV A^+ ions trapped in Ag, Au, Al and Pb and Kr^+ ions trapped in Ur[118], during continuous heating of the targets. Again multiple peak structures were observed and in metals such as Au, Al and Pb, considerable gas evolution occurred at and above the melting temperature. In all metals some evolution occurred below the melting temperatures, in Au and Pb there was a more or less continuous, but small evolution from 100°C up to their respective melting temperatures. In Ag however, there were broad release peaks at 180°C, 680°C and 860°C with a roughly constant release rate from 200°C to 500°C and very little release above the melting temperature. In Al, large peaks occurred at 470°C and 500°C as well as considerable release above the melting temperature. There was clearly a relationship to the nature of the target, since, for example two groups of peaks associated with the release of Kr^+ ions from Ur, are below the α–β phase transition and the other group in the β–γ phase regions. In this material it was notable that for low heating rates ($\sim$3°K/min) most gas release occurred between 700°K and 1000°K (β and γ phases) but for higher rates ($\sim$9°K/min) most of the release occurred below 700°K suggesting that in some metals at least, gas atom motion and release is conditioned by phase transformations and the rate at which they proceed.

Ivanovskii and Rhadzabov[75] have also measured the thermal desorption of 2.5 keV A^+ ions trapped in Ti films. They find two peaks in the desorption spectrum, at 300°C and $\sim$500°C, but that there is also a continuous release of gas up to 1100°C. If the Ti film was continuously deposited during bombardment, then subsequent thermal desorption showed that a larger fraction of gas was released in the 500°C $\rightarrow$ 1000°C range although the peaks at lower temperatures were retained. This certainly suggests that the low temperature peaks are associated with near surface gas and that the higher temperature release arises from diffusion of more deeply penetrating ions, since simultaneous growth of the film during bombardment will give rise to a larger fraction of gas located more deeply from the final surface.

Kelly[50, 51] also obtained evidence of the importance of the target structure in determining the release of trapped gas from metals and metallic oxides. In one set of experiments Argon and Xenon gas were irradiated with neutrons in the presence of Nb, Nb_2O_5, SiO_2, and TiO_2 targets in powder or rod form (n, γ) reactions took place and recoiling gas atoms became imbedded in the targets. The targets were then heated in 100°C steps from 50°C to 1000°C and the fraction of gas recovered at each temperature step recorded, i.e. an integral method of recovery. Because of the rather large temperature increments it is not justifiable to attempt differentiation of the fractional release/temperature curves, example of which are shown for A and Xe in TiO_2 in Figure 8.37 to obtain release rate/

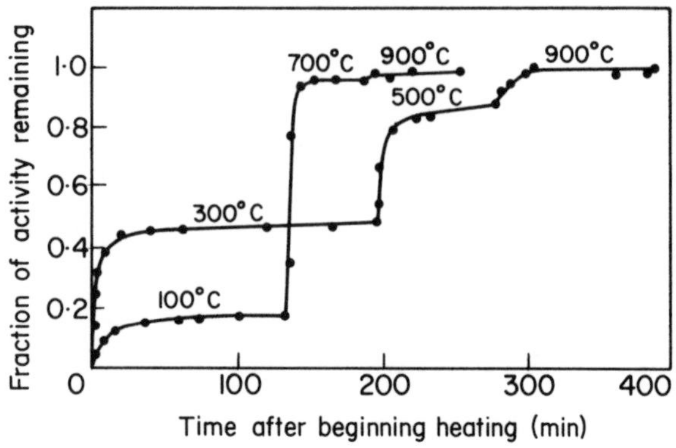

Fig. 8.37 Release of ^{125}Xe activity which had become "attached" to TiO_2 powder following (n, γ) events in the Xe gas, as a function of time during heating. Two typical experiments are shown, where the temperatures are raised rapidly to several constant values (shown on the plateaux) (viz. Ref. 8.50)

temperature functions. It is evident from this Figure however that release continued more or less uniformly up to about 600°C after which a smaller quantity was recovered. Similar results were obtained for all the other systems investigated and there was little apparent difference between the release of trapped A and Xe.

Subsequently Kelly and Brown[119, 120, 121] irradiated Al, Al_2O_3, Ta, Ta_2O_5, Ag and Au targets with Xe^+ ions from an accelerator with energies between 200 eV and 40 keV and also, through use of the above nuclear reaction method, achieved low energies (<1 keV) and again studied the integral release/temperature behaviour. Typical release curves for Al and Al_2O_3 are shown in Figure 8.38 and for Ta and Ta_2O_5 in Figure 8.39, for Ag in Figure 8.40 and Au in Figure 8.41.

The general characteristics of these curves are as follows:- For low incident ion energies (<4 keV) there is a considerable proportion of the gas released continuously below 500°C, for all targets except Al (in stage I). Further gas is released between this temperature and the melting temperature, this fraction becoming of increasing importance as both the ion energy and the quantity of gas trapped are increased. In Ta, Ag and Au two temperature intervals (stages II and III) over which different fractions of gas are released are also discernible (e.g. in Ta, 600°C-800°C

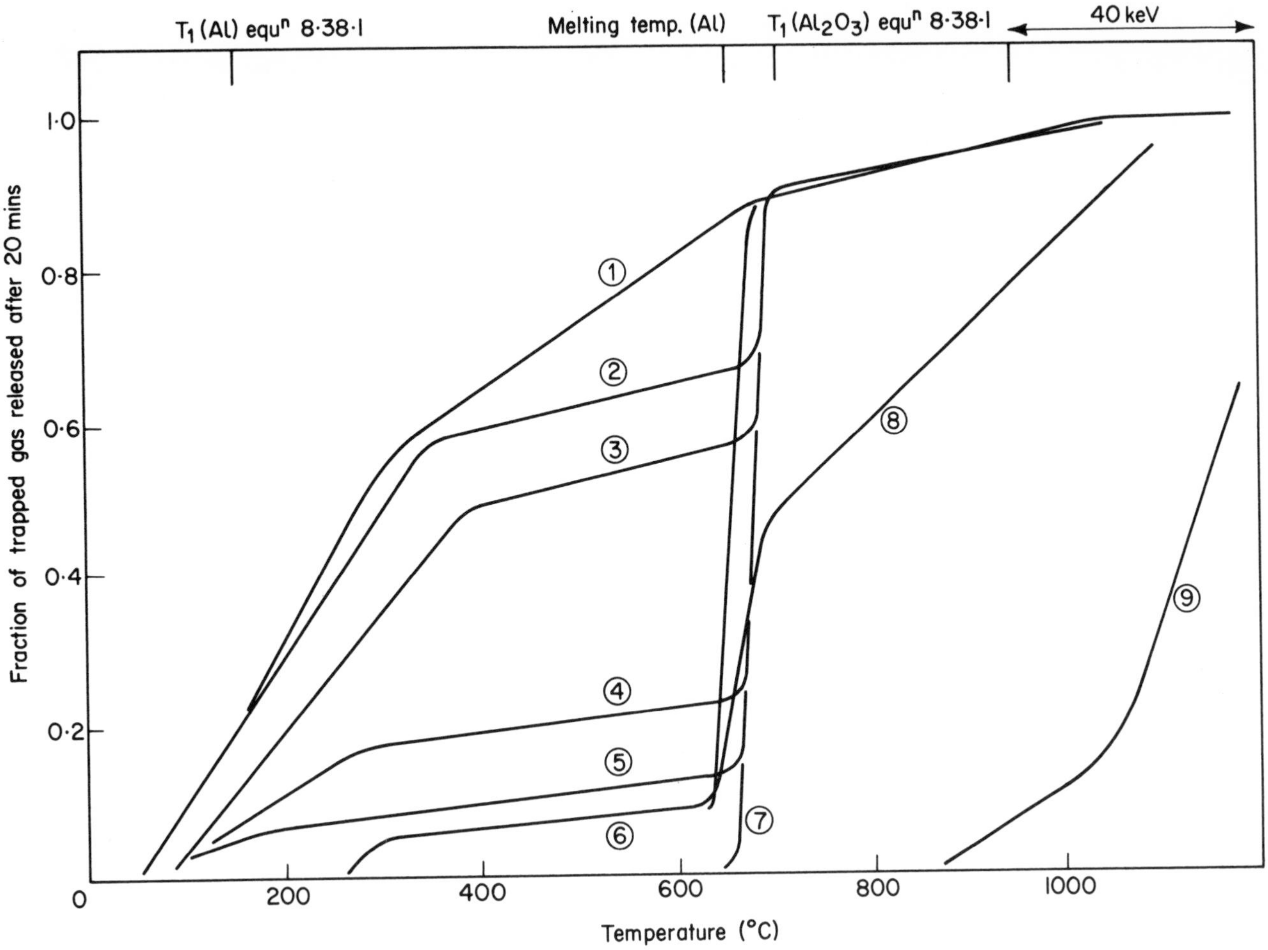

Fig. 8. 38 Fraction of Xe^+ ions trapped in Al (powder and sheet) and Al_2O_3 (Powder, Sapphire) released after 20 mins at the temperatures shown (viz. Ref. 8. 121)

Key to Fig. 8. 38
Curve (1) Corresponds to Xe "attached" to Al_2O_3 powder following (n, γ) events.
Curve (2) Corresponds to 0. 5 keV Xe^+ ions ($\sim 4 \times 10^{13}$ ions/cm^2) injected into Al sheet.
Curve (3) Corresponds to Xe "attached" to Al powder following (n, γ) events.
Curve (4) Corresponds to 1. 0 keV Xe^+ ions ($\sim 4 \times 10^{13}$ ions/cm^2) injected into Al sheet.
Curve (5) Corresponds to 2. 5 kev Xe^+ ions ($\sim 4 \times 10^{13}$ ions/cm^2) injected into Al sheet.
Curve (6) Corresponds to 40 kev Xe^+ ions ($\sim 4 \times 10^{13}$ ions/cm^2) injected into Al sheet (apparent "burn mark" on Al)
Curve (7) Corresponds to 19 and 40 kev Xe^+ ions ($\sim 4 \times 10^{11}$ ions/cm^2 and $\sim 4 \times 10^{13}$ ions/cm^2 respectively) injected into Al sheet.
Curve (8) Corresponds to 40 kev Xe^+ ions ($\sim 4 \times 10^{13}$ ions/cm^2) injected in Al sheet (target exposed to 1 torr of air during heating)
Curve (9) Corresponds to 40 kev Xe^+ ions ($\sim 4 \times 10^{13}$ ions/cm^2) injected into Al_2O_3 (sapphire).
T_1 is the temperature at which 10% of trapped gas should be released according to Equa 8. 38. 1 assuming appropriate values for the diffusion energy in Al and Al_2O_3

and 800°C-1000°C). The higher temperature interval containing higher proportions of trapped gas as the total quantity of gas trapped is increased. In all targets stage II is apparent to some extent, again depending upon the ion energy and trapped gas dose. Finally, at and above, the target melting temperature stage IV gas release occurs with Al (to a smaller extent with Au targets) but not at all with Al_2O_3. In the case of Al, the release near the melting temperature was associated with fragmentation of a surface oxide layer allowing simultaneous release of trapped gas. The contamination of the Al surface with oil and carbon films during bombardment also led to a considerable release of Xe at 300°C rather than at the melting temperature and Kelly and Brown[119] suggest this as a possible reason for the difference in the quantities released at the melting temperature observed in their own and in Tucker and Norton's[117] work. In addition there was an extra release in Ta preoxidised at about 500°C which was associated with oxide dissolution. The release at the melting temperature in the case of Au was also considerably less than observed by Tucker and Norton[117] for A^+ ions.

Although we will discuss the interpretation of these results in full shortly, we may point out that Kelly and Brown[119, 121] suggested that gas release in stage II was the result of normal gas diffusional migration, in stage I it was the result of migration along lower energy paths than normally associated with diffusion and produced by radiation damage effects and that in stage III, the agglomeration of gas atoms to form bubbles and their migration caused gas release.

Kelly and Matzke[122, 123] later extended these measurements to studies of gas release of 5 and 9 keV Kr^+ ions and α recoil radon and fission recoil Xenon

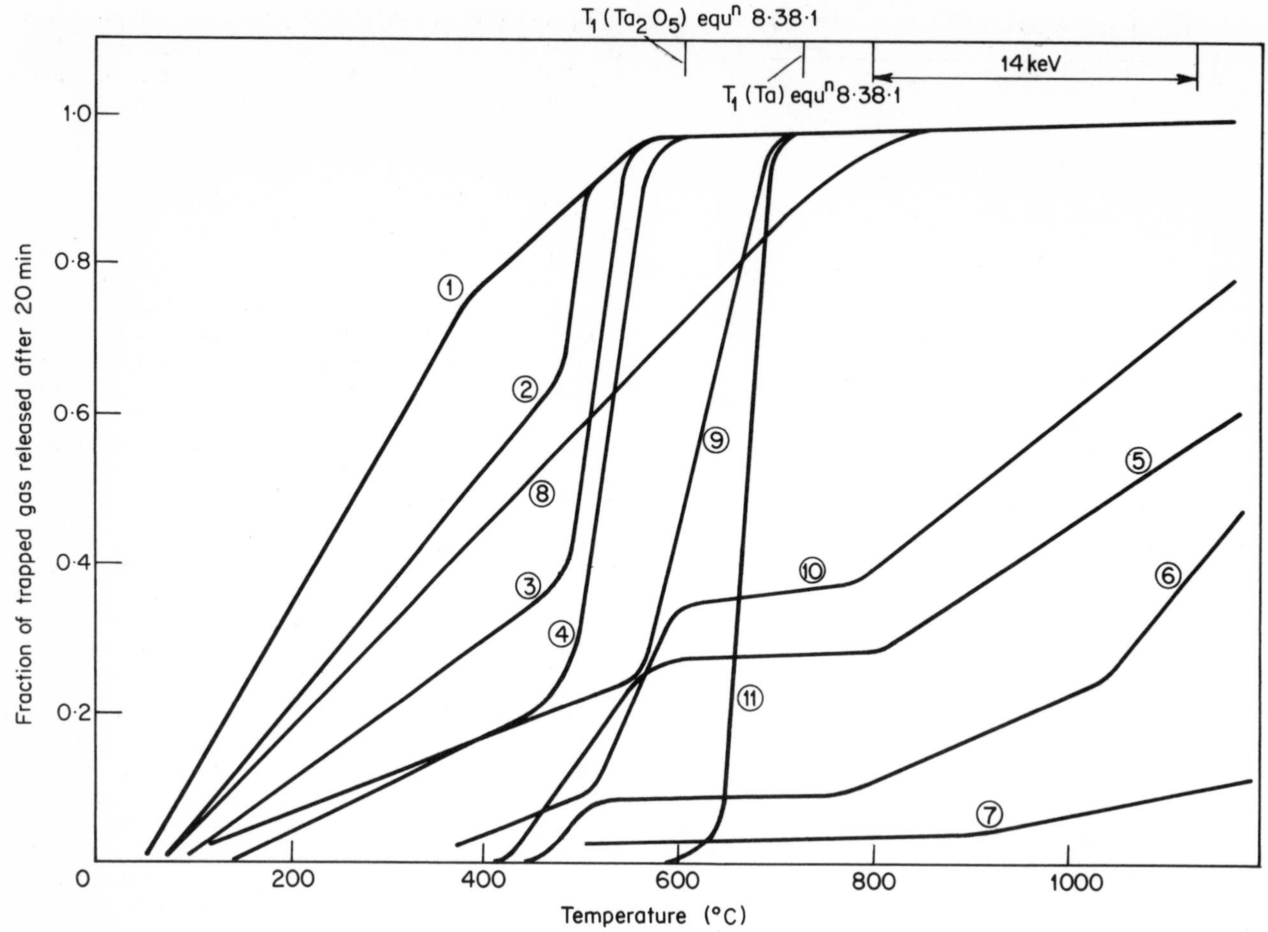

Fig. 8. 39 Fraction of Xe^+ ions trapped in Ta (powder and sheet) and Ta_2O_5 (powder and an anodic layer on Ta) released after 20 mins at the temperatures shown (viz. Ref. 8. 121)

Key to Fig. 8. 39
Curve (1) Corresponds to Xe "attached" to Ta powder following (n, γ) events
Curve (2) Corresponds to 0. 2 kev Xe^+ ions ($\sim 4 \times 10^{13}$ ions/cm^2) injected into Ta sheet
Curve (3) Corresponds to 0. 5 kev Xe^+ ions ($\sim 4 \times 10^{13}$ ions/cm^2) injected into Ta sheet
Curve (4) Corresponds to 1. 0 kev Xe^+ ions ($\sim 4 \times 10^{13}$ ions/cm^2) injected into Ta sheet
Curve (5) Corresponds to 14 kev Xe^+ ions ($\sim 4 \times 10^{13}$ ions/cm^2) injected into Ta sheet
Curve (6) Corresponds to 40 kev Xe^+ ions ($\sim 4 \times 10^{13}$ ions/cm^2) injected into Ta sheet
Curve (7) Corresponds to 40 kev Xe^+ ions ($\sim 2 \times 10^{16}$ ions/cm^2) injected into Ta sheet
Curve (8) Corresponds to Xe "attached" to Ta_2O_5 powder following (n, γ) events
Curve (9) Corresponds to 1. 0 kev Xe^+ ions ($\sim 4 \times 10^{13}$ ions/cm^2) injected into Ta_2O_5 anodic film.
Curve (10) Corresponds to 40 kev Xe^+ ions ($\sim 4 \times 10^{13}$ ions/cm^2) injected into Ta_2O_5 anodic film (target exposed to 1 torr air during heating)
Curve (11) Corresponds to 40 kev Xe^+ ions ($\sim 4 \times 10^{13}$ ions/cm^2) injected into Ta_2O_5 anodic film

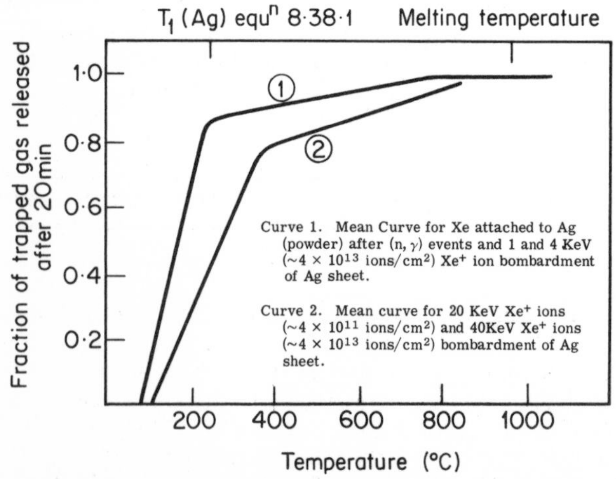

Fig. 8. 40 Fraction of Xe^+ ions trapped in Ag (powder & sheet) released after 20 mins at the temperatures shown (viz. Ref. 8. 121)

injected into single crystal CaF_2, BaF_2, UO_2, KCl and α-Al_2O_3 and sintered ThO_2 and ThO_2-UO_2. In CaF_2 evidence of both stage I damage induced and stage II normal diffusion were found and a similar result, with a preponderance of stage II normal diffusion release was observed in BaF_2, UO_2 and ThO_2 and ThO_2-UO_2 mixtures also evidenced considerable normal diffusion with a small stage I component whilst KCl showed a small stage I diffusion component. α-Al_2O_3 also shows evidence of both components and damage processes are most important at low bombardment energies. In none of the above materials was it possible to unequivocally identify a stage III release process with the formation and migration of gas bubbles but in several cases this could be partly explained by the rather low temperatures at which the materials evaporate rapidly and so the gas escapes with the solid rather than aggregating.

Brown and Matzke[124] also studied gas release of 40 keV Xe^+ ions up to a dose of 10^{10} ions/cm^2 from

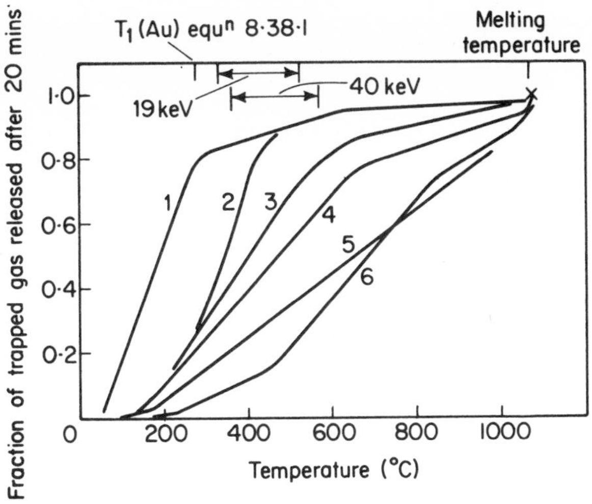

Fig. 8. 41 Fraction of Xe^+ ions trapped in Au sheet released after 20 mins at the temperatures shown (viz. Ref. 8. 121)

Key to Fig. 8. 41
Curve (1) Corresponds to 1. 0 kev Xe^+ ions ($\sim 4 \times 10^{13}$ ions/cm^2) injected into Au sheet
Curve (2) Corresponds to 4. 0 kev Xe^+ ions ($\sim 4 \times 10^{31}$ ions/cm^2) injected into Au sheet
Curve (3) Corresponds to 14. 0 kev Xe^+ ions ($\sim 4 \times 10^{13}$ ions/cm^2) injected into Au sheet
Curve (4) Corresponds to 19. 0 kev Xe^+ ions ($\sim 4 \times 10^{11}$ ions/cm^2) injected into Au sheet
Curve (5) Corresponds to 37. 0 kev Xe^+ ions ($\sim 4 \times 10^{13}$ ions/cm^2) injected into Au sheet
Curve (6) Corresponds to 40. 0 kev Xe^+ ions ($\sim 4 \times 10^{13}$ ions/cm^2) injected into Au sheet

KCl, KBr, KI, NaCl, UO_2 and ThO_2 and found no evidence of stage I release but complete release in stage II. On the other hand MgO and CaF_2 bombarded crystals revealed both stages I and II recovery and low energy electron diffraction studies of the surface showed no observable damage for the former six materials but considerable damage in the latter two materials which annealed out during stage I recovery. The fact that the former materials are all of the B.C.C. structure which tends to allow easy interstitial diffusion appears to be significant. In an attempt to determine the importance of normal diffusion processes, UO_2 was doped with La_2O_3 and Ytt_2O_3 which reduces the normal Ur diffusion coefficient and Nb_2O_5 which increases the normal Ur diffusion, before Xe ion bombardment. For low Xe bombardment doses there was very little change in stage II recovery, but for higher doses the stage II recovery was decreased and a marked stage III appeared. This suggests, as observed by Kelly and Ruedl[125, 126] that the enhanced vacancy concentration produced by the bombardment can promote bubble formation and increase stage III at the expense of stage II, but that for small normal chemical dopants there is insufficient vacancy production to enhance stage II.

Matzke and Whitton[124b] have recently attempted to further correlate the release of trapped gas from some ceramics and ionic crystals with damage induced by the injected (40 keV Kr^+ and Xe^+) ions. High energy ions were used, at doses from 8×10^{10} to 2×10^{16} ions/cm^2, so that these were trapped relatively deeply in the targets and surface effects, which may influence stage 1 recovery, were minimised. Radiation damage was explored using reflection electron diffraction (at 100 keV) and observing the patterns from the crystals, before, and after bombardment and following subsequent thermal annealing. Single crystals of NaCl, KCl, KBr, KI, MgO, CaO, NiO, CaF_2, BaF_2, UO_2, ThO_2, UC, TiO_2 and α-Al_2O_3, and sintered specimens of UO_2, ThO_2 and U_3O_8 were examined.

In the case of the cubic crystals (NaCl, KCl, KBr, KI, CaO, NiO, CaF_2, BaF_2, UO_2 and ThO_2, there was no evidence of damage up to ion doses as large as 2×10^{16} ions/cm^2, and very little injected gas was recovered (< 10%) in stage 1 (up to 0. 4 of the melting temperature which was taken to define the temperature below which no bulk diffusion would be evidenced). In Mgo and the anisotropic TiO_2, α-Al_2O_3 and U_3O_8 however there was a continued degradation in the diffraction pattern as the dose was increased up to the maximum. In all these cases also, stage I gas release was observed, whilst the prebombardment diffraction pattern was also restored, in the stage I temperature interval during annealing.

In the case of MgO, where experiments were conducted at lower energies, (down to 0. 5 keV) it was found that the gas release became more pronounced in stage I the lower the ion energy, whilst in this material, and in TiO_2, α-Al_2O_3 and U_3O_8, the proportional release of gas in stage I increased with increasing dose.

It thus appears that, in these materials which are more readily disordered by bombardment, the gas release is attendant upon subsequent thermal reordering. It is possible that diffusion in the damaged amorphous material proceeds with lower activation energies than in crystalline material and thus reordering and gas release occur in stage I. In fact, it was shown that the stage I release in these materials would be described by gas diffusion with a continuum of activation energies up to the bulk diffusion energy.

Tosic and Perovic[127] have also examined the release of Xe ions injected at various energies between 12 and 80 keV into Al, Ag and Ta targets. In none of these targets was release which could be identified with stage I observed but this is not surprising since release commenced at temperatures which could be controlled by dissolution of a surface oxide skin e.g. about 600°C in Al, 200°C in Ag and 400°C in Ta. Release extended over a further 500°C in each case however, a larger proportionate release fraction occurring at higher temperatures as the bombarding energy was increased, due it was believed to the longer path length for the diffusing ions. Further work by Jokic and Pervoic[128] with Xe ions incident on polycrystalline and single crystal copper substantiated this result and revealed a further, very interesting feature displayed in Figure 8. 42. When 40 keV Xe^+ was incident on the (110), (100) and (111) faces of single crystal copper, the post bombardment release spectrum was displaced to higher temperatures in the order written above. Since the channelling processes discussed in Chapter 5 also increase in this order it is natural to suppose that the displacement to higher temperatures is associated with deeper ion penetration, as proposed by Kelly and Brown[121].

Work by Kelly and Ruedl[125] who observed the release of 9 keV Kr^+ ions trapped in Pt foils, and also examined the damage pattern in the target electron microscopically, tended to confirm this picture of stage III migration. At low ion doses (7×10^{13} ions/cm^2) dots and loops were observed in the target and these persisted up to above 500°C during heating although a small amount of gas release occurred (~10%). In the next 150°C interval the loops and dots disappeared and 70% of the gas was released. Finally between

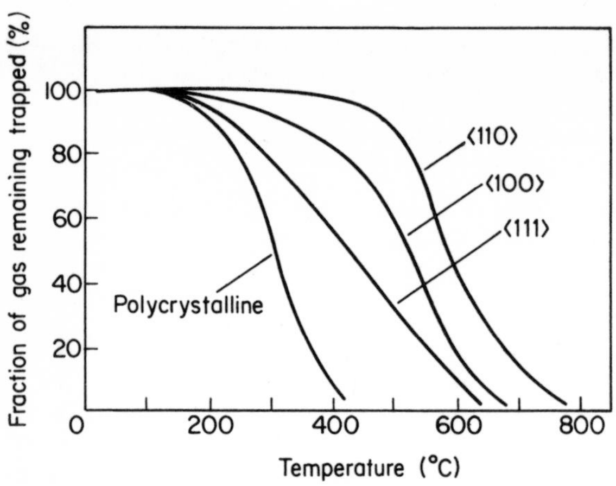

Fig. 8. 42 The fraction of Xe^+ ions: initially trapped in single crystal & polycrystalline Cu or 40 kev, released after 20 minutes at the temperatures shown The direction of ion incidence is indicated (viz. Ref. 8. 128)

650°C and 850°C patches of bubbles appeared and almost all trapped gas was released. In targets bombarded with a high ion dose (7×10^{16} ions/cm^2) the initial damage pattern was a complex tangle of loops and heating up to 650°C produced only a 30% recovery of gas. Further heating produced a uniform distribution of bubbles and 70% recovery of gas to 850°C. The final 30% was recovered above 850°C and was ascribed to bubble migration. It is very probable that the gas release between 500°C and 850°C, in the normal diffusion range, is associated with the disappearance of the dislocations in this temperature range and therefore governed by some form of self diffusion process for the metal.

Kelly and Ruedl[126] also studied Al targets after 9 keV Ne^+ ion bombardment, by electron microscopy and found dislocation tangle formation of bubbles within the up to 500°C and then formation of bubbles within the material and bubble like pockets near the surface upon heating above 600°C. Since very little gas escaped at the lower temperatures it was felt that the oxide skin was impermeable to the trapped gas and bubbles form formed beneath the surface as the gas became mobile. Only upon dissolving the oxide skin could this gas be released.

These authors[126] also studied the depth distribution of 9 keV trapped Kr^+ ions in Pt and 40 keV Xe^+ ions in Al by using the sputtering technique described in Chapter 5. As expected the range distributions were approximately exponential in both cases, before heating the target, with a median range of 9 keV Kr^+ in Pt of ~36 atom layers. After heating to 850°C however (in stage II) the median range increased threefold since the surface concentration fell but the deeper penetration increased. On further heating to 1000°C (in stage III where bubbles are observed) there was a further surface concentration diminution but not much change in the deeper component. This suggests that the bubbles actually form and grow during stage II heating rather than being spontaneously nucleated during bombardment. In the case of 40 keV Xe^+ in Al, heating to 350°C (in stage II) has virtually no effect on the Xe penetration distribution but further heating to 450°C increases both the near surface and deep penetrating components. Finally heating to 600°C removes the surface gas, presumably by the release of the bubbles trapped by the oxide skin.

Jacobson and Wehner[129] and Macrae and Gobeli[130] have also been able to correlate the release of trapped gas from Ge and some III-V compounds respectively with the annealing of surface radiation damage inflicted by ion bombardment up to 1 keV via examination of the surfaces with low energy electron diffraction. Again it appears that gas release is conditioned by damage annealing and vacancy motion.

Morrison et al[131, 132] also studied the release of Xe^{133} from ceramic oxides by heating after injection of high energy recoil atoms produced in fission events from UO_2. These authors also found considerable gas release at temperatures below those expected for normal diffusion, in addition to some release at the expected temperature. The former process was once again ascribed to the damage promoted diffusion to be discussed shortly.

Auskern[133] reported an anomalous low temperature release of fission induced Xe from UC with a temperature release function similar to that measured by Kelly and Brown[121] whilst similar fission gas release from UO_2[134, 135] and graphite[136] have also been studied. The interpretation was again in terms of a damage enhanced diffusion process.

Finally Koch[104], Thulin[105], Fluit et al[106], Almen and Bruce[77] and Bergjstrom et al[120] have given qualitative information on the release of trapped inert gas atoms from various metals. Thulin[105] observed that 8. 5% of 40 keV Xe^+ ions trapped in Al were released below 350°C, in disagreement with Kelly and Brown's[119, 121] results but closer to Tucker and Norton's[117] data but contaminant carbon films were probably present and as shown by Kelly and Brown[119] this allows gas release at lower temperatures.

Almen and Bruce[77] observed 80% recovery of 40 keV Kr^+ ions trapped in non annealed Ag by heating to 450°C but only 20% recovery upon heating to 550°C in annealed Ag, again in agreement with Kelly and Brown's[119] results and exhibiting the importance of the target structure in conditioning the diffusion processes. On the other hand no effect of mechanical work or annealing upon the release of 40 keV Kr^+ ions from Ni, Mo or Ta was observed and only 40% of the trapped gas was released by heating Ta to 600°C and 10% by heating Ni or Pt to this temperature.

Moore et al[137] have observed the release of He, previously trapped at 10 keV in Al and Ag targets by heating the targets after bombardment and found evidence of considerable release of gas over a wide temperature range extending at least as far as 635°C. The results of these workers suggest operation of a continuous spectrum of release activation energies. In addition to the experiments with glass and metal surfaces, Jech has studied the thermal release of trapped inert gases from several compounds[138, 139, 140]. The gas was introduced into the solid by running a high frequency discharge (15-30 kV, 1. 9mc/s) in Kr, Xe or Ra at pressures between 1×10^{-2} and 5 torr in the neighbourhood of the target material. Although it was not possible to determine target ion currents and energies two types of treatment were distinguishable. One, a labelling treatment where the discharge was run at high pressure (5 torr) and low voltage (15 kV) for a short time (3 secs.) and the second where the discharge conditions were (1×10^{-2} torr, 30 kV, 30 secs.) Ions were trapped in both cases but in the latter conditions the effective ion dose and energy were undoubtedly much larger. Upon heating the targets at a constant rate, the same type of release curves as observed for glass were obtained[138, 139] as shown by the curves for RbCl,

CsCl, KCl and NaCl with a low Xenon dose in Figure 8.43. Each curve shows a maximum, which was

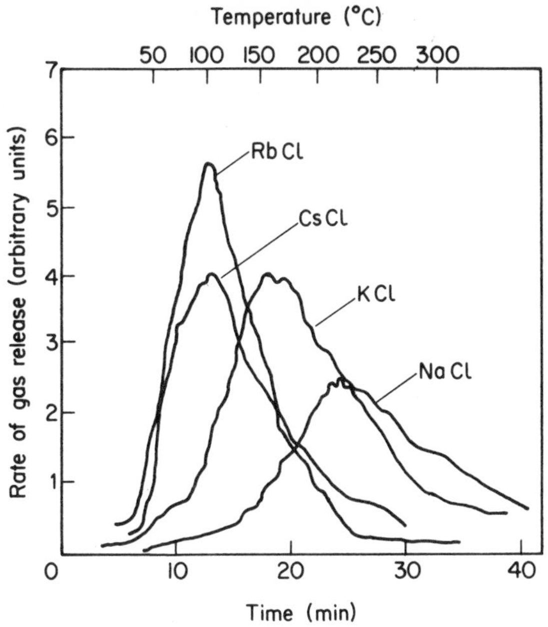

Fig. 8.43 The rate of release of Xe, from Alkali metal chlorides during heating (viz. Ref. 8.139)

independent of whether Xe or Ra was employed, and release was almost totally complete by heating to 400°C. The temperature at which maximum rate occurred decreased with increasing cation mass in the series of chlorides. It is interesting to note that Nelson et al[141] observed a peak in the radiation induced ionic conductivity recovery of reactor irradiated KCl at 170°C, close to the peak in release rate observed by Jech at 160°–170°C, whilst Kobayashi[142, 143] found that the density change in proton irradiated NaCl annealed rapidly between 220°C and 230°C, and as we saw earlier Kelly and Matzke[122] have observed a gas release component of Kr from KCl in this temperature range. Jech[140] subsequently extended these measurements to investigate the effects of trapping two ion species in LiF, Diamond and Magnesium hydroxide. Figure 8, 44a shows the release spectrum of a small low energy dose of Kr^{85} from a LiF sample whilst Figure 8.44b shows release of the same dose of Kr from LiF sample which had received a large dose of higher energy Xe ions. Both curves show a peak at 250°C but the latter indicates an extra release with a broad peak between 400°C and 500°C. On the other hand similar curves for release of trapped Kr from a Xe bombarded diamond, show an enhancement of a low temperature release process at 300°C and some elimination of higher temperature release, viz. Figures. 8.45a and b. Similar enhancement of a peak at 300°C occurred in the Kr release spectrum from magnesium hydroxide by prebombardment with Xe ions and simultaneous diminution of a peak at 400°C as shown in Figures 8.46a and b.

These results are similar in nature to a few exploratory measurements made with ion bombarded glass by James and Carter[43] and a further experiment by Jech[140] gave identical results to observations on glass by Smeaton et al[144]. Jech[140] observed that, if during heating, the temperature of Kr bombarded LiF was held constant, gas evolution ceased after a short period and upon cooling to room temperaure, and reheating, evolution did not resume until the target temperature was higher than the earlier stable value.

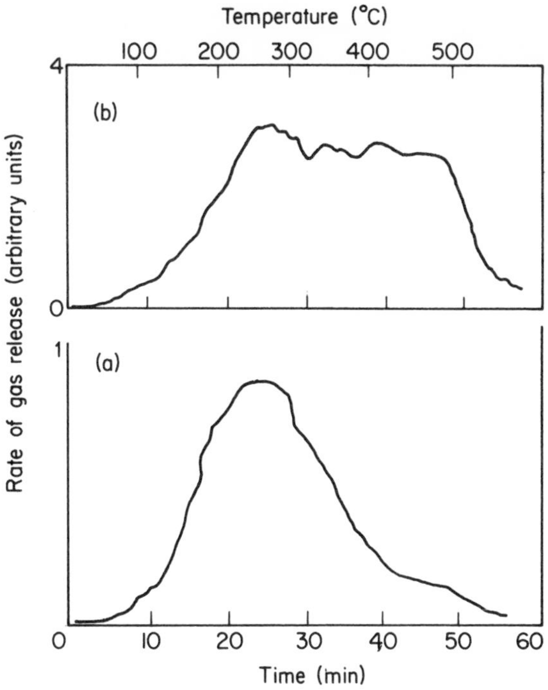

Fig. 8.44 Rate of Kr release from a diamond sample during heating. (a) untreated sample. (b) Sample exposed to a Xe discharge at 0.02 torr for 30 seconds (viz. Ref. 8.140)

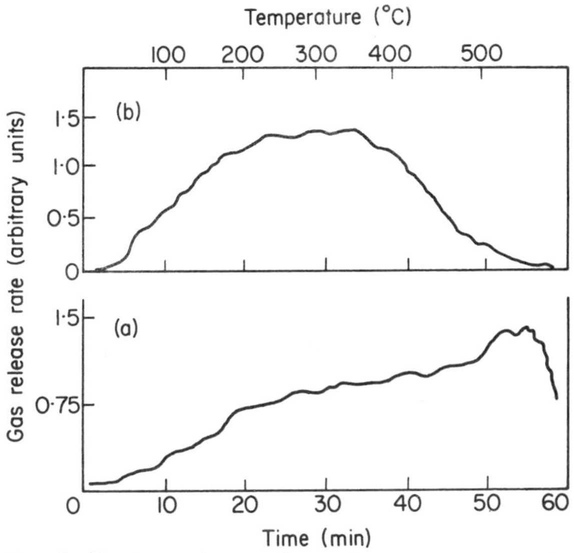

Fig. 8.45 Rate of Kr release from a LiF sample during heating. (a) untreated Sample. (b) Sample exposed to a Xe dishcarge at 0.025 torr for 20 seconds (viz. Ref. 8.140)

Comparison with other irradiation experiments is also fruitful here since Burton and Neubert[145] observed that LiF exposed to low neutron doses exhibited damage which showed recovery at about 260°C, due to interstitial-vacancy annealing, but at larger doses the annealing spectrum extended above 500°C (c.f. Figure 8.44). In addition, radiation induced dilatation and stored energy release in reactor irradiated diamond exhibit[146] an annealing peak at about 300°C, again close to the pronounced peak in Xe and Kr bombarded diamond and the less obvious but undoubtedly present peak in Kr bombarded diamond.

Maddix and Allen[21-23] observed that the release rate of He, Ne, A and Kr from quartz after trapping at tem-

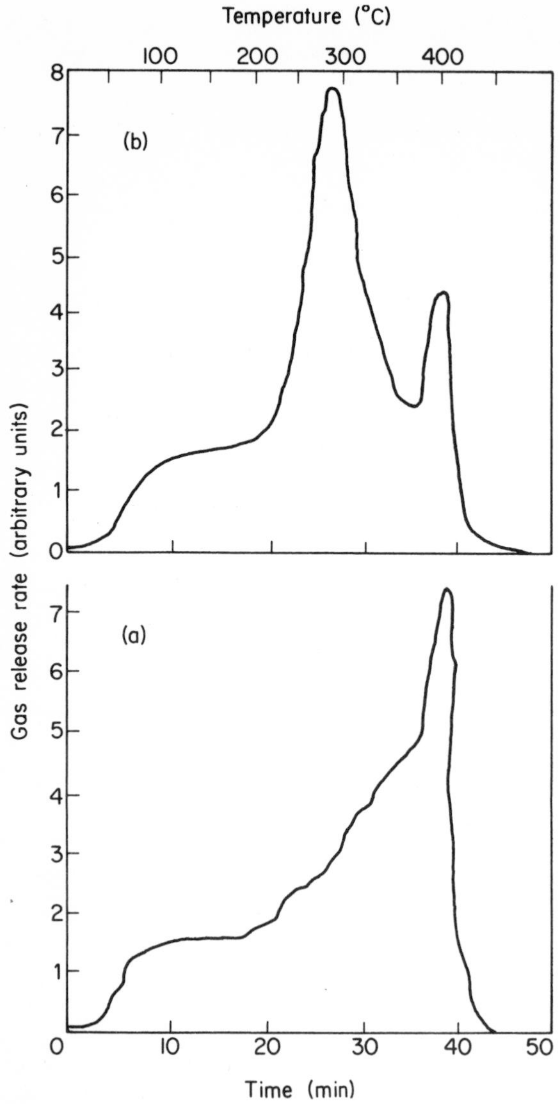

Fig. 8.46 Rate of Kr release from a magnesium hydroxide sample during heating
a) Untreated sample
b) Sample exposed to a Xe discharge at 0.023 torr for 10 seconds (viz. Ref. 8.140)

peratures > 200°C, followed a $(\text{time})^{-1/2}$ relation closely, at all desorption temperatures up to about 800°C, suggesting a normal diffusional release only. Indeed the energies of activation for diffusion deduced from the recovery data are close to known values and suggest that indiffusion must occur in this particular system at the bombardment temperatures with possible simultaneous annealing of surface damage.

8.8. MECHANISMS OF GAS RELEASE.

8.8.1. Since the results just described reveal that gas release processes occur both during and after bombardment at the bombardment temperature, and at an accelerated rate during post bombardment heating, it is clear that these release processes are thermally activated and are presumably the result of gas atom migration through and from the target by some form of diffusion process. In the introduction to this Chapter we outlined the possible forms that such diffusion effects could take and it is useful to reiterate these here. Since the energetic ions are driven into and trapped in the target in some form of depth distribution, it is quite probable that these atoms can then diffuse via normal processes, i.e. interstitialcy or vacancy motion, under the driving force of the gas atom or vacancy concentration gradient. This form of diffusion would proceed with an activation energy equivalent to that for gas atom migration through the target obtained in conventional diffusion measurements or, if the vacancies move, to the energy for self diffusion. In addition the energetic ions will leave considerable damage in their wake and often become trapped in non normal configurations of lattice atoms. The energies required for gas atom release from these special 'sites' and migration along the damaged paths may be considerably different to those encountered in normal diffusion, and this radiation induced diffusion may be more effective than normal diffusion at different temperatures. Because of the possibility of many different atomic configurations surrounding the trapped atom, and a variety of damage paths, it is very probable that this form of diffusion would be excited with a large number, or even a continuous spectrum of activation energies. At low bombardment energies, where the ion penetration is so small that gas atoms are trapped predominantly in, and just below, the surface, one may still expect gas migration and release from damage induced sites and in this case, since only one or two jumps are required for the trapped atom to re-enter the gas phase, the release process should be rather simple. A possible mechanism for this 'damage diffusion' is the migration of radiation produced vacancies, which allows simultaneous gas movement, with energies lower than normal vacancy diffusion values and which are conditioned by their promimity to the surface.

For large gas concentrations, coupled with extensive vacancy production, as obtains with high energy ions, one may expect agglomeration of the isolated atoms into gas bubbles, and the migration of these will be determined by somewhat different processes to individual atom migration, including pressure and temperature gradients. Although we have already presented results snowing the importance of bubble formation and migration, we will defer further discussion of these until Section 8.10 where a more thorough theoretical and experimental summary is given.

Finally we should mention gas release processes which accompany target phase changes or activation of surface processes such as oxide dissolution or carbon film dissociation and spontaneous release of gas trapped beneath the superficial skin. Easily oxidised targets such as Al will exhibit this effect as Kelly and Brown's[121] results show, as will contaminated targets.

The two situations in which we will be interested are (1) Gas release whilst there is no simultaneous ion trapping, i.e. post bombardment release and (2) Gas release coincident with ion trapping, i.e. gas release during bombardment. Although case (1) implies that case (2) has already operated, this former situation is more amenable to analysis since a gas source term is not required in the defining diffusion equations. The results of this analysis can then be inserted into case (2) to determine the influence of simultaneous release upon trapping.

8.8.2. Gas Release at Elevated Temperatures.

If we suppose that ions have been injected into a target, forming a concentration distribution which varies with depth according to C(X, O) i.e. an initial pre-migration distribution and if conventional diffusion theory is applicable, then these trapped atoms can migrate under the concentration gradient according to Fick's diffusion law[147], such that

$$D \frac{\partial^2 C(x,t)}{\partial x^2} = -\frac{\partial C(x,t)}{\partial t} \quad 8.34.1.$$

assuming motion in the x direction only, with a Diffusion coefficient D.

This diffusion coefficient D is generally related to the temperature through the formula $D = D_o \exp(-Q/RT)$. 8.34.2 where Q is the activation energy for the diffusion process, assumed for the present to be single valued, and D_o, the preexponential factor is generally considered to be temperature and concentration independent. (Examples where such a supposition is invalid may be found in the texts of Crank,[147] Jost[148] and Barrier[149].)

Solution of Equation 8.34.1 is possible and relatively simple if the initial distribution C(X, O) is known (viz Crank[147], Jost[148] and Barrer[149]) and if suitable boundary conditions can be imposed, e.g. $C(\infty,\infty) \to O$; $C(o,t) = O$ since trapped atoms emerge at the gas-solid interface.

Of more fundamental importance than the solution to Equation 8.34.1 however, is whether this Equation is in fact applicable to the case of gas atom migration in solid targets. Generally speaking, the Fick diffusion equation is applied to a physical situation in which there is a continuous variation of concentration with distance and time[150]. In the present case trapped atoms may be considered to be fixed in adjacent lattice planes with discrete separation distances between each trapped atom, over which an atom must jump in order to migrate. One therefore really requires the finite difference form of Equation 8.34.1 to describe the kinetics of the gas migration. Kelly[51, 151] has shown that in this case, the diffusion of atoms is governed by a difference equation of the form

$$C(x, t+\Delta t) = \left(1 - \frac{\Delta t}{\tau}\right).\beta\, c(x,t) + \frac{\Delta t}{\tau}.\frac{\beta}{2}$$

$$\{c(x-\lambda, t) + c(x+\lambda, t)\} \quad 8.35.1.$$

where λ is the lattice spacing, τ the mean time an atom remains bound in a site and β the probability that a migrating atom jumps into a new lattice plane at each migration and $\Delta t \ll \tau$

If the concentration gradient is low this equation simplifies to Equation 8.34.1 with

$$D = \frac{\beta\lambda^2}{2\tau} \quad 8.35.2.$$

but for larger, discontinuous gradients, one can simplify Equation 8.35.1 only to

$$\frac{\partial c(x,t)}{\partial t} = -k\, c(x,t) + \frac{k}{2}\{c(x-\lambda,t) + c(x+\lambda,t)\}$$

where $k = \frac{2D}{\lambda^2}$ and therefore varies with temperature according to Equation 8.34.2

For the simple case where all gas is initially trapped at one plane, p beneath the surface of an infinite target, i.e. a well defined range, probably representative of low energy ions, the solution of the normal diffusion equation is

$$C(x,t) = \frac{C_\phi}{\sqrt{2\pi kt}} \left\{ \frac{\exp -\left[\frac{(p-x)^2}{\lambda}\right]}{2kt} - \frac{\exp\left[-\frac{(p+x)^2}{\lambda}\right]}{2kt} \right\} \quad 8.36.1$$

for $x = o, \lambda, 2\lambda, 3\lambda \ldots$.

The fraction of gas released at a time t, may then be obtained as

$$F = \frac{1}{C_\phi}\{C_o - \sum_{x=o}^{\infty} c(x,t) \quad 8.36.2$$

or approximated by

$$F \approx \frac{2}{\sqrt{\pi}} \int_{\sqrt{2kt}}^{\infty} e^{-u^2}\, du = \operatorname{erfc} p/\sqrt{2kt} \quad 8.36.3.$$

Kelly[151] has shown that the corresponding solution to the difference Equation 8.35.1 is

$$C(r\lambda, t) = C_o \exp(-kt)\{I_{p-r}(kt) - I_{p+r}(kt)\} \quad 8.37.1$$

and $I_n(Z)$ is the modified Bessel function of the first kind. The fraction of gas released at a time t, may also be written

$$F = \frac{1}{C_o}\left(C_o - \sum_{r=o}^{\infty} C(r\lambda, t)\right) \quad 8.37.2.$$

or

$$F = 1 - \exp(-kt)\{I_o(kt) + I_p(kt) + 2[I_1(kt) +$$

$$I_2(kt) + \ldots I_{p-1}(kt)]\} \quad 8.37.3.$$

For gas atoms trapped in the first lattice plane below the surface Equation 8.36.3 reduces to

$$F \simeq \operatorname{erfc} 1/\sqrt{2kt} \quad 8.36.4.$$

and equation 8.37.3 to

$$F \simeq 1 - \exp(-kt)[I_0(kt) + I_1(kt)] \quad 8.37.4.$$

and the behaviour of F with time for both approximations is shown in Figure 8.47. For $F \gtrsim 0.4$ the curves

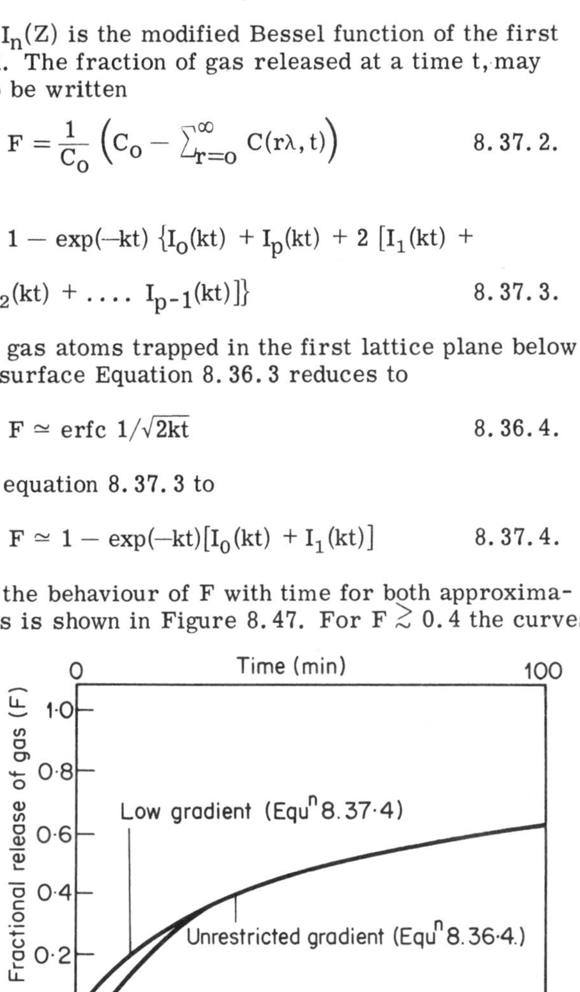

Fig. 8.47 Fractional release of gas as a function of time due to diffusion from a plane source, using an unrestricted gradient (Ficks Law and equn 8.36.4) and the low gradient (finite difference form of Fick's Law and equn 8.37.4) (viz. Ref. 8.51) Time (minutes)

are identical, suggesting that normal diffusion theory is applicable at least for $kt \gtrsim 1.5$. However Figure 8.47 does suggest that normal diffusion theory does predict too low a release rate for short times.

Since agreement is satisfactory for large kt, one can use either theory to predict the fractional release of gas at a given temperature, for a given value of k (i.e. D and hence activation energy Q) provided t is sufficiently large. In Figure 8.48 the fractional release after 30 minutes is shown for increasing temperatures for two values of Q, 25K cal/mole and 60 K cal/mole, assuming the gas to be initially trapped in the first subsurface plane. It is immediately clear that temperature ranges of ±25°C and ±50°C about mean temperatures of 90°C and 550°C are sufficient to remove almost all gas migrating with energies of 25 or 60 K cal/mole respectively.

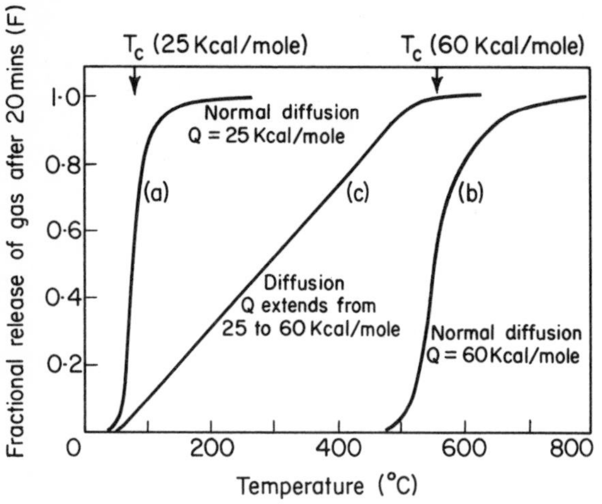

Fig. 8.48 Fractional release of gas after 20 mins at the temperatures shown for gas initially located 1 lattice plane from the surface
a) For one diffusion energy Q = 25 Kcal/mode
b) For one diffusion energy Q = 60 Kcal/mode
c) For a uniform distribution of diffusion energies between 25 and 60 Kcal/mode (viz. Ref. 8.51)

Equations 8.36.3 and 8.37.3 also illustrate the fact that the fractional release depends upon the depth of the initial plane of trapping below the surface. One can extend the solutions to equations 8.36, 37 for a source of strength C_o located at p. to cover the case of an initial depth distribution of gas where $C_{r\lambda}$ is a function of $r\lambda$. However equally interesting information is derived simply by considering the fractional release from a plane source of gas trapped more deeply in the target. One can then employ Equation 8.36.3 to predict temperatures T_1 and T_2 at which 10% and 90% of trapped gas will be released in a specified time for a given energy of activation Q. One can also define a characteristic temperature T_c at

at which 50% of gas is released during the observation time. If one takes a time of 20 minutes, and a value of

$$k_o = \frac{2D_o}{\lambda^2} = 10^{13}\ sec^{-1}*.$$

which is frequently accepted as being a reasonable value, one obtains

$$T_1 = \frac{Q}{76-9.2\ \log_{10}p} \qquad 8.38.1.$$

$$T_2 = \frac{Q}{66-9.2\ \log_{10}p} \qquad 8.38.2.$$

$$T_c \simeq \frac{Q}{71-9.2\ \log_{10}p} \qquad 8.38.3.$$

where the temperatures are measured in °K.

Table 8.8 illustrates values of T_1 and T_2 for gas atoms initially trapped at 1, 10 or 100 atomic layers from the surface for two values of the activation energy for migration, 40 K cal/mole and 80 K cal/mole respectively. As anticipated, all temperatures

TABLE 8.8. (Ref. 8.121).

Numerical examples of release by normal diffusion.

Distance of diffusing material from surface (atom layers)	Temperature at which the fractional, F, reaches the values 0.1 or 0.9 in 20 minutes.			
	F = 0.1 (Q = 40 kcal)	F = 0.9	F = 0.1 (Q = 80 kcal)	F = 0.9
1	245°C	335°C	765°C	945°C
10	325	435	920	1140
100	420	575	1115	1420

T_1, T_c and T_2 increase with increasing penetration depth, and moreover the temperature interval $T_2 - T_1 = \Delta T$ over which release is completed also increases with increasing depth. However, even for 100 atomic layers penetration $T_c \simeq 290°C$ and $\Delta T = 90°C$ for Q = 40 K cal/mole and $T_c \simeq 1270°C$ and $\Delta T = 305°C$ for Q = 80 K cal/mole. We can thus assert that on the basis of a single valued diffusion energy and a single penetration depth a release spectrum which peaks at a temperature T, say 200°C, will only exhibit release over a rather narrow temperature range (≃ ±40°C). A range distribution of a factor of 10 only increases this temperature range by a comparatively small amount and Kelly and Brown[121] and Kelly and Matzke[122] have given appropriate formulae for initial trapped atom distribution functions of the forms $\exp(-p\lambda)$; $p\lambda(\exp(-p\lambda))$. For the form $\exp(-p\lambda)$ with a median value of $p_m\lambda$ one obtains

$$T_1 \simeq \frac{Q}{83-4.6\ \log_{10}[p_m^2/t_{min}]} \qquad 8.38.4$$

$$T_2 \simeq \frac{Q}{67-4.6\ \log_{10}[p_m^2/t_{min}]} \qquad 8.38.5$$

$$T_c \approx \frac{Q}{75-4.6\ \log_{10}[p_m^2/t_{min}]} \qquad 8.38.6$$

where t is release time in minutes and k_o has been taken as $10^{15}\ sec^{-1}$. For the distribution $p\lambda\ \exp(-p\lambda)$ with a median value of $p_m\lambda$ one finds that the first constants in the denominators of T_1, T_2 and T_c are changed to 81, 68 and 75 respectively. We may also note that if one assumes an activation energy of as low as 4 K cal/mole (approximate surface adsorption energies for inert gases on solids), one requires an effective penetration depth of 10^6 lattice spacings to give T_2 = room temperature.

The preceding analysis applies to gas atoms which migrate with the normal activation energy for diffusion and where diffusion proceeds according to the concentration gradient of trapped atoms. A rather different situation occurs when gas atoms are trapped

* This value of k_o has been questioned by Kelly & Brown[121] on the basis of observed values of D_o in metals. They suggest an improved value of $k_o = 10^{15\pm1}$. which leads to rather different values of the constant in equation 8.38.

in various configurations of target atoms or migrate to the surface along special circuits created by damage effects. In these cases each trapped atom may migrate to the surface independent of other atoms with an energy of activation necessary either to remove the trapped atom from the retaining target atom cluster or to itself migrate along the damaged path or to allow vacancy migration along this path. A particularly interesting case of this mechanism is where low energy ions come to rest just below the target surface and essentially require only one jump to re-enter the gas phase. The diffusion equation is simplified in this case since there is essentially no concentration gradient, and one obtains a simple rate equation

$$\frac{\partial c}{\partial t} = -\frac{c}{\tau} \qquad 8.39.1.$$

where τ is the sticking time for trapped atoms and is related to temperature in an analogous manner to the diffusion coefficient, D, via the Frenkel[152] relation

$$\tau = \tau_0 \exp(Q/RT) \qquad 8.39.2.$$

with $\tau_0 \simeq 10^{-13}$ secs.

We have already considered the solutions to Equation 8.39.1 in Chapter 6 for the case where the temperature T is constant and where T varies with time. Recapitulating those results it is found that gas release occurs rapidly at a temperature T such that the time constant is of the order of the experimental time (tens and hundreds of seconds), and that for an activation energy Q, the characteristic temperature is given by

$$T_c \approx \frac{Q}{72} \qquad 8.40.1.$$

If the temperatures is varied during gas release, from a value below T_c through and above T_c, the solution to Equation 8.39.1 depends upon the exact manner in which the temperature is varied with time. Generally speaking the release rate increases from almost zero at temperatures $T < T_c$ to a maximum at $T = T_c$ and then decreases again to zero, for $T > T_c$. The temperature T_m at which the release rate reaches a maximum may be deduced by differentation of Equation 8.39.1. For a linearly increasing temperature/time function $T = a + bt$ it can be shown that $T_m \simeq \frac{Q}{C}$ where C lies between 65 and 75 depending upon the temperature rate of increase.

The temperature range over which release occurs rapidly may also be specified by determining the temperatures T_a, below T_m and T_b, above T_m at which the release rate is e^{-1} of the maximum release rate (i.e. 34%). For the linear temperature/time function T_a and T_b are given by:-

$$T_a = \frac{Q}{C-2.4} \qquad 8.40.2.$$

$$T_b = \frac{Q}{C+3.6} \qquad 8.40.3.$$

It is evident that T_m and T_c are almost identical, whilst T_a and T_b are only slightly above and below T_m respectively.

It is further clear that T_a and T_b are essentially identical to the values of T_1 and T_2 deduced in Kelly's[51,151] treatment for unit penetration depth.

We should mentioned however that in the derivation of T_a and T_b it is essentially assumed that gas migrates only out from the surface. In the diffusion equation if the source is plane, gas can migrate in both directions, but initially there is no concentration gradient therefore there should be no diffusion. Since the process is really a random walk problem however, gas will diffuse both ways, initially corresponding to a desorption type of rate law but then rapidly converting to the diffusion problem as a gradient is established. Consequently, for gas release on this basis the release rate/temperature curve is sharply peaked, with a small peak width $\Delta T = T_b - T_a$. The narrowness of the peaks is best shown with reference to Figure 8.49. where release rate/temperature functions are shown for several values of Q between 20 and 50 K cal/mole.

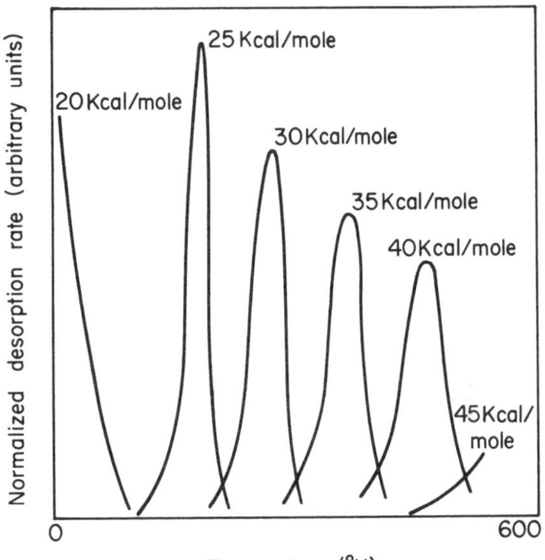

Fig. 8.49 Desorption rate divided by initial gas concentration, as a function of temperature during heating, for single step desorption and different desorption energies from 20 to 45 Kcal/mole (viz. Ref. 8.15)

It is notable that atoms bound with energies less than about 22 K cal/mole are rapidly released even at room temperature.

If, therefore, experiments reveal broadly peaked release rate/temperature functions, one must conclude that either a wide variety of penetration depths occurs or that a spectrum of activation energies for gas release operates, (each release function contributing a fraction to the overall release rate) or both occur simultaneously. Inspection of experimental conditions help to decide which is the probable cause.

A factor which assists in determination of the gas release mechanism is the minimum characteristic temperature at which rapid release occurs. For a normal diffusion process of activation energy Q, this temperature will be that at which gas is released from just below the surface, i.e. $T_c \simeq Q/71$.

Gas release will then continue until gas is exhausted from deeper levels as the temperature is increased, but the minimum characteristic temperature will be determined by the activation energy for normal diffusion of the gas in the solid.

For a damage induced diffusion process, release will also occur at a minimum characteristic temperature T_c^1, but this will be determined by an activation energy Q^1 which is not necessarily equal to that for normal diffusion. Thus one might expect, if $Q^1 < Q$, gas release at temperatures considerably below those where normal diffusional release occurs. We should note that if T_b is the bombardment temperature, then all gas which is trapped with an activation energy less than $Q_b \cong 71\ T_b$ will be rapidly released even at the bombardment temperature. Thus a lower limit to observable diffusion energies is dicated by the operating temperature and is approximately 71 T_b. For room temperature bombardment this implies that release of any atoms bound with energies less than $\simeq$ 22 K cal/mole will occur before observations commence.

We will now apply these ideas to the experimental data summarised earlier. Unfortunately, values for normal activation energies for diffusion of inert gas atoms in solids are scarce and the best that one can do is to quote data which has some relevance to the experimental data. In the case of glass, Barrer[149] and Alpert, Buritz and Rogers[153] have obtained values of the activation energy for diffusion for He in Pyrex of 5-6 K cal/mole whilst T'sai and Hogness[154] deduced a value of 9.5 K cal/mole for Ne in Silica and Leiby and Chen[155] obtained a similar value for Ne in Vycor glass. On the other hand Barrer[149] measured values between 18-31 K cal/mole for oxygen, nitrogen and air and 32 K cal/mole for Argon in fused silica, whilst Reynolds[156] reports a value of 42 K cal/mole for Argon in a Potash-lime silica. The former, low values, < 10 K cal/mole for He and Ne suggest characteristic release temperatures for these gases of ~140°K, so that, if normal diffusional release only operated, no gas would ever be trapped at room temperature. The latter, higher values for Argon, > 30 K cal/mole, however, gives a characteristic temperature ~140°C, so that if only normal diffusion operated, gas would not be released below a temperature of about 120°C. The fact that all inert gases are trapped in glass at room temperature and are released continuously between room temperature and 400°C, can only mean that some form of damage diffusion dominates the release in this case, for He and Ne, largely damage paths or surface contaminant films allow the gas to remain trapped but for the other gases it is possible that some part of the release cycle is due to normal diffusion. We shall return to a further discussion of this target material shortly.

Federighi[157] has evaluated the self diffusion energy of Al to be 30.6 K cal/mole whilst Lindner and Matzke[158] have determined Q for Em in Al_2O_3 to be 70 K cal/mole. The former value predicts a value of T_c = 150°C, whilst the latter, 700°C. It is uncertain whether one can use such values for the cases of trapped Ar or Xe in Al or Al_2O_3 but it is clear from the data of Tucker and Norton[117] and Kelly and Brown[119, 121] that gas release occurs both above and below the respective temperatures. Presumably the gas release above T_c can be ascribed to normal diffusion motion, but in the case of Al this is only a small component of the total release. The large release at 500°C observed by Tucker and Norton[117] has been attributed to dissolution of the superficial oxide layer by Kelly and Brown[119, 121] whilst the gas release below T_c in these cases was attributed to decomposition of oil contaminant films.

Tobin[159] has obtained a value of ~37.5 K cal/mole for the system Xe-Ag (from considerations of the self diffusion energy in this metal) and this leads to a value of T_c = 250°C. Both Tucker and Norton[117] and Kelly and Brown[119, 121] observed gas emission below and above this temperature, and some at least of the release above T_c is characteristic of normal diffusion. Below T_c, damage diffusion must be considered active. It is notable that the proportion of the release above T_c increases as the bombarding ion energy (and thus the penetration depth) increases, whereas damage diffusion is predominant for low energies where the damage is confined to the surface layers. Similar results are obtained for the case of the gold targets where Okkerse[160] has determined Q for Au-Au to be 39.4 K cal/mole with a value of T_c = 275°C. Release is observed both above and below T_c, with a predominance of the fraction above T_c at increased ion energies. The observations by Kelly and Brown[119, 121] and Tucker and Norton[117] that at large ion doses, a considerable fraction of gas is released near and above the melting temperature suggests that appreciable gas bubble formation and migration may be important in this case.

No activation energy data is available for Ta or Ta_2O_5 but the wide temperature range over which gas release occurs suggests operation of both damage and normal diffusion, the former predominating at low ion energies. Gas release at high temperatures in saturated Ta again implies gas bubble formation and migration.

In lead, values lying between 24.2 and 32.2 K cal/mole have been reported by Nachtrieb and Handler[161] for the Pb-Pb diffusion energy, whereas Tucker and Norton's[117] data show continuous release from 50°C to the melting temperature and a major fraction of the release above this temperature. Again one interprets this as showing damage, normal and gas bubble type migration.

The evolution of Kr from Ur, for which a diffusion energy $\lesssim$ 95 K cal/mole has been reported[162] shows multiple peak structure both below and above the $\alpha \rightarrow \beta$ phase transition and the fraction of gas released in each phase depends upon the heating rate. These results indicate the simultaneous presence of damage diffusion, normal diffusion and a process which proceeds at a rate determined by the transition rate from one phase to another. Since the release is markedly different at temperatures quite remote from the phase change temperature it appears that the presence of gas and of course damage may modify the structure so that the phase changes occur at different temperatures. In the release experiments reported by Kelly and Matzke[122] from ionic crystals and sinters, these authors were able to show that, in addition to the normal diffusion process, the derived energies of which generally agreed quite well with known diffusion, damage enhanced processes also occurred.

A most interesting result is obtained in the inert gas—W release scheme where Kornelsen[72] detected six well defined peaks in the release spectrum, the T_c's of which were almost independent of the trapped gas species. Values of the self diffusion energy for the W-W system have been found to be in the region of 120-135 K cal/mole (Henning[163] and Peterson[164]), and extrapolating the results of Tobin[159] for inert gases in silver, suggest values for Q for inert gases in tungsten of about 100 K cal/mole. This value is close to that derived for peak f in Kornelsen's[72] measurements (100-105 K cal/mole) and suggests that the final peak is therefore associated with normal diffusion. Since this peak becomes of increasing importance as the bombarding ion energy is increased, this conclusion tends to be confirmed. The peaks at lower temperatures, and therefore energies, may therefore be associated with damage diffusion processes, and since these occur down to low bombardment energies, one could ascribe them to differing configurations of target atoms surrounding the trapped atoms. On the other hand, since the ion penetration is low, there will be considerable strain fields surrounding the trapped atoms which extend to the surface and it is very possible that the lower energy peaks are associated with self diffusion of tungsten atoms on different surface planes which expose the gas atoms and these are ejected by the strain fields. This, of course, is another configuration dependent process, but depends more on the properties of tungsten than on damage induced properties.

Kornelsen's[199, 200] studies with single crystal W tends to confirm that the low energy peaks are indeed associated with target structure, since there is a considerable difference between release spectra from different planes, whilst both Kornelsen's[199, 200] and Erents and Carter's[201] observations with very low energy ions, where damage would appear to be impossible suggest again that the lower energy peaks are correlated with the surface properties of the tungsten.

On the other hand, damage certainly is inflicted by the ions and part of the release spectrum in Stage I may be associated with abnormal diffusion through the damaged layer. The peak widths in Kornelsen's[72], Burtt et al's[69] and Colligon and Leck's[70] data are too wide to be associated with discrete activation energies however (c.f. the values of T_1 and T_2 or T_a and T_b and the curves in Figure 8.33, 34) so that each peak is associated with a range of energies of about 10 K cal/mole. The most probable values for the Q's derived from Kornelsen's[72] data are shown in Table 8.9.

TABLE 8.9. (Ref. 8.72).

Activation energies of various peaks.

Q (kcal/mole) of peak:

Gas	a	b	c	d	e	f
Ne	34.4	46.8	53.0	66.8	94	105
A	36.3	43.0	52.2	64.5	86	102
Kr	33.2	41.0	51.5	62.0	86	100
Xe	33.3	41.7	50.7	60.8	91	105

Jech's[138, 139, 140] data for inert gases trapped in Alkali halide crystals, diamond and magnesium hydroxide, also show a wide temperature release spectrum typical of damage diffusion. The effects of bombarding with different ion species and enhancing parts of the release spectrum confirm that the ion induced damage is responsible for the wide spectrum of activation energies. It is notable that both in LiF and diamond, peaks in the gas release spectrum appear to possess similar activation energies to those associated with radiation damage annealing, suggesting that some gas release is itself associated with a reorientation of the target atoms via perhaps the vacancy migration.

Auskern[133] suggested that the release of fission induced Xe from UC was also determined by a damage enhanced diffusion process. In particular, since the trapped Xe was located close to damage produced vacancies, the energy of activation for Xe migration would only include the energy for migration and not for vacancy formation, as is required for normal diffusion. Thus the lower values (27-35 K cal/mole) than measured self diffusion energies (85 K cal/mole) were to be expected, and were in fact in good agreement with known activation energies for annealing of damage or plastic recovery (25-38 K cal/mole) in this material. This scheme has also been adopted by Kelly[123] to explain the observed gap between the upper stage I release temperature and the lower stage II release temperature of Kr from Pt[125] and of Kornelsen's[72] two sets of separated peaks. Thus stage I was believed to result from migration of vacancies from the surface region, with energies conditioned by surface proximity considerations or by damaged regions. The upper limit for this migration energy would then be the same as the energy for migration of vacancies in the bulk material, whilst the lower stage II migration energy corresponds to the energy for vacancy formation and migration, which will be higher than stage I. Corkhill and Carter[165] have in fact confirmed directly that the gas released in the lower temperature peaks is located nearer the surface. Monoenergetic 2 keV Kr^+ ions were injected into a polycrystalline W target and post bombardment heating showed a similar peak structure to that of Kornelsen[72] for the Kr release. If, before heating however, the W was bombarded with 1 or 4 keV A^+ ions to sputter away the tungsten, subsequent heating showed that most of the low temperature part of the spectrum was removed before any of the higher energy part was affected, i.e. the A^+ ions were sputtering away tungsten and gas trapped near the initial surface before the deeply located gas was approached. The independence of Q values on the trapped species in Kornelsen's [72] work also suggest that the target atom or vacancy motion may be the important parameter in damage controlled gas emission. We shall return to this question again in Section 8.9.

We therefore note that in many cases of gas release from bomarded targets there is a component which can only be ascribed to a damage controlled diffusion or re-orientation process, with a minimum activation energy which is invariably dictated by the bombardment temperature. Thus, at room temperature, observable gas release processes are associated with energies in the region of 22 K cal/mole. Measurements at lower temperature (viz. Carter's[27] and Hobson and Edmond's[116] results for glass, and some observations by Kelly[50] on Argon trapped in TiO_2) show that gas may also be trapped with even lower activation energies than normally deduced, and that a spectrum of release energies may be continuous down to very low energies. One suspects that such spectra would be observed for most target materials provided that the bombardment temperature was adequately specified. The upper energy limit for damage diffusion is often the same as the energy for normal diffusion although it is not impossible that a gap between the two energies could exist. We should note that the heating schedule will not only cause gas release but will tend to anneal radiation damage so that gas which is not released by a damage diffusion controlled process may eventually be simply trapped in a 'normal' diffusion configuration and the gas release would occur with the activation energy typical of this latter process.

As we have seen there is very considerable evidence for a normal diffusion component in the desorption spectra. Thus Kelly and Brown's[119, 121] and Kelly and Matzke's[122] results show a 'normal' diffusion component for almost all target materials, whilst Kelly and Ruedl's[125, 126] observation of dislocation annealing during Stage II desorption illustrates quite unequivocally that a similar migration process is responsible for both, i.e. the normal vacancy diffusion. It would appear that the normal diffusion component is greatest when the ion energy is large, ensuring deep penetration and hence absence of surface interactions, and both Kelly and Brown's[121] observations of increased stage II release as the ion energy is increased and Jokic and Perovic's[128] measurement of increased release temperature along the most open channelling directions support this belief.

The important questions now remain of how to obtain activation energy spectra from measured release curves, and how to interpret these in terms of the possible damage effects and normal diffusion. For the time being we will concentrate our attention on the first question of how to determine the spectra. If the activation energy spectrum is composed of well defined, discrete values, the deduction of the individual values of Q_i is quite straightforward since these give quite distinctive and well separated peaks in the recovery rate/temperature transient at characteristic temperatures $T_i \approx Q_i/C$. It is readily deduced whether the activation energies are discrete or not by inspection of the width of each peak as defined by the difference T_b-T_a. Thus the energy spectrum for the release of inert gases from W deduced by Kornelsen[72] was shown to be composed of quite well defined activation energies with the values shown in Table 8.9 but with a small energy spread about each value.

If however, the gas release occurs more or less continuously over a wide temperature range, such as occurs with inert gas release from glass[15, 16] and in the metals studied by Kelly and Brown[119, 121] and Tucker and Norton[117], then this is indicative of a more or less continuous activation energy spectrum, and gas release at any temperature is composed of contributions from several closely spaced energies.

If the number of atoms trapped in sites (damage configurations) of release energy Q_i is n_i, then the rate of gas release from these sites may be written.

$$-\frac{dn_i}{dt} = n_i/\tau_i \qquad 8.41.1$$

where

$$\tau_i = \tau_0 \exp(Q_i/RT) \qquad 8.41.2$$

This equation may be solved formally to give

$$n_i = n_{i0} \exp\{-\int_0^t dt/\tau_i\} \qquad 8.41.3.$$

or

$$\frac{dn_i}{dt} = -\frac{n_{i0}}{\tau} \exp\{-\int_0^t dt/\tau_i\} \qquad 8.41.3.$$

If the temperature is varied with time, then this equation must be solved with the particular functional dependence of the temperature, since τ_i will vary with temperature, and thus time.

If, in addition, the number of atoms n_{i0}, initially trapped with energy Q_i is a function of this energy, $n_{i0} = \rho(Qi)$ then the total gas release at a time t is

$$\int_{Q_1}^{Q_2} \frac{dn_i}{dt} . dQ_i$$

where the limiting activation energies are Q_1 and Q_2. Thus the measured gas release rate,

$$\frac{dn}{dt} = -\int_{Q_1}^{Q_2} \frac{\rho(Q_i)}{\tau_i} \exp\left(-\int_0^t \frac{dt}{t_i}\right) dQ_i \qquad 8.42$$

From the observed gas release rate/temperature curve it is not generally possible to determine the function $\rho(Q_i)$ analytically, but a graphical method of solution has been developed by Carter and Leck[15, 16] to determine the activation energy spectrum for inert gases trapped in glass.

Basically one determines the limiting activation energies Q_1 and Q_2, from lower and upper temperatures T_L and T_U at which release is observed. The energy interval is then split into a number of finite steps Q_i and theoretical release transients are computed for each energy, as shown in Figure 8.49. This may be accomplished by numerical integration of

$$\exp -\int_0^t \frac{dt}{\tau_i}$$

for the particular time variation of T used. In the case of glass the temperature/time function was of the form T = a + bt, so that

$$\tau_{i_t} = \tau_{i0} \exp\{Q_i/R(a + bt)\}$$

Each release transient is weighted with an undetermined constant and the total release rate at a number of times, or temperatures is compared with the observed release rate function, so that a set of linear simultaneous equations is obtained. Solution of these equations then gives the n_{i0} values and thus the function $\rho(Q_i)$. Carter and Leck[15, 16] used 30 values of Q_i spaced at 1 K cal/mole intervals between 20 and 50 K cal/mole and obtained the activation energy spectrum for inert gases in glass shown in Figure 8.50. The same procedure can be applied to all the other release spectra described earlier, with, if necessary smaller intervals between the assumed Q_i's to achieve greater resolution of the spectrum.

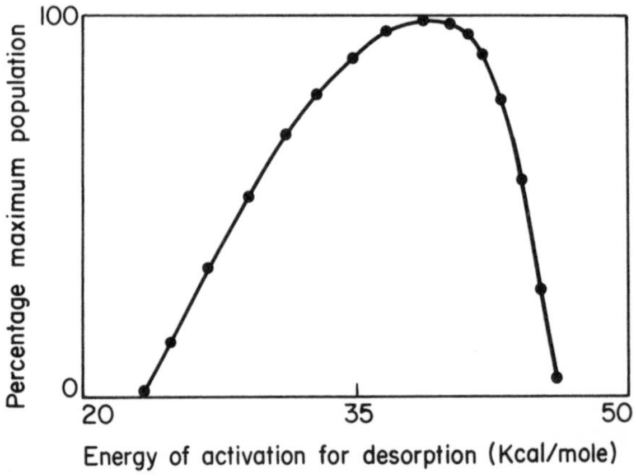

Fig. 8.50 The proportion of A atoms trapped in Pyrex glass as a function of the activation energy for desorption (computed from Fig. 8.30 viz. Ref. 8.15)

Although we have employed the one jump approximation to determine the spectra, a similar procedure can be applied using equations 8.37 if it is believed that gas is located over a depth distribution in addition to an energy spectrum. In the case of glass just cited it is probably justified to use the approximate method since the ion bombardment energy is so low that they are injected only just below the surface.

Although evaluation of the energy spectrum for a general distribution presents some difficulties, there is one special case of some interest and importance. This is where the trapped atoms are uniformly distributed between the two energies Q_1 and Q_2[51, 95, 96].

If there are n_0 trapped atoms between energy limits Q_1 and Q_2 the number initially trapped per unit energy interval

$$= \frac{n_0}{Q_2-Q_1} \qquad 8.43.1.$$

and in a range

$$\delta Q_i = \frac{n_0 \delta Q_i}{Q_2-Q_1}$$

The rate of gas release from sites in this energy range at a constant temperature T is then

$$-\frac{dn_i}{dt} = +\frac{n_i}{\tau_i}\delta Q_i$$

which is readily solved to give

$$\frac{dn_i}{dt} = -\frac{n_0}{Q_2-Q_1}\frac{\exp(-t/\tau_i)\ \delta Q_i}{\tau_i} \qquad 8.43.2.$$

The total rate of gas release is thus

$$\frac{dn}{dt} = -\frac{n_0}{Q_2-Q_1}\int_{Q_1}^{Q_2} \exp(-t/\tau_i\frac{dQ_i}{\tau_i} \qquad 8.43.3.$$

The integral is readily evaluated[95, 96] on substitution $\tau_i = \tau_0 \exp(Q_i/RT)$ (and thence $\delta Q_i = \frac{\delta \tau_i}{\tau_i}. RT$) Thus

$$\frac{dn}{dt} = \frac{n_0 RT}{Q_2-Q_1}\cdot\frac{1}{t}\{\exp(-t/\tau_1) - \exp(-t/\tau_2)\} \qquad 8.43.4.$$

This equation indicates that, for short times where $t \lesssim \tau_1$ $(= \tau_0 \exp(Q_1/RT))$ the re-emission rate is

$$\frac{n_0 RT}{Q_2-Q_1}\cdot\frac{1}{t}\{\exp(-t/\tau_1) - 1\}$$

since

$$t \ll \tau_2\ (= \tau_0 \exp(Q_2/RT))$$

which may be expanded to

$$\frac{n_0 RT}{Q_2-Q_1} \qquad 8.44.1.$$

i.e. a constant. For large times, where $t \gg \tau_1$ but $t < \tau_2$ the release rate is approximately

$$\frac{n_0 RT}{Q_2-Q_1}\cdot\frac{1}{t}$$

and this persists up to very long times, where $t \approx \tau_2$ and the release rate tends to zero. Essentially this equation shows that at a given time t gas is exhausted from the lowest energy sites Q_1 up to sites whose binding energy Q_i is determined by $t = \tau_i = \tau_0 \exp(Q_i/RT)$. This may be appreciated by noting that the release rate at a time t from sites of energy between Q_1 and Q_i is

$$\int_{Q_1}^{Q_i}\frac{dn_i}{dt}\cdot dQ_i = \frac{n_0 RT}{Q_2-Q_1}\cdot\frac{1}{t}\left(\exp-\frac{t}{\tau_1} - \exp-\frac{t}{\tau_i}\right) \qquad 8.45.1.$$

which, for $t \gg \tau_i$ tends to zero.

The fraction of trapped gas removed at this temperature is therefore

$$\frac{n_0 . Q_i - Q_1}{Q_2 - Q_1}$$

and according to Equation 8.45.1 is a linear function of the temperature T. The same result is obtained upon actual evaluation of the quantity of gas released n_r from

$$n_0 - \int_{Q_1}^{Q_2} n_i dQ_i = n_0 - \frac{n_0}{Q_2-Q_1}\int_{Q_1}^{Q_2}\exp(-t/\tau_i)dQ_i$$

at the time t.

Again substitution of $\tau_i = \tau_0 \exp(Q_i/RT)$ leads to the result[51] for the fraction of gas released $\frac{n_r}{n_0} = F$.

$$= 1 + \frac{RT}{Q_2-Q_1}\left\{E_i\left[-\frac{t}{\tau_0}\exp(-Q_1/RT)\right] + E_i\left[-\frac{t}{\tau_0}\exp-\frac{Q_2}{RT}\right]\right\} \qquad 8.46.1.$$

where E_i is the exponential integral defined by

$$-E_i(Z) = \int_Z^\infty \frac{e^{-u}}{u}du = -\log_e \gamma_0 Z + \frac{Z}{1|\underline{1}} - \frac{Z^2}{2|\underline{2}} + \ldots.$$

and γ_0 is a constant.

If the temperature T is above that required for rapid release of gas trapped with energy Q_1 but below that for rapid release of gas trapped with energy Q_2 then

$$-E_i\left(-\frac{t}{\tau_0}\exp(-Q_1 RT)\right) \to 0$$

and

$$-E_i\left(-\frac{t}{\tau_0}\exp(-Q_2/RT)\right) \to -\log_e\frac{\gamma_0 t}{\tau_0} + \frac{Q_2}{RT}$$

Hence

$$F \simeq \frac{RT}{Q_2-Q_1}\log_e\frac{\gamma_0 t}{\tau_0} - \frac{Q_1}{Q_2-Q_1} \qquad 8.46.2.$$

which illustrates the linear dependence of the fractional release upon T.

If the temperature is now raised to a new value T^1 a further fraction of gas

$$n_0 \cdot \frac{Q_j - Q_i}{Q_2 - Q_1}$$

is released in the same time t, between the energy limits Q_i and Q_j, where $t = \tau_0 \exp(Q_j/RT)$ and again this fraction is proportional to the new temperature T^1.

Thus, if the temperature is raised in a series of

stages, the fraction of gas removed at each step is directly proportional to the individual temperatures. This result is clearly representative of much of the data obtained by Kelly and Brown[121] in the 'damage diffusion' region, and one can therefore conclude that their results generally imply a uniform distribution of trapped gas in the activation energy spectrum. We may also note that the temperature T_2 at the termination of this spectrum is generally close to the characteristic temperature for normal diffusion, so that there is, in fact, a continuous spectrum.

It is more difficult to obtain an analytical expression for the instantaneous gas release rate when the temperature is raised continuously, but one can reasonably extrapolate (Ref. Grant and Carter[166], Erents, Grant and Carter[167]) the above result to the case where the temperature intervals are small, and eventually vanishing, so that the fraction of gas released during continuous temperature increase should also be proportional to the temperature and the rate of gas release should be approximately constant. This result is applicable to the early portions of the gas release spectra from Ag, Au and Pb observed by Tucker and Norton[117] and a uniform spectral distribution is again implicit.

It therefore appears that this special distribution function has some quite practical significance, and we shall shortly discuss a further important application.

8.8.3. Gas release at the bombardment temperature.

Since gas release occurs at elevated temperature after bombardment one may also anticipate release processes at the bombardment temperature both during and after bombardment.

For ions which have a depth trapping function p(x), one may write for the rate of trapping in the depth interval δx at x.

$$\frac{\partial C}{\partial t} = Bp(x) - D\frac{\partial^2 C}{\partial x^2} \qquad 8.47.1.$$

where the second term describes diffusion across the boundaries at x and $x + \delta x$, with a constant diffusion coefficient D.

If the surface is receding at a rate v due to sputtering, one can generalise this equation, for the depth $\xi = x - vt$ below the instantaneous surface,

$$\frac{\partial C}{\partial t} = Bp(\xi) - D\frac{\partial^2 C}{\partial \xi^2} \qquad 8.47.2.$$

which is readily transformed to

$$\frac{\partial c}{\partial t} = D\frac{\partial^2 C}{\partial x^2} + v\frac{\partial c}{\partial x} + Bp(x) \qquad 8.47.3.$$

This equation has been solved for three cases. First Equation 8.23.1 is the equivalent form for diffusionless trapping with the solution given by Equation 8.26.1 which, as we have already discussed may possess some validity for certain ion/target combinations. Kuchai and Rodin[168] have also solved Equation 8.47.3 employing the approximation that the ion range has a specific value L and there is no spread in ranges. Although, as we have seen in Chapter 5 this is hardly a physically reasonable situation, except perhaps for very low energy ions, it is interesting to note the solution to this situation, viz.

$$N(t) = \frac{BL^2}{v\sqrt{\pi}}\left\{\frac{1}{2}\frac{\sqrt{Dt}}{L}\frac{\exp L/\sqrt{4Dt} - \frac{v}{2}\sqrt{\frac{t}{D}}}{v^2t/4D - L^2/4Dt}\right\}^2$$

$$+ \exp\frac{vR}{2D}\int_0^{\frac{\sqrt{Dt}}{L}} \exp\left(-\frac{v^2L^2}{4D^2}.p + \frac{1}{4p^2}\right)dp \qquad 8.48.1.$$

where p is an arbitrary variable.

A saturation limit for the total quantity of gas trapped is determined at $t = \infty$ as

$$N_\infty = BL/v = nL/s_t \qquad 8.48.2.$$

just the result for diffusionless sputtering determined earlier (for a unique ion range) and the assumption employed by Kuchai and Rodin[168] that $\eta = 1$. Robinson[169] has also solved Equation 8.47.3 for a physically more realistic situation where the range has an arbitrary distribution p(x). In order to achieve a solution one must also postulate suitable boundary conditions, one of which $c \to o, x \to \infty$, is obviously quite acceptable. Another boundary condition imposed by Robinson[169] was that the surface concentration c(o, t) was equivalent to that if diffusion effects were absent i.e. as given in the Equation 8.28.2. Thus

$$c(o, t) = \frac{B}{v}\int_0^{vt} p(x)dx$$

Whether or not this is in fact a legitimate condition is open to doubt, and indeed, the more common assumption of diffusion theory that $c(o, t) = o$ appears to be equally valid. However, as shown by Robinson[169], whilst this arbitrary assumption for c(o, t) does change the time dependence of the rate of gas trapping and the total quantity of gas eventually trapped in a particular manner it does reveal that there is in fact such a time dependence, which may be different for different boundary conditions.

Robinson[169] solved Equation 8.47.3 using Fourier Transform methods in essentially the same manner as that developed by Kuchai and Rodin[168] but the analysis is rather involved and will not be reproduced in full here. The final result for the total quantity of gas trapped at a time t is

$$Nt = B/v\left[\eta\overline{L} + \frac{D}{v}\int_0^{vt} p(x)dx\right] - \frac{B}{2v}\int_0^{\infty} p(x)dx$$

$$\left\{(vt + x)e\frac{vx}{D}\operatorname{erfc}\left(\frac{vt + x}{\sqrt{4Dt}}\right)\right\} +$$

$$+ \frac{B}{2v}\int_0^{\infty} p(x)dx\left\{(vt-x)\operatorname{erfc}\frac{(vt-x)}{\sqrt{4Dt}}\right\}$$

$$- \frac{BD}{v^2}\int_0^{vt} p(x)dx\left\{\left(1 + \frac{v(vt-x)}{2D}\operatorname{erfc}\left[\frac{v(vt-x)}{2D}\right]^{1/2}\right) +\right.$$

$$\left.\left(\frac{v(vt-x)}{\pi D}^{1/2}\exp - \left[\frac{v(vt-x)}{4D}\right]\right)\right\} \qquad 8.49.1.$$

where $\overline{L}$ is the mean penetration depth defined earlier. For large times the error functions vanish and give

$$N_\infty \to nB\left\{\int_0^{\infty}\frac{p(x)dx}{v}\right\}\left\{\overline{L} + \frac{D}{v}\right\} \qquad 8.49.2.$$

which shows a different form than that for a unique range.

For diffusionless trapping this relation reduces to

$$N_\infty \to \frac{B}{v}\eta \int_0^x xp(x)dx$$

identical to Equation 8.26. There is an apparent disagreement between the results of Kuchai and Rodin[168], and of Robinson[169], since the former predicts a saturation level which is diffusion independent, whilst the latter deduces a dependence upon this parameter. One is inclined to accept the latter theory since Kuchai and Rodin's[168] defining equation did not include a source term (of the form $B\delta(\xi-L)$ but equated build up at $\xi = L$ to the diffusion across the plane at ξ. In addition, both equations 8.49.1 and 8.49.2 show that the quantity of gas trapped at any time decreases with increasing bombardment rate and this will be valid whether diffusion is of the normal type, or is enhanced by radiation damage. Consequently one would expect, in the presence of a diffusion process, that the quantity of gas trapped would depend upon the individual parameters of bombardment rate and time and not only upon their product, bombardment dose. The results of Almen and Bruce[77] for Kr on Al and Sn targets illustrate this behaviour, and indeed N_∞ appears to follow a dependence of the form $N_\infty \propto \frac{1}{B}$ as expected from Equation 8.49.2. Other ion target combinations showed no such effect however, a result also confirmed with 250 eV → 4 keV He, A and Xe ions in W by Corkhill and Carter[74], and one must conclude that the diffusion effects may only exist for certain combinations. Although Robinson[169] employed a specific form for c(o, t), any time dependent boundary conditions would also lead to a time dependence of the quantity of gas trapped and further experimental observations in this field will allow more precise stipulation of these boundary conditions.

One apparent failure of this simple theory is that only one diffusion constant D, typical of one thermally activated process, is considered whereas the experimental evidence so far presented, suggests operation of activation energy spectra. Reformation and solution of Equation 8.47.3 for such a special distribution of D is extremely complex, but simplification is possible if the one jump diffusion theory is postulated, as is probably legitimate for damage induced diffusion. In this case the defining equation for the rate of gas build up in trapping sites of time constant τ_i is

$$\frac{dn_i}{dt} = B\eta_i \frac{(n_{si}-n_i)}{n_{si}} - Bs_i\, f(n_i) - \frac{n_i}{\tau_i} \qquad 8.50.1.$$

Where the first term on the right hand side describes trapping into a maximum number of ith type sites n_{si}, the second term describes bombardment induced re-emission through the functional dependence $f(n_i)$ and the effective sputtering constant s_i and the final term describes spontaneous release due to damage controlled diffusion.

To be precise the final term is in fact

$$-\int_0^t \frac{1}{\tau_i}\frac{dn_i}{dt'}dt' \qquad 8.51.$$

where $\frac{dn_i}{dt'}$ is the instantaneous rate of gas trapping at any time t before t′ and this is of course simply $-\frac{n_i}{\tau_i}$. A further simplification results from the experimental observations in low energy ion bombarded glass and metals that for small quantities of gas trapped ($n_i \leqslant 0.1\, n_{si}$ the bombardment induced re-emission function $f(n_i) = cn_i$ and indeed this term is negligibly small for $n_i \lesssim 10^{-2}\, n_{si}$. Equation 8.50.1 therefore simplifies to

$$\frac{dn_i}{dt} = a\,B - bBn_i - n_i/\tau_i \qquad 8.50.2.$$

where

$$a = \eta_i,\; b = \frac{\eta_i + n_{si}s_i}{n_s'}$$

or

$$\frac{dn_i}{dt} = A - \frac{n_i}{\tau_i'} \qquad 8.50.3.$$

where

$$A = B\eta_i \text{ and } \frac{1}{\tau'_i} = Bb + \frac{1}{\tau_i}$$

This equation is solved simply to

$$n_i = A\tau_i'\{1 - \exp(-t/\tau'_i)\} \qquad 8.50.4.$$

and eventually, after a long period

$$n_{i\infty} \to A\tau i \qquad 8.50.5.$$

whereas, for short bombardment times

$$n_i \approx B\eta_i\, t \qquad 8.50.6.$$

These relations indicate that the populations of ith type sites build up to a dynamic equilibrium limit which depends upon the bombardment rate and the effective time constant τ_i' at a rate which also depends upon this effective time constant τ_i'.

The effective time constant τ_i' is itself composed of contributions from the thermal release time constant and from bombardment induced release and maximum site availability considerations.

The initial population is seen to increase independently of these parameters however. Thus for sites where the thermal time constant $\tau_i = \tau_0 \exp(Q_i/RT)$ is small compared with $B(\eta_i/n_{si} + si)$ this former time constant dominates the final population distribution, but for sites where the thermal time constant is large compared with $B(\eta_i/n_{si} + si)$ this latter time constant conditions the final population distribution. Unfortunately precise data for η_i, n_{si} and s_i is not available for either glass or metal targets but from the data observed by Cobic et al[14] and James and Carter[42, 43] for glass targets one can estimate $\eta_i \approx 0.2$, $n_{si} \approx 3 \times 10^{15}$ per unit energy interval and $s_i = 10^{-14}$ per unit energy interval, i.e. $b \approx 10^{-14}/cm^2$. For a normal surface bombardment rate of 3×10^{11} ions/cm²/sec this suggests a maximum population and bombardment induced time constant $\frac{1}{bB}$ of approximately 300 seconds. At room temperature atoms trapped with energies in the region of 21-22 K cal/mole possess this order of thermal time constant, so that the build up of atoms with energies somewhat less than this value (~20 K cal/mole) will be conditioned by their thermal time constant, but atoms trapped with energies $\gtrsim$ 25 K cal/mole will be little effected by the thermal processes. Confirmation of this latter prediction is afforded when it is remembered that the shape of the spectral distribution curve for gases trapped in glass in Figure 8.30 was found, to be virtually independent of the total dose (and therefore time) above an energy in the region of $\gtrsim$ 25 K cal/mole i.e. the final form of the n/Q (or n/τ_i') spectrum depends only upon the relative values of η_i, n_{si} and s_i for sites with Q > 25 K cal/mole. The build-up of gas in sites with binding energies $\lesssim$ 25 K cal/mole has not been studied in a similar way and indeed this would be difficult without immediate refrigeration after trapping, since upon cessation of trapping at normal temperatures, gas evolves from these sites very rapidly (i.e. $\tau \approx$ experimental observation times). This spontaneous emission process itself, however, suggests that a study of its behaviour will clarify the situation for trapping energies < 25 K cal/mole and the experiments of Smeaton et al[96] for glass targets help to elucidate the process.

If we consider Equation 8.50.4 for small values of the trapping time, then the quantity of gas trapped in any energy interval δQ_i is simply proportional to $B\eta_i\ \delta Q_i$ i.e. a uniform spectral distribution of gas. Upon cessation of bombardment, gas is then re-emitted from these sites according to the simple Equation

$$\frac{dni}{dt} = -\frac{CB\eta i\ \delta Qi}{\tau_i} \qquad 8.52.$$

For a uniform energy spectral distribution of trapped atoms between limits Q_1 and Q_2 we have already noted that the total gas release rate, for times $\tau_1 < t < \tau_2$, is proportional to t^{-1} (viz Equation 8.43.4) and Smeaton et al have reported just this behaviour.

As the bombardment time is increased, at a fixed bombardment rate B, gas builds up in individual sites according to Equation 8.50.4 and it is clear that this results in preferential build up in sites with the larger effective time constants τ_i' i.e. n_i increases with increasing τ_i. This is of course physically logical since gas is trapped for longer periods before release for larger trapping time constants. Erents, Grant and Carter[170] have shown how it is possible to solve exactly an analogous form to Equation 8.43 when the gas spectral distribution is an arbitrary function $n(Q_i) = f(Q_i)$. Thus, one may expand the function $f(Q_i)$ $f(Q_i) = a + be^{\alpha_1 Q_i} + Ce^{\alpha_2 Q_i} \ldots\ldots$ 8.53 and show both analytically and graphically, that for $f(Q_i)$ as an increasing function of Q_i, the rate of gas release at $\tau_1 < t < \tau_2$ is still adequately described by a form $\frac{dn}{dt} = -Kt^{-m}$ where $o < m < 1$. It is also found that m decreases as the spectra become more heavily weighted towards higher energies i.e. as the trapping time increases. Once again Smeaton et al[96] found that the release rate of gas after long trapping times was described by the above relation with m decreasing with increasing trapping time (viz. Figure 8.28). In addition Equation 8.50.4 predicts that the departure from a uniform spectral distribution will be less, for a given trapping time, the larger the bombardment rate, since Bb then dominates the trapping time constants for all values of τ_i. Smeaton et al[96] also report an increase of m with increasing bombardment rate expected from this behaviour. (again viz. Figure 8.28). These authors[96] also show that above a certain bombardment rate there is no further change in the index m for any given pumping time and this is interpreted as indicating that trapping is completely dictated by maximum available population and bombardment induced emission considerations.

It is also evident that for short pumping times, as much gas will be trapped in low release energy sites as in higher energy sites, so that a considerable fraction of trapped gas may be subsequently recovered. For longer trapping times, gas will build up preferentially in the higher energy sites so that the fraction of gas recovered will diminish, a fact also observed by Smeaton et al and by other investigators using both static and dynamic bombardment conditions. Thus, gas recovery at the bombardment temperature gives information on the activation energy spectral distribution between about 18 and 25 K cal/mole, which supplements the data obtained from elevated temperature gas release giving the spectra above 25 K cal/mole. For the case of glass the release data for long bombardment times and rates, where bombardment induced phenomena are important, indicates a distribution which increases with Q up to 25 K cal/mole, just as the elevated temperature recovery data predicts a rising f(Q) dependence above this energy.

We should note that this model can also explain the various t^{-m} release rate functions reported by different authors for differing bombardment conditions. Cavaleru et al[91, 92] have also interpreted their release data from glass in terms of sites of different release energy, but because of the method of presentation of the results suggest the existence of only two such types of sites with binding energies of about 20 and 25 K cal/mole respectively. We have seen, however, that this data may be re-interpreted in the same way as Smeaton et al's results[96], so that a spectrum of activation energies is probable.

In particular the t^{-1} dependence (up to 1/10th. saturation coverage) observed under static bombardment conditions by Varnerin and Carmichael[29], and Fox and Knoll[49], is illustrative of a quite uniform site energy population distribution over a wide energy range (since bombardment times from about 1 second up to 10^5 seconds gave this behaviour). This t^{-1} dependence was observed over an effectively wide range of bombardment rates and times and this suggests that the effective time constant is dominated by the bB term. It is improbable that a large value of bB results from a large value of the sputtering coefficient, since as we have already seen, Carmichael and Trendelenberg's[80] values for this parameter are of the order 0.1-1. A more probable reason is that the maximum number of available sites is small and some evidence of this is to be found in the fact that Carmichael and his collaborators[29,81] observed that the re-emission rate was given by $\frac{kn_T}{t}$ where n_T was the quantity of gas trapped and k was a constant with values between 0.01 and 4×10^{-3} depending upon the ion species. According to the simple theory developed above, the re-emission rate should be given by

$\frac{RT}{Q_2 - Q_1} \cdot \frac{n_T}{t}$. Since the inverse time dependence of the release rate is observed up to times of 10^4 secs. at room temperature, $\frac{RT}{Q_2 - Q_1}$ is of order 0.1 which leads one to believe that of the total quantity of gas trapped, less than 10% is trapped in the low energy range. i.e. the saturation values for n_{si} in this energy range are small.

We may also note that Kelly and Brown's[119, 121] and Tucker and Norton's[117] elevated temperature gas release data also suggest a uniform site population distribution at energies greater than 25 K cal/mole even under saturation conditions and a continuation of this spectrum to lower energies seems valid. Although these studies were typical of high incident energy ions, we may note that Kornelsen's[72] low ion energy data for tungsten are also suggestive of a uniform site population towards the low energy end of the release spectrum.

We should point out that both Carmichael and his collaborators[29, 81] and Blodgett and Vanderslice[87] have attempted interpretation of their data in terms of the diffusion controlled mechanism with a single activation energy. For such a process, and an initial penetration function uniform with depth, solution of Equation 8.34.1 readily shows that the release rate is proportional to $t^{-1/2}$ whilst some other penetration function might be expected to give a t^{-1} dependence. However, a diffusion controlled process with a single activation energy Q should give a linear dependence of the logarithmic fractional recovery at a given time upon the reciprocal temperature during bombardment, with a slope equal to Q. Blodgett and Vanderslice[87] have in fact observed such an approximate temperature dependence from -75°C to +150°C but arrive at the result that $Q = 4$ K cal/mole. We have already shown that such a low activation energy is only reconcilable with re-emission data if the ion penetration depth is $\gtrsim 10^6$ Å, which is rather large for 100 eV Argon ions in glass. Such a result could equally well be obtained if the population energy spectrum is increasing with energy, and of an approximate form $f(Q) = ae^{\alpha Q}$. This type of energy spectrum was in fact observed in the elevated temperature release studies by Carter and Leck[15, 16].

Another fact which mitigates against the concept of a single diffusion energy is the experimental observation by Smeaton et al[144] and Jech[140] that upon heating a bombarded target to a given temperature, then cooled and finally reheated, thermal re-emission only recommences at the high temperature. If the release process was diffusion controlled with a single activation energy then heating and cooling would only cause a redistribution of gas atoms and immediately upon reheating, gas would be released at all temperatures. The observations are readily explained on the basis of an activation energy spectrum however since all gas with activation energies less than about 71 T is removed by heating to a temperature T. Subsequent cooling and reheating does not cause further release until the temperature again exceeds T where higher energy sites are activated. We may also note that such an activation energy spectrum readily explains the results obtained by Cobic, Carter and Leck[14] for glass and Almen and Bruce[77] for metals, that the ion trapping efficiency decreases with increasing target temperature. As the bombardment temperature is increased, ions only remain trapped for times significantly greater than observation times in sites of energy 71T. Thus a smaller fraction of the activation energy spectrum is effective in trapping gas as the target temperature increases, so η falls. It is significant that Cobic et al[14] found that the temperatures for which $\eta \to 0$ for glass surfaces were similar to the temperatures where gas release tends to zero during temperature cycling after bombardment at room temperature.

The increased availability of trapping sites with time constants greater than the experimental time also explains the results of Carter[27] and Cobic et al[14], Hobson and Edmonds[116] and Kelly[50] that increased gas trapping occurs at lower than room temperature.

On the other hand the results of Maddix and Allen[21, 22, 23] which we have previously seen give anomalously large trapped gas populations, also showed a $t^{-1/2}$ release rate dependence. However, these authors measured an activation energy of about 40 K cal/mole for A and about 11 K cal/mole for He and Ne in quartz which are much more acceptable results, and it appears that in this case normal diffusion may have been dominant. The quartz wall temperature may have been sufficiently large in these experiments to clear all damage diffusion sites and leave normal diffusion as the only operative process. It is possible that during bombardment the incident ions are initially trapped in damage configurations but they then diffuse, at the high bombardment temperatures, into the bulk. Cobic et al[44] also invoked such a possibility to explain the very large quantities of He which may be trapped in Pyrex glass and a similar interpretation may apply to the trapping of He in Ni. We may also note that in investigations in which inert gases have been introduced by nuclear decay processes uniformly throughout various materials, evidence of only a normal diffusion with the expected diffusion energy has been found[171, 172].

In view of the fact that a normal diffusional component is frequently observed in gas desorption, it is perhaps necessary to give a further brief consideration to the influence this process exerts on both sorption and desorption characteristics. In most of the ion-solid combinations we have discussed, it is very unlikely that normal diffusion occurred during trapping since the target temperatures were too small, nor does it appear that radiation enhanced processes are generally active. However in the studies of gas trapping in quartz surfaces by Maddix and Allen[21, 22, 23], the operating temperatures were sufficiently large to allow normal diffusion processes and, it is believed, accounted for the extremely large quantities of trapped gas and the $(\text{time})^{-1/2}$ dependence of both trapping and recovery processes. Although we discussed effects occurring during trapping in Section 8.7.2. it is appropriate to consider the process again here, since our treatment is based essentially on the arguments leading to Equations 8.50. and is equally valid for the post bombardment release process.

If we assume that the ion penetration depth is small, and single valued, but that in addition to trapping and release processes, trapped gas can diffuse into the target during bombardment, Equation 8.50.1 can be rewritten, for atoms trapped with a single time constant

$$\frac{dn_i}{dt} = B\eta_i \frac{(n_{si}-n_i)}{n_{si}} - Bs_i\, f(n_i) - \frac{n_i}{\tau_i} - g(n_i) \qquad 8.54.1.$$

where g(n) is the rate at which trapped gas can diffuse into the solid from the plane source at the surface.

Exact solution of 8.54.1. is possible only if n_i (and thence $g(n_i)$) are known but it is clear that n_i will eventually reach a dynamic equilibrium value when the ion trapping is just balanced by gas release and in-diffusion. If it is assumed that in-diffusion always occurs only from an essentially plane source, one can immediately write, from standard diffusion theory

$$g(n_i) = n_i \sqrt{D/\pi t} \qquad 8.55.$$

For large bombardment rates ($B = 10^{19}$ ions/cm²/

sec. in the work of Maddix and Allen[21, 22, 23]), the trapping and desorption processes will generally be much larger than the in-diffusion rate and so in determining n_i, the term $g(n_i)$ can, be ignored, whilst again, for simplification, we can assume that bombardment induced re-emission processes are unimportant. Thus 8.54.1. is solved to

$$n_i = \frac{B\tau_i}{1 + \frac{\eta . B\tau_i}{n_{si}}}\left\{1 - \exp\left[-\frac{t}{\tau_i}\left(1 + \frac{\eta B\tau_i}{n_{si}}\right)\right]\right\} \qquad 8.56.1.$$

or at dynamic equilibrium

$$n_f = B\tau_i/1 + \frac{\eta B\tau_i}{n_{si}} \qquad 8.56.2.$$

Equation 8.56.2. can now be used with 8.55 to give the in-diffusion rate when surface saturation is attained i.e.

$$g(n_i) = \frac{B\tau_i}{1 + \frac{\eta B\tau_i}{n_{si}}}\left(\frac{D_0}{\pi t}\right)^{1/2} \exp\left(-\frac{Q}{2RT}\right) \qquad 8.57.1.$$

This illustrates that the rate of in-diffusion should, after an initial interval to build up the surface concentration n_f, vary as $t^{-1/2}$, and just this behaviour has been reported by Maddix and Allen[21, 22, 23] for sorption of He, Ne and A in quartz. Further, from the temperature dependence of $g(n_i)$, one could in principle, obtain the activation energy for diffusion Q. However τ_i also varies in an exponential manner with temperature according to the Frenkel[152] equation. $\tau = \tau_0 \exp(Q_s/RT)$ where Q_s is the surface trapping energy. If we assume that $Q_s = Q$, i.e. that surface trapped atoms possess the same trapping energy as the diffusion energy, which is expected to be true near temperatures where diffusion occurs rapidly and low energy trapping sites are rapidly cleared, then

$$g(n_i) \propto B \exp(Q/2RT) \qquad 8.57.2.$$

and Q can be deduced.

Maddix and Allen[21, 22, 23] have determined Q for He, Ne and A, by this method and obtained values close to the accepted data.

Inspection of 8.57.1. shows that, as T(and τ) increases, $g(n_i)$ should increase, reach a maximum, since at lower temperatures the surface density is large but the diffusion rate is small, whilst at higher temperatures the situation is reversed. Again Maddix and Allen[21, 22, 23] observed this form of temperature variation.

If, during trapping, the bombarding flux of ions is removed, gas atoms are re-emitted from the diffusion profile, which, according to Jost[148] will be exponentially decreasing with depth, and the rate of gas re-emission can be determined. Maddix and Allen[21, 22, 23], have performed the necessary calculations and once again determined Q, from the temperature variation, to be close to accepted values for He, Ne and A in quartz.

We should comment that the behaviour observed by the above authors is in fact only typical of the system employed, since generally the bombarding ion flux and the surface temperatures were high enough to allow both sufficient surface population and a high in-diffusion rate. In ion beam experiments (and other ionization tube methods) the surface ion fluxes are smaller by many orders of magnitude and the target temperatures too low, to allow a sufficiently high surface atom density or inwards migration. Thus, in these experiments, saturation is generally determined by surface erosion by sputtering. In Maddix and Allen's[21, 22, 23] work this, and radiation damage were minimised by using low energy ions. In fact this work differs only from conventional gaseous permeation studies in that the ions are injected beyond the surface potential barrier dynamically, rather than by the normal surface atomic relaxation. We thus conclude that from all the experimental evidence it appears that for most ion/target combinations at particular temperatures a certain proportion of the thermal release phenomenon is the result of gas re-emission from spectra of activated energy sites produced by damage to the lattice. In certain cases a uniformly populated spectrum is a sufficiently good approximation to the gas distribution. It now remains to investigate the nature of these damage trapping sites. There is also considerable evidence for a normal diffusional release, and the necessary conditions for this appear to be either a sufficiently high target temperature during trapping to ensure indiffusion or a high ion energy to ensure deep penetration.

8.9. THE LOCATION OF TRAPPED GAS

We have seen that in many cases, gas release occurs at temperatures different from those expected on the basis of the normal thermal diffusion process. Those occurring below the 'normal diffusion temperature range', we have ascribed to the production of damage sites and/or paths, those above this temperature range, to gas bubble formation and migration. Before considering the nature of these two processes in further detail we should discuss the location of trapped gas atoms which are released by the 'normal diffusion process'. Before diffusion such atoms are presumably located in the lattice position in which they would normally dissolve independently of the manner in which they had entered the target. Rimmer and Cottrell[173] have discussed the solution of inert gas atoms in simple metals such as copper and we will summarize their computational methods and results here. These authors considered three possible gas atom configurations (1) Interstitial solution (2) Substitutional solution where the gas atom displaces a lattice atom to become accommodated and (3) Substitutional solution where thermal vacancies are available and allow strain release. It was shown that the total energy of solution was made up of the strain energy introduced by the presence of the dissolved atom and the loss of cohesive energy at the site of this atom.

The magnitude of the strain energy was computed by inserting a trial gas atom at an appropriate lattice position and relaxing neighbouring atoms by variable distances. The interatomic potential between copper atoms (assuming a Huntington potential[174]) and between a copper atom and the inert gas atom (obtained from a combination of Cu-Cu atom, and mutual inert gas atom potentials obtained from data by Buckingham[175] and Stewart[176] (for A), Mason and Rice[177], Slater and Kirkwood[178] (for He), Buckingham (for Ne)[175] and Beattie[179] (for Kr and Xe)) were then used to determine the total strain energy as a function of the copper atomic displacements, and the equilibrium displacements were deduced when this strain energy was a minimum.

Because of the high resonance and ionization potentials of the inert gases these would be expected to retain their electrons when in solution and these would therefore not contribute noticeably to cohesion of the lattice. Thus the dissolved atom could be treated as occupying a vacancy of equivalent volume, the energy of which is known to be contributed mainly by the conduction electrons in a monovalent metal. Following the methods of Friedel[180] and Fumi[181], the increase in electronic energy was shown to be $\frac{4}{15} E_F$ per atomic volume occupied by the gas atom (E_F is the conduction band width). In addition the increase in electronic energy in the dilated lattice surrounding the trapped atom was also included. These contributions to the cohesive energy were evaluated when the equilibrium lattice configuration had been determined.

Finally, in the case of substitutional solution without free vacancies the energy necessary to create a vacancy and the resulting interstitial were added (using Huntingtons values of $E_{1V} \simeq 1$ ev and $E_i \simeq 4.5$ eV) whereas for the case where free vacancies were available and could be captured by the gas atom, only the energy of the vacancy E_{1V} was added.

From these considerations Rimmer and Cottrell[173] deduced the energies of solution of the five inert gases in Cu for assumed interstitial and both substitutional positions, with the results given in Table 8.10 (The two columns for A, Kr and Xe represent data obtained with different gas interatomic potentials). It is clear from this Table that A, Kr and Xe atoms will always dissolve substitutionally, whether free vacancies are available or not. Neon should also dissolve substitutionally when thermal vacancies are available (or vacancies induced by radiation damage), but in the absence of vacancies, interstitital solution would be preferred. The same situation would obtain for He atoms.

Because of the large strain energy involved in the substitutional solution of Xe it is quite probable that this atom would tend to relax the strain by capturing further vacancies and this would be rather easy in a damaged lattice. In addition, clustering of several gas atoms and association with a number of vacancies, would allow considerable strain relaxation since the lattice atoms around the larger periphery of the cluster would be more easily re-arranged. In this way bubble nucleation would be a favourable process and would be very probable in an ion bombardment damaged target.

We see already from the above discussion that the dissolution process can be considerably modified by the presence of vacancies (thermally or damage induced) and thus in an ion bombarded lattice one may anticipate normal diffusion, between the sites of normal solution, damage diffusion due to capture of vacancies or along otherwise modified paths, and bubble formation and migration.

Present knowledge of normal diffusion energies is limited, but, as seen in our earlier discussion there appears to be a number of experimental observations of gas release along diffusion paths with energies which correspond reasonably well with anticipated normal diffusion energies. Unfortunately no detailed gas release measurements have been made with a Cu target and different bombarding ions so that the Rimmer and Cottrell[173] analysis cannot be applied. However there have been numerous measurements of gas release which can only be explained on the basis of a damage enhanced diffusion process. The activation energy spectra for these processes appear to extend generally below the normal diffusion energy down to an energy determined by the bombardment temperature, but as in the case of He^+ and Ne^+ ions in glass[14, 15, 16] the damage diffusion activation energy spectrum appears to extend above the normal diffusion energy. In fact in amorphous glass[15, 16], as in polycrystalline tungsten[72] targets, there is little difference between the release energy spectra of the five inert gases from He to Xe. This suggests that it is a property of the target which determines the gas release rather than the bombarding ion species, since according to the Rimmer-Cottrell[173] analysis different ions should follow quite different diffusional behaviour. In the absence of any detailed experimental observations of the lattice configurations surrounding trapped atoms in a target, one can only speculate upon the influence of the target. According to the

TABLE 8.10. (Ref. 8.173).

Energies of Solution of Inert Gases in Copper

Type of Solution	Energy Terms	He	Ne	A(a)	A(b)	Kr(c)	Kr(d)	Xe(c)	Xe(d)
Interstitial	Strain	1.7	3.4	10.6	7.7	14.9	10.8	24.5	17.5
	Electronic	0.8	1.2	3.0	2.3	4.6	3.0	6.5	4.9
	E_i	2.5	4.6	13.6	10.0	19.5	13.8	31.0	22.4
Substitutional with thermal vacancies	Strain	0	0.3	2.2	1.7	3.8	2.7	7.8	5.7
	Electronic	0	0.1	0.7	0.5	1.4	0.8	2.4	1.5
	E_{1V}	1.0	1.0	1.0	1.0	1.0	1.0	1.0	1.0
	E_{S2}	1.0	1.4	3.9	3.2	6.2	4.5	11.2	8.2
Substitutional with no thermal vacancies	$E_{S1} = E_{S2} + E_i$	5.5	5.9	8.4	7.7	10.7	9.0	15.7	12.7

(a) Ref. 8.175. (b) Ref. 8.176. (c) Ref. 8.179. (d) Ref. 8.177.

computer calculations of Beeler and Besco[182] the damage inflicted by an energetic ion on a single crystal target can result in the production of a wide variety of vacancy and interstitial cluster configurations, including dislocations of various types and sizes each of which may be associated with trapped atoms. The release energy spectrum therefore may be representative of the energies of rearrangement of these configurations back to the normal lattice structure which will tend to be a function of the lattice atoms only. Isolated vacancies will also be produced near the surface by the bombardment. Gas release may occur since in the rearranging cluster the vacancies are close to the surface, the energies of motion will be less than for normal migration. On the other hand the annealing of dislocations in the same temperature range as normal diffusional release, as observed in Au by Ogilvie et al[183] tends to support this model and Kelly and Ruedl's[125, 126] observations with Pt show that this diffusional release is associated with dislocation disappearance, which occur with normal migration energy. We should remember that if rearrangement processes occur with an energy Q_1 and this merely frees a gas atom for normal diffusion with an activation energy Q_2, then if $Q_2 > Q_1$ gas release will not be observed until a temperature commensurate with Q_2 is reached. Thus atoms trapped near the surface which are released in the rearrangement process will evolve at temperatures conditioned by Q_1, but more deeply located atoms may only evolve at temperatures characteristic of Q_2. Consequently release of gas trapped after high bombardment energies will show preferential normal diffusion release as found by Kelly and Brown[121]. For rearrangement processes where $Q_1 > Q_2$ gas release will always be conditioned by damage diffusion.

In an amorphous target such as glass one may anticipate that a quite broad spectrum of activation energies could exist because of the gross heterogenity of the target material. In polycrystalline tungsten[72], the observation of relatively discrete peaks superimposed on a continuous background spectrum may suggest the operation of a few prefered types of damage configuration (e.g. a trapped gas atom associated with definite numbers of vacancies) or surface atomic plane but because of the polycrystallinity these may exist below superficial planes of random orientation which smears out the well defined spectrum. Kornelsen's[119, 200] observations with single crystal targets do in fact reveal the importance of the target structure, whilst the low energy He data of Erents and Carter[201] suggests that damage is not necessary to account for all gas release in stage I. The equally valid explanation for 'damage diffusion' developed by Auskern[133] and Kelly[123] should also be given prominence however. In this model the vacancies produced by the bombardment migrate with energies less than that for normal diffusion and conditioned by surface proximity. It may well be that stage I release consists of contributions due to both surface proximity considerations and due to damage induced effects. An urgent need exists for further experiments in this field using single crystal targets, with which some closer comparison with theoretical data may be possible.

Although it is not fruitful to further pursue damage diffusion processes at this stage, a considerable amount of evidence has been accumulated on another form of migration which we have mentioned, viz. bubble formation and migration and we conclude this Chapter with a discussion of this topic.

8.10. BUBBLE FORMATION AND MIGRATION.

Because of the considerable vacancy production during ion irradiation, and because the strain energy associated with a trapped atom-vacancy aggregate is generally less than that for the atom trapped in a normal substitutional or interstitial site, one may expect some gas atom-vacancy agglomeration in an ion bombarded target. This should be particularly prevalent when the trapped atom and vacancy concentrations are large as will occur with large ion doses and high ion energies. As we shall see these are just the conditions under which gas bubbles (consisting of gas and vacancies) have been experimentally observed in electron microscopic examination. We have already mentioned these experimental observations in Chapter 6 and earlier in this Chapter and we shall now discuss these in greater detail and attempt an explanation of the measurements. In addition to gas bubble production as a result of ion bombardment, Helium, Krypton and Xenon gas bubbles have been observed to form in reactor materials due to nuclear reaction and transmutation effects, and although we shall not describe these further here, the production of gas bubbles in materials clearly has some practical significance.

Barnes and his collaborators[184, 185, 186], have been most active in investigating this topic and in early electron microscopic studies[184] of the injection of ~30 MeV α particles into Be, Cu, Al and U at 200°C showed that no observable He bubbles formed (i.e. with sizes above the 20 Å resolution of the microscope) even when the α particle dose was equivalent to insertion of 1 Atom% of He atoms in the trapping region. Upon heating to 650°C after bombardment however, Helium bubbles were observed to form in initially well defined regions. These regions included the free surface, if He atoms had come to rest there, grain boundaries, and some non coherent twin boundaries and dislocation lines, but never at coherent twin boundaries. During the initial stages of heating the bubbles formed close to the boundaries but subsequently this region extended away from the boundary until all the region initially containing stopped He atoms were filled with bubbles. At this later stage however some of the regions close to the boundaries often became denuded of bubbles. The simple explanation of these observations was that at sufficiently high temperatures, vacancies could be generated at a source, such as a free surface or grain boundary and these would migrate to and agglomerate with trapped He atoms to form bubbles. The regions closest to the trapped atoms precipitated bubbles first, then, once these bubbles were stabilised, the vacancies migrated to more remote parts of the lattice to precipitate further bubbles. If vacancies were generated at a boundary then their flow to the bubbles would result in a counter flow of lattice atoms to the boundary so that atoms would build up at the boundary and leave an apparently bubble denuded region close to the boundary. Since this was observed at some boundaries it was concluded that vacancies were truly generated there. At non denuded boundaries however it was believed that these were behaving merely as conductors of vacancies from, and lattice atoms back to, a true vacancy source. Such conducting boundaries were identified as grain boundaries adjacent to twinned boundaries. This concept of vacancy conduction and lattice atom counter conduction was confirmed by showing that the extra atomic content of denuded target near boundaries was balanced by the vacancies in the bubbles (which were of order 3000 Å diameter). The actual bubble nucleation sites were not identified in this work, but subsequent investigations by Barnes Barnes[185] and Mazey[186] showed that small vacancy clusters (radius 20 Å were formed during α particle irradiation of Al and Cu at 350°C, and, in regions of the target containing trapped He, these clusters grew and precipitated into He bubbles of ~40 Å radius, upon heating to temperatures between 450°and 750°C. The observed lack of further bubble growth during bombardment was presumably a result of insufficient vacancy production which could migrate to and enlarge the bubbles. It is interesting to note that, from measurement of the bubble diameters and bubble density Barnes and Mazey[186] calculated the He content of the bubbles in the targets to be $\sim 10^{-3}$ atom‰. It is very tempting to interpret this as showing that the bubbles contained all the entrapped He atoms and that small bubbles at least could be nucleated spontaneously in a displacement spike type of process or by collision of ions with dislocation loops.

Nelson[187] bombarded Cu, Ag, Au and Al with 60 keV, He^+, A^+ and Xe^+ ions at temperatures between 20°C and 500°C and also observed gas bubble formation with the mean bubble radius increasing from < 20 Å at 20°C to 135 Å at 500°C. This result again suggested that some bubbles must have been nucleated spontaneously via a damage induced process, possibly upon the small dislocation loops, but that the bubble size could be increased when the supply of vacancies from various sources by thermal activation was increased, and when gas atom migration may have been rapid to allow agglomeration. Indeed Nelson[187] concludes, as we have suggested above, that all gas is nucleated into some bubble form by damage events which provide the necessary vacancies, at least at the high ion energies used in his investigations. At low temperatures the bubble sizes may only be small of course, but as the temperature is increased trapped gas may migrate quickly to the nucleation sites and form larger bubbles. On the other hand, Kelly and Ruedl[125] observed that bubbles only nucleated during heating of Kr^+ ion irradiated Pi, and since most gas is released via normal diffusion in this system it appears that very little spontaneous nucleation occurred. The situation may well vary with ion energy and dose however. Gas bubble formation has also been observed by Brebec et al[188], Castaing and Jouffrey[189] and Jouffrey[190] during relatively low energy (< 4 keV) bombardment of silver and gold. Jouffrey[190] observed the formation of bubbles of Argon ($\lesssim$ 20Å diameter) after bombarding Au targets with 4 keV ions at temperatures around 200°C to a dose of about 5×10^{15} ions/cm^2. Gas bubbles formed throughout the irradiated area but preferentially upon dislocation loops, and it was noted that enhanced bubble production occurred if the target was heated to 250°C following bombardment. These results indicate that even with low energy ions, sufficient nucleation sites must be formed for gas bubbles to form by vacancy capture. Because the ion penetration depth is short it is probable that many vacancies migrate to the nucleation sites from the free surface.

As we saw in Chapter 6 Jouffrey[190] also observed production of small dots, diameter < 40 Å, during ion bombardment at room temperature, and which subsequently disappeared on heating to 165°C. We suggested earlier that these were vacancy clusters and it seems probable that these were the nucleation sites for the Argon bubble formation. Indirect evidence of the formation of gas bubbles has been obtained by Kaminsky[191] who observed that 125 keV D^+ ions bombarding copper released pulses of previously trapped D atoms. The pulse sizes were such as to suggest bursting of gas bubbles at the surface, and it was believed that these minor explosions were probably the cause of etch pit formation during bombardment. Primak[192] has also observed that high energy protons or He^+ ions cause stress relaxation and surface cracking of silica, and this has been interpreted as due to the growth of sub surface gas bubbles.

We may also note an effect of gas bubble production investigated by Ghosh, Beevers and Barnes[143]. These authors found that in the regions of α particle bombarded Cu containing He bubbles, there was a considerable hardening, and this was attributed to pinning of dislocations by the gas bubbles.

A further deleterious effect of bubble formation is the volume expansion of gas-containing solids, and Barnes and his co workers have shown that this is a result of bubble migration, to which we now turn our attention. Barnes and Mazey[194] bombarded Cu films to a 0.1 atomic percent concentration of He with 38 MeV particles and then pulse heated these films to 800°C in the electron microscope itself. Bubbles of various sizes were present and these were observed to move rapidly and all in the same direction with velocities in the region of 1000 Å/sec.

The velocities of smaller bubbles were higher than those of larger bubbles and apparently the bubble velocity was inversely proportional to the bubble radius. Quite frequently bubbles were observed to meet the free surface and burst, releasing their trapped gas, whilst small bubbles were observed to collide and combine to form a larger bubble. In these cases the total surface area of the combining bubbles, radii r_1 and r_2 was preserved in the resultant bubble, radius R, so that $r_1^2 + r_2^2 = R^2$. On the other hand some cases were observed where small bubbles contacted larger bubbles for long periods of time without apparent coalescence, and this suggested that strain fields surrounded the smaller bubbles at least. Further, bubbles were only observed to change size via the coalescence process and these facts revealed that the He did not redissolve into the lattice during heating. Because of this bubble migration and coalescence the volume occupied by the bubbles increases and so the target material swells, and Barnes[195] and Greenwood and Speight[196] have constructed simple theories on these lines to explain swelling, which is of considerable practical importance, in irradiated reactor materials. Although the details of the calculations need not concern us here, some of the basic principles invoked by these authors to explain bubble migration are relevant to our discussion.

Although the exact mechanism of initial bubble nucleation is still rather nebulous, one can comment upon the physical properties of these bubbles once formed. Since Barnes and Mazey's[194] results indicated that stable bubbles do not acquire or lose further gas or vacancies during migration one may assume that each is in thermodynamic equilibrium with the target. If such is the case the gas pressure within the bubble will balance the forces exerted by the lattice upon the bubble. These forces will be due to the intrinsic strength of the lattice σ^1, any external pressure exerted on the target P^1 and the surface tension force between gas atoms and the target, which for a bubble of radius r is $2\gamma/r$ where γ is the surface energy and is generally of the order 10^3 ergs/cm^2. Assuming the gas in the bubbles to obey the perfect gas laws, one obtains, for a bubble radius r.

$$\frac{2\gamma}{r} + \sigma^1 + P^1 \frac{4\pi}{3} r^3 = mkT \qquad 8.58.1.$$

where m is the number of atoms in the bubble, k is Boltzmann's constant and T the absolute temperature. If there are n bubbles of equal size per sq. cm. of target, then since σ^1 and P^1 are generally small compared with $2\gamma/r$ one obtains

$$\frac{8\pi}{3} n\gamma r^2 = MkT \qquad 8.58.2.$$

where M is the effective number of gas atoms/cm^2. This was the expression used by Barnes[195] to determine M in the case quoted above for He atoms in Cu. If two bubbles of radii r_1 and r_2 containing m_1 and m_2 gas atoms respectively coalesce to form a bubble of radius R then according to the above model

$$\frac{8\pi}{3} \gamma R^2 = (m_1 + m_2)kT = \frac{8\pi}{3} \gamma(r_1{}^2 + r_2{}^2) \qquad 8.59.$$

i.e. the total surface area is preserved as observed by Barnes and Mazey[194]. Such bubbles will normally not migrate over appreciable distances in a uniformly heated target, since they will not experience any forces driving them. They may however oscillate on an atomic scale because of several possible causes. These could include vacancies entering a bubble which implies effective movement (and enlargement) of the bubble in a counter direction to the vacancy motion, evaporation of lattice atoms from one part of the bubble surface to another, or surface migration of lattice atoms over the bubble surface. Lack of bubble enlargement or target disappearance in targets where bubbles were almost of the same dimensions as the target led Barnes and Mazey to discount the first two of the above processes and it was concluded that only surface diffusion of lattice atoms over a bubble surface could cause bubble motion. Since surface migration is a random process one might expect bubble oscillation when in equilibrium, but if there was some force promoting more rapid surface diffusion in a specific direction one could anticipate net bubble migration. Such a specificity of surface diffusion could occur if there was a temperature gradient, and Barnes and Mazey[194] attribute their observations of bubble migration in impulse heated thin targets to just this cause. Another possible driving force would be the tension exerted by climbing dislocations on the bubbles and Barnes[195] suggests that this is the reason for bubble coalescence and swelling in bulk materials where temperature gradients and macroscopic strains are non existent.

Greenwood and Speight[196] obtained a general expression for bubble migration velocity due to surface diffusion as follows:-

Consider a bubble of diameter na (where a is the width of atomic spacings in the lattice) which will have a volume $\frac{\pi}{6}(na)^3$ and πn^2 lattice atoms around its surface. Each surface atom can jump a distance a and the frequency of this occurrence will be $\nu \exp(-Q_s/kT)$ where Q_s is the energy of surface diffusion and ν a frequency factor of order 10^{13}. The bubble of volume $\frac{\pi}{6}(na)^3$ is equivalent volume to $\frac{\pi n^3}{6}$ lattice atoms, so that each time a lattice atom jumps a distance a, the bubble moves an effective distance $\frac{6a}{\pi n^3}$ in the opposite direction. The jump frequency of all surface atoms on the bubble is $\pi n^2 \nu \exp(-Q_s/kT)$ and so the effective bubble diffusion coefficient can be approximated by $\frac{1}{6}^{th}$ the product of the jump frequency and the square of the jump distance (c.f. Equation 8.35.2 for 3 dimensional movement) i.e.

$$D_B \cong \frac{6}{\pi n^4} \nu a^2 \exp(-Q_s/kT) \qquad 8.60.$$

If an energy gradient, grad ϕ exists in the lattice, such as a temperature gradient, then the energy difference per atomic spacing $\Delta Q = a$ grad ϕ. Thus atoms moving in the direction of the gradient must overcome a barrier of only $Q_s - \frac{\Delta Q}{2}$ approximately, and opposite the gradient, $Q_s + \frac{\Delta Q}{2}$. Consequently the number of jumps made by a bubble along this gradient per second is given by

$$\nu_g \cong \frac{1}{4} A\pi n^2 \nu \left\{ \exp\left[-\frac{Q_s - \frac{\Delta Q}{2}}{kT}\right] - \exp\left[-\frac{Q_s + \frac{\Delta Q}{2}}{kT}\right] \right\} \qquad 8.61.1.$$

where A is a constant deduced from geometrical considerations to be 2/3.

Since $\Delta Q \ll Q_s$, one obtains

$$\nu_g \cong \frac{\pi}{6} n^2 \nu \frac{\Delta Q}{kT} \exp - \frac{Q_s}{kT} \qquad 8.61.2.$$

Further, since the bubbles jump distance is $\frac{6a}{\pi n^3}$ the bubble drift velocity along the energy gradient, v, is given by

$$v \approx \frac{\nu a}{n} \frac{\Delta Q}{kT} \exp(-Q_s/kT) \qquad 8.62.1.$$

or

$$v \approx \frac{\nu a^2 \text{ grad } \phi}{nkT} \exp(-Q_s/kT) \qquad 8.62.2.$$

Since grad ϕ is the driving force F and the bubble radius is na/2. We see that $v = \frac{3D_s}{kT} \frac{a}{r} F$ where D_s is the lattice atom surface diffusion coefficient. For bubbles of 300 Å diameter, Barnes and Mazey[194] observed a velocity of 1000 Å/sec which, using values for $Q_s = 0.7$ eV (as obtained by Choi and Shewmon[197]) and $T \approx 1100°C$, leads to an energy gradient of about 12 eV/cm or a temperature gradient of about 10^5°C/cm which Barnes and Mazey[194] considered to be a feasible value in their pulse heating experiments.

Barnes[195] has also quoted a form for v, applicable to face centred materials, (whereas the above treatment refers to an isotropic medium) as

$$v_{f.c} \cong \frac{1}{8\pi} \frac{D_s}{kT}\left(\frac{a_o}{r}\right)^4 \cdot F_b \qquad 8.62.3.$$

where a_o is the lattice parameter and F_b the driving force per bubble. Since the bubble is equivalent to $\pi n^3/6$ (or $\frac{8\pi}{6}(r/a)^3$) lattice atoms in the isotropic case, the driving force per bubble F_b is $\frac{8\pi}{6}(r/a)^3$. F i.e.

$$v \cong \frac{18}{8\pi} \frac{D_s}{kT} (a/r)^4 . F_b \qquad 8.62.4.$$

for the isotropic case. It is apparent that in both cases the bubble velocity varies inversely as the bubble radius for a given driving force F and this was observed by Barnes and Mazey[194]. In the case of swelling in bulk targets due to bubble migration under the influence of dislocation movement, the driving force is believed to be independent of bubble diameter and Barnes[195] has shown that such an assumption leads to a simple theory of swelling which agrees well with experimental data.

Although the basic details of bubble migration are adequately described by the simple theory outlined above, Barnes[195] suggests that the gas in small bubbles does not obey the perfect gas laws and the corrections to the law indicate that fewer gas atoms occupy smaller bubbles than given by Equation 2. 58. 2.

For the larger bubbles in an f.c.c. metal the ratio of the number of gas atoms in a bubble to the number of vacancies is given by

$$\frac{8\pi r^2 \gamma}{3kT} / \frac{16\pi}{3} (r/a)^3$$

i.e. $\gamma a^3/2kTr$. Consequently larger bubbles require a higher vacancy concentration. For a 10 Å radius Helium bubble at room temperature, a simple calculation (allowing for a Van der Waals type deviation from the perfect gas law) shows that this contains about 100 gas atoms and about 3 times this number of vacancies. For even smaller bubbles or heavier gas atoms the number of gas atoms per bubble falls considerably whilst the number of vacancies tends to remain between 3 and 10 times the number of gas atoms. It is therefore not inconceivable that single atoms injected into targets at low energy can form bubbles either by capturing damage induced vacancies, or since the atoms reside close to the surface, from the surface itself. One may anticipate this bubble nucleation to be most favourable at temperatures where vacancies are mobile as observed by Barnes and Mazey[186, 194] in α particle irradiated Cu and Al and by Jouffrey[190] in Argon ion bombarded Au, since vacancy agglomerates could be larger, and capture a larger percentage of the injected gas. In glass and metals irradiated at room temperature one may therefore expect some bubble nucleation, but it is impossible to estimate what percentage of the trapped gas will reside in such configurations and what proportion in other damage created configurations. It is possible that during post bombardment heating, whereas some gas atoms are released from damage sites into the gas phase, other atoms nucleate to form bubbles, which are only released at a higher temperature where bubbles migrate freely. Such a competitive process might operate in favour of bubble formation where the ion energy and penetration is high so that the gas atoms have more chance of nucleation before escape, and where the ion dose is large so that the trapped atom and nucleation site densities are large. These are just the circumstances in which Kelly and Brown[121] observe a gas release which they ascribe to bubble migration.

One may attempt an estimate of the thermal release rate of gas bubbles of radius r, since according to Equation 8. 60 the bubble diffusion coefficient is

$$\frac{6a^4}{16\pi r^4} \nu a^2 \exp(-Q_s/kT)$$

This suggests that a time constant τ_B for bubbles requiring one jump to reach the surface is of the order of $r_s m^2$. For bubbles containing only a few gas atoms the time constant is thus of order τ_s. At room temperature τ_s, and thus τ_B, is of the order of 1 second for Cu with $Q_s \approx 0.7$ ev. For larger bubbles the time constants increase only relatively slowly, and it does not seem generally possible that gas release during heating (which show very wide time constant spectra) is due to gradual release of increasingly larger bubbles in the absence of temperature gradients. It is therefore inferred that the thermal release spectra from glass and metals in the 'damage diffusion' region is only partly explicable on a bubble release process. On the other hand release near and above normal diffusion temperatures may well be due to bubble formation and migration as suggested by Kelly and Brown[121] since the more readily available vacancies may allow bubble growth. One consequence of gas release due to bubble migration would be that gas emission should take the form of bursts of gas as the bubble errupts at the surface. A useful experiment would be to study the continuity of gas release with a high sensitivity detector from targets where no temperature gradients existed and determine whether the bubble bursting process was operating.

We should also note an effect, suggested by Kelly[198], that the presence of gas bubbles should exert on the diffusion and desorption of individually trapped gas atoms. Bubbles dispersed throughout the target should act as trapping centres for diffusing atoms, and as a result both the desorption and in diffusion should be reduced. Further Kelly[198] suggests that a final exponential tail on the diffusion profile should exist following heating and claims that Kornelsens'[72] and Kelly and Ruedl's[126] data supports this belief.

We therefore conclude that in low energy ion bombarded targets, at least three types of gas trapping and release process can operate. Firstly gas can be trapped in damage induced configurations which require energies of activation for re-arrangement and/or migration less than the normal diffusion energy. Secondly gas may be trapped in the sites it would normally occupy when dissolved in the lattice and gas migration would be conditioned by the normal activation energy for diffusion in the particular ion target combination. Finally some of the injected ions may be trapped in bubbles of various sizes, the sizes increasing with target temperature as more vacancies become available for bubble stabilisation and where gas atoms can migrate more freely to the nucleation sites.

In the experimental work currently available one is able to tentatively distinguish these three regions, and further investigations should allow some more definitive statement of the processes involved in gas trapping.

REFERENCES

1. Plücker, J. (1958) Pogg. Ann. **105,** 84
2. Pietsch, E. (1926) Ergebn. exakt. Naturw. **5,** 213
3. Dushman, S. (1946) Scientific Foundations of Vacuum Technique. John Wiley & Sons. Inc. New York (1949)
4. Alpert, D. (1958) Handbuch. der. Physik. Springer-Verlag. Berlin. Vol. **12,** 1958 p. 693
5. Carter, G. (1959) Vacuum **9,** 190
6. Grant, W. A. and Carter, G. (1965) Vacuum **15,** 477
7. Strotzer, G. (1958) Zeits Angew. Phys. **10,** 207 & (1959) Z. Angew. Phys. **11,** 223
8. Leck, J. (1957-1964) Pressure Measurement in Vacuum Systems. Chapman & Hall. London 1957 & 1964
9. Bayard, R. T. and Alpert, D. (1950) Rev. Sci. Instrum. **21,** 571
10. Penning, F. M. (1937) Physica **4,** 71
11. Schwarz, H. (1940) Zeits. f. Phys. **117,** 23
12. Alpert, D. (1953) J. Appl. Phys. **24,** 860
13. Varnerin, L. J. and Carmichael, J. H. (1955) J. Appl. Phys. **26,** 782
14. Cobic, B., Carter, G. and Leck, J. H. (1961) Brit. J. Appl. Phys. **12,** 288
15. Carter, G. and Leck, J. H. (1961) Proc. Roy. Soc. **A261,** 303.
16. Carter, G. and Leck, J. H. (1960) Seventh National Symposium of the American Vacuum Society. Pergamon Press. Oxford (1961) p. 339
17. Bills, D. G. and Carleton, N. P. (1958) J. Appl. Phys. **29,** 692
18. Grant, W. A. and Carter, G. (1965) Proc. 7th International Conference on Phenomena in Ionized Gases. Belgrade. Yugoslavia. (To be Published)
19. Bloomer, R. N. and Haine, M. E. (1953) Vacuum. **3,** 128
20. James, L. H. and Carter, G. (1962) Brit. J. Appl. Phys. **13,** 3
21. Maddix, H. and Allen, M. A. (1963) Tenth National Vacuum Symposium of the American Vacuum Society. Macmillan Book Co. London p. 197
22. Maddix, H. and Allen, M. A. (1965) J. Vac. Sci. & Technol. **2,** 221
23. Maddix, H. S., Gregory, J. and Allen, M. A. (1962-1965) 10 Quarterly Progress Reports. Microwave Associates Inc. Burlington. Massachussetts. U.S.A. on Contract No. DA-36-039-AMC-00097(E)
24. Young, J. R. (1956) J, Appl. Phys. **27,** 926
25. Carter, G. (1959) Natures London **183,** 1619
26. Carter, G. and Leck, J. H. (1960) Advances in Vacuum Science & Technology. Vol. 1. Pergamon Press. London (1960) p. 463
27. Carter, G. (1959) Ph. D. Thesis. The University of Liverpool
28. Carter, G. and Leck, J. H. (1959) Brit. J. Appl. Phys. **10,** 364
29. Varnerin L. J. and Carmichael, J. H. (1957) J. Appl. Phys. **28,** 913
30. Cobic, B., Carter, G. and Leck, J. H. (1961) Vacuum **11,** 247
31. James, L. H. and Carter, G. (1962) J. Elec. & Control. **12,** 63
32. Comsa, G. and Musa, G. (1957) J. Sci. Instrum. **34,** 291
33. Comsa, G. and Musa, G. (1957) Stud. Cercet. de. Fizica **8,** (2), 119
34. Comsa, G. (1960) Stud. Cercet. de Fizica **11,** 645
35. Schulz, G. J. (1957) J. Appl. Phys. **28,** 1149
36. Jenkins, R. O. and Trodden, W. G. (1960) Vacuum **10,** 319
37. Florescu, N. A. (1964) Vacuum **14,** 47
38. James, L. H. (1962) Ph. D. Thesis. The University of Liverpool
39. Comsa, G. and Iosifescu, B. (1961) 8th National Vacuum Symposium of the American Vacuum Society. Pergamon Press. Oxford (1962) p. 43
40. Comsa, G. (1962) Cesk. Casop. pro. Fys. **5-6A.** 634
41. Comsa, G. (1963) Proc. Symp. Electr. Vac. Phys. Academic Press; New York
42. James, L. H. and Carter, G. (1963) Brit. J. Appl. Phys. **14,** 147
43. James, L. H., Leck, J. H. and Carter, G. (1964) Brit. J. Appl. Phys. **15,** 681
44. Cobic, B., Carter, G. and Leck, J. H. (1961) Brit. J. Appl. Phys. **12,** 384
45. Teloy, E. (1965) 3rd International Vacuum Congress. Stuttgart. Germany (1965) (To be Published)
46. Kay, E. and Winters, H. F. (1965) Proc. 3rd International Vacuum Congress. Stuttgart. Germany (1965) (To be Published)
47. Winters, H. F. (1965) J. Chem. Phys. (To be Published)
48. Robinson, N. W. and Berz, F. (1959) Vacuum **9,** 48
49. Fox, R. E. and Knoll, J. S. (1960) Seventh National Vacuum Symposium of the American Vacuum Society. Pergamon Press. Oxford (1961) p. 364
50. Kelly, R. (1961) Can. J. Chem. **39,** 664
51. Kelly, R. (1961) Can. J, Chem. **39,** 2411
52. Langmuir, I. (1913) J. Amer. Chem. Soc. **35,** 931
53. Langmuir, I. (1915) J. Amer. Chem. Soc. **37,** 417
54. Langmuir, I. (1918) J. Amer. Chem. Soc. **40,** 1361
55. Schlier, R. E. (1958) J. Appl. Phys. **29,** 1162
56. Young, J. R. (1959) J. Appl. Phys. **30,** 1671
57. LeGoff, P. and Letort, M. (1957) J. Chem. Phys. **54,** 3
58. Becker, J. A., Becker, E. J. and Brandes, R. G. (1961) J. Appl. Phys. **32,** 411
59. Johnson, M. C. (1929) Proc. Roy. Soc. (London) **A123,** 603
60. Johnson, M. C. (1931) Proc. Roy. Soc. (London) **A132,** 67
61. De Boer, J. H. and Lehr, J. J. (1933) Z. Physik. Chem. **B22,** 423
62. De Boer, J. H. and Van Steenis, J. (1952) Kominkl. Ned. Akad. Wetenschap Proc. **B55,** 578
63. Hickmott, T. W. (1960) J. Appl, Phys. **31,** 128
64. Hickmott, T. W. and Ehrlich, G. (1958) J. Phys. Chem. Solids. **5,** 47
65. Jaeckel, R. and Teloy, E. (1961) 8th National Vacuum Symposium of the American Vacuum Society. Pergamon Press. Oxford (1962) Vol. **1**
66. Donaldson, E. E., Winters, M. F. and Horne, D. E. (1963) Conf. on Adsorption of Vacuum Deposited Metal Films. University of Liverpool (1963) Unpublished
67. and (1964) 11th National Vacuum Symposium of the American Vacuum Society
68. Carter, G., James, L. H. and Leck, J. H. (1962) Vacuum **12,** 213
69. Burtt, R. B., Colligon, J. S. and Leck, J. H. (1961) Brit. J. Appl. Phys. **12,** 396

70. Colligon, J. S. and Leck, J. H. (1961) Eighth National Vacuum Symposium of the American Vacuum Society. Vol. 1. Pergamon Press. Oxford (1962) p. 275

71. Kornelsen, E. V. (1961) Eight National Vacuum Symposium of the American Vacuum Society Vol. **1.** Pergamon Press Oxford (1962) p. 281

72. Kornelsen E. V. (1964) Can. J. Phys. **42,** 364

73. McCargo, M., Davies, J. A. and Brown, F. (1963) Can. J. Phys. **41,** 123

74. Corkhill, D. P. and Carter, G. (1965) Proc. Conference on Electromagnetic Isotage Separators, Related Ion Accelerators, and their Application to Physics. Aarhus. Denmark (1965) (To be Published)

75. Ivanovskii, G. F. and Radzhabov, T. D. (1965) Zhur. Tekh. Fiz. **35,** 1312. English Translation in Soviet Physics. Tech. Phys. **10,** 1017, (1965)

76. Brown, F. and Davies, J. A. (1963) Can. J. Phys. **41,** 844

77. Almen, O. and Bruce, G. (1961) J. Nucl. Instrum. Methods **11,** 257

78. Almen, O. and Bruce, G. (1961) J. Nucl. Instrum. Methods **11,** 279

79. Abrahamson, A. A. (1963) Phys. Rev. **130,** 693

80. Carmichael, J. H. and Trendelenburg, E. A. (1958) J. Appl. Phys. **29,** 1570

81. Carmichael, J. H. and Knoll, J. S. (1958) Westinghouse Scientific Paper. 6-94436-1-P1 and 1958 Fifth National Vacuum Symposium of the American Vacuum Society 1958. Pergamon Press. Oxford p. 18

82. Von Meyern, W. (1933) Zeits. f. Physik **84,** 531

83. Von Meyern, W. (1934) Zeits f. Physik **91,** 727

84. Bartholomew, C. Y. and La Padula, A. R. (1960) J. Appl. Phys. **31,** 445

85. Carter, G., Colligon, J. S. and Leck, J. H. (1962) Proc. Phys. Soc. London **79,** 299

86. Vernerin, L. J. and Carmichael, J. H. (1955) Phys. Rev. **99,** 1662, and Westinghouse Research Report 71F191-R6. 1955

87 Blodgett, K. B. and Vanderslice, T. A. (1961) Eighth National Vacuum Symposium of the American Vacuum Society. Pergamon Press. Oxford (1962) p. 400

88. Hobson, J. P. (1961) Eighth National Vacuum Symposium of the American Vacuum Society. Pergamon Press. Oxford, 1962 p. 26

89. Hobson, J. P. (1961) Eighth National Vacuum Symposium of the American Vacuum Society. Pergamon Press. Oxford, 1962 p. 146

90. Hobson, J. P. (1961) Vacuum **11,** 16

91. Cavaleru, A., Comsa, G. and Iosifescu, B. (1964) Brit. J, Appl. Phys. **15,** 161

92. and Cavaleru, A., Comsa, G. and Iosifescu, B. (1965) 3rd International Vacuum Congress. Stuttgart. Germany

93. Baker F. A. and Giorgi T. A. (1960) Brit. J. Appl. Phys. **11,** 433

94. Baker, F. A. (1962) Le Vide **99,** 256

95. Smeaton, G. P., Carter, G. and Leck, J. H. (1962) Ninth National Vacuum Symposium of the American Vacuum Society. Macmillan Book Co. Ltd. London (1963) p. **491**

96. Smeaton, G. P., Leck, J. H. and Carter, G. (1963) Suppl. Al. Nuovo Cimento Series 1. Vol. **1.** 548

97. Cobic, B. and Carter, G. (1962) Le Vide **100**

98. James, L. H. and Carter, G. (1963) 9th National Symposium of the American Vacuum Society. Macmillan Book Co. Ltd. London p. 502

99. Brown, E. A. and Leck, J. H. (1955) Brit. J. Appl. Phys. **6,** 161

100. De Angelis, H. M. (1962) J. Appl. Phys. **33,** 2657

101. Blodgett, K. B. and Vanderslice, T. A. (1960) J. Appl. Phys. **31,** 1017

102. Bartholomew, C. and La Padula, A. R. (1964) J. Appl. Phys. **35,** 2570

103. Kornelsen, E. V. (1964) Vakuum Technik **13,** 6

104. Koch, J. (1948) Nature (London) **161,** 566

105 Thulin, S. (1954) Arkiv. f. Fysik **9,** 107

106. Fluit, J. M., Snoek, C. and Kistemaker, J. (1964) Physica. **30,** 144

107. Schwarz, H. (1944) Zeits, F. Physik **122,** 437

108. Carmichael, J. H. and Waters, P. M. (1962) J. Appl. Phys. **33,** 1470

109. Wehner, G. K. (1961) General Mills Electronic Group. Report No. 2309

110. Wehner, G. K. and Jorgenson, G. V. (1965) 3rd International Vacuum Congress. Stuttgart. Germany (1965) (To be Published) and J. Appl. Phys. **36,** 2672 (1965)

111. Colligon, J. S. (1961) Vacuum **5/6,** 272

112. Davies, J. A., Domeij, B. and Uhler, J. (1963) Arkiv f. Fysik **24,** 377

113. Davies, J. A., Brown, F. and McCargo, M. (1963) Can. J. Phys. **41,** 829

114. Piercy, G. R., McCargo, M., Brown, F. and Davies, J. A. (1964) Can J. Phys. **42,** 1116

115. Davies, J. A., Ball, G. C., Brown, F. and Domeij, B. (1964) Can J. Phys. **42,** 1070

116. Hobson, J. P. and Edmonds, T. (1963) Can J. Phys. **41,** 827

117. Tucker, C. W. and Norton, F. J. (1960) J. Nucl. Mat. **2,** 329

118. Tucker, C. W. and Norton, F. J. (1960) J. Nucl. Mat. **2,** 350

119. Kelly, R. and Brown, F. (1963) J. Nucl. Instrum. Methods **21,** 265

120. Bergstrom, I., Brown, F., Davies, J. A., Geiger, J. S., Graham, R. L., Kelly, R. (1963) J. Nucl. Instrum. Methods **21,** 249

121. Kelly, R. and Brown, F. (1965) Acta. Met. **13,** 169

122. Kelly, R. and Matzke, H. J. (1965) J. Nucl. Mat. **17,** 179

123. Kelly, R. (1965) Proc. Conf. on Electromagnetic Isotope Separators, Related Ion Accelerators and their Application to Physics. Aarhus. Denmark. To be Published

124a. Brown, F. and Matzke, H. J. (1965) Proc. Conf. on Electromagnetic Isotope Separators, Related Ion Accelerators and their Application to Physics. Aarhus. Denmark (1965) To be Published

124b. Matzke, H. J. and Whitton, J. L. (1966) Can J. Phys. **44,** 995

125. Kelly, R. and Ruedl, E. (1964) 3rd European Regional Conference on Electron Microscopy. Prague (1964)

126. Kelly, R. and Ruedl, E. (1965) Phys. Stat. Solidi **12,** and **1965.** J. Nucl. Mat. **16,** 89

127. Tosic, D. and Perovic, B. (1965) Proc. Conf. on Electromagnetic Isotope Separators. Related Ion Accelerators and their Application to Physics. Aarhus. Denmark (1965) To be Published

128. Jokic, T. and Perovic, B. (1965) Proc. 7th International Conf. on Phenomena in Ionised Gases. Belgrade (1965)

129. Jacobson, R. L. and Wehner, G. K. (1965) J. Appl. Phys. **36,** 2674

130. Macrae, A. V. and Gobeli, G. W. (1964) J. Appl. Phys. **35,** 1629

131. Morrison, D. L. and Elleman, T. S. and Sunderman, D. N. (1964) J. Appl. Phys. **35,** 1616

132. Bauer, A. A., Bugl, A., Cocks, G. G., Elleman, T. S., Howes, T. E., Morrison, D. L., and Winslow, F. R. (1963) Battelle Report BM1-1611 (1963)

133. Auskern, A. (1964) J. Amer. Ceram. Soc. **47**, 390

134. Lustman, B. (1962) Ceram. Abstr. p. 106

135. Davies, D. and Long, G. (1963) A.E.R.E. report (Harwell) Memo. M. 969

136. Findlay, J. R. and Laing, T. F. (1962) J. Nucl. Mat. **7**, 182

137. Moore, W. J., Logan, S. R., Lutter, L. C. and Brown, S. N. (1962) Le Bombardment Ionique. C.N.R.S. Bellevue. Paris (1962) p. 35

138. Jech, C. (1960) Int. J. of App. Radiation and Isotopes **8**, 179

139. Jech, C. (1962) Phys. Stat. Sol. **2**, 1299

140. Jech, C. (1964) Phys. Stat. Sol **4**, 499

141. Nelson, C. M., Sproull, R. L. and Caswell, R. S. (1953) Phys. Rev. **90**, 364

142. Kobayashi, H. (1956) Phys. Rev. **102**, 348

143. Kobayashi, H. (1957) Phys. Rev. **107**, 41

144. Smeaton, G. P., Carter, G. and Leck, J. H. (1963) Brit. J. Appl. Phys. **15**, 205

145. Burton, M. and Neubert, T. J. (1956) J. Appl. Phys. 27, 557

146. Billington, D. S. and Crawford, J. H. (1961) Radiation Damage in Solids. Princeton University Press. Princeton (1961) p. 295

147. Crank, J. (1957) The mathematics of diffusion. Oxford University Press. London (1957)

148. Jost, W. (1952) Diffusion in Solids. Liquids and Gases. Academic Press Inc.; New York (1952)

149. Barrer, R. M. (1951) Diffusion in and Through Solids. Cambridge University Press; London (1951)

150. Shewmon, P. G. (1963) Diffusion in Solids. McGraw-Hill. Book Co. Inc. New York (1963)

151. Kelly, R. (1964) Acta Met. **12**, 123

152. Frenkel, I. (1924) Zeits. f. Physik **26**, 117

153. Alpert, D., Buritz, R. S. and Rogers, W. A. (1954) J. Appl. Phys. **25**, 868

154. T'sai, L. S. and Hogness, T. R. (1932) J. Phys. Chem. **36**, 2595

155. Leiby, C. C. and Chen, C. L. (1960) J. Appl. Phys. **31**, 268

156. Reynolds, M. B. (1957) J. Amer. Ceram. Soc. **40**, 395

157. Federighi, T. (1959) Phil. Mag. **4**, 502

158. Lindner, R. and Matzke, Hj. (1960) Zeits. f. Naturforschung, Naturforschung **15A**, 1082

159. Tobin, J. M. (1959) Acta. Met. **7**, 701

160. Okkerse, B. (1956) Phys. Rev. **103**, 1246

161. Nachtrieb, N. and Handler, G. (1955) J. Chem. Phys. **23**, 1569

162. Reynolds, M. B. (1956) Nucl. Sci. Eng. **1**, 374

163. Herring, C. (1953) Structures and Properties of solid surfaces. Ed. by Gomer and Smith. University of Chicago Press. Chicago. p. 66

164. Peterson, N. L. (1960) Wright Air Development (U.S.A.) Report WADD—TR 60-793

165. Corkhill, D. P. and Carter, G. (1965) Phys. Letters **18**, 264

166. Grant, W. A. and Carter, G. (1965) Vacuum **15**, 13

167. Erents, K., Grant, W. A. and Carter, G. (1965) Vacuum **15**, 529

168. Kuchai, S. A. and Rodin, A. M. (1958) Atomnaya Energiya **4**, 202. English Translation in Soviet J. Atomic Energy (1958) **4**, 277

169. Robinson, M. T. (1962) Appl. Phys. Letters **1**, **49**

170. Erents, K., Grant, W. A. and Carter, G. (1965) Surface Science **3**, 480

171. Anderson, J. S., Bevan, D. J. M. and Burden, J. P. (1963) Proc. Roy. Soc. (London) **A272**, 15

172. Lagerwall, T. (1962) Nukleonik **4**, 158

173. Rimmer, D. C. and Cottrell, A. H. (1957) Phil. Mag. **2**, 1345

174. Huntington, H. B. (1953) Phys. Rev. **91**, 1092

175. Buckingham, R. A. (1938) Proc. Roy. Soc. **A168**, 264

176. Stewart, J. W. (1956) J. Phys. Chem. Solids. **1**, 146

177. Mason, E. A. and Rice, W. E. (1954) J. Chem. Phys. **22**, 483

178. Slater, J. C. and Kirkwood, J. G. (1931) Phys. Rev. **37**, 652

179. Beattie, J. A., Brierley, J. S. and Barriault, R. J. (1952) J. Chem. Phys. **20**, 1615

180. Friedel, J, (1954) Adv. in Phys. **3**, 446

181. Fumi, F. G. (1955) Phil. Mag. **46**, 1007

182. Beeler, J. R. and Besco, D. G. (1962) Radiation Damage in Solids. Vol. 1. International Atomic Energy Agency. Vienna (1962) p. 43

183. Ogilvie, G. J., Sanders, J. V. and Thomson, A. A. (1963) J. Phys. Chem. Solids. **24**, 247

184. Barnes, R. S. (1960) Phil. Mag. **5**, 635

185. Barnes, R. S. (1961) Disc. Farad. Soc. **31**, 38

186. Barnes, R. S. and Mazey, D. J. (1960) Phil. Mag. **5**, 1247

187. Nelson, R. S. (1964) Phil. Mag. **9**, 343

188. Brebec, G., Levy, V., Leteutre, J. and Adda, Y. (1962) Le Bombardment Ionique. C.N.R.S. Bellevue, Paris. (1962) p. 63

189. Castaing, R. and Jouffrey, B. (1963) J. de Microscopie **2**, 6

190. Jouffrey, B. (1963) J. de. Microscopie **2**, 45

191. Kaminsky, M. (1964) Institute of Petroleum/ASTM Mass Spectrometry Symposium. Paris (1964)

192. Primak, W. (1964) J. Appl. Phys. **35**, 1342

193. Ghosh, T. K., Beevers, C. J. and Barnes, R. S. (1960-61) J. Inst. Metals **89**, 125

194. Barnes, R. S. and Mazey, D. J. (1963) Proc. Roy. Soc. **275**, 47

195. Barnes, R. S. (1963) U.K.A.E.A. Report No. A.E.R.E R4429

196. Greenwood, G.W. and Speight, M. V. (1963) J. Nucl. Mat. **10**, 140

197. Choi, J. Y. and Shewmon, P. G. (1962) Trans. Mat. Soc. A.I.M.E. **224**, 589

198. Kelly, R. and Matzke, Hj. (1966) To be Published in J. Nucl. Mat

199. Kornelsen, E. V. (1965) Bull. Radio and Elec. Engineering Division Nat. Res. Council. Canada. Vol. 15, No. **4** p. 36

200. Kornelsen, E. V, (1966) Bull, Radio and Elec. Engineering Division Nat. Res. Council. Canada. Vol. **16**, No. 1 p. 38

201. Errents, K. and Carter, G. (1966) Vacuum **16**, To be Published

CHAPTER 9

Ion Bombardment Techniques and Applications

9.1 INTRODUCTION

In the preceding chapters we have discussed the many phenomena associated with ion bombardment of surfaces. Here we discuss the principal techniques for producing ion beams to undertake the foregoing investigations and also briefly describe several useful applications of bombardment phenomena.

9.2 PRODUCTION OF ION BEAMS

The problem facing the designer of an ion beam apparatus is basically two-fold (1) Selection of an ion source which will produce a sufficiently intense beam of tolerable energy spread and, where possible, (2) Construction of lens system to utilize the ions produced most efficiently; introducing momentum or energy analyzing devices where desired. The designer may wish to incorporate additional intermediate focus points with a view to obtaining differential pumping across the narrow slit or aperture and thereby improve the vacuum in the vicinity of the target surface. As the second part of the problem discussed above is essentially one of Electron Optics and its solution is very dependent upon the particular experiment under study, a full treatment will not be presented here. We confine our discussion therefore to the available types of ion source, their performance and method of operation.

9.2.1 Electron Impact ion source

The electron impact source is one of the most widely used in mass spectrometers because of its inherent low energy spread and ability to produce reasonably intense ion beams. This particular ion source was developed by Bleakney[1] and Nier[2 3] and is of the form illustrated in Fig. 9.1. Electrons are produced at the tungsten filament and accelerated into the ionization

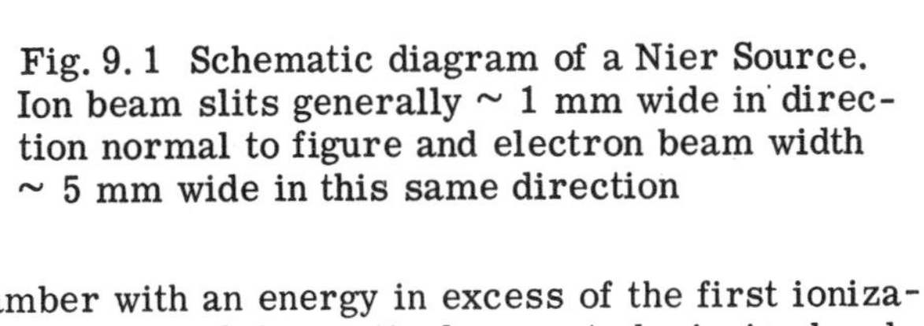

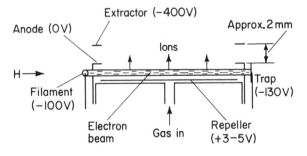

Fig. 9.1 Schematic diagram of a Nier Source. Ion beam slits generally ~ 1 mm wide in direction normal to figure and electron beam width ~ 5 mm wide in this same direction

chamber with an energy in excess of the first ionization potential of the particular gas to be ionized and near the peak in the ionization efficiency curve. This usually means electron energies of 70-100 volts. The electron beam is collimated by narrow slits as it enters the ionization chamber thus forming a narrow ribbon and a magnetic field constrains the electrons within this ribbon shape as they traverse the ionizing region. The electrons then exit via a similar slit and are collected at the trap which is generally held a few tens of volts more positive than the ionization chamber. As they traverse the ionization chamber these electrons undergo inelastic collisions with the gas atoms causing ejection of an electron and ions are formed along the narrow band enclosed by the electron ribbon. By making the repeller plate a few volts positive and the extractor negative these ions find themselves on a potential hill and are accelerated out of the ion source.

General parameters for the source are as follows:-

Trap current	10-100 μA.
Collimating field	100 gauss
Energy spread	0.05 eV
Ion intensity	10^{-9} A
Source pressure	10^{-4} Torr

The ion intensity may be improved to more than 10^{-7} A by increasing the source pressure to 0.5×10^{-3} Torr and by using higher electron currents (1 mA) and extractor fields (500 V). However under these conditions the mode of operation is essentially that of a low voltage arc source and the energy spread of the resulting beam is not as low; approaching values from 2 to 3 eV.

The electron current to the trap must be monitored if stable ion beams are to be produced and this is usually performed by an electronic stabilizing circuit which automatically adjusts the tungsten filament heating current to increase or decrease the electron emission.

Tungsten filaments are generally preferred as a source of the electron stream, but they become very unstable in operation if the W_2C layer which forms at the surface is disturbed, e.g. by introducing an oxidizing gas. A good stabilizing circuit could counteract these functions but there would still be a widely varying temperature on the tungsten filament. Rhenium may be used instead of tungsten as it does not form a carbide layer although it has the disadvantage of a high evaporation rate for a given electron emission.

The performance of a Nier source has been shown by Barnard[4] to be improved in efficiency by a factor of five by the introduction of a 0.01" diameter canal which feeds the gas into the source at the ionizing electron stream. This prevents filling the entire source chamber with unwanted gas which may attenuate the electron beam and it minimizes ion production in a region not contributing to the useful current output of the source. The lower source pressure reduces the probability of ion-molecule collisions which would cause a fraction of the beam to be defocused and lost. This refinement is not so useful for low pressure (10^{-4} to 10^{-6} Torr) operation of Nier sources, possibly due to the difficulty of aligning the canal with the ion extractor system. In conventional electron bombardment sources the extracted ion beam increases with increasing source chamber gas pressure until a maximum is reached; further increases of pressure above this point only attenuate the ion beam. The effect of the gas jet described above however is to raise the effective pressure in the ionization region thus improving the gas efficiency of the source: an increase of a factor of 1000 over conventional sources is possible with careful alignment of the jet and the magnetic field which constrains the ionizing electron beam.

9.2.2 Vacuum Spark source

This type of ion source was developed by Dempster[6 7] for determination of the isotopic constitutions of the elements, for which task it had the advantage over heated filament discharge sources in that no hydrides were formed so that confusion in identifying a real isotope from a spectrum containing the parent element plus one, two or more hydrogen atoms was avoided. More recently this source has been established as the only ion source suitable for the general chemical analysis of solid materials[8 9 10 11] as the sensitivities for different elements differ by less than an order of magnitude.

The spark source is of little use for controlled ion-surface studies as the energy spread of the ion beam produced is large (up to 1000 eV) and many multiply charged species are produced together with complex molecular ions. Useful currents after energy selection are less than 10^{-10} A which is too low for clean surface studies of secondary processes. However, if the ion energy is not important, the vacuum spark is convenient for the production of very intense beams. Maximum current densities which can be extracted are given by

$$j_{max\ i,e} \doteq e\, n_{i,e}\, (2\, kT_e/M_{i,e})^{1/2} \qquad 9.1$$

where the suffix i or e refers to ion or electron currents, e is the electron charge, k Boltzmann's constant, $M_{i,e}$ the mass of the ion or electron, $n_{i,e}$ the plasma density (approximately 10^{15}-10^{16} (cm^{-3}) and T_e the electron temperature ($\sim 2 \times 10^5$ °K). Thus current densities as high as 10-100 A/cm^2 for ions and 1000 A/cm^2 for electrons can be obtained. Suladze and Plyutto[11a] have described a version of this source which will produce H^+ currents of 5-15 A/cm^2 in pulses of 10^{-6} second duration with an energy spread of 10^3-10^4 eV.

Fig. 9.2 shows the principal elements of a simple spark source. If the material to be analyzed is a conductor then the electrodes may be constructed

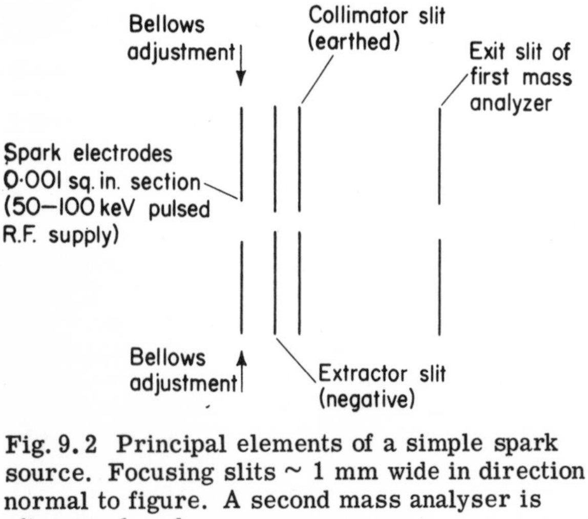

Fig. 9.2 Principal elements of a simple spark source. Focusing slits ~ 1 mm wide in direction normal to figure. A second mass analyser is often employed.

directly from it. If not, a powdered form of the sample must be mixed with graphite and formed into an electrode. Electrodes are normally of 0.001 square inch section by ½ inch long and can be manipulated from outside the vacuum by a bellows arrangement.

In operation a high voltage 50 to 100 kV pulsed r.f. supply is applied between the rods, the use of short pulses ensuring that appreciable thermal selection cannot occur due to differing evaporation rates. Ions formed in the spark are extracted by applying a negative voltage to the first slit and are collimated by a second earthed slit into the first of two consecutive mass analyzers. Ion currents are generally difficult to detect due to the r.f. supply upsetting electronic amplifier circuits. However Gorman et al[12] have shown that the ion current fluctuations can largely be eliminated by arranging to measure the ratio of two ionic currents.

Woolston and Honig[13] have carried out a thorough investigation of the energy spread of ions produced in the r.f. spark source and have found that the distributions were greatly affected by ion source parameters such as spark gap width and r.f. spark voltage. The actual energy spreads were found to exceed one thousand volts and even the maxima in the energy distributions changed when source parameters were adjusted. Consequently this type of source has little to recommend it for controlled studies of ion-surface interactions.

Typical operating characteristics of the spark source are:-

R.F. pulsed supply	50-100 kV
Source pressure	10^{-6} Torr
Sample size (electrode)	100 mgm.
Ion current	10^{-10} A
Energy spread	100-1000 eV
Sensitivity w.r.t. iron for most species	0.8-3.0

9.2.3 Thermal Ionization sources

The operation of a thermal ionization source relies on the fact that when an atom or molecule evaporates from a surface there is a finite probability that it will be ejected as a positive ion. Datz and Taylor[14] have shown the ratio of ionized to neutral atoms is given by

$$\frac{n^+}{n^0} = \frac{1 - r^+}{1 - r^0} \cdot \frac{g^+}{g^0} \exp \frac{\phi - E_i}{kT} \qquad 9.2.$$

where n^+, n^0 are the numbers of positive ions and neutral atoms respectively, r^+ and r^0 the internal reflection coefficients, g^+ and g^0 appropriate statistical weighting factors, E_i the ionization potential of the atom, ϕ the work function of the surface, k Boltzmann's constant and T the absolute temperature of the surface. It is clear that, to a first approximation,

$$n^+/n^0 = A \exp(\phi - E_i/kT) \qquad 9.3.$$

where A is a constant so that the critical factor in determining the ion to neutral ratio is the magnitude of $\phi - E_i$. For $\phi - E_i \gg kT$ nearly complete ionization will occur as observed for the vapours of alkali metals in contact with heated tungsten and nickel surfaces[14]. Target temperatures should in this case be maintained as low as possible provided they are sufficient to re-evaporate the ionizable vapours. For

$E_i > \phi$ ionization probability is low and here one must use the maximum practicable temperature to produce the optimum ion-atom ratio.

Two methods of heating the material are employed to form ions; one using a single filament which comprises simply a wire or ribbon on which the sample is placed, the other a multiple filament arrangement[15 16] where the sample is evaporated from one filament and ionizes on contact with a second heated filament. The second method has the great advantage in that the temperature of the evaporating filament can be independently controlled to promote a reasonable evaporation rate whilst the ionizing filament can be maintained at the optimum temperature for thermal excitation. However the single filament performance can be improved somewhat by adding a small quantity of powdered fused borax to the solution on the filament which, on heating, melts and forms a glass-like bead. The sample is thus in good thermal and electrical contact with the filament and an improvement in ion intensity of the order of a factor five can often be obtained by this treatment.

Extraction of the ion beam is normally carried out by designing a strong immersion ion lens which will form a demagnified image of the filament (see fig. 9. 3). Care must be taken to eliminate ions formed on the heating filaments in the multiple-filament source and this is usually ensured by either applying a small negative potential to them[16], or, by arranging a defocusing lens system which accepts ions from the central ionizing filament but de-focuses ions from the evaporator filaments.

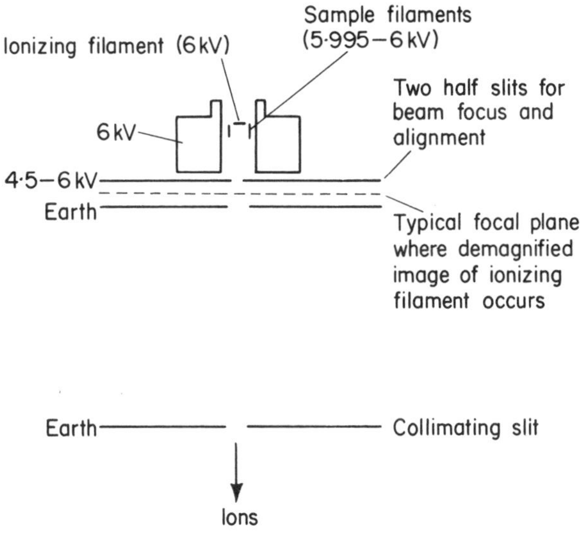

Fig. 9. 3 Electrode assembly for extracting ion beams from a thermal ionization ion source (viz. Ref. 9. 16)

The principal disadvantages of this type of source are:

(1) The need for replacement of sample material which usually demands the introduction of a vacuum-lock assembly.

(2) The rapid fluctuation in source intensity as the test material is used up.

However, it has considerable advantages where small samples of material are required to be ionized and the energy spread of the ion beam produced is of thermal dimensions only, so is minimal. Typical operating characteristics of a thermal ionization source are:-

Ionizing filament potential	6 kV
Evaporating filament potentials	5. 995 kV
Source enclosure	6 kV
Extractor slit	4. 5-6 kV
Exit slit	0 V
Collimating slit	0 V

Filament temperatures depend critically on the samples to be ionized. Inghram and Chupka[15] used a temperature of 2500°K on the ionizing filament and 1250°K on the evaporating filament for the production of Gd^+ ion beams from a 25 microgramme sample of Gd_2O_3.

A novel surface ionization type of source for producing ionic or atomic beams has been described by Rubin[17]. Here the ionization of an alkali vapour was promoted by the filament of a triode type of electrode arrangement. The ions were accelerated to the anode of the structure and focused into a small hole in it. The anode was a boxed-in region where charge exchange could take place due to collisions of the ion beam with the atoms of the alkali metal vapour. With such an arrangement neutral beams with energies of 15 to 200 eV could be extracted.

An interesting combination of a vapour source and electron bombardment ion source has been described by Tyrrell et al[18] who have modified the triple filament source of Inghram and Chupka[15] by mounting a crucible box (which has a slit opposite the right-hand filament) on the supports of Inghram's left-hand filament and lowering the centre filament. Samples were placed on the centre filament which was heated and electrons emitted from the remaining right-hand filament were accelerated into the box where they ionized the vapour. Typical operating parameters were:

Electron filament	4-4. 5 A
Vapour filament	0-6 A
Electron accelerator voltage	10-100 volts
Electron current	0. 5-1. 5 mA

This modified source was capable of producing ion currents stable to 1 in 10^3 decaying as the material forming the vapour was used. Memory effects were found to be very small, less than 1 in 10^6 for the worst case tested (tellurium). The source was capable of analyzing samples of weight less than five micrograms of nickel, tellurium, antimony, copper and cadmium, and is clearly of great use for production of ion beams of solid species.

9. 2. 4 The High Voltage Gas Discharge ion source

Aston[19] was a pioneer of this type of ion source which comprises basically a set of two electrodes placed some tens of centimetres apart to which is applied a voltage of 10-60 kV. Vapour between the plates at a pressure between 10^{-3} and 10^{-1} Torr is ionized as the medium breaks down and the ions formed are accelerated through a hole in the cathode and proceed to the mass or energy analyzers. Although currents produced by this ion source are exceptionally large (of order 1 milliamp) the ion energy spread is also large and equal to the voltage supplied (depending whether the ion was formed near the cathode or the anode) so that this type of source is generally unsuitable for controlled bombardment experiments.

9.2.5 The Low Voltage Arc source

This low voltage arc source was developed by Koch[20] for isotope separation of small quantities of material. The discharge is maintained between a heated filament and an anode which are separated by a capillary section as illustrated in Fig. 9.4. Ions from the positive ion sheath, which forms the outermost part of the arc, are accelerated transversely as they emerge form the small hole in the capillary wall.

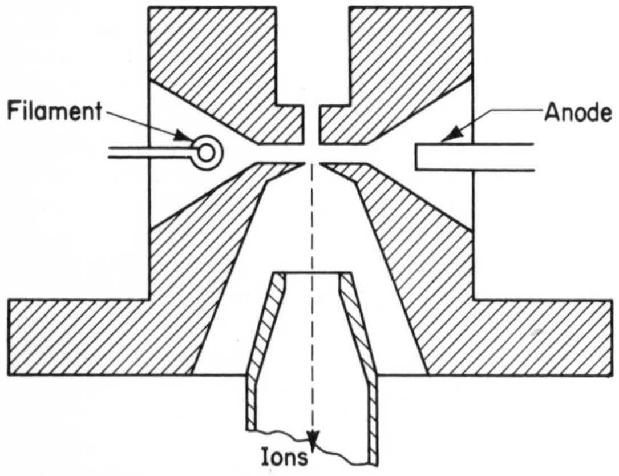

Fig. 9.4 Low-voltage capillary-arc discharge source. (viz. Ref. 9.20)

The capillary envelope may be eliminated provided a suitable magnetic field is applied in which case the operating pressure of the discharge can be slightly reduced but the inherent energy spread is then larger than for the simple capillary source. The principal advantage of this second mode of operation is however that the source can now be used for ionization of solid materials, these materials being vapourized in an oven adjacent to the arc, or, by electron bombardment using electrons from an auxiliary filament.

Typical parameters for this type of source are:

Pressure	2×10^{-3} Torr
Ion current	100-200 μA
Energy spread	0.2 eV
Arc voltage	100 volts
Arc current	0.2-1 A.

9.2.6 Mercury Pool Cathode Discharge

This is basically a low voltage arc discharge with a liquid mercury pool replacing the conventional cathode. The source was first successfully used by Fetz[21] and has been extensively used in the modified form illustrated in Fig. 7.1 (Chapter 7) by Wehner[22]. An auxiliary discharge is first started by discharging a condenser through the ignitor. This auxiliary arc carries a current of approximately 3 A and the cathode spot becomes anchored to a molybdenum strip immersed in the mercury pool. The main discharge runs at 2.5 A with 30 volts between the main anode and the cathode and is separated from the auxiliary discharge by a graphite grid which increases the plasma density in the target region.

The target itself is supported in the manner of a Langmuir probe in the main discharge and is usually spherical. The ion sheath forming around this negative probe causes the field to be radial so that ion bombardment is essentially normal to the spherical surface. For plane targets the bombardment is normal at the centre, but the current density and angle of incidence vary rapidly toward the extreme edges and a 'guard-ring' is essential to carry the current in this non-linear region. An interesting development of the mercury pool system has been to re-arrange the electrode structure in the main discharge region and provide a re-entrant liquid nitrogen trap[23]. The mercury vapour can thus be frozen out and noble gases introduced for production of inert gas ions. In this modified system (see Fig. 9.5) the main discharge is constricted by a magnetic field. Typical working conditions for this type of ion source are:-

Main discharge current	2-5 A
Main discharge voltage	30 V
Ion current density at target	5 mA/cm^2
Energy spread	5-10 eV

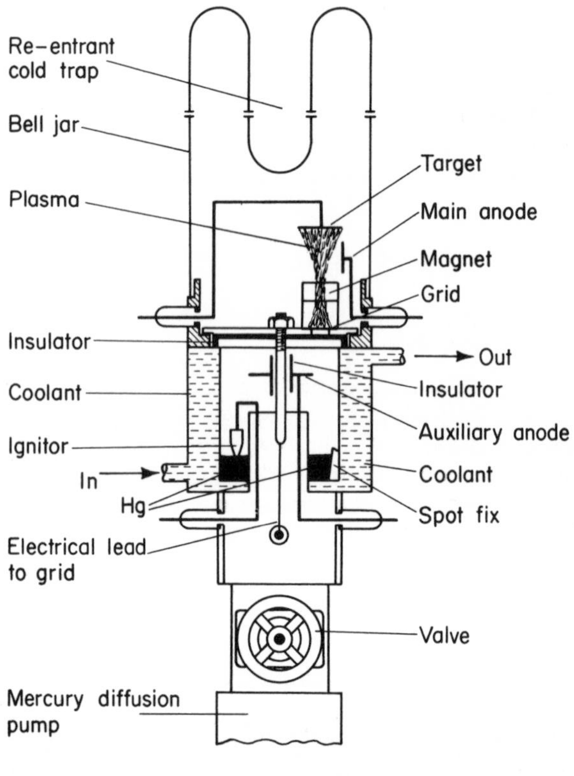

Fig. 9.5 Mercury pool discharge apparatus modified to produce noble gas ions. (viz. Ref. 9.23)

The principal disadvantage of these sources is that the target must be supported within the discharge where the background mercury pressure is of the order 10^{-5} Torr and the test gas 10^{-3} Torr. The angle of incidence and energy of the beam are poorly defined and the secondary electron emission component puts ion current values in error by an unknown quantity. However, the ion current intensities attained far outweigh those possible by most other techniques so that this form of beam production is often very useful, as witnessed by Wehner's noteworthy contribution to sputtering knowledge (see Chapter 7).

An alternative discharge-type ion source also employed by Wehner et al[24] uses an oxide cathode from a commercial thyratron and is illustrated in Fig. 9. 6. Parameters for this source are:

Working pressure	1-40 mTorr
Main discharge current	1-5 A
Main discharge voltage	25-65 volts (depending on gas to be ionized)
Target ion current density	3-15 mA/cm^2
Ion energy spread	
(full discharge volt drop)	25-65 eV

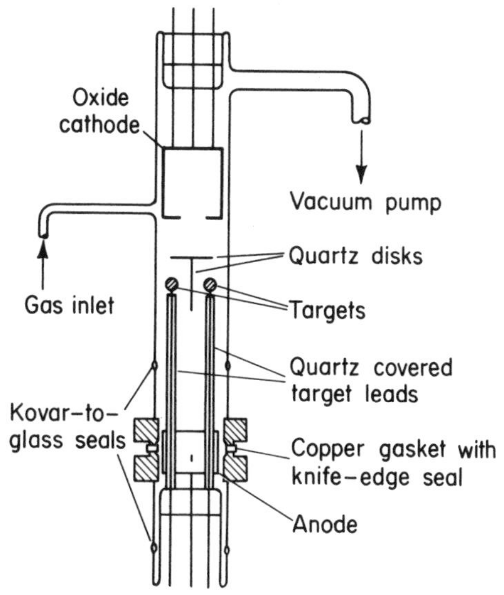

Fig. 9. 6 Oxide cathode discharge ion source (viz. Ref. 9. 23)

The disadvantages of this type of source are similar to those of the mercury pool except that the mercury contamination is eliminated. An additional disadvantage of this particular source is the shielding techniques which are necessary to protect from damage the oxide filament upon exposure of the system to the atmosphere.

9. 2. 7 Oscillating Discharge sources

These sources are basically modified forms of the Philips Ionization Gauge (or Penning Gauge) and comprise a hollow cylindrical anode and two plane circular cathodes placed at each end of the anode. A magnetic field is applied parallel to the anode cylinder axis constraining any electrons to move in tight helices as they pass from cathode to anode region. The electrons thus pass through the anode to the second cathode where they are reflected and proceed to oscillate betwen these two cathodes until they are lost from the discharge. The probability of an electron making an ionizing collision is thus relatively large and a discharge can be maintained at pressures in the region 10^{-4} to 10^{-3} Torr.

Ions may be extracted through a small hole (order $1/8$" diameter) in one of the cathodes. Barnett et al[25] rather ingeniously extracted the ions, after they had passed through the cathode aperture, through a shaped canal which was located in the centre of one of their magnet pole pieces supplying the collimating field for the discharge. Typical operating parameters for this source are:

Anode-Cathode voltage	7. 5 kV
Extractor canal voltage	5 kV negative with respect to the cathode
Magnetic field	600 Gauss
Ion currents	1 mA or above (within discharge)
Energy spread	25 eV
Source pressure	10^{-4}-10^{-3} Torr
Power consumption	100 watts with electromagnet, 20-30 watts with permanent magnet
Gas consumption	2 cc/hr.

The principal advantage of this type of ion source is the absence of a heated filament which cracks pump oil vapours and has a limited life. However, the energy spread of the ions is high, insulation problems between cathode and anode are severe and it is difficult to extract a reasonably intense ion current from this type of source for controlled ion bombardment experiments.

A simple modification to the Nier Source converts it into an oscillating electron source of the type described by Heil[26], (Fig. 9. 7) Finkelstein and Smith[27], Kistemaker[28], and Almén and Nielsen[29]. Here the electrons emanating from one filament are reflected by the second filament after traversing the ionizing region and proceed to oscillate back and forth, thus increasing the probability of ionization. The source can operate under normal discharge conditions with very weak electron currents, but when the currents are sufficiently strong a 'superstate' condition exists where a brightly glowing plasma may be seen.

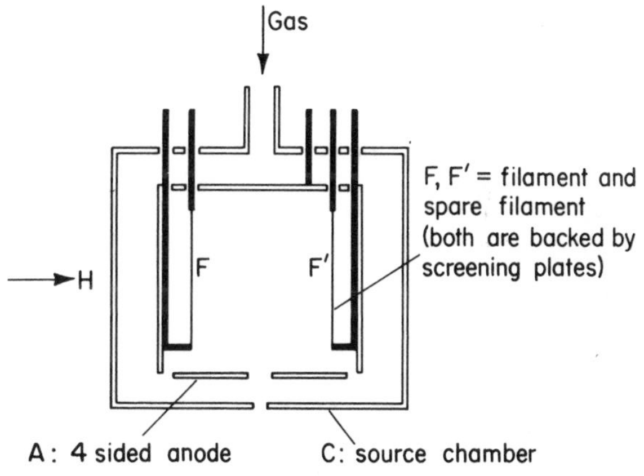

Fig. 9. 7 Principal electrode arrangement in a Heil source

Sources of this type have been known to produce ion currents of the order 100 μA at a discharge voltage of 100 volts and pressure of 10^{-3} Torr.

Cobic et al[29a] describe an oscillatory discharge source of magnetron structure which can be used for production of ion beams of solid materials. The principal elements of the source are illustrated in Fig. 9. 8 and comprise an anode cylinder with its axis parallel to a magnetic field and a filament extending along this same axis. Material to be ionized is dedeposited along the central region of the filament in the form of a paste comprising the powdered solid, acetone and collodion and is heated to a red heat in atmosphere to form a stable layer. Operation of the

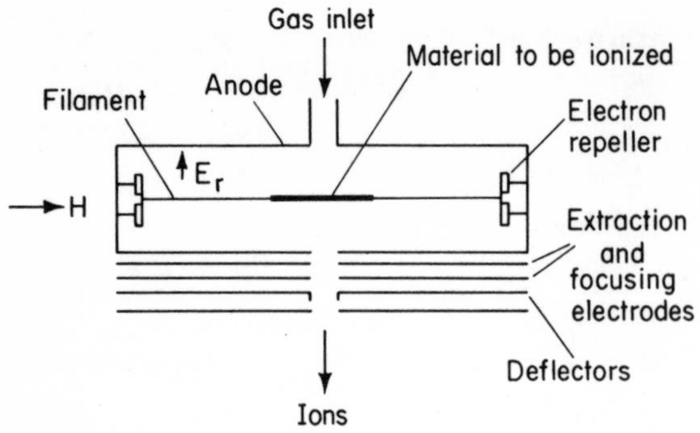

Fig. 9. 8 Electrode arrangement in the magnetron solid-ion source of Cobic et al[29a]

discharge is by emission of electrons from the untreated ends of the filament when it is heated. These electrons are accelerated by a radial field, E_p, between the anode cylinder and the filament, but owing to the magnetic field are constrained to follow helical paths about the filament axis. Electron reflectors at each end of the discharge region prevent loss of useful electron current so that considerable ionization of the vapour emitted from the hot central portion of the filament occurs. To promote stable operation the discharge chamber is filled with a low (10^{-7} Torr) pressure of argon. Typical operating parameters of this source are:

Filament current	5 A
Anode voltage	120-200 V
Anode current	10 mA
Magnetic field	300 Gauss
Charge	0.5-2 mgm/hr
Energy spread	$\sim$ 4 eV
Ion current (after mass analysis)	$\sim 10^{-11}$-10^{-10}A

This type of source is thus very useful for production of ion beams from solid samples and has been used for ionization of Sb, La, Nd_2O_3, Cu, Ni, Ce_2O_3, Ti, Ir, ZrO_2, Ta and Re. Sensitivities for all these samples varied by just over an order of magnitude.

A similar source has been described by Magnuson et al[29b] again having the magnetic and anode cylinder axes coincident, but extracting the ions along this same axis. Two filaments were used by Magnuson et al one producing electrons for ionization and the other acting as a heater for the material to be ionized. The advantage of this source was that the sample can be introduced in a crucible rather than coating the filament. Very pure beams of N_2^+, Zn^+, Al^+, Cu^+, Ag^+, Au^+ and Fe^+ ions were produced at about 600 eV and of intensity expected by space charge limitations, i.e. about 85 μA for N_2^+ and 56 μA for Zn^+.

9.2.8 The Radio-Frequency ion source

An alternative method of producing an ion beam without using a heated filament is by coupling the gas discharge tube to an r-f tuned circuit and applying a high frequency field. This method was successfully developed by Thonemann et al[30 31] and depends for its operation on the electrons gaining energy from the r-f field and ionising gas atoms in their oscillatory path. The ions are extracted by a negative electrode as indicated in Fig. 9. 9 and can then be focused by a simple electrostatic lens array onto a target.

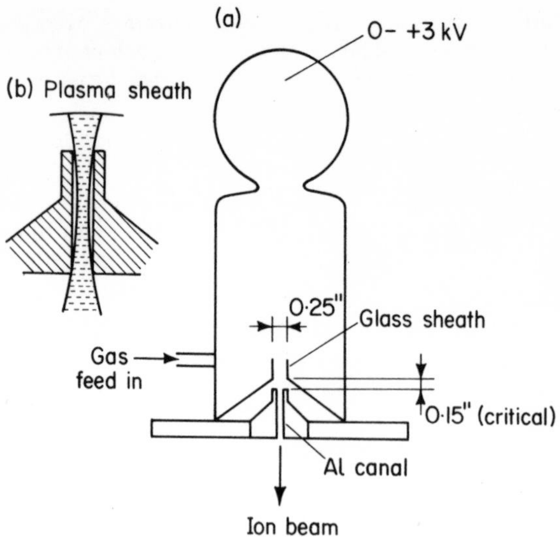

Fig. 9. 9 (a) R. F. ion source
(b) Optimum extraction conditions in an r-f source

Eubank et al[32] have carried out a thorough study of the performance of the r-f ion source as a function of the r-f power input, frequency, discharge pressure and extracting voltage. They concluded that it was the plasma density and source geometry which governed the optimum conditions for running the ion source. The plasma density could be optimized either by running at high r-f power and a low discharge pressure or vice-versa. It was considered that the shape of the space-charge sheath surrounding the extractor canal would vary with extractor voltage and optimum extractor conditions were assumed to occur when the envelope of the ion beam just skimmed the entrance and exit ports of the extractor canal with a waist at the canal mid-point. (Fig. 9. 9b). A thorough review of r-f discharge sources has been presented by Blanc and Degeilh[33] who list the principal physical details of all published sources of this type. Typical operating conditions for the r-f ion source are as follows:

Discharge pressure	10^{-2} to 10^{-3} Torr
r.f. power	300 watts at 10-30 mc/s
Extractor voltage	3 kV
Magnetic field	40 Gauss
Ion density	$10^{11}/cm^3$
Extracted ion current	10 mA
Energy spread	20-100 eV

The energy spread of the r-f source is exceptionally large (20-100 eV) making this type of source useful only for high energy bombardment experiments. The source is however, particularly useful for the production of proton beams, Eubank et al quote that as much as 91% of the extracted current in their apparatus comprised protons; this compares with beams of only 1% protons obtained in electron impact ion sources.

9.2.9 Duo-Plasmatron ion source

The duo-plasmatron ion source was first described in 1956 by von Ardenne[34] and has since been widely used as an intense source of ions particularly for high energy bombardment applications.

A schematic diagram of this type of source is presented in Fig. 9. 10. Electrons are emitted by the filament

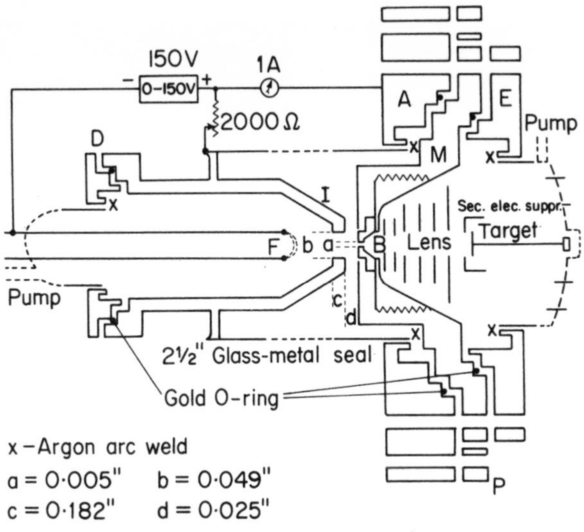

Fig. 9.10 The duo-plasmatron ion source (viz. Ref. 9.35)

F and accelerated towards the anode through the gas to be ionized which is present at a pressure of 10-50 millitorr. An arc strikes between the filament and anode and is confined to form a .005 inch spot at the latter electrode by introducing:

1. a conical intermediate electrode, I, which is held at a potential approximately half-way between the filament and anode and
2. a magnetic field which converges to the desired .005 inch aperture at the anode.

The magnetic field constrains the electrons so that ionization in the arc is limited to a small region extending right through the aperture in the anode. Thus there is an intense plasma at the output side of the nozzle from which either ions or electrons may be extracted and focused. The excess pressure of gas in the ion source region promotes rapid flow through the nozzle and thereby pushes even more ionized components into the extraction region.

As the anode aperture has to dissipate the entire discharge wattage of the arc current it becomes extremely hot and must therefore be constructed of a high melting point low vapour pressure material. A molybdenum button is often used, designed so that it can easily be replaced as the intense ion bombardment causes severe sputtering which widens the aperture.

The magnetic field is usually produced by a solenoid surrounding flange D, the flux circuit comprising: a mild steel cylinder (enclosing the solenoid and nearly touching the anode flange), the anode itself, and the intermediate lens cone which is constructed of a suitable magnetic vacuum material, (certain types of stainless steel are satisfactory). In practice the required field is reasonably small and can often be provided by residual magnetism in the components. Tawara and Suganomata[36] describe a compact version of this type of source which uses ferrite permanent ring magnets which, as they are electrically non-conducting, can be sandwiched firmly between the intermediate and anode electrode structures. Platinum mesh filaments impregnated with barium have been found by Moak et al[37] to be much superior to the conventional untreated tungsten ribbons. Initial a.c. heating is required, but, once the arc has struck, the heat dissipated at the filament surface is usually sufficient to maintain the required emission of electrons.

Extraction of the ion beam can conveniently be carried out by a shaped electrode with the conventional Pierce geometry, though Sreenivasan et al[35] have found that a double einzel lens arrangement brings the ions to a focus just as efficiently.

Typical operating parameters of this type of source are:

Arc current	0.25-0.75 A.
Arc voltage	40-70 V (depending on type of gas in source)
Pressure	50 mTorr
Extractor volts	2-3 kV
Target current	100-400 $\mu A/cm^2$
Energy spread	6-10 eV

The source can produce substantial electron or negative ion currents by reversing the polarity of the extractor voltage.

Moak et al[37] have shown that a beam of up to 5 mA of electrons and 11 mA of H^- ions could be obtained when the source is operated in this mode.

9.2.10 Field Ionization source

The field ion source is basically a field ion microscope with a hole in the image screen to allow the ions, which are formed in the intense field at the tip of a sharpened tungsten wire, to pass through and be focused into a beam. Currents produced by the source are extremely low however, the energy spread is high and operation is difficult owing to the high voltages involved, so for surface interaction studies this type of source is of little use.

Typical operating conditions are

Field	5 volts per angstrom
Energy spread	20-40 eV
Target current	10^{-11} A

9.2.11 Bombardment ion source

The bombardment source, or sputtering ion source as it is often called, relies on the production of ionic species of a given target material when it is bombarded by ions of another species. It has a great advantage over the spark source which is the main alternative method of producing ions from a solid sample in that the secondary currents are stable and the energy spread is not as large. The principal disadvantage is however that an ion source and focusing system is required for the primary beam and a further analyzer and energy selector for the secondary beam. Liebl and Herzog[39] describe an apparatus with a duoplasmatron primary ion source which produces 10-12 keV argon ions of 1 mA intensity. Secondary emission coefficients are such that the ejected ion current is only of the order 10^{-8}-10^{-7} A. and the energy spread will be the same magnitude as the ejection energies of sputtered atoms discussed in Chapter 7, i.e. 10-20 eV.

This source is thus rather complex and is not satisfactory for studies of clean surface interactions. Where ions of solid materials are required the triple filament thermal ionization source[15,16], the magnetron source of Cobic et al[29a], or, a more recent sputtering ion source of Hill and Nelson[39a] would be more efficient, the thermal sources producing ion beams with a lower energy spread.

9.3 APPLICATIONS OF ION BOMBARDMENT

9.3.1 Introduction

Although studies of ion bombardment phenomena have been carried out for over a hundred years much of the work was of a basic nature and was designed to learn more about sputtering and the various ionic and electronic emissions which occurred. Only since 1950 have applications of various ion bombardment processes become of importance. The main applications of ion bombardment will be briefly discussed here and it is clear that they are of a widespread nature. Ion bombardment is now used to clean surfaces, to carry out micro-machining, to produce thin films, especially for micro-circuits, and is the basic process responsible for the action of modern high speed oil-free pumping devices.

In the following, sections 9.3.2 to 9.3.8 describe useful applications which depend essentially on the sputtering process, sections 9.3.9 to 9.3.11 applications deriving from injection phenomena and sections 9.3.12 to 9.3.15 applications which rely on emission of charged particles during bombardment.

9.3.2 Bombardment cleaning

The production of an atomically clean surface is a problem often encountered in processes designed to produce thin films, for example in the production of micro-circuits. Conventional cleaning methods, which include chemical etching, electro-polishing, high temperature heating and ultrasonic cleaning, are generally cumbersome and are selective in their mode of attack. In 1935 Strong[40] showed that ion bombardment of bases for mirror telescopes was adequate to produce a clean substrate for the deposition of the reflecting material; the thin films forming without blistering or producing cloudy layers as would have occurred if the substrates were in any way contaminated. The process devised by Strong involved immersing the mirror base into a glow discharge. Many variations of this technique have since been employed, the samples to be cleaned usually being placed in the cathode dark space, or, in the positive column region, though in the latter case they have to be shielded from high speed electrons which otherwise encourage the formation of polymeric films on the surface.

The principal shortcoming of bombardment cleaning technique has been that the surface layers become severely damaged as discussed fully in Chapter 6. However a carefully planned series of cycles of annealing and bombardment can be devised which will leave the surfaces atomically clean and undamaged, as has been demonstrated by Farnsworth et al[41]. The optimum conditions established by Farnsworth et al were:

(1) A vacuum of the order 10^{-9} Torr

(2) Thorough out-gassing of the samples at 500-1000°C for several days

(3) Irradiation of the samples with argon ions of about 0.5 keV energy and 1 mA/cm^2 intensity for one hour.

(4) Annealing of the samples at 500°C.

(5) Repeating operations 3 and 4 several times and concluding with a quick anneal.

Using the ion-electron emission coefficient, and the gas absorption rate as a monitor of target cleanliness Hagstrum et al[42] have shown that the above cycle enables surfaces to be maintained clean, with contamination levels less than 0.05 monolayers whilst Haneman[43], using electron diffraction techniques, has shown that the above surfaces were also undamaged.

Thus ion bombardment provides a useful cleaning method which is applicable to cleaning of metals, alloys, semiconductors, or dielectrics. It is not selective in its cleaning action, although stable oxide layers tend to persist and must be bombarded with heavier inert gases at high (20-30 keV) energies, and, provided the correct procedure is always adopted, undamaged atomically clean surfaces can be produced.

9.3.3 Bombardment as a means of thinning samples

Removal of metal during ion bombardment is difficult to avoid but, controlled removal of uniform thin layers of the bombarded surface is almost equally difficult to attain. The only work on this technique appears to have been carried out by Fisher and Weber[44] who have developed a method for removing micron layers of metal from cylindrical specimens placed in a fairly high pressure discharge plasma. Typical working parameters were found to be

Discharge voltage	1.5 kV
Discharge current	1 mA
Gas pressure (krypton)	0.3 Torr

Investigations of a more general nature on thinning of specimens by ion bombardment are more numerous. Ion bombardment thinning has several advantages over the conventional electrolytic techniques which may be listed as follows:

(1) It can be universally employed to all species

(2) No contamination of the specimen by the electrolyte can occur

(3) The thin specimens usually have a thick rim due to the concentration of the ion beams at a focus, this makes handling the specimen easier and further ensures a good thermal contact with the thinned region under study.

The principal arguments against the bombardment technique are:

(1) Relatively complex apparatus is required,

(2) the operation must be carried out in vacuum which takes time to attain and,

(3) selective etching and deposition of the bombarding gas can occur.

However, all the disadvantages can be accepted if the specimen is one which does not readily respond to the electrolytic method. The selective etching can be minimized by using low bombarding energies and the sorbed gases may be reliberated by gently baking the specimen.

Paulus and Reverchon[45] have shown that ceramics, which because of their porosity are extremely difficult to thin uniformly by electrolytic means, can be successfully thinned by bombarding with 6 keV oxygen ions at angles of incidence near grazing. The use of such oblique bombardments was suggested to avoid formation of a large number of wells in the surface and also to increase the sputtering yield, thus accelerating the process. Simultaneous bombardment of the specimen from both sides was carried out to avoid buckling the sample as it reached its ultimate thinned size.

Genty[46] has carried out a thorough comparison of ion bombardment and electrolytic thinning techniques and concluded that the bombardment method was very successful provided that energies less than 2 keV were used, otherwise selective sputtering was found to occur which led to the appearance of approximately regular striations when the sample was viewed in the electron microscope. The bombardment was shown to have no selective effect on joints in the materials and perturbation due to the introduction of dislocations was seen to be unimportant.

9.3.4 Micro-machining by ion bombardment

By carefully producing a well focused intense ion beam it is a relatively simple matter to allow the erosion to continue and thereby produce fine holes of the order of a few microns diameter in foils of materials some tens of microns in thickness.

Rozenfel'd and Makarov[47] describe a simple discharge tube with a hole in the cathode which collimates the ions produced in the plasma and focuses them onto the sample to be drilled. Materials such as tantalum, nichrome, molybdenum, steel and diamond have been successfully drilled by this technique in times of the order several minutes for the metallic specimens and up to one hour for the diamond samples The final diameters of the fine holes produced were fairly random however, varying over a range from 7 to 40 microns. Raether[48] has described the bombardment of a 50 μ silicon monocrystal with ion beams from both sides in an experiment designed to produce uniform thin films. He has shown that the resulting section through the material is wedge shaped each side of the hole, and suggests that this is due to a variation in ion current density from the hole centre outwards. We mention this work here as the shape of the drilled section is perhaps the reason for the discrepancy in diameter of ion drilled holes in the work described above. Clearly the actual hole edge must be extremely thin and slight changes in the duration of the bombardment may make considerable differences to the final diameter of the resulting aperture.

An elegant method of producing very thin (500 Å) gold strands has been described by Broers[49]. An electron beam focused to a 100 Å diameter spot is swept over a selected area of a thin film of gold and polymerizes a resist layer along its path. Subsequent ion bombardment can remove the substrate film except where it is protected and hence, after prolonged bombardment a set of fine miniature strands of gold remain (less than 500 Å in width). A technique such as this could be readily adopted to produce masks for use during evaporation or sputtering of thin film circuits; the electron beam profile could be programmed and subsequent bombardment would produce a reproducible and accurate mask structure.

Thus ion beam drilling has immediate applications in micro-circuit development and for drilling materials which could otherwise present severe machining problems. The application is a relatively new one and much work will have to be done to compile reproducible machining data.

9.3.5 Ion etching

As we have already seen in Chapter 7 surfaces bombarded by ion beams develop characteristic etch patterns from which much can be learnt about the distribution of dislocations and grain boundaries in the sample under investigation. Thus ion bombardment provides an alternative technique to chemical etching for developing surface irregularities and has the following advantages over the latter:

(1) Ion bombardment of all types of material is possible whereas chemical etching is limited to certain specimens, for example structures of alloys, silicides, carbides and borides can be developed by ion bombardment whereas all other methods are extremely difficult.

(2) The investigations can be carried out at any selected specimen temperature whereas in chemical methods the temperature range is limited.

(3) No contamination of the surfaces by chemical etchant occurs, although this advantage is off-set to some extent by the damage introduced into the crystal by the irradiation.

Wehner[50] has shown that, not only can the surface irregularities be observed by ion bombardment etching, but also the predominant crystal face can be determined by the characteristic etch patterns produced. For example, for 100 eV mercury ion bombardment of monocrystalline germanium a (100) surface was shown to form pits with four-fold symmetry, whilst a (111) surface produced pits with three-fold symmetry and a (110) surface two-fold symmetrical pits. The basic mechanism involved in the selective decoration of surfaces due to ion bombardment is clear from an understanding of the principles of sputtering discussed in Chapter 7. Energy is introduced into the crystal by the incoming particles and is dissipated in collisions which predominate in directions of closest atomic packing. Thus atoms are preferentially ejected from the densest atomic places in the crystal so that selective erosion of the edges of these dense planes occurs. The effect produces an inverse pattern to that obtained by chemical etching where it is the least dense planes which are preferentially eroded away.

9.3.6 Production of thin films by sputtering

With the advent of micro-circuit techniques production of controlled thin films of various materials as resistors, inductors, or, capacitors is a very important problem and sputtering techniques of producing such films are proving extremely successful; especially where deposition of alloys or oxides of particular metals are required as, in these cases, the conventional evaporation techniques fail.

The deposition of material by sputtering in conventional glow-discharge apparatus has the disadvantage that the ejected atoms leave the sputtered surface in uncontrollable directions so that, for deposition of useful circuit patterns, masks have to be placed over the substrate. An alternative technique at present under investigation by Probyn[50a] and Medved[50b] is to produce a metal ion beam which can then be swept across the substrate surface in a controlled manner. The deposition could thus be programmed and completely automatic and the construction of masks would be avoided.

The most common materials required for sputtering of micro-circuit components are presented in Table 9.1.

A diagrammatic sketch of a thin film depositing apparatus is presented in Fig. 9.11. The discharge surrounds both substrate and target the latter being left electrically floating at first to allow the plasma

TABLE 9.1

Principal materials used for the production of microcircuit components

Capacitors	Tantalum
Conductors	Beryllium-Copper, Aluminium
Resistors	Tantalum, Tungsten, Nichrome
Inductors	Permalloy
Semi-conductors	Silicon, Germanium
Dielectrics	Tantalum-Pentoxide

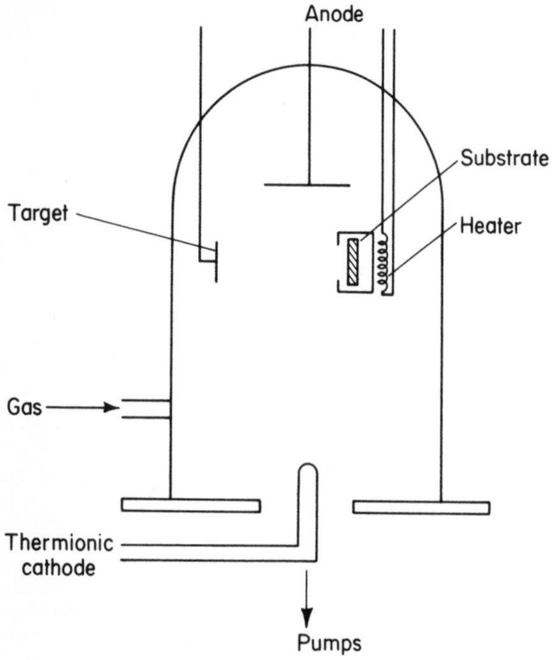

Fig. 9.11 Principal elements of a thin film deposition apparatus

to clean the substrate surface by bombardment. The substrate can also be heated during this interval after which the target is connected to a negative voltage of the order 1 kV when sputtering commences. Sputtered atoms traverse the one-centimetre distance to the substrate where they are deposited and eventually build up a complete film, the thickness of which can be controlled, by experience of the prevailing conditions, to within 1% over an area of the order one square inch. If a particular pattern of deposition is required the substrate must be protected by a suitably designed mask.

Variations of this simple deposition apparatus enable production of non-inductive low-noise resistors[51], tantalum capacitors[52], thin film diodes[53] and high sensitivity bolometers[54]. An improvement in the quality of the thin films has been shown to occur when an alternating voltage is applied between the sputtered cathode surface and the substrate. Frerichs[55] demonstrated that, provided the discharge conditions were adjusted so that more current flowed during the half-cycle when the target was negative than when positive, a net transfer of material to the substrate occurred and relatively pure films were obtainable under fairly 'dirty' experimental conditions.

Bombardment of the substrate during the half-cycle when it was negative was believed to assist in the preferential removal of adsorbed contaminant gases. Maissel and Schaible[56] have shown that provided the substrate was suitably 'biased' throughout the experiment, the deposition could be carried out continuously under d.c. conditions with similar success to the a.c. technique of Frerichs. For bias voltages of up to 20 volts the resistivity of the films was found to increase and Maissel et al concluded that at these low potentials the argon ions did not clean the surface and became trapped. This factor is an important one as in most deposition experiments the substrate is allowed to electrically 'float' and will often charge up to these low negative-bias values thereby causing production of films with exceptionally high resistivities. At higher bias voltages the resistivity decreases sharply to values less than 40 μ-ohm-cm at 200 volts after which it proceeds to increase slightly, this latter trend being ascribed to the stresses induced in the films during irradiation.

It was noted that the sputtered films produced by the 'bias' technique did not adhere to the substrate as well as those produced on a substrate at a floating potential and this was considered to be due to the removal by bombardment of the initial oxide layer which Benjamin and Weaver[57] have shown to be necessary for good adhesion. This problem was eliminated by Maissel et al by biasing the substrate positive initially and allowing a small percentage of oxygen into the sys-system with the argon. After half a minute the bias was then switched negative to 200 volts at which value most of the factors disturbing production of pure films were eliminated.

Maissel and Schaible demonstrated that the bias technique has several distinct advantages over straightforward deposition as follows:

(1) Oxygen contamination: resulting films had resistivities varying by only a factor of four whereas variation in conventional apparatus due to the presence of oxygen in the film is several orders of magnitude.

(2) Cathode impurities: in conventional deposition methods impurities may be sputtered from the cathode and be deposited on the substrate. Although the effect on the resistivity is not very large it is seen to be greatly reduced by employing the bias technique.

(3) Film thickness: for films exceeding 500 Å the bias technique ensures resistivities which are relatively independent of film thickness. For thinner films their own rather high resistance decreases the effective bias so that the process is not successful.

(4) Chemical cleaning: introduction of small amounts of forming gas (N_2 + 10% H_2) into the sputtering atmosphere was shown by Maissel et al[58] to reduce the resistivity of tantalum films to about a quarter of the value which would be obtained for un-biased deposition in the pure argon sputtering atmosphere. This additional process is of no advantage when the bias of −200 volts is applied; in other words the ionic bombardment of the substrate is as efficient as the chemical action of the forming gas in maintaining a clean surface.

Work by Kay[59] contradicts the preceding findings as he was able to demonstrate that uniaxial permalloy films with reproducible characteristics could be obtained regardless of the potential at which the substrate was held and, further, that there was no evidence of oxide compounds forming within or at the substrate surface. The substrate temperature was, however, accurately maintained at 350°C throughout the deposition and this factor may have been significant in maintaining an adequately clean surface and have eliminated the need for the bombardment cleaning employed by Maissel et al[56].

The importance of oxidation in determining the properties of thin sputtered films is apparent in work by the Bell Telephone Laboratories[60] who were able to produce films with resistivities as high as 10 kilo-ohms per square by sputtering tantalum in a partial oxygen atmosphere. After sputtering, the surfaces of the films were electrolytically oxidized to 'trim' their resistance values and to protect the final resistor. Temperature coefficients of resistance varied between +100 and −500 parts per million per degree centigrade. These workers have further shown that films with resistance less than 200 ohms per square could be deposited by sputtering in a nitrogen atmosphere. Maissel[61] has shown that the introduction of 0. 1% oxygen into the discharge promotes the production of more stable tantalum films. The resistivity of these films did in fact still change when they were heated in air, but approached a stable value within twenty hours. However the absolute magnitudes of the resistors were not by any means reproducible. Maissel has suggested that the reason is that the penetration of the oxygen into grain boundaries causes the instability in the resistance values. Schaible and Maissel[62] concluded that resistance values would be more stable were atoms of a good conducting material introduced into the grain boundaries and they were able to demonstrate that tantalum films doped with gold produced very stable resistors. The resistance still increased by about 8% when heated for ten hours in air at 250°C, but these films were superior to the oxygen treated samples for frequencies up to 2000 Mc/sec.

9. 3. 7 Determination of crystal orientations by ion bombardment

It was seen in chapter 7 that atoms ejected from monocrystalline samples during ion bombardment were characteristically ejected in directions corresponding to the close-packed atom rows in the crystal structure (i.e. ⟨111⟩ directions in bcc crystals and ⟨110⟩ in fcc), an effect first described by Wehner[63]. Cunningham and Ng-Yelim[64,65] have devised an apparatus utilizing the above effect in which the reproductibility of spots is so consistent that the orientations of bombarded crystals can be interpreted to within 3° by studying the ejection patterns. The apparatus consisted basically of a low-pressure glow-discharge ion source from which a fairly intense beam of ions could be extracted and focused to a sharp point (100 mA onto 2 mm square). Targets were placed at the centre of a hemispherical section of a ping-pong ball and the principal ejection directions recorded by pricking the dense point of the deposits on this hemisphere with a pin. Reference to a calibrated standard was then carried out and the particular spots and their relative directions to the target normal (marked by a hole through which the incident ion beam passed) could be determined. Hence the particular crystal face could be specified. Investigations carried out on the face-centred cubic silver, copper and aluminium samples showed that the close-packed ⟨110⟩ spots were the best guide to the surface orientation. For body-centred cubic crystals, iron, beta-brass, and tungsten however the close-packed ⟨111⟩ directions were not reliable due to additional 'satellite' deposits in the ⟨111⟩ directions caused by a ejection of a surface atom which has relaxed from its normal ⟨111⟩ position. Cunningham et al have found that the orientation of bcc crystals is best interpolated from the positions of ⟨100⟩ spots which, although less intense, are more reliable.

A comparison of the method with results obtained by x-ray analysis is given in Table 9. 2 and it is clear that the ion bombardment technique is a reliable and inexpensive method of determining the orientation of a crystalline material.

TABLE 9. 2 (Ref. 9. 64)

Comparison of x-ray and ion bombardment data for crystal orientation determinations.

Sample	direction of surface normal by x-rays	by ion bombardment
Silver 1	22° to ⟨111⟩	22° to ⟨111⟩
Silver 2	18° to ⟨100⟩	20° to ⟨100⟩
Silver 3	12° to ⟨111⟩	13° to ⟨111⟩
Silver 4	10° to ⟨111⟩	12° to ⟨111⟩
Silver 5	8° to ⟨110⟩	4° to ⟨110⟩
Silver 6	2° to ⟨100⟩	3° to ⟨100⟩
Silver 7	7° to ⟨110⟩	4° to ⟨110⟩
Aluminium	3° to ⟨100⟩	4° to ⟨100⟩
Iron	8° to ⟨100⟩	10° to ⟨100⟩
Tungsten	3° to ⟨100⟩	3° to ⟨100⟩
Tungsten	2° to ⟨111⟩	2° to ⟨111⟩

9. 3. 8 Sputter and Getter Ion Pumping

Getter ion pumps have become of great importance during recent years when it was realized that the oil contamination introduced by conventional pumping systems was preventing attainment of ultra-high vacua and, more important, was interfering with clean surface experiments and applications of ultra high vacuum environment to evaporation of thin films, space simulation and particle accelerators. The principle of gettering has been well established for many years in that certain gettering materials, such as barium, titanium, zirconium, molybdenum, when cooled from high temperatures, or, upon being evaporated, will remove gases from a system at a rate which declines as the surface is saturated with gas. The disadvantage of using a simple getter was that the surfaces became saturated with gas, so that pumping of large quantities of gas was impossible. An alternative established method of pumping was that of ion pumping in a triode gauge where it was observed that the positive ions were buried in the ion collector and the gauge walls with the resultant removal of gas, although pumping speeds were extremely low. This is discussed more fully in Chapter 8.

The getter-ion pump, as the name implies, combines both the above processes. The arrangement is similar to a cold-cathode Penning Gauge with titanium, or other gettering material, as the cathode and is illustrated in Fig. 9. 12. A high positive voltage is applied between the anode and cathode. Electrons are constrained by the magnetic field to move in directions parallel to the anode axis, and thus oscil-

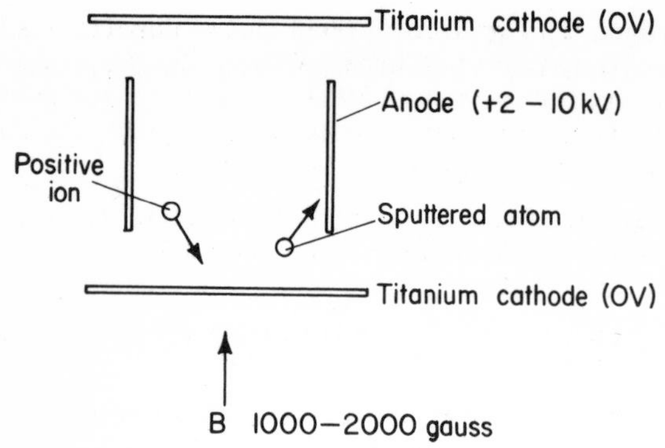

Fig. 9. 12 Typical configuration of electrodes in a getter ion pump

late between the two cathodes until they make an ionizing collision. Ions are accelerated towards the cathode where they react chemically with the getter material, cause sputtering of atoms of the getter, or, are simply buried in the cathode surface. A large majority of the sputtered atoms fall onto the anode where they produce a new surface thereby burying underneath any chemically sorbed gases. Thus, both the anode and cathode surfaces are continually being changed and the sorptive surfaces are thus continuously replenished so that the pumping action can continue over extremely long periods. Typical pumping speeds for various gases are indicated in Table 9. 3. It is clear that the inert gases are not pumped as efficiently, the only mechanism for these gases being injection into regions of the cathode where the deposition of material exceeds the erosion by sputtering.

TABLE 9. 3

Pumping speed relative to nitrogen of VacIon pumps for various gases

(by courtesy of Varian Associates Ltd.[66])

Nitrogen	1. 00
Oxygen	0. 57
Argon, Krypton, Xenon	0. 01 (0. 06 for super pumps)*
Hydrogen	2. 7
Deuterium	1. 9
Helium	0. 10
Neon	0. 05 (O. 15 for super pumps)*
Carbon Dioxide, Water Vapour, Carbon Monoxide	1. 0
Light Hydrocarbons	0. 90-1. 60

* Super pumps are those with slotted cathodes as discussed in text

In practice pump assemblies comprise an array of the modules indicated in Fig. 9. 12 the anodes forming a honeycomb pattern and thus the effect is to increase the pumping speed of the system many times. With such arrays pumps with speeds up to 500 litres per second (for air) have been constructed. An improvement in the pumping speed for inert gases can be made by, either, machining slots into the cathodes, or, by introducing an extra grid structure at each side of the anode. The final result of either technique is similar in that it encourages bombardment of the cathode obliquely. The reader will remember from Chapter 7 that sputtering yields at oblique incidence are higher than those obtained at normal incidence so that, in the case of the slotted cathode, a net removal of material from the sides of the slots and a net build up at the back of the cathode is anticipated. This does in fact occur so that a large part of the back face of the cathode slot acts as a sink for the inert gas ions. Improvement in pumping speed by a factor of 5 or 6 for the inert gases can be obtained by this simple modification, and, more important, the so called 'argon instability' encountered in pumps with plain cathodes due to the release of previously sorbed argon by sputtering, is eliminated by introducing the slots or extra grids.

Starting procedure for getter ion pump involves reducing the system pressure to 10^{-2} Torr or less with a suitable pump: usually a zeolite sorption pump is employed to avoid contaminating the system with oil. Once the getter pump starts the zeolite system can be valved off.

The getter pump is thus a most useful application of two aspects of ion bombardment: sorption and sputtering. It has many advantages over conventional oil-pumped systems among which can be listed:

(1) Fundamentally clean, hence no refrigerated baffle required.

(2) Use of continuous fore-pumping eliminated.

(3) No water cooling so that system is portable.

(4) Power failures not serious.

(5) Mechanically robust

(6) Uniform pumping speed over a wide pressure range (10^{-2}-10^{-10} Torr)

(7) The discharge current gives an indication of pressure

(8) Long life; due to continuous production of fresh gettering surfaces.

Hirsch[67] has described experiments with getter-ion pumps which have an auxiliary heated filament to produce extra ionizing electrons. The improvement in pumping speed is not however very large, varying by a one third power law of the useful emission current. Pumps with this extra source of electrons were however able to run with comparative speeds at much lower anode voltages and lower magnetic fields; for example a conventional 2. 5 l/sec pump would require 3 kV and 1000 gauss whilst the thermionically assisted pumps required only 270 volts and 250 gauss for the same pumping speed.

9. 3. 9 Collection of bombarding ions

In 1948 Koch[68] described an experiment which utilized the sorption effect discussed in Chapter 8 to enable the separation of neon isotopes. Neon ions were produced in a mass spectrometer which was capable of resolving the isotopes and ions of one of these were injected into the collector of the spectrometer at an energy of 60 keV. After the target had been bombarded for about an hour with an ion current of approximately 3 mA/cm^2 it was transferred to a geissler tube which was sealed off and evacuated to a pressure of about one millitorr. Spectrographic analysis of a glow discharge of the gas liberated on heating the target indicated it was extremely pure neon, although quantities obtained were very small (approximately 5×10^{14} atoms/cm^2). Clearly much improvement in collection efficiency is required to make this technique feasible for even small scale industrial use. The method has the advantage however that it is versatile and any selected gas within the range of the mass spectrometer can be collected and held for future analysis. This collection technique has been used on a wide scale for the production of sources of radioactive atoms.

One of the most important aspects of the collection of bombarding ions is the possibility of direct deposition of a metal ion beam pattern. Such a process would enable production of micro-circuits without the need for manufacture of masks and has the following additional advantages over conventional evaporative techniques.

(i) thin film resistors can be 'trimmed' in production

(ii) the ion beam can be purified, therefore allowing deposition of extremely pure circuit components,

(iii) similarly, dopant ions can be purified and precise amounts may be administered,

(iv) thin oxide barriers can be penetrated by the bombarding ions to make good ohmic contacts and,

(v) the process lends itself to programming and could thus be made completely automatic.

The main problem lies in the production of the metallic ion beam which must be well focused, (about 0.002 inch diameter spot) be reasonably intense, and have an energy less than that at which it sputters previously deposited atoms in the ratio one atom per ion; otherwise the film will not build up. Researches on metal ion beams for this purpose are being carried out by Probyn[50a], Medved[50b], and Wolter[68a,b]. Wolter[68b] has shown that, for the deposition to be reasonably rapid, the ion beam must be focused over as short a distance as practicable; i.e. a rapidly converging beam. Unfortunately such a beam is difficult to sweep across a substrate but Wolter has managed to overcome this problem and produce thin films of chromium, copper, and silver with reasonably reproducible electrical characteristics. If the beam is scanned horizontally lines of deposit are produced and a density distribution in the vertical direction shows the film to be bell-shaped; a broad maximum corresponding to the centre of the incident beam and rapidly thinning at the edges. Films were shown to be keyed to the substrate significantly better than the corresponding evaporated films. Results are thus so far extremely promising and the problem now resolves into devising a technique for switching-in a sequence of different ion beams to deposit more complex patterns in a reliable manner.

9.3.10 Injection of ions into semiconductors

A basic requirement in the manufacture of semi-conductor components is the ability to introduce controlled amounts of certain impurities into the samples to act as acceptors or donors. The process requires extremely careful control when carried out by conventional chemical methods where, usually, equilibrium conditions are established between the semiconductor surface and the dopant. As we have seen in Chapter 8 impurities can be introduced into the surface regions of a target by bombarding it with an energetic beam of the impurity ions and it is not surprising that semi-conductor junctions treated in this manner show marked improvement in their characteristics; the back voltage can be increased by an order of magnitude whilst the ratio of the forward current to the back can be increased by two to three orders of magnitude[69,70,71] Ohl[69] describes a bombardment technique for improving the properties of pure silicon where 3 keV He^+ ions at 5 $\mu A/cm^2$ intensity were fired for a period of two minutes at the silicon target which was heated to 300°C.

The advantages of the ion bombardment method of introducing donor levels are principally:

(1) The variations in the forward and back currents obtained by ion bombardment are easily reproducible

(2) The ion beam can be masked to produce many doping configurations

(3) By varying the ion energy the doping can be extended to greater depths in the surface or maintained solely at the surface (which is ideal for production of solar cells)

(4) Doping with new species, which could not otherwise be introduced, becomes possible. For example, McCaldin and Widmer[72] have introduced sodium ions into silicon to produce donor centres at concentrations of the order 10^{19} per square centimetre. A wide range of new Fermi-levels can thus be introduced which may allow production of semi-conductors with unique electrical properties, for example ZnO has never been doped p-type, but a suitable treatment with the correct ion beam may make this feasible.

(5) The damage introduced during the ion bombardment can usually be annealed out at reasonably low temperatures (300-400°C). This is the maximum temperature required by the process and is far less than that demanded by alloying or diffusion techniques. Thus the host crystal is less likely to absorb unwanted impurities.

(6) Certain materials can be super-saturated with the dopant ions and thus increase the carrier density above that obtainable by conventional techniques. In the work of McCaldin and Widmer (mentioned above) the sodium concentration is some factor 10^3 higher than the equilibrium concentration.

(7) By introducing ions into single crystals in 'channel' directions (see Chapter 5) the impurities will travel distances of the order 100 Å or more. Thus the doped region is at a considerable depth below the surface and is thereby protected from surface damage. Further, the impurity ions sorbed in this manner are not as easily liberated by heating as in polycrystalline ion doping processes since they have to diffuse further to the surface and the thermal energy available is insufficient for the sorbed atom to use the same 'channel' route out of the crystal.

The principal disadvantage of the bombardment method of doping is that the host crystal is damaged by the irradiation, the concentration of displaced atoms being much greater than the concentration of impurity atoms. However, by selecting suitable bombardment conditions, it can usually be arranged for the chemical properties of the injected ions to predominate, even though the impurities represent only several atomic percent of the parent semi-conductor. The damage to the crystal can in turn assist the doping by providing defects which act as carrier sites. Cussins[70] has shown that for bombardment of antimony the defects act as acceptor impurities. Cussins showed further that, for all types of bombarding ion on germanium, the resulting change in the Fermi level could be ascribed solely to the radiation damage and was independent of the chemical nature of the doping ion.

The same is not true for silicon where experiments on bombardment doping of point contact junctions by Ohl et al[69, 73] and Thornton et al[74] show that the reverse breakdown voltage of 5 volts for silicon increases to 15 volts after bombardment by helium ions and to 130 volts after bombardment by oxygen ions, so it is possible that the chemical nature of the bombarding ions is important in this case. The effect of the radiation damage alone on silicon will certainly move the Fermi-level toward the centre of the band gap thus making the semi-conductor intrinsic. This type of silicon is useful in high voltage rectifier applications[69,74] and for photo-electric devices[73]. The lifetime of the carriers induced by ion bombardment are lower however than those formed by the conventional epitaxial growth technique of producing near-intrinsic silicon surfaces.

Whilst there is no doubt that the ion is trapped by the semi-conductors in this form of doping it is not clear whether its final site will correspond to the solution sites attained by conventional methods. After the bombardment a region supersaturated with parent interstitials, vacancies and impurity atoms will exist and thorough annealing must be carried out to ensure that the impurity atoms 'jostle' into substitutional sites where possible. Care must be taken not to select too high an annealing temperature for this process otherwise the effect of the bombardment will be eliminated completely, the impurity atoms being ejected in gaseous form (as described in Chapter 8) at temperatures above 500°C. Alvager et al[75] report that an extensive post-bombardment anneal is required to move ion-injected phosphorus into the desired substitutional sites in silicon, and to remove the radiation damage. Even when the impurity atoms are established in the host crystal the concentration gradient near the surface will encourage diffusion, and evaporation of the impurity species. For this reason certain combinations of impurity and host materials are impractical e.g. germanium supersaturated with lithium precipitates the lithium at room temperature within a few hours[76,77].

The reader should now be aware of the fact that, although ion bombardment doping is simple in principle, much preliminary work on any new combination of doping ion and host crystal must be carried out to attain optimum conditions. For example, the target temperature is a critical factor, as was observed by McCaldin and Widmer[72] who found that, for 10 keV Cs^+ bombardment of silicon the resistivity was of the order 10^{-6} mho/cm^2 at 300°C and 2×10^{-4} mho/cm^2 at 500°C. Once established however the procedure is relatively simple and the resulting doped semi-conductors are found to have properties very similar to those obtained by conventional means (for combinations where comparisons can be made). In the work of Alvager et al[75] mentioned above, for example, the resulting phosphorus-doped silicon possessed identical properties to the semi-conductor obtained by conventional methods.

9.3.11 Alteration of chemical reaction rates at surfaces

In recent years it has been observed that ion bombardment of surfaces can either accelerate a subsequent chemical reaction at the surface, or, produce a passive surface which is highly resistant to oxidation. The former process generally occurs where the surface is simply damaged; the etch pits and dislocations which are generated providing a larger effective surface area for the reaction to take place. Surface passivation is due to the presence of sorbed ions which both reduce the effective surface area by occupying vacant lattice sites and also protect the surface beneath them from immediate erosion.

Mihama et al[78-81] have shown that monocrystalline FeS_2 targets immediately show diffraction patterns representing Fe_3O_4 when ions of air at 10 keV energy strike the surface, although Gribi[82] believes that it is the residual oxygen in the system which contributes to the Fe_3O_4 formation, the ion beam merely acting as a catalyst by disturbing fresh areas of surface. Gribi was able to add to this hypothesis in an experiment where he cooled the experimental chamber with liquid nitrogen (thereby reducing the thermal energy of the residual oxygen atoms) and showed that the surface oxidation was considerably reduced.

Mihama et al further observed that the oxidation in their experiments began in the neighbourhood of faults in the crystal. A similar effect was observed by Trillat et al[83,84,85] for nitrogen ions striking a nickel target, the nickel changing into nickel nitrate within a few seconds.

Sosnovsky[86] has described the effects of ion bombardment on the catalytic activity of silver crystals of various orientations in the decomposition of formic acid. (111) (110) and (100) silver surfaces were bombarded with argon ions of energy 14-1400 eV and the subsequent reaction rates, after annealing in vacuo at 250°C for at least 18 hours, were studied. The change in the catalyst was found to depend on the crystal face studied and was an important function of the bombarding energy, exhibiting a maximum catalytic rate after 500 eV bombardment of a (110) surface and after 46-300 eV bombardment of a (100) surface. Sosnovsky proposed that the increase in catalytic activity was brought about by the presence of dislocations and sorbed argon atoms, which provided additional active sites for the catalytic process.

Passivation of uranium by argon ion bombardment has been observed by Haymann et al[87,88,89]. His 'treated' sample of the normally readily-oxidizable uranium was seen to remain bright for several months whilst a similar untreated target was rapidly covered by a dull layer of UO_2. A similar effect was found for aluminium target bombarded by helium, the bombardment producing a compound similar to an alloy of helium-aluminium which possessed great neutrality with respect to oxidation.

Hondros and Benard[90] have demonstrated that the rate of oxidation of copper can be greatly inhibited by prior bombardment with a 1-3 keV argon ion beam of 1-5 mA/cm^2 intensity for 30 to 60 minutes. They concluded that the reduction of some 30% in oxidizing rate was due to the sorbed argon atoms in the surface layers of the copper targets; a view which was strengthened by the fact that the passivity can be eliminated by heating the targets for several hours at 500°C subsequent to the irradiation and thereby allowing the argon atoms to desorb.

In conclusion therefore we can state with certainty that many chemical reactions are affected by a preliminary treatment with ion bombardment. The principal effects of the bombardment appear to be a damaging action to the surface which increases the effective surface area and causes quicker reaction rates, or, sorption of a foreign gas which forms a type of *alloy*, resistant to chemical attack. The conditions required for a given treatment are critical and much further study is required before the effect could be put into commercial application. The scope of the treatment is further limited to materials which will not be heated to temperatures greater than 300-500°C at which the beneficial effects of the bombardment are generally eliminated.

9. 3. 12 Auger electron emission as a clean surface monitor

It was stressed in Chapter 3 that reliable results for the Auger ejection process could only be obtained if the surfaces under investigation were atomically clean. Once clean surfaces have been produced however and the secondary emission coefficient γ evaluated then the surface purity can be checked by performing a secondary emission experiment and comparing the measured value of γ with the known value for a clean surface.

Hagstrum et al[42] have demonstrated that this technique can detect a surface concentration of foreign atoms which amount to a few percent of a monolayer. Figures 3. 27 and 3. 28 show the change in electron emission yield and energy distribution as the tungsten surface was cleaned from its original un-treated condition. The difference between curves 1 and 4 in both cases is quite distinct, the latter most definitely representing the characteristics for an atomically clean tungsten surface.

An original, but less sensitive, method for observing surface cleanliness has been described by Anderson[91] which is based on the examination of atomic ejection patterns. Monocrystalline nickel targets were bombarded with mercury ions and it was found that on a temperature-pressure plot of the form shown in Fig. 9. 13 a distinct dividing line could be drawn between a region where clear ejection spots characteristic of the nickel (100) surface were observed and a region where the spots were diffuse and similar to those obtained for polycrystalline surfaces. Anderson presents a theoretical treatment showing that the transition to diffuse spots can be interpreted to be the results of a two dimensional condensation of mercury atoms and, further, that the heat of adsorption is 0. 69 eV per atom.

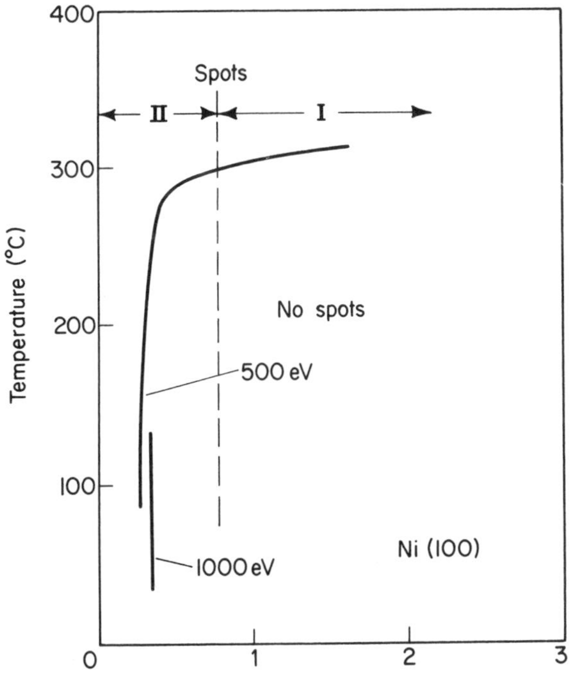

Fig. 9. 13 Curve of target temperature vs Hg pressure for Ni (100) showing regions where spot patterns were and were not observed during Hg^+ ion bombardment (viz. Ref. 9. 91)

9. 3. 13 Secondary electron emission for probing p-n junctions

An interesting application of the secondary electron emission phenomenon has been described by Spivak et al[92 93] for obtaining images of activated cold cathodes or p-n junctions. The specimen was bombarded by an ion beam and the secondary electrons focused onto a large screen. For studying the p-n junctions a voltage was applied to the junction in the cut-off direction. This produced a field distortion of the form indicated in Fig. 9. 14. Secondary electrons (which left the surface normally before applying this voltage) were now ejected into a distorted field and their paths are indicated in the figure. Hence the p-n junction was represented on the luminescent screen by a dark region and the position of the p-n junction could thus be directly viewed. Further experiments of Spivak et al demonstrated that the width of the p-n junction increased with the magnitude of the reverse voltage applied to the semi-conductor. Results for the width of the junction were higher than those obtained by conventional capacitance methods due to fringing of the distorted field, but the secondary emission method is an extremely simple direct-viewing one and is therefore of much use. Further, by viewing the electron mirror image of the surface superimposed on the secondary emission pattern, Spivak et al were able to evaluate the variation of potential across the p-n junction. If a reverse voltage was applied to the junction then the overall potential on the specimen varied with respect to that on the electron gun cathode and, at some point, the potential on the surface was equal to that of the electron gun cathode. At potentials more negative than this the normal electron mirror image would dominate the screen whilst at potentials

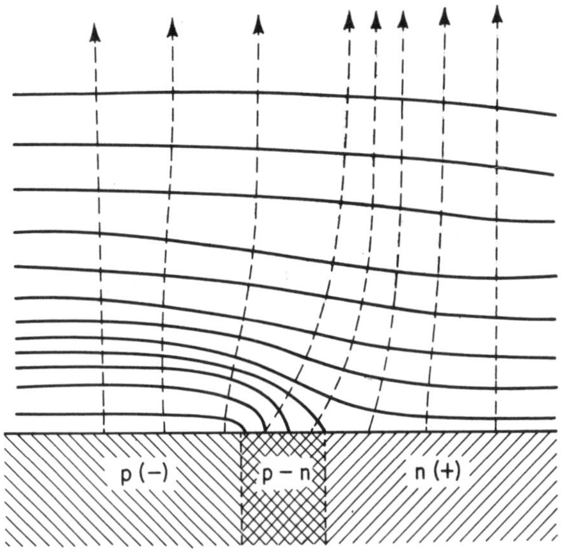

Fig. 9. 14 Illustrating field distortion and secondary electron paths at a p-n junction (viz. Ref. 9. 92)

more positive the mirror image vanished and the secondary emission pattern dominated. By slowly varying the voltage between the electron cathode and the specimen the movement of this changeover region could be plotted and related to the distance across the p-n junction as indicated in fig. 9. 15. This elegant application of secondary emission provides an extremely useful probe for p-n junctions and measurements far more accurate than those possible by conventional probe techniques are easily obtained.

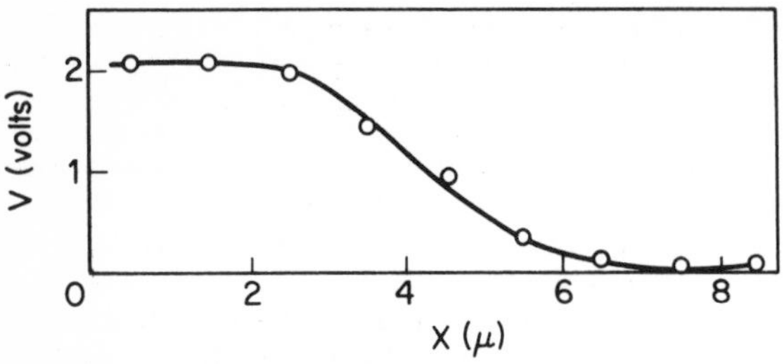

Fig. 9. 15 Distribution of potential over a p-n junction as measured by the electron mirror technique (viz. Ref. 9. 92)

9. 3. 14 Ion neutralization spectroscopy

We concluded Chapter 3 with the remark that further studies of potential ejection of electrons could lead to a better understanding of electron state densities in solids. Hagstrum and his co-workers[93a, b] have already made much progress in this field and have recently developed an elegant technique known as Ion Neutralization Spectroscopy (INS) in which information on the electron state densities in a material is extracted from the experimental electron energy distributions obtained by low energy He^+, Ne^+, and A^+ ion bombardment. The method is offered as an alternative to soft x-ray and photo-electron spectroscopy (SXS and PES, respectively) and has the advantage over these latter techniques in that INS is critically dependent on surface contamination and can therefore be used to investigate electron state density distributions for a thin layer of one material on another.

The mathematics of the process is protracted and will not be presented here. However the basic steps are straightforward and can be listed as follows:

(1) The external electron energy distributions $X_k(E)$ for three ion species at two energies K are determined experimentally (usually He^+, Ne^+, and A^+ at 5 and 10 eV).

(2) From these the de-broadened distributions are obtained using the observation that broadening is a linear function of ion velocity (broadening is discussed fully in Chapter 3, section 3. 4. 8).

(3) The $X_0(E)$ functions are then divided by an escape probability function P(E) to obtain the internal electron energy function F(E). P(E) is a three parameter function with the parameters chosen so that the functions for the three ions is the same (where they overlap) except for a possible normalizing factor.

(4) The energy variable is changed to give F(G) where G is the band energy level and is measured positively down from the Fermi level.

(5) The function F(G) is unfolded to obtain U(G).

This 'unfolding' stage is perhaps the most difficult step to visualize. It arises because there are two electrons participating in each Auger transition. If we look at the electrons contributing to an internal energy E to E + dE we find that they arise from pairs of electrons in energy levels equally disposed above and below a level G which is half-way between E and the ground state of the incoming atom ($-E_i$ (S)). If the number in the levels Δ above and below G is $N_v(G + \Delta)$ and $N_v(G - \Delta)$, respectively, then the total contribution to the energy E (i.e. to energy G, changing the variable) is

$$F(G) = \int_0^G U(G + \Delta)\, U(G - \Delta)\, d\Delta$$

where U(G) is a function which includes the state density $N_v(G)$ and is proportional to it if the matrix element factors are equal for the two electrons involved and are independent of G. In an elementary way one can consider that, whereas $N_v(G)$ is the state density variation of electrons in the solid, U(G) is the density variation of those electrons which actually participate in the Auger transition.

Assuming that U(G) does adequately represent the state density variation Hagstrum and Becker[93a] have presented data for Cu(110) and Ni(111) surfaces and shown that the method yields similar state density variations to that of PES, for example;

1. the d-band peaks were observed at G = 2-4 eV for copper and G = 0. 2 eV for Ni and

2. the peak at G = 6. 5 eV was observed for copper.

Differences with the PES method were apparent however in that the copper d-band was narrower and did not exhibit a double peak, also there was no observable peak at G = 4. 5 eV in the nickel results. However the method of INS does appear to be very promising and much credit is due to Hagstrum and his co-workers for developing this new technique.

9. 3. 15 Secondary ion emission for analysis of surface conditions and target materials

This particular application of ion bombardment was pioneered by Honig[94] who fired the inert gases Ne^+, A^+, Kr^+ and Xe^+ at silver, germanium, germanium-silicon alloy, graphite, coal and silicon carbide surfaces and mass analyzed the secondary species. Peaks of the parent target material were readily detected as already discussed in Chapter 4 (section 4. 4) and indicated in Tables 4. 1 and 4. 2. For silver bombarded by 300-400 eV Xe^+ ions the relative abundance decreased in the order Ag_1^+, Ag_2^+, Ag_3^+, Ag_2O^-, Ag_2^- and $Ag_2O_2^-$, respectively. Impurity species of Na^+ and K^+ were present at similar intensities to the silver peak itself whilst Mg^+ and Fe^+ were observed only weakly and decreased in importance as the bombardment continued. Species characteristic of sorbed impurities Hg, H_2O, CO, CO_2 and hydrocarbons were also present in the spectrum at intermediate strengths.

Honig was thus able to demonstrate that the ion bombardment technique was a useful tool which would provide much useful qualitative information about specimen surfaces. He further attempted to use the technique as a quantitative analyzer to determine the percentage composition of a Ge-Si alloy (11% Si by density) by comparing the magnitudes of the Ge^+ and Si_1^+ peaks. Results conclusively showed that the method was not accurate, percentage compositions predicted by the method being a linear function of ion energy and varying from 6 to 20%.

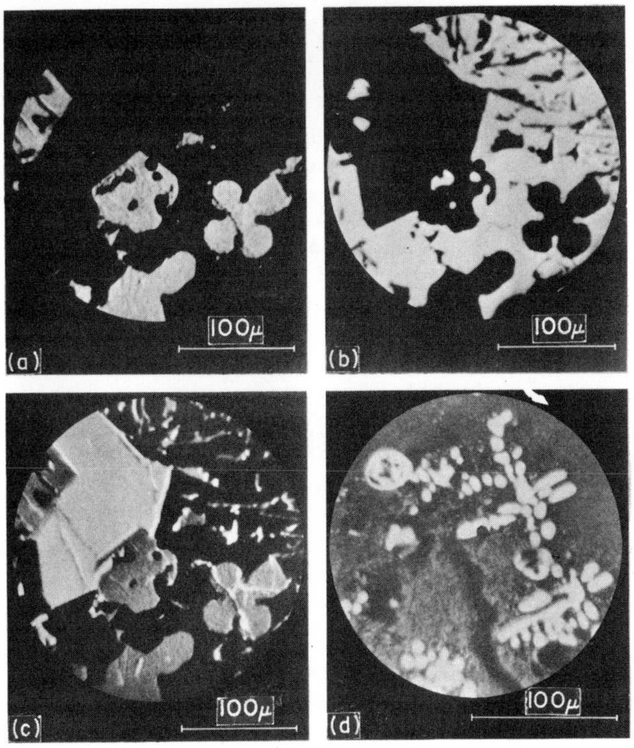

Plate 9. 1. a Distribution of magnesium in an alloy Al-Mg-Si (unpolished). Image obtained with 24 Mg^+ ions

b Distribution of aluminium in the same region of the specimen observed in 'a'. Image obtained with $_{27}Al^+$ ions

c Distribution of silicon in the same region of the specimen observed in 'a'. Image obtained with $_{28}Si^+$ ions

d Image obtained with $_{63}Cu^+$ ions on a bulk copper specimen containing nodules of the oxide Cu_2O

(viz. Ref. 9. 96)

This limitation of the technique has been illustrated in similar experiments by Bradley[95] and Castaing et al[96]. However the technique is still a most useful analytical tool as can be clearly seen from the photographs of an Al-Mg-Si alloy (plate 9. 1). To obtain these pictures an ion beam was fired at approximately 45° to the specimen surface and the ejected ions extracted normal to the target and focused by an electrostatic lens. A magnetic analyzer was then employed to separate the different ion species and the selected beam struck an image-converter which converted the ion pattern to an equivalent electron beam pattern. Finally the electrons were fired at a luminescent display screen and the photographs of plate 9. 1 obtained; different ion patterns being displayed for different settings of the magnetic analyzer field.

A cascade mass spectrometer has been described by Collins and McHugh[97] for qualitative analysis of unknown target compounds. The apparatus comprises essentially two 180° mass-analyzers maintained end to end so that the target port of the first analyzer corresponded to the ion source port of the second, the sample to be investigated being situated at the cusp of the ion trajectory. The primary ions strike the sample normally after traversing the first 180° sector. The specimen is evaporated onto a tungsten filament which is mounted in a simple surface ionization source for the analysis. Secondary particles leaving the specimen are ionized and extracted into the second 180° main analyzer. A magnetic electron-multiplier magnifies the small secondary currents at the final collector, currents being typically 10^5 ions/sec or approximately 10^{-14} A. Many types of metal have been analyzed by this technique, but it is still in an elementary stage.

REFERENCES

1. Bleakney, W. (1929) Phys Rev. **34**, 157
2. Nier, A.O. (1940) Rev. Sci. Instr. **11**, 212
3. Nier, A.O. (1947) Rev. Sci. Instr. **18**, 398
4. Barnard, G.B. (1956) Mass Spectrometer Researches Report. D.S.I.R. H.M.S.O. London
5. Edmonds, P.H. and Hasted, J.B. (1963) Proc. Third Internatl. Conf. of Electronic and Atomic Collisions. North Holland Publishing Co.; Amsterdam
6. Dempster, A.J. (1935) Proc. Am. Phil. Soc. **75**, 755
7. Dempster, A.J. (1936) Rev. Sci. Instr. **7**, 46
8. Hannay, N.B. (1954) Rev. Sci. Instr. **25**, 644
9. Hannay, N.B. and Ahearn, A.J. (1954) Analyt. Chem. **26**, 1056
10. Waldron, J.D. (1956) Research (London) **9**, 306
11. Craig, R.D., Errock, G.A. and Waldron, J.D. (1959) Advances in Mass Spectrometry. p. 136 Pergamon Press; London

11a. Suladze, K.V. and Plyutto, A.A. (1965) Zh. tekh. fiz. **35**, 1298. English translation in Soviet Phys.-Tech. Phys. (1966) **10**, 1006

12. Gorman, J.G., Jones, E.J. and Hipple, J.A. (1951) Analyt. Chem. **23**, 438
13. Woolston, J.R. and Honig, R.E. (1964) Rev. Sci. Instr. **35**, 69
14. Datz, S. and Taylor, E.H. (1956) J. Chem. Phys. **25**, 289
15. Inghram, M.G. and Chupka, W.A. (1953) Rev. Sci. Instr. **24**, 518
16. Craig, R.D. (1959) J. Sci. Instr. **36**, 38
17. Rubin, K., Dittner, P. and Bederson, B. (1964) Rev. Sci. Instr. Notes **35**, 1720
18. Tyrell, A.C., Roberts, J.W., and Ridley, R.G. (1965) J. Sci. Instr. **42**, 806
19. Aston, F.W. (1942) Mass Spectra and Isotopes. Edward Arnold (Publishers) Ltd.; London
20. Koch, J. (1953) Mass Spectroscopy in Physics Research, NBS. circular No. 522 p. 165 Washington
21. Fetz, H. (1940) Ann. Physik **37**, 1
22. Wehner, G.K. (1956) Phys. Rev. **108**, 35
23. Stuart, R.V. (1962) Trans. 8th National Vacuum Symposium Washington (1961) **1**, 252 Pergamon Press Inc. New York
24. Laegreid, N., Wehner, G.K. and Meckel, B.B. (1959) J. Appl. Phys. **30**, 514
25. Barnett, C.F., Stier, P.M. and Evans, G.E. (1953) Rev. Sci. Instr. **24**, 394
26. Heil, H. (1944) Zeits. f. Physik **120**, 212
27. Finkelstein, A.T. and Smith, L.P. (1940) Rev. Sci. Instr. **11**, 94
28. Kistemaker, J. (1953) Mass Spectroscopy in Physics Research N.B.S. Circular No. 522, p. 179 Washington
29. Almén, O. and Nielsen, K.O. (1956) Electromagnetically Enriched Isotopes and Mass Spectrometry p. 23 Butterworth & Co. Ltd.; London

29a. Cobić, B., Perović, B. and Tošić, D. (1965) Rev. Sci. Instr. **36**, 1844

29b. Magnuson, G.D., Carlston, C.E., Mahadevan, P. and Comeaux, A.R. (1965) Rev. Sci. Instr. **36**, 136

30. Thonemann, P.C., Moffatt, J., Roaf, D. and Sanders, J.H. (1948) Proc. Phys. Soc. (London) **61**, 483
31. Thonemann, P.C. and Harrison, E.R. (1958) A.E.R.E. Report No. GP/R 1190
32. Eubank, H.P., Peck, R.A. Jr. and Truell, R. (1954) Rev. Sci. Instr. **25**, 989
33. Blanc, D. and Degeilh, A. (1961) J. Phys. Radium **22**, 230
34. Ardenne, M. Von, (1956) Tabellen der Elektronenphysik Ionenphysik and Übermikroskopie. Deutscher Verlag der Wissenschaften, Berlin
35. Screenivasan, T. and Carter, G. (1964) J. Electronics and Control **17**, 159
36. Tawara, H. and Suganomata, S. (1964) Nuclear Instr. and Methods **31**, 353
37. Moak, C.D., Banta, H.E., Thurston, J.N., Johnson, J.W. and King, R.F. (1959) Rev. Sci. Instr. **30**, 694
38. Pierce, J.R. (1954) The Theory and Design of Electron Beams. D. Van Nostrand and Co. Inc., New York
39. Liebl, H.J. and Herzog, R.F.K. (1963) J. Appl. Phys. **34**, 2893

39a. Hill, K.J. and Nelson, R.S. (1965) Nucl. Instrum. and Methods, **38**, 15

40. Strong, J. (1935) Rev. Sci. Instr. **6**, 97
41. Farnsworth, H.E., Schlier, R.E., George, T.H. and Burger, R.M. (1958) J. Appl. Phys. **29**, 1150 and 1195
42. Hagstrum, H.D. and D'Amico, C.D. (1960) J. Appl. Phys. **31**, 715
43. Haneman, D. (1960) Phys. Rev. **119**, 563 and 567
44. Fisher, T.F. and Weber, C.E. (1952) J. Appl. Phys. **23**, 181
45. Paulus, M. and Reverchon, F. (1962) Le Bombardment Ionique. Colloques Internationale du Centre National de la Recherche Scientifique. Bellevue, Paris Dec. (1962) **113**, 223
46. Genty, B. (1962) Le Bombardment Ionique. Colloques Internationale du Centre National de la Recherche Scientifique. Bellevue, Paris Dec. (1962) **113**, 95
47. Rozenfel'd, L.B. and Makarov, A.I. (1961) Izv. Akad. Nauk (SSSR) ser. fiz. **25**, 754. English translation in Bull. Acad. Sci. USSR, Physics Series (1961) **25**, 764
48. Raether, H. (1962) Le Bombardment Ionique. Colloques Internationale du Centre National de la Recherche Scientifique. Bellevue, Paris Dec. (1962) **113**, 129
49. Broers, A.N. (1964) Symposium on Electron Beam Processes for Micro-Electronics. Paper No. 15 Malvern July, 1964
50. Wehner, G.K. (1955) Advances in Electronics and Electron Physics, **7**, 239

50a. Probyn, B.A. (1964) Proc. 11th Meeting of Dielectrics and Evaporation Group. Inst. Physics, London, 20 October. Reported in Vacuum (1965) **15**, 315

50b. Medved, D.B. (1965) Proc. Electron and Laser Beam Symposium Pennsylvania State Univ. 31 Mar-2 April

51. Holland, L. and Siddal, G. (1953) Vacuum **3**, 245 and 375
52. Berry, R.W. and Sloan, D.J. (1959) Proc. Inst. Radio Engrs. **51**, 1040
53. Magill, P.J. (1963) Proc. Inst. Electronic and Electrical Engrs. **51**, 1040
54. Itterbeek, A. von, Greve L. de., Lanileir, R. and Celis, R. (1949) Physica **15**, 962
55. Frerichs, R. (1962) J. Appl. Phys. **33**, 1898
56. Maissel, L.I. and Schaible, P.M. (1965) J. Appl. Phys. **36**, 237
57. Benjamin, P. and Weaver, C. (1961) Proc. Roy. Soc. London **A261**, 516

58. Maissel, L. I., Hecht R. J. and Silcox, N. W. (1963) Proc. I.E.E.E. Electronic Components Conference, Washington D.C. (1963)

59. Kay, E. (1965) J. Electrochem. Soc. **112**, 590

60. Bell Telephone Laboratories (1963) Brit. Communications and Electronics 10 July, 553

61. Maissel, L. I. (1963) Transactions of 9th Vacuum Symposium Los Angeles 1962, 169 Macmillan-Pergamon; New York

62. Schaible, P. M. and Maissel, L. I. (1963) Transactions of 9th Vacuum Symposium Los Angeles 1962, 190 Macmillan-Pergamon; New York

63. Wehner, G. K. (1955) J. Appl. Phys. **26**, 1056

64. Cunningham, R. L. and Ng-Yelim, J. (1964) J. Appl. Phys. **35**, 2185

65. Cunningham, R. L. and Ng-Yelim, J. (1965) Rev. Sci. Instr. **36**, 54

66. Varian Associates Ltd. Booklet. 'New Large Cell Vaclon Pump Instruction Manual' Table IV-1 p. 27

67. Hirsch, E. H. (1964) J. Sci. Instr. **41**, 426

68. Koch, J. (1948) Nature **161**, 566

68a. Wolter, A. R. (1965) 4th Proc. Micro-electronics Symposium St. Louis Miss. Reported in IEEE Journal **2A**, 1 (1965)

68b. Wolter, A. R. (1966) 2nd Internatl. Conf. on Electron and Ion Beam Science and Technology; to be published

69. Ohl, R. S. (1952) Bell System Tech. J. **31**, 104

70. Cussins, W. D. (1955) Proc. Phys. Soc. **B. 68**, 213

71. Fainshtein, S. M. and Lysogorov, O. S. (1958) Zh. tekhn. fiz. **28**, 493 English translation in Soviet Phys. -Tech. Phys. (1959) **3**, 464

72. McCaldin, J. O. and Widmer, A. E. (1963) J. Phys. Chem. Solids **24**, 1073

73. Kingsbury, E. F. and Ohl R. S. (1952) Bell System Tech. J. **31**, 802

74. Thornton, C. G. and Hanley, L. D. (1955) Proc. Inst. Radio Engrs. **43**, 186

75. Alvager, T. and Hansen, N. J. (1962) Rev. Sci. Instr. **33**, 567

76. Morin, F. and Reiss, H. (1957) J. Phys. Chem. Solids **3**, 196

77. Carter, J. R. and Swalin, R. A. (1960) J. Appl. Phys. **31**, 1191

78. Trillat, J. J. and Mihama K. (1959) Comptes Rendus Acad. Sci. **248**, 2827

79. Mihama, K. (1960) Métaux **219**, 418

80. Mihama, K. (1960) Fourth Conf. on Electron Microscopy, p 414 Springer-Verlag Berlin

81. Mihama, K. and Trillat, J. J. (1960) Bull. Sté. Fran. Microsc. International Kongr. Electronen Mikroskopie 4 Berlin (1958) **1**, 414

82. Gribi, M. (1962) Le Bombardment Ionique. Colloques Internationale du Central National de la Recherche Scientifique Bellevue Paris Dec. (1962) **113**, 77

83. Trillat, J. J., Tertian, L. andTerao, N. (1956) Comptes Rendus Acad. Sci. **243**, 7 and 666

84. Trillat, J. J., Tertian, L. and Terao, N. (1957) Bull. Sté. Chim. France **6**, 804

85. Trillat, J. J., Lecomte, C. and Tertian, L. (1957) Comptes Rendus Acad. Sci. **244**, 596

86. Sosnovsky, H. M. C. (1959) J. Phys. Chem. Solids **10**, 304

87. Haymann, P. (1960) Comptes Rendus Acad. Sci. **251**, 85

88. Haymann, P. (1960) J. Chim. Phys. **572**, 580

89. Haymann, P. and Lecomte, C. (1960) Comptes Rendus Acad. Sci. **250**, 530

90. Hondros, E. D. and Benard, J. (1962) Le Bombardment Ionique Colloques Internationale du Centre National de la Recherche Scientifique Bellevue Paris Dec. (1962) **113**

91. Anderson, G. S. (1965) J. Appl. Phys. **36**, 1558

92. Sedov, N. N., Spivak, G. V. and Ivanov, R. D. (1962) Izv. Akad. Nauk. SSSR Ser. fiz. 26, 1332 English translation in Bull. Acad. Sci. (USSR) Physics Series (1963) **26**, 1355

93. Spivak, G. V. and Lukatskaya, R. A. (1951) Izv. Akad. Nauk SSSR. ser. fiz. **15**, 434

93a. Hagstrum, H. D. and Becker, G. E. (1966) Phys. Rev. Letters **16**. A543

93b. Pretzer, D. D. and Hagstrum, H. D. (1966) Surf. Sci. **4**, 265

94. Honig, R. E. (1958) J. Appl. Phys. **29**, 549

95. Bradley, R. C. (1959) J. Appl. Phys. **30**, 1

96. Castaing, R. and Slodzian, G. (1962) J. de Microscopie **1**, 395

97. Collins, T. L. and McHugh, J. A. (1965) Advances in Mass Spectrometry **3**, Proc. ASTM Mass Spectrometry Symposium, Paris (1964). Institute of Petroleum, London

Index